Improve Your Grade!

Access included with any new book.

Registration will let you:

- Check your preparedness for A&P by taking *Get Ready for A&P* tests

- Prepare for exams by taking practice tests and quizzes

- Master tough concepts in A&P using interactive tutorials and animations

- Prepare for lab practicals by taking lab practicals in *Practice Anatomy Lab™* 2.0

www.myaandp.com

TO REGISTER

1. Go to www.myaandp.com

2. Click "Register."

3. Follow the on-screen instructions to create your login name and password.

Your Access Code is:

Note: If there is no silver foil covering the access code, it may already have been redeemed, and therefore may no longer be valid. In that case, you can purchase access online using a major credit card or PayPal account. To do so, go to www.myaandp.com, click "Buy Access," and follow the on-screen instructions.

TO LOG IN

1. Go to www.myaandp.com

2. Click "Log In."

3. Pick your book cover.

4. Enter your login name and password.

5. Click "Log In."

Hint:
Remember to bookmark the site after you log in.

Technical Support:
http://247pearsoned.custhelp.com

Brief Contents

About the Authors

We dedicate this work to our students both present and past, who always inspire us to "push the envelope."

Elaine N. Marieb

For Elaine N. Marieb, taking the student's perspective into account has always been an integral part of her teaching style. Dr. Marieb began her teaching career at Springfield College, where she taught anatomy and physiology to physical education majors. She then joined the faculty of the Biological Science Division of Holyoke Community College in 1969 after receiving her Ph.D. in zoology from the University of Massachusetts at Amherst. While teaching at Holyoke Community College, where many of her students were pursuing nursing degrees, she developed a desire to better understand the relationship between the scientific study of the human body and the clinical aspects of the nursing practice. To that end, while continuing to teach full time, Dr. Marieb pursued her nursing education, which culminated in a Master of Science degree with a clinical specialization in gerontology from the University of Massachusetts. It is this experience, along with stories from the field—including those of former students now in health careers—that has informed the development of the unique perspective and accessibility for which her texts and laboratory manuals are known.

In her ongoing commitment to students and her realization of the challenges they face, Dr. Marieb has given generously to provide opportunities for students to further their education. She contributes to the New Directions, New Careers Program at Holyoke Community College by funding a staffed drop-in center and by providing several full-tuition scholarships each year for women who are returning to college after a hiatus or attending college for the first time and who would be unable to continue their studies without financial support. She funds the E. N. Marieb Science Research Awards at Mount Holyoke College, which promotes research by undergraduate science majors, and has underwritten renovation and updating of one of the biology labs in Clapp Laboratory at that college. Dr. Marieb is also a contributor to the University of Massachusetts at Amherst where she generously provided funding for reconstruction and instrumentation of a cutting-edge cytology research laboratory that bears her name. Recognizing the severe national shortage of nursing faculty, she underwrites the Nursing Scholars of the Future Grant Program at the university.

In 1994, Dr. Marieb received the Benefactor Award from the National Council for Resource Development, American Association of Community Colleges, which recognizes her ongoing sponsorship of student scholarships, faculty teaching awards, and other academic contributions to Holyoke Community College. In May 2000, the science building at Holyoke Community College was named in her honor.

Dr. Marieb is an active member of the Human Anatomy and Physiology Society (HAPS) and the American Association for the Advancement of Science (AAAS). Additionally, while actively engaged as an author, Dr. Marieb serves as a consultant for the Benjamin Cummings *Interactive Physiology*® CD-ROM series. This text—*Human Anatomy & Physiology*, Eighth Edition—is the latest expression of her commitment to the needs of students in their pursuit of the study of A&P.

When not involved in academic pursuits, Dr. Marieb is a world traveler and has vowed to visit every country on this planet. Shorter term, she serves on the board of directors of the famed Marie Selby Botanical Gardens and on the scholarship committee of the Women's Resources Center of Sarasota County. She is an enthusiastic supporter of the local arts and enjoys a competitive match of doubles tennis.

Katja Hoehn

Dr. Katja Hoehn is an instructor in the Department of Chemical and Biological Sciences at Mount Royal College in Calgary, Canada. Dr. Hoehn's first love is teaching. Her teaching excellence has been recognized by several awards during her 14 years at Mount Royal College. These include a PanCanadian Educational Technology Faculty Award (1999), a Teaching Excellence Award from the Students' Association of Mount Royal College (2001), and the Mount Royal College Distinguished Faculty Teaching Award (2004).

Dr. Hoehn received her M.D. (with Distinction) from the University of Saskatchewan, and her Ph.D. in Pharmacology from Dalhousie University. In 1991, the Dalhousie Medical Research Foundation presented her with the Max Forman (Jr.) Prize for excellence in medical research. During her Ph.D. and postdoctoral studies, she also pursued her passion for teaching by presenting guest lectures to first- and second-year medical students at Dalhousie University and at the University of Calgary.

Dr. Hoehn has been a contributor to several books and has written numerous research papers in Neuroscience and Pharmacology. She oversaw the recent revision of the Benjamin Cummings *Interactive Physiology*® CD-ROM series modules, and coauthored the newest module, *The Immune System.*

Dr. Hoehn is also actively involved in the Human Anatomy and Physiology Society (HAPS). When not teaching, she likes to spend time outdoors with her husband and two boys, compete in triathlons, and play Irish flute.

To the Student: How to Use This Book

Introduce yourself to the chapter

Chapter outlines provide a preview of the chapter and let you know where you're going.

Focus on key concepts

Student objectives have been integrated into the chapter and give you a preview of what content is to come and what you are expected to learn.

NEW! Check Your Understanding questions ask you to stop, think, and to check your understanding of key concepts at the end of major sections.

Homeostatic Imbalance sections are integrated within the text and alert you to the consequences of body systems not functioning optimally. These pathological conditions are integrated with the text to clarify and illuminate normal functioning.

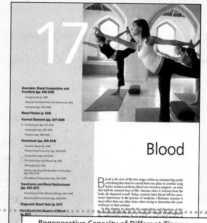

Blood

Blood is the river of life that surges within us, transporting nearly everything that must be carried from one place to another. Long before modern medicine, blood was viewed as magical—an elixir that held the mystical force of life—because when it drained from the body, life departed as well. Today, centuries later, blood still has enormous importance in the practice of medicine. Clinicians examine it more often than any other tissue when trying to determine the cause of disease in their patients.

In this chapter, we describe the composition and functions of this life-sustaining fluid.

Regenerative Capacity of Different Tissues

The different tissues vary widely in their capacity for regeneration. Epithelial tissues, bone, areolar connective tissue, dense irregular connective tissue, and blood-forming tissue regenerate extremely well. Smooth muscle and dense regular connective tissue have a moderate capacity for regeneration, but skeletal muscle and cartilage have a weak regenerative capacity. Cardiac muscle and the nervous tissue in the brain and spinal cord have virtually no *functional* regenerative capacity, and they are routinely replaced by scar tissue. However, recent studies have shown that some unexpected (and highly selective) cellular division occurs in both these tissues after damage, and efforts are under way to coax them to regenerate better.

In nonregenerating tissues and in exceptionally severe wounds, fibrosis totally replaces the lost tissue. Over a period of months, the fibrous mass shrinks and becomes more and more compact. The resulting scar appears as a pale, often shiny area composed mostly of collagen fibers. Scar tissue is strong, but it lacks the flexibility and elasticity of most normal tissues. Also, it cannot perform the normal functions of the tissue it has replaced.

HOMEOSTATIC IMBALANCE

Scar tissue that forms in the wall of the urinary bladder, heart, or other muscular organ may severely hamper the function of that organ. The normal shrinking of the scar reduces the internal volume of an organ and may hinder or even block movement of substances through a hollow organ. Scar tissue hampers muscle's ability to contract and may interfere with its normal excitation by the nervous system. In the heart, these problems may lead to progressive heart failure. In irritated visceral organs, particularly following abdominal surgery, adjacent organs together. Such adhesions can prevent the normal shifting about (churning) of loops of the intestine, dangerously obstructing the flow of foodstuffs through Adhesions can also restrict heart movements and immobil joints. ■

CHECK YOUR UNDERSTANDING

21. What are the three main steps of tissue repair?
22. Why does a deep injury to the skin result in abundant scar tissue formation?

For answers, see Appendix G.

Developmental Aspects of Tissues

▶ Indicate the embryonic origin of each tissue class.
▶ Briefly describe tissue changes that occur with age.

One of the first events of embryonic development is the formation of the three **primary germ layers**, which lie one atop next like a three-layered cellular pancake. From superficial deep, these layers are the **ectoderm**, **mesoderm** (mez'o-derm and **endoderm**. As shown in Figure 4.13, these primary germ layers then specialize to form the four primary tissues epithelium, nervous tissue, muscle, and connective tissue—th make up all body organs.

By the end of the second month of development, the primary tissues have appeared, and all major organs are in place. In general, tissue cells remain mitotic and produce the rapid growth that occurs before birth. The division of nerve cells however, stops or nearly stops during the fetal period. After birth, the cells of most other tissues continue to divide until adult body size is achieved. Cellular division then slows great

Illustrated tables summarize complex information and serve as a "one-stop shopping" study tool.

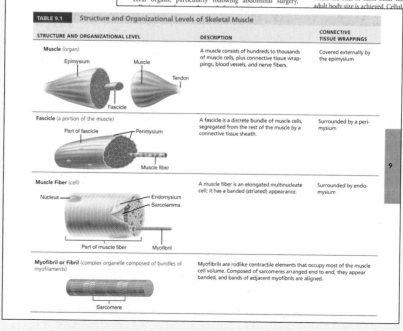

TABLE 9.1	Structure and Organizational Levels of Skeletal Muscle	
STRUCTURE AND ORGANIZATIONAL LEVEL	**DESCRIPTION**	**CONNECTIVE TISSUE WRAPPINGS**
Muscle (organ) Epimysium, Muscle, Tendon, Fascicle	A muscle consists of hundreds to thousands of muscle cells, plus connective tissue wrappings, blood vessels, and nerve fibers.	Covered externally by the epimysium
Fascicle (a portion of the muscle) Part of fascicle, Perimysium, Muscle fiber	A fascicle is a discrete bundle of muscle cells, segregated from the rest of the muscle by a connective tissue sheath.	Surrounded by a perimysium
Muscle Fiber (cell) Nucleus, Endomysium, Sarcolemma, Part of muscle fiber, Myofibril	A muscle fiber is an elongated multinucleate cell; it has a banded (striated) appearance.	Surrounded by endomysium
Myofibril or Fibril (complex organelle composed of bundles of myofilaments) Sarcomere	Myofibrils are rodlike contractile elements that occupy most of the muscle cell volume. Composed of sarcomeres arranged end to end, they appear banded, and bands of adjacent myofibrils are aligned.	

Follow complex processes step-by-step

NEW! Focus figures help you grasp tough topics in A&P by walking you through carefully developed step-by-step illustrations that use a big-picture layout and dramatic art to provide a context for understanding the process.

Figure 9.8 FOCUS Events at the Neuromuscular Junction

When a nerve impulse reaches a neuromuscular junction, acetylcholine (ACh) is released. Upon binding to sarcolemma receptors, ACh causes a change in sarcolemma permeability leading to a change in membrane potential.

Action potential (AP)

Myelinated axon of motor neuron

Nucleus

Axon terminal of neuromuscular junction

Sarcolemma of the muscle fiber

① Action potential arrives at axon terminal of motor neuron.

② Voltage-gated Ca²⁺ channels open and Ca²⁺ enters the axon terminal.

Ca²⁺

Synaptic vesicle containing ACh

Axon terminal of motor neuron

Mitochondrion

Synaptic cleft

③ Ca²⁺ entry causes some synaptic vesicles to release their contents (acetylcholine) by exocytosis.

Fusing synaptic vesicles

ACh

Junctional folds of sarcolemma

④ Acetylcholine, a neurotransmitter, diffuses across the synaptic cleft and binds to receptors in the sarcolemma.

Sarcoplasm of muscle fiber

⑤ ACh binding opens ion channels that allow simultaneous passage of Na⁺ into the muscle fiber and K⁺ out of the muscle fiber. More Na⁺ ions enter than K⁺ ions leave and this produces a local change in the membrane potential (depolarization).

Na⁺ K⁺

Postsynaptic membrane ion channel opens; ions pass.

⑥ ACh effects are terminated by its enzymatic breakdown in the synaptic cleft by acetylcholinesterase.

ACh Degraded ACh

Na⁺

Postsynaptic membrane ion channel closed; ions cannot pass.

Acetylcholinesterase

K⁺

286

A&PFlix View this animation at myA&P

Overview provides a quick summary of the key idea of the figure.

Big picture orientation provides you with a concrete starting point for the process.

Step text walks you through the process step-by-step.

Visualize structures

NEW! Stunning 3-D anatomy art
is rendered in a dramatically more dynamic, realistic style with vibrant, saturated colors to help you visualize key anatomical structures.

Brachiocephalic trunk

Left comm... artery

Left subcl...

Superior vena cava

Aortic arch

Right pulmonary artery

Ligamentu...

Ascending aorta

Left pulmo...

Pulmonary trunk

Left pulmo...

Right pulmonary veins

Auricle of **left atrium**

Right atrium

Circumflex...

Right coronary artery (in coronary sulcus)

Left corona... (in corona...

Anterior cardiac vein

Left ventr...

Right ventricle

Right marginal artery

Great cardiac vein

Small cardiac vein

Anterior interventricular artery (in anterior interventricular sulcus)

Inferior vena cava

Apex

Bone

Tendon

Epimysium

Epimysium

Perimysium

Endomysium

Muscle fiber in middle of a fascicle

(b)

Blood vessel

Fascicle (wrapped by perimysium)

Endomysium (between individual muscle fibers)

Muscle fiber

Perimysium   Fascicle

NEW! Bone art features
realistic bone color and texture with a consistent style from figure to figure.

Compact bone   Spongy bone

Blood vessels continue into medullary cavity containing marrow

Central (Haversian) canal

Osteon (Haversian system)

Endosteum lining bony canals and covering trabeculae

Circumferential lamellae

Perforating (Volkmann's) canal

(a)

Perforating (Sharpey's) fibers

Periosteal blood vessel

Lamellae

Periosteum

Nerve

Vein

Artery

Lamellae

Central canal

Canaliculus

Osteocyte in a lacuna

Lacunae

(b)

(c)

Interstitial lamellae

Lacuna (with osteocyte)

Make connections

MAKING CONNECTIONS

System Connections
Homeostatic Interrelationships Between the Integumentary System and Other Body Systems

Endocrine System
- Skin protects endocrine organs; converts some hormones to their active forms; synthesizes a vitamin D precursor
- Androgens produced by the endocrine system activate sebaceous glands and are involved in regulation of hair growth

Cardiovascular System
- Skin protects cardiovascular organs; prevents fluid loss from body; serves as blood reservoir
- Cardiovascular system transports oxygen and nutrients to skin and removes wastes from skin; provides substances needed by skin glands to make their secretions

Lymphatic System/Immunity
- Skin protects lymphatic organs; prevents pathogen invasion; dendritic cells and macrophages help activate the immune system
- Lymphatic system prevents edema by picking up excessive leaked fluid; immune system protects skin cells

Respiratory System
- Skin protects respiratory organs; hairs in nose help filter out dust from inhaled air
- Respiratory system furnishes oxygen to skin cells and removes carbon dioxide via gas exchange with blood

Digestive System
- Skin protects digestive organs; provides vitamin D needed for calcium absorption; performs some of the same chemical conversions as liver cells
- Digestive system provides needed nutrients to the skin

Urinary System
- Skin protects urinary organs; excretes salts and some nitrogenous wastes in sweat
- Urinary system activates vitamin D precursor made by keratinocytes; disposes of nitrogenous wastes of skin metabolism

Reproductive System
- Skin protects reproductive organs; cutaneous receptors respond to erotic stimuli; highly modified sweat glands (mammary glands) produce milk. During pregnancy, skin stretches to accommodate growing fetus; changes in skin pigmentation may occur

Skeletal System
- Skin protects bones; skin synthesizes a vitamin D precursor needed for normal calcium absorption and deposit of bone (calcium) salts, which make bones hard
- Skeletal system provides support for skin

Muscular System
- Skin protects muscles
- Active muscles generate large amounts of heat, which increases blood flow to the skin and may promote activation of sweat glands of skin

Nervous System
- Skin protects nervous system organs; cutaneous sensory receptors for touch, pressure, pain, and temperature located in skin (see Figure 5.1)
- Nervous system regulates diameter of blood vessels in skin; activates sweat glands, contributing to thermoregulation; interprets cutaneous sensation; activates arrector pili muscles

166

Closer Connections
The Integumentary System and Interrelationships with the Nervous, Cardiovascular, and Lymphatic/Immune Systems

First and foremost, our skin is a barrier. Like the skin of a grape, it keeps its contents juicy and whole. The skin is also a master at self (wound) repair, and interacts intimately with other body systems by making vitamin D (necessary for hard bones) and other potent molecules, all the while protecting deeper tissues from damaging external agents. Perhaps the most crucial roles of the skin in terms of overall body homeostasis are those it plays with the nervous, cardiovascular, and lymphatic systems. These interactions are detailed next.

Nervous System
The whole body benefits from the skin's interaction with the nervous system. The skin houses the tiny sensory receptors that provide a great deal of information about our external environment—its temperature, the pressure exerted by objects, and the presence of dangerous substances. What if we stepped on broken glass or hot pavement but did not have neural monitors in our skin? If we did not actually see, hear, taste, or smell such a damaging event, no reports would be sent to the nervous system. Consequently, the nervous system would be left "in the dark," unable to evaluate the need for a response and to order the steps needed to protect us from further damage or to get first aid.

Nervous and Cardiovascular System
Skin provides the site both for sensing external temperature and for responding to temperature changes. Dermal blood vessels (cardiovascular system organs) and sweat glands (controlled by

the nervous system) play crucial roles in thermoregulation. So too do blood and the hot and cold receptors in the skin. When we are chilled, our blood loses heat to retain body heat by constricting dermal blood vessels. When body and blood temperature rises, dermal vessels dilate and sweating begins.

Thermoregulation is vital: When the body overheats, life-threatening changes occur. Chemical reactions speed up, and as the temperature continues to rise vital proteins are destroyed and cells die. Cold has the opposite effect; cellular activity slows and ultimately stops.

Lymphatic System/Immunity
The role of the skin in immunity is complex. Keratinocytes in the skin manufacture interferons (proteins that block viral infection) and other proteins important to the immune response. Epidermal dendritic cells in the skin interact with antigens (foreign substances) that have penetrated the stratum corneum. The dendritic cells then migrate to lymphatic organs, where they present bits of the antigens to cells that will mount the immune response against them. This "messenger" function alerts the immune system early on to the presence of pathogens in the body.

Even a mild sunburn disrupts the normal immune response because UV radiation disables the skin's presenter cells. This effect may explain why many people infected by the cold sore virus tend to have a cold sore eruption after sun exposure.

Clinical Connections
Integumentary System

A terrible collision between a trailer truck and a bus has occurred on Route 91. Several of the passengers are rushed to area hospitals for treatment. We will follow a few of these people in clinical case studies that will continue through the book from one organ system to the next.

Case study: Examination of Mrs. DeStephano, a 45-year-old woman, reveals several impairments of homeostasis. Relative to her integumentary system, the following comments are noted on her chart:

- Epidermal abrasions of the right arm and shoulder
- Severe lacerations of the right cheek and temple
- Cyanosis apparent

The lacerated areas are cleaned, sutured, and bandaged by the emergency room (ER) personnel, and Mrs. DeStephano is admitted for further tests.

Relative to her signs:
1. What protective mechanisms are impaired or deficient in the abraded areas?
2. Assuming that bacteria are penetrating the dermis in these areas, what remaining skin defenses might act to prevent further bacterial invasion?
3. What benefit is conferred by suturing the lacerations? (Hint: See Chapter 4, p. 144.)
4. Mrs. DeStephano's cyanotic skin may hint at what additional problem (and impairment of what body systems or functions)?

(Answers in Appendix G)

167

Chapter 9 Muscles and Muscle Tissue · 313

A CLOSER LOOK
Athletes Looking Good and Doing Better with Anabolic Steroids?

Society loves a winner and top athletes reap large social and monetary rewards. It is not surprising that some will grasp at anything that might increase their performance—including "juice," or anabolic steroids. These drugs are variants of the male sex hormone testosterone engineered by pharmaceutical companies. They were introduced in the 1950s to treat anemia and certain muscle-wasting diseases and to prevent muscle atrophy in patients immobilized after surgery. Testosterone is responsible for the increase in muscle and bone mass and other physical changes that occur during puberty and converts boys into men.

Convinced that megadoses of steroids could produce enhanced masculinizing effects in grown men, many athletes and bodybuilders were using them by the early 1960s. Investigations of the so-called Balco Scandal have stunned fans of major league baseball players with revelations in 2004 and since of rampant steroid use by Barry Bonds, of the San Francisco Giants, and many other elite athletes. It is still going strong. In October of 2007, Marion Jones, one of the most celebrated of women athletes of all time, admitted that she was using performance-enhancing steroids when she won five gold medals in the 2000 Olympics. Furthermore, steroid use today is not confined to athletes. Indeed, it is estimated that nearly one in every 10 young men has tried them, and the practice is also spreading among young women.

It is difficult to determine the extent of anabolic steroid use because most international competitions ban the use of drugs. Users (and prescribing physicians or drug dealers) are naturally reluctant to talk about it, and users stop doping before the event, aware that evidence of drug use is hard to find a week after its use is stopped. Additionally, "underground" suppliers of performance-enhancing drugs keep producing new versions of designer steroids that evade standard antidoping tests. The Olympic Analytical Laboratory in Los Angeles rocked the sports world in November of 2003 when it revealed that a number of elite athletes tested positive for tetrahydrogestrinone (THG), a designer steroid not previously known or tested for. Nonetheless, there is little question that

many professional bodybuilders and athletes competing in events that require muscle strength (e.g., shot put, discus throwing, and weight lifting) are heavy users. Sports figures such as football players have also admitted to using steroids as an adjunct to training, diet, and psychological preparation for games. These athletes claim that anabolic steroids enhance muscle mass and strength, and raise oxygen-carrying capability owing to greater red blood cell volume.

Typically, bodybuilders who use steroids combine high doses (up to 200 mg/day) via injection or transdermal skin patches with heavy resistance training. Intermittent use begins several months before an event, and commonly entails the use of many anabolic steroid supplements (a method called stacking). Doses are increased gradually as the competition nears.

Do the drugs do all that is claimed? Research studies report increased isometric strength and body weight in steroid users. While these are results weight lifters dream about, for runners and others requiring fine muscle coordination and endurance these changes may not translate into improved performance. The "jury is still out" on this question.

Do the alleged advantages of steroids outweigh their risks? Absolutely not. Physicians say they cause bloated faces (Cushingoid sign of steroid excess); acne and hair loss; shriveled testes and infertility; damage to the liver that promotes liver cancer; and changes in blood cholesterol levels that may predispose users to coronary heart disease. In addition, females can develop masculine characteristics

such as smaller breasts, enlarged clitoris, excess body hair, and thinning scalp hair. The psychiatric hazards of anabolic steroid use may be equally threatening: Recent studies indicate that one-third of users suffer serious mental problems. Depression, delusions, and manic behavior—in which users undergo Jekyll-and-Hyde personality swings and become extremely violent (termed 'roid rage)—are all common.

A more recent arrival on the scene, sold over the counter as a "nutritional performance-enhancer," is androstenedione, which is converted to testosterone in the body. Though it is taken orally (and much of it is destroyed by the liver soon after ingestion), the few milligrams that survive temporarily boost testosterone levels. Reports of its use by baseball great Mark McGwire before he retired, and of athletic wanna-bes from the fifth grade up sweeping the supplement off the drug store shelves, are troubling, particularly since it is not regulated by the U.S. Food and Drug Administration (FDA) and its long-term effects are unpredictable and untested. A study at Massachusetts General Hospital found that males who took androstenedione developed higher levels of the female hormone estrogen as well as testosterone, raising the risk of feminizing effects such as enlarged breasts. Youths with elevated levels of estrogen or testosterone may enter puberty early, stunting bone growth and leading to shorter-than-normal adult height. Some people admit to a willingness to try almost anything to win, short of killing themselves. Are they unwittingly doing this as well?

Learn the language

Phonetic spellings are provided for words that may be unfamiliar to you to help you with pronunciation.

Color-coded chapter and unit tabs help you find information quickly and easily.

Word roots listed on the inside back cover will help you learn the special vocabulary of anatomy and physiology.

Review what you've learned

Review questions at the end of each chapter, including multiple choice/matching, short answer, and Critical Thinking and Clinical Application questions, help you evaluate your progress.

Chapter summaries with page references provide excellent study aids.

Answers to Check Your Understanding, Clinical Connections, and end-of-chapter Multiple Choice and Matching Review Questions can be found in Appendix G.

The following are sample textbook pages shown as illustrations:

200 UNIT 2 Covering, Support, and Movement of the Body

trunk, and (3) protects the brain, spinal cord, and the organs in the thorax. As we will see later in this chapter, the bones of the appendicular skeleton, which allow us to interact with and manipulate our environment, are appended to the axial skeleton.

CHECK YOUR UNDERSTANDING

1. What are the three main parts of the axial skeleton?
2. Which part of the skeleton—axial or appendicular—is important in protecting internal organs?

For answers, see Appendix G.

The Skull

► Name, describe, and identify the skull bones. Identify their important markings.
► Compare and contrast the major functions of the cranium and the facial skeleton.

The **skull** is the body's most complex bony structure. It is formed by *cranial* and *facial bones*, 22 in all. The cranial bones, or *cranium* (kra'ne-um), enclose and protect the fragile brain and furnish attachment sites for head and neck muscles. The facial bones (1) form the framework of the face, (2) contain cavities for the special sense organs of sight, taste, and smell, (3) provide openings for air and food...

Cranium

The eight cranial bones are the paired parietal and temporal bones and the unpaired frontal, occipital, sphenoid, and ethmoid bones.

Frontal Bone

The shell-shaped **frontal bone** (Figures 7.4a, 7.5, and 7.7) forms the anterior cranium.

Parietal Bones and the Major Sutures

The two large **parietal bones** are curved, rectangular bones that form most of the superior and lateral aspects of the skull.

Word Roots, Prefixes, Suffixes, and Combining Forms

---

170 UNIT 2 Covering, Support, and Movement of the Body

REVIEW QUESTIONS

Multiple Choice/Matching

(Some questions have more than one correct answer. Select the best answer or answers from the choices given.)

Short Answer Essay Questions

Critical Thinking and Clinical Application Questions

CHAPTER SUMMARY

The Skin (pp. 149–155)

1. The skin, or integument, is composed of two discrete tissue layers, an outer epidermis and a deeper dermis, resting on subcutaneous tissue, the hypodermis.

Epidermis (pp. 150–152)

2. The epidermis is an avascular, keratinized sheet of stratified squamous epithelium. Most epidermal cells are keratinocytes. Scattered among the keratinocytes in the deepest epidermal layers are melanocytes, epidermal dendritic cells, and tactile cells.

3. From deep to superficial, the strata, or layers of the epidermis, are the basale, spinosum, granulosum, lucidum, and corneum. The stratum lucidum is absent in thin skin. The mitotically active stratum basale is the source of new cells for epidermal growth. The most superficial layers are increasingly keratinized and less viable.

Dermis (pp. 152–153)

4. The dermis, composed mainly of dense, irregular connective tissue, is well supplied with blood vessels, lymphatic vessels, and nerves. Cutaneous receptors, glands, and hair follicles reside within the dermis.

5. The more superficial papillary layer exhibits dermal papillae that protrude into the epidermis above, as well as dermal ridges. Dermal ridges and epidermal ridges together form the friction ridges that produce fingerprints.

6. In the deeper, thicker reticular layer, the connective tissue fibers are much more densely interwoven. Less dense regions between the collagen bundles produce cleavage, or tension, lines in the skin. Points of tight dermal attachment to the hypodermis produce dermal folds, or flexure lines.

Check your readiness

Get Ready for A&P gets you prepared for your A&P course. Take the diagnostic test to see where you need review.

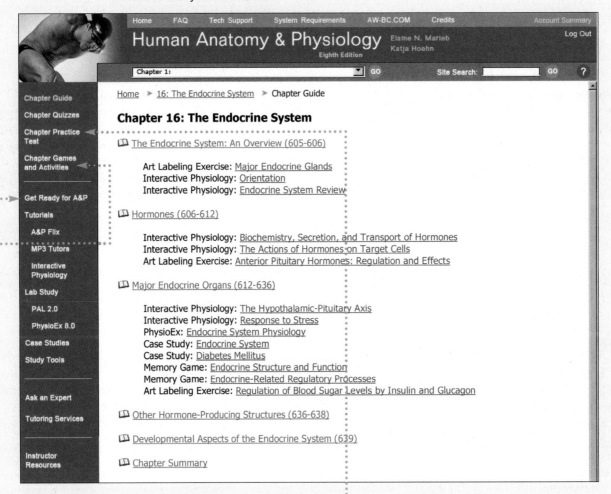

Prepare for exams

Chapter Quizzes and Practice Tests help you assess your understanding of the chapter and prepare for your exams.

Games and activities featuring Art Labeling Exercises, Memory Games, and Crossword Puzzles and Histology, Bone, and Muscle Reviews. Also included are new **MP3 Tutor Sessions** that carefully coach you through the most difficult A&P concepts including calcium regulation, the visual pathway, and gas exchange during respiration.

Chapter Guide

Chapter Quizzes

Chapter Practice
Test

Chapter Games
and Activities

Get Ready for A&P

Tutorials

A&P Flix

MP3 Tutors

Interactive
Physiology

Lab Study

PAL 2.0

PhysioEx 8.0

Case Studies

Study Tools

Ask an Expert

Tutoring Services

Instructor
Resources

Master tough concepts in A&P

NEW! A&P Flix animations provide carefully developed step-by-step explanations with dramatic 3-D representations of structures that show action and movement of processes, thereby bringing difficult-to-teach A&P concepts to life. Each animation includes gradable quizzes as well as study sheets for practice and assessment.

Interactive Physiology® **10-System Suite,** an award-winning tutorial program with a new module on the Immune System, tutors you in key physiological concepts and helps you advance beyond memorization to a genuine understanding of complex processes.

Access the A&P lab 24/7

NEW! Practice Anatomy Lab™ 2.0 allows you to view hundreds of images of the human cadaver, anatomical models, histology slides, the cat, and the fetal pig and to take practice quizzes and simulated lab practical exams.

PhysioEx™ laboratory simulations allow you to conduct simulated experiments as part of your A&P lab.

Preface

As educators, clinically trained individuals, and perennial students, we are continually challenged by the learning mind. What works best to get students over conceptual hurdles and to help them apply new information to the world they personally understand? Our clinical backgrounds have served our teaching and writing purposes well. Perhaps even more important, our clinical experience has allowed us to view our presentations through our students' eyes and from the vantage points of their career interests.

For this edition, as for those preceding it, feedback from both student and instructor reviews indicated areas of the text that needed to be revised for clarity, timeliness, and just plain reduction of verbal meatiness. Overall, feedback was positive, verifying that the approach of explaining fundamental principles and unifying themes first as a strong base for all that comes later is still viable. Furthermore, it is clear that backing up these explanations with comfortable analogies and familiar examples enhances the students' understanding of the workings of the human body.

Unifying Themes

Three integrating themes that organized, unified, and set the tone of the first edition of this text continue to be valid and are retained in this edition. These themes are:

Interrelationships of body organ systems. The fact that nearly all regulatory mechanisms require interaction of several organ systems is continually emphasized. For example, Chapter 25, which deals with the structure and function of the urinary system, discusses the vital importance of the kidneys not only in maintaining adequate blood volume to ensure normal blood circulation, but also in continually adjusting the chemical composition of blood so that all body cells remain healthy. The unique Making Connections feature is the culmination of this approach and should help students think of the body as a dynamic community of interdependent parts rather than as a number of isolated structural units.

Homeostasis. The normal and most desirable condition of body functioning is homeostasis. Its loss or destruction always leads to some type of pathology—temporary or permanent. Pathological conditions are integrated with the text to clarify and illuminate normal functioning, not as an end in and of themselves. For example, Chapter 19, which deals with the structure and function of blood vessels, explains how the ability of healthy arteries to expand and recoil ensures continuous blood flow and proper circulation. The chapter goes on to discuss the effects on homeostasis when arteries lose their elasticity: high blood pressure and all of its attendant problems. These homeostatic imbalances are indicated visually by a pink symbol with a fulcrum:

Whenever students see the imbalance symbol in text, the concept of disease as a loss of homeostasis is reinforced.

Complementarity of structure and function. Students are encouraged to understand the structure of an organ, a tissue, or a cell as a prerequisite to comprehending its function.

Concepts of physiology are explained and related to structural characteristics that promote or allow the various functions to occur. For example, the lungs can act as a gas exchange site because the walls of their air sacs present an incredibly thin barrier between blood and air.

NEW TO THE EIGHTH EDITION

The Eighth Edition represents a monumental revision with an entirely new art program and text presentation that build upon the hallmark strengths of the previous seven editions. With every edition, our goal is powerful but simple—to make anatomy and physiology as engaging, accurate, and relevant as possible for both you and your students. The changes to the Eighth Edition are all driven by the needs of today's students, as we seek to make the learning of key concepts in A&P as easy as possible for them. Key concepts are important because of the overwhelming amount of material in this course. Mastering this material gives students an anchor and structure for managing this wealth of information. Below are the ways in which we've revised the Eighth Edition to make this book the one where learning happens most effectively, followed by a detailed list of specific chapter-by-chapter content changes.

A whole new art program. The drive for this revision began as a simple list. We sat down together and created a chapter-by-chapter list of the key concepts in A&P where students struggle the most. This list became the basis for our art revision plans. We first boiled it down to some of the toughest topics to get our list of Focus figures. This new Focus feature highlights tough topics in A&P and walks students step-by-step through complex processes that are difficult to teach and visualize. In each case, we scrutinized the process and worked through countless revisions to break it down in the most logical and easy-to-follow way possible for students. We hope you'll be as pleased with the results as we are.

We also revised and reconceptualized many of the process figures in the book to make them easier to follow and to learn from. Where appropriate we have added blue step text that serves as our author voice guiding students step-by-step through complex processes. The blue text clearly separates the process steps from the labels, making the figures easy to navigate.

Flipping through the Eighth Edition, you can see that our new art is dynamic, three-dimensional, and realistic, with dramatic views and perspectives that use vibrant, saturated colors. Using our list of key concepts, we targeted critical figures in anatomy and worked closely with the artistic team on making these figures superior in rendering and in conveying the key pedagogical information and structures that students need to learn from the figure, striking a perfect balance between realism and teaching effectiveness.

Finally, we've also added a wealth of new figures and photos to enhance learning, many of which are listed below.

Improved text presentation. New text features also serve to focus students on key concepts. We have integrated the student objectives to fall within the chapter, giving students a preview in smaller chunks of what they are expected to learn in a given section. We've also added new Check Your Understanding questions that ask students to stop, think, and check their understanding of key concepts at the end of major sections. These changes along with a brand-new design make the book easier than ever to study from and navigate. We have also edited the text throughout with a refined writing style that retains our hallmark analogies and accessible, friendly style while using simpler, more concise language and shorter paragraphs. These changes make the text easier for students to manage as they face the challenging amount of information in this course.

Factual updates and accuracy. As authors we pride ourselves on keeping our book as up-to-date and as accurate as possible in all areas—a monumental task that requires painstaking selectivity. Although information changes even as a textbook goes to press, be assured that our intent and responsibility to update was carried out to the best of our ability. We have incorporated updates from current research in the field as much as possible; many of these updates are included below in the chapter-by-chapter changes. A more complete list, along with references for selected updates, is available from your Pearson sales representative and in the Instructor Guide to Text and Media.

Chapter-by-Chapter Changes

Chapter 1 The Human Body: An Orientation
- New PET scan for A Closer Look on medical imaging

Chapter 2 Chemistry Comes Alive
- Updated information on molecular chaperones

Chapter 3 Cells: The Living Units
- New step art for exocytosis (Figure 3.14)
- Updated discussion of types of endocytosis accompanied by new endocytosis step art (Figure 3.12)

- New Figure 3.13 provides a comparison of three types of endocytosis
- New Figure 3.20 with step text on the signaling mechanism for targeting new proteins to the ER
- New Focus on Primary Active Transport: The Na$^+$-K$^+$ Pump (Figure 3.10)
- New Focus on G Proteins (Figure 3.16)
- New Focus on Mitosis (Figure 3.33)
- New diagrams accompany photos in figure showing the effects of varying tonicities on living red blood cells (Figure 3.9)
- New photomicrographs accompany all cell organelle illustrations, including new Figure 3.28 on microvilli
- Revised text and new figures for transcription (Figure 3.35) and translation (Figure 3.37).
- New information on the origin of peroxisomes based on recent research

Chapter 4 Tissue: The Living Fabric
- New Figure 4.1: Overview of four tissue types
- New photomicrographs for pseudostratified ciliated columnar epithelium (Figure 4.3d), goblet cells (Figure 4.4), and elastic connective tissue (Figure 4.8f)
- New Table 4.1 compares four main classes of connective tissue
- Updated A Closer Look on cancer

Chapter 5 The Integumentary System
- New Figure 5.3: Two regions of the dermis, with three new photomicrographs
- New Figure 5.4: Dermal modifications result in characteristic skin markings, with one new photomicrograph
- New photos: partial and full thickness burns (Figure 5.10)

Chapter 6 Bones and Skeletal Tissue
- New Figure 6.4 shows comparative morphology of bone cells
- New Figure 6.14 shows that vigorous exercise can lead to large increases in bone strength
- Updated information on homocysteine as a marker of low bone mass density and bone frailty; additional information on age-related bone changes and treatments

Chapter 7 The Skeleton
- New photo of midsagittal section of the skull (Figure 7.5c)
- New photos for inferior and superior views of the skull (Figures 7.6b, 7.7b)
- New photos of the sphenoid bone, superior and posterior views (Figure 7.9)
- New photo of right lateral view of the maxilla (Figure 7.11)
- New MRI of lumbar region in sagittal section showing herniated disc (Figure 7.17)
- New photo of midsagittal section of the thorax (Figure 7.22)
- New X ray of the foot (Figure 7.34)
- New Figure 7.37: The C-shaped spine of a newborn infant
- New Homeostatic Imbalance: xiphoid process projecting posteriorly

Chapter 8 Joints
- Figure 8.1 expanded to show a comparison of different types of fibrous joints; added gomphosis
- Added new views for knee, shoulder, and mandible joint

Chapter 9 Muscles and Muscle Tissue
- New Focus on Events at the Neuromuscular Junction (Figure 9.8)
- New Focus on Excitation-Contraction Coupling (Figure 9.11)
- New Focus on the Cross Bridge Cycle (Figure 9.12)
- New Figure 9.7: Phases leading to muscle fiber contraction
- New Figure 9.20: Comparison of energy sources used during short-duration and prolonged-duration exercise
- New Figure 9.24: Cross section of the three types of fibers in skeletal muscle
- New Figure 9.30: Formation of a multinucleate skeletal muscle fiber by fusion of myoblasts

Chapter 10 The Muscular System
- New cadaver photo of the anterior and lateral regions of the neck (Figure 10.9c)
- New cadaver photo of superficial muscles of the thorax (Figure 10.13b)
- New cadaver photo of muscles crossing the shoulder and elbow joint (Figure 10.14d)
- New cadaver photo of superficial muscles of the superior gluteal region (Figure 10.20b)

Chapter 11 Fundamentals of the Nervous System and Nervous Tissue
- New Focus on Resting Membrane Potential (Figure 11.8)
- New Focus on Action Potential (Figure 11.11)
- New Focus on Chemical Synapse (Figure 11.17)
- Updated role of satellite cells
- Updated discussion of nitric oxide and carbon dioxide; added paragraph on new class of neurotransmitter endo-cannabinoids
- Updated the roles of neurotropins in signaling the growth cone during neuronal development
- Updated information in A Closer Look on overcoming cocaine addiction
- Updated information on neurotransmitters (histamine, somatostatin, substance P, CCK) in Table 11.3
- New Figure 11.10: The spread and decay of a graded potential
- New Figure 11.15: Action potential propagation in unmyelinated and myelinated axons
- New photo, a neuronal growth cone (Figure 11.24)

Chapter 12 The Central Nervous System
- Updated location of cortex receiving vestibular input based on new fMRI studies
- New Homeostatic Imbalance on brain tumors in different regions of the brain: the anterior association area and the posterior parietal region

- Updated discussion of regulation of respiratory rhythm in the medulla
- Updated discussion of occurrence of theta waves in adult electroencephalogram
- Updated mechanisms of onset of sleep and wakefulness, the role of orexins (hypocretins) in narcolepsy, and recent finding that orexin antagonists promote sleep in humans
- Updated survival of strokes and stroke treatment
- Updated cause and treatment of Parkinson's disease
- Updated treatments for Alzheimer's disease
- New Figure 12.17 on the cerebellum with side-by-side illustration and photo showing a sagittal view
- New photo of frontal section of the brain (Figure 12.10)
- New photo of inferior view of the brain showing the regions of the brain stem (Figure 12.14)
- New EEG photo (Figure 12.20)

Chapter 13 The Peripheral Nervous System and Reflex Activity
- Updated axon regrowth and treating spinal cord injuries
- Updated Homeostatic Imbalance on cause and treatment of trigeminal neuralgia
- Updated origin and course of the accessory nerves (CN XI)
- New Focus on the Stretch Reflex (Figure 13.17)
- New cadaver photo of the brachial plexus (Figure 13.9)
- New cadaver photo of the sacral plexus (Figure 13.11)
- New Homeostatic Imbalance on hyperalgesia and phantom limb pain

Chapter 14 The Autonomic Nervous System
- New Homeostatic Imbalance on autonomic neuropathy

Chapter 15 The Special Senses
- Updated laser procedures to correct myopia
- Updated the mechanism of light adaptation in rods
- Updated odor signal processing
- Updated taste cell specificity
- Updated the mechanism of transduction for all five taste modalities
- Updated treatment of age-related macular degeneration

Chapter 16 The Endocrine System
- New Figure 16.7 on regulation of thyroid hormone secretion
- Updated hormones released by the thymus and by adipose tissue
- Added new information about incretins and osteocalcin
- Simplified and updated A Closer Look on diabetes mellitus

Chapter 17 Blood
- Updated discussion of erythropoietin—new understanding of how hypoxia induces erythropoiesis
- Updated treatment of sickle-cell anemia—new drug clotrimazole

Chapter 18 The Cardiovascular System: The Heart
- New cadaver photo of frontal section of the heart (Figure 18.4f)
- New photomicrograph of cardiac muscle (Figure 18.11)

Chapter 19 The Cardiovascular System: Blood Vessels
- Updated function of pericytes
- Updated relationship between obesity and hypertension
- Updated development of arteries and veins
- Updated systolic blood pressure as a better predictor of complications of hypertension in those older than 50
- Updated hypertension and its treatment—angiotensin II receptor blockers

Chapter 20 The Lymphatic System and Lymphoid Organs and Tissues
- Updated information on Hassall's corpuscles from current research

Chapter 21 The Immune System: Innate and Adaptive Body Defenses
- Added dermcidin—an important antimicrobial in human sweat
- Updated number of types of human TLRs
- Updated information that dendritic cells can obtain foreign antigens from infected cells through gap junctions
- Updated role of the T_H2 type of helper T cells in immunity
- Updated statistics on HIV/AIDS
- Updated treatments of autoimmune diseases and multiple sclerosis
- Added new type of T_H cell, T_H17
- New Figure 21.2 on phagocytosis
- New SEM of a dendritic cell (Figure 21.10)
- New computer-generated image of an antibody (Figure 21.14)
- New Homeostatic Imbalance on parasitic worms

Chapter 22 The Respiratory System
- Updated role of alveolar type II cells in innate immunity
- Updated mechanism for hypercapnia following administration of oxygen to patients with COPD
- Updated therapy for cystic fibrosis
- New photomicrograph showing a portion of the tracheal wall (Figure 22.6)

Chapter 23 The Digestive System
- New X ray of the mouth of a child showing the permanent incisors forming (Figure 23.10)
- New photomicrograph of small intestine villus (Figure 23.22)
- New photo of a peptic ulcer lesion and SEM of *H. pylori* bacteria (Figure 23.16)
- Updated discussion of the process of HCl formation within the parietal cells
- Expanded section on histology of the small intestine wall; added function of Paneth cells' secretions

Chapter 24 Nutrition, Metabolism, and Body Temperature Regulation
- Vitamin and mineral tables have been simplified for ease of student learning

- New sections and coverage of obesity, short- and long-term regulation of food intake, and additional regulatory factors
- New photo, atomic force microscopy, reveals the structure of energy-converting ATP synthase rotor rings (Figure 24.10)

Chapter 25 The Urinary System
- New photo of a frontal section of kidney (Figure 25.3)
- New photomicrograph of cut nephron tubules in new figure of renal cortical tissue and renal tubules (Figure 25.6)
- New intravenous pyelogram (Figure 25.19)
- Updated structure and possible function of extra-glomerular mesangial cells
- New Homeostatic Imbalance on chronic renal disease and renal failure

Chapter 26 Fluid, Electrolyte, and Acid-Base Balance
- Added clarification of difference between edema and hypotonic hydration
- New paragraph on angiotensin II

Chapter 27 The Reproductive System
- New SEM of sperm (Figure 27.8)
- New photomicrograph of the endometrium and its blood supply (Figure 27.13)
- New photo of mammogram procedure, plus new photos of a normal mammogram compared to one showing a tumor (Figure 27.16)
- New photomicrographs showing stages of follicular development (Figure 27.18)
- New section on erectile dysfunction
- Added new human papillomavirus vaccine
- Expanded discussion of interactions along the hypothalamic-pituitary-ovarian axis with reconceptualized figure
- Updated transmission of herpes virus
- Updated descent of the testes
- Updated hormone replacement therapy for women

Chapter 28 Pregnancy and Human Development
- New photomicrograph of a blastocyst that has just adhered to the uterine endometrium (Figure 28.5)
- New Figure 28.8 showing detailed anatomy of the vascular relationships in the mature decidua basalis
- New Figure 28.13, flowchart showing major derivatives of the embryonic germ layers
- Updated information on the initiation of labor and on contraception

Chapter 29 Heredity
- New photomicrograph of human sex chromosomes (Figure 29.5)
- New Figure 29.8 comparing amniocentesis and chorionic villus sampling
- Updated discussion of stem cells
- Updated discussion of epigenetics and nontraditional methods of gene regulation

Supplements for the Instructor

NEW! Instructor Resource DVD

(0-321-50704-5)

This media tool organizes all instructor media resources by chapter into one convenient package that allows you to easily and quickly pull together a lecture and to show animations, including brand-new A&P Flix, from your PowerPoint® presentations. The IRDVD contains:

- **NEW! A&P Flix**
  Movie-quality A&P Flix animations of key concepts invigorate classroom lectures. These animations provide carefully developed, step-by-step explanations with dramatic 3-D representations of structures that show action and movement of processes, bringing A&P concepts to life. Using the A&P Flix animations, you can help students visualize tough-to-teach A&P concepts such as muscle actions, excitation-contraction coupling, generation of an action potential, and more. These animations can be launched directly from your PowerPoint presentations.

  Note: *these animations are available on the myA&P™ companion website with gradable quizzes as well as printable study sheets for practice and assessment.*

- **All art, photos, and tables** from the book in JPEG and PowerPoint format, as well as all photos from *A Brief Atlas of the Human Body,* Second Edition. Labels have been enlarged in easy-to-read type for optimal viewing in large lecture halls.

- **Instructor Guide to Text and Media**

- **Test Bank**

- **Illustrations offered in customizable PowerPoint formats,** including Label-Edit Art with editable leaders and labels and Step-Edit Art that walks through multistep figures step-by-step.

- **Quiz Show Game chapter reviews** that encourage student interaction

- **Updated, customizable PowerPoint Lecture Outline slides,** available for every chapter, that combine lecture notes, illustrations with editable labels, photos, tables, and animations.

- **Active Lecture Questions** (for use with or without clickers) that stimulate effective classroom discussions and check comprehension

BONUS!
IRDVD includes Practice Anatomy Lab 2.0 Instructor Resource DVD

PAL IRDVD includes customizable images from PAL 2.0 in JPEG and PowerPoint format. PowerPoint slides also include embedded links to relevant animations and PRS-enabled active lecture questions for use with or without clickers. Quizzes and lab practical are available in Microsoft Word and Computerized Test Bank formats.

(For a description of PAL, please see page xix.)

myA&P™ Website now includes everything students need to practice, review, and self-assess for both the A&P lecture *and* lab.

- **NEW! *Get Ready for A&P*, Second Edition** helps students prepare for the A&P course through Pre-Tests, Post-Tests with Study Plans, tutorials, animations, activities, and an integrated E-Book.

- Chapter-specific resources include Chapter Quizzes and brand new Chapter Practice Tests; Games and Activities, featuring Art Labeling Exercises, Memory Games, and Crossword Puzzles; Histology, Bone, and Muscle Reviews; Flashcards; a Glossary; and more!

- *Interactive Physiology*® 10-System Suite includes a new module on the immune system.

- **NEW! Practice Anatomy Lab™ 2.0** is an indispensable virtual anatomy practice tool that gives students 24/7 access to the most widely used lab specimens (includes self-study quizzes and gradable lab practicals).

- **PhysioEx™ 8.0** supplements traditional wet labs safely and cost-effectively (includes gradable quizzes and printable review sheets).

- **Instructor Gradebook** allows instructors to track student assessment.

- **Instructor Resource Section** includes IP Exercise Sheet Answer Key, and items from the IRDVD, including JPEG images (labeled and unlabeled sets), Label-Edit Art and Step-Edit Art, Active Lecture Questions, and Quiz Show Game Questions.

Course Management

CourseCompass™

This nationally hosted, dynamic, interactive online course management system is powered by Blackboard, the leading platform for Internet-based learning tools. This easy-to-use and customizable program enables professors to tailor content to meet individual course needs. Includes all of the content from myA&P™.

WebCT and Blackboard

These open-access cartridges are loaded with rich content, including assessment items, self-study quizzes, case studies, a histology tutorial, reference tools, and hundreds of fun games, animations, and anatomy labeling exercises.

NEW! New assessment items in the course management system of your choice, including CourseCompass, Blackboard, WebCT, and others. In addition to the Gradeable Quizzes from the myA&P™ Website and the Test Bank, you will now have access to Instructor Test Item assessments for:

- *Get Ready for A&P* (Diagnostic and Cumulative Tests and Chapter Pre- and Post-Tests).

- *Interactive Physiology*®
- PhysioEx™ 8.0
- Quizzes and lab practicals from Practice Anatomy Lab™ 2.0, including images and questions not available in the student product. Instructors can modify the questions to reflect the content they want their students to be quizzed and tested on.
- Post-Test versions of the new Chapter Practice Tests on the myA&P™ Website.

Instructor Guide to Text and Media

(0-321-55876-6)

This fully revised guide includes detailed objectives, lecture outlines, activities, online media resources, answers to end-of-chapter questions, and *Interactive Physiology*® exercise sheets and answer key. All the illustrations from the text are indexed as thumbnails in the Visual Resource Guide so you can easily locate and make the best use of the available media.

Printed Test Bank

(0-321-55884-7)

With more than 3600 test questions, this Test Bank has been updated with new and revised questions that cover all major topics at a range of difficulty levels. All questions in the printed Test Bank are available in Word and TestGen formats on the IRDVD. Both electronic options are cross-platform and allow instructors to easily generate and customize tests.

Transparency Acetates

(0-321-55888-X)

This package includes all illustrations, photos, and tables from the text—approximately 800 images—with labels that have been enlarged for easy viewing in the classroom or lecture hall.

Human Anatomy & Physiology Laboratory Manuals

Elaine N. Marieb's three widely used and acclaimed laboratory manuals complement this textbook and are designed to meet the varying needs of most laboratory courses: *Human Anatomy & Physiology Laboratory Manual: Cat Version*, Ninth Edition Update; *Main Version*, Eighth Edition Update; and *Pig Version*, Ninth Edition Update. Included with each laboratory manual is the PhysioEx™ 8.0 CD-ROM and a registration code for online access. PhysioEx™ 8.0 features 12 experiments and a Histology Tutorial.

Supplements for the Student

NEW! Practice Anatomy Lab™ 2.0 CD-ROM

(0-321-54725-X)

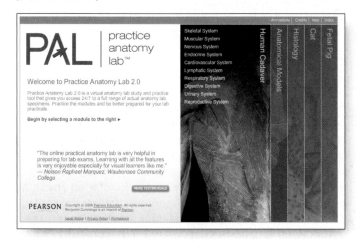

Practice Anatomy Lab™ 2.0 is a virtual anatomy study and practice tool that gives you 24/7 access to a full range of actual lab specimens, including:
- Human cadaver
- Anatomical models
- Histology slides
- Cat dissections
- Fetal pig dissections

Each module includes hundreds of images as well as interactive tools for reviewing the specimens, learning and hearing the names of anatomical structures, seeing animations, and taking multiple choice quizzes and fill-in-the-blank lab practical exams.

PAL 2.0 features include:
- All-new Human Cadaver module
- Fully rotatable human skull and 17 other rotatable skeletal structures
- 3-D animations of origins, insertions, actions, and innervations of over 65 individual muscles
- Greatly expanded Histology module

Interactive Physiology® 10-System Suite

Interactive Physiology® will give you the help you need to grasp some of the most difficult concepts in A&P. This award-winning tutorial system features ten modules containing in-depth, fully narrated, animated tutorials and engaging quizzes covering key physiological processes and concepts. *Interactive Physiology®* is a highly effective program that provides the tools you need to advance beyond simple memorization to a genuine understanding of the most difficult concepts in A&P.

Modules
- Muscular System
- Nervous System I
- Nervous System II
- Cardiovascular System
- Respiratory System
- Urinary System
- Fluids & Electrolytes
- Endocrine System
- Digestive System
- **NEW!** Immune System

myA&P™

Please see How to Use myA&P **for a description (p. x).**

Get Ready for A&P, Second Edition

(0-321-55695-X)
This book and online component
was created to help you be better
prepared for your A&P course.
This hands-on book helps you get
up to speed in your knowledge of
basic study skills, math review,
basic chemistry, cell biology,
anatomical terminology, and the
human body. Features include
pre-tests, guided explanations
followed by interactive quizzes
and exercises, and end-of-chapter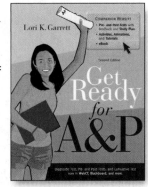
cumulative tests. The online component includes a gradable
diagnostic pre-test and post-test, self-study quizzes with
feedback, animations and links, a glossary, and flashcards. It
is available via myA&P™.

New to the Second Edition
- New topics have been added, including coverage of pH,
  energy, and meiosis, as well as tips on how to minimize
  anxiety surrounding tests, and more.
- A more robust Companion Website includes new
  activities and tutorials on key topics and new myeBook
  content.
- A new preface for instructors explains how to use the
  book.
- All assessments are now available in course management
  platforms, including WebCT, Blackboard, and
  CourseCompass™. Separate Instructor Test Item versions
  of the Diagnostic Test, Cumulative Test, and the chapter
  Pre- and Post-Tests can now be easily imported into these
  course management systems.

A Brief Atlas of the Human Body, Second Edition

This full-color atlas is bundled with every new copy of
the text, and includes 107 bone and 47 soft-tissue
photographs with easy-to-read labels. This new edition
of the atlas contains a brand-new, comprehensive histology
photomicrograph section with more
than 50 slides of basic tissue and organ
systems. Featuring photos taken by
renowned biomedical photographer
Ralph Hutchings, this high-quality
photographic atlas makes an excellent
resource for the classroom and laboratory,
and is referenced in appropriate figure
legends throughout the text.

Study Guide

(0-321-55873-1)
Revised to accompany the Eighth Edition of *Human
Anatomy & Physiology,* the study guide offers a wide variety
of exercises that address different learning styles and call
on students to develop their critical-thinking abilities. The
three major sections, Building the Framework, Challenging
Yourself, and Covering All Your Bases, help students build a
base of knowledge using recall, reasoning, and imagination
that can be applied to solving problems in both clinical and
nonclinical situations.

The Tutor Center

Free tutoring is available to students with a valid myA&P™
course ID number from their instructor. The Tutor Center is
staffed with qualified A&P instructors who can tutor students
on all the materials covered in the text. Tutoring content is
restricted to the text material, and tutors will discuss only
answers that are provided in the textbook. After an instructor
authorizes student access to this service, students can contact
the Tutor Center by phone, email, fax, or the Internet. The
Tutor Center is open five days a week. For more information,
visit www.aw-bc.com/tutorcenter.

Additional Supplements Available from Benjamin Cummings

*Anatomy & Physiology Coloring Workbook: A Complete
Study Guide,* Ninth Edition By Elaine N. Marieb

The Physiology Coloring Book, Second Edition By Wynn
Kapit, Robert I. Macey, Esmail Meisami

The Anatomy Coloring Book, Third Edition By Wynn Kapit
and Lawrence M. Elson

Human Cadaver Dissection Videos By Rose Leigh Vines, et al.

Student Video Series for Human Anatomy & Physiology,
Volume 1

Student Video Series for Human Anatomy & Physiology,
Volume 2

Acknowledgments

Harmonizing "Oh, happy day," we could hardly express our joy at coming to the end of this Eighth Edition update. This revision, like the ones that preceded it, is a major one. It has consumed most of our day and night hours for nearly two years. Text has been streamlined, rewritten for currency, or reorganized. As usual, it's been difficult to keep up to date in the very broad field of anatomy and physiology, and then a wrenching ordeal to decide how much of it to use in the new edition. We want our students to be informed intellectually, but how rich a diet that requires is a persistent question.

Though text revision is demanding, our task there was nothing compared to the Herculean effort of a whole new art program for the book. Literally every figure in the book has been touched in some way. These modifications ranged from light touches such as color changes or text editing for brevity, to art modifications for enhanced three-dimensionality (particularly in anatomy pieces), revisions for greater clarity, or a whole new conceptualization and rendering for better pedagogy. We are really excited about an entirely new feature—the Focus Feature. These one- to two-page displays showcase major concepts that students traditionally have trouble with, such as generation of an action potential, excitation-contraction coupling, or G protein mechanisms. In most cases the feature uses text that concisely states each step, accompanied by exceptionally instructive and evocative art. We are excited about this feature and hope that you will be too.

The sponsoring editor for this edition, Serina Beauparlant, has supported every aspect of this revision—sometimes too much! Serina is insightful and dedicated to producing the best educational product possible (both text and multimedia). She is a true human dynamo. Frank Ruggirello, publisher for this edition, has backed Serina up in the most effective way possible (with $). Thank you Frank. Project editor for this text is again the conscientious and competent Sabrina Larson. Wrestling with schedule deadlines, picking up manuscript loose ends, and trying to make overwhelmed authors work more quickly have made her life these many months a nightmare, we are sure. But she survived and still speaks to us. Derek Perrigo, our marketing manager, has efficiently kept us abreast of the pulse of the marketplace—keeping in touch with professors and students and providing feedback on what they do or don't like about the text and media products. Stacey Weinberger's expertise as manufacturing buyer has served us well. A resounding dollop of gratitude also goes to those on the editorial team with whom we have had little or no personal contact but who have provided valuable services for the revision: Erik Fortier, media producer, and Nicole Graziano, assistant editor, for the Eighth Edition.

We also want to thank the following reviewers who provided us with their expertise and constructive criticism to improve the art and text presentation. Their input resulted in the continued excellence and accuracy of this text.

Kurt Albertine, *University of Utah Medical School*
C. Thomas G. Appleton, *University of Western Ontario*
Barbie Baker, *Florida Community College–Jacksonville*
Sherry Bowen, *Indian River College*
Virginia Brooks, *Oregon Health and Science University*
Bruce Buttler, *Canadian University College*
Mary Beth Dawson, *Kingsborough Community College*
Trevor Day, *University of Calgary*
Randall Fameree, *Athens Technical College*
Patty Finkenstadt, *Phoenix College*
Lynn Gargan, *Tarrant County Community College*
Cynthia Gill, *Hampshire College*
William Hoover, *Bunker Hill Community College*
Mark Hubley, *Prince George's Community College*
Jody Johnson, *Arapahoe Community College*
John C. Koch, *John Tyler Community College*
John Lepri, *University of North Carolina–Greensboro*
Jane Marone, *University of Illinois at Chicago*
Justin Moore, *American River College*
Karen Payne, *Chattanooga State Technical Community College*
Louise Petroka, *Gateway Community College*
Brandon Poe, *Springfield Tech Community College*
David Quadagno, *Florida State University–Emeritus*
Saeed Rahmanian, *Roane State Community College*
Charles Roselli, *Oregon Health and Science University*
Pamela Siergiej, *Roane State Community College*
Tom Swensen, *Ithaca College*
Carol Veil, *Anne Arundel Community College*
Amy Way, *Lock Haven University*
Kelly Young, *California State University, Long Beach*

Additionally, we want to acknowledge Katja's colleagues at Mount Royal College (Trevor Day, Janice Meeking, Izak Paul, Michael Pollock, and Ruth Pickett-Seltner) for stimulating discussions of the text, which they embraced as their own cause, providing feedback on changes and options. We are also grateful to Yvonne Baptiste-Szymanski, Niagara County Community College, Mark Taylor, Baylor University, and Linda Porter, Midlands Technical College, for conducting student user diaries with their classes and gathering valuable feedback directly from our student users.

Once again Wendy Earl Productions handled the production of this text. As always, Wendy Earl, the managing editor, selects highly qualified people to work with her. Michele Mangelli, production supervisor extraordinaire, guided us through the schedule with an expert hand. Her efficient management style and excellent problem-solving skills headed off many a storm, which the whole team appreciated. Laura Southworth, the art development manager, was charged with being the developmental editor for all the art, ensuring the consistency of the art program to encourage automatic learning, helping to conceptualize and construct the Focus Features and all new pieces. All we had to say to Laura is "I don't like this piece of art; can't we do something to reconfigure it for more interest . . . more clarity . . . ?" Two days later there would be a mailer with a great new conceptualization of that figure. Laura is an enthusiastic, can-do woman and we love her! Recognition for a job well done is due Kristin Piljay, photo researcher, and David Novak, art coordinator. Jim Perkins helped us to reorganize key flowcharts in the book, for which we thank him. The talented artists at Imagineering and at Electronic Publishing Services generated the new art pieces conceived for this edition, and made changes requested on existing art. It is their art that puts the zing in the book. We'd also like to thank Precison Graphics who assisted in establishing the new art style for this edition. The new text design is the handiwork of Mark Ong, and the exciting cover image is a stunning photo of 16-time Olympic medalist, Michael Phelps. As always, a monumental thank-you goes to Anita Wagner, ultra-conscientious copyeditor. She edits with a light hand, all the while double-checking all statistics, drug names, and other technical data. Our text developmental editor, Annie Reid, did a great job helping us to rid the book of redundancies and unclear text. We are also fortunate to have Martha Ghent returning as proofreader for this edition. We thank Izak Paul for meticulously proofreading each chapter as well. In addition, Michael Wiley from the University of Toronto checked many pieces of anatomy art for accuracy. As has been the practice with this text, Aptara assembled the final pages with their customary expertise led by their extremely talented and organized Los Angeles Project Manager, Sandie Sigrist Allaway.

Once again, Dr. Marieb's husband, Harvey Howell, served as a sounding board for some of her ideas, manned the copy machine, and ran the manuscript to the FedEx box daily with nary a complaint during the unbelievably busy days. Thanks also to Katja's husband, Dr. Lawrence W. Haynes, who as a fellow physiologist has provided invaluable assistance to her during the course of the revision. She also thanks her children, Eric and Stefan Haynes, who are an inspiration and a joy.

Well, our tenure on this edition is over, but there will be another edition three years hence. We would really appreciate hearing from you concerning your opinion—suggestions and constructive criticisms—of this text. It is this type of feedback that provides the basis of each revision, and underwrites its improvement.

Elaine N. Marieb

Elaine N. Marieb

Katja Hoehn

Katja Hoehn

Elaine N. Marieb and Katja Hoehn
Anatomy and Physiology
Benjamin Cummings Science
1301 Sansome Street
San Francisco, CA 94111

Contents

20 The Lymphatic System and Lymphoid Organs and Tissues   752

21 The Immune System: Innate and Adaptive Body Defenses   766

Appendices

26. Which of the following is *not* a possible cause of conduction deafness? (**a**) impacted cerumen, (**b**) middle ear infection, (**c**) cochlear nerve degeneration, (**d**) otosclerosis.

27. Which of the following are intrinsic eye muscles? (**a**) superior rectus, (**b**) orbicularis oculi, (**c**) smooth muscles of the iris and ciliary body, (**d**) levator palpebrae superioris.

28. Which lies closest to the exact posterior pole of the eye? (**a**) optic nerve, (**b**) optic disc, (**c**) macula lutea, (**d**) point of entry of central artery into the eye.

29. Otoliths (ear stones) are (**a**) a cause of deafness, (**b**) a type of hearing aid, (**c**) important in equilibrium, (**d**) the rock-hard petrous temporal bones.

Short Answer Essay Questions

30. Why do you often have to blow your nose after crying?
31. How do rods and cones differ functionally?
32. Where is the fovea centralis, and why is it important?
33. Describe the response of rhodopsin to light stimuli. What is the outcome of this cascade of events?
34. Since there are only three types of cones, how can you explain the fact that we see many more colors?
35. Where are the olfactory receptors, and why is that site poorly suited for their job?
36. Each olfactory cell responds to a single odorant molecule. True or false? Explain your choice.
37. Name the five primary taste qualities and the cranial nerves that serve the sense of taste.
38. Describe the effect of aging on the special sense organs.

Critical Thinking and Clinical Application Questions

1. During an ophthalmoscopic examination, Mrs. James was found to have bilateral papilledema. Further investigation indicated that this condition resulted from a rapidly growing intracranial tumor. First, define papilledema. Then, explain its presence in terms of Mrs. James's diagnosis.

2. Sally, a 9-year-old girl, told the clinic physician that her "ear lump hurt" and she kept "getting dizzy and falling down." As she told her story, she pointed to her mastoid process. An otoscopic examination of the external acoustic meatus revealed a red, swollen eardrum, and her throat was inflamed. Her condition was described as mastoiditis with secondary labyrinthitis (inflammation of the labyrinth). Describe the most likely route of infection and the infected structures in Sally's case. Also explain the cause of her dizziness and falling.

3. Mr. Gaspe appeared at the eye clinic complaining of a chip of wood in his eye. No foreign body was found, but the conjunctiva was obviously inflamed. What name is given to this inflammatory condition, and where would you look for a foreign body that has been floating around on the eye surface for a while?

4. Mrs. Orlando has been noticing flashes of light and tiny specks in her right visual field. When she begins to see a "veil" floating before her right eye, she makes an appointment to see the eye doctor. What is your diagnosis? Is the condition serious? Explain.

5. David Norris, an engineering student, has been working in a disco to earn money to pay for his education. After about eight months, he notices that he is having problems hearing high-pitched tones. What is the cause-and-effect relationship here?

6. Assume that a tumor in the pituitary gland or hypothalamus is protruding inferiorly and compressing the optic chiasma. What could be the visual outcome?

7. Four-year-old Gary Zammer is brought to the ophthalmologist for a routine checkup on his vision. Gary is an albino. How do you think albinism affects vision?

8. Right before Jan, a senior citizen, had a large plug of earwax cleaned from her ear, she developed a constant howling sound in her ear that would not stop. It was very annoying and stressful, and she had to go to counseling to learn how to live with this awful noise. What was her condition called?

9. During an anatomy and physiology lab exercise designed to teach the use of the ophthalmoscope, you notice that your lab partner has difficulty seeing objects in the darkened room. Upon examining her retina through the ophthalmoscope, you observe streaks and patches of dark pigmentation at the back of the eye. What might this condition be?

10. Henri, a chef in a five-star French restaurant, has been diagnosed with leukemia. He is about to undergo chemotherapy, which will kill rapidly dividing cells in his body. He needs to continue working between bouts of chemotherapy. What consequences of chemotherapy would you predict that might affect his job as a chef?

15

16

The Endocrine System

Y ou don't have to watch *CSI* to experience action-packed drama. Molecules and cells inside your body have dynamic adventures on microscopic levels all the time. For instance, when insulin molecules, carried passively along in the blood, attach to protein receptors of nearby cells, the response is dramatic: Glucose molecules begin to disappear from the blood into the cells, and cellular activity accelerates. Such is the power of the second great control system of the body, the **endocrine system**, which interacts with the nervous system to coordinate and integrate the activity of body cells.

The Endocrine System: An Overview

▶ Indicate important differences between hormonal and neural controls of body functioning.

▶ List the major endocrine organs, and describe their body locations.

▶ Distinguish between hormones, paracrines, and autocrines.

The means of control and the speed of the endocrine system are very different from those of the nervous system. The nervous system regulates the activity of muscles and glands via electrochemical impulses delivered by neurons, and those organs respond within milliseconds. The endocrine system influences metabolic activity by means of *hormones* (*hormone* = to excite), which are chemical messengers released into the blood to be transported throughout the body. Binding of a hormone to cellular receptors initiates responses that typically occur after a lag period of seconds or even days. But, once initiated, those responses tend to be much more prolonged than those induced by the nervous system.

Hormonal targets ultimately include most cells of the body, and hormones have widespread and diverse effects. The major processes controlled and integrated by these "mighty molecules" are reproduction; growth and development; maintenance of electrolyte, water, and nutrient balance of the blood; regulation of cellular metabolism and energy balance; and mobilization of body defenses. As you can see, the endocrine system orchestrates processes that go on for relatively long periods, in some instances continuously. The scientific study of hormones and the endocrine organs is called **endocrinology**.

Compared with other organs of the body, those of the endocrine system are small and unimpressive. Indeed, to collect 1 kg (2.2 lb) of hormone-producing tissue, you would need to collect all the endocrine tissue from eight or nine adults! Unlike the arrangement in most organ systems, the endocrine organs are not grouped together in the body. Instead, endocrine organs are widely scattered about the body.

As we explained in Chapter 4, there are two kinds of glands. *Exocrine glands* produce nonhormonal substances, such as sweat and saliva, and have ducts that carry these substances to a membrane surface. **Endocrine glands**, also called *ductless glands*, produce hormones and lack ducts. They release their hormones into the surrounding tissue fluid (*endo* = within; *crine* = to secrete), and they typically have a rich vascular and lymphatic drainage that receives their hormones. Most of the hormone-producing cells in endocrine glands are arranged in cords and branching networks—a situation that maximizes contact between them and the capillaries surrounding them.

The endocrine glands include the pituitary, thyroid, parathyroid, adrenal, and pineal glands (**Figure 16.1**). The hypothalamus, along with its neural functions, produces and releases hormones, so we can consider the hypothalamus a **neuroendocrine organ**. In addition, several organs, such as the pancreas, gonads (ovaries and testes), and placenta, contain endocrine tissue and also perform other functions.

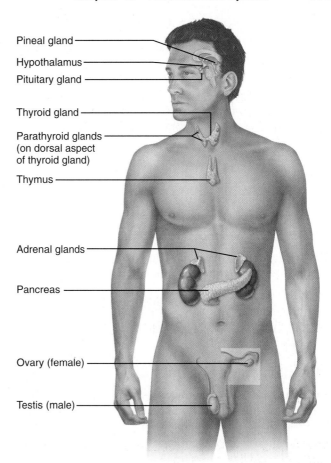

Pineal gland
Hypothalamus
Pituitary gland
Thyroid gland
Parathyroid glands (on dorsal aspect of thyroid gland)
Thymus
Adrenal glands
Pancreas
Ovary (female)
Testis (male)

Figure 16.1 Location of selected endocrine organs of the body.

16

Many other organs also contain scattered endocrine cells or small clusters of endocrine cells. For example, adipose cells release leptin, the thymus releases thymic hormones, and hormone-producing cells are found in the walls of the small intestine, stomach, kidneys, and heart—organs whose chief functions have little to do with hormone production. We describe these other hormone-producing structures on pp. 624–625.

Some physiologists include local chemical messengers—autocrines and paracrines—as part of the endocrine system, but that is not the consensus. Hormones are long-distance chemical signals that travel in blood or lymph throughout the body. **Autocrines** are chemicals that exert their effects on the same cells that secrete them. For example, certain prostaglandins released by smooth muscle cells cause those smooth muscle cells to contract. **Paracrines** also act locally but affect cell types other than those releasing the paracrine chemicals. For example, somatostatin released by one population of pancreatic cells inhibits the release of insulin by a different population of pancreatic cells.

HOMEOSTATIC IMBALANCE

Certain tumor cells, such as those of some cancers of the lung or pancreas, synthesize hormones identical to those made in normal endocrine glands. However, they do so in an excessive and uncontrolled fashion leading to problems due to hormone-mediated pathology. ■

CHECK YOUR UNDERSTANDING

1. For each of the following statements, indicate whether it applies more to the endocrine system or the nervous system: rapid; discrete responses; controls growth and development; long-lasting responses.
2. Which two endocrine glands are found in the neck?
3. What is the difference between a hormone and a paracrine?

For answers, see Appendix G.

Hormones

▶ Describe how hormones are classified chemically.

▶ Describe the two major mechanisms by which hormones bring about their effects on their target tissues.

▶ List three kinds of interaction of different hormones acting on the same target cell.

▶ Explain how hormone release is regulated.

The Chemistry of Hormones

Hormones are chemical substances, secreted by cells into the extracellular fluids, that regulate the metabolic function of other cells in the body. Although a large variety of hormones are produced, nearly all of them can be classified chemically as either amino acid based or steroids.

Most hormones are **amino acid based**. Molecular size varies widely in this group—from simple amino acid derivatives (which include amines and thyroxine constructed from the amino acid tyrosine), to peptides (short chains of amino acids), to proteins (long polymers of amino acids).

The **steroids** are synthesized from cholesterol. Of the hormones produced by the major endocrine organs, only gonadal and adrenocortical hormones are steroids.

If we also consider the **eicosanoids** (i-ko′să-noyds), which include *leukotrienes* and *prostaglandins*, we must add a third chemical class. These biologically active lipids (made from arachidonic acid) are released by nearly all cell membranes. Leukotrienes are signaling chemicals that mediate inflammation and some allergic reactions. Prostaglandins have multiple targets and effects, ranging from raising blood pressure and increasing the expulsive uterine contractions of birth to enhancing blood clotting, pain, and inflammation.

Because the effects of eicosanoids are typically highly localized, affecting only nearby cells, they generally act as paracrines and autocrines and do not fit the definition of the true *hormones*, which influence distant targets. For this reason, we will not consider this class of hormonelike chemicals here. Instead, we note their important effects in later chapters as appropriate.

Mechanisms of Hormone Action

All major hormones circulate to virtually all tissues, but a given hormone influences the activity of only certain tissue cells, referred to as its **target cells**. Hormones bring about their characteristic effects on target cells by *altering* cell activity. In other words, they increase or decrease the rates of normal cellular processes.

The precise response depends on the target cell type. For example, when the hormone epinephrine binds to certain smooth muscle cells in blood vessel walls, it stimulates them to contract. Epinephrine binding to cells other than muscle cells may have a different effect, but it does not cause those cells to contract.

A hormonal stimulus typically produces one or more of the following changes:

1. Alters plasma membrane permeability or membrane potential, or both, by opening or closing ion channels
2. Stimulates synthesis of proteins or regulatory molecules such as enzymes within the cell
3. Activates or deactivates enzymes
4. Induces secretory activity
5. Stimulates mitosis

How does a hormone communicate with its target cell? In other words, how is hormone receptor binding harnessed to the intracellular machinery needed for hormone action? The answer depends on the chemical nature of the hormone and the cellular location of the receptor, but hormones act at receptors in one of two general ways. On the one hand, *water-soluble hormones* (all amino acid–based hormones except thyroid hormone) act on *receptors in the plasma membrane*. These receptors are coupled via regulatory molecules called G proteins to one or more intracellular second messengers which mediate the target cell's response. On the other hand, *lipid-soluble hormones* (steroid and thyroid hormones) act on *intracellular receptors*, which directly activate genes.

This will be easy for you to remember if you think about *why* the hormones must bind where they do. Receptors for water-soluble hormones must be in the plasma membrane since these hormones *cannot* enter the cell, and receptors for lipid-soluble steroid and thyroid hormones are inside the cell because these hormones *can* enter the cell. Of course, things are not quite that clear-cut. Recent research has shown that steroid hormones exert some of their more immediate effects via plasma membrane receptors, and the second messengers of some water-soluble hormones can turn genes on.

Plasma Membrane Receptors and Second-Messenger Systems

With the exception of thyroid hormone, all amino acid–based hormones exert their signaling effects through intracellular **second messengers** generated when a hormone binds to a receptor on the plasma membrane. You are already familiar with one of these second messengers, **cyclic AMP**, which is used by neurotransmitters (Chapter 11) and olfactory receptors (Chapter 15).

The Cyclic AMP Signaling Mechanism As you recall, this mechanism involves the interaction of three plasma membrane components to determine intracellular levels of cyclic AMP

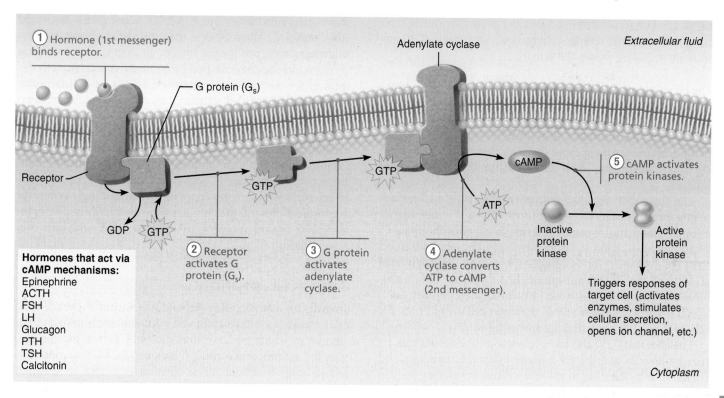

Figure 16.2 Cyclic AMP second-messenger mechanism of water-soluble hormones.

(cAMP)—a hormone receptor, a G protein, and an effector enzyme (adenylate cyclase). **Figure 16.2** illustrates these steps:

1. **Hormone binds receptor.** The hormone, acting as the **first messenger**, binds to its receptor on the plasma membrane.

2. **Receptor activates G protein.** Hormone binding causes the receptor to change shape, allowing it to bind a nearby inactive **G protein**. The G protein is activated as the guanosine diphosphate (GDP) bound to it is displaced by the high-energy compound *guanosine triphosphate* (*GTP*). The G protein behaves like a light switch: It is "off" when GDP is bound to it, and "on" when GTP is bound.

3. **G protein activates adenylate cyclase.** The activated G protein (moving along the membrane) binds to the effector enzyme **adenylate cyclase**. Some G proteins (G_s) *stimulate* adenylate cyclase (as shown in Figure 16.2), but others (G_i) *inhibit* adenylate cyclase. Eventually, the GTP bound to the G protein is hydrolyzed to GDP and the G protein becomes inactive once again. (The G protein cleaves the terminal phosphate group off GTP in much the same way that ATPase enzymes hydrolyze ATP.)

4. **Adenylate cyclase converts ATP to cyclic AMP.** For as long as activated G_s is bound to it, adenylate cyclase generates the *second messenger* cAMP from ATP.

5. **Cyclic AMP activates protein kinases.** cAMP, which is free to diffuse throughout the cell, triggers a cascade of chemical reactions by activating *protein kinase A*. **Protein kinases** are enzymes that *phosphorylate* (add a phosphate group to) various proteins, many of which are other enzymes. Be-

cause phosphorylation activates some of these proteins and inhibits others, a variety of processes may be affected in the same target cell at the same time.

This type of intracellular enzymatic cascade has a huge amplification effect. Each activated adenylate cyclase generates large numbers of cAMP molecules, and a single kinase enzyme can catalyze hundreds of reactions. As the reaction cascades through one enzyme intermediate after another, the number of product molecules increases dramatically at each step. Receptor binding of a single hormone molecule can generate millions of final product molecules!

The sequence of reactions set into motion by cAMP depends on the type of target cell, the specific protein kinases it contains, and the substrates within that cell available for phosphorylation by the protein kinase. For example, in thyroid cells, binding of thyroid-stimulating hormone promotes synthesis of the thyroid hormone thyroxine; in liver cells, binding of glucagon activates enzymes that break down glycogen, releasing glucose to the blood. Since some G proteins inhibit rather than activate adenylate cyclase, thereby reducing the cytoplasmic concentration of cAMP, even slight changes in levels of antagonistic hormones can influence a target cell's activity. Examples of hormones that act via cyclic AMP second-messenger systems are listed in Figure 16.2.

The action of cAMP persists only briefly because the molecule is rapidly degraded by the intracellular enzyme **phosphodiesterase**. While at first glance this may appear to be a problem, it is quite the opposite. Because of the amplification effect, most hormones need to be present only briefly to cause the desired results. Continued production of hormones then prompts continued cellular activity, and no extracellular controls are necessary to stop the activity.

The PIP₂-Calcium Signaling Mechanism Cyclic AMP is the activating second messenger in some tissues for at least ten amino acid–based hormones, but some of the same hormones (such as epinephrine) act through a different second-messenger system in other tissues. In one such mechanism, called the PIP₂-calcium signaling mechanism, intracellular calcium ions act as a final mediator.

Like the cAMP signaling mechanism, the PIP₂-calcium signaling mechanism involves a G protein (G_q) and a membrane-bound effector, in this case an enzyme called **phospholipase C**. Phospholipase C splits a plasma membrane phospholipid called **PIP₂** (**p**hosphatidyl **i**nositol bis**p**hosphate) into **diacylglycerol** (**DAG**) and **inositol trisphosphate** (**IP₃**). DAG, like cAMP, activates a protein kinase enzyme (protein kinase C in this case), which triggers responses within the target cell. In addition, IP_3 releases Ca^{2+} from intracellular storage sites.

The liberated Ca^{2+} also takes on a second-messenger role, either by directly altering the activity of specific enzymes and channels or by binding to the intracellular regulatory protein **calmodulin**. Once Ca^{2+} binds to calmodulin, it activates enzymes that amplify the cellular response.

Hormones known to act on their target cells via the PIP₂ mechanism include thyrotropin-releasing hormone (TRH), antidiuretic hormone (ADH), gonadotropin-releasing hormone (GnRH), oxytocin, and epinephrine.

Other Signaling Mechanisms Other hormones that bind plasma membrane receptors act on their target cells through different signaling mechanisms. For example, cyclic guanosine monophosphate (cGMP) is a second messenger for selected hormones.

Insulin (and other growth factors) work without second messengers. The insulin receptor is a *tyrosine kinase* enzyme that is activated by autophosphorylation (addition of phosphate to several of its own tyrosines) when insulin binds. The activated insulin receptor provides docking sites for intracellular *relay proteins* that, in turn, initiate a series of protein phosphorylations that trigger specific cell responses.

In certain instances, any of the second messengers mentioned—and the hormone receptor itself—can cause changes in intracellular Ca^{2+} levels.

Intracellular Receptors and Direct Gene Activation

Being lipid soluble, steroid hormones (and, strangely, thyroid hormone, a small iodinated amine) diffuse into their target cells where they bind to and activate an intracellular receptor **(Figure 16.3)**. The activated receptor-hormone complex then makes its way to the nuclear chromatin, where the hormone receptor binds to a region of DNA (a *hormone response element*) specific for it. (The exception to these generalizations is that thyroid hormone receptors are always bound to DNA even in the absence of thyroid hormone.) This interaction "turns on" a gene, that is, prompts transcription of DNA to produce a messenger RNA (mRNA). The mRNA is then translated on the cytoplasmic ribosomes, producing specific protein molecules. These proteins include enzymes that promote the metabolic activities induced by that particular hormone and, in some cases, promote synthesis of either structural proteins or proteins to be exported from the target cell.

In the absence of hormone, the receptors are bound up in receptor-chaperonin complexes. These associations seem to keep the receptors from binding to DNA and perhaps protect them from proteolysis. (Check back to Chapter 2, pp. 50–51, if your recall of molecular chaperones needs a jog.) When the hormone *is* present, the complex dissociates, which allows the hormone-bound receptor to bind to DNA and influence transcription.

Target Cell Specificity

In order for a target cell to respond to a hormone, the cell must have *specific* protein receptors on its plasma membrane or in its interior to which that hormone can bind. For example, receptors for adrenocorticotropic hormone (ACTH) are normally found only on certain cells of the adrenal cortex. By contrast, thyroxine is the principal hormone stimulating cellular metabolism, and nearly all body cells have thyroxine receptors.

A hormone receptor responds to hormone binding by prompting the cell to perform, or turn on, some gene-determined "preprogrammed" function. As such, hormones are molecular triggers rather than informational molecules. Although binding of a hormone to a receptor is the crucial first step, target cell activation by hormone-receptor interaction depends equally on three factors: (1) blood levels of the hormone, (2) relative numbers of receptors for that hormone on or in the target cells, and (3) *affinity* (strength) of the binding between the hormone and the receptor. All three factors change rapidly in response to various stimuli and changes within the body. As a rule, for a given level of hormone in the blood, a large number of high-affinity receptors produces a pronounced hormonal effect, and a smaller number of low-affinity receptors results in reduced target cell response or outright endocrine dysfunction.

Receptors are dynamic structures. In some instances, target cells form more receptors in response to rising blood levels of the specific hormones to which they respond, a phenomenon called **up-regulation**. In other cases, prolonged exposure to high hormone concentrations desensitizes the target cells, so that they respond less vigorously to hormonal stimulation. This **down-regulation** involves loss of receptors and prevents the target cells from overreacting to persistently high hormone levels.

Hormones influence the number and affinity not only of their own receptors but also of receptors that respond to other hormones. For example, progesterone induces a loss of estrogen receptors in the uterus, thus antagonizing estrogen's actions. On the other hand, estrogen causes the same cells to produce more progesterone receptors, enhancing their ability to respond to progesterone.

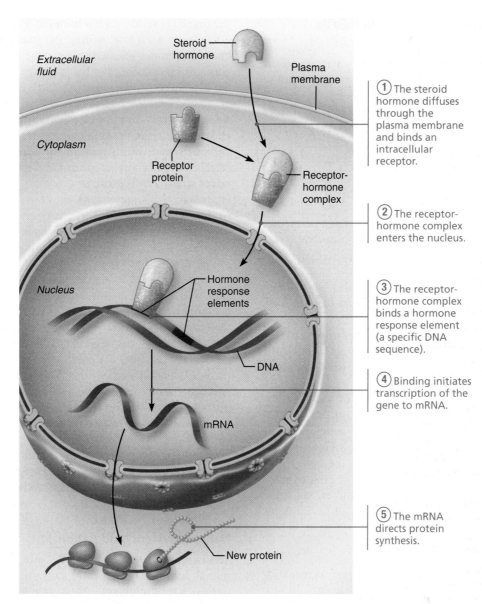

Figure 16.3 Direct gene activation mechanism of lipid-soluble hormones. Steroid hormone is illustrated. Thyroid hormone binds its receptor in the nucleus.

Within the figure:

Extracellular fluid

Steroid hormone

Plasma membrane

① The steroid hormone diffuses through the plasma membrane and binds an intracellular receptor.

Cytoplasm

Receptor protein

Receptor-hormone complex

② The receptor-hormone complex enters the nucleus.

Nucleus

Hormone response elements

③ The receptor-hormone complex binds a hormone response element (a specific DNA sequence).

DNA

④ Binding initiates transcription of the gene to mRNA.

mRNA

⑤ The mRNA directs protein synthesis.

New protein

Half-Life, Onset, and Duration of Hormone Activity

Hormones are potent chemicals, and they exert profound effects on their target organs at very low concentrations. Hormones circulate in the blood in two forms—free or bound to a protein carrier. In general, lipid-soluble hormones (steroids and thyroid hormone) travel in the bloodstream attached to plasma proteins. Most others circulate without carriers.

The concentration of a circulating hormone in blood at any time reflects (1) its rate of release, and (2) the speed at which it is inactivated and removed from the body. Some hormones are rapidly degraded by enzymes in their target cells, but most are removed from the blood by the kidneys or liver, and their breakdown products are excreted from the body in urine or, to a lesser extent, in feces. As a result, the length of time for a hormone's blood level to decrease by half, referred to as its **half-life**, varies from a fraction of a minute to a week. The water-soluble hormones exhibit the shortest half-lives.

How long does it take for a hormone to have an effect? The time required for hormone effects to appear varies greatly. Some hormones provoke target organ responses almost immediately, while others, particularly the steroid hormones, require hours to days before their effects are seen. Additionally, some hormones are secreted in a relatively inactive form and must be activated in the target cells.

The duration of hormone action is limited, ranging from 10 seconds to several hours, depending on the hormone. Effects may disappear rapidly as blood levels drop, or they may persist for hours after very low hormone levels have been reached. Because of these many variations, hormonal blood levels must be precisely and individually controlled to meet the continuously changing needs of the body.

Interaction of Hormones at Target Cells

Understanding hormonal effects is a bit more complicated than you might expect because multiple hormones may act on the same target cells at the same time. In many cases the result of such an interaction is not predictable, even when you know the effects of the individual hormones. Here we will look at three types of hormone interaction—permissiveness, synergism, and antagonism.

Permissiveness is the situation when one hormone cannot exert its full effects without another hormone being present. For example, the development of the reproductive system is largely regulated by reproductive system hormones, as we might expect. However, thyroid hormone is necessary (has a permissive effect) for normal *timely* development of reproductive structures. Without thyroid hormone, reproductive system development is delayed.

Synergism of hormones occurs in situations where more than one hormone produces the same effects at the target cell and their combined effects are amplified. For example, both glucagon (produced by the pancreas) and epinephrine cause the liver to release glucose to the blood. When they act together, the amount of glucose released is about 150% of what is released when each hormone acts alone.

When one hormone opposes the action of another hormone, the interaction is called **antagonism**. For example, insulin, which lowers blood glucose levels, is antagonized by glucagon, which acts to raise blood glucose levels. How does antagonism occur? Antagonists may compete for the same receptors, act through different metabolic pathways, or even, as noted in the progesterone-estrogen interaction at the uterus, cause down-regulation of the receptors for the antagonistic hormone.

Control of Hormone Release

The synthesis and release of most hormones are regulated by some type of **negative feedback system** (see Chapter 1). In such a system, some internal or external stimulus triggers hormone secretion. As hormone levels rise, they cause target organ effects, which then inhibit further hormone release. As a result, blood levels of many hormones vary only within a narrow range.

Endocrine Gland Stimuli

Three major types of stimuli trigger endocrine glands to manufacture and release their hormones: *humoral* (hu′mer-ul), *neural*, and *hormonal* stimuli.

Humoral Stimuli Some endocrine glands secrete their hormones in direct response to changing blood levels of certain critical ions and nutrients. These stimuli are called *humoral stimuli* to distinguish them from hormonal stimuli, which are also bloodborne chemicals. The term *humoral* harks back to the ancient use of the term *humor* to refer to various body fluids (blood, bile, and others).

Humoral stimuli are the simplest endocrine controls. For example, cells of the parathyroid glands monitor the body's crucial blood Ca^{2+} levels. When they detect a decline from normal values, they secrete parathyroid hormone (PTH) **(Figure 16.4a)**.

Because PTH acts by several routes to reverse that decline, blood Ca^{2+} levels soon rise, ending the initiative for PTH release. Other hormones released in response to humoral stimuli include insulin, produced by the pancreas, and aldosterone, one of the adrenal cortex hormones.

Neural Stimuli In a few cases, nerve fibers stimulate hormone release. The classic example of neural stimuli is sympathetic nervous system stimulation of the adrenal medulla to release catecholamines (norepinephrine and epinephrine) during periods of stress (Figure 16.4b).

Hormonal Stimuli Finally, many endocrine glands release their hormones in response to hormones produced by other endocrine organs, and the stimuli in these cases are called hormonal stimuli. For example, release of most anterior pituitary hormones is regulated by releasing and inhibiting hormones produced by the hypothalamus, and many anterior pituitary hormones in turn stimulate other endocrine organs to release their hormones (Figure 16.4c). As blood levels of the hormones produced by the final target glands increase, they inhibit the release of anterior pituitary hormones and thus their own release.

This hypothalamic–pituitary–target endocrine organ feedback loop lies at the very core of endocrinology, and it will come up many times in this chapter. Hormonal stimuli promote rhythmic hormone release, with hormone blood levels rising and falling in a specific pattern.

Although these three types of stimuli are typical of most systems that control hormone release, they are by no means all-inclusive or mutually exclusive, and some endocrine organs respond to multiple stimuli.

Nervous System Modulation

The nervous system can modify both "turn-on" factors (hormonal, humoral, and neural stimuli) and "turn-off" factors (feedback inhibition and others) that affect the endocrine system. Without this added safeguard, endocrine system activity would be strictly mechanical, much like a household thermostat. A thermostat can maintain the temperature at or around its set value, but it cannot sense that your grandmother visiting from Florida feels cold at that temperature and reset itself accordingly. *You* must make that adjustment. In your body, it is the nervous system that makes certain adjustments to maintain homeostasis by overriding normal endocrine controls.

For example, the action of insulin and several other hormones normally keeps blood glucose levels in the range of 90–110 mg/100 ml of blood. However, when your body is under severe stress, blood glucose levels rise because the hypothalamus and sympathetic nervous system centers are strongly activated. In this way, the nervous system ensures that body cells have sufficient fuel for the more vigorous activity required during periods of stress.

CHECK YOUR UNDERSTANDING

4. Name the two major chemical classes of hormones. Which class consists entirely of lipid-soluble hormones? Name the only hormone in the other chemical class that is lipid soluble.

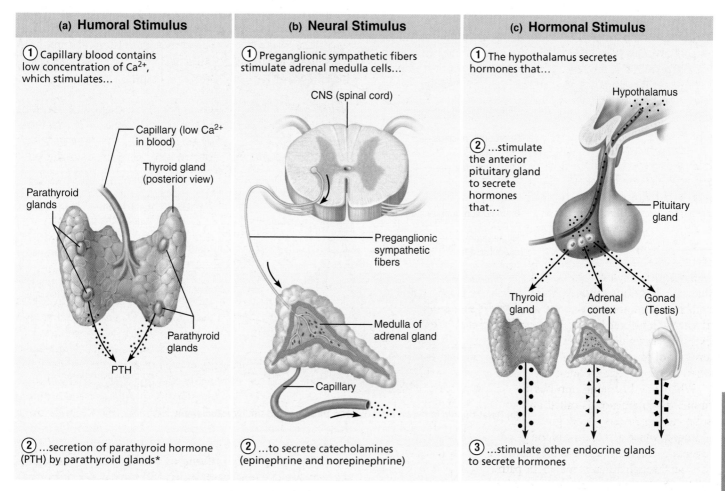

Figure 16.4 Three types of endocrine gland stimuli.
*PTH increases blood Ca^{2+} (see Figure 16.12).

5. Consider the signaling mechanisms of water-soluble and lipid-soluble hormones. In each case, where are the receptors found and what is the final outcome?

6. What are the three types of stimuli that control hormone release?

For answers, see Appendix G.

The Pituitary Gland and Hypothalamus

▶ Describe structural and functional relationships between the hypothalamus and the pituitary gland.

▶ List and describe the chief effects of anterior pituitary hormones.

▶ Discuss the structure of the posterior pituitary, and describe the effects of the two hormones it releases.

Securely seated in the sella turcica of the sphenoid bone, the tiny **pituitary gland**, or **hypophysis** (hi-pof′ĭ-sis; "to grow under"),

secretes at least nine hormones. Usually said to be the size and shape of a pea, this gland is more accurately described as a pea on a stalk. Its stalk, the funnel-shaped **infundibulum**, connects the gland to the hypothalamus superiorly (Figure 16.5).

In humans, the pituitary gland has two major lobes. One lobe is neural tissue and the other is glandular. The **posterior pituitary** (lobe) is composed largely of pituicytes (glia-like supporting cells) and nerve fibers (Figure 16.5). It releases **neurohormones** (hormones secreted by neurons) received ready-made from the hypothalamus. Consequently, this lobe is a hormone-storage area and not a true endocrine gland in the precise sense. The posterior lobe plus the infundibulum make up the region called the **neurohypophysis** (nu″ro-hi-pof′ĭ-sis), a term commonly used (incorrectly) to indicate the posterior lobe alone.

The **anterior pituitary** (lobe), or **adenohypophysis** (ad″ĕ-no-hi-pof′ĭ-sis), is composed of glandular tissue (*adeno* = gland). It manufactures and releases a number of hormones (Table 16.1 on pp. 606–607).

Arterial blood is delivered to the pituitary via hypophyseal branches of the internal carotid arteries. The veins leaving the pituitary drain into the dural sinuses.

16

Paraventricular nucleus

Supraoptic nucleus

Optic chiasma

Infundibulum (connecting stalk)

Hypothalamic-hypophyseal tract

Axon terminals

Posterior lobe of pituitary

Hypothalamus

Inferior hypophyseal artery

Oxytocin
ADH

① Hypothalamic neurons synthesize oxytocin and ADH.

② Oxytocin and ADH are transported along the hypothalamic-hypophyseal tract to the posterior pituitary.

③ Oxytocin and ADH are stored in axon terminals in the posterior pituitary.

④ Oxytocin and ADH are released into the blood when hypothalamic neurons fire.

(a) Relationship between the posterior pituitary and the hypothalamus

Hypothalamic neuron cell bodies

Superior hypophyseal artery

Hypophyseal portal system

• Primary capillary plexus

• Hypophyseal portal veins

• Secondary capillary plexus

Anterior lobe of pituitary

TSH, FSH, LH, ACTH, GH, PRL

Hypothalamus

① When appropriately stimulated, hypothalamic neurons secrete releasing and inhibiting hormones into the primary capillary plexus.

② Hypothalamic hormones travel through the portal veins to the anterior pituitary where they stimulate or inhibit release of hormones from the anterior pituitary.

③ Anterior pituitary hormones are secreted into the secondary capillary plexus.

(b) Relationship between the anterior pituitary and the hypothalamus

Figure 16.5 **Relationships of the pituitary gland and hypothalamus.**

Pituitary-Hypothalamic Relationships

The contrasting histology of the two pituitary lobes reflects the dual origin of this tiny gland. The posterior lobe is actually part of the brain. It derives from a downgrowth of hypothalamic tissue and maintains its neural connection with the hypothalamus via a nerve bundle called the **hypothalamic-hypophyseal tract**, which runs through the infundibulum (Figure 16.5). This tract arises from neurons in the **supraoptic** and **paraventricular nuclei** of the hypothalamus. These neurosecretory cells synthesize two neurohormones and transport them along their axons to the posterior pituitary. Oxytocin (ok″sĭ-to′sin) is made primarily by the paraventricular neurons, and antidiuretic hormone (ADH) primarily by the supraoptic neurons. When these hypothalamic neurons fire, they release the stored hormones into a capillary bed in the posterior pituitary for distribution throughout the body.

The glandular anterior lobe originates from a superior outpocketing of the oral mucosa (*Rathke's pouch*) and is formed from epithelial tissue. After touching the posterior lobe, the anterior lobe loses its connection with the oral mucosa and adheres to the neurohypophysis. There is no direct neural connection between the anterior lobe and hypothalamus, but there is a vascular connection. Specifically, the **primary capillary plexus** in the infundibulum communicates inferiorly via the small **hypophyseal portal veins** with a **secondary capillary plexus** in the anterior lobe. The primary and secondary capillary plexuses and the intervening hypophyseal portal veins make up the **hypophyseal portal system** (Figure 16.5). Note that a *portal system* is an unusual arrangement of blood vessels in which a capillary bed feeds into veins, which in turn feed into another capillary bed. Via this portal system, **releasing** and **inhibiting hormones** secreted by neurons in the ventral hypothalamus circulate to the anterior pituitary, where they regulate secretion of its hormones. All these hypothalamic regulatory hormones are amino acid based, but they vary in size from a single amine to peptides to proteins.

Anterior Pituitary Hormones

The anterior pituitary has traditionally been called the "master endocrine gland" because many of the numerous hormones it produces regulate the activity of other endocrine glands. In recent years, however, it has been dethroned by the hypothalamus, which is now known to control the activity of the anterior pituitary.

Researchers have identified six distinct anterior pituitary hormones, all of them proteins (Table 16.1). In addition, a large molecule with the tongue-twisting name **pro-opiomelanocortin (POMC)** (pro″o″pe-o-mah-lan′o-kor″tin) has been isolated from the anterior pituitary. POMC is a *prohormone*, that is, a large precursor molecule that can be split enzymatically into one or more active hormones. POMC is the source of adrenocorticotropic hormone, two natural opiates (an enkephalin and a beta endorphin, described in Chapter 11), and *melanocyte-stimulating hormone* (*MSH*). In amphibians, reptiles, and other animals MSH stimulates melanocytes to increase synthesis of melanin pigment, but this is not an important function of MSH in hu-

mans. In humans and other mammals, MSH is a CNS neurotransmitter involved in the control of appetite. Although low levels of MSH are found in plasma, its role in the periphery is not yet well understood.

When the anterior pituitary receives an appropriate chemical stimulus from the hypothalamus, one or more of its hormones are released by certain of its cells. Although many different hormones pass from the hypothalamus to the anterior lobe, each target cell in the anterior lobe distinguishes the messages directed to it and responds in kind—secreting the proper hormone in response to specific releasing hormones, and shutting off hormone release in response to specific inhibiting hormones.

Four of the six anterior pituitary hormones—thyroid-stimulating hormone, adrenocorticotropic hormone, follicle-stimulating hormone, and luteinizing hormone—are **tropins** or **tropic hormones** (*tropi* = turn on, change), which are hormones that regulate the secretory action of other endocrine glands. All anterior pituitary hormones except for growth hormone affect their target cells via a cyclic AMP second-messenger system.

Growth Hormone

Growth hormone (**GH**; *somatotropin*) is produced by cells called **somatotrophs** of the anterior lobe and has both growth-promoting and metabolic actions, summarized in **Figure 16.6**. Although GH stimulates most body cells to increase in size and divide, its major targets are the bones and skeletal muscles. Stimulation of the epiphyseal plate leads to long bone growth, and stimulation of skeletal muscles promotes increased muscle mass.

Essentially an anabolic (tissue-building) hormone, GH promotes protein synthesis, and it encourages the use of fats for fuel, thus conserving glucose. Most growth-promoting effects of GH are mediated indirectly by **insulin-like growth factors** (**IGFs**), a family of growth-promoting proteins produced by the liver, skeletal muscle, bone, and other tissues. IGFs produced by the liver act as hormones, while IGFs produced in other tissues act locally within those tissues (as paracrines). Specifically, IGFs stimulate actions required for growth: (1) uptake of nutrients from the blood and their incorporation into proteins and DNA, allowing growth by cell division; and (2) formation of collagen and deposition of bone matrix.

Acting directly, GH exerts metabolic effects. It mobilizes fats from fat depots for transport to cells, increasing blood levels of fatty acids. It also decreases the rate of glucose uptake and metabolism. In the liver, it encourages glycogen breakdown and release of glucose to the blood. The elevation in blood glucose levels that occurs as a result of this *glucose sparing* is called the *anti-insulin effect* of GH, because its effects are opposite to those of insulin.

Secretion of GH is regulated chiefly by two hypothalamic hormones with antagonistic effects. **Growth hormone–releasing hormone (GHRH)** stimulates GH release, while **growth hormone–inhibiting hormone (GHIH)**, also called **somatostatin** (so″mah-to-stat′in), inhibits it. GHIH release is (presumably) triggered by the feedback of GH and IGFs. Rising levels of GH also feed back to inhibit its own release. As indicated in Table 16.1, a number of secondary triggers also influence GH release. Typically, GH secretion has a daily cycle, with the highest

Figure 16.6 Growth-promoting and metabolic actions of growth hormone (GH).

levels occurring during evening sleep. The total amount secreted daily peaks during adolescence and then declines with age.

Besides inhibiting growth hormone secretion, GHIH blocks the release of thyroid-stimulating hormone. GHIH is also produced in various locations in the gut, where it inhibits the release of virtually all gastrointestinal and pancreatic secretions—both endocrine and exocrine.

HOMEOSTATIC IMBALANCE

Both hypersecretion and hyposecretion of GH may result in structural abnormalities. Hypersecretion in children results in **gigantism** because GH targets the still-active epiphyseal (growth) plates. The person becomes abnormally tall, often reaching a height of 2.4 m (8 feet), but has relatively normal body proportions. If excessive amounts of GH are secreted after the epiphyseal plates have closed, **acromegaly** (ak″ro-meg′ah-le) results. Literally translated as "enlarged extremities," this condition is characterized by overgrowth of bony areas still responsive to GH, namely bones of the hands, feet, and face. Hypersecretion usually results from an anterior pituitary tumor that churns out excessive amounts of GH. The usual treatment

is surgical removal of the tumor, but this surgery does not reverse anatomical changes that have already occurred.

Hyposecretion of GH in adults usually causes no problems. GH deficiency in children results in slowed long bone growth, a condition called **pituitary dwarfism**. Such individuals attain a maximum height of 1.2 m (4 feet), but usually have fairly normal body proportions. Lack of GH is often accompanied by deficiencies of other anterior pituitary hormones, and if thyroid-stimulating hormone and gonadotropins are lacking, the individual will be malproportioned and will fail to mature sexually as well. Fortunately, human GH is produced commercially by genetic engineering techniques. When pituitary dwarfism is diagnosed before puberty, growth hormone replacement therapy can promote nearly normal somatic growth.

The availability of synthetic GH also has a downside. Athletes and the elderly have been tempted to use GH for its bodybuilding properties, and some parents have used GH in an attempt to give their children additional height. However, while muscle mass increases, there is no objective evidence for an increase in muscle strength in either athletes or the elderly, and only minimal increases in stature occur in normal children. Moreover, taking GH can lead to fluid retention, joint and muscle pain, diabetes, and may promote cancer. ■

Thyroid-Stimulating Hormone

Thyroid-stimulating hormone (TSH), or **thyrotropin**, is a tropic hormone that stimulates normal development and secretory activity of the thyroid gland. Its release follows the hypothalamic–pituitary–target endocrine organ feedback loop described earlier and shown in Figure 16.7. TSH release from cells of the anterior pituitary called **thyrotrophs** is triggered by the hypothalamic peptide **thyrotropin-releasing hormone (TRH)**. Rising blood levels of thyroid hormones act on both the pituitary and the hypothalamus to inhibit TSH secretion.

Adrenocorticotropic Hormone

Adrenocorticotropic hormone (ACTH) (ah-dre″no-kor″tĭ-ko-trōp′ik), or **corticotropin**, is secreted by the **corticotrophs** of the anterior pituitary. ACTH stimulates the adrenal cortex to release corticosteroid hormones, most importantly glucocorticoids that help the body to resist stressors. ACTH release, elicited by hypothalamic **corticotropin-releasing hormone (CRH)**, has a daily rhythm, with levels peaking in the morning, shortly before awakening. Rising levels of glucocorticoids feed back and block secretion of CRH and ACTH release. Internal and external factors that alter the normal ACTH rhythm by triggering CRH release include fever, hypoglycemia, and stressors of all types.

Gonadotropins

Follicle-stimulating hormone (FSH) and **luteinizing hormone (LH)** (lu′te-in-īz″ing) are referred to collectively as **gonadotropins**. They regulate the function of the gonads (ovaries and testes). In both sexes, FSH stimulates gamete (sperm or egg) production and LH promotes production of gonadal hormones. In females, LH works with FSH to cause an egg-containing ovarian follicle to mature. LH then independently triggers ovulation and promotes synthesis and release of ovarian hormones. In males, LH stimulates the interstitial cells of the testes to produce the male hormone testosterone.

Gonadotropins are virtually absent from the blood of prepubertal boys and girls. During puberty, the **gonadotrophs** of the anterior pituitary are activated and gonadotropin levels begin to rise, causing the gonads to mature. In both sexes, gonadotropin release by the anterior pituitary is prompted by **gonadotropin-releasing hormone (GnRH)** produced by the hypothalamus. Gonadal hormones, produced in response to the gonadotropins, feed back to suppress FSH and LH release.

Prolactin

Prolactin (PRL) is a protein hormone structurally similar to GH. Produced by the **lactotrophs**, PRL stimulates the gonads of some animals (other than humans) and is considered a gonadotropin by some researchers. Its only well-documented effect in humans is to stimulate milk production by the breasts (*pro* = for; *lact* = milk). The role of prolactin in males is not well understood.

Unlike the other anterior pituitary hormones, PRL release is controlled primarily by an inhibitory hormone, **prolactin-**

Figure 16.7 Regulation of thyroid hormone secretion. TRH = thyrotropin-releasing hormone, TSH = thyroid-stimulating hormone.

inhibiting hormone (PIH), now known to be *dopamine (DA)*, which prevents prolactin secretion. Decreased PIH secretion leads to a surge in PRL release. There are a number of *prolactin-releasing factors*, including TRH, but their exact roles are not well understood.

In females, prolactin levels rise and fall in rhythm with estrogen blood levels. Estrogen stimulates prolactin release, both directly and indirectly. A brief rise in prolactin levels just before the menstrual period partially accounts for the breast swelling and tenderness some women experience at that time, but because this PRL stimulation is so brief, the breasts do not produce milk. In pregnant women, PRL blood levels rise dramatically toward the end of pregnancy, and milk production becomes possible. After birth, the infant's suckling stimulates release of prolactin-releasing factors in the mother, encouraging continued milk production and availability.

HOMEOSTATIC IMBALANCE

Hypersecretion of prolactin is more common than hyposecretion (which is not a problem in anyone except women who choose to nurse). In fact, hyperprolactinemia is the most frequent abnormality of anterior pituitary tumors. Clinical signs include inappropriate lactation, lack of menses, infertility in females, and impotence in males. ■

The Posterior Pituitary and Hypothalamic Hormones

The posterior pituitary, made largely of the axons of hypothalamic neurons, stores antidiuretic hormone (ADH) and oxytocin that have been synthesized and forwarded by hypothalamic neurons of the supraoptic and paraventricular nuclei. These hormones are later released "on demand" in response to nerve impulses from the same hypothalamic neurons.

ADH and oxytocin, each composed of nine amino acids, are almost identical. They differ in only two amino acids, and yet they have dramatically different physiological effects, summarized in Table 16.1. ADH influences body water balance, and

TABLE 16.1	Pituitary Hormones: Summary of Regulation and Effects		
HORMONE (CHEMICAL STRUCTURE AND CELL TYPE)	**REGULATION OF RELEASE**	**TARGET ORGAN AND EFFECTS**	**EFFECTS OF HYPOSECRETION ↓ AND HYPERSECRETION ↑**

 Anterior Pituitary Hormones

Growth hormone (GH) (Protein, somatotroph)	**Stimulated** by GHRH* release, which is triggered by low blood levels of GH as well as by a number of secondary triggers including hypoglycemia, increases in blood levels of amino acids, low levels of fatty acids, exercise, other types of stressors, and estrogens **Inhibited** by feedback inhibition exerted by GH and IGFs, and by hyperglycemia, hyperlipidemia, obesity, and emotional deprivation via either increased GHIH* (somatostatin) or decreased GHRH* release	 Liver, muscle, bone, cartilage, and other tissues: anabolic hormone; stimulates somatic growth; mobilizes fats; spares glucose Growth-promoting effects mediated indirectly by IGFs	↓ Pituitary dwarfism in children ↑ Gigantism in children; acromegaly in adults
Thyroid-stimulating hormone (TSH) (Glycoprotein, thyrotroph)	**Stimulated** by TRH* and indirectly by pregnancy and (in infants) cold temperature **Inhibited** by feedback inhibition exerted by thyroid hormones on anterior pituitary and hypothalamus and by GHIH*	 Thyroid gland: stimulates thyroid gland to release thyroid hormones	↓ Cretinism in children; myxedema in adults ↑ Hyperthyroidism; effects similar to those of Graves' disease, in which antibodies mimic TSH
Adrenocorticotropic hormone (ACTH) (Polypeptide of 39 amino acids, corticotroph)	**Stimulated** by CRH;* stimuli that increase CRH release include fever, hypoglycemia, and other stressors **Inhibited** by feedback inhibition exerted by glucocorticoids	 Adrenal cortex: promotes release of glucocorticoids and androgens (mineralocorticoids to a lesser extent)	↓ Rare ↑ Cushing's disease
Follicle-stimulating hormone (FSH) (Glycoprotein, gonadotroph)	**Stimulated** by GnRH* **Inhibited** by feedback inhibition exerted by inhibin, and estrogen in females and testosterone in males	 Ovaries and testes: in females, stimulates ovarian follicle maturation and estrogen production; in males, stimulates sperm production	↓ Failure of sexual maturation ↑ No important effects

oxytocin stimulates contraction of smooth muscle, particularly that of the uterus and breasts.

Oxytocin

A strong stimulant of uterine contraction, **oxytocin** is released in significantly higher amounts during childbirth (*oxy* = rapid; *tocia* = childbirth) and in nursing women. The number of oxytocin receptors in the uterus peaks near the end of pregnancy, and uterine smooth muscle becomes more and more sensitive to the hormone's stimulatory effects. Stretching of the uterus and cervix as birth nears dispatches afferent impulses to the hypothalamus, which responds by synthesizing oxytocin and triggering its release from the posterior pituitary. Oxytocin acts via the PIP_2-Ca^{2+} second-messenger system to mobilize Ca^{2+}, allowing stronger contractions. As blood levels of oxytocin rise, the expulsive contractions of labor gain momentum and finally end in birth.

TABLE 16.1	(continued)		
HORMONE (CHEMICAL STRUCTURE AND CELL TYPE)	**REGULATION OF RELEASE**	**TARGET ORGAN AND EFFECTS**	**EFFECTS OF HYPOSECRETION ↓ AND HYPERSECRETION ↑**
Luteinizing hormone (LH) (Glycoprotein, gonadotroph)	**Stimulated** by GnRH* **Inhibited** by feedback inhibition exerted by estrogen and progesterone in females and testosterone in males	Ovaries and testes: in females, triggers ovulation and stimulates ovarian production of estrogen and progesterone; in males, promotes testosterone production	As for FSH
Prolactin (PRL) (Protein, lactotroph)	**Stimulated** by decreased PIH*; release enhanced by estrogens, birth control pills, breast-feeding, and dopamine-blocking drugs **Inhibited** by PIH* (dopamine)	Breast secretory tissue: promotes lactation	↓ Poor milk production in nursing women ↑ Inappropriate milk production (galactorrhea); cessation of menses in females; impotence in males

 Posterior Pituitary Hormones (Made by Hypothalamic Neurons and Stored in Posterior Pituitary)

Oxytocin (Peptide mostly from neurons in paraventricular nucleus of hypothalamus)	**Stimulated** by impulses from hypothalamic neurons in response to cervical/uterine stretching and suckling of infant at breast **Inhibited** by lack of appropriate neural stimuli	Uterus: stimulates uterine contractions; initiates labor; breast: initiates milk ejection	Unknown
Antidiuretic hormone (ADH) or **vasopressin** (Peptide, mostly from neurons in supraoptic nucleus of hypothalamus)	**Stimulated** by impulses from hypothalamic neurons in response to increased osmolality of blood or decreased blood volume; also stimulated by pain, some drugs, low blood pressure **Inhibited** by adequate hydration of the body and by alcohol	Kidneys: stimulates kidney tubule cells to reabsorb water	↓ Diabetes insipidus ↑ Syndrome of inappropriate ADH secretion (SIADH)

*Indicates hypothalamic releasing and inhibiting hormones: GHRH = growth hormone–releasing hormone; GHIH = growth hormone–inhibiting hormone; TRH = thyrotropin-releasing hormone; CRH = corticotropin-releasing hormone; GnRH = gonadotropin-releasing hormone; PIH = prolactin-inhibiting hormone

Oxytocin also acts as the hormonal trigger for milk ejection (the "letdown" reflex) in women whose breasts are producing milk in response to prolactin. Suckling causes a reflex-initiated release of oxytocin, which targets specialized myoepithelial cells surrounding the milk-producing glands. As these cells contract, milk is forced from the breast into the infant's mouth. Both childbirth and milk ejection result from *positive feedback mechanisms* and are described in more detail in Chapter 28.

Both natural and synthetic oxytocic drugs are used to induce labor or to hasten normal labor that is progressing slowly. Less frequently, oxytocic drugs are used to stop postpartum bleeding (by compressing ruptured blood vessels at the placental site) and to stimulate the milk ejection reflex.

Until recently, oxytocin's role in males and nonpregnant, nonlactating females was unknown, but studies reveal that this potent peptide plays a role in sexual arousal and orgasm when the body is already primed for reproduction by sex hormones. Then, it may be responsible for the feeling of sexual satisfaction that results from that interaction. In nonsexual relationships, it is thought to promote nurturing and affectionate behavior, that is, it acts as a "cuddle hormone."

Antidiuretic Hormone

Diuresis (di″u-re′sis) is urine production, so an *antidiuretic* is a substance that inhibits or prevents urine formation. **Antidiuretic hormone (ADH)** prevents wide swings in water balance, helping the body avoid dehydration and water overload. Hypothalamic neurons called *osmoreceptors* continually monitor the solute concentration (and thus the water concentration) of the blood. When solutes threaten to become too concentrated (as might follow excessive perspiration or inadequate fluid intake), the osmoreceptors transmit excitatory impulses to the hypothalamic neurons, which synthesize and release ADH. Liberated into the blood by the posterior pituitary, ADH targets the kidney tubules via cAMP. The tubule cells respond by reabsorbing more water from the forming urine and returning it to the bloodstream. As a result, less urine is produced and blood solute concentration decreases. As the solute concentration of the blood declines, the osmoreceptors stop depolarizing, effectively ending ADH release. Other stimuli triggering ADH release include pain, low blood pressure, and such drugs as nicotine, morphine, and barbiturates.

Drinking alcoholic beverages inhibits ADH secretion and causes copious urine output. The dry mouth and intense thirst of the "hangover" reflect this dehydrating effect of alcohol. As might be expected, ADH release is also inhibited by drinking excessive amounts of water. *Diuretic drugs* antagonize the effects of ADH and cause water to be flushed from the body. These drugs are used to manage some cases of hypertension and the edema (water retention in tissues) typical of congestive heart failure.

At high blood concentrations, ADH causes vasoconstriction, primarily of the visceral blood vessels. This response targets different ADH receptors found on vascular smooth muscle. Under certain conditions, such as severe blood loss, exceptionally large amounts of ADH are released, causing a rise in blood pressure. The alternative name for this hormone, **vasopressin**, reflects this particular effect.

HOMEOSTATIC IMBALANCE

One result of ADH deficiency is **diabetes insipidus**, a syndrome marked by the output of huge amounts of urine and intense thirst. The name of this condition (*diabetes* = overflow; *insipidus* = tasteless) distinguishes it from diabetes mellitus (*mel* = honey), in which insulin deficiency causes large amounts of blood glucose to be lost in the urine. At one time, urine was tasted to determine which type of diabetes the patient was suffering from.

Diabetes insipidus can be caused by a blow to the head that damages the hypothalamus or the posterior pituitary. In either

case, ADH release is deficient. Though inconvenient, the condition is not serious when the thirst center is operating properly and the person drinks enough water to prevent dehydration. However, it can be life threatening in unconscious or comatose patients, so accident victims with head trauma must be carefully monitored.

Hypersecretion of ADH occurs in children with meningitis, may follow neurosurgery or hypothalamic injury, or results from ectopic ADH secretion by cancer cells (particularly pulmonary cancers). It also may occur after general anesthesia or administration of certain drugs. The resulting condition, *syndrome of inappropriate ADH secretion* (*SIADH*), is marked by retention of fluid, headache and disorientation due to brain edema, weight gain, and decreased solute concentration in the blood. SIADH management requires fluid restriction and careful monitoring of blood sodium levels. ■

CHECK YOUR UNDERSTANDING

7. What is the key difference between the way the hypothalamus communicates with the anterior pituitary and the way it communicates with the posterior pituitary?
8. List the four anterior pituitary hormones that are tropic hormones and name their target glands.
9. Anita drank too much alcohol one night and suffered from a headache and nausea the next morning. What caused these "hangover" effects?

For answers, see Appendix G.

The Thyroid Gland

▶ Describe important effects of the two groups of hormones produced by the thyroid gland.

▶ Follow the process of thyroxine formation and release.

Location and Structure

The butterfly-shaped **thyroid gland** is located in the anterior neck, on the trachea just inferior to the larynx (Figure 16.1 and Figure 16.8a). Its two lateral *lobes* are connected by a median tissue mass called the *isthmus*. The thyroid gland is the largest pure endocrine gland in the body. Its prodigious blood supply (from the *superior* and *inferior thyroid arteries*) makes thyroid surgery a painstaking (and bloody) endeavor.

Internally, the gland is composed of hollow, spherical **follicles** (Figure 16.8b). The walls of each follicle are formed largely by cuboidal or squamous epithelial cells called *follicle cells*, which produce the glycoprotein **thyroglobulin** (thi″ro-glob′u-lin). The central cavity, or lumen, of the follicle stores **colloid**, an amber-colored, sticky material consisting of thyroglobulin molecules with attached iodine atoms. *Thyroid hormone* is derived from this iodinated thyroglobulin.

The *parafollicular cells*, another population of endocrine cells in the thyroid gland, produce *calcitonin*, an entirely different hormone. The parafollicular cells lie in the follicular epithelium but protrude into the soft connective tissue that separates and surrounds the thyroid follicles.

Hyoid bone

Thyroid cartilage

Epiglottis

Common carotid artery

Superior thyroid artery

Inferior thyroid artery

Isthmus of thyroid gland

Trachea

Left subclavian artery

Left lateral lobe of thyroid gland

Aorta

Colloid-filled follicles

Follicle cells

Parafollicular cell

(a) Gross anatomy of the thyroid gland, anterior view

(b) Photomicrograph of thyroid gland follicles (125×)

Figure 16.8 **The thyroid gland.**

Thyroid Hormone

Often referred to as the body's major metabolic hormone, **thyroid hormone (TH)** is actually two iodine-containing amine hormones, **thyroxine** (thi-rok′sin), or **T$_4$**, and **triiodothyronine** (tri″i-o″do-thi′ro-nēn), or **T$_3$**. T$_4$ is the major hormone secreted by the thyroid follicles. Most T$_3$ is formed at the target tissues by conversion of T$_4$ to T$_3$. Very much like one another, these hormones are constructed from two linked tyrosine amino acids. The principal difference is that T$_4$ has four bound iodine atoms, and T$_3$ has three (thus, T$_4$ and T$_3$).

TH affects virtually every cell in the body, as summarized in **Table 16.2** (p. 612). Like steroids, TH enters a target cell, binds to intracellular receptors within the cell's nucleus, and initiates transcription of mRNA for protein synthesis. By turning on transcription of genes concerned with glucose oxidation, TH increases basal metabolic rate and body heat production. This effect is known as the hormone's **calorigenic effect** (*calorigenic* = heat producing). Because TH provokes an increase in the number of adrenergic receptors in blood vessels, it plays an important role in maintaining blood pressure. Additionally, it is important in regulating tissue growth and development. It is critical for normal skeletal and nervous system development and maturation and for reproductive capabilities.

Synthesis

The thyroid gland is unique among the endocrine glands in its ability to store its hormone extracellularly and in large quanti-

ties. In the normal thyroid gland, the amount of stored colloid remains relatively constant and is sufficient to provide normal levels of hormone release for two to three months.

When TSH from the anterior pituitary binds to receptors on follicle cells, their *first* response is to secrete stored thyroid hormone. Their *second* response is to begin synthesizing more colloid to "restock" the follicle lumen. As a general rule, TSH levels are lower during the day, peak just before sleep, and remain high during the night. Consequently, thyroid hormone release and synthesis follows a similar pattern.

Let's examine how follicle cells synthesize thyroid hormone. The following numbers correspond to steps 1–7 in **Figure 16.9**:

① **Thyroglobulin is synthesized and discharged into the follicle lumen.** After being synthesized on the ribosomes of the thyroid's follicle cells, thyroglobulin is transported to the Golgi apparatus, where sugar molecules are attached and the thyroglobulin is packed into transport vesicles. These vesicles move to the apex of the follicle cell, where they discharge their contents into the follicle lumen to become part of the stored colloid.

② **Iodide is trapped.** To produce the functional iodinated hormones, the follicle cells must accumulate iodides (anions of iodine, I$^-$) from the blood. Iodide trapping depends on active transport. (The intracellular concentration of I$^-$ is over 30 times higher than that in blood.) Once trapped inside the follicle cell, iodide then moves into the follicle lumen by facilitated diffusion.

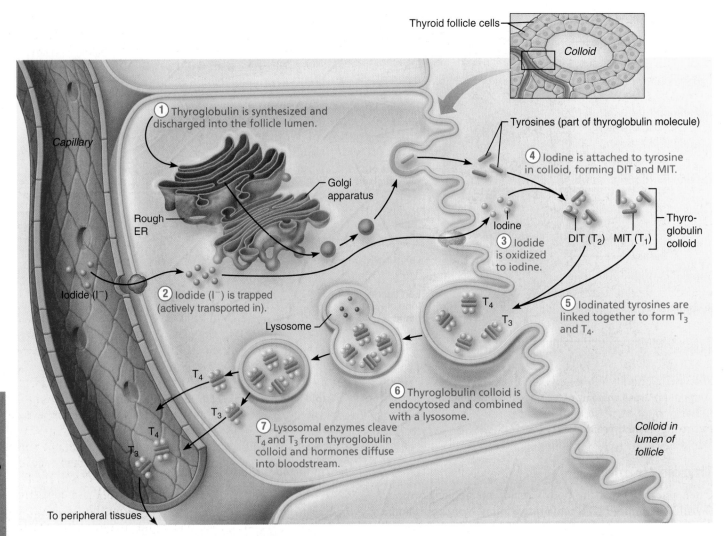

Figure 16.9 Synthesis of thyroid hormone. Only a few tyrosines of the thyroglobulins in the colloid are illustrated. The colloid is represented by the unstructured yellow substance outside of the cells.

(3) **Iodide is oxidized to iodine.** At the border of the follicle cell and colloid, iodides are oxidized (by removal of electrons) and converted to iodine (I_2).

(4) **Iodine is attached to tyrosine.** Once formed, iodine is attached to tyrosine amino acids that form part of the thyroglobulin colloid. This iodination reaction occurs at the junction of the follicle cell apex and the colloid and is mediated by peroxidase enzymes. Attachment of one iodine to a tyrosine produces **monoiodotyrosine** (**MIT** or T_1), and attachment of two iodines produces **diiodotyrosine** (**DIT** or T_2).

(5) **Iodinated tyrosines are linked together to form T_3 and T_4.** Enzymes in the colloid link MIT and DIT together. Two linked DITs result in T_4, and coupling of MIT and DIT produces T_3. At this point, the hormones are still part of the thyroglobulin colloid.

(6) **Thyroglobulin colloid is endocytosed.** In order to secrete the hormones, the follicle cells must reclaim iodinated thyroglobulin by endocytosis and combine the vesicles with lysosomes.

(7) **Lysosomal enzymes cleave T_4 and T_3 from thyroglobulin and the hormones diffuse from the follicle cell into the**

bloodstream. The main hormonal product secreted is T_4. Some T_4 is converted to T_3 before secretion, but most T_3 is generated in the peripheral tissues.

Transport and Regulation

Most released T_4 and T_3 immediately binds to transport proteins, most importantly *thyroxine-binding globulins* (*TBGs*) produced by the liver. Both T_4 and T_3 bind to target tissue receptors, but T_3 binds much more avidly and is about 10 times more active. Most peripheral tissues have the enzymes needed to convert T_4 to T_3 by removing one iodine atom.

The negative feedback loop that regulates blood levels of TH is shown in Figure 16.7. Falling TH blood levels trigger release of *thyroid-stimulating hormone* (*TSH*), and ultimately of more TH. Rising TH levels feed back to inhibit the hypothalamic–anterior pituitary axis, temporarily shutting off the stimulus for TSH release.

Conditions that increase body energy requirements, such as pregnancy and exposure of infants to cold, stimulate the hypothalamus to secrete *thyrotropin-releasing hormone* (*TRH*),

(a)

(b)

Figure 16.10 Thyroid disorders. (a) An enlarged thyroid (goiter) of a Bangladeshi boy.
(b) Exophthalmos of Graves' disease.

which triggers TSH release, and in such instances, TRH overcomes the negative feedback controls. The thyroid gland then releases larger amounts of thyroid hormones, enhancing body metabolism and heat production.

Factors that inhibit TSH release include GHIH, dopamine, and rising levels of glucocorticoids. Excessively high blood iodide concentrations also inhibit TH release.

HOMEOSTATIC IMBALANCE

Both overactivity and underactivity of the thyroid gland can cause severe metabolic disturbances. Hypothyroid disorders may result from some thyroid gland defect or secondarily from inadequate TSH or TRH release. They also occur when the thyroid gland is removed surgically and when dietary iodine is inadequate.

In adults, the full-blown hypothyroid syndrome is called **myxedema** (mik″sĕ-de′mah; "mucous swelling"). Symptoms include a low metabolic rate; feeling chilled; constipation; thick, dry skin and puffy eyes; edema; lethargy; and mental sluggishness (but not mental retardation). If myxedema results from lack of iodine, the thyroid gland enlarges and protrudes, a condition called **endemic** (en-dem′ik), or *colloidal*, **goiter** (Figure 16.10a). The follicle cells produce colloid but cannot iodinate it and make functional hormones. The pituitary gland secretes increasing amounts of TSH in a futile attempt to stimulate the thyroid to produce TH, but the only result is that the follicles accumulate more and more *unusable* colloid. Untreated, the thyroid cells eventually "burn out" from frantic activity, and the gland atrophies.

Before the marketing of iodized salt, parts of the midwestern United States were called the "goiter belt." Goiters were common there because these areas had iodine-poor soil and no access to iodine-rich seafood. Depending on the cause, myxedema can be reversed by iodine supplements or hormone replacement therapy.

Like many other hormones, the important effects of TH depend on a person's age and development. Severe hypothyroidism in infants is called **cretinism** (kre′tĭ-nizm). The child is mentally retarded and has a short, disproportionately sized body and a thick tongue and neck. Cretinism may reflect a genetic deficiency of the fetal thyroid gland or maternal factors, such as lack of dietary iodine. It is preventable by thyroid hormone replacement therapy if diagnosed early enough, but developmental abnormalities and mental retardation are not reversible once they appear.

The most common hyperthyroid pathology is an autoimmune disease called **Graves' disease**. In this condition, a person makes abnormal antibodies directed against thyroid follicle cells. Rather than destroying these cells, as antibodies normally do, these antibodies paradoxically mimic TSH and continuously stimulate TH release. Typical symptoms include an elevated metabolic rate; sweating; rapid, irregular heartbeat; nervousness; and weight loss despite adequate food intake. *Exophthalmos*, protrusion of the eyeballs, may occur if the tissue behind the eyes becomes edematous and then fibrous (Figure 16.10b). Treatments include surgical removal of the thyroid gland or ingestion of radioactive iodine (^{131}I), which selectively destroys the most active thyroid cells. ∎

Calcitonin

Calcitonin is a polypeptide hormone produced by the **parafollicular**, or **C, cells** of the thyroid gland. Its effect is to lower blood Ca^{2+} levels, antagonizing the effects of parathyroid hormone produced by the parathyroid glands, which we consider in the next section. Calcitonin targets the skeleton, where it (1) inhibits osteoclast activity, inhibiting bone resorption and release of Ca^{2+} from the bony matrix, and (2) stimulates Ca^{2+} uptake and incorporation into bone matrix. As a result, calcitonin has a bone-sparing effect.

Excessive blood levels of Ca^{2+} (approximately 20% above normal) act as a humoral stimulus for calcitonin release, whereas declining blood Ca^{2+} levels inhibit C cell secretory activity. Calcitonin regulation of blood Ca^{2+} levels is short-lived but extremely rapid.

Calcitonin does not appear to play an important role in calcium homeostasis in humans. For example, calcitonin does not need to be replaced in patients whose thyroid gland has been

TABLE 16.2	Major Effects of Thyroid Hormone (T$_4$ and T$_3$) in the Body		
PROCESS OR SYSTEM AFFECTED	NORMAL PHYSIOLOGICAL EFFECTS	EFFECTS OF HYPOSECRETION	EFFECTS OF HYPERSECRETION
Basal metabolic rate (BMR)/ temperature regulation	Promotes normal oxygen use and BMR; calorigenesis; enhances effects of sympathetic nervous system	BMR below normal; decreased body temperature and cold intolerance; decreased appetite; weight gain; reduced sensitivity to catecholamines	BMR above normal; increased body temperature and heat intolerance; increased appetite; weight loss
Carbohydrate/lipid/protein metabolism	Promotes glucose catabolism; mobilizes fats; essential for protein synthesis; enhances liver's synthesis of cholesterol	Decreased glucose metabolism; elevated cholesterol/triglyceride levels in blood; decreased protein synthesis; edema	Enhanced catabolism of glucose, proteins, and fats; weight loss; loss of muscle mass
Nervous system	Promotes normal development of nervous system in fetus and infant; promotes normal adult nervous system function	In infant, slowed/deficient brain development, retardation; in adult, mental dulling, depression, paresthesias, memory impairment, hypoactive reflexes	Irritability, restlessness, insomnia, personality changes, exophthalmos (in Graves' disease)
Cardiovascular system	Promotes normal functioning of the heart	Decreased efficiency of pumping action of the heart; low heart rate and blood pressure	Increased sensitivity to catecholamines leads to rapid heart rate and possible palpitations; high blood pressure; if prolonged, heart failure
Muscular system	Promotes normal muscular development and function	Sluggish muscle action; muscle cramps; myalgia	Muscle atrophy and weakness
Skeletal system	Promotes normal growth and maturation of the skeleton	In child, growth retardation, skeletal stunting and retention of child's body proportions; in adult, joint pain	In child, excessive skeletal growth initially, followed by early epiphyseal closure and short stature; in adult, demineralization of skeleton
Gastrointestinal system	Promotes normal GI motility and tone; increases secretion of digestive juices	Depressed GI motility, tone, and secretory activity; constipation	Excessive GI motility; diarrhea; loss of appetite
Reproductive system	Promotes normal female reproductive ability and lactation	Depressed ovarian function; sterility; depressed lactation	In females, depressed ovarian function; in males, impotence
Integumentary system	Promotes normal hydration and secretory activity of skin	Skin pale, thick, and dry; facial edema; hair coarse and thick	Skin flushed, thin, and moist; hair fine and soft; nails soft and thin

removed. However, calcitonin is given therapeutically to patients to treat Paget's disease (a bone disease described in Chapter 6, p. 191).

The Parathyroid Glands

▶ Indicate general functions of parathyroid hormone.

The tiny, yellow-brown **parathyroid glands** are nearly hidden from view in the posterior aspect of the thyroid gland (Figure 16.11a). There are usually four of these glands, but the number varies from one individual to another—as many as eight have been reported, and some may be located in other regions of the neck or even in the thorax. The parathyroid's glandular cells are arranged in thick, branching cords containing scattered *oxyphil cells* and large numbers of smaller **chief cells** (Figure 16.11b). The chief cells secrete parathyroid hormone. The function of the oxyphil cells is unclear.

Discovery of the parathyroid glands was accidental. Years ago, surgeons were baffled by the observation that most patients recovered uneventfully after partial (or even total) thyroid gland removal, while others suffered uncontrolled muscle spasms and severe pain, and subsequently died. It was only after several such tragic deaths that the parathyroid glands were discovered and their hormonal function, quite different from that of the thyroid gland hormones, became known.

Parathyroid hormone (PTH), or *parathormone*, the protein hormone of these glands, is the single most important hormone controlling the calcium balance of the blood. Precise control of calcium levels is critical because Ca^{2+} homeostasis is essential for so many functions, including transmission of nerve impulses, muscle contraction, and blood clotting.

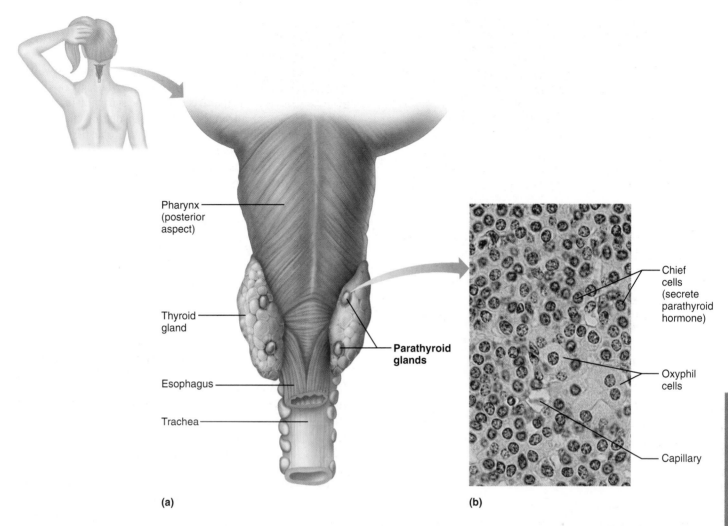

Pharynx (posterior aspect)

Thyroid gland

Esophagus

Trachea

Parathyroid glands

Chief cells (secrete parathyroid hormone)

Oxyphil cells

Capillary

(a)

(b)

Figure 16.11 The parathyroid glands. (a) The parathyroid glands are located on the posterior aspect of the thyroid gland and may be more inconspicuous than depicted. **(b)** Photomicrograph of parathyroid gland tissue (500×).

PTH release is triggered by falling blood Ca^{2+} levels and inhibited by rising blood Ca^{2+} levels. PTH increases Ca^{2+} levels in blood by stimulating three target organs: the skeleton (which contains considerable amounts of calcium salts in its matrix), the kidneys, and the intestine **(Figure 16.12)**.

PTH release ① stimulates osteoclasts (bone-resorbing cells) to digest some of the bony matrix and release ionic calcium and phosphates to the blood; ② enhances reabsorption of Ca^{2+} [and excretion of phosphate (PO_4^{3-})] by the kidneys; and ③ promotes activation of vitamin D, thereby increasing absorption of Ca^{2+} by the intestinal mucosal cells. Vitamin D is required for absorption of Ca^{2+} from food, but the vitamin is ingested or produced by the skin in an inactive form. For vitamin D to exert its physiological effects, it must first be converted by the kidneys to its active vitamin D_3 form, *calcitriol* (1,25-dihydroxycholecalciferol). PTH stimulates this transformation.

HOMEOSTATIC IMBALANCE

Hyperparathyroidism is rare and usually results from a parathyroid gland tumor. In hyperparathyroidism, calcium is leached from the bones, and the bones soften and deform as their mineral salts are replaced by fibrous connective tissue. In *osteitis fibrosa cystica*, a severe example of this disorder, the bones have a moth-eaten appearance on X rays and tend to fracture spontaneously. The resulting abnormally elevated blood Ca^{2+} level (hypercalcemia) has many outcomes, but the two most notable are (1) depression of the nervous system, which leads to abnormal reflexes and weakness of the skeletal muscles, and (2) formation of kidney stones as excess calcium salts precipitate in the kidney tubules. Calcium deposits may also form in soft tissues throughout the body and severely impair vital organ functioning, a condition called *metastatic calcification*.

Hypoparathyroidism, or PTH deficiency, most often follows parathyroid gland trauma or removal during thyroid surgery. However, an extended deficiency of dietary magnesium (required for PTH secretion) can cause functional hypoparathyroidism. The resulting hypocalcemia (low blood Ca^{2+}) increases the excitability of neurons and accounts for the classical symptoms of *tetany* such as loss of sensation, muscle twitches, and convulsions. Untreated, the symptoms progress to respiratory paralysis and death. ■

16

Hypocalcemia (low blood Ca²⁺) stimulates parathyroid glands to release PTH.

Rising Ca²⁺ in blood inhibits PTH release.

— Bone

① PTH activates osteoclasts: Ca²⁺ and PO₄³⁻ released into blood.

② PTH increases Ca²⁺ reabsorption in kidney tubules.

— Kidney

③ PTH promotes kidney's activation of vitamin D, which increases Ca²⁺ absorption from food.

— Intestine

— Blood-stream

•ᵉ• Ca²⁺ ions

▲▴ PTH molecules

Figure 16.12 Effects of parathyroid hormone on bone, the kidneys, and the intestine. The effect on the intestine is indirect via activated vitamin D.

CHECK YOUR UNDERSTANDING

10. What is the major effect of thyroid hormone? Parathyroid hormone? Calcitonin?
11. Name the cells that release each of the three hormones listed above.

For answers, see Appendix G.

The Adrenal (Suprarenal) Glands

▶ List hormones produced by the adrenal gland, and cite their physiological effects.

The paired **adrenal glands** are pyramid-shaped organs perched atop the kidneys (*ad* = near; *renal* = kidney), where they are enclosed in a fibrous capsule and a cushion of fat (see Figure 16.1 and Figure 16.13). They are also often referred to as the **suprarenal glands** (*supra* = above).

Each adrenal gland is structurally and functionally two endocrine glands. The inner **adrenal medulla**, more like a knot of nervous tissue than a gland, is part of the sympathetic nervous system. The outer **adrenal cortex**, encapsulating the medulla and forming the bulk of the gland, is glandular tissue derived from embryonic mesoderm. Each region produces its own set of hormones summarized in **Table 16.3** (p. 617), but all adrenal hormones help us cope with stressful situations.

The Adrenal Cortex

The adrenal cortex synthesizes well over two dozen steroid hormones, collectively called **corticosteroids**. The multistep steroid synthesis pathway begins with cholesterol, and involves varying intermediates depending on the hormone being formed. Unlike the amino acid–based hormones, steroid hormones are not stored in cells. Consequently, their rate of release in response to stimulation depends on their rate of synthesis.

The large, lipid-laden cortical cells are arranged in three layers or zones (Figure 16.13). The cell clusters forming the superficial **zona glomerulosa** (zo′nah glo-mer″u-lo′sah) produce mineralocorticoids, hormones that help control the balance of minerals and water in the blood. The principal products of the middle **zona fasciculata** (fah-sik″u-la′tah) cells, arranged in more or less linear cords, are the metabolic hormones called glucocorticoids. The cells of the innermost **zona reticularis** (rĕ-tik″u-lar′is), abutting the adrenal medulla, have a netlike arrangement. These cells mainly produce small amounts of adrenal sex hormones, or gonadocorticoids. Note, however, that the two innermost layers of the adrenal cortex share production of glucocorticoids and gonadocorticoids, although each layer predominantly produces one type.

Mineralocorticoids

The essential function of **mineralocorticoids** is to regulate the electrolyte (mineral salt) concentrations in extracellular fluids, particularly of Na⁺ and K⁺. The single most abundant cation in extracellular fluid is Na⁺, and the amount of Na⁺ in the body largely determines the volume of the extracellular fluid—where Na⁺ goes, water follows. Changes in Na⁺ concentration lead to changes in blood volume and blood pressure. Moreover, the regulation of a number of other ions, including K⁺, H⁺, HCO₃⁻ (bicarbonate), and Cl⁻ (chloride), is coupled to that of Na⁺. The extracellular concentration of K⁺ is also critical—it sets the resting membrane potential of all cells and determines how easily action potentials are generated in nerve and muscle. Not surprisingly, Na⁺ and K⁺ regulation are crucial to overall body homeostasis. Their regulation is the primary job of **aldosterone** (al-dos′ter-ōn), the most potent mineralocorticoid. Aldosterone accounts for more than 95% of the mineralocorticoids produced.

Aldosterone reduces excretion of Na⁺ from the body. Its primary target is the distal parts of the kidney tubules, where it stimulates Na⁺ reabsorption and water retention accompanied by elimination of K⁺ and, in some instances, alterations in the

Adrenal gland
• Medulla
• Cortex

Kidney

Cortex

Medulla

Capsule
Zona glomerulosa
Zona fasciculata
Zona reticularis
Adrenal medulla

Hormones secreted
Aldosterone

Cortisol and androgens

Epinephrine and NE

(a) Drawing of the histology of the adrenal cortex and a portion of the adrenal medulla

(b) Photomicrograph (160×)

Figure 16.13 Microscopic structure of the adrenal gland.

acid-base balance of the blood (by H^+ excretion). Aldosterone also enhances Na^+ reabsorption from perspiration, saliva, and gastric juice. Because aldosterone's regulatory effects are brief (lasting approximately 20 minutes), plasma electrolyte balance can be precisely controlled and modified continuously. The mechanism of aldosterone activity involves the synthesis and activation of proteins required for Na^+ transport such as Na^+-K^+ ATPase, the pump that exchanges Na^+ for K^+.

In this discussion we are focusing on the major roles of bloodborne aldosterone produced by the adrenal cortex, but aldosterone is also secreted by cardiovascular organs. There it is a paracrine and plays a completely different role in cardiac regulation.

Aldosterone secretion is stimulated by decreasing blood volume and blood pressure, and rising blood levels of K^+. The reverse conditions inhibit aldosterone secretion. Four mechanisms regulate aldosterone secretion, but the first two are by far the most important (**Figure 16.14** and Table 16.3):

1. **The renin-angiotensin mechanism.** The renin-angiotensin mechanism (re′nin an″je-o-ten′sin) influences both blood volume and blood pressure by regulating the release of aldosterone and therefore Na^+ and water reabsorption by the kidneys. Specialized cells of the *juxtaglomerular apparatus* in the kidneys become excited when blood pressure (or blood volume) declines. These cells respond by releasing **renin** into the blood. Renin cleaves off part of the plasma protein **angiotensinogen** (an″je-o-ten′sin-o-gen), triggering an enzymatic cascade leading to the formation

of **angiotensin II**, a potent stimulator of aldosterone release by the glomerulosa cells.

However, the renin-angiotensin mechanism does much more than trigger aldosterone release, and all of its effects are ultimately involved in raising the blood pressure. We describe these additional effects in detail in Chapters 25 and 26.

2. **Plasma concentrations of potassium.** Fluctuating blood levels of K^+ directly influence the zona glomerulosa cells in the adrenal cortex. Increased K^+ stimulates aldosterone release, whereas decreased K^+ inhibits it.

3. **ACTH.** Under normal circumstances, ACTH released by the anterior pituitary has little or no effect on aldosterone release. However, when a person is severely stressed, the hypothalamus secretes more corticotropin-releasing hormone (CRH), and the resulting rise in ACTH blood levels steps up the rate of aldosterone secretion to a small extent. The increase in blood volume and blood pressure that results helps ensure adequate delivery of nutrients and respiratory gases during the stressful period.

4. **Atrial natriuretic peptide (ANP).** Atrial natriuretic peptide, a hormone secreted by the heart when blood pressure rises, fine-tunes blood pressure and sodium-water balance of the body. One of its major effects is to inhibit the renin-angiotensin mechanism. It blocks renin and aldosterone secretion and inhibits other angiotensin-induced mechanisms that enhance water and Na^+ reabsorption. Consequently, ANP's overall influence is to decrease blood pressure by allowing Na^+ (and water) to flow out of the body in urine (*natriuretic* = producing salty urine).

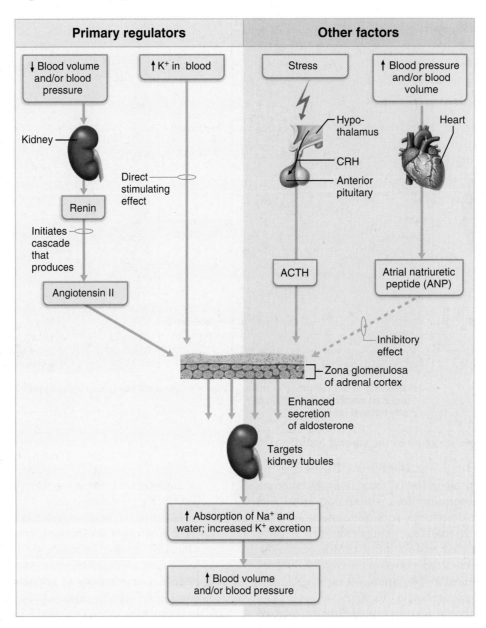

Figure 16.14 Major mechanisms controlling aldosterone release from the adrenal cortex.

![balance icon] HOMEOSTATIC IMBALANCE

Hypersecretion of aldosterone, a condition called *aldosteronism*, typically results from adrenal tumors. Two major sets of problems result: (1) hypertension and edema due to excessive Na⁺ and water retention, and (2) accelerated excretion of potassium ions. If K⁺ loss is extreme, neurons become nonresponsive and muscle weakness (and eventually paralysis) occurs. *Addison's disease*, a hyposecretory disease of the adrenal cortex, generally involves a deficient output of both mineralocorticoids and glucocorticoids, as we will describe shortly. ∎

Glucocorticoids

Essential to life, the **glucocorticoids** influence the energy metabolism of most body cells and help us to resist stressors. Under normal circumstances, they help the body adapt to inter-

mittent food intake by keeping blood glucose levels fairly constant, and maintain blood pressure by increasing the action of vasoconstrictors. However, severe stress due to hemorrhage, infection, or physical or emotional trauma evokes a dramatically higher output of glucocorticoids, which helps the body negotiate the crisis. Glucocorticoid hormones include **cortisol (hydrocortisone)**, **cortisone**, and **corticosterone**, but only cortisol is secreted in significant amounts in humans. As for all steroid hormones, the basic mechanism of glucocorticoid action on target cells is to modify gene activity.

Glucocorticoid secretion is regulated by negative feedback. Cortisol release is promoted by ACTH, triggered in turn by the hypothalamic releasing hormone CRH. Rising cortisol levels feed back to act on both the hypothalamus and the anterior pituitary, preventing CRH release and shutting off ACTH and cortisol secretion. Cortisol secretory bursts, driven by patterns of

TABLE 16.3	Adrenal Gland Hormones: Summary of Regulation and Effects		
HORMONE	**REGULATION OF RELEASE**	**TARGET ORGAN AND EFFECTS**	**EFFECTS OF HYPERSECRETION ↑ AND HYPOSECRETION ↓**
Adrenocortical Hormones			
Mineralocorticoids (chiefly aldosterone)	Stimulated by renin-angiotensin mechanism (activated by decreasing blood volume or blood pressure), elevated blood K^+ levels, and ACTH (minor influence); inhibited by increased blood volume and pressure, and decreased blood K^+ levels	Kidneys: increase blood levels of Na^+ and decrease blood levels of K^+; since water reabsorption accompanies sodium retention, blood volume and blood pressure rise	↑ Aldosteronism ↓ Addison's disease
Glucocorticoids (chiefly cortisol)	Stimulated by ACTH; inhibited by feedback inhibition exerted by cortisol	Body cells: promote gluconeogenesis and hyperglycemia; mobilize fats for energy metabolism; stimulate protein catabolism; assist body to resist stressors; depress inflammatory and immune responses	↑ Cushing's syndrome ↓ Addison's disease
Gonadocorticoids (chiefly androgens, converted to testosterone or estrogens after release)	Stimulated by ACTH; mechanism of inhibition incompletely understood, but feedback inhibition not seen	Insignificant effects in males; responsible for female libido; development of pubic and axillary hair in females; source of estrogen after menopause	↑ Virilization of females (adrenogenital syndrome) ↓ No effects known
Adrenal Medullary Hormones			
Catecholamines (epinephrine and norepinephrine)	Stimulated by preganglionic fibers of the sympathetic nervous system	Sympathetic nervous system target organs: effects mimic sympathetic nervous system activation; increase heart rate and metabolic rate; increase blood pressure by promoting vasoconstriction	↑ Prolonged fight-or-flight response; hypertension ↓ Unimportant

16

eating and activity, occur in a definite pattern throughout the day and night. Cortisol blood levels peak shortly before we arise in the morning. The lowest levels occur in the evening just before and shortly after we fall asleep. The normal cortisol rhythm is interrupted by acute stress of any variety as higher CNS centers override the (usually) inhibitory effects of elevated cortisol levels and trigger CRH release. The resulting increase in ACTH blood levels causes an outpouring of cortisol from the adrenal cortex.

Stress results in a dramatic rise in blood levels of glucose, fatty acids, and amino acids, all provoked by cortisol. Cortisol's prime metabolic effect is to provoke *gluconeogenesis*, that is, the formation of glucose from fats and proteins. In order to "save" glucose for the brain, cortisol mobilizes fatty acids from adipose tissue and encourages their increased use for energy. Under cortisol's influence, stored proteins are broken down to provide building blocks for repair or for making enzymes to be used in metabolic processes. Cortisol enhances the sympathetic nervous system's vasoconstrictive effects, and the rise in blood pressure and circulatory efficiency that results helps ensure that these nutrients are quickly distributed to the cells.

Note that *ideal amounts of glucocorticoids promote normal function*, but cortisol excess is associated with significant anti-

inflammatory and anti-immune effects. Excessive levels of glucocorticoids (1) depress cartilage and bone formation, (2) inhibit inflammation by decreasing the release of inflammatory chemicals, (3) depress the immune system, and (4) promote changes in cardiovascular, neural, and gastrointestinal function. Recognition of the effects of glucocorticoid hypersecretion has led to widespread use of glucocorticoid drugs to control symptoms of many chronic inflammatory disorders, such as rheumatoid arthritis or allergic responses. However, these potent drugs are a double-edged sword. Although they relieve some of the symptoms of these disorders, they also cause the undesirable effects of excessive levels of these hormones.

HOMEOSTATIC IMBALANCE

The pathology of glucocorticoid excess, **Cushing's syndrome**, may be caused by an ACTH-releasing pituitary tumor (in which case, it is called **Cushing's disease**); by an ACTH-releasing malignancy of the lungs, pancreas, or kidneys; or by a tumor of the adrenal cortex. However, it most often results from the clinical administration of pharmacological doses (doses higher than those found in the body) of glucocorticoid drugs. The syndrome is characterized by persistent elevated blood glucose levels

(a) Patient before onset.

(b) Same patient with Cushing's syndrome. The white arrow shows the characteristic "buffalo hump" of fat on the upper back.

Figure 16.15 **The effects of excess glucocorticoid.**

16

(*steroid diabetes*), dramatic losses in muscle and bone protein, and water and salt retention, leading to hypertension and edema. The so-called *cushingoid signs* (Figure 16.15) include a swollen "moon" face, redistribution of fat to the abdomen and the posterior neck (causing a "buffalo hump"), a tendency to bruise, and poor wound healing. Because of enhanced anti-inflammatory effects, infections may become overwhelmingly severe before producing recognizable symptoms. Eventually, muscles weaken and spontaneous fractures force the person to become bedridden. The only treatment is removal of the cause—be it surgical removal of the offending tumor or discontinuation of the drug.

Addison's disease, the major hyposecretory disorder of the adrenal cortex, usually involves deficits in both glucocorticoids and mineralocorticoids. Its victims tend to lose weight; their plasma glucose and sodium levels drop, and potassium levels rise. Severe dehydration and hypotension are common. Corticosteroid replacement therapy at physiological doses (doses typical of those normally found in the body) is the usual treatment. ∎

Gonadocorticoids (Sex Hormones)

The bulk of the **gonadocorticoids** secreted by the adrenal cortex are weak **androgens**, or male sex hormones, such as *androstenedione* and *dehydroepiandrosterone* (*DHEA*). These are converted to the more potent male hormone, *testosterone*, in the tissue cells or to estrogens (female sex homones) in females. The adrenal cortex also makes small amounts of female hormones (estradiol and other estrogens). The amount of gonadocorticoids produced by the adrenal cortex is insignificant compared with the amounts made by the gonads during late puberty and adulthood.

The exact role of the adrenal sex hormones is still in question, but because adrenal androgen levels rise continuously between the ages of 7 and 13 in both boys and girls, it is assumed that these hormones contribute to the onset of puberty and the appearance of axillary and pubic hair during that time. In adult women adrenal androgens are thought to be responsible for the sex drive, and they may account for the estrogens produced after menopause when ovarian estrogens are no longer produced. Control of gonadocorticoid secretion is not completely understood. Release seems to be stimulated by ACTH, but the gonadocorticoids do not appear to exert feedback inhibition on ACTH release.

HOMEOSTATIC IMBALANCE

Since androgens predominate, hypersecretion of gonadocorticoids causes *adrenogenital syndrome* (masculinization). In adult males, these effects of elevated gonadocorticoid levels may be obscured, since testicular testosterone has already produced virilization, but in prepubertal males and in females, the results can be dramatic. In the young man, maturation of the reproductive organs and appearance of the secondary sex characteristics occur rapidly, and the sex drive emerges with a vengeance. Females develop a beard and a masculine pattern of body hair distribution, and the clitoris grows to resemble a small penis. ∎

The Adrenal Medulla

We discussed the adrenal medulla in Chapter 14 as part of the autonomic nervous system, so our coverage here is brief. The spherical **chromaffin cells** (kro′maf-in), which crowd around

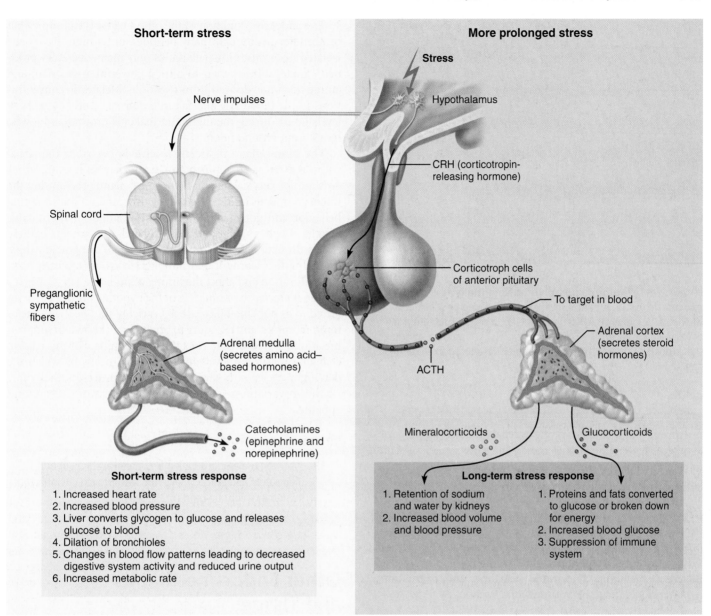

Figure 16.16 Stress and the adrenal gland. Stressful stimuli cause the hypothalamus to activate the adrenal medulla via sympathetic nerve impulses and the adrenal cortex via hormonal signals.

blood-filled capillaries and sinusoids, are modified ganglionic sympathetic neurons that synthesize the *catecholamines* **epinephrine** and **norepinephrine (NE)** via a molecular sequence from tyrosine to dopamine to NE to epinephrine.

When the body is activated to fight-or-flight status by some short-term stressor, the sympathetic nervous system is mobilized. Blood glucose levels rise, blood vessels constrict and the heart beats faster (together raising the blood pressure), blood is diverted from temporarily nonessential organs to the heart and skeletal muscles, and preganglionic sympathetic nerve endings weaving through the adrenal medulla signal for release of catecholamines, which reinforce and prolong the fight-or-flight response.

Unequal amounts of the two hormones are stored and released. Approximately 80% is epinephrine and 20% norepi-

nephrine. With a few exceptions, the two hormones exert the same effects (see Table 14.2, p. 536). Epinephrine is the more potent stimulator of metabolic activities, bronchial dilation, and increased blood flow to skeletal muscles and the heart, but norepinephrine has the greater influence on peripheral vasoconstriction and blood pressure. Epinephrine is used clinically as a heart stimulant and to dilate the bronchioles during acute asthmatic attacks.

Unlike the adrenocortical hormones, which promote long-lasting body responses to stressors, catecholamines cause fairly brief responses. The interrelationships of the adrenal hormones and the hypothalamus, the "director" of the stress response, are depicted in **Figure 16.16**.

Pancreatic islet (of Langerhans)
- α (Glucagon-producing) cells
- β (Insulin-producing) cells

Pancreatic acinar cells (exocrine)

Figure 16.17 Photomicrograph of differentially stained pancreatic tissue. A pancreatic islet is surrounded by acinar cells (stained blue–gray), which produce the exocrine product (enzyme-rich pancreatic juice). The β cells of the islets that produce insulin are stained pale pink, and the α cells that produce glucagon are bright pink (230×).

HOMEOSTATIC IMBALANCE

A deficiency of hormones of the adrenal medulla is not a problem because these hormones merely intensify activities set into motion by the sympathetic nervous system neurons. Unlike glucocorticoids and mineralocorticoids, adrenal catecholamines are not essential for life. On the other hand, hypersecretion of catecholamines, sometimes arising from a chromaffin cell tumor called a *pheochromocytoma* (fe-o-kro″mo-si-to′mah), produces symptoms of uncontrolled sympathetic nervous system activity—**hyperglycemia** (elevated blood glucose), increased metabolic rate, rapid heartbeat and palpitations, hypertension, intense nervousness, and sweating. ■

CHECK YOUR UNDERSTANDING

12. List the three classes of hormones released from the adrenal cortex and for each briefly state its major effect(s).

For answers, see Appendix G.

The Pineal Gland

▶ Briefly describe the importance of melatonin.

The tiny, pine cone–shaped **pineal gland** hangs from the roof of the third ventricle in the diencephalon (see Figure 16.1). Its secretory cells, called **pinealocytes**, are arranged in compact cords and clusters. Lying between pinealocytes in adults are dense particles containing calcium salts ("brain-sand" or "pineal sand"). These salts are radiopaque, making the pineal gland a handy landmark for determining brain orientation in X rays.

The endocrine function of the pineal gland is still somewhat of a mystery. Although many peptides and amines have been isolated from this minute gland, its only major secretory product is **melatonin** (mel″ah-to′nin), a powerful antioxidant and amine hormone derived from serotonin. Melatonin concentrations in the blood rise and fall in a diurnal (daily) cycle. Peak levels occur during the night and make us drowsy, and lowest levels occur around noon.

The pineal gland indirectly receives input from the visual pathways (retina → suprachiasmatic nucleus of hypothalamus → superior cervical ganglion → pineal gland) concerning the intensity and duration of daylight. In some animals, mating behavior and gonadal size vary with changes in the relative lengths of light and dark periods, and melatonin mediates these effects. In children, melatonin may have an antigonadotropic effect. In other words, it may inhibit precocious (too early) sexual maturation and affect the timing of puberty.

The *suprachiasmatic nucleus* of the hypothalamus, an area referred to as our "biological clock," is richly supplied with melatonin receptors, and exposure to bright light (known to suppress melatonin secretion) can reset the clock timing. For this reason, changing melatonin levels may also be a means by which the day/night cycles influence physiological processes that show rhythmic variations, such as body temperature, sleep, and appetite.

CHECK YOUR UNDERSTANDING

13. Synthetic melatonin supplements are available, although their safety and efficacy have not been proved. What do you think they might be used for?

For answers, see Appendix G.

Other Endocrine Glands and Tissues

So far, we've examined the endocrine role of the hypothalamus and of glands dedicated solely to endocrine function. We will now consider a set of organs that contain endocrine tissue but also have other major functions. These include the pancreas, gonads, and placenta.

The Pancreas

▶ Compare and contrast the effects of the two major pancreatic hormones.

Located partially behind the stomach in the abdomen, the soft, triangular **pancreas** is a mixed gland composed of both endocrine and exocrine gland cells (see Figure 16.1). Along with the thyroid and parathyroids, it develops as an outpocketing of the epithelial lining of the gastrointestinal tract. *Acinar cells,* forming the bulk of the gland, produce an enzyme-rich juice that is carried by ducts to the small intestine during digestion.

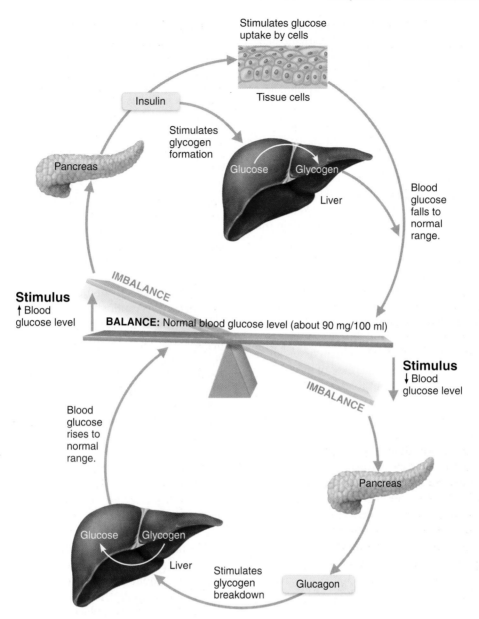

Figure 16.18 Regulation of blood glucose levels by insulin and glucagon from the pancreas.

Scattered among the acinar cells are approximately a million **pancreatic islets** (also called **islets of Langerhans**), tiny cell clusters that produce pancreatic hormones **(Figure 16.17)**. The islets contain two major populations of hormone-producing cells, the glucagon-synthesizing **alpha (α) cells** and the more numerous insulin-producing **beta (β) cells**. These cells act as tiny fuel sensors, secreting glucagon and insulin appropriately during the fasting and fed states. In this way insulin and glucagon are intimately but independently involved in the regulation of blood glucose levels. Their effects are antagonistic: Insulin is a *hypoglycemic* hormone, whereas glucagon is a *hyperglycemic* hormone **(Figure 16.18)**. Some islet cells also synthesize other peptides in small amounts. These include *somatostatin*, *pancreatic polypeptide* (*PP*), and others. However, we will not deal with these here.

Glucagon

Glucagon (gloo′kah-gon), a 29-amino-acid polypeptide, is an extremely potent hyperglycemic agent. One molecule of this hormone can cause the release of 100 million molecules of glucose into the blood! The major target of glucagon is the liver, where it promotes the following actions:

1. Breakdown of glycogen to glucose (*glycogenolysis*) (Figure 16.18)
2. Synthesis of glucose from lactic acid and from noncarbohydrate molecules (*gluconeogenesis*)
3. Release of glucose to the blood by liver cells, causing blood glucose levels to rise

A secondary effect is a fall in the amino acid concentration in the blood as the liver cells sequester these molecules to make new glucose molecules.

Humoral stimuli, mainly falling blood glucose levels, prompt the alpha cells to secrete glucagon. However, sympathetic nervous system stimulation and rising amino acid levels (as might follow a protein-rich meal) are also stimulatory. Glucagon release is suppressed by rising blood glucose levels, insulin, and somatostatin.

Insulin

Insulin is a small (51-amino-acid) protein consisting of two amino acid chains linked by disulfide (–S–S–) bonds. It is synthesized as part of a larger polypeptide chain called **proinsulin**. The middle portion of this chain is then excised by enzymes, releasing functional insulin. This "clipping" process occurs in the secretory vesicles just before insulin is released from the beta cell.

Insulin's effects are most obvious when we have just eaten. Its main effect is to lower blood glucose levels (Figure 16.18), but it also influences protein and fat metabolism. Circulating insulin lowers blood glucose levels in three main ways. (1) Insulin enhances membrane transport of glucose (and other simple sugars) into body cells, especially muscle and fat cells. (It does *not* accelerate glucose entry into liver, kidney, and brain tissue, all of which have easy access to blood glucose regardless of insulin levels. However, insulin does have important roles in the brain—it participates in neuronal development, feeding behavior, and learning and memory.) (2) Insulin inhibits the breakdown of glycogen to glucose, and (3) it inhibits the conversion of amino acids or fats to glucose. These inhibiting effects counter any metabolic activity that would increase plasma levels of glucose.

How does insulin act at the cellular level? Insulin activates its receptor (a tyrosine kinase enzyme), which phosphorylates specific proteins, beginning the cascade that leads to increased glucose uptake and insulin's other effects. After glucose enters a target cell, insulin binding triggers enzymatic activities that

1. Catalyze the oxidation of glucose for ATP production
2. Join glucose molecules together to form glycogen
3. Convert glucose to fat (particularly in adipose tissue)

As a rule, energy needs are met first, followed by glycogen formation. Finally, if excess glucose is still available, it is converted to fat. Insulin also stimulates amino acid uptake and protein synthesis in muscle tissue. In summary, insulin sweeps glucose out of the blood, causing it to be used for energy or converted to other forms (glycogen or fats), and it promotes protein synthesis and fat storage.

Pancreatic beta cells are stimulated to secrete insulin chiefly by elevated blood glucose levels, but also by rising plasma levels of amino acids and fatty acids, and release of acetylcholine by parasympathetic nerve fibers. As body cells take up glucose and other nutrients, and plasma levels of these substances drop, insulin secretion is suppressed.

Other hormones also influence insulin release. For example, any hyperglycemic hormone (such as glucagon, epinephrine, growth hormone, thyroxine, or glucocorticoids) called into action as blood glucose levels drop indirectly stimulates insulin release by promoting glucose entry into the bloodstream. Somatostatin and sympathetic nervous system activation depress insulin release. As you can see, blood glucose levels represent a balance of humoral, neural, and hormonal influences.

Insulin is the major hypoglycemic factor that counterbalances the many hyperglycemic hormones.

HOMEOSTATIC IMBALANCE

Diabetes mellitus (DM) results from either hyposecretion or hypoactivity of insulin. When insulin is absent or deficient, blood glucose levels remain high after a meal because glucose is unable to enter most tissue cells. Ordinarily, when blood glucose levels rise, hyperglycemic hormones are not released, but when hyperglycemia becomes excessive, the person begins to feel nauseated, which precipitates the fight-or-flight response. This response results, inappropriately, in all the reactions that normally occur in the hypoglycemic (fasting) state to make glucose available—that is, glycogenolysis, lipolysis (breakdown of fat), and gluconeogenesis. Consequently, the already high blood glucose levels soar even higher, and excesses of glucose begin to be lost from the body in the urine (*glycosuria*).

When sugars cannot be used as cellular fuel, more fats are mobilized, resulting in high fatty acid levels in the blood, a condition called lipidemia or lipemia. In severe cases of diabetes mellitus, blood levels of fatty acids and their metabolites (acetoacetic acid, acetone, and others) rise dramatically. The fatty acid metabolites, collectively called **ketones** (ke'tōnz) or **ketone bodies**, are organic acids. When they accumulate in the blood, the blood pH drops, resulting in **ketoacidosis**, and ketone bodies begin to spill into the urine (*ketonuria*). Severe ketoacidosis is life threatening. The nervous system responds by initiating rapid deep breathing (hyperpnea) to blow off carbon dioxide from the blood and increase blood pH. (We will explain the physiological basis of this mechanism in Chapter 22.) If untreated, ketoacidosis disrupts heart activity and oxygen transport, and severe depression of the nervous system leads to coma and death.

The three cardinal signs of diabetes mellitus are polyuria, polydipsia, and polyphagia. The excessive glucose in the kidney filtrate acts as an osmotic diuretic (that is, it inhibits water reabsorption by the kidney tubules), resulting in **polyuria**, a huge urine output that leads to decreased blood volume and dehydration. Serious electrolyte losses also occur as the body rids itself of excess ketone bodies. Ketone bodies are negatively charged and carry positive ions out with them, and as a result, sodium and potassium ions are also lost from the body. Because of the electrolyte imbalance, the person gets abdominal pains and may vomit, and the stress reaction spirals even higher. Dehydration stimulates hypothalamic thirst centers, causing **polydipsia**, or excessive thirst. The final sign, **polyphagia**, refers to excessive hunger and food consumption, a sign that the person is "starving in the land of plenty." Although plenty of glucose is available, it cannot be used, and the body starts to utilize its fat and protein stores for energy metabolism. **Table 16.4** summarizes the consequences of insulin deficiency. DM is the focus of *A Closer Look* on pp. 626–627.

Hyperinsulinism, or excessive insulin secretion, results in low blood glucose levels, or **hypoglycemia**. This condition triggers the release of hyperglycemic hormones, which cause anxiety, nervousness, tremors, and weakness. Insufficient glucose delivery to the brain causes disorientation, progressing to convulsions, unconsciousness, and even death. In rare cases, hyperinsulinism re-

TABLE 16.4   Symptoms of Insulin Deficit (Diabetes Mellitus)

ORGANS/TISSUES INVOLVED	ORGAN/TISSUE RESPONSES TO INSULIN DEFICIENCY	RESULTING CONDITIONS		SIGNS AND SYMPTOMS
		IN BLOOD	IN URINE	
Liver Adipose tissue Muscle	Decreased glucose uptake and utilization	Hyperglycemia	Glycosuria Osmotic diuresis	Polyuria (and dehydration, soft eyeballs) Polydipsia (and fatigue, weight loss) Polyphagia
Liver	Glycogenolysis			
Liver Muscle	Protein catabolism and gluconeogenesis			
Liver Adipose tissue	Lipolysis and ketogenesis	Lipidemia and ketoacidosis	Ketonuria Loss of Na^+, K^+; electrolyte and acid-base imbalances	Acetone breath Hyperpnea Nausea, vomiting, abdominal pain Cardiac irregularities Central nervous system depression; coma

sults from an islet cell tumor. More commonly, it is caused by an overdose of insulin and is easily treated by ingesting some sugar. ■

CHECK YOUR UNDERSTANDING

14. You've just attended a football game with your friend, Sharon, who is diabetic. While you aren't aware of Sharon having had more than one beer during the game, she is having trouble walking straight, her speech is slurred, and she is not making sense. What does it mean when we say Sharon is diabetic? What is the most likely explanation for Sharon's current behavior?

15. Diabetes mellitus and diabetes insipidus are both due to lack of a hormone. Which hormone causes which? What symptom do they have in common? What would you find in the urine of a patient with one but not the other?

For answers, see Appendix G.

The Gonads and Placenta

▶ Describe the functional roles of hormones of the testes, ovaries, and placenta.

The male and female **gonads** produce steroid sex hormones, identical to those produced by adrenal cortical cells (see Figure 16.1). The major distinction is the source and relative amounts produced. The release of gonadal hormones is regulated by gonadotropins, as described earlier.

The paired *ovaries* are small, oval organs located in the female's abdominopelvic cavity. Besides producing ova, or eggs, the ovaries produce several hormones, most importantly **estrogens** and **progesterone** (pro-jes′tĕ-rōn). Alone, the estrogens are responsible for maturation of the reproductive organs and the appearance of the secondary sex characteristics of females at puberty. Acting with progesterone, estrogens promote breast development and cyclic changes in the uterine mucosa (the menstrual cycle).

The male *testes*, located in an extra-abdominal skin pouch called the scrotum, produce sperm and male sex hormones, primarily **testosterone** (tes-tos′tĕ-rōn). During puberty, testosterone initiates the maturation of the male reproductive organs and the appearance of secondary sex characteristics and sex drive. In addition, testosterone is necessary for normal sperm production and maintains the reproductive organs in their mature functional state in adult males.

The *placenta* is a temporary endocrine organ. Besides sustaining the fetus during pregnancy, it secretes several steroid and protein hormones that influence the course of pregnancy. Placental hormones include estrogens and progesterone (hormones more often associated with the ovary), and human chorionic gonadotropin (hCG).

We will discuss the roles of the gonadal, placental, and gonadotropic hormones in detail in Chapters 27 and 28, where we consider the reproductive system and pregnancy.

CHECK YOUR UNDERSTANDING

16. Which of the two chemical classes of hormones introduced at the beginning of this chapter do the gonadal hormones belong to? Which major endocrine gland secretes hormones of this same chemical class?

For answers, see Appendix G.

Hormone Secretion by Other Organs

▶ Name a hormone produced by the heart.

▶ State the location of enteroendocrine cells.

▶ Briefly explain the hormonal functions of the kidney, skin, adipose tissue, bone, and thymus.

Other hormone-producing cells occur in various organs of the body, including the following, summarized in **Table 16.5**:

1. **Heart.** The atria contain some specialized cardiac muscle cells that secrete **atrial natriuretic peptide**. ANP prompts the kidneys to increase their production of salty urine and inhibits aldosterone release by the adrenal cortex. In this way, ANP decreases the amount of sodium in the extracellular fluid, thereby reducing blood volume and blood pressure (see Figure 16.14).

2. **Gastrointestinal tract.** *Enteroendocrine cells* are hormone-secreting cells sprinkled in the mucosa of the gastrointestinal (GI) tract. These scattered cells release several peptide hormones that help regulate a wide variety of digestive functions, some of which are summarized in Table 16.5. Enteroendocrine cells also release amines such as serotonin, which act as paracrines, diffusing to and influencing nearby target cells without first entering the bloodstream. Enteroendocrine cells are sometimes referred to as *paraneurons* because they are similar in certain ways to neurons and many of their hormones and paracrines are chemically identical to neurotransmitters.

3. **Kidneys.** Interstitial cells in the kidneys secrete **erythropoietin** (ĕ-rith″ro-poi′ĕ-tin; "red-maker"), a protein hormone that signals the bone marrow to increase production of red blood cells. The kidneys also release **renin**, the hormone that acts as an enzyme to initiate the renin-angiotensin mechanism of aldosterone release described earlier.

4. **Skin.** The skin produces **cholecalciferol**, an inactive form of vitamin D_3, when modified cholesterol molecules in epidermal cells are exposed to ultraviolet radiation. This compound then enters the blood via the dermal capillaries, is modified in the liver, and becomes fully activated in the kidneys. The active form of vitamin D_3, **calcitriol**, is an essential regulator of the carrier system that intestinal cells use to absorb Ca^{2+} from ingested food. Without this vitamin, the bones become soft and weak.

5. **Adipose tissue.** Adipose cells release **leptin**, which serves to tell your body how much stored energy (as fat) you have. The more fat you have, the more leptin there will be in your blood. As we describe in Chapter 24, leptin binds to CNS neurons concerned with appetite control, producing a sensation of satiety. It also appears to stimulate increased energy expenditure. Two other hormones released by adipose cells both affect the sensitivity of cells to insulin. *Resistin* is an insulin antagonist, while *adiponectin* enhances sensitivity to insulin.

6. **Skeleton.** Osteoblasts in bone secrete *osteocalcin*, a hormone that prods pancreatic beta cells to divide and secrete more insulin. It also restricts fat storage by adipocytes, and triggers the release of adiponectin. As a result, glucose handling is improved and body fat is reduced. Osteocalcin levels are low in type 2 diabetes, and increasing its level may offer a new treatment approach.

7. **Thymus.** Located deep to the sternum in the thorax is the lobulated **thymus** (see Figure 16.1). Large and conspicuous in infants and children, the thymus diminishes in size throughout adulthood. By old age, it is composed largely of adipose and fibrous connective tissues.

   Thymic epithelial cells secrete several different families of peptide hormones, including **thymulin, thymopoietins,** and **thymosins** (thi′mo-sinz). These hormones are thought to be involved in the normal development of *T lymphocytes* and the immune response, but their roles are not well understood. Although still called hormones, they mainly act locally as paracrines. We describe the thymus in Chapter 20 in our discussion of the lymphoid organs and tissues.

CHECK YOUR UNDERSTANDING

17. What hormone does the heart produce and what is its function?
18. What is the function of the hormone produced by the skin?

For answers, see Appendix G.

Developmental Aspects of the Endocrine System

▶ Describe the effects of aging on endocrine system functioning.

Hormone-producing glands arise from all three embryonic germ layers. Endocrine glands derived from mesoderm produce steroid hormones. All others produce amines, peptides, or protein hormones.

Though not usually considered important when describing hormone effectiveness, exposure to many environmental pollutants has been shown to disrupt endocrine function. These pollutants include many pesticides, industrial chemicals, arsenic, dioxin, and other soil and water pollutants. So far, sex hormones, thyroid hormone, and glucocorticoids have proved vulnerable to the effects of such pollutants. Interference with glucocorticoids, which turn on many genes that may suppress cancer, may help to explain the high cancer rates in certain areas of the country.

Barring exposure to environmental pollutants, and hypersecretory and hyposecretory disorders, most endocrine organs operate smoothly throughout life until old age. Aging may bring about changes in the rates of hormone secretion, breakdown, and excretion, or in the sensitivity of target cell receptors. Endocrine functioning in the elderly is difficult to research, however, because it is frequently altered by the chronic illnesses common in that age group.

TABLE 16.5	Selected Examples of Hormones Produced by Organs Other Than the Major Endocrine Organs			
SOURCE	**HORMONE**	**CHEMICAL COMPOSITION**	**TRIGGER**	**TARGET ORGAN AND EFFECTS**
Adipose tissue	Leptin	Peptide	Secretion proportional to fat stores; increased by nutrient uptake	Brain: suppresses appetite; increases energy expenditure
Adipose tissue	Resistin, adiponectin	Peptides	Unknown	Fat, muscle, liver: resistin antagonizes insulin's action and adiponectin enhances it
GI tract mucosa				
▪ Stomach	Gastrin	Peptide	Secreted in response to food	Stomach: stimulates glands to release hydrochloric acid (HCl)
▪ Duodenum (of small intestine)	Intestinal gastrin	Peptide	Secreted in response to food, especially fats	Stomach: stimulates HCl secretion and gastrointestinal tract motility
▪ Duodenum	Secretin	Peptide	Secreted in response to food	Pancreas and liver: stimulates release of bicarbonate-rich juice; Stomach: inhibits secretory activity
▪ Duodenum	Cholecystokinin (CCK)	Peptide	Secreted in response to food	Pancreas: stimulates release of enzyme-rich juice; Gallbladder: stimulates expulsion of stored bile; Hepatopancreatic sphincter: causes sphincter to relax, allowing bile and pancreatic juice to enter duodenum
▪ Duodenum (and other gut regions)	Incretins [glucose-dependent insulinotropic peptide (GIP) and glucagon-like peptide 1 (GLP-1)]	Peptide	Secreted in response to glucose in intestinal lumen	Pancreas: enhances insulin release and inhibits glucagon release caused by increased blood glucose
Heart (atria)	Atrial natriuretic peptide	Peptide	Secreted in response to stretching of atria (by rising blood pressure)	Kidney: inhibits sodium ion reabsorption and renin release; adrenal cortex: inhibits secretion of aldosterone; decreases blood pressure
Kidney	Erythropoietin (EPO)	Glycoprotein	Secreted in response to hypoxia	Red bone marrow: stimulates production of red blood cells
Kidney	Renin	Peptide	Secreted in response to low blood pressure or plasma volume, or sympathetic stimulation	Acts as an enzyme to initiate renin-angiotensin mechanism of aldosterone release; returns blood pressure to normal
Skeleton	Osteocalcin	Peptide	Unknown	Increases insulin production and insulin sensitivity
Skin (epidermal cells)	Cholecalciferol (provitamin D_3)	Steroid	Activated by the kidneys to active vitamin D_3 (calcitriol) in response to parathyroid hormone	Intestine: stimulates active transport of dietary calcium across intestinal cell membranes
Thymus	Thymulin, thymopoietins, thymosins	Peptides	Unknown	Mostly act locally as paracrines; involved in T lymphocyte development and in immune responses

16

A CLOSER LOOK
Sweet Revenge: Taming the DM Monster?

Few medical breakthroughs have been as electrifying as the discovery of insulin in 1921, an event that changed diabetes mellitus from a death sentence to a survivable disease. Nonetheless, DM is still a huge health problem: Determining blood glucose levels accurately and maintaining desirable levels sorely challenge our present biotechnology. Let's take a closer look at the characteristics and challenges of type 1 and type 2, the major forms of diabetes mellitus.

More than 1 million Americans have **type 1 diabetes mellitus**, formerly called *insulin-dependent diabetes mellitus* (*IDDM*). Symptoms appear suddenly, usually before age 15, following a long asymptomatic period during which the beta cells are destroyed by the immune system. Consequently, type 1 diabetics effectively lack insulin.

Type 1 diabetes susceptibility genes have been localized on several chromosomes, indicating that type 1 diabetes is an example of a multigene autoimmune response. However, some investigators believe that *molecular mimicry* is at least part of the problem: Some foreign substance (for example, a virus) has entered the body and is so similar to certain self (beta cell) proteins that the immune system attacks the beta cells as well as the invader.

Indeed, elegant studies on certain strains of diabetic mice, stressed by infections or other irritants, demonstrated that they produced increasing amounts of a particular stress protein (heat shock protein 60) and also churned out antibodies against that stress protein. When fragments of the stress protein called p277 were injected into other mice showing early signs of diabetes, the beta cells were spared from the autoimmune attack. Recent clinical trials in which newly diagnosed diabetics were given the fragment as a drug (called DiaPep277) have yielded conflicting results, with some studies showing less need for insulin and others showing no effect.

Type 1 diabetes is difficult to control and patients typically develop long-term vascular and neural problems. The lipidemia and high blood cholesterol levels typical of the disease can lead to severe vascular complications including atherosclerosis, strokes, heart attacks, renal shutdown, gangrene, and blindness.

Nerve damage leads to loss of sensation, impaired bladder function, and impotence. Female type 1 diabetics also tend to have lumpy breasts and to undergo premature menopause, which increases their risk for cardiac problems.

Hyperglycemia is the culprit behind these complications, and the closer to normal blood glucose levels are held, the less likely complications are. Continuous glucose monitors make this much easier than relying upon finger pricks. Currently, frequent insulin injections (up to four times daily, or better yet, by a continuous infusion pump) are recommended to reduce vascular and renal complications. While some glucose sensors can talk directly to insulin pumps, problems with automatically calculating the amount of insulin to dispense mean patients must still make these decisions. In this way, such combined devices still fall short of being a true "artificial pancreas." A number of alternative insulin delivery methods exist—insulin inhalers are now approved for use and insulin patches may be on the horizon.

Pancreatic islet cell transplants have become increasingly successful in helping type 1 diabetics. Still, only 33% of patients

---

Structural changes in the anterior pituitary occur with age. The amount of connective tissue increases, vascularization decreases, and the number of hormone-secreting cells declines. These changes may or may not affect hormone production. In women, for example, blood levels and the release rhythm of ACTH remain constant, but levels of gonadotropins increase with age. GH levels decline in both sexes, which partially explains muscle atrophy in old age.

The adrenal glands also show structural changes with age, but normal controls of cortisol appear to persist as long as a person is healthy and not stressed. Chronic stress, on the other hand, drives up blood levels of cortisol and appears to contribute to hippocampal (and memory) deterioration. Plasma levels of aldosterone are reduced by half in old age, but this change may reflect a decline in renin release by the kidneys, which become less responsive to renin-evoking stimuli. No age-related differences have been found in the release of catecholamines by the adrenal medulla.

The gonads, particularly the ovaries, undergo significant changes with age. In late middle age, the ovaries decrease in size and weight, and they become unresponsive to gonadotropins. As female hormone production declines dramatically, the ability to bear children ends, and problems associated with estrogen deficiency, such as arteriosclerosis and osteoporosis, begin to occur. Testosterone production by the testes also wanes with age, but this effect usually is not seen until very old age.

Glucose tolerance (the ability to dispose of a glucose load effectively) begins to deteriorate as early as the fourth decade of life. Blood glucose levels rise higher and return to resting levels more slowly in the elderly than in young adults. The fact that the islet cells continue to secrete near-normal amounts of insulin leads researchers to conclude that decreasing glucose tolerance with age may reflect declining receptor sensitivity to insulin (pre–type 2 diabetes).

Thyroid hormone synthesis and release diminish somewhat with age. Typically, the follicles are loaded with colloid in the elderly, and fibrosis of the gland occurs. Basal metabolic rate declines with age. Mild hypothyroidism is only one cause of this decline. The increase in body fat relative to muscle is equally important, because muscle tissue is more active metabolically than fat.

The parathyroid glands change little with age, and PTH levels remain fairly normal throughout life. Estrogens protect women

A CLOSER LOOK
(continued)

need no injected insulin after two years. The need for long-term immunosuppression limits this treatment to only those diabetics who cannot control their blood glucose by any other means.

Over 90% of known DM cases are **type 2 diabetes mellitus**, formerly called *non-insulin-dependent diabetes mellitus* (*NIDDM*), which grows increasingly common with age and with the increasing size of our waistlines. About 12 million people in the U.S. have been diagnosed with type 2 diabetes, and roughly half as many are believed to be undiagnosed victims. Type 2 diabetics are at risk for the same complications as type 1 diabetics—heart disease, amputations, kidney failure, and blindness.

A hereditary predisposition is particularly striking in this diabetic group. About 25–30% of Americans carry a gene that predisposes them to type 2 diabetes, with nonwhites affected to a much greater extent. If an identical twin has type 2 diabetes mellitus, the probability that the other twin will have the disease is virtually 100%. Most type 2 diabetics produce insulin, but the insulin receptors are unable to respond to it, a phenomenon called **insulin resistance**. Mutations in any one of several genes could lead to insulin resistance.

Lifestyle factors also play a role: Type 2 diabetics are almost always overweight and sedentary. Adipose cells of obese people overproduce a number of signaling chemicals including *tumor necrosis factor alpha* and *resistin*, which may alter the enzymatic cascade triggered by insulin binding. The Diabetes Prevention Program, a major clinical trial, showed that weight loss and regular exercise can lower the risk of type 2 diabetes dramatically, even for people at high risk.

In many cases type 2 diabetes can be managed solely by exercise, weight loss, and a healthy diet. Some type 2 diabetics also benefit from oral medications that lower blood glucose or reduce insulin resistance. A promising new class of drugs targets the incretin hormones normally secreted by the gut, enhancing glucose-dependent insulin release from pancreatic beta cells using a normal physiological pathway. However, most type 2 diabetics must eventually inject insulin.

While we cannot yet cure diabetes, biotechnology promises to continue to improve control of blood glucose levels and thereby tame the monster that is diabetes.

---

against the demineralizing effects of PTH, but estrogen production wanes after menopause, leaving older women vulnerable to the bone-demineralizing effects of PTH and osteoporosis.

CHECK YOUR UNDERSTANDING

19. In the elderly, the decline in levels of which hormone is associated with muscle atrophy? With osteoporosis in women?

For answers, see Appendix G.

In this chapter, we have covered the general mechanisms of hormone action and have provided an overview of the major endocrine organs, their chief targets, and their most important physiological effects, as summarized in *Making Connections* on p. 628. However, every one of the hormones discussed here comes up in at least one other chapter, where its actions are described as part of the functional framework of a particular organ system. For example, we described the effects of PTH and calcitonin on bone mineralization in Chapter 6 along with the discussion of bone remodeling.

RELATED CLINICAL TERMS

Hirsutism (her′soot-izm; *hirsut* = hairy, rough) Excessive hair growth; usually refers to this phenomenon in women and reflects excessive androgen production.

Hypophysectomy (hi-pof″ĭ-sek′to-me) Surgical removal of the pituitary gland.

Prolactinoma (pro-lak″tĭ-no′mah; *oma* = tumor) The most common type (30–40% or more) of pituitary gland tumor; evidenced by hypersecretion of prolactin and menstrual disturbances in women.

Psychosocial dwarfism Dwarfism (and failure to thrive) resulting from stress and emotional disorders that suppress hypothalamic release of growth hormone–releasing hormone and thus anterior pituitary secretion of growth hormone.

Thyroid storm (thyroid crisis) A sudden and dangerous increase in all of the symptoms of hyperthyroidism due to excessive amounts of circulating TH. Symptoms of this hypermetabolic state include fever, rapid heart rate, high blood pressure, dehydration, nervousness, and tremors. Precipitating factors include severe infection, excessive intake of TH supplements, and trauma.

Homeostatic Interrelationships Between the Endocrine System and Other Body Systems

Integumentary System

- Androgens cause activation of sebaceous glands; estrogen increases skin hydration
- Skin produces cholecalciferol (provitamin D)

Skeletal System

- PTH regulates calcium blood levels; growth hormone, T_3, T_4, and sex hormones are necessary for normal skeletal development
- The skeleton provides some protection to endocrine organs, especially to those in the brain, chest, and pelvis

Muscular System

- Growth hormone is essential for normal muscular development; other hormones (thyroxine and catecholamines) influence muscle metabolism
- Muscular system mechanically protects some endocrine glands; muscular activity elicits catecholamine release

Nervous System

- Many hormones (growth hormone, thyroxine, sex hormones) influence normal maturation and function of the nervous system
- Hypothalamus controls anterior pituitary function and produces two hormones

Cardiovascular System

- Several hormones influence blood volume, blood pressure, and heart contractility; erythropoietin stimulates red blood cell production
- Blood is the main transport medium of hormones; heart produces atrial natriuretic peptide

Lymphatic System/Immunity

- Lymphocytes "programmed" by thymic hormones seed the lymph nodes; glucocorticoids depress the immune response and inflammation
- Chemical messengers of the immune system stimulate the release of cortisol and ACTH; lymph provides a route for transport of hormones

Respiratory System

- Epinephrine influences ventilation (dilates bronchioles)
- Respiratory system provides oxygen; disposes of carbon dioxide; converting enzyme in lungs converts angiotensin I to angiotensin II

Digestive System

- GI hormones and paracrines influence GI function; activated vitamin D necessary for absorption of calcium from diet; catecholamines influence digestive motility and secretory activity
- Digestive system provides nutrients to endocrine organs

Urinary System

- Aldosterone and ADH influence renal function; erythropoietin released by kidneys influences red blood cell formation
- Kidneys activate vitamin D (considered a hormone)

Reproductive System

- Hypothalamic, anterior pituitary, and gonadal hormones direct reproductive system development and function; oxytocin and prolactin involved in birth and breast-feeding
- Gonadal hormones feed back to influence endocrine system function

16

THE ENDOCRINE SYSTEM and Interrelationships with the Nervous and Reproductive Systems

Like most body systems, the endocrine system performs many functions that benefit the body as a whole. For example, without insulin, thyroxine, and various other metabolic hormones, body cells would be unable to get or use glucose, and would die. Likewise, total body growth is beholden to the endocrine system, which coordinates the growth spurts with increases in skeletal and muscular mass so that we don't look out of proportion most of the time. But the interactions that are most noticeable and crucial are those that the endocrine system has with the nervous and the reproductive systems, and they begin before birth.

Nervous System

The influence of hormones on behavior is striking. While we are still in the wet darkness of our mother's uterus, testosterone—or lack of it—is determining the "sex" of our brain. If testosterone is produced by the exceedingly tiny male testes, then certain areas of the brain enlarge, develop large numbers of androgen receptors, and thereafter determine the so-called masculine aspects of behavior (aggressiveness, etc.). Conversely, in the absence of testosterone, the brain is feminized. At puberty, Mom and Dad's "little angels," driven by raging hormones, turn into strangers. The surge of androgens—produced first by the adrenal cortices, and then by the maturing gonads—produces an often thoughtless aggressiveness and galloping sex drive, typically long before the cognitive abilities of the brain can rein them in.

Neural involvement in hormonal affairs is no less striking. Not only is the hypothalamus an endocrine organ in its own right, but it also effectively regulates the bulk of hormonal activity via its hormonal or neural controls of the pituitary and adrenal medulla. And that's just on a normal day. The effects of trauma on the hypothalamic-pituitary axis can be far-reaching. Lack of loving care to a newborn baby results in failure to thrive; exceptionally vigorous athletic training in the pubertal female can result in bone wasting and infertility. The shadow the nervous system casts over the endocrine system is long indeed.

Reproductive System

The reproductive system is totally dependent on hormones to "order up the right organs" to match our genetic sex. Testosterone secretion by the testes of male embryos directs formation of the male reproductive tract and external genitalia. Without testosterone, female structures develop—regardless of gonadal sex. The next crucial period is puberty, when gonadal sex hormone production rises and steers maturation of the reproductive organs, bringing them to their adult structure and function. Without these hormonal signals, the reproductive organs remain childlike and the person cannot produce offspring.

Pregnancy invites more endocrine system interactions with the reproductive system. The placenta, a temporary endocrine organ, churns out estrogens and progesterone, which help maintain the pregnancy and prepare the mother's breasts for lactation, as well as a number of other hormones that influence maternal metabolism. During and after birth, oxytocin and prolactin take center stage to promote labor and delivery, and then milk production and ejection. Other than feedback inhibition exerted by its sex hormones on the hypothalamic-pituitary axis, the influence of reproductive organs on the endocrine system is negligible.

16

Endocrine System

Case study: We have a new patient to consider today. Mr. Gutteman, a 70-year-old male, was brought into the ER in a comatose state and has yet to come out of it. It is obvious that he suffered severe head trauma—his scalp was badly lacerated, and he has an impacted skull fracture. His initial lab tests (blood and urine) were within normal limits. His fracture was repaired and the following orders (and others) were given:

- Check qh (every hour) and record: spontaneous behavior, level of responsiveness to stimulation, movements, pupil size and reaction to light, speech, and vital signs.
- Turn patient q4h and maintain meticulous skin care and dryness.

1. Explain the rationale behind these orders.

On the second day of his hospitalization, the aide reports that Mr. Gutteman is breathing irregularly, his skin is dry and flaccid, and that she has emptied his urine reservoir several times during the day. Upon receiving this information, the physician ordered

- Blood and urine tests for presence of glucose and ketones
- Strict I&O (fluid intake and output recording)

Mr. Gutteman is found to be losing huge amounts of water in urine and the volume lost is being routinely replaced (via IV line). Mr. Gutteman's blood and urine tests are negative for glucose and ketones.

Relative to these findings:

2. What would you say Mr. Gutteman's hormonal problem is and what do you think caused it?

3. Is it life threatening? (Explain your answer.)

(Answers in Appendix G)

CHAPTER SUMMARY

Media study tools that could provide you additional help in reviewing specific key topics of Chapter 16 are referenced below.

iP = *Interactive Physiology*

1. The nervous and endocrine systems are the major controlling systems of the body. The nervous system exerts rapid controls via nerve impulses; the endocrine system's effects are mediated by hormones and are more prolonged.

The Endocrine System: An Overview   (pp. 595–596)

1. Hormonally regulated processes include reproduction; growth and development; maintaining electrolyte, water, and nutrient balance; regulating cellular metabolism and energy balance; and mobilization of body defenses.
2. Endocrine organs are ductless, well-vascularized glands that release hormones directly into the blood or lymph. They are small and widely separated in the body.
3. The purely endocrine organs are the pituitary, thyroid, parathyroid, adrenal, and pineal glands. The hypothalamus is a neuroendocrine organ. The pancreas, gonads, and placenta also have endocrine tissue.
4. Local chemical messengers, not generally considered part of the endocrine system, include autocrines, which act on the cells that secrete them, and paracrines, which act on a different cell type nearby.

iP Endocrine System; Topic: Endocrine System Review, p. 3.

Hormones   (pp. 596–601)

The Chemistry of Hormones   (p. 596)

1. Most hormones are steroids or amino acid based.

iP Endocrine System; Topic: Biochemistry, Secretion, and Transport of Hormones, p. 3.

Mechanisms of Hormone Action   (pp. 596–598)

2. Hormones alter cell activity by stimulating or inhibiting characteristic cellular processes of their target cells.
3. Cell responses to hormone stimulation may involve changes in membrane permeability; enzyme synthesis, activation, or inhibition; secretory activity; gene activation; and mitosis.
4. Second-messenger mechanisms employing G proteins and intracellular second messengers are a common means by which amino acid–based hormones interact with their target cells. In the cyclic AMP system, the hormone binds to a plasma membrane receptor that couples to a G protein. When the G protein is activated, it in turn couples to adenylate cyclase, which catalyzes the synthesis of cyclic AMP from ATP. Cyclic AMP initiates reactions that activate protein kinases and other enzymes, leading to cellular response. The PIP_2-calcium signaling mechanism, involving phosphatidyl inositol, is another important second-messenger system. Other second messengers are cyclic GMP and calcium.

iP Endocrine System; Topic: The Actions of Hormones on Target Cells, pp. 3–7.

5. Steroid hormones (and thyroid hormone) enter their target cells and effect responses by activating DNA, which initiates messenger RNA formation leading to protein synthesis.

Target Cell Specificity   (p. 598)

6. The ability of a target cell to respond to a hormone depends on the presence of receptors, within the cell or on its plasma membrane, to which the hormone can bind.
7. Hormone receptors are dynamic structures. Changes in number and sensitivity of hormone receptors may occur in response to high or low levels of stimulating hormones.

iP Endocrine System; Topic: The Actions of Hormones on Target Cells, p. 3.

Half-Life, Onset, and Duration of Hormone Activity (p. 599)

8. Blood levels of hormones reflect a balance between secretion and degradation/excretion. The liver and kidneys are the major organs that degrade hormones; breakdown products are excreted in urine and feces.
9. Hormone half-life and duration of activity are limited and vary from hormone to hormone.

Interaction of Hormones at Target Cells   (p. 600)

10. Permissiveness is the situation in which one hormone must be present in order for another hormone to exert its full effects.
11. Synergism occurs when two or more hormones produce the same effects in a target cell and their results together are amplified.
12. Antagonism occurs when a hormone opposes or reverses the effect of another hormone.

Control of Hormone Release   (pp. 600–601)

13. Humoral, neural, or hormonal stimuli activate endocrine organs to release their hormones. Negative feedback is important in regulating hormone levels in the blood.
14. The nervous system, acting through hypothalamic controls, can in certain cases override or modulate hormonal effects.

iP Endocrine System; Topic: The Hypothalamic–Pituitary Axis, pp. 4 and 5.

The Pituitary Gland and Hypothalamus   (pp. 601–608)

Pituitary-Hypothalamic Relationships   (p. 603)

1. The pituitary gland hangs from the base of the brain by a stalk and is enclosed by bone. It consists of a hormone-producing glandular portion (anterior pituitary or adenohypophysis) and a neural portion (posterior pituitary or neurohypophysis), which is an extension of the hypothalamus.
2. The hypothalamus (a) regulates the hormonal output of the anterior pituitary via releasing and inhibiting hormones and (b) synthesizes two hormones that it exports to the posterior pituitary for storage and later release.

Anterior Pituitary Hormones   (pp. 603–605)

3. Four of the six anterior pituitary hormones are tropic hormones that regulate the function of other endocrine organs. Most anterior pituitary hormones exhibit a diurnal rhythm of release, which is subject to modification by stimuli influencing the hypothalamus.
4. Growth hormone (GH) is an anabolic hormone that stimulates growth of all body tissues but especially skeletal muscle and bone. It may act directly, or indirectly, via insulin-like growth factors

(IGFs). GH mobilizes fats, stimulates protein synthesis, and inhibits glucose uptake and metabolism. Its secretion is regulated by growth hormone–releasing hormone (GHRH) and growth hormone–inhibiting hormone (GHIH), or somatostatin. Hypersecretion causes gigantism in children and acromegaly in adults; hyposecretion in children causes pituitary dwarfism.

5. Thyroid-stimulating hormone (TSH) promotes normal development and activity of the thyroid gland. Thyrotropin-releasing hormone (TRH) stimulates its release; negative feedback of thyroid hormone inhibits it.

6. Adrenocorticotropic hormone (ACTH) stimulates the adrenal cortex to release corticosteroids. ACTH release is triggered by corticotropin-releasing hormone (CRH) and inhibited by rising glucocorticoid levels.

7. The gonadotropins—follicle-stimulating hormone (FSH) and luteinizing hormone (LH)—regulate the functions of the gonads in both sexes. FSH stimulates sex cell production; LH stimulates gonadal hormone production. Gonadotropin levels rise in response to gonadotropin-releasing hormone (GnRH). Negative feedback of gonadal hormones inhibits gonadotropin release.

8. Prolactin (PRL) promotes milk production in humans. Its secretion is inhibited by prolactin-inhibiting hormone (PIH).

The Posterior Pituitary and Hypothalamic Hormones (pp. 605–608)

9. The posterior pituitary stores and releases two hypothalamic hormones, oxytocin and antidiuretic hormone (ADH).

10. Oxytocin stimulates powerful uterine contractions, which trigger labor and delivery of an infant, and milk ejection in nursing women. Its release is mediated reflexively by the hypothalamus and represents a positive feedback mechanism.

11. Antidiuretic hormone stimulates the kidney tubules to reabsorb and conserve water, resulting in small volumes of highly concentrated urine and decreased plasma osmolality. ADH is released in response to high solute concentrations in the blood and inhibited by low solute concentrations in the blood. Hyposecretion results in diabetes insipidus.

The Thyroid Gland (pp. 608–612)

1. The thyroid gland is located in the anterior neck. Thyroid follicles store colloid containing thyroglobulin, a glycoprotein from which thyroid hormone is derived.

2. Thyroid hormone (TH) includes thyroxine (T_4) and triiodothyronine (T_3), which increase the rate of cellular metabolism. Consequently, oxygen use and heat production rise.

3. Secretion of thyroid hormone, prompted by TSH, requires reuptake of the stored colloid by the follicle cells and splitting of the hormones from the colloid for release. Rising levels of thyroid hormone feed back to inhibit the anterior pituitary and hypothalamus.

4. Most T_4 is converted to T_3 (the more active form) in the target tissues. These hormones act by turning on gene transcription and protein synthesis.

5. Graves' disease is the most common cause of hyperthyroidism; hyposecretion causes cretinism in infants and myxedema in adults.

6. Calcitonin, produced by the parafollicular (C) cells of the thyroid gland in response to rising blood calcium levels, inhibits bone matrix resorption and enhances calcium deposit in bone. It is not normally important in calcium homeostasis.

iP Endocrine System; Topic: The Hypothalamic–Pituitary Axis, p. 6.

The Parathyroid Glands (pp. 612–614)

1. The parathyroid glands, located on the dorsal aspect of the thyroid gland, secrete parathyroid hormone (PTH), which causes an increase in blood calcium levels. It targets bone, the kidneys, and the intestine (indirectly via vitamin D activation). PTH is the key hormone for calcium homeostasis.

2. PTH release is triggered by falling blood calcium levels and is inhibited by rising blood calcium levels.

3. Hyperparathyroidism results in hypercalcemia and all its effects and in extreme bone wasting. Hypoparathyroidism leads to hypocalcemia, evidenced by tetany and respiratory paralysis.

The Adrenal (Suprarenal) Glands (pp. 614–620)

1. The paired adrenal (suprarenal) glands sit atop the kidneys. Each adrenal gland has two functional portions, the cortex and the medulla.

The Adrenal Cortex (pp. 614–618)

2. The cortex produces three groups of steroid hormones from cholesterol.

3. Mineralocorticoids (primarily aldosterone) regulate sodium ion reabsorption and potassium ion excretion by the kidneys. Sodium ion reabsorption leads to water reabsorption, and increases in blood volume and blood pressure. Release of aldosterone is stimulated by the renin-angiotensin mechanism, rising potassium ion levels in the blood, and ACTH. Atrial natriuretic peptide inhibits aldosterone release.

4. Glucocorticoids (primarily cortisol) are important metabolic hormones that help the body resist stressors by increasing blood glucose, fatty acid and amino acid levels, and blood pressure. High levels of glucocorticoids depress the immune system and the inflammatory response. ACTH is the major stimulus for glucocorticoid release.

5. Gonadocorticoids (mainly androgens) are produced in small amounts throughout life.

6. Hypoactivity of the adrenal cortex results in Addison's disease. Hypersecretion can result in aldosteronism, Cushing's syndrome, and adrenogenital syndrome.

The Adrenal Medulla (pp. 618–620)

7. The adrenal medulla produces catecholamines (epinephrine and norepinephrine) in response to sympathetic nervous system stimulation. Its catecholamines enhance and prolong the fight-or-flight response to short-term stressors. Hypersecretion leads to symptoms typical of sympathetic nervous system overactivity.

iP Endocrine System; Topic: Response to Stress, pp. 5–8.

The Pineal Gland (pp. 620)

1. The pineal gland is located in the diencephalon. Its primary hormone is melatonin, which influences daily rhythms and may have an antigonadotropic effect in humans.

Other Endocrine Glands and Tissues (pp. 620–624)

The Pancreas (pp. 620–623)

1. The pancreas, located in the abdomen close to the stomach, is both an exocrine and an endocrine gland. The endocrine portion (pancreatic islets) releases insulin and glucagon and smaller amounts of other hormones to the blood.

2. Glucagon, released by alpha (α) cells when blood levels of glucose are low, stimulates the liver to release glucose to the blood.

16

3. Insulin is released by beta (β) cells when blood levels of glucose (and amino acids) are rising. It increases the rate of glucose uptake and metabolism by most body cells. Hyposecretion or hypoactivity of insulin results in diabetes mellitus; cardinal signs are polyuria, polydipsia, and polyphagia.

iP Endocrine System; Topic: The Actions of Hormones on Target Cells, pp. 5 and 8.

The Gonads and Placenta   (p. 623)

4. The ovaries of the female, located in the pelvic cavity, release two main hormones. The ovarian follicles begin to secrete estrogens at puberty under the influence of FSH. Estrogens stimulate maturation of the female reproductive system and development of the secondary sex characteristics. Progesterone is released in response to high blood levels of LH. It works with estrogens in establishing the menstrual cycle.

5. The testes of the male begin to produce testosterone at puberty in response to LH. Testosterone promotes maturation of the male reproductive organs, development of secondary sex characteristics, and production of sperm by the testes.

6. The placenta produces hormones of pregnancy—estrogens, progesterone, and others.

Hormone Secretion by Other Organs   (p. 624)

7. Many body organs not normally considered endocrine organs contain cells that secrete hormones. Examples include the heart (atrial natriuretic peptide); gastrointestinal tract organs (gastrin, secretin, incretins, and others); the kidneys (erythropoietin and renin); skin (cholecalciferol); adipose tissue (leptin, resistin, and adiponectin); bone (osteocalcin); and thymus (thymic hormones).

8. The thymus, located in the upper thorax, declines in size and function with age. Its hormones, thymulin, thymosins, and thymopoietins, are important to the normal development of the immune response.

Developmental Aspects of the Endocrine System   (pp. 624, 626–627)

1. Endocrine glands derive from all three germ layers. Those derived from mesoderm produce steroid hormones; the others produce the amino acid–based hormones.

2. The natural decrease in function of the female's ovaries during late middle age results in menopause.

3. The efficiency of all endocrine glands seems to decrease gradually as aging occurs. This change leads to a generalized increase in the incidence of diabetes mellitus and a lower metabolic rate.

REVIEW QUESTIONS

Multiple Choice/Matching

(Some questions have more than one correct answer. Select the best answer or answers from the choices given.)

1. The major stimulus for release of parathyroid hormone is (**a**) hormonal, (**b**) humoral, (**c**) neural.

2. The anterior pituitary secretes all but (**a**) antidiuretic hormone, (**b**) growth hormone, (**c**) gonadotropins, (**d**) TSH.

3. A hormone not involved in glucose metabolism is (**a**) glucagon, (**b**) cortisone, (**c**) aldosterone, (**d**) insulin.

4. Parathyroid hormone (**a**) increases bone formation and lowers blood calcium levels, (**b**) increases calcium excretion from the body, (**c**) decreases calcium absorption from the gut, (**d**) demineralizes bone and raises blood calcium levels.

5. Choose from the following key to identify the hormones described.

   Key: (**a**) aldosterone   (**e**) oxytocin
         (**b**) antidiuretic hormone (**f**) prolactin
         (**c**) growth hormone   (**g**) T$_4$ and T$_3$
         (**d**) luteinizing hormone   (**h**) TSH

   _____ (1) important anabolic hormone; many of its effects mediated by IGFs

   _____ (2) cause the kidneys to conserve water and/or salt (two choices)

   _____ (3) stimulates milk production

   _____ (4) tropic hormone that stimulates the gonads to secrete sex hormones

   _____ (5) increases uterine contractions during birth

   _____ (6) major metabolic hormone(s) of the body

   _____ (7) causes reabsorption of sodium ions by the kidneys

   _____ (8) tropic hormone that stimulates the thyroid gland to secrete thyroid hormone

   _____ (9) secreted by the posterior pituitary (two choices)

   _____(10) the only steroid hormone in the list

6. A hypodermic injection of epinephrine would (**a**) increase heart rate, increase blood pressure, dilate the bronchi of the lungs, and increase peristalsis, (**b**) decrease heart rate, decrease blood pressure, constrict the bronchi, and increase peristalsis, (**c**) decrease heart rate, increase blood pressure, constrict the bronchi, and decrease peristalsis, (**d**) increase heart rate, increase blood pressure, dilate the bronchi, and decrease peristalsis.

7. Testosterone is to the male as what hormone is to the female? (**a**) luteinizing hormone, (**b**) progesterone, (**c**) estrogen, (**d**) prolactin.

8. If anterior pituitary secretion is deficient in a growing child, the child will (**a**) develop acromegaly, (**b**) become a dwarf but have fairly normal body proportions, (**c**) mature sexually at an earlier than normal age, (**d**) be in constant danger of becoming dehydrated.

9. If there is adequate carbohydrate intake, secretion of insulin results in (**a**) lower blood glucose levels, (**b**) increased cell utilization of glucose, (**c**) storage of glycogen, (**d**) all of these.

10. Hormones (**a**) are produced by exocrine glands, (**b**) are carried to all parts of the body in blood, (**c**) remain at constant concentration in the blood, (**d**) affect only non-hormone-producing organs.

11. Some hormones act by (**a**) increasing the synthesis of enzymes, (**b**) converting an inactive enzyme into an active enzyme, (**c**) affecting only specific target organs, (**d**) all of these.

12. Absence of thyroid hormone would result in (**a**) increased heart rate and increased force of heart contraction, (**b**) depression of the CNS and lethargy, (**c**) exophthalmos, (**d**) high metabolic rate.

13. Chromaffin cells are found in the (**a**) parathyroid gland, (**b**) anterior pituitary gland, (**c**) adrenal gland, (**d**) pineal gland.

14. Atrial natriuretic peptide secreted by the heart has exactly the opposite function of this hormone secreted by the zona glomerulosa: (**a**) antidiuretic hormone, (**b**) epinephrine, (**c**) calcitonin, (**d**) aldosterone, (**e**) androgens.

16

Short Answer Essay Questions

15. Define hormone.

16. Which type of hormone receptor—plasma membrane bound or intracellular—would be expected to provide the most long-lived response to hormone binding and why?

17. (a) Describe the body location of each of the following endocrine organs: anterior pituitary, pineal gland, pancreas, ovaries, testes, and adrenal glands. (b) List the hormones produced by each organ.

18. Name two endocrine glands (or regions) that are important in the stress response, and explain why they are important.

19. The anterior pituitary is often referred to as the master endocrine organ, but it, too, has a "master." What controls the release of anterior pituitary hormones?

20. The posterior pituitary is not really an endocrine gland. Why not? What is it?

21. A colloidal, or endemic, goiter is not really the result of malfunction of the thyroid gland. What does cause it?

22. How are the hyperglycemia and lipidemia of insulin deficiency linked?

23. Name a hormone secreted by a muscle cell and two hormones secreted by neurons.

24. List some problems that elderly people might have as a result of decreasing hormone production.

Critical Thinking and Clinical Application Questions

1. Richard Neis had symptoms of excessive secretion of PTH (high blood calcium levels), and his physicians were certain he had a parathyroid gland tumor. Yet when surgery was performed on his neck, the surgeon could not find the parathyroid glands at all. Where should the surgeon look next to find the tumorous parathyroid gland?

2. Mary Morgan has just been brought into the emergency room of City General Hospital. She is perspiring profusely and is breathing rapidly and irregularly. Her breath smells like acetone (sweet and fruity), and her blood glucose tests out at 650 mg/100 ml of blood. She is in acidosis. What hormone drug should be administered, and why?

3. Johnny, a 5-year-old boy, has been growing by leaps and bounds; his height is 100% above normal for his age. He has been complaining of headaches and vision problems. A CT scan reveals a large pituitary tumor. (a) What hormone is being secreted in excess? (b) What condition will Johnny exhibit if corrective measures are not taken? (c) What is the probable cause of his headaches and visual problems?

4. Sean, a 42-year-old single father, goes to his physician complaining of nausea and chronic fatigue. He reports having felt fatigued and listless for about half a year, but he had attributed this to stress. He has lost considerable weight and, strangely, his skin has a healthy tan, even though he spends long hours at work and rarely ventures outside. His doctor finds very low blood pressure and a rapid, weak pulse. Blood tests show that Sean does not have anemia, but his plasma glucose, cortisol, and Na^+ are low, and his plasma K^+ is high. His doctor orders an ACTH stimulation test, in which Sean's secretion of cortisol is measured after he is given a synthetic form of ACTH. (a) What would account for Sean's low plasma Na^+ and high plasma K^+? (b) What is the reason for doing an ACTH stimulation test? (c) What gland is primarily affected if ACTH *does not* cause a normal elevation of cortisol secretion? What is this abnormality called? (d) What gland is primarily affected if ACTH does cause an elevation of cortisol secretion?

5. Roger Proulx has severe arthritis and has been taking prednisone (a glucocorticoid) for two months. He isn't feeling well, complains of repeated "colds," and is extremely "puffy" (edematous). Explain the reason for these symptoms.

Access everything you need to practice, review, and self-assess for both your A&P lecture and lab courses at **myA&P** (www.myaandp.com). There, you'll find powerful online resources, including chapter quizzes and tests, games, A&P Flix animations with quizzes, *Interactive Physiology*® with quizzes, MP3 Tutor Sessions, Practice Anatomy Lab™, and more to help you get a better grade in your course.

17

Blood

B lood is the river of life that surges within us, transporting nearly everything that must be carried from one place to another. Long before modern medicine, blood was viewed as magical—an elixir that held the mystical force of life—because when it drained from the body, life departed as well. Today, centuries later, blood still has enormous importance in the practice of medicine. Clinicians examine it more often than any other tissue when trying to determine the cause of disease in their patients.

In this chapter, we describe the composition and functions of this life-sustaining fluid that serves as a transport "vehicle" for the organs of the cardiovascular system. To get started, we need a brief overview of blood circulation, which is initiated by the pumping action of the heart. Blood exits the *heart* via *arteries*, which branch repeatedly until they

Figure 17.1 **The major components of whole blood.**

become tiny *capillaries*. By diffusing across the capillary walls, oxygen and nutrients leave the blood and enter the body tissues, and carbon dioxide and wastes move from the tissues to the bloodstream. As oxygen-deficient blood leaves the capillary beds, it flows into *veins*, which return it to the heart. The returning blood then flows from the heart to the lungs, where it picks up oxygen and then returns to the heart to be pumped throughout the body once again. Now let us look more closely at the nature of blood.

Overview: Blood Composition and Functions

▶ Describe the composition and physical characteristics of whole blood. Explain why it is classified as a connective tissue.

▶ List eight functions of blood.

Components

Blood is the only fluid tissue in the body. It appears to be a thick, homogeneous liquid, but the microscope reveals that blood has both cellular and liquid components. Blood is a specialized type of connective tissue in which living blood cells, called the *formed elements,* are suspended in a nonliving fluid matrix called *plasma* (plaz′mah). The collagen and elastic fibers typical of other connective tissues are absent from blood, but dissolved fibrous proteins become visible as fibrin strands during blood clotting.

If we spin a sample of blood in a centrifuge, the heavier formed elements are packed down by centrifugal force and the less dense plasma remains at the top **(Figure 17.1)**. Most of the reddish mass at the bottom of the tube is *erythrocytes* (ĕ-rith′ro-sīts; *erythro* = red), the red blood cells that transport oxygen. A thin, whitish layer called the **buffy coat** is present at the erythrocyte-plasma junction. This layer contains *leukocytes* (*leuko* = white), the white blood cells that act in various ways to protect the body, and *platelets*, cell fragments that help stop bleeding.

Erythrocytes normally constitute about 45% of the total volume of a blood sample, a percentage known as the **hematocrit** (he-mat′o-krit; "blood fraction"). Normal hematocrit values vary. In healthy males the norm is 47% ± 5%; in females it is 42% ± 5%. Leukocytes and platelets contribute less than 1% of blood volume. Plasma makes up most of the remaining 55% of whole blood.

Physical Characteristics and Volume

Blood is a sticky, opaque fluid with a characteristic metallic taste. As children, we discover its saltiness the first time we stick a cut finger into our mouth. Depending on the amount of oxygen it is carrying, the color of blood varies from scarlet (oxygen rich) to dark red (oxygen poor).

Blood is more dense than water and about five times more viscous, largely because of its formed elements. Blood is slightly alkaline, with a pH between 7.35 and 7.45, and its temperature (38°C or 100.4°F) is always slightly higher than body temperature.

Blood accounts for approximately 8% of body weight. Its average volume in healthy adult males is 5–6 L (about 1.5 gallons), somewhat greater than in healthy adult females (4–5 L).

Functions

Blood performs a number of functions, all concerned in one way or another with distributing substances, regulating blood levels of particular substances, or protecting the body.

Distribution

Distribution functions of blood include

■ Delivering oxygen from the lungs and nutrients from the digestive tract to all body cells.

■ Transporting metabolic waste products from cells to elimination sites (to the lungs for elimination of carbon dioxide, and to the kidneys for disposal of nitrogenous wastes in urine).

■ Transporting hormones from the endocrine organs to their target organs.

17

Regulation

Regulatory functions of blood include

- Maintaining appropriate body temperature by absorbing and distributing heat throughout the body and to the skin surface to encourage heat loss.
- Maintaining normal pH in body tissues. Many blood proteins and other bloodborne solutes act as buffers to prevent excessive or abrupt changes in blood pH that could jeopardize normal cell activities. Additionally, blood acts as the reservoir for the body's "alkaline reserve" of bicarbonate atoms.
- Maintaining adequate fluid volume in the circulatory system. Salts (sodium chloride and others) and blood proteins act to prevent excessive fluid loss from the bloodstream into the tissue spaces. As a result, the fluid volume in the blood vessels remains ample to support efficient blood circulation to all parts of the body.

Protection

Protective functions of blood include

- Preventing blood loss. When a blood vessel is damaged, platelets and plasma proteins initiate clot formation, halting blood loss.
- Preventing infection. Drifting along in blood are antibodies, complement proteins, and white blood cells, all of which help defend the body against foreign invaders such as bacteria and viruses.

Blood Plasma

▶ Discuss the composition and functions of plasma.

Blood **plasma** is a straw-colored, sticky fluid (Figure 17.1). Although it is mostly water (about 90%), plasma contains over 100 different dissolved solutes, including nutrients, gases, hormones, wastes and products of cell activity, ions, and proteins. **Table 17.1** summarizes the major plasma components.

Plasma proteins are the most abundant plasma solutes, accounting for about 8% by weight of plasma volume. Except for hormones and gamma globulins, most plasma proteins are produced by the liver. Plasma proteins serve a variety of functions, but they are *not* taken up by cells to be used as fuels or metabolic nutrients as are most other plasma solutes, such as glucose, fatty acids, and amino acids.

Albumin (al-bu′min) accounts for some 60% of plasma protein. It acts as a carrier to shuttle certain molecules through the circulation, is an important blood buffer, and is the major blood protein contributing to the plasma osmotic pressure (the pressure that helps to keep water in the bloodstream). (Sodium ions are the other major solute contributing to blood osmotic pressure.)

The makeup of plasma varies continuously as cells remove or add substances to the blood. However, assuming a healthy diet, plasma composition is kept relatively constant by various homeostatic mechanisms. For example, when blood protein levels drop undesirably, the liver makes more proteins. When the blood starts to become too acidic (acidosis), both the respiratory

TABLE 17.1	Composition of Plasma
CONSTITUENT	**DESCRIPTION AND IMPORTANCE**
Water	90% of plasma volume; dissolving and suspending medium for solutes of blood; absorbs heat
Solutes Plasma proteins	8% (by weight) of plasma volume; all contribute to osmotic pressure and maintain water balance in blood and tissues; all have other functions (transport, enzymatic, etc.) as well
▪ Albumin	60% of plasma proteins; produced by liver; main contributor to osmotic pressure
▪ Globulins	36% of plasma proteins
alpha, beta	Produced by liver; most are transport proteins that bind to lipids, metal ions, and fat-soluble vitamins
gamma	Antibodies released by plasma cells during immune response
▪ Fibrinogen	4% of plasma proteins; produced by liver; forms fibrin threads of blood clot
Nonprotein nitrogenous substances	By-products of cellular metabolism, such as urea, uric acid, creatinine, and ammonium salts
Nutrients (organic)	Materials absorbed from digestive tract and transported for use throughout body; include glucose and other simple carbohydrates, amino acids (digestion products of proteins), fatty acids, glycerol and triglycerides (fat products), cholesterol, and vitamins
Electrolytes	Cations include sodium, potassium, calcium, magnesium; anions include chloride, phosphate, sulfate, and bicarbonate; help to maintain plasma osmotic pressure and normal blood pH
Respiratory gases	Oxygen and carbon dioxide; oxygen mostly bound to hemoglobin inside RBCs; carbon dioxide transported dissolved in plasma as bicarbonate ion or CO_2, or bound to hemoglobin in RBCs
Hormones	Steroid and thyroid hormones carried by plasma proteins

system and the kidneys are called into action to restore plasma's normal, slightly alkaline pH. Body organs make dozens of adjustments, day in and day out, to maintain the many plasma solutes at life-sustaining levels.

CHECK YOUR UNDERSTANDING

1. What is the hematocrit? What is its normal value?
2. List two protective functions of blood.
3. Are plasma proteins used as fuel for body cells? Explain your answer.

For answers, see Appendix G.

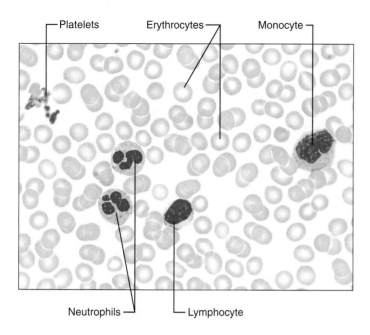

Figure 17.2 **Photomicrograph of a human blood smear stained with Wright's stain.** (640×)

Figure 17.3 **Structure of erythrocytes.** Notice the distinctive biconcave shape.

Formed Elements

The **formed elements** of blood, *erythrocytes*, *leukocytes*, and *platelets*, have some unusual features. (1) Two of the three are not even true cells: Erythrocytes have no nuclei or organelles, and platelets are cell fragments. Only leukocytes are complete cells. (2) Most of the formed elements survive in the bloodstream for only a few days. (3) Most blood cells do not divide. Instead, they are continuously renewed by division of cells in red bone marrow, where they originate.

If you examine a stained smear of human blood under the light microscope, you will see disc-shaped red blood cells, a variety of gaudily stained spherical white blood cells, and some scattered platelets that look like debris **(Figure 17.2)**. Erythrocytes vastly outnumber the other types of formed elements. Table 17.2 on p. 645 summarizes the important characteristics of the formed elements.

Erythrocytes

▶ Describe the structure, function, and production of erythrocytes.

▶ Describe the chemical makeup of hemoglobin.

▶ Give examples of disorders caused by abnormalities of erythrocytes. Explain what goes wrong in each disorder.

Structural Characteristics

Erythrocytes or **red blood cells (RBCs)** are small cells, about 7.5 μm in diameter. Shaped like biconcave discs—flattened discs with depressed centers—they appear lighter in color at their thin centers than at their edges **(Figure 17.3)**. Consequently, erythrocytes look like miniature doughnuts when viewed with a microscope. Mature erythrocytes are bound by a plasma membrane, but lack a nucleus (are *anucleate*) and have essentially no organelles. In fact, they are little more than "bags" of *hemoglobin* (*Hb*), the RBC protein that functions in gas transport. Other proteins are present, such as antioxidant enzymes that rid the body of harmful oxygen radicals, but most function mainly to maintain the plasma membrane or promote changes in RBC shape.

For example, the biconcave shape of an erythrocyte is maintained by a network of proteins, especially one called *spectrin*, attached to the cytoplasmic face of its plasma membrane. The spectrin net is deformable, giving erythrocytes flexibility to change shape as necessary—to twist, turn, and become cup shaped as they are carried passively through capillaries with diameters smaller than themselves—and then to resume their biconcave shape.

The erythrocyte is a superb example of complementarity of structure and function. It picks up oxygen in the capillary beds of the lungs and releases it to tissue cells across other capillaries throughout the body. It also transports some 20% of the carbon dioxide released by tissue cells back to the lungs. Three structural characteristics contribute to erythrocyte gas transport functions:

1. Its small size and biconcave shape provide a huge surface area relative to volume (about 30% more surface area than comparable spherical cells). The biconcave disc shape is ideally suited for gas exchange because no point within the cytoplasm is far from the surface.
2. Discounting water content, an erythrocyte is over 97% hemoglobin, the molecule that binds to and transports respiratory gases.
3. Because erythrocytes lack mitochondria and generate ATP by anaerobic mechanisms, they do not consume any of the oxygen they are transporting, making them very efficient oxygen transporters indeed.

17

(a) **Hemoglobin consists of globin (two alpha and two beta polypeptide chains) and four heme groups.**

(b) **Iron-containing heme pigment.**

Figure 17.4 **Structure of hemoglobin.**

Erythrocytes are the major factor contributing to blood viscosity. Women typically have a lower red blood cell count than men [4.3–5.2 million cells per microliter (1 μl = 1 mm^3) of blood versus 5.1–5.8 million cells/μl respectively]. When the number of red blood cells increases beyond the normal range, blood viscosity rises and blood flows more slowly. Similarly, as the number of red blood cells drops below the lower end of the range, the blood thins and flows more rapidly.

Function

Erythrocytes are completely dedicated to their job of transporting respiratory gases (oxygen and carbon dioxide). **Hemoglobin,** the protein that makes red blood cells red, binds easily and reversibly with oxygen, and most oxygen carried in blood is bound to hemoglobin. Normal values for hemoglobin are 14–20 grams per 100 milliliters of blood (g/100 ml) in infants, 13–18 g/100 ml in adult males, and 12–16 g/100 ml in adult females.

Hemoglobin is made up of the protein **globin** bound to the red **heme** pigment. Globin consists of four polypeptide chains—two alpha (α) and two beta (β)—each binding a ring-like heme group (Figure 17.4a). Each heme group bears an atom of iron set like a jewel in its center (Figure 17.4b). A hemoglobin molecule can transport four molecules of oxygen because each iron atom can combine reversibly with one molecule of oxygen. A single red blood cell contains about 250 million hemoglobin molecules, so each of these tiny cells can scoop up about 1 billion molecules of oxygen!

The fact that hemoglobin is contained in erythrocytes, rather than existing free in plasma, prevents it (1) from breaking into fragments that would leak out of the bloodstream (through the rather porous capillary membranes) and (2) from contributing to blood viscosity and osmotic pressure.

Oxygen loading occurs in the lungs, and the direction of transport is from lungs to tissue cells. As oxygen-deficient blood moves through the lungs, oxygen diffuses from the air sacs of the lungs into the blood and then into the erythrocytes, where it binds to hemoglobin. When oxygen binds to iron, the hemoglobin, now called **oxyhemoglobin,** assumes a new three-dimensional shape and becomes ruby red. In the tissues, the process is reversed. Oxygen detaches from iron, hemoglobin resumes its former shape, and the resulting **deoxyhemoglobin,** or *reduced hemoglobin,* becomes dark red. The released oxygen diffuses from the blood into the tissue fluid and then into the tissue cells.

About 20% of the carbon dioxide transported in the blood combines with hemoglobin, but it binds to globin's amino acids rather than to the heme group. This formation of **carbaminohemoglobin** (kar-bam″ ĭ-no-he″mo″-glo′bin) occurs more readily when hemoglobin is in the reduced state (dissociated from oxygen). Carbon dioxide loading occurs in the tissues, and the direction of transport is from tissues to lungs, where carbon dioxide is eliminated from the body. We describe the loading and unloading of these respiratory gases in Chapter 22.

Production of Erythrocytes

Blood cell formation is referred to as **hematopoiesis** (hem″ah-to-poi-e′sis), or **hemopoiesis** (*hemo, hemato* = blood; *poiesis* = to make). This process occurs in the **red bone marrow,** which is composed largely of a soft network of reticular connective tissue bordering on wide blood capillaries called *blood sinusoids.*

Stem cell   Committed cell   Developmental pathway ⟶

Phase 1
Ribosome synthesis

Phase 2
Hemoglobin accumulation

Phase 3
Ejection of nucleus

Hemocytoblast   Proerythroblast   Early erythroblast   Late erythroblast   ⌐Normoblast⌐   Reticulocyte   Erythrocyte

Figure 17.5 Erythropoiesis: genesis of red blood cells. Reticulocytes are released into the bloodstream. The myeloid stem cell, the phase intermediate between the hemocytoblast and the proerythroblast, is not illustrated.

Within this network are immature blood cells, macrophages, fat cells, and *reticular cells* (which secrete the fibers). In adults, red marrow is found chiefly in the bones of the axial skeleton and girdles, and in the proximal epiphyses of the humerus and femur.

Each type of blood cell is produced in different numbers in response to changing body needs and different regulatory factors. As blood cells mature, they migrate through the thin walls of the sinusoids to enter the bloodstream. On average, the marrow turns out an ounce of new blood containing some 100 billion new cells each and every day.

The various formed elements have different functions, but there are similarities in their life histories. All arise from the same type of *stem cell*, the **hemocytoblast** (*cyte* = cell, *blast* = bud), or pluripotent **hematopoietic stem cell**. These undifferentiated precursor cells reside in the red bone marrow. The maturation pathways of the various formed elements differ, however, and once a cell is *committed* to a specific blood cell pathway, it cannot change. This commitment is signaled by the appearance of membrane surface receptors that respond to specific hormones or growth factors, which in turn "push" the cell toward further specialization.

Erythrocyte production, or **erythropoiesis** (ĕ-rith″ro-poi-e′sis) begins when a hemocytoblast descendant called a **myeloid stem cell** is transformed into a **proerythroblast** (Figure 17.5). Proerythroblasts, in turn, give rise to the **early (basophilic) erythroblasts** that produce huge numbers of ribosomes. During these first two phases, the cells divide many times. Hemoglobin is synthesized and iron accumulates as the early erythroblast is transformed into a **late erythroblast** and then a **normoblast**. The "color" of the cell cytoplasm changes as the blue-staining ribosomes become masked by the pink color of hemoglobin. When a normoblast has accumulated almost all of its hemoglobin, it ejects most of its organelles. Additionally, its nuclear functions end and its nucleus degenerates and is pinched off, allowing the cell to collapse inward and eventually assume the biconcave shape. The result is the **reticulocyte** (essentially a young erythrocyte), so named

because it still contains a scant *reticulum* (network) of clumped ribosomes.

The entire process from hemocytoblast to reticulocyte takes about 15 days. The reticulocytes, filled almost to bursting with hemoglobin, enter the bloodstream to begin their task of oxygen transport. Usually they become fully mature erythrocytes within two days of release as their ribosomes are degraded by intracellular enzymes.

Reticulocytes account for 1–2% of all erythrocytes in the blood of healthy people. **Reticulocyte counts** provide a rough index of the *rate* of RBC formation—reticulocyte counts below or above this percentage range indicate abnormal rates of erythrocyte formation.

Regulation and Requirements for Erythropoiesis

The number of circulating erythrocytes in a given individual is remarkably constant and reflects a balance between red blood cell production and destruction. This balance is important because having too few erythrocytes leads to tissue hypoxia (oxygen deprivation), whereas having too many makes the blood undesirably viscous. To ensure that the number of erythrocytes in blood remains within the homeostatic range, new cells are produced at the incredibly rapid rate of more than 2 million per second in healthy people. This process is controlled hormonally and depends on adequate supplies of iron, amino acids, and certain B vitamins.

Hormonal Controls The direct stimulus for erythrocyte formation is provided by **erythropoietin (EPO)**, a glycoprotein hormone (Figure 17.6). Normally, a small amount of EPO circulates in the blood at all times and sustains red blood cell production at a basal rate. The kidneys play the major role in EPO production, although the liver produces some. When certain kidney cells become *hypoxic* (i.e., have inadequate oxygen), oxygen-sensitive enzymes are unable to carry out their normal functions of degrading an intracellular signaling molecule called hypoxia-inducible factor (HIF). As HIF accumulates, it accelerates the synthesis and release of erythropoietin.

17

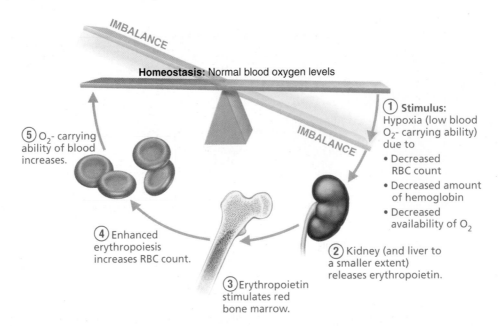

Figure 17.6 Erythropoietin mechanism for regulating erythropoiesis.

The drop in normal blood oxygen levels that triggers EPO formation can result from

1. Reduced numbers of red blood cells due to hemorrhage or excessive RBC destruction
2. Insufficient hemoglobin per RBC (as in iron deficiency)
3. Reduced availability of oxygen, as might occur at high altitudes or during pneumonia

Conversely, too many erythrocytes or excessive oxygen in the bloodstream depresses erythropoietin production. Note that it is not the number of erythrocytes in blood that controls the rate of erythropoiesis. Instead, control is based on their ability to transport enough oxygen to meet tissue demands.

Bloodborne erythropoietin stimulates red marrow cells that *are already committed* to becoming erythrocytes, causing them to mature more rapidly. One to two days after erythropoietin levels rise in the blood, a marked increase in the rate of reticulocyte release (and hence reticulocyte count) occurs. Notice that hypoxia (oxygen deficit) does not activate the bone marrow directly. Instead it stimulates the kidneys, which in turn provide the hormonal stimulus that activates the bone marrow.

HOMEOSTATIC IMBALANCE

Renal dialysis patients whose kidneys have failed produce too little EPO to support normal erythropoiesis. Consequently, they routinely have red blood cell counts less than half that of healthy individuals. Genetically engineered (recombinant) EPO has helped such patients immeasurably but has also become a substance of abuse in athletes—particularly in professional bike racers and marathon runners seeking increased stamina and performance. However, the consequences can be deadly. By injecting EPO, healthy athletes increase their normal hematocrit from 45% to as much as 65%. Then, with the dehydration that occurs in a long race, the blood concentrates even further,

becoming a thick, sticky "sludge" that can cause clotting, stroke, and heart failure. ■

The male sex hormone *testosterone* also enhances EPO production by the kidneys. Because female sex hormones do not have similar stimulatory effects, testosterone may be at least partially responsible for the higher RBC counts and hemoglobin levels seen in males. Also, a wide variety of chemicals released by leukocytes, platelets, and even reticular cells stimulates bursts of RBC production.

Dietary Requirements The raw materials required for erythropoiesis include the usual nutrients and structural materials—amino acids, lipids, and carbohydrates. Iron is essential for hemoglobin synthesis. Iron is available from the diet, and its absorption into the bloodstream is precisely controlled by intestinal cells in response to changing body stores of iron.

Approximately 65% of the body's iron supply (about 4000 mg) is in hemoglobin. Most of the remainder is stored in the liver, spleen, and (to a much lesser extent) bone marrow. Free iron ions (Fe^{2+}, Fe^{3+}) are toxic, so iron is stored inside cells as protein-iron complexes such as **ferritin** (fer′ĭ-tin) and **hemosiderin** (he″ mo-sid′er-in). In blood, iron is transported loosely bound to a transport protein called **transferrin**, and developing erythrocytes take up iron as needed to form hemoglobin **(Figure 17.7)**. Small amounts of iron are lost each day in feces, urine, and perspiration. The average daily loss of iron is 1.7 mg in women and 0.9 mg in men. In women, the menstrual flow accounts for the additional losses.

Two B-complex vitamins—vitamin B_{12} and folic acid—are necessary for normal DNA synthesis. Thus, even slight deficits jeopardize rapidly dividing cell populations, such as developing erythrocytes.

Fate and Destruction of Erythrocytes

Red blood cells have a useful life span of 100 to 120 days (Figure 17.7). Their anucleate condition carries with it some important limitations. Red blood cells are unable to synthesize new proteins, to grow, or to divide. Erythrocytes become "old" as they lose their flexibility and become increasingly rigid and fragile, and their contained hemoglobin begins to degenerate. They become trapped and fragment in smaller circulatory channels, particularly in those of the spleen. For this reason, the spleen is sometimes called the "red blood cell graveyard."

Dying erythrocytes are engulfed and destroyed by macrophages. The heme of their hemoglobin is split off from globin. Its core of iron is salvaged, bound to protein (as ferritin or hemosiderin), and stored for reuse. The balance of the heme group is degraded to **bilirubin** (bil″ĭ-roo′bin), a yellow pigment that is released to the blood and binds to albumin for transport (Figure 17.7, ⑤). Bilirubin is picked up by liver cells, which in turn secrete it (in bile) into the intestine, where it is metabolized to *urobilinogen*. Most of this degraded pigment leaves the body in feces, as a brown pigment called *stercobilin*. The protein (globin) part of hemoglobin is metabolized or broken down to amino acids, which are released to the circulation.

Disposal of hemoglobin spilled from red blood cells to the blood (as occurs in sickle-cell anemia or hemolytic anemia) takes a similar but much more rapid course to avoid toxic buildup of iron in blood. Released hemoglobin is captured by the plasma protein *haptoglobin* and the complex is phagocytized by macrophages.

Erythrocyte Disorders

Most erythrocyte disorders can be classified as anemias or polycythemias. We describe the many varieties and causes of these conditions next.

Anemias Anemia (ah-ne′me-ah; "lacking blood") is a condition in which the blood has abnormally low oxygen-carrying capacity. It is a *sign* of some disorder rather than a disease in and of itself. Its hallmark is blood oxygen levels that are inadequate to support normal metabolism. Anemic individuals are fatigued, often pale, short of breath, and chilly. Common causes of anemia include the following:

1. **An insufficient number of red blood cells.** Conditions that reduce the red blood cell count include blood loss, excessive RBC destruction, and bone marrow failure.

    Hemorrhagic anemias (hem″o-raj′ik) result from blood loss. In acute hemorrhagic anemia, blood loss is rapid (as might follow a severe stab wound); it is treated by blood replacement. Slight but persistent blood loss (due to hemorrhoids or an undiagnosed bleeding ulcer, for example) causes chronic hemorrhagic anemia. Once the primary problem is resolved, normal erythropoietic mechanisms replace the deficient blood cells.

    In *hemolytic anemias* (he″mo-lit′ik), erythrocytes rupture, or lyse, prematurely. Hemoglobin abnormalities, transfusion of mismatched blood, and certain bacterial and parasitic infections are possible causes.

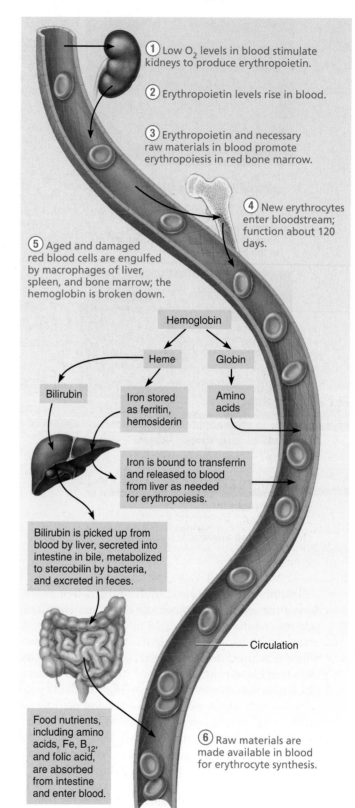

① Low O₂ levels in blood stimulate kidneys to produce erythropoietin.

② Erythropoietin levels rise in blood.

③ Erythropoietin and necessary raw materials in blood promote erythropoiesis in red bone marrow.

④ New erythrocytes enter bloodstream; function about 120 days.

⑤ Aged and damaged red blood cells are engulfed by macrophages of liver, spleen, and bone marrow; the hemoglobin is broken down.

Hemoglobin

Heme

Globin

Bilirubin

Iron stored as ferritin, hemosiderin

Amino acids

Iron is bound to transferrin and released to blood from liver as needed for erythropoiesis.

Bilirubin is picked up from blood by liver, secreted into intestine in bile, metabolized to stercobilin by bacteria, and excreted in feces.

Circulation

Food nutrients, including amino acids, Fe, B₁₂, and folic acid, are absorbed from intestine and enter blood.

⑥ Raw materials are made available in blood for erythrocyte synthesis.

Figure 17.7 Life cycle of red blood cells.

Val His Leu Thr Pro Glu Glu ⋯
1   2   3   4   5   6   7   146

(a) Normal erythrocyte has normal hemoglobin amino acid sequence in the beta chain.

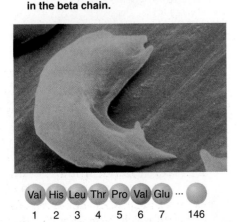

Val His Leu Thr Pro Val Glu ⋯
1   2   3   4   5   6   7   146

(b) Sickled erythrocyte results from a single amino acid change in the beta chain of hemoglobin.

Figure 17.8 Sickle-cell anemia. Scanning electron micrographs (5700×).

Aplastic anemia may result from destruction or inhibition of the red marrow by certain drugs and chemicals, ionizing radiation, or viruses. In most cases, the cause is unknown. Because marrow destruction impairs formation of *all* formed elements, anemia is just one of its signs. Defects in blood clotting and immunity are also present. Blood transfusions provide a stopgap treatment until stem cells harvested from a donor's blood, bone marrow, or umbilical cord blood can be transplanted.

2. **Low hemoglobin content.** When hemoglobin molecules are normal, but erythrocytes contain fewer than the usual number, a nutritional anemia is always suspected.

Iron-deficiency anemia is generally a secondary result of hemorrhagic anemias, but it also results from inadequate intake of iron-containing foods and impaired iron absorption. The erythrocytes produced, called **microcytes**, are small and pale. The obvious treatment is iron supplements, but if chronic hemorrhage is the cause, red cell transfusions may also be needed.

When athletes exercise vigorously, their blood volume expands and can increase by as much as 35% over time. Since this increased volume effectively dilutes the blood

components, a test for the iron content of the blood at such times would indicate iron-deficiency anemia. However, this illusion of iron deficiency, called **athlete's anemia**, is reversed as blood components return to physiological levels within a week or so after the athlete resumes a normal level of activity.

Pernicious anemia is due to a deficiency of vitamin B_{12}. Because meats, poultry, and fish provide ample amounts of the vitamin, diet is rarely the problem except for strict vegetarians. A substance called **intrinsic factor**, produced by the stomach mucosa, must be present for vitamin B_{12} to be absorbed by intestinal cells. In most cases of pernicious anemia, intrinsic factor is deficient. Consequently, the developing erythrocytes grow but do not divide, and large, pale cells called **macrocytes** result. Pernicious anemia is an autoimmune disease in which the stomach mucosa atrophies, and it most often affects the elderly. Treatment involves regular intramuscular injections of vitamin B_{12} or application of a B_{12}-containing gel (Nascobal) to the nasal lining once a week.

3. **Abnormal hemoglobin.** Production of abnormal hemoglobin usually has a genetic basis. Two such examples, thalassemia and sickle-cell anemia, can be serious, incurable, and sometimes fatal diseases. In both diseases the globin part of hemoglobin is abnormal and the erythrocytes produced are fragile and rupture prematurely.

Thalassemias (thal″ah-se′me-ahs; "sea blood") are typically seen in people of Mediterranean ancestry, such as Greeks and Italians. One of the globin chains is absent or faulty, and the erythrocytes are thin, delicate, and deficient in hemoglobin. There are many subtypes of thalassemia, classified according to which hemoglobin chain is affected and where, ranging in severity from mild to so severe that monthly blood transfusion is required.

In **sickle-cell anemia**, the havoc caused by the abnormal hemoglobin, *hemoglobin S* (*HbS*), results from a change in just one of the 146 amino acids in a beta chain of the globin molecule! (See **Figure 17.8**.) This alteration causes the beta chains to link together under low-oxygen conditions, forming stiff rods so that hemoglobin S becomes spiky and sharp. This, in turn, causes the red blood cells to become crescent shaped when they unload oxygen molecules or when the oxygen content of the blood is lower than normal, as during vigorous exercise and other activities that increase metabolic rate.

The stiff, deformed erythrocytes rupture easily and tend to dam up in small blood vessels. These events interfere with oxygen delivery, leaving the victims gasping for air and in extreme pain. Bone and chest pain are particularly severe, and infection and stroke are common sequels. Blood transfusion is still the standard treatment for an acute sickle-cell crisis, but preliminary results using inhaled nitric oxide to dilate blood vessels are promising.

Sickle-cell anemia occurs chiefly in black people who live in the malaria belt of Africa and among their descendants. It strikes nearly one of every 400 black newborns in the United States. Globally, 300–500 million people are infected with malaria and more than a million die each year. While individuals with two copies of the sickle-cell gene have sickle-cell anemia, individuals with only one copy of the gene (the sickle-cell trait) have a better chance of surviving in regions where malaria is present. Their cells only sickle under abnormal circumstances, most importantly when they are infected with malaria. Sickling appears to reduce the parasites' ability to survive and enhances macrophages' ability to destroy infected RBCs and the parasites they contain.

Several treatment approaches focus on preventing RBCs from sickling. Fetal hemoglobin (HbF) does not "sickle," even in those destined to have sickle-cell anemia. *Hydroxyurea*, a drug used to treat chronic leukemia, switches the fetal hemoglobin gene back on. This drug dramatically reduces the excruciating pain and overall severity and complications of sickle-cell anemia (by 50%). Another drug, clotrimazole, reduces sickling by blocking ion channels in the RBC membrane, keeping ions and water inside the cell. Other approaches being tested include oral arginine to stimulate nitric oxide production and dilate blood vessels, stem cell transplants, and gene therapy to deliver genes for synthesizing normal beta chains.

Polycythemia Polycythemia (pol″e-si-the′me-ah; "many blood cells") is an abnormal excess of erythrocytes that increases blood viscosity, causing it to sludge, or flow sluggishly. *Polycythemia vera*, a bone marrow cancer, is characterized by dizziness and an exceptionally high RBC count (8–11 million cells/µl). The hematocrit may be as high as 80% and blood volume may double, causing the vascular system to become engorged with blood and severely impairing circulation.

Secondary polycythemias result when less oxygen is available or EPO production increases. The secondary polycythemia that appears in individuals living at high altitudes is a normal physiological response to the reduced atmospheric pressure and lower oxygen content of the air in such areas. RBC counts of 6–8 million/µl are common in such people. Severe polycythemia is treated by blood dilution, in other words, removing some blood and replacing it with saline.

Blood doping, practiced by some athletes competing in aerobic events, is artificially induced polycythemia. Some of the athlete's red blood cells are drawn off and then reinjected a few days before the event. The erythrocytes are quickly replaced because the erythropoietin mechanism is triggered shortly after blood removal. Then, when the stored blood is reinfused, a temporary polycythemia results. Since red blood cells carry oxygen, the additional infusion should translate into increased oxygen-carrying capacity due to a higher hematocrit, and hence greater endurance and speed. Other than the risk of stroke and heart failure due to high hematocrit and high blood viscosity described earlier, blood doping seems to work. However, the practice is considered unethical and has been banned from the Olympic Games.

4. How many molecules of oxygen can each hemoglobin molecule transport? What part of the hemoglobin binds the oxygen?

5. Patients with advanced kidney disease often have anemia. Explain the connection.

For answers, see Appendix G.

Leukocytes

▶ List the classes, structural characteristics, and functions of leukocytes.

▶ Describe how leukocytes are produced.

▶ Give examples of leukocyte disorders, and explain what goes wrong in each disorder.

General Structural and Functional Characteristics

Leukocytes (*leuko* = white), or **white blood cells (WBCs)**, are the only formed elements that are complete cells, with nuclei and the usual organelles. Accounting for less than 1% of total blood volume, leukocytes are far less numerous than red blood cells. On average, there are 4800–10,800 WBCs/µl of blood.

Leukocytes are crucial to our defense against disease. They form a mobile army that helps protect the body from damage by bacteria, viruses, parasites, toxins, and tumor cells. As such, they have some special functional characteristics. Red blood cells are confined to the bloodstream, and they carry out their functions in the blood. But white blood cells are able to slip out of the capillary blood vessels—a process called **diapedesis** (di″ah-pĕ-de′sis; "leaping across")—and the circulatory system is simply their means of transport to areas of the body (mostly loose connective tissues or lymphoid tissues) where they are needed to mount inflammatory or immune responses.

As we explain in more detail in Chapter 21, the signals that prompt WBCs to leave the bloodstream at specific locations are cell adhesion molecules displayed by endothelial cells forming the capillary walls at sites of inflammation. Once out of the bloodstream, leukocytes move through the tissue spaces by **amoeboid motion** (they form flowing cytoplasmic extensions that move them along). By following the chemical trail of molecules released by damaged cells or other leukocytes, a phenomenon called **positive chemotaxis**, they can pinpoint areas of tissue damage and infection and gather there in large numbers to destroy foreign substances or dead cells.

Whenever white blood cells are mobilized for action, the body speeds up their production and twice the normal number may appear in the blood within a few hours. A *white blood cell count* of over 11,000 cells/µl is **leukocytosis**. This condition is a normal homeostatic response to an infection in the body.

Leukocytes are grouped into two major categories on the basis of structural and chemical characteristics. *Granulocytes* contain obvious membrane-bound cytoplasmic granules, and *agranulocytes* lack obvious granules. We provide general information about the various leukocytes next. More details appear in **Figure 17.9** and **Table 17.2**.

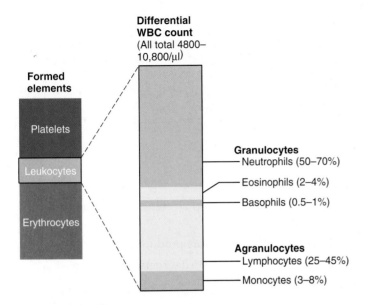

Figure 17.9 Types and relative percentages of leukocytes in normal blood. (The relationship of the formed elements in the left column is not shown to scale. Erythrocytes comprise nearly 98% of the formed elements, and leukocytes and platelets together account for the remaining 2+%.)

Students are often asked to list the leukocytes in order from most abundant to least abundant. The following phrase may help you with this task: **N**ever **l**et **m**onkeys **e**at **b**ananas (neutrophils, lymphocytes, monocytes, eosinophils, basophils).

Granulocytes

Granulocytes (gran′u-lo-sīts), which include neutrophils, basophils, and eosinophils, are all roughly spherical in shape. They are larger and much shorter lived (in most cases) than erythrocytes. They characteristically have lobed nuclei (rounded nuclear masses connected by thinner strands of nuclear material), and their membrane-bound cytoplasmic granules stain quite specifically with Wright's stain. Functionally, all granulocytes are phagocytes to a greater or lesser degree.

Neutrophils **Neutrophils** (nu′tro-filz) are the most numerous of the white blood cells, accounting for 50–70% of the WBC population. Neutrophils are about twice as large as erythrocytes.

The neutrophil cytoplasm stains pale lilac and contains very fine granules (of two varieties) that are difficult to see (Table 17.2 and **Figure 17.10a**). They are called neutrophils (literally, "neutral-loving") because their granules take up both *basic* (blue) and *acidic* (red) *dyes*. Together, the two types of granules give the cytoplasm a lilac color. Some of these granules contain hydrolytic enzymes, and are regarded as lysosomes. Others, especially the smaller granules, contain a potent "brew" of antimicrobial proteins, called **defensins**.

Neutrophil nuclei consist of three to six lobes. Because of this nuclear variability, they are often called **polymorphonuclear leukocytes (PMNs)** or simply **polys** (*polymorphonuclear =* many shapes of the nucleus). (However, some authorities use this term to refer to all granulocytes.)

Neutrophils are our body's bacteria slayers, and their numbers increase explosively during acute bacterial infections such as meningitis and appendicitis. Neutrophils are chemically attracted to sites of inflammation and are active phagocytes. They are especially partial to bacteria and some fungi, and bacterial killing is promoted by a process called a respiratory burst. In the **respiratory burst**, oxygen is actively metabolized to produce potent germ-killer oxidizing substances such as bleach and hydrogen peroxide, and defensin-mediated lysis occurs. It appears that when the granules containing defensins are merged with a microbe-containing phagosome, the defensins form peptide "spears" that pierce holes in the membrane of the ingested "foe."

(a) Neutrophil; multilobed nucleus

(b) Eosinophil; bilobed nucleus, red cytoplasmic granules

(c) Basophil; bilobed nucleus, purplish-black cytoplasmic granules

(d) Small lymphocyte; large spherical nucleus

(e) Monocyte; kidney-shaped nucleus

Figure 17.10 Leukocytes. In each case the leukocytes are surrounded by erythrocytes. (All 1850×, Wright's stain.)

TABLE 17.2	Summary of Formed Elements of the Blood				
CELL TYPE	ILLUSTRATION	DESCRIPTION*	CELLS/μL (mm³) OF BLOOD	DURATION OF DEVELOPMENT (D) AND LIFE SPAN (LS)	FUNCTION
Erythrocytes (red blood cells, RBCs)		Biconcave, anucleate disc; salmon-colored; diameter 7–8 μm	4–6 million	D: about 15 days LS: 100–120 days	Transport oxygen and carbon dioxide
Leukocytes (white blood cells, WBCs)		Spherical, nucleated cells	4800–10,800		
Granulocytes					
▪ Neutrophil		Nucleus multilobed; inconspicuous cytoplasmic granules; diameter 10–12 μm	3000–7000	D: about 14 days LS: 6 hours to a few days	Phagocytize bacteria
▪ Eosinophil		Nucleus bilobed; red cytoplasmic granules; diameter 10–14 μm	100–400	D: about 14 days LS: about 5 days	Kill parasitic worms; complex role in allergy and asthma
▪ Basophil		Nucleus bilobed; large purplish-black cytoplasmic granules; diameter 10–14 μm	20–50	D: 1–7 days LS: a few hours to a few days	Release histamine and other mediators of inflammation; contain heparin, an anticoagulant
Agranulocytes					
▪ Lymphocyte		Nucleus spherical or indented; pale blue cytoplasm; diameter 5–17 μm	1500–3000	D: days to weeks LS: hours to years	Mount immune response by direct cell attack or via antibodies
▪ Monocyte		Nucleus U or kidney shaped; gray-blue cytoplasm; diameter 14–24 μm	100–700	D: 2–3 days LS: months	Phagocytosis; develop into macrophages in the tissues
Platelets		Discoid cytoplasmic fragments containing granules; stain deep purple; diameter 2–4 μm	150,000–400,000	D: 4–5 days LS: 5–10 days	Seal small tears in blood vessels; instrumental in blood clotting

* Appearance when stained with Wright's stain.

Eosinophils Eosinophils (e″o-sin′o-filz) account for 2–4% of all leukocytes and are approximately the size of neutrophils. Their deep red nucleus usually resembles an old-fashioned telephone receiver—it has two lobes connected by a broad band of nuclear material (Table 17.2 and Figure 17.10b).

Large, coarse granules that stain from brick red to crimson with acid (eosin) dyes pack the cytoplasm. These granules are lysosome-like and filled with a unique variety of digestive enzymes. However, unlike typical lysosomes, they lack enzymes that specifically digest bacteria.

The most important role of eosinophils is to lead the counterattack against parasitic worms, such as flatworms (tapeworms and flukes) and roundworms (pinworms and hookworms) that are too large to be phagocytized. These worms are ingested in food (especially raw fish) or invade the body via the skin and then typically burrow into the intestinal or respiratory mucosae. Eosinophils reside in the loose connective tissues at the same body sites, and when they encounter a parasitic worm "prey," they gather around and release the enzymes from their cytoplasmic granules onto the parasite's surface, digesting it away. Eosinophils have complex roles in many other diseases including allergy and asthma. While they contribute to the tissue damage that occurs in many immune processes, we are also beginning to recognize them as important modulators of the immune response.

17

Basophils   Basophils are the rarest white blood cells, averaging only 0.5–1% of the leukocyte population. Their cytoplasm contains large, coarse, histamine-containing granules that have an affinity for the basic dyes (*basophil* = base loving) and stain purplish-black (Figure 17.10c). *Histamine* is an inflammatory chemical that acts as a vasodilator (makes blood vessels dilate) and attracts other white blood cells to the inflamed site; drugs called antihistamines counter this effect. The deep purple nucleus is generally U or S shaped with one or two conspicuous constrictions.

Granulated cells similar to basophils, called *mast cells*, are found in connective tissues. Although mast cell nuclei tend to be more oval than lobed, the cells are similar microscopically, and both cell types bind to a particular antibody (immunoglobulin E) that causes the cells to release histamine. However, they arise from different cell lines.

Agranulocytes

The **agranulocytes** include lymphocytes and monocytes, WBCs that lack *visible* cytoplasmic granules. Although they are similar structurally, they are functionally distinct and unrelated cell types. Their nuclei are typically spherical or kidney shaped.

Lymphocytes   Lymphocytes, accounting for 25% or more of the WBC population, are the second most numerous leukocytes in the blood. When stained, a typical lymphocyte has a large, dark-purple nucleus that occupies most of the cell volume. The nucleus is usually spherical but may be slightly indented, and it is surrounded by a thin rim of pale-blue cytoplasm (Table 17.2 and Figure 17.10d). Lymphocyte diameter ranges from 5 to 17 μm, but they are often classified according to size as small (5–8 μm), medium (10–12 μm), and large (14–17 μm).

Large numbers of lymphocytes exist in the body, but only a small proportion of them (mostly the small lymphocytes) are found in the bloodstream. In fact, lymphocytes are so called because most are closely associated with lymphoid tissues (lymph nodes, spleen, etc.), where they play a crucial role in immunity. **T lymphocytes (T cells)** function in the immune response by acting directly against virus-infected cells and tumor cells. **B lymphocytes (B cells)** give rise to *plasma cells*, which produce **antibodies** (immunoglobulins) that are released to the blood. (We describe B and T lymphocyte functions in Chapter 21.)

Monocytes   Monocytes account for 3–8% of WBCs. They have an average diameter of 18 μm and are the largest leukocytes. They have abundant pale-blue cytoplasm and a darkly staining purple nucleus, which is distinctively U or kidney shaped (Table 17.2 and Figure 17.10e).

When circulating monocytes leave the bloodstream and enter the tissues, they differentiate into highly mobile **macrophages** with prodigious appetites. Macrophages are actively phagocytic, and they are crucial in the body's defense against viruses, certain intracellular bacterial parasites, and *chronic* infections such as tuberculosis. As we explain in Chapter 21, macrophages are also important in activating lymphocytes to mount the immune response.

Production and Life Span of Leukocytes

Like erythropoiesis, **leukopoiesis**, or the production of white blood cells, is stimulated by chemical messengers. These messengers, which can act either as paracrines or hormones, are glycoproteins that fall into two families of hematopoietic factors, **interleukins** and **colony-stimulating factors**, or **CSFs**. The interleukins are numbered (e.g., IL-3, IL-5), but most CSFs are named for the leukocyte population they stimulate—for example, *granulocyte-CSF* (*G-CSF*) stimulates production of granulocytes. Hematopoietic factors, released by supporting cells of the red bone marrow and mature WBCs, not only prompt the white blood cell precursors to divide and mature, but also enhance the protective potency of mature leukocytes.

Many of the hematopoietic hormones (EPO and several of the CSFs) are used clinically to stimulate the bone marrow of cancer patients who are receiving chemotherapy (which suppresses the marrow) and of those who have received stem cell transplants, and to beef up the protective responses of AIDS patients.

Figure 17.11 shows the pathways of leukocyte differentiation, starting with the hematopoietic stem cell, or hemocytoblast, that gives rise to all of the formed elements in the blood. An early branching of the pathway divides the **lymphoid stem cells**, which produce lymphocytes, from the **myeloid stem cells**, which give rise to all other formed elements. In each granulocyte line, the committed cells, called **myeloblasts** (mi′ĕ-lo-blasts″), accumulate lysosomes, becoming **promyelocytes**. The distinctive granules of each granulocyte type appear next in the **myelocyte** stage and then cell division stops. In the subsequent stage, the nuclei arc, producing the **band cell** stage. Just before granulocytes leave the marrow and enter the circulation, their nuclei constrict, beginning the process of nuclear segmentation.

The bone marrow stores mature granulocytes and usually contains about ten times more granulocytes than are found in the blood. The normal ratio of granulocytes to erythrocytes produced is about 3:1, which reflects the much shorter life span (0.25 to 9.0 days) of the granulocytes. Most die combating invading microorganisms.

Despite their similar appearances, the two types of agranulocytes have very different lineages. Monocytes are derived from myeloid stem cells, and share a common precursor with neutrophils that is not shared with the other granulocytes. Cells following the monocyte line pass through the **monoblast** and **promonocyte** stages before leaving the bone marrow and becoming monocytes (Figure 17.11d). Lymphocytes derive from the lymphoid stem cell and progress through the **lymphoblast** and **prolymphocyte** stages (Figure 17.11e). The prolymphocytes leave the bone marrow and travel to the lymphoid tissues, where their further differentiation occurs (as we describe in Chapter 21). Monocytes may live for several months, whereas the life span of lymphocytes varies from a few hours to decades.

Leukocyte Disorders

Overproduction of abnormal leukocytes occurs in leukemia and infectious mononucleosis. At the opposite pole, **leukopenia** (loo″ko-pe′ne-ah) is an abnormally low white blood cell count

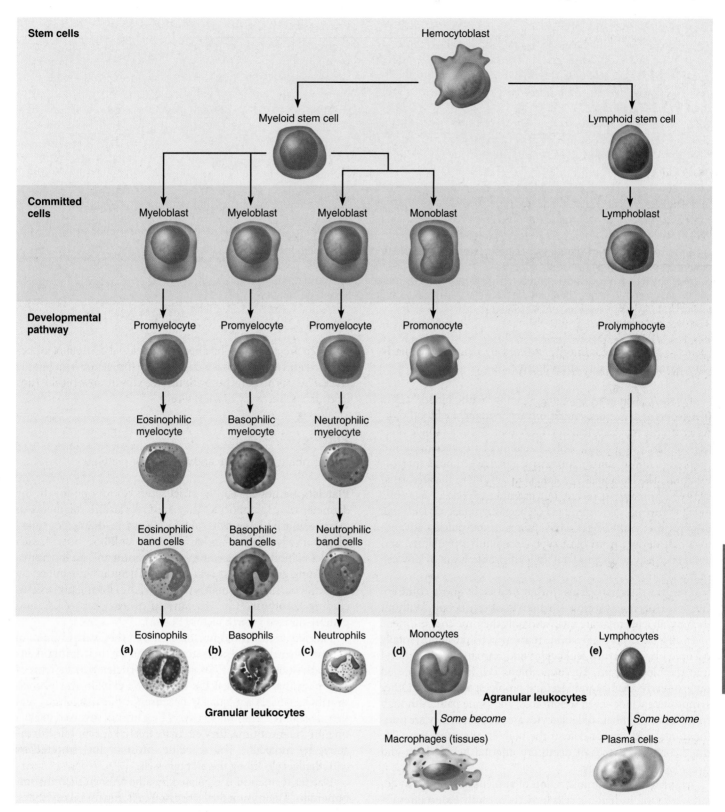

Stem cells

Hemocytoblast

Myeloid stem cell

Lymphoid stem cell

Committed cells

Myeloblast

Myeloblast

Myeloblast

Monoblast

Lymphoblast

Developmental pathway

Promyelocyte

Promyelocyte

Promyelocyte

Promonocyte

Prolymphocyte

Eosinophilic myelocyte

Basophilic myelocyte

Neutrophilic myelocyte

Eosinophilic band cells

Basophilic band cells

Neutrophilic band cells

Eosinophils
(a)

Basophils
(b)

Neutrophils
(c)

Monocytes
(d)

Lymphocytes
(e)

Granular leukocytes

Agranular leukocytes

Some become

Some become

Macrophages (tissues)

Plasma cells

17

Figure 17.11 **Leukocyte formation.** Leukocytes arise from ancestral stem cells called hemocy-toblasts. **(a–c)** Granular leukocytes develop via a sequence involving myeloblasts. **(d)** Monocytes, like granular leukocytes, are progeny of the myeloid stem cell and share a common precursor with neutrophils (not shown). **(e)** Only lymphocytes arise via the lymphoid stem cell line.

Stem cell   Developmental pathway

Hemocytoblast   Megakaryoblast   Promegakaryocyte   Megakaryocyte   Platelets

Figure 17.12 Genesis of platelets. The hemocytoblast gives rise to cells that undergo several mitotic divisions unaccompanied by cytoplasmic division to produce megakaryocytes. The cytoplasm of the megakaryocyte becomes compartmentalized by membranes, and the plasma membrane then fragments, liberating the platelets. (Intermediate stages between the hemocytoblast and megakaryoblast are not illustrated.)

(*penia* = poverty), commonly induced by drugs, particularly glucocorticoids and anticancer agents.

Leukemias   The term *leukemia,* literally "white blood," refers to a group of cancerous conditions involving white blood cells. As a rule, the renegade leukocytes are members of a single *clone* (descendants of a single cell) that remain unspecialized and proliferate out of control, impairing normal red bone marrow function. The leukemias are named according to the abnormal cell type primarily involved. For example, *myelocytic leukemia* involves myeloblast descendants, whereas *lymphocytic leukemia* involves the lymphocytes. Leukemia is *acute* (quickly advancing) if it derives from blast-type cells like lymphoblasts, and *chronic* (slowly advancing) if it involves proliferation of later cell stages like myelocytes.

The more serious acute forms primarily affect children. Chronic leukemia is seen more often in elderly people. Without therapy, all leukemias are fatal, and only the time course differs.

In all leukemias, the red bone marrow becomes almost totally occupied by cancerous leukocytes and immature WBCs flood into the bloodstream. The other blood cell lines are crowded out, so severe anemia and bleeding problems also result. Other symptoms include fever, weight loss, and bone pain. Although tremendous numbers of leukocytes are produced, they are nonfunctional and cannot defend the body in the usual way. The most common causes of death are internal hemorrhage and overwhelming infections.

Irradiation and administration of antileukemic drugs to destroy the rapidly dividing cells have successfully induced remissions (symptom-free periods) lasting from months to years. Stem cell transplants are used in selected patients when compatible donors are available.

Infectious Mononucleosis   Once called the kissing disease, *infectious mononucleosis* is a highly contagious viral disease most often seen in young adults. Caused by the Epstein-Barr virus, its hallmark is excessive numbers of agranulocytes, many of which are atypical. The affected individual complains of being tired and achy, and has a chronic sore throat and a low-grade fever. There is no cure, but with rest the condition typically runs its course to recovery in a few weeks.

Platelets

▶ Describe the structure and function of platelets.

Platelets are not cells in the strict sense. About one-fourth the diameter of a lymphocyte, they are cytoplasmic fragments of extraordinarily large cells (up to 60 μm in diameter) called **megakaryocytes** (meg"ah-kar'e-o-sītz). In blood smears, each platelet exhibits a blue-staining outer region and an inner area containing granules that stain purple. The granules contain an impressive array of chemicals that act in the clotting process, including serotonin, Ca^{2+}, a variety of enzymes, ADP, and platelet-derived growth factor (PDGF).

Platelets are essential for the clotting process that occurs in plasma when blood vessels are ruptured or their lining is injured. By sticking to the damaged site, platelets form a temporary plug that helps seal the break. (We explain this process shortly.) Platelets age quickly because they are anucleate, and they degenerate in about 10 days if they are not involved in clotting. In the meantime, they circulate freely, kept mobile but inactive by molecules (nitric oxide, prostacyclin) secreted by endothelial cells lining the blood vessels.

Platelet formation is regulated by a hormone called **thrombopoietin**. Their immediate ancestral cells, the megakaryocytes, are progeny of the hemocytoblast and the myeloid stem cell, but their formation is quite unusual (**Figure 17.12**). In this line, repeated mitoses of the **megakaryoblast** occur, but cytokinesis does not. The final result is the megakaryocyte (literally "big nucleus cell"), a bizarre cell with a huge, multilobed nucleus and a large cytoplasmic mass.

When formed, the megakaryocyte presses up against a sinusoid (the specialized type of capillary in the red marrow) and sends cytoplasmic extensions through the sinusoid wall into the bloodstream. These extensions rupture, releasing the platelet fragments like stamps being torn from a sheet of postage stamps and seeding the blood with platelets. The plasma membranes associated with each fragment quickly seal around the cytoplasm to form the grainy, roughly disc-shaped platelets (see Table 17.2), each with a diameter of 2–4 μm. Each microliter of blood contains between 150,000 and 400,000 of the tiny platelets.

CHECK YOUR UNDERSTANDING

6. Which WBCs turn into macrophages in tissues? Which other WBC is a voracious phagocyte?
7. Platelets are called "thrombocytes" in other animals. Which term that you've just learned relates to this name? What does this term mean?
8. Amos has leukemia. Even though his WBC count is abnormally high, Amos is prone to severe infections, bleeding, and anemia. Explain.

For answers, see Appendix G.

Hemostasis

▶ Describe the process of hemostasis. List factors that limit clot formation and prevent undesirable clotting.

▶ Give examples of hemostatic disorders. Indicate the cause of each condition.

Normally, blood flows smoothly past the intact blood vessel lining (endothelium). But if a blood vessel wall breaks, a whole series of reactions is set in motion to accomplish **hemostasis** (he″mo-sta′sis), or stoppage of bleeding (*stasis* = halting). Without this plug-the-hole defensive reaction, we would quickly bleed out our entire blood volume from even the smallest cuts.

The hemostasis response is fast, localized, and carefully controlled. It involves many *clotting factors* normally present in plasma as well as some substances that are released by platelets and injured tissue cells. During hemostasis, three steps occur in rapid sequence: ① vascular spasm, ② platelet plug formation, and ③ coagulation, or blood clotting. Blood loss at the site is permanently prevented when fibrous tissue grows into the clot and seals the hole in the blood vessel. Now let's look at each of the three steps in more detail, as shown in **Figure 17.13**.

Vascular Spasm

In the first step, the damaged blood vessels respond to injury by constricting (vasoconstriction) (Figure 17.13, ①). Factors that trigger this **vascular spasm** include direct injury to vascular smooth muscle, chemicals released by endothelial cells and platelets, and reflexes initiated by local pain receptors. The spasm mechanism becomes more and more efficient as the amount of tissue damage increases, and is most effective in the smaller blood vessels. The spasm response is valuable because a strongly constricted artery can significantly reduce blood loss

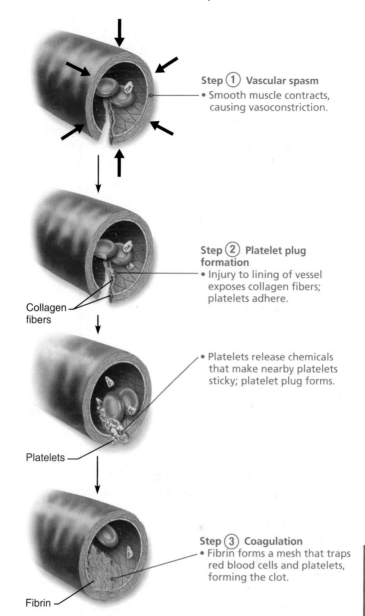

Step ① Vascular spasm
• Smooth muscle contracts, causing vasoconstriction.

Collagen fibers

Step ② Platelet plug formation
• Injury to lining of vessel exposes collagen fibers; platelets adhere.

• Platelets release chemicals that make nearby platelets sticky; platelet plug forms.

Platelets

Step ③ Coagulation
• Fibrin forms a mesh that traps red blood cells and platelets, forming the clot.

Fibrin

Figure 17.13 Events of hemostasis.

for 20–30 minutes, allowing time for platelet plug formation and blood clotting to occur.

Platelet Plug Formation

In the second step, platelets play a key role in hemostasis by aggregating (sticking together), forming a plug that temporarily seals the break in the vessel wall (Figure 17.13, ②). They also help to orchestrate subsequent events that lead to blood clot formation.

As a rule, platelets do not stick to each other or to the smooth endothelial linings of blood vessels. Intact endothelial cells release nitric oxide and a prostaglandin called **prostacyclin** (or *PGI₂*). Both chemicals prevent platelet aggregation in undamaged tissue and restrict aggregation to the site of injury.

However, when the endothelium is damaged and underlying collagen fibers are exposed, platelets adhere tenaciously to the collagen fibers. A large plasma protein called von Willebrand

Phase 1

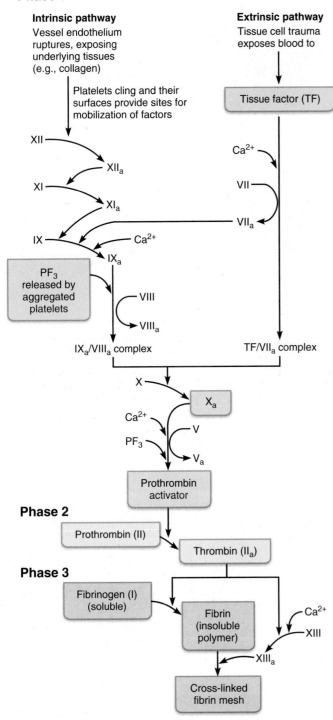

Figure 17.14 The intrinsic and extrinsic pathways of blood clotting (coagulation). The subscript "a" indicates the activated procoagulant.

factor stabilizes bound platelets by forming a bridge between collagen and platelets. Platelets swell, form spiked processes, become stickier, and release chemical messengers including the following:

- **Adenosine diphosphate (ADP):** a potent aggregating agent that causes more platelets to stick to the area and release their contents

- **Serotonin** and **thromboxane A₂** (throm-boks′ān; a short-lived prostaglandin derivative): messengers that enhance vascular spasm and platelet aggregation

As more platelets aggregate, they release more chemicals, aggregating more platelets, and so on, in a positive feedback cycle. Within one minute, a platelet plug is built up, further reducing blood loss. Platelets alone are sufficient for sealing the thousands of minute rips and holes that occur unnoticed as part of the daily wear and tear in your smallest blood vessels. Because platelet plugs are loosely knit, larger breaks need additional reinforcement.

Coagulation

The third step, **coagulation** or **blood clotting**, reinforces the platelet plug with fibrin threads that act as a "molecular glue" for the aggregated platelets (Figure 17.13, ③). The resulting blood clot (fibrin mesh) is quite effective in sealing larger breaks in a blood vessel. Blood is transformed from a liquid to a gel in a multistep process that involves a series of substances called **clotting factors**, or **procoagulants** (Table 17.3).

Most clotting factors are plasma proteins synthesized by the liver. They are numbered I to XIII according to the order of their discovery; hence, the numerical order does not reflect their reaction sequence. All (except tissue factor) normally circulate in blood in inactive form until mobilized. Although vitamin K is not directly involved in coagulation, this fat-soluble vitamin is required for the synthesis of four of the clotting factors (Table 17.3).

Figure 17.14 illustrates the way clotting factors act together to form a clot. The coagulation sequence looks intimidating at first glance, but two things will help you cope with its complexity. First, realize that in most cases, *activation turns clotting factors into enzymes* by clipping off a piece of the protein, causing it to change shape. Once one clotting factor is activated, it activates the next in sequence, and so on, in a cascade. (In Figure 17.14, we use the subscript "a" to denote the activated clotting factor.) Two important exceptions to this generalization are fibrinogen and Ca^{2+}, as we will see below.

The second strategy that will help you cope is to recognize that coagulation occurs in three phases, each with a specific end point:

- *Phase 1: Two pathways to prothrombin activator.* A complex substance called *prothrombin activator* is formed.
- *Phase 2: Common pathway to thrombin.* Prothrombin activator converts a plasma protein called *prothrombin* into *thrombin*, an enzyme.
- *Phase 3: Common pathway to the fibrin mesh.* Thrombin catalyzes the joining of *fibrinogen* molecules present in plasma to a *fibrin mesh*, which traps blood cells and effectively seals the hole until the blood vessel can be permanently repaired.

Now let's consider the three phases in detail.

Phase 1: Two Pathways to Prothrombin Activator

Clotting may be initiated by either the **intrinsic** or the **extrinsic pathway**. In the body both pathways are usually triggered by the

TABLE 17.3	**Blood Clotting Factors (Procoagulants)**			
FACTOR NUMBER	**FACTOR NAME**	**NATURE**	**SOURCE**	**PATHWAY; FUNCTION**
I	Fibrinogen	Plasma protein	Liver	Common pathway; converted to fibrin (insoluble weblike substance of clot)
II	Prothrombin	Plasma protein	Liver*	Common pathway; converted to thrombin (converts fibrinogen to fibrin)
III	Tissue factor (TF)	Plasma membrane glycoprotein	Tissue cells	Activates extrinsic pathway
IV	Calcium ions (Ca^{2+})	Inorganic ion	Plasma	Needed for essentially all stages of coagulation process; always present
V	Proaccelerin	Plasma protein	Liver, platelets	Common pathway
VI[†]				
VII	Proconvertin	Plasma protein	Liver*	Both extrinsic and intrinsic pathways
VIII	Antihemophilic factor (AHF)	Plasma protein	Liver	Intrinsic pathway; deficiency results in hemophilia A
IX	Plasma thromboplastin component (PTC)	Plasma protein	Liver*	Intrinsic pathway; deficiency results in hemophilia B
X	Stuart factor	Plasma protein	Liver*	Common pathway
XI	Plasma thromboplastin antecedent (PTA)	Plasma protein	Liver	Intrinsic pathway; deficiency results in hemophilia C
XII	Hageman factor	Plasma protein; activated by negatively charged surfaces (e.g., glass)	Liver	Intrinsic pathway; activates plasmin; initiates clotting in vitro; activation initiates inflammation
XIII	Fibrin stabilizing factor (FSF)	Plasma protein	Liver, bone marrow	Cross-links fibrin, forming a strong, stable clot

*Synthesis requires vitamin K
[†]Number no longer used; substance now believed to be same as factor V

same tissue-damaging events. Clotting of blood outside the body (such as in a test tube) is initiated *only* by the intrinsic pathway. Before we examine the "why" of these differences, let's see what these pathways have in common.

Pivotal components in both pathways are negatively charged membranes, particularly those on platelets containing phosphatidylserine, also known as **PF₃** (platelet factor 3). Many intermediates of both pathways can be activated only in the presence of PF₃. The intermediate steps of each pathway *cascade* toward a common intermediate, factor X (Figure 17.14). Once factor X has been activated, it complexes with calcium ions, PF₃, and factor V to form **prothrombin activator**. This is usually the slowest step of the blood clotting process, but once prothrombin activator is present, the clot forms in 10 to 15 seconds.

The intrinsic and extrinsic pathways usually work together and are interconnected in many ways, but there are significant differences between them. The *intrinsic pathway* is

- Triggered by negatively charged surfaces such as activated platelets, collagen, or glass. (This is why this pathway can initiate clotting in a test tube.)
- Called *intrinsic* because the factors needed for clotting are present *within* (intrinsic to) the blood.
- Slower because it has many intermediate steps.

The *extrinsic pathway* is

- Triggered by exposing blood to a factor found in tissues underneath the damaged endothelium. This factor is called **tissue factor (TF)** or **factor III.**
- Called *extrinsic* because the tissue factor it requires is *outside* of blood.
- Faster because it bypasses several steps of the intrinsic pathway. In severe tissue trauma, it can promote clot formation in 15 seconds.

Phase 2: Common Pathway to Thrombin

Prothrombin activator catalyzes the transformation of the plasma protein **prothrombin** to the active enzyme **thrombin**.

Phase 3: Common Pathway to the Fibrin Mesh

Thrombin catalyzes the transformation of the *soluble* clotting factor **fibrinogen** into **fibrin**. The fibrin molecules then polymerize (join together) to form long, hairlike, *insoluble* fibrin strands. (Notice that, unlike other clotting factors, activating fibrinogen does not convert it into an enzyme, but instead allows it to polymerize.) The fibrin strands glue the platelets together and make a web that forms the structural basis of the

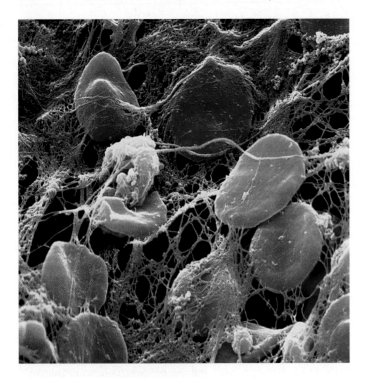

Figure 17.15 Scanning electron micrograph of erythrocytes trapped in a fibrin mesh. (2700×)

clot. Fibrin makes plasma become gel-like and traps formed elements that try to pass through it (Figure 17.15).

In the presence of calcium ions, thrombin also activates **factor XIII (fibrin stabilizing factor)**, a cross-linking enzyme that binds the fibrin strands tightly together, forming a fibrin mesh. Cross-linking further strengthens and stabilizes the clot, effectively sealing the hole until the blood vessel can be permanently repaired.

Factors that inhibit clotting are called **anticoagulants**. Whether or not blood clots depends on a delicate balance between clotting factors and anticoagulants. Normally, anticoagulants dominate and clotting is prevented, but when a vessel is ruptured, procoagulant activity in that area increases dramatically and a clot begins to form. Clot formation is normally complete within 3 to 6 minutes after blood vessel damage.

Clot Retraction and Repair

Within 30 to 60 minutes, the clot is stabilized further by a platelet-induced process called **clot retraction**. Platelets contain contractile proteins (actin and myosin), and they contract in much the same manner as muscle cells. As the platelets contract, they pull on the surrounding fibrin strands, squeezing **serum** (plasma minus the clotting proteins) from the mass, compacting the clot and drawing the ruptured edges of the blood vessel more closely together.

Even as clot retraction is occurring, the vessel is healing. **Platelet-derived growth factor (PDGF)** released by platelet degranulation stimulates smooth muscle cells and fibroblasts to divide and rebuild the wall. As fibroblasts form a connective tissue patch in the injured area, endothelial cells, stimulated by vascular endothelial growth factor (VEGF), multiply and restore the endothelial lining.

Fibrinolysis

A clot is not a permanent solution to blood vessel injury, and a process called **fibrinolysis** removes unneeded clots when healing has occurred. This cleanup detail is crucial because small clots are formed continually in vessels throughout the body. Without fibrinolysis, blood vessels would gradually become completely blocked.

The critical natural "clot buster" is a fibrin-digesting enzyme called **plasmin**, which is produced when the plasma protein **plasminogen** is activated. Large amounts of plasminogen are incorporated into a forming clot, where it remains inactive until appropriate signals reach it. The presence of a clot in and around the blood vessel causes the endothelial cells to secrete **tissue plasminogen activator (tPA)**. Activated factor XII and thrombin released during clotting also serve as plasminogen activators. As a result, most plasmin activity is confined to the clot, and any plasmin that strays into the plasma is quickly destroyed by circulating enzymes. Fibrinolysis begins within two days and continues slowly over several days until the clot is finally dissolved.

Factors Limiting Clot Growth or Formation

Factors Limiting Normal Clot Growth

Once the clotting cascade has begun, it continues until a clot is formed. Normally, two homeostatic mechanisms prevent clots from becoming unnecessarily large: (1) swift removal of clotting factors, and (2) inhibition of activated clotting factors. For clotting to occur in the first place, the concentration of activated procoagulants must reach certain critical levels. Clot formation in rapidly moving blood is usually curbed because the activated clotting factors are diluted and washed away. For the same reasons, further growth of a forming clot is hindered when it contacts blood flowing normally.

Other mechanisms block the final step in which fibrinogen is polymerized into fibrin. They work by restricting thrombin to the clot or by inactivating it if it escapes into the general circulation. As a clot forms, almost all of the thrombin produced is bound onto the fibrin threads. This is an important safeguard because thrombin also exerts positive feedback effects on the coagulation process prior to the common pathway. Not only does it speed up the production of prothrombin activator by acting indirectly through factor V, but it also accelerates the earliest steps of the intrinsic pathway by activating platelets. By binding thrombin, fibrin effectively acts as an anticoagulant, preventing the clot from enlarging and thrombin from acting elsewhere.

Thrombin not bound to fibrin is quickly inactivated by **antithrombin III**, a protein present in plasma. Antithrombin III and **protein C**, another protein produced in the liver, also inhibit the activity of other intrinsic pathway procoagulants.

Heparin, the natural anticoagulant contained in basophil and mast cell granules, is also found on the surface of endothelial cells. It inhibits thrombin by enhancing the activity of antithrombin III. Like most other clotting inhibitors, heparin also inhibits the intrinsic pathway.

Factors Preventing Undesirable Clotting

As long as the endothelium is smooth and intact, platelets are prevented from clinging and piling up. Also, antithrombic substances—nitric oxide and prostacyclin—secreted by the endothelial cells normally prevent platelet adhesion. Additionally, vitamin E quinone, a molecule formed in the body when vitamin E reacts with oxygen, is a potent anticoagulant.

Disorders of Hemostasis

Blood clotting is one of nature's most elegant creations, but it sometimes goes awry. The two major disorders of hemostasis are at opposite poles. **Thromboembolic disorders** result from conditions that cause undesirable clot formation. **Bleeding disorders** arise from abnormalities that prevent normal clot formation. **Disseminated intravascular coagulation (DIC)** involves both widespread clotting and severe bleeding.

Thromboembolic Conditions

Despite the body's many safeguards, undesirable intravascular clotting, called "hemostasis in the wrong place" by some, sometimes occurs. A clot that develops and persists in an *unbroken* blood vessel is called a **thrombus**. If the thrombus is large enough, it may block circulation to the cells beyond the occlusion and lead to death of those tissues. For example, if the blockage occurs in the coronary circulation of the heart (coronary thrombosis), the consequences may be death of heart muscle and a fatal heart attack.

If the thrombus breaks away from the vessel wall and floats freely in the bloodstream, it becomes an **embolus** (plural: *emboli*). An embolus ("wedge") is usually no problem until it encounters a blood vessel too narrow for it to pass through. Then it becomes an **embolism**, obstructing the vessel. For example, emboli that become trapped in the lungs (pulmonary embolisms) dangerously impair the ability of the body to obtain oxygen. A cerebral embolism may cause a stroke. Drugs that dissolve blood clots (such as tPA) and innovative medical techniques for removing clots are described in *A Closer Look* in Chapter 19 (pp. 702–703).

Conditions that roughen the vessel endothelium, such as atherosclerosis or inflammation, cause thromboembolic disease by allowing platelets to gain a foothold. Slowly flowing blood or blood stasis is another risk factor, particularly in bedridden patients and those taking a long flight in economy-class seats. In this case, clotting factors are not washed away as usual and accumulate so that clot formation finally becomes possible.

A number of drugs, most importantly aspirin, heparin, and warfarin, are used clinically to prevent undesirable clotting in patients at risk for heart attack or stroke. **Aspirin** is an antiprostaglandin drug that inhibits thromboxane A_2 formation

(in this way, it blocks platelet aggregation and platelet plug formation). Clinical studies of men taking low-dose aspirin (one aspirin every two days) over several years demonstrated a 50% reduction in incidence of heart attack.

Heparin (see above) is also prescribed as an anticoagulant drug, as is warfarin, an ingredient in rat poison. Administered in injectable form, heparin is the anticoagulant most used in the hospital (for preoperative and postoperative cardiac patients and for those receiving blood transfusions). Taken orally, **warfarin** (Coumadin) is a mainstay of outpatient treatment to reduce the risk of stroke in those prone to atrial fibrillation, a condition in which blood pools in the heart. Warfarin works via a different mechanism than heparin—it interferes with the action of vitamin K in the production of some procoagulants (see Impaired Liver Function below).

Disseminated Intravascular Coagulation

DIC is a situation in which widespread clotting occurs in intact blood vessels and the residual blood becomes unable to clot. Blockage of blood flow accompanied by severe bleeding follows. DIC is most commonly encountered as a complication of pregnancy or a result of septicemia or incompatible blood transfusions.

Bleeding Disorders

Anything that interferes with the clotting mechanism can result in abnormal bleeding. The most common causes are platelet deficiency (thrombocytopenia) and deficits of some procoagulants, which can result from impaired liver function or certain genetic conditions.

Thrombocytopenia A condition in which the number of circulating platelets is deficient, **thrombocytopenia** (throm″bo-si″to-pe′ne-ah) causes spontaneous bleeding from small blood vessels all over the body. Even normal movement leads to widespread hemorrhage, evidenced by many small purplish spots, called *petechiae* (pe-te′ke-e), on the skin. Thrombocytopenia can arise from any condition that suppresses or destroys the red bone marrow, such as bone marrow malignancy, exposure to ionizing radiation, or certain drugs. A platelet count of under 50,000/μl of blood is usually diagnostic for this condition. Transfusions of concentrated platelets provide temporary relief from bleeding.

Impaired Liver Function When the liver is unable to synthesize its usual supply of procoagulants, abnormal, and often severe, bleeding occurs. The causes can range from an easily resolved vitamin K deficiency (common in newborns and after taking systemic antibiotics) to nearly total impairment of liver function (as in hepatitis or cirrhosis). Liver cells require vitamin K for production of the clotting factors, and dietary deficiencies are rarely a problem because bacteria that reside in the large intestine produce vitamin K. However, vitamin K deficiency can occur if fat absorption is impaired, because vitamin K is a fat-soluble vitamin that is absorbed into the blood along with fats. In liver disease, the nonfunctional liver cells fail to produce not only the procoagulants, but also bile that is required for fat and vitamin K absorption.

Hemophilias The term **hemophilia** refers to several different hereditary bleeding disorders that have similar signs and symptoms. *Hemophilia A*, or *classical hemophilia*, results from a deficiency of **factor VIII (antihemophilic factor)**. It accounts for 77% of cases. *Hemophilia B* results from a deficiency of factor IX. Both types are X-linked conditions and so occur primarily in males. *Hemophilia C*, a less severe form of hemophilia seen in both sexes, is due to a lack of factor XI. The relative mildness of this form, as compared to the A and B forms, reflects the fact that the procoagulant (factor IX) that factor XI activates may also be activated by factor VII (see Figure 17.14).

Symptoms of hemophilia begin early in life. Even minor tissue trauma causes prolonged bleeding into tissues that can be life threatening. Commonly, the person's joints become seriously disabled and painful because of repeated bleeding into the joint cavities after exercise or trauma. Hemophilias are managed clinically by transfusions of fresh plasma or injections of the appropriate purified clotting factor. These therapies provide relief for several days but are expensive and inconvenient.

In addition, the dependence of patients with hemophilia on blood transfusions or factor injections has caused other problems. In the past, many became infected by the hepatitis virus and, beginning in the early 1980s, by HIV, a blood-transmitted virus that depresses the immune system and causes AIDS. (See Chapter 21.) New infections are now avoided as a result of new testing methods for HIV, availability of genetically engineered clotting factors, and hepatitis vaccines.

CHECK YOUR UNDERSTANDING

9. What are the three steps of hemostasis?

10. What is the key difference between fibrinogen and fibrin? Between prothrombin and thrombin? Between most factors before and after they are activated?

11. Which bleeding disorder results from not having enough platelets? From absence of clotting factor VIII?

For answers, see Appendix G.

Transfusion and Blood Replacement

▶ Describe the ABO and Rh blood groups. Explain the basis of transfusion reactions.

▶ Describe fluids used to replace blood volume and the circumstances for their use.

The human cardiovascular system is designed to minimize the effects of blood loss by (1) reducing the volume of the affected blood vessels, and (2) stepping up the production of red blood cells. However, the body can compensate for only so much blood loss. Losses of 15–30% cause pallor and weakness. Loss of more than 30% of blood volume results in severe shock, which can be fatal.

Transfusion of Red Blood Cells

Whole blood transfusions are routine when blood loss is rapid and substantial. In all other cases, infusions of **packed red cells** (whole blood from which most of the plasma has been removed) are preferred for restoring oxygen-carrying capacity. The usual blood bank procedure involves collecting blood from a donor and then mixing it with an anticoagulant, such as certain citrate or oxalate salts, which prevents clotting by binding calcium ions. The shelf life of the collected blood at 4°C is about 35 days. Because blood is such a valuable commodity, it is most often separated into its component parts so that each component can be used when and where it is needed.

Human Blood Groups

People have different blood types, and transfusion of incompatible blood can be fatal. RBC plasma membranes, like those of all body cells, bear highly specific glycoproteins at their external surfaces, which identify each of us as unique from all others. These glycoproteins serve as *antigens*, which are anything the body perceives as foreign, including bacteria and their toxins, viruses, cancer cells, or mismatched RBCs. One person's RBC proteins may be recognized as foreign if transfused into someone with a different red blood cell type, and the transfused cells may be agglutinated (clumped together) and destroyed. Since these RBC antigens promote agglutination, they are more specifically called **agglutinogens** (ag″loo-tin′o-jenz).

At least 30 groups of naturally occurring RBC antigens are found in humans, and many variants occur in individual families ("private antigens") rather than in the general population. The presence or absence of each antigen allows each person's blood cells to be classified into several different blood groups. Antigens determining the ABO and Rh blood groups cause vigorous transfusion reactions (in which the foreign erythrocytes are destroyed) when they are improperly transfused. For this reason, blood typing for these antigens is always done before blood is transfused.

Other antigens (such as the MNS, Duffy, Kell, and Lewis factors) are mainly of legal or academic importance. Because these factors cause weak or no transfusion reactions, blood is not specifically typed for them unless the person is expected to need several transfusions, in which case the many weak transfusion reactions could have cumulative effects. Here we describe only the ABO and Rh blood groups.

ABO Blood Groups As shown in Table 17.4, the **ABO blood groups** are based on the presence or absence of two agglutinogens, type A and type B. Depending on which of these a person inherits, his or her ABO blood group will be one of the following: A, B, AB, or O. The O blood group, which has neither agglutinogen, is the most common ABO blood group in white, black, Asian, and Native Americans. AB, with both antigens, is least prevalent. The presence of either the A or the B agglutinogen results in group A or B, respectively.

TABLE 17.4	ABO Blood Groups							
	FREQUENCY (% OF U.S. POPULATION)				**RBC ANTIGENS (AGGLUTINOGENS)**	**ILLUSTRATION**	**PLASMA ANTIBODIES (AGGLUTININS)**	**BLOOD THAT CAN BE RECEIVED**
BLOOD GROUP	**WHITE**	**BLACK**	**ASIAN**	**NATIVE AMERICAN**				
AB	4	4	5	<1	A B		None	A, B, AB, O (Universal recipient)
B	11	20	27	4	B		Anti-A (a)	B, O
A	40	27	28	16	A		Anti-B (b)	A, O
O	45	49	40	79	None		Anti-A (a) Anti-B (b)	O (Universal donor)

Unique to the ABO blood groups is the presence in the plasma of *preformed antibodies* called **agglutinins**. The agglutinins act against RBCs carrying ABO antigens that are *not* present on a person's own red blood cells. A newborn lacks these antibodies, but they begin to appear in the plasma within two months and reach adult levels between 8 and 10 years of age. As indicated in Table 17.4, a person with neither the A nor the B antigen (group O) possesses both anti-A and anti-B antibodies, also called *a* and *b agglutinins* respectively. Those with group A blood have anti-B antibodies, while those with group B have anti-A antibodies. Neither antibody is produced by AB individuals.

Rh Blood Groups There are 50 different types of Rh agglutinogens, each of which is called an **Rh factor**. Only three of these, the C, D, and E antigens, are fairly common. The Rh blood typing system is so named because one Rh antigen (agglutinogen D) was originally identified in *rhesus* monkeys. Later, the same antigen was discovered in humans. Most Americans (about 85%) are Rh$^+$ (Rh positive), meaning that their RBCs carry the D antigen. As a rule, a person's ABO and Rh blood groups are reported together, for example, O$^+$, A$^-$, and so on.

Unlike the ABO system antibodies, anti-Rh antibodies are not spontaneously formed in the blood of Rh$^-$ (Rh negative) individuals. However, if an Rh$^-$ person receives Rh$^+$ blood, the immune system becomes sensitized and begins producing anti-Rh antibodies against the foreign antigen soon after the transfusion. Hemolysis does not occur after the first such transfusion because it takes time for the body to react and start making

antibodies. But the second time, and every time thereafter, a typical transfusion reaction occurs in which the recipient's antibodies attack and rupture the donor RBCs.

HOMEOSTATIC IMBALANCE

An important problem related to the Rh factor occurs in pregnant Rh$^-$ women who are carrying Rh$^+$ babies. The first such pregnancy usually results in the delivery of a healthy baby. But, when bleeding occurs as the placenta detaches from the uterus, the mother may be sensitized by her baby's Rh$^+$ antigens that pass into her bloodstream. If so, she will form anti-Rh antibodies unless treated with RhoGAM before or shortly after she has given birth. (The same precautions are taken in women who have miscarried or aborted the fetus.) RhoGAM is a serum containing anti-Rh agglutinins. By agglutinating the Rh factor, it blocks the mother's immune response and prevents her sensitization.

If the mother is not treated and becomes pregnant again with an Rh$^+$ baby, her antibodies will cross through the placenta and destroy the baby's RBCs, producing a condition known as **hemolytic disease of the newborn**, or **erythroblastosis fetalis**. The baby becomes anemic and hypoxic. In severe cases, brain damage and even death may result unless transfusions are done *before* birth to provide the fetus with more erythrocytes for oxygen transport. Additionally, one or two *exchange transfusions* (see Related Clinical Terms, p. 658) are done after birth. The baby's Rh$^+$ blood is removed, and Rh$^-$ blood is infused. Within six weeks, the transfused Rh$^-$ erythrocytes have been broken down and replaced with the baby's own Rh$^+$ cells. ■

Blood being tested

Serum

Anti-A   Anti-B

Type AB (contains agglutinogens A and B; agglutinates with both sera)

RBCs

Type A (contains agglutinogen A; agglutinates with anti-A)

Type B (contains agglutinogen B; agglutinates with anti-B)

Type O (contains no agglutinogens; does not agglutinate with either serum)

Figure 17.16 Blood typing of ABO blood types. When serum containing anti-A or anti-B agglutinins is added to a blood sample diluted with saline, agglutination will occur between the agglutinin and the corresponding agglutinogen (A or B).

Transfusion Reactions: Agglutination and Hemolysis

When mismatched blood is infused, a **transfusion reaction** occurs in which the donor's red blood cells are attacked by the recipient's plasma agglutinins. (Note that the donor's plasma antibodies may also be agglutinating the host's RBCs, but they are so diluted in the recipient's circulation that this does not usually present a serious problem.)

The initial event, agglutination of the foreign red blood cells, clogs small blood vessels throughout the body. During the next few hours, the clumped red blood cells begin to rupture or are destroyed by phagocytes, and their hemoglobin is released into the bloodstream. (When the transfusion reaction is exceptionally severe, the RBCs are lysed almost immediately.)

These events lead to two easily recognized problems: (1) The oxygen-carrying capability of the transfused blood cells is disrupted, and (2) the clumping of red blood cells in small vessels hinders blood flow to tissues beyond those points. Less apparent, but more devastating, is the consequence of hemoglobin escaping into the bloodstream. Circulating hemoglobin passes freely into the kidney tubules, causing cell death and renal shutdown. If shutdown is complete (acute renal failure), the person may die.

Transfusion reactions can also cause fever, chills, low blood pressure, rapid heartbeat, nausea, vomiting, and general toxicity, but in the absence of renal shutdown, these reactions are rarely lethal. Treatment of transfusion reactions is directed toward preventing kidney damage by administering fluid and diuretics to increase urine output, diluting and washing out the hemoglobin.

As indicated in Table 17.4, group O red blood cells bear neither the A nor the B antigen, so theoretically this blood group is the **universal donor**. Indeed, some laboratories are developing methods to enzymatically convert other blood types to type O by clipping off the extra (A- or B-specific) sugar molecule. Since group AB plasma is devoid of antibodies to both A and B antigens, group AB people are theoretically **universal recipients** and can receive blood transfusions from any of the ABO groups. However, these classifications are misleading, because they do not take into account the other agglutinogens in blood that can trigger transfusion reactions.

The risk of transfusion reactions and transmission of life-threatening infections (particularly with HIV) from pooled blood transfusions has increased public interest in **autologous transfusions** (*auto* = self). In autologous transfusions, the patient *predonates* his or her own blood, and it is stored and immediately available if needed during or after an operation. They are particularly sought by people considering elective surgery who are in no immediate danger. Iron supplements are given, and as long as the patient's preoperative hematocrit is at least 30%, one unit (400–500 ml) of blood can be collected every four days, with the last unit taken 72 hours prior to surgery.

Blood Typing

It is crucial to determine the blood group of both the donor and the recipient *before* blood is transfused. **Figure 17.16** briefly outlines the general procedure for determining ABO blood type. Because it is so critical that blood groups be compatible, cross matching is also done. *Cross matching* tests for agglutination of donor RBCs by the recipient's serum, and of the recipient's RBCs by the donor serum. Typing for the Rh factors is done in the same manner as ABO blood typing.

Restoring Blood Volume

When a patient's blood volume is so low that death from shock is imminent, there may not be time to type blood, or appropriate whole blood may be unavailable. Such emergencies demand that blood *volume* be replaced immediately to restore adequate circulation.

Fundamentally, blood consists of proteins and cells suspended in a salt solution. Replacing lost blood volume essentially consists of replacing that isotonic salt solution. *Normal saline* or a *multiple electrolyte solution* that mimics the electrolyte composition of plasma (for example, *Ringer's solution*) are the preferred choices. You might think that it would be important to add materials to mimic the osmotic properties of albumin in blood, and indeed this has been widely practiced. However, studies have shown that **plasma expanders** such as *purified human serum albumin*, *hetastarch*, and *dextran* provide no benefits over much cheaper electrolyte solutions and are associated with significant complications of their own. Volume replacement restores adequate circulation but cannot, of course,

17

replace the oxygen-carrying capacity of the lost red blood cells. Research on ways to replace that capability by using artificial blood substitutes is ongoing.

CHECK YOUR UNDERSTANDING

12. Nigel is told he has type B blood. Which ABO antibodies does he have in his plasma? Which agglutinogens are on his RBCs? Could he donate blood to an AB recipient? Could he receive blood from an AB donor? Explain.

For answers, see Appendix G.

Diagnostic Blood Tests

▶ Explain the diagnostic importance of blood testing.

A laboratory examination of blood yields information that can be used to evaluate a person's current state of health. For example, in some anemias, the blood is pale and yields a low hematocrit. A high fat content (*lipidemia*) gives blood plasma a yellowish hue and forecasts possible problems in those with heart disease. How well a diabetic is controlling diet and blood sugar levels is routinely determined by blood glucose tests. Infections are signaled by leukocytosis and, if severe, larger than normal buffy coats in the hematocrit.

Microscopic studies of blood can reveal variations in the size and shape of erythrocytes that indicate iron deficiency or pernicious anemia. Furthermore, a determination of the relative proportion of individual leukocyte types, a **differential white blood cell count**, is a valuable diagnostic tool. For example, a high eosinophil count may indicate a parasitic infection or an allergic response somewhere in the body.

A number of tests provide information on the status of the hemostasis system. For example, the ability of blood to clot is assessed by determining the **prothrombin time**, and a **platelet count** is done when thrombocytopenia is suspected.

Two batteries of tests—a SMAC (SMA20, CHEM-20, or similar series) and a **complete blood count (CBC)**—are routinely ordered during physical examinations and before hospital admissions. SMAC is a blood *chemistry* profile. The CBC includes counts of the different types of formed elements, a hematocrit, measurements of hemoglobin content, and size of RBCs. Together these tests provide a comprehensive picture of a person's general health status in relation to normal blood values.

Appendix F contains a listing of the normal values for selected blood tests.

Developmental Aspects of Blood

▶ Describe changes in the sites of blood production and in the type of hemoglobin produced after birth.

▶ Name some blood disorders that become more common with age.

Early in fetal development blood cells form at many sites—the fetal yolk sac, liver, and spleen, among others—but by the seventh month, the red marrow has become the primary hematopoietic area and remains so (barring serious illness) throughout life. If there is a severe need for blood cell production, however, the liver and the spleen may resume their fetal blood-forming roles. Additionally, inactive yellow bone marrow regions (essentially fatty tissue) may reconvert to active red marrow.

Blood cells develop from collections of mesenchymal cells, called *blood islands*, derived from the mesoderm germ layer. The fetus forms a unique hemoglobin, **hemoglobin F**, that has a higher affinity for oxygen than does adult hemoglobin (hemoglobin A). It contains two alpha and two gamma (γ) polypeptide chains per globin molecule, instead of the paired alpha and beta chains typical of hemoglobin A. After birth, fetal erythrocytes carrying hemoglobin F are rapidly destroyed by the liver, and the baby's erythroblasts begin producing hemoglobin A.

The most common blood diseases that appear during aging are chronic leukemias, anemias, and clotting disorders. However, these and most other age-related blood disorders are usually precipitated by disorders of the heart, blood vessels, or immune system. For example, the increased incidence of leukemias in old age is believed to result from the waning efficiency of the immune system, and abnormal thrombus and embolus formation reflects the progress of atherosclerosis, which roughens the blood vessel walls.

CHECK YOUR UNDERSTANDING

13. Emily Wong, 17, is brought to the ER with a fever, headache, and stiff neck. You suspect bacterial meningitis. Would you expect to see an elevated neutrophil count in a differential WBC count? Explain.
14. How is hemoglobin F different from adult hemoglobin?

For answers, see Appendix G.

17

Blood serves as the vehicle that the cardiovascular system uses to transport substances throughout the body, so it could be considered the servant of the cardiovascular system. On the other hand, without blood, the normal functions of the heart and blood vessels are impossible. So perhaps the organs of the cardiovascular system, described in Chapters 18 and 19, are subservient to blood. The point of this circular thinking is that blood and the cardiovascular system organs are vitally intertwined in their common functions—to see that nutrients, oxygen, and other vital substances reach all tissue cells of the body and to relieve the cells of their wastes.

Blood chemistry tests Chemical analysis of substances in the blood, e.g., glucose, iron, or calcium determinations, protein tests, bilirubin content, and pH.

Blood fraction Any one of the components of whole blood that has been separated out from the other blood components, such as platelets or clotting factors.

Bone marrow biopsy A sample of red bone marrow is obtained by needle aspiration (typically from the anterior or posterior iliac crest), and is examined to diagnose disorders of blood-cell formation, leukemia, various marrow infections, and anemias resulting from damage to or failure of the marrow.

Exchange transfusion A technique of alternating removal of patient's blood and infusion of donor blood until a large fraction of the patient's blood has been replaced; used to treat fetal blood incompatibilities and poisoning victims.

Hematology (hem″ah-tol′o-je) Study of blood.

Hematoma (hem″ah-to′mah) Accumulated, clotted blood in the tissues usually resulting from injury; visible as "black and blue" marks or bruises; eventually absorbed naturally unless infections develop.

Hemochromatosis (he″mo-kro″mah-to′sis) An inherited disorder of iron overload in which the intestine absorbs too much iron from the diet. The iron builds up in body tissues, where it oxidizes to form compounds that poison those organs (especially joints, liver, and pancreas).

Myeloproliferative disorder All-inclusive term for a group of proliferative disorders including leukoerythroblastic anemia involving fibrosis of the bone marrow, polycythemia vera, and leukemia.

Plasmapheresis (plaz″mah-fe-re′sis) A process in which blood is removed, its plasma is separated from formed elements, and the formed elements are returned to the patient or donor. The most important application is removal of antibodies or immune complexes from the blood of individuals with autoimmune disorders (multiple sclerosis, myasthenia gravis, and others). Also used by blood banks to collect plasma for burn victims and to obtain plasma components for therapeutic use.

Septicemia (sep″ti-se′me-ah; *septos* = rotten) Situation of excessive and harmful levels of bacteria or their toxins in the blood; also called blood poisoning.

CHAPTER SUMMARY

Media study tools that could provide you additional help in reviewing specific key topics of Chapter 17 are referenced below.

iP = *Interactive Physiology*

Overview: Blood Composition and Functions (pp. 635–636)

Components (p. 635)

1. Blood is composed of formed elements and plasma. The hematocrit is a measure of one formed element, erythrocytes, as a percentage of total blood volume.

Physical Characteristics and Volume (p. 635)

2. Blood is a viscous, slightly alkaline fluid representing about 8% of total body weight. Blood volume of a normal adult is about 5 L.

Functions (pp. 635–636)

3. Distribution functions include delivery of oxygen and nutrients to body tissues, removal of metabolic wastes, and transport of hormones.

4. Regulation functions are maintenance of body temperature, of constant blood pH, and of adequate fluid volume.

5. Protective functions include hemostasis and prevention of infection.

Blood Plasma (p. 636)

1. Plasma is a straw-colored, viscous fluid and is 90% water. The remaining 10% is solutes, such as nutrients, respiratory gases, salts, hormones, and proteins. Plasma makes up 55% of whole blood.

2. Plasma proteins, most made by the liver, include albumin, globulins, and fibrinogen. Albumin is an important blood buffer and contributes to the osmotic pressure of blood.

Formed Elements (pp. 637–649)

1. Formed elements, accounting for 45% of whole blood, are erythrocytes, leukocytes, and platelets. All formed elements arise from hemocytoblasts in red bone marrow.

Erythrocytes (pp. 637–643)

2. Erythrocytes (red blood cells) are small, biconcave cells containing large amounts of hemoglobin. They have no nucleus and few organelles. Spectrin allows the cells to change shape as they pass through tiny capillaries.

3. Oxygen transport is the major function of erythrocytes. In the lungs, oxygen binds to iron atoms in hemoglobin molecules, producing oxyhemoglobin. In body tissues, oxygen dissociates from iron, producing deoxyhemoglobin.

4. Red blood cells begin as hemocytoblasts and, through erythropoiesis, proceed from the proerythroblast (committed cell) stage to the erythroblast (early and late), normoblast, and reticulocyte stages. During this process, hemoglobin accumulates and the organelles and nucleus are extruded. Differentiation of reticulocytes is completed in the bloodstream.

5. Erythropoietin and testosterone enhance erythropoiesis.

6. Iron, vitamin B_{12}, and folic acid are essential for production of hemoglobin.

7. Red blood cells have a life span of approximately 120 days. Old and damaged erythrocytes are removed from the circulation by macrophages of the liver and spleen. Released iron from hemoglobin is stored as ferritin or hemosiderin to be reused. The balance of the heme group is degraded to bilirubin and secreted in bile. Amino acids of globin are metabolized or recycled.

iP **Respiratory System; Topic: Gas Transport, pp. 3–5, 11–17.**

8. Erythrocyte disorders include anemias and polycythemia.

Leukocytes (pp. 643–648)

9. Leukocytes are white blood cells. All are nucleated, and all have crucial roles in defending against disease. Two main categories exist: granulocytes and agranulocytes.

10. Granulocytes include neutrophils, basophils, and eosinophils. Basophils contain histamine, which enhances migration of leukocytes to inflammatory sites and promotes vasodilation. Neutrophils are active phagocytes. Eosinophils attack parasitic worms and their numbers increase during allergic reactions.

11. Agranulocytes have crucial roles in immunity. They include lymphocytes—the "immune cells"—and monocytes which differentiate into macrophages.

12. Leukopoiesis is directed by colony-stimulating factors and interleukins released by supporting cells of the red bone marrow and mature WBCs.

13. Leukocyte disorders include leukemias and infectious mononucleosis.

Platelets (pp. 648–649)

14. Platelets are fragments of large, megakaryocytes formed in red marrow. When a blood vessel is damaged, platelets form a plug to help prevent blood loss and play a central role in the clotting cascade.

Hemostasis (pp. 649–654)

1. Hemostasis is prevention of blood loss. The three major phases of hemostasis are vascular spasm, platelet plug formation, and blood coagulation.

Vascular Spasm and Platelet Plug Formation (pp. 649–650)

2. Spasms of smooth muscle in blood vessel walls and accumulation of platelets (platelet plug) at the site of vessel injury provide a temporary means of stopping or slowing blood loss until coagulation occurs.

Coagulation (pp. 650–652)

3. Coagulation of blood may be initiated by either the intrinsic or the extrinsic pathway. Platelet phospholipid (PF_3) is crucial to both pathways. Tissue factor (factor III) exposed by tissue injury allows the extrinsic pathway to bypass many steps of the intrinsic pathway. A series of activated procoagulants oversees the intermediate steps of each cascade. The pathways converge as prothrombin is converted to thrombin.

Clot Retraction and Repair (p. 652)

4. After a clot is formed, clot retraction occurs. Serum is squeezed out and the ruptured vessel edges are drawn together. The vessel is repaired by smooth muscle, connective tissue, and endothelial cell proliferation and migration.

Fibrinolysis (p. 652)

5. When healing is complete, clot digestion (fibrinolysis) occurs.

Factors Limiting Clot Growth or Formation (pp. 652–653)

6. Abnormal expansion of clots is prevented by removal of coagulation factors in contact with rapidly flowing blood and by inhibition of activated blood factors. Prostacyclin (PGI_2) and nitric oxide secreted by the endothelial cells help prevent undesirable (unnecessary) clotting.

Disorders of Hemostasis (pp. 653–654)

7. Thromboembolic disorders involve undesirable clot formation, which can block vessels. DIC is a condition of bodywide clotting in undamaged blood vessels and subsequent hemorrhages.

8. Thrombocytopenia, a deficit of platelets, causes spontaneous bleeding from small blood vessels. Hemophilia is caused by a genetic deficiency of certain coagulation factors. Liver disease can also cause bleeding disorders because many coagulation proteins are formed by the liver.

Transfusion and Blood Replacement (pp. 654–657)

Transfusion of Red Blood Cells (pp. 654–656)

1. Whole blood transfusions are given to replace severe and rapid blood loss. Packed RBCs are given to replace lost O_2-carrying capacity.

2. Blood group is based on agglutinogens (antigens) present on red blood cell membranes.

3. When mismatched blood is transfused, the recipient's agglutinins (plasma antibodies) clump the foreign RBCs; the clumped cells are then lysed. Blood vessels may be blocked by clumped RBCs. Released hemoglobin may precipitate in the kidney tubules, causing renal shutdown.

4. Before whole blood can be transfused, it must be typed and cross matched so that transfusion reactions are avoided. The most important blood groups for which blood must be typed are the ABO and Rh groups.

Restoring Blood Volume (pp. 656–657)

5. Plasma volume can be replaced with balanced electrolyte solutions, and these are generally preferred over plasma expanders.

Diagnostic Blood Tests (p. 657)

1. Diagnostic blood tests can provide large amounts of information about the current status of the blood and of the body as a whole.

Developmental Aspects of Blood (p. 657)

1. Fetal hematopoietic sites include the yolk sac, liver, and spleen. By the seventh month of development, the red bone marrow is the primary blood-forming site.

2. Blood cells develop from blood islands derived from mesoderm. Fetal blood contains hemoglobin F. After birth, hemoglobin A is formed.

3. The major blood-related problems associated with aging are leukemia, anemia, and thromboembolic disease.

REVIEW QUESTIONS

Multiple Choice/Matching

(Some questions have more than one correct answer. Select the best answer or answers from the choices given.)

1. The blood volume in an adult averages approximately (a) 1 L, (b) 3 L, (c) 5 L, (d) 7 L.

2. The hormonal stimulus that prompts red blood cell formation is (a) serotonin, (b) heparin, (c) erythropoietin, (d) thrombopoietin.

3. All of the following are true of RBCs except (a) biconcave disc shape, (b) life span of approximately 120 days, (c) contain hemoglobin, (d) contain nuclei.

4. The most numerous WBC is the (**a**) eosinophil, (**b**) neutrophil, (**c**) monocyte, (**d**) lymphocyte.

5. Blood proteins play an important part in (**a**) blood clotting, (**b**) immunity, (**c**) maintenance of blood volume, (**d**) all of the above.

6. The white blood cell that releases histamine and other inflammatory chemicals is the (**a**) basophil, (**b**) neutrophil, (**c**) monocyte, (**d**) eosinophil.

7. The blood cell that can become an antibody-secreting cell is the (**a**) lymphocyte, (**b**) megakaryocyte, (**c**) neutrophil, (**d**) basophil.

8. Which of the following does not promote multiple steps in the clotting pathway? (**a**) PF_3, (**b**) factor XI, (**c**) thrombin, (**d**) Ca^{2+}.

9. The normal pH of the blood is about (**a**) 8.4, (**b**) 7.8, (**c**) 7.4, (**d**) 4.7.

10. Suppose your blood was found to be AB positive. This means that (**a**) agglutinogens A and B are present on your red blood cells, (**b**) there are no anti-A or anti-B antibodies in your plasma, (**c**) your blood is Rh^+, (**d**) all of the above.

Short Answer Essay Questions

11. (**a**) Define formed elements and list their three major categories. (**b**) Which is least numerous? (**c**) Which comprise(s) the buffy coat in a hematocrit tube?

12. Discuss hemoglobin relative to its chemical structure, its function, and the color changes it undergoes during loading and unloading of oxygen.

13. If you had a high hematocrit, would you expect your hemoglobin determination to be low or high? Why?

14. What nutrients are needed for erythropoiesis?

15. (**a**) Describe the process of erythropoiesis. (**b**) What name is given to the immature cell type released to the circulation? (**c**) How does it differ from a mature erythrocyte?

16. Besides the ability to move by amoeboid motion, what other physiological attributes contribute to the function of white blood cells in the body?

17. (**a**) If you had a severe infection, would you expect your WBC count to be closest to 5000, 10,000, or 15,000/μl? (**b**) What is this condition called?

18. (**a**) Describe the appearance of platelets and state their major function. (**b**) Why should platelets not be called "cells"?

19. (**a**) Define hemostasis. (**b**) List the three major phases of coagulation. Explain what initiates each phase and what the phase accomplishes. (**c**) In what general way do the intrinsic and extrinsic mechanisms of clotting differ? (**d**) What ion is essential to virtually all stages of coagulation?

20. (**a**) Define fibrinolysis. (**b**) What is the importance of this process?

21. (**a**) How is clot overgrowth usually prevented? (**b**) List two conditions that may lead to unnecessary (and undesirable) clot formation.

22. How can liver dysfunction cause bleeding disorders?

23. (**a**) What is a transfusion reaction and why does it happen? (**b**) What are its possible consequences?

24. How can poor nutrition lead to anemia?

25. What blood-related problems are most common in the aged?

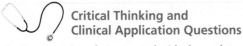

Critical Thinking and Clinical Application Questions

1. Cancer patients being treated with chemotherapeutic drugs designed to destroy rapidly dividing cells are monitored closely for changes in their red and white blood counts. Why so?

2. Mary Healy, a young woman with severe vaginal bleeding, is admitted to the emergency room. She is three months pregnant, and the physician is concerned about the volume of blood she is losing. (**a**) What type of transfusion will probably be given to this patient? (**b**) What blood tests will be performed before starting the transfusion?

3. Alan Forsythe, a middle-aged college professor from Boston, is in the Swiss Alps studying astronomy during his sabbatical leave. He has been there for two days and plans to stay the entire year. However, he notices that he is short of breath when he walks up steps and tires easily with any physical activity. His symptoms gradually disappear, and after two months he feels fine. Upon returning to the United States, he has a complete physical exam and is told that his erythrocyte count is higher than normal. (**a**) Attempt to explain this finding. (**b**) Will his RBC count remain at this higher-than-normal level? Why or why not?

4. A young child is diagnosed as having acute lymphocytic leukemia. Her parents cannot understand why infection is a major problem for Janie when her WBC count is so high. Can you provide an explanation for Janie's parents?

5. Mrs. Ryan, a middle-aged woman, appears at the clinic complaining of multiple small hemorrhagic spots in her skin and severe nosebleeds. While taking her history, the nurse notes that Mrs. Ryan works as a rubber glue applicator at a local factory. Rubber glue contains benzene, which is known to be toxic to red marrow. Using your knowledge of physiology, explain the connection between the bleeding problems and benzene.

6. A reticulocyte count indicated that 5% of Tyler's red blood cells were reticulocytes. His blood test also indicated he had polycythemia and a hematocrit of 65%. Explain the connection between these three facts.

7. In 1998, the U.S. Food and Drug Administration approved the nation's first commercial surgical glue to control bleeding during certain surgeries. Called Tisseel, it forms a flexible mesh over an oozing blood vessel to help stem bleeding within five minutes. This sealant is made from two blood proteins that naturally cause blood to clot when they latch together. Name these proteins.

8. Jenny, a healthy young woman, had a battery of tests during a physical for a new job. Her RBC count was at the higher end of the normal range at that time, but four weeks later it was substantially elevated beyond that. When asked if any circumstances had changed in her life, she admitted to taking up smoking. How might her new habit explain her higher RBC count?

9. Mr. Chu has been scheduled for surgery to have his arthritic hip replaced. His surgeon tells him he must switch from aspirin to acetaminophen for pain control before his surgery. Why?

18

The Cardiovascular System: The Heart

The ceaselessly beating heart has intrigued people for centuries. The ancient Greeks believed the heart was the seat of intelligence. Others thought it was the source of emotions. While these theories have proved false, we do know that emotions affect heart rate. When your heart pounds or occasionally skips a beat, you become acutely aware of how much you depend on this dynamic organ for your very life.

Despite its vital importance, the heart does not work alone. Indeed, it is part of the cardiovascular system, which includes the miles of blood vessels that run through the body. Day and night, tissue cells take in nutrients and oxygen and excrete wastes. Cells can make such exchanges only with their immediate environment, so some means of

(a)

(b)

Posterior

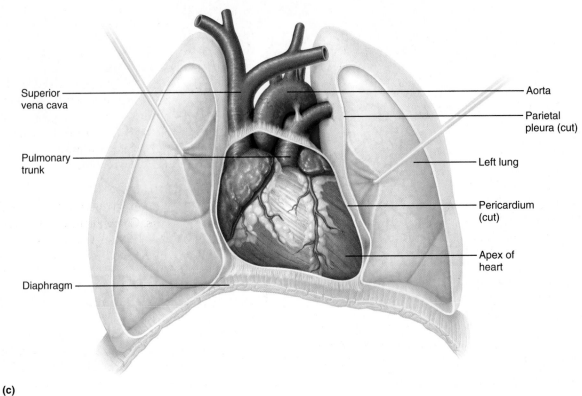

(c)

Figure 18.1 Location of the heart in the mediastinum. (a) Relationship of the heart to the sternum, ribs, and diaphragm in a person who is lying down (the heart is slightly inferior to this position in a standing person). **(b)** Inferior view of a cross section showing the heart's relative position in the thorax. **(c)** Relationship of the heart and great vessels to the lungs.

changing and renewing that environment is necessary to ensure a continual supply of nutrients and to prevent a buildup of wastes. The cardiovascular system provides the transport system "hardware" that keeps blood continuously circulating to fulfill this critical homeostatic need.

Stripped of its romantic cloak, the **heart** is no more than the transport system pump, and the hollow blood vessels are the delivery routes. Using blood as the transport medium, the heart continually propels oxygen, nutrients, wastes, and many other substances into the interconnecting blood vessels that service body cells. We consider blood and blood vessels separately in

Chapters 17 and 19, respectively. In this chapter we focus on the structure and function of the heart.

Heart Anatomy

▶ Describe the size, shape, location, and orientation of the heart in the thorax.

▶ Name the coverings of the heart.

▶ Describe the structure and function of each of the three layers of the heart wall.

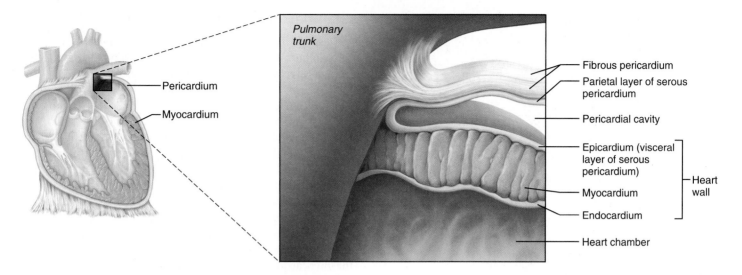

Figure 18.2 The pericardial layers and layers of the heart wall.

Size, Location, and Orientation

The modest size and weight of the heart belie its incredible strength and endurance. About the size of a fist, the hollow, cone-shaped heart has a mass of between 250 and 350 grams—less than a pound (Figure 18.1).

Snugly enclosed within the **mediastinum** (me″de-ah-sti′num), the medial cavity of the thorax, the heart extends obliquely for 12 to 14 cm (about 5 inches) from the second rib to the fifth intercostal space (Figure 18.1a). As it rests on the superior surface of the diaphragm, the heart lies anterior to the vertebral column and posterior to the sternum. The lungs flank the heart laterally and partially obscure it (Figure 18.1b, c). Approximately two-thirds of its mass lies to the left of the midsternal line; the balance projects to the right.

Its broad, flat **base**, or posterior surface, is about 9 cm (3.5 in) wide and directed toward the right shoulder. Its **apex** points inferiorly toward the left hip. If you press your fingers between the fifth and sixth ribs just below the left nipple, you can easily feel the **apical impulse** caused by the apex of your beating heart contacting the chest wall.

Coverings of the Heart

The heart is enclosed in a double-walled sac called the **pericardium** (per″ĭ-kar′de-um; *peri* = around, *cardi* = heart) (Figure 18.2). The loosely fitting superficial part of this sac is the **fibrous pericardium**. This tough, dense connective tissue layer (1) protects the heart, (2) anchors it to surrounding structures, and (3) prevents overfilling of the heart with blood.

Deep to the fibrous pericardium is the **serous pericardium**, a thin, slippery, two-layer serous membrane. Its **parietal layer** lines the internal surface of the fibrous pericardium. At the superior margin of the heart, the parietal layer attaches to the large arteries exiting the heart, and then turns inferiorly and continues over the external heart surface as the **visceral layer**, also called the **epicardium** ("upon the heart"), which is an integral part of the heart wall.

Between the parietal and visceral layers is the slitlike **pericardial cavity**, which contains a film of serous fluid. The serous membranes, lubricated by the fluid, glide smoothly past one another during heart activity, allowing the mobile heart to work in a relatively friction-free environment.

HOMEOSTATIC IMBALANCE

Pericarditis, inflammation of the pericardium, roughens the serous membrane surfaces. Consequently, as the beating heart rubs against its pericardial sac, it creates a creaking sound (*pericardial friction rub*) that can be heard with a stethoscope. Pericarditis is characterized by pain deep to the sternum. Over time, it may lead to adhesions in which the visceral and parietal pericardia stick together and impede heart activity. In severe cases, the situation changes and *large* amounts of inflammatory fluid seep into the pericardial cavity. This excess fluid compresses the heart, limiting its ability to pump blood. This condition in which the heart is compressed by fluid is called *cardiac tamponade* (tam″pŏ-nād′), literally, "heart plug." Physicians treat it by inserting a syringe into the pericardial cavity and draining off the excess fluid. ■

Layers of the Heart Wall

The heart wall, richly supplied with blood vessels, is composed of three layers: the epicardium, the myocardium, and the endocardium (Figure 18.2).

As we have noted, the superficial **epicardium** is the visceral layer of the serous pericardium. It is often infiltrated with fat, especially in older people.

The middle layer, the **myocardium** ("muscle heart"), is composed mainly of cardiac muscle and forms the bulk of the heart. It is the layer that contracts. In this layer, the branching cardiac muscle cells are tethered to one another by crisscrossing connective tissue fibers and arranged in spiral or circular *bundles*

18

Cardiac muscle bundles

Figure 18.3 The circular and spiral arrangement of cardiac muscle bundles in the myocardium of the heart.

(Figure 18.3). These interlacing bundles effectively link all parts of the heart together.

The connective tissue fibers form a dense network, the **fibrous skeleton of the heart**, that reinforces the myocardium internally and anchors the cardiac muscle fibers. This network of collagen and elastic fibers is thicker in some areas than others. For example, it constructs ropelike rings that provide additional support where the great vessels issue from the heart and around the heart valves (see Figure 18.8a, p. 671). Without this support, the vessels and valves might eventually become stretched because of the continuous stress of blood pulsing through them. Additionally, because connective tissue is not electrically excitable, the fibrous skeleton limits the direct spread of action potentials across the heart to specific pathways.

The third layer, the **endocardium** ("inside the heart"), is a glistening white sheet of endothelium (squamous epithelium) resting on a thin connective tissue layer. Located on the inner myocardial surface, it lines the heart chambers and covers the fibrous skeleton of the valves. The endocardium is continuous with the endothelial linings of the blood vessels leaving and entering the heart.

CHECK YOUR UNDERSTANDING

1. The heart is in the mediastinum. Just what is the mediastinum?
2. From inside to outside, list the layers of the heart wall and the coverings of the heart.
3. What is the purpose of the serous fluid inside the pericardial cavity?

For answers, see Appendix G.

Chambers and Associated Great Vessels

▶ Describe the structure and functions of the four heart chambers. Name each chamber and provide the name and general route of its associated great vessel(s).

The heart has four chambers (**Figure 18.4e**)—two superior **atria** (a′tre-ah) and two inferior **ventricles** (ven′trĭ-klz). The internal partition that divides the heart longitudinally is called the **interatrial septum** where it separates the atria, and the **interventricular septum** where it separates the ventricles. The right ventricle forms most of the anterior surface of the heart. The left ventricle dominates the inferoposterior aspect of the heart and forms the heart apex.

Two grooves visible on the heart surface indicate the boundaries of its four chambers and carry the blood vessels supplying the myocardium. The **coronary sulcus** (Figure 18.4b, d), or *atrioventricular groove*, encircles the junction of the atria and ventricles like a crown (*corona* = crown). The **anterior interventricular sulcus**, cradling the anterior interventricular artery, marks the anterior position of the septum separating the right and left ventricles. It continues as the **posterior interventricular sulcus**, which provides a similar landmark on the heart's posteroinferior surface.

Atria: The Receiving Chambers

Except for small, wrinkled, protruding appendages called **auricles** (or′ĭ-klz; *auricle* = little ear), which increase the atrial volume somewhat, the right and left atria are remarkably free of distinguishing surface features. Internally, the right atrium has two basic parts (Figure 18.4c): a smooth-walled posterior part and an anterior portion in which the walls are ridged by bundles of muscle tissue. Because these bundles look like the teeth of a comb, these muscle bundles are called **pectinate muscles** (*pectin* = comb). The posterior and anterior regions of the right atrium are separated by a C-shaped ridge called the *crista terminalis* ("terminal crest"). In contrast, the left atrium is mostly smooth and pectinate muscles are found only in the auricle. The interatrial septum bears a shallow depression, the **fossa ovalis** (o-vă′lis), that marks the spot where an opening, the *foramen ovale*, existed in the fetal heart (Figure 18.4c, e).

Functionally, the atria are receiving chambers for blood returning to the heart from the circulation (*atrium* = entryway). The atria are relatively small, thin-walled chambers because they need contract only minimally to push blood "downstairs" into the ventricles. As a rule, they contribute little to the propulsive pumping activity of the heart.

Blood enters the *right atrium* via three veins (Figure 18.4c–e): (1) The **superior vena cava** returns blood from body regions superior to the diaphragm; (2) the **inferior vena cava** returns blood from body areas below the diaphragm; and (3) the **coronary sinus** collects blood draining from the myocardium.

Four **pulmonary veins** enter the *left atrium*, which makes up most of the heart's base. These veins, which transport blood from the lungs back to the heart, are best seen in a posterior view (Figure 18.4d).

Aortic arch
(fat covered)

Pulmonary trunk

Auricle of
right atrium

Auricle of
left atrium

Anterior
interventricular
artery

Right ventricle

Apex of heart
(left ventricle)

(a) Anterior aspect (pericardium removed)

Brachiocephalic trunk

Superior vena cava

Right pulmonary artery

Ascending aorta

Pulmonary trunk

Right pulmonary veins

Right atrium

Right coronary artery
(in coronary sulcus)

Anterior cardiac vein

Right ventricle

Right marginal artery

Small cardiac vein

Inferior vena cava

Left common carotid
artery

Left subclavian artery

Aortic arch

Ligamentum arteriosum

Left pulmonary artery

Left pulmonary veins

Auricle of
left atrium

Circumflex artery

Left coronary artery
(in coronary sulcus)

Left ventricle

Great cardiac vein

Anterior interventricular
artery (in anterior
interventricular sulcus)

Apex

(b) Anterior view

Figure 18.4 Gross anatomy of the heart. In diagrammatic views, vessels transporting
oxygen-rich blood are red; those transporting oxygen-poor blood are blue.

18

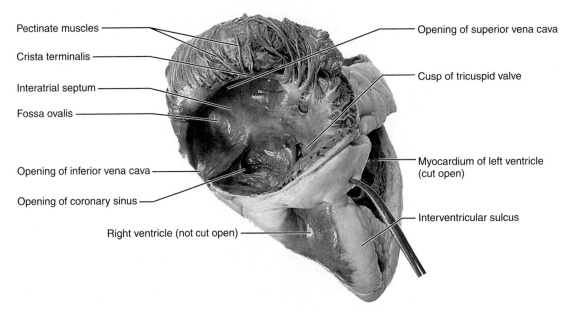

Pectinate muscles

Crista terminalis

Interatrial septum

Fossa ovalis

Opening of inferior vena cava

Opening of coronary sinus

Right ventricle (not cut open)

Opening of superior vena cava

Cusp of tricuspid valve

Myocardium of left ventricle (cut open)

Interventricular sulcus

(c) Right anterior view of the internal aspect of the right atrium

Aorta

Left pulmonary artery

Left pulmonary veins

Auricle of left atrium

Left atrium

Great cardiac vein

Posterior vein of left ventricle

Left ventricle

Apex

Superior vena cava

Right pulmonary artery

Right pulmonary veins

Right atrium

Inferior vena cava

Coronary sinus

Right coronary artery (in coronary sulcus)

Posterior interventricular artery (in posterior interventricular sulcus)

Middle cardiac vein

Right ventricle

(d) Posterior surface view

Figure 18.4 *(continued)* **Gross anatomy of the heart.** In **(c)**, the anterior wall of the atrium has been opened and folded superiorly.

(e) Frontal section

(f) Photograph; view similar to (e)

Figure 18.4 *(continued)* **Gross anatomy of the heart.**

18

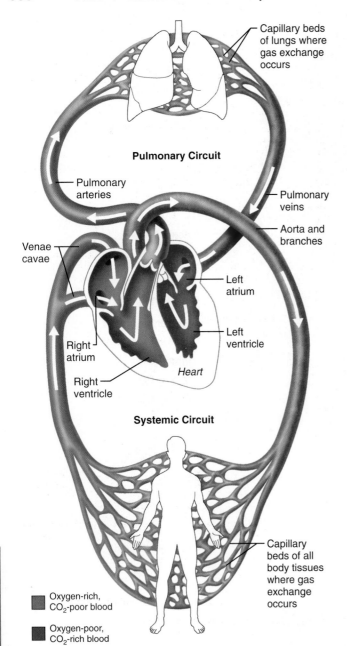

Figure Labels:
- Capillary beds of lungs where gas exchange occurs
- **Pulmonary Circuit**
- Pulmonary arteries
- Pulmonary veins
- Aorta and branches
- Venae cavae
- Left atrium
- Left ventricle
- *Heart*
- Right atrium
- Right ventricle
- **Systemic Circuit**
- Oxygen-rich, CO₂-poor blood
- Oxygen-poor, CO₂-rich blood
- Capillary beds of all body tissues where gas exchange occurs

Figure 18.5 The systemic and pulmonary circuits. The right side of the heart pumps blood through the pulmonary circuit* (to the lungs and back to the left side of the heart). The left side of the heart pumps blood via the systemic circuit to all body tissues and back to the right side of the heart.

*For simplicity, the actual number of two pulmonary arteries and four pulmonary veins has been reduced to one each.

Ventricles: The Discharging Chambers

Together the ventricles (*ventr* = underside) make up most of the volume of the heart. As already mentioned, the right ventricle forms most of the heart's anterior surface and the left ventricle dominates its posteroinferior surface. Marking the internal walls of the ventricular chambers are irregular ridges of muscle called **trabeculae carneae** (trah-bek′u-le kar′ne-e; "crossbars of flesh"). Still other muscle bundles, the conelike

papillary muscles, which play a role in valve function, project into the ventricular cavity (Figure 18.4e).

The ventricles are the discharging chambers or actual pumps of the heart. The difference in function between atria and ventricles is reflected in the much more massive ventricular walls (Figure 18.4e and f). When the ventricles contract, blood is propelled out of the heart into the circulation. The right ventricle pumps blood into the **pulmonary trunk**, which routes the blood to the lungs where gas exchange occurs. The left ventricle ejects blood into the **aorta** (a-or′tah), the largest artery in the body.

Pathway of Blood Through the Heart

▶ Trace the pathway of blood through the heart.

Until the sixteenth century, people believed that blood moved from one side of the heart to the other by seeping through pores in the septum. We now know that the heart passages open not from one side to the other but vertically. The heart is actually two side-by-side pumps, each serving a separate blood circuit (Figure 18.5). The blood vessels that carry blood to and from the lungs form the **pulmonary circuit** (*pulmo* = lung), which serves gas exchange. The blood vessels that carry the functional blood supply to and from all body tissues constitute the **systemic circuit**.

The right side of the heart is the *pulmonary circuit pump*. Blood returning from the body is relatively oxygen-poor and carbon dioxide–rich. It enters the right atrium and passes into the right ventricle, which pumps it to the lungs via the pulmonary trunk (Figure 18.4e). In the lungs, the blood unloads carbon dioxide and picks up oxygen. The freshly oxygenated blood is carried by the pulmonary veins back to the left side of the heart.

Notice how unique this circulation is. Elsewhere in the body, veins carry relatively oxygen-poor blood to the heart, and arteries transport oxygen-rich blood from the heart. Exactly the opposite oxygenation conditions exist in veins and arteries of the pulmonary circuit.

The left side of the heart is the *systemic circuit pump*. Freshly oxygenated blood leaving the lungs is returned to the left atrium and passes into the left ventricle, which pumps it into the aorta. From there the blood is transported via smaller systemic arteries to the body tissues, where gases and nutrients are exchanged across the capillary walls. Then the blood, once again loaded with carbon dioxide and depleted of oxygen, returns through the systemic veins to the right side of the heart, where it enters the right atrium through the superior and inferior venae cavae. This cycle repeats itself continuously.

Equal volumes of blood are pumped to the pulmonary and systemic circuits at any moment, but the two ventricles have very unequal workloads. The pulmonary circuit, served by the right ventricle, is a short, low-pressure circulation. In contrast, the systemic circuit, associated with the left ventricle, takes a long pathway through the entire body and encounters about five times as much friction, or resistance to blood flow.

This functional difference is revealed in the anatomy of the two ventricles (Figure 18.4e and **Figure 18.6**). The walls of the

Figure 18.6 Anatomical differences between the right and left ventricles. The left ventricle has a thicker wall and its cavity is basically circular. The right ventricle cavity is crescent shaped and wraps around the left ventricle.

left ventricle are three times as thick as those of the right ventricle, and its cavity is nearly circular. The right ventricular cavity is flattened into a crescent shape that partially encloses the left ventricle, much the way a hand might loosely grasp a clenched fist. Consequently, the left ventricle can generate much more pressure than the right and is a far more powerful pump.

Coronary Circulation

▶ Name the major branches and describe the distribution of the coronary arteries.

Although the heart is more or less continuously filled with blood, this blood provides little nourishment to heart tissue. (The myocardium is too thick to make diffusion a practical means of nutrient delivery.) How, then, does the heart get nourishment?

The **coronary circulation**, the functional blood supply of the heart, is the shortest circulation in the body. The arterial supply of the coronary circulation is provided by the *right* and *left coronary arteries,* both arising from the base of the aorta and encircling the heart in the coronary sulcus **(Figure 18.7a)**. The **left coronary artery** runs toward the left side of the heart and then divides into its major branches: the **anterior interventricular artery** (also known clinically as the *left anterior descending artery*), which follows the anterior interventricular sulcus and supplies blood to the interventricular septum and anterior walls of both ventricles; and the **circumflex artery**, which supplies the left atrium and the posterior walls of the left ventricle.

The **right coronary artery** courses to the right side of the heart, where it also gives rise to two branches: the **right marginal artery**, which serves the myocardium of the lateral right side of the heart, and the **posterior interventricular artery**, which runs to the heart apex and supplies the posterior ventricular walls.

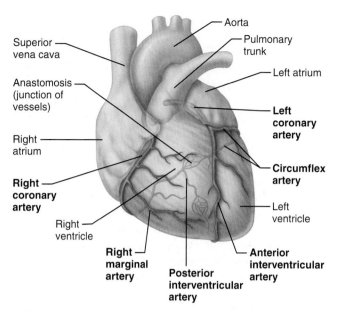

(a) The major coronary arteries

(b) The major cardiac veins

Figure 18.7 Coronary circulation. In both drawings, lighter-tinted vessels are more posterior in the heart.

Near the apex of the heart, this artery merges (anastomoses) with the anterior interventricular artery. Together the branches of the right coronary artery supply the right atrium and nearly all the right ventricle.

The arterial supply of the heart varies considerably. For example, in 15% of people, the left coronary artery gives rise to *both* the anterior and posterior interventricular arteries. In about 4% of people, a single coronary artery supplies the whole heart. Additionally, there may be both right and left marginal arteries. There are many anastomoses (junctions) among the coronary arterial branches. These fusing networks provide additional (*collateral*) routes for blood delivery to the heart muscle, but are not robust enough to supply adequate nutrition when a coronary artery is suddenly occluded (blocked). Complete blockage leads to tissue death and heart attack.

18

The coronary arteries provide an intermittent, pulsating blood flow to the myocardium. These vessels and their main branches lie in the epicardium and send branches inward to nourish the myocardium. They deliver blood when the heart is relaxed, but are fairly ineffective when the ventricles are contracting because they are compressed by the contracting myocardium. Although the heart represents only about 1/200 of the body's weight, it requires about 1/20 of the body's blood supply. As might be expected, the left ventricle receives the most plentiful blood supply.

After passing through the capillary beds of the myocardium, the venous blood is collected by the **cardiac veins**, whose paths roughly follow those of the coronary arteries. These veins join together to form an enlarged vessel called the **coronary sinus**, which empties the blood into the right atrium. The coronary sinus is obvious on the posterior aspect of the heart (Figure 18.7b). The sinus has three large tributaries: the **great cardiac vein** in the anterior interventricular sulcus; the **middle cardiac vein** in the posterior interventricular sulcus; and the **small cardiac vein**, running along the heart's right inferior margin. Additionally, several **anterior cardiac veins** empty directly into the right atrium anteriorly.

HOMEOSTATIC IMBALANCE

Blockage of the coronary arterial circulation can be serious and sometimes fatal. **Angina pectoris** (an-ji′nah pek′tor-is; "choked chest") is thoracic pain caused by a fleeting deficiency in blood delivery to the myocardium. It may result from stress-induced spasms of the coronary arteries or from increased physical demands on the heart. The myocardial cells are weakened by the temporary lack of oxygen but do not die. Far more serious is prolonged coronary blockage, which can lead to a **myocardial infarction (MI)**, commonly called a **heart attack**. Because adult cardiac muscle is essentially amitotic, most areas of cell death are repaired with noncontractile scar tissue. Whether or not a person survives a myocardial infarction depends on the extent and location of the damage. Damage to the left ventricle, which is the systemic pump, is most serious. ■

CHECK YOUR UNDERSTANDING

4. Which side of the heart acts as the pulmonary pump? The systemic pump?
5. Which of the following statements are true? (a) The left ventricle wall is thicker than the right ventricle wall. (b) The left ventricle pumps blood at a higher pressure than the right ventricle. (c) The left ventricle pumps more blood with each beat than the right ventricle. Explain.
6. Name the two main branches of the right coronary artery.

For answers, see Appendix G.

Heart Valves

▶ Name the heart valves and describe their location, function, and mechanism of operation.

Blood flows through the heart in one direction: from atria to ventricles and out the great arteries leaving the superior aspect of the heart. Four valves enforce this one-way traffic (Figure 18.4e and **Figure 18.8**). They open and close in response to differences in blood pressure on their two sides.

Atrioventricular Valves

The two **atrioventricular (AV) valves**, one located at each atrial-ventricular junction, prevent backflow into the atria when the ventricles are contracting. The right AV valve, the **tricuspid valve** (tri-kus′pid), has three flexible cusps (flaps of endocardium reinforced by connective tissue cores). The left AV valve, with two flaps, is called the **mitral valve** (mi′tral) because of its resemblance to the two-sided bishop's miter or hat. It is sometimes called the *bicuspid valve*. Attached to each AV valve flap are tiny white collagen cords called **chordae tendineae** (kor″de ten″dĭ′ne-e; "tendonous cords"), "heart strings" which anchor the cusps to the papillary muscles protruding from the ventricular walls (Figure 18.8c, d).

When the heart is completely relaxed, the AV valve flaps hang limply into the ventricular chambers below and blood flows into the atria and then through the open AV valves into the ventricles (**Figure 18.9a**). When the ventricles contract, compressing the blood in their chambers, the intraventricular pressure rises, forcing the blood superiorly against the valve flaps. As a result, the flap edges meet, closing the valve (Figure 18.9b).

The chordae tendineae and the papillary muscles serve as guy-wires to anchor the valve flaps in their *closed* position. If the cusps were not anchored in this manner, they would be blown upward into the atria, in the same way an umbrella is blown inside out by a gusty wind. The papillary muscles contract with the other ventricular musculature so that they take up the slack on the chordae tendineae as the full force of ventricular contraction hurls the blood against the AV valve flaps.

Semilunar Valves

The **aortic** and **pulmonary (semilunar, SL) valves** guard the bases of the large arteries issuing from the ventricles (aorta and pulmonary trunk, respectively) and prevent backflow into the associated ventricles. Each SL valve is fashioned from three pocketlike cusps, each shaped roughly like a crescent moon (*semilunar* = half-moon).

Like the AV valves, the SL valves open and close in response to differences in pressure. In the SL case, when the ventricles are contracting and intraventricular pressure *rises above* the pressure in the aorta and pulmonary trunk, the SL valves are forced open and their cusps flatten against the arterial walls as the blood rushes past them (**Figure 18.10a**). When the ventricles relax, and the blood (no longer propelled forward by the pressure of ventricular contraction) flows backward toward the heart, it fills the cusps and closes the valves (Figure 18.10b).

We complete the valve story by noting what seems to be an important omission—there are no valves guarding the entrances of the venae cavae and pulmonary veins into the right and left atria, respectively. Small amounts of blood *do* spurt back into these vessels during atrial contraction, but backflow is

Figure 18.8 Heart valves. (a) Superior view of the two sets of heart valves (atria removed). The paired atrioventricular valves are located between atria and ventricles; the two semilunar valves are located at the junction of the ventricles and the arteries issuing from them. **(b)** Photograph of the heart valves, superior view. **(c)** Photograph of the tricuspid valve. This bottom-to-top view shows the valve as seen from the right ventricle. **(d)** Coronal section of the heart. (See also *A Brief Atlas of the Human Body*, Figures 58 and 60.)

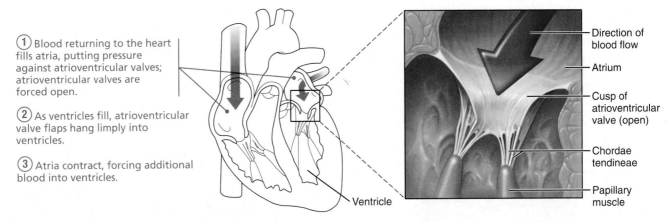

① Blood returning to the heart fills atria, putting pressure against atrioventricular valves; atrioventricular valves are forced open.

② As ventricles fill, atrioventricular valve flaps hang limply into ventricles.

③ Atria contract, forcing additional blood into ventricles.

Direction of blood flow

Atrium

Cusp of atrioventricular valve (open)

Chordae tendineae

Papillary muscle

Ventricle

(a) AV valves open; atrial pressure greater than ventricular pressure

① Ventricles contract, forcing blood against atrioventricular valve cusps.

② Atrioventricular valves close.

③ Papillary muscles contract and chordae tendineae tighten, preventing valve flaps from everting into atria.

Atrium

Cusps of atrioventricular valve (closed)

Blood in ventricle

(b) AV valves closed; atrial pressure less than ventricular pressure

Figure 18.9 **The atrioventricular valves.**

minimal because of the inertia of the blood and because as it contracts, the atrial myocardium compresses (and collapses) these venous entry points.

HOMEOSTATIC IMBALANCE

Heart valves are simple devices, and the heart—like any mechanical pump—can function with "leaky" valves as long as the impairment is not too great. However, severe valve deformities can seriously hamper cardiac function. An *incompetent valve* forces the heart to repump the same blood over and over because the valve does not close properly and blood backflows. In valvular *stenosis* ("narrowing"), the valve flaps become stiff (typically because of scar tissue formation following endocarditis or calcium salt deposit) and constrict the opening. This stiffness compels the heart to contract more forcibly than normal. In both instances, the heart's workload increases and, ultimately, the heart may be severely weakened.

Under such conditions, the faulty valve (most often the mitral valve) is replaced with a mechanical valve, a pig or cow heart valve chemically treated to prevent rejection, or cryopreserved valves from human cadavers. Heart valves tissue-engineered from a patient's own cells grown on a biodegradable scaffold are being developed. ■

CHECK YOUR UNDERSTANDING

7. What is the function of the papillary muscles and chordae tendineae?

For answers, see Appendix G.

Cardiac Muscle Fibers

▶ Describe the structural and functional properties of cardiac muscle, and explain how it differs from skeletal muscle.

▶ Briefly describe the events of cardiac muscle cell contraction.

Although similar to skeletal muscle, cardiac muscle displays some special anatomical features that reflect its unique blood-pumping role.

Microscopic Anatomy

Cardiac muscle, like skeletal muscle, is striated, and it contracts by the sliding filament mechanism. However, in contrast to the long, cylindrical, multinucleate skeletal muscle fibers, cardiac

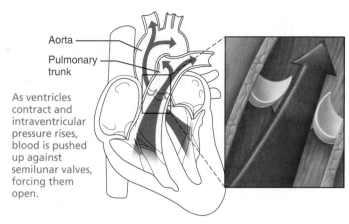

Aorta

Pulmonary trunk

As ventricles contract and intraventricular pressure rises, blood is pushed up against semilunar valves, forcing them open.

(a) Semilunar valves open

As ventricles relax and intraventricular pressure falls, blood flows back from arteries, filling the cusps of semilunar valves and forcing them to close.

(b) Semilunar valves closed

Figure 18.10 The semilunar valves.

cells are short, fat, branched, and interconnected. Each fiber contains one or at most two large, pale, *centrally* located nuclei **(Figure 18.11a)**. The intercellular spaces are filled with a loose connective tissue matrix (the *endomysium*) containing numerous capillaries. This delicate matrix is connected to the fibrous skeleton, which acts both as a tendon and as an insertion, giving the cardiac cells something to pull or exert their force against.

Skeletal muscle fibers are independent of one another both structurally and functionally. By contrast, the plasma membranes of adjacent cardiac cells interlock like the ribs of two sheets of corrugated cardboard at dark-staining junctions called **intercalated discs** (in-ter′kah-la″ted; *intercala* = insert) (Figure 18.11). These discs contain anchoring *desmosomes* and *gap junctions* (cell junctions discussed in Chapter 3). The desmosomes prevent adjacent cells from separating during contraction, and the gap junctions allow ions to pass from cell to cell, transmitting current across the entire heart. Because cardiac cells are electrically coupled by the gap junctions, the myocardium *behaves* as a single coordinated unit, or **functional syncytium**.

Large mitochondria account for 25–35% of the volume of cardiac cells (compared with only 2% in skeletal muscle) and give cardiac cells a high resistance to fatigue. Most of the re-

maining volume is occupied by myofibrils composed of fairly typical sarcomeres. The sarcomeres have Z discs, A bands, and I bands that reflect the arrangement of the thick (myosin) and thin (actin) filaments composing them. However, in contrast to skeletal muscle, the myofibrils of cardiac muscle cells vary greatly in diameter and branch extensively, accommodating the abundant mitochondria that lie between them. This difference produces a banding pattern less dramatic than that seen in skeletal muscle.

The system for delivering Ca^{2+} is less elaborate in cardiac muscle cells. The T tubules are wider and fewer than in skeletal muscle and they enter the cells once per sarcomere at the Z discs. (Recall that T tubules are invaginations of the sarcolemma. In skeletal muscle, the T tubules invaginate twice per sarcomere, at the A band–I band junctions.) The cardiac sarcoplasmic reticulum is simpler and lacks the large terminal cisternae seen in skeletal muscle. Consequently, no *triads* are seen in cardiac muscle fibers.

Mechanism and Events of Contraction

Although heart muscle and skeletal muscle are contractile tissues, they have some fundamental differences:

1. **Means of stimulation.** Each skeletal muscle fiber must be stimulated to contract by a nerve ending, but some cardiac muscle cells are self-excitable. These cells can initiate not only their own depolarization, but that of the rest of the heart as well, in a spontaneous and rhythmic way. We describe this property, called **automaticity**, or **autorhythmicity**, in the next section.
2. **Organ versus motor unit contraction.** In skeletal muscle, all cells of a given motor unit (but not necessarily all motor units of the muscle) are stimulated and contract at the same time. Impulses do not spread from cell to cell. In cardiac muscle, the heart either contracts as a unit or doesn't contract at all. This coordinated action occurs because gap junctions electrically tie all cardiac muscle cells together into a single contractile unit. Consequently, the depolarization wave travels across the heart from cell to cell via ion passage through the gap junctions.
3. **Length of absolute refractory period.** In cardiac muscle cells, the absolute refractory period (the inexcitable period when Na^+ channels are still open or inactivated) lasts approximately 250 ms, nearly as long as the contraction **(Figure 18.12)**. Contrast this to the short refractory periods of 1–2 ms in skeletal muscle fibers, in which contractions last 15–100 ms. The long cardiac refractory period normally prevents tetanic contractions, which would stop the heart's pumping action.

Having probed the major differences between cardiac and skeletal muscle tissues, let's now look at their similarities. As with skeletal muscle, cardiac muscle contraction is triggered by action potentials that sweep across cell membranes. About 1% of cardiac fibers are *autorhythmic* ("self-rhythm"), having the special ability to depolarize spontaneously and thus pace the heart. The bulk of heart muscle, however, is composed of

(a)

(b)

Figure 18.11 Microscopic anatomy of cardiac muscle. (a) Photomicrograph of cardiac muscle (600×). Notice that the cardiac muscle cells are short, branched, and striated. The dark-staining areas are intercalated discs, or junctions, between adjacent cells. **(b)** Components of intercalated discs and cardiac muscle fibers.

contractile muscle fibers responsible for the heart's pumping activity. In these cells, the sequence of events leading to contraction is similar to that in skeletal muscle fibers:

- Depolarization opens a few **voltage-gated fast Na$^+$ channels** in the sarcolemma, allowing extracellular Na$^+$ to enter. This influx initiates a positive feedback cycle that causes the rising phase of the action potential (and reversal of the membrane potential from −90 mV to nearly +30 mV; Figure 18.12, ①). The period of Na$^+$ influx is very brief, because the sodium channels quickly inactivate and the Na$^+$ influx stops.

- Transmission of the depolarization wave down the T tubules (ultimately) causes the sarcoplasmic reticulum (SR) to release Ca^{2+} into the sarcoplasm.

- Excitation-contraction coupling occurs as Ca^{2+} provides the signal (via troponin binding) for cross bridge activation and couples the depolarization wave to the sliding of the myofilaments.

These three steps are common to both skeletal and cardiac muscle cells (see Figure 9.11), but the two muscle types differ in how the SR is stimulated to release Ca^{2+}. Let's take a look.

Some 10–20% of the Ca^{2+} needed for the calcium pulse that triggers contraction enters the cardiac cells from the extracellular space. Once inside, it stimulates the SR to release the other 80% of the Ca^{2+} needed. Ca^{2+} is barred from entering nonstimulated cardiac fibers, but when Na$^+$-dependent membrane depolarization occurs, the voltage change also opens channels

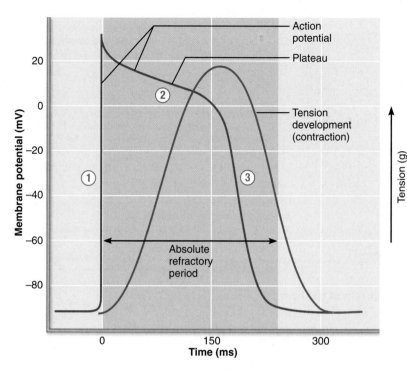

① **Depolarization** is due to Na⁺ influx through fast voltage-gated Na⁺ channels. A positive feedback cycle rapidly opens many Na⁺ channels, reversing the membrane potential. Channel inactivation ends this phase.

② **Plateau phase** is due to Ca²⁺ influx through slow Ca²⁺ channels. This keeps the cell depolarized because few K⁺ channels are open.

③ **Repolarization** is due to Ca²⁺ channels inactivating and K⁺ channels opening. This allows K⁺ efflux, which brings the membrane potential back to its resting voltage.

Figure 18.12 The action potential of contractile cardiac muscle cells. Relationship between the action potential, period of contraction, and absolute refractory period in a single ventricular cell.

that allow Ca^{2+} entry from the extracellular space. These channels are called **slow Ca^{2+} channels** because their opening is delayed a bit. The local influxes of Ca^{2+} through these channels trigger opening of nearby Ca^{2+}-sensitive channels in the SR tubules, which liberate bursts of Ca^{2+} ("calcium sparks") that dramatically increase the intracellular Ca^{2+} concentration.

Although Na^+ channels have inactivated and repolarization has begun by this point, the calcium surge across the sarcolemma prolongs the depolarization potential briefly, producing a **plateau** in the action potential tracing (Figure 18.12, ②). At the same time, few K^+ channels are open, which also prolongs the plateau and prevents rapid repolarization. As long as Ca^{2+} is entering, the cells continue to contract. Notice in Figure 18.12 that muscle tension develops during the plateau, and peaks just after the plateau ends.

Notice also that the duration of the action potential and contractile phase is much greater in cardiac muscle than in skeletal muscle. In skeletal muscle, the action potential typically lasts 1–2 ms and the contraction (for a single stimulus) 15–100 ms. In cardiac muscle, the action potential lasts 200 ms or more (because of the plateau), and tension development persists for 200 ms or more, providing the sustained contraction needed to eject blood from the heart.

After about 200 ms, the slope of the action potential tracing falls rapidly (Figure 18.12, ③). This repolarization results from inactivation of Ca^{2+} channels and opening of voltage-gated K^+ channels, which allows a rapid loss of potassium from the cell that restores the resting membrane potential. During repolarization, Ca^{2+} is pumped back into the SR and the extracellular space.

Energy Requirements

Cardiac muscle has more mitochondria than skeletal muscle does, reflecting its greater dependence on oxygen for its energy metabolism. Unlike skeletal muscle, which can contract for prolonged periods, even during oxygen deficits, by carrying out anaerobic respiration, the heart relies almost exclusively on aerobic respiration. As a result, cardiac muscle cannot incur much of an oxygen deficit and still operate effectively.

Both types of muscle tissue use multiple fuel molecules, including glucose and fatty acids. But cardiac muscle is much more adaptable and readily switches metabolic pathways to use whatever nutrient supply is available, including lactic acid generated by skeletal muscle activity. Consequently, the real danger of an inadequate blood supply to the myocardium is lack of oxygen, not of nutrient fuels.

HOMEOSTATIC IMBALANCE

When a region of heart muscle is deprived of blood (is ischemic), the oxygen-starved cells begin to metabolize anaerobically, producing lactic acid. The rising H^+ level that results hinders the cardiac cells' ability to produce the ATP they need to pump Ca^{2+} into the extracellular fluid. The resulting increase in intracellular H^+ and Ca^{2+} levels causes the gap junctions (which are usually open) to close, electrically isolating the damaged cells and forcing generated action potentials to find alternate routes to the cardiac cells beyond them. If the ischemic area is large, the pumping activity of the heart as a whole may be severely impaired, leading to a heart attack. ∎

18

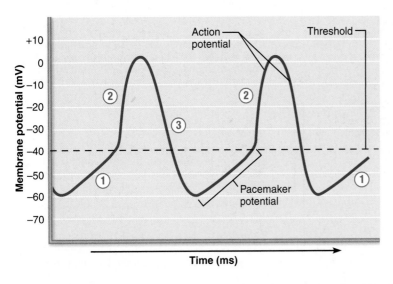

① **Pacemaker potential** This slow depolarization is due to both opening of Na⁺ channels and closing of K⁺ channels. Notice that the membrane potential is never a flat line.

② **Depolarization** The action potential begins when the pacemaker potential reaches threshold. Depolarization is due to Ca²⁺ influx through Ca²⁺ channels.

③ **Repolarization** is due to Ca²⁺ channels inactivating and K⁺ channels opening. This allows K⁺ efflux, which brings the membrane potential back to its most negative voltage.

Figure 18.13 Pacemaker and action potentials of autorhythmic cells of the heart.

CHECK YOUR UNDERSTANDING

8. For each of the following, state whether it applies to skeletal muscle, cardiac muscle, or both: (a) refractory period is almost as long as the contraction; (b) source of Ca²⁺ for contraction is *only* SR; (c) AP exhibits a plateau phase; (d) has troponin; (e) has triads.

9. Cardiac muscle cannot go into tetany. Why?

For answers, see Appendix G.

Heart Physiology

Electrical Events

▶ Name the components of the conduction system of the heart, and trace the conduction pathway.

▶ Draw a diagram of a normal electrocardiogram tracing. Name the individual waves and intervals, and indicate what each represents.

▶ Name some abnormalities that can be detected on an ECG tracing.

The ability of cardiac muscle to depolarize and contract is intrinsic. In other words, it is a property of heart muscle and does not depend on the nervous system. Even if all nerve connections to the heart are severed, the heart continues to beat rhythmically, as demonstrated by transplanted hearts. Nevertheless, the healthy heart is amply supplied with autonomic nerve fibers that can alter the basic rhythm of heart activity set by intrinsic factors.

Setting the Basic Rhythm: The Intrinsic Conduction System

The independent, but coordinated, activity of the heart is a function of (1) the presence of gap junctions, and (2) the activity of the heart's "in-house" conduction system. The **intrinsic**

cardiac conduction system consists of noncontractile cardiac cells specialized to initiate and distribute impulses throughout the heart, so that it depolarizes and contracts in an orderly, sequential manner. In this way, the heart beats as a coordinated unit. Let's look at how this system works.

Action Potential Initiation by Autorhythmic Cells Unlike unstimulated contractile cells of the heart (and neurons and skeletal muscle fibers), which maintain a stable resting membrane potential, the **autorhythmic cells** making up the intrinsic conduction system do *not*. Instead, they have an *unstable resting potential* that continuously depolarizes, drifting slowly toward threshold. These spontaneously changing membrane potentials, called **pacemaker potentials** or **prepotentials**, initiate the action potentials that spread throughout the heart to trigger its rhythmic contractions **(Figure 18.13)**.

The pacemaker potential is due to the special properties of the ion channels in the sarcolemma. In these cells, hyperpolarization at the end of an action potential leads to both closing of K⁺ channels and opening of slow Na⁺ channels. The Na⁺ influx alters the balance between K⁺ loss and Na⁺ entry, and the membrane interior becomes less and less negative (more positive; Figure 18.13, ①). Ultimately, at threshold (approximately −40 mV), **Ca²⁺ channels** open, allowing explosive entry of Ca²⁺ from the extracellular space. As a result, in autorhythmic cells, it is the influx of Ca²⁺ (rather than Na⁺) that produces the rising phase of the action potential and reverses the membrane potential (Figure 18.13, ②).

As in other excitable cells, the falling phase of the action potential and repolarization reflect opening of K⁺ channels and K⁺ efflux from the cell (Figure 18.13, ③). Once repolarization is complete, K⁺ channels close, K⁺ efflux declines, and the slow depolarization to threshold begins again.

Sequence of Excitation Autorhythmic cardiac cells are found in the following areas (Figure 18.14): sinoatrial (si″no-a′tre-al) node, atrioventricular node, atrioventricular bundle, right and left bundle branches, and ventricular walls (as Purkinje fibers).

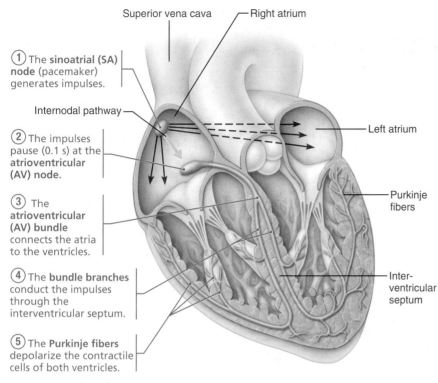

① The **sinoatrial (SA) node** (pacemaker) generates impulses.

Internodal pathway

② The impulses pause (0.1 s) at the **atrioventricular (AV) node.**

③ The **atrioventricular (AV) bundle** connects the atria to the ventricles.

④ The **bundle branches** conduct the impulses through the interventricular septum.

⑤ The **Purkinje fibers** depolarize the contractile cells of both ventricles.

Superior vena cava

Right atrium

Left atrium

Purkinje fibers

Inter-ventricular septum

(a) Anatomy of the intrinsic conduction system showing the sequence of electrical excitation

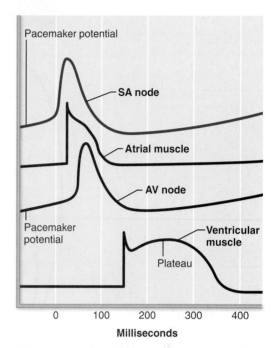

Pacemaker potential

SA node

Atrial muscle

AV node

Pacemaker potential

Ventricular muscle

Plateau

Milliseconds

(b) Comparison of action potential shape at various locations

Figure 18.14 Cardiac intrinsic conduction system and action potential succession during one heartbeat.

Impulses pass across the heart in order from ① to ⑤ following the yellow pathway in **Figure 18.14a.**

① **Sinoatrial node.** The crescent-shaped **sinoatrial (SA) node** is located in the right atrial wall, just inferior to the entrance of the superior vena cava. A minute cell mass with a mammoth job, the SA node typically generates impulses about 75 times every minute. (Its inherent rate in the absence of extrinsic neural and hormonal factors is closer to 100 times per minute.) The SA node sets the pace for the heart as a whole because no other region of the conduction system or the myocardium has a faster depolarization rate. For this reason, it is the heart's **pacemaker**, and its characteristic rhythm, called **sinus rhythm**, determines heart rate.

② **Atrioventricular node.** From the SA node, the depolarization wave spreads via gap junctions throughout the atria and via the *internodal pathway* to the **atrioventricular (AV) node**, located in the inferior portion of the interatrial septum immediately above the tricuspid valve. At the AV node, the impulse is delayed for about 0.1 s, allowing the atria to respond and complete their contraction before the ventricles contract. This delay reflects the smaller diameter of the fibers here and the fact that they have fewer gap junctions for current flow. Consequently, the AV node conducts impulses more slowly than other parts of the system, just as traffic slows when cars are forced to merge into two lanes from four. Once through the AV node, the signaling impulse passes rapidly through the rest of the system.

③ **Atrioventricular bundle.** From the AV node, the impulse sweeps to the **atrioventricular bundle** (also called the **bundle of His**) in the superior part of the interventricular septum. Although the atria and ventricles abut each other, they are *not* connected by gap junctions. The AV bundle is the *only* electrical connection between them. The balance of the AV junction is insulated by the nonconducting fibrous skeleton of the heart.

④ **Right and left bundle branches.** The AV bundle persists only briefly before splitting into two pathways—the **right** and **left bundle branches**, which course along the interventricular septum toward the heart apex.

⑤ **Purkinje fibers.** Essentially long strands of barrel-shaped cells with few myofibrils, the **Purkinje fibers** (pur-kin′je) complete the pathway through the interventricular septum, penetrate into the heart apex, and then turn superiorly into the ventricular walls. The bundle branches excite the septal cells, but the bulk of ventricular depolarization depends on the large Purkinje fibers and, ultimately, on cell-to-cell transmission of the impulse via gap junctions between the ventricular muscle cells. Because the left ventricle is much larger than the right, the Purkinje network is more elaborate in that side of the heart.

The total time between initiation of an impulse by the SA node and depolarization of the last of the ventricular muscle cells is approximately 0.22 s (220 ms) in a healthy human heart.

18

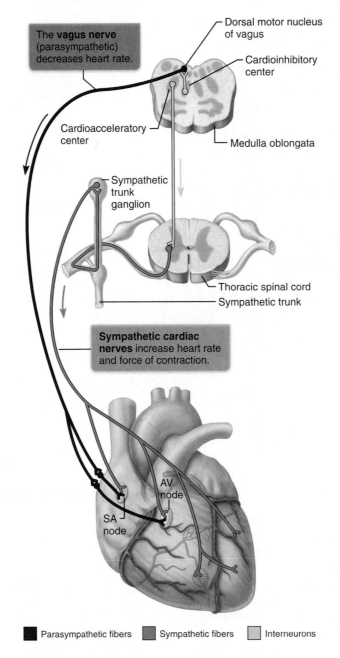

Figure 18.15 Autonomic innervation of the heart.

Ventricular contraction almost immediately follows the ventricular depolarization wave. The wringing motion of contraction begins at the heart apex and moves toward the atria, following the direction of the excitation wave through the ventricle walls. This contraction ejects some of the contained blood *superiorly* into the large arteries leaving the ventricles.

The various autorhythmic cardiac cells have different rates of spontaneous depolarization. The SA node normally drives the heart at a rate of 75 beats per minute. Without SA node input, the AV node would depolarize only about 50 times per minute. Likewise, the AV bundle and the Purkinje fibers would depolarize only about 30 times per minute without input from the AV node (though they conduct very rapidly). Note that these slower

"pacemakers" cannot dominate the heart unless faster pacemakers stop functioning.

The cardiac conduction system coordinates and synchronizes heart activity. Without it, the impulse would travel much more slowly through the myocardium—at the rate of 0.3 to 0.5 m/s as opposed to several meters per second in most parts of the conduction system. This slower rate would allow some muscle fibers to contract well before others, resulting in reduced pumping effectiveness.

HOMEOSTATIC IMBALANCE

Defects in the intrinsic conduction system can cause irregular heart rhythms, or **arrhythmias** (ah-rith′me-ahz), uncoordinated atrial and ventricular contractions, and even **fibrillation**, a condition of rapid and irregular or out-of-phase contractions in which control of heart rhythm is taken away from the SA node by rapid activity in other heart regions. The heart in fibrillation has been compared with a squirming bag of worms. Fibrillating ventricles are useless as pumps; and unless the heart is defibrillated quickly, circulation stops and brain death occurs.

Defibrillation is accomplished by electrically shocking the heart, which interrupts its chaotic twitching by depolarizing the entire myocardium. The hope is that "with the slate wiped clean" the SA node will begin to function normally and sinus rhythm will be reestablished. Implantable cardioverter defibrillators (ICDs) are available that continually monitor heart rhythms and can slow an abnormally fast heart rate or emit an electrical shock if the heart begins to fibrillate.

A defective SA node may have several consequences. An **ectopic focus** (ek-top′ik), which is an abnormal pacemaker, may appear and take over the pacing of heart rate, or the AV node may become the pacemaker. The pace set by the AV node (**junctional rhythm**) is 40 to 60 beats per minute, slower than sinus rhythm but still adequate to maintain circulation.

Occasionally, ectopic pacemakers appear even when the SA node is operating normally. A small region of the heart becomes hyperexcitable, sometimes as a result of too much caffeine (several cups of coffee) or nicotine (excessive smoking), and generates impulses more quickly than the SA node. This leads to a *premature contraction* or **extrasystole** (ek″strah-sis′to-le) before the SA node initiates the next contraction. Then, because the heart has a longer time for filling, the next (normal) contraction is felt as a thud. As you might guess, premature *ventricular* contractions (PVCs) are most problematic.

Because the only route for impulse transmission from atria to ventricles is through the AV node, any damage to the AV node interferes with the ability of the ventricles to receive pacing impulses. This is referred to as a **heart block**. In total heart block no impulses get through and the ventricles beat at their intrinsic rate, which is too slow to maintain adequate circulation. In partial heart block, only some of the atrial impulses reach the ventricles. In both cases, artificial pacemakers are used to recouple the atria to the ventricles as necessary. These programmable devices speed up in response to increased physical activity just as a normal heart would, and many can send diagnostic information to the patient's doctor via the telephone. ∎

Modifying the Basic Rhythm: Extrinsic Innervation of the Heart

Although the basic heart rate is set by the intrinsic conduction system, fibers of the autonomic nervous system modify the marchlike beat and introduce a subtle variability from one beat to the next. The sympathetic nervous system (the "accelerator") increases both the rate and the force of heartbeat. The parasympathetic activation (the "brakes") slows the heart. We explain these neural controls later—here we discuss the anatomy of the nerve supply to the heart.

The cardiac centers are located in the medulla oblongata. The **cardioacceleratory center** projects to sympathetic neurons in the T_1–T_5 level of the spinal cord. These preganglionic neu-

Figure 18.16 **An electrocardiogram tracing (lead I).** The three normally recognizable deflections (waves) and the important intervals are labeled.

rons, in turn, synapse with ganglionic neurons in the cervical and upper thoracic sympathetic trunk (**Figure 18.15**). From there, postganglionic fibers run through the cardiac plexus to the heart where they innervate the SA and AV nodes, heart muscle, and the coronary arteries.

The **cardioinhibitory center** sends impulses to the parasympathetic dorsal vagus nucleus in the medulla, which in turn sends inhibitory impulses to the heart via branches of the vagus nerves. Most parasympathetic ganglionic motor neurons lie in ganglia in the heart wall and their fibers project most heavily to the SA and AV nodes.

Electrocardiography

The electrical currents generated in and transmitted through the heart spread throughout the body and can be detected with an **electrocardiograph**. A graphic record of heart activity is called an **electrocardiogram** (**ECG** or **EKG**; *kardio* is Greek for "heart"). An ECG is a composite of all the action potentials generated by nodal and contractile cells at a given time (**Figure 18.16**) and is *not*, as sometimes assumed, a tracing of a single action potential.

Recording electrodes (leads) are positioned at various sites on the body surface. In a clinical setting, 12 leads are typically

18

① Atrial depolarization, initiated by the SA node, causes the P wave.

② With atrial depolarization complete, the impulse is delayed at the AV node.

③ Ventricular depolarization begins at apex, causing the QRS complex. Atrial repolarization occurs.

④ Ventricular depolarization is complete.

⑤ Ventricular repolarization begins at apex, causing the T wave.

⑥ Ventricular repolarization is complete.

☐ Depolarization   ■ Repolarization

Figure 18.17 The sequence of depolarization and repolarization of the heart related to the deflection waves of an ECG tracing.

used. Three are bipolar leads that measure the voltage difference either between the arms or between an arm and a leg, and nine are unipolar leads. Together the 12 leads provide a fairly comprehensive picture of the heart's electrical activity.

A typical ECG has three distinguishable waves or *deflections* (Figure 18.16). The first, the small **P wave**, lasts about 0.08 s and results from movement of the depolarization wave from the SA node through the atria. Approximately 0.1 s after the P wave begins, the atria contract.

The large **QRS complex** results from ventricular depolarization and precedes ventricular contraction. It has a complicated shape because the paths of the depolarization waves through the ventricular walls change continuously, producing corresponding changes in current direction. Additionally, the time required for each ventricle to depolarize depends on its size relative to the other ventricle. Average duration of the QRS complex is 0.08 s.

The **T wave** is caused by ventricular repolarization and typically lasts about 0.16 s. Repolarization is slower than depolarization, so the T wave is more spread out and has a lower amplitude (height) than the QRS wave. Because atrial repolarization takes place during the period of ventricular excitation, the wave representing atrial repolarization is normally obscured by the large QRS complex being recorded at the same time.

The **P-Q interval** is the time (about 0.16 s) from the beginning of atrial excitation to the beginning of ventricular excitation. Sometimes called the **P-R interval** because the Q wave tends to be very small, it includes atrial depolarization (and contraction) as well as the passage of the depolarization wave through the rest of the conduction system.

During the **S-T segment** of the ECG, when the action potentials of the ventricular myocytes are in their plateau phases, the entire ventricular myocardium is depolarized. The **Q-T interval**, lasting about 0.38 s, is the period from the beginning of ventricular depolarization through ventricular repolarization. The relationship of the parts of an ECG to the sequence of depolarization and repolarization of the heart is illustrated in **Figure 18.17**.

In a healthy heart, the size, duration, and timing of the deflection waves tend to be consistent. For this reason, changes in the pattern or timing of the ECG may reveal a diseased or damaged heart or problems with the heart's conduction system **(Figure 18.18)**. For example, an enlarged R wave hints of enlarged ventricles, an S-T segment that is elevated or depressed indicates cardiac ischemia, and a prolonged Q-T interval reveals a repolarization abnormality that increases the risk of ventricular arrhythmias.

CHECK YOUR UNDERSTANDING

10. Which part of the intrinsic conduction system directly excites ventricular myocardial cells? In which direction does the depolarization wave travel across the ventricles?

11. Describe the electrical event in the heart that occurs during each of the following: (a) the QRS wave of the ECG; (b) the T wave of the ECG; (c) the P-Q interval of the ECG.

For answers, see Appendix G.

(a) Normal sinus rhythm.

(b) Junctional rhythm. The SA node is nonfunctional, P waves are absent, and heart is paced by the AV node at 40–60 beats/min.

(c) Second-degree heart block. Some P waves are not conducted through the AV node; hence more P than QRS waves are seen. In this tracing, the ratio of P waves to QRS waves is mostly 2:1.

(d) Ventricular fibrillation. These chaotic, grossly irregular ECG deflections are seen in acute heart attack and electrical shock.

Figure 18.18 Normal and abnormal ECG tracings.

Heart Sounds

▶ Describe normal heart sounds, and explain how heart murmurs differ.

During each heartbeat, two sounds can be distinguished by auscultating (listening to) the thorax with a stethoscope. These **heart sounds**, often described as lub-dup, are associated with closing of heart valves. (The timing of heart sounds in the cardiac cycle is shown at the top of Figure 18.20.)

The basic rhythm of the heart sounds is lub-dup, pause, lub-dup, pause, and so on, with the pause indicating the period when the heart is relaxing. The first sound occurs as the AV valves close. It signifies the point when ventricular pressure rises above atrial pressure (the beginning of ventricular systole, discussed in the next section). The first sound tends to be

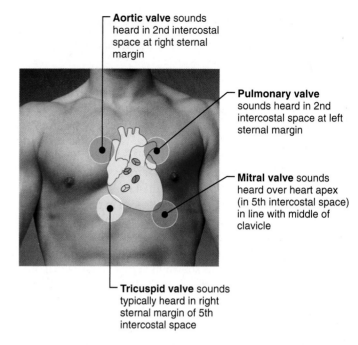

Aortic valve sounds heard in 2nd intercostal space at right sternal margin

Pulmonary valve sounds heard in 2nd intercostal space at left sternal margin

Mitral valve sounds heard over heart apex (in 5th intercostal space) in line with middle of clavicle

Tricuspid valve sounds typically heard in right sternal margin of 5th intercostal space

Figure 18.19 Areas of the thoracic surface where the heart sounds can best be detected.

louder, longer, and more resonant than the second. The second sound occurs as the SL valves snap shut at the beginning of ventricular relaxation (diastole) resulting in a short, sharp sound.

Because the mitral valve closes slightly before the tricuspid valve does, and the aortic SL valve generally snaps shut just before the pulmonary valve, it is possible to distinguish the individual valve sounds by auscultating four specific regions of the thorax (Figure 18.19). Notice that these four points, while not directly superficial to the valves (because the sounds take oblique paths to reach the chest wall), do handily define the four corners of the normal heart. Knowing normal heart size and location is essential for recognizing an enlarged (and often diseased) heart.

⚖ HOMEOSTATIC IMBALANCE

Abnormal heart sounds are called **heart murmurs**. Blood flows silently as long as the flow is smooth and uninterrupted. If it strikes obstructions, however, its flow becomes turbulent and generates heart murmurs that can be heard with a stethoscope. Heart murmurs are fairly common in young children (and some elderly people) with perfectly healthy hearts, probably because their heart walls are relatively thin and vibrate with rushing blood.

Most often, however, murmurs indicate valve problems. If a valve fails to close completely, a swishing sound is heard as the blood backflows or regurgitates through the partially open valve *after* the valve has (supposedly) closed. Such valves are termed *insufficient* or *incompetent*. If a valve fails to open completely, its narrow opening restricts blood flow *through* the valve. Such valves are termed *stenotic*. In a stenotic aortic valve, for instance, a high-pitched sound or click can be detected when the valve should be wide open during systole, but is not. ∎

18

Mechanical Events: The Cardiac Cycle

▶ Describe the timing and events of the cardiac cycle.

The heart undergoes some dramatic writhing movements as it alternately contracts, forcing blood out of its chambers, and then relaxes, allowing its chambers to refill with blood. The terms **systole** (sis′to-le) and **diastole** (di-as′to-le) refer respectively to these *contraction* and *relaxation* periods. The **cardiac cycle** includes *all* events associated with the blood flow through the heart during one complete heartbeat—atrial systole and diastole followed by ventricular systole and diastole. These mechanical events always *follow* the electrical events seen in the ECG.

The cardiac cycle is marked by a succession of pressure and blood volume changes in the heart. Because blood circulates endlessly, we must choose an arbitrary starting point for one turn of the cardiac cycle. As shown in Figure 18.20, which outlines what happens in the left side of the heart, we begin our explanation with the heart in total relaxation: Atria and ventricles are quiet, and it is mid-to-late diastole.

① **Ventricular filling: mid-to-late diastole.** Pressure in the heart is low, blood returning from the circulation is flowing passively through the atria and the open AV valves into the ventricles, and the aortic and pulmonary valves are closed. Approximately 80% of ventricular filling occurs during this period, and the AV valve flaps begin to drift toward the closed position. (The remaining 20% is delivered to the ventricles when the atria contract toward the end of this phase.)

Now the stage is set for atrial systole. Following depolarization (P wave of ECG), the atria contract, compressing the blood in their chambers. This causes a sudden slight rise in atrial pressure, which propels residual blood out of the atria into the ventricles. At this point the ventricles are in the last part of their diastole and have the maximum volume of blood they will contain in the cycle, a volume called the *end diastolic volume* (*EDV*). Then the atria relax and the ventricles depolarize (QRS complex). Atrial diastole persists through the rest of the cycle.

② **Ventricular systole.** As the atria relax, the ventricles begin contracting. Their walls close in on the blood in their chambers, and ventricular pressure rises rapidly and sharply, closing the AV valves. The split-second period when the ventricles are completely closed chambers and the blood volume in the chambers remains constant as the ventricles contract is called the **isovolumetric contraction phase** (i″so-vol″u-met′rik).

Ventricular pressure continues to rise and when it finally exceeds the pressure in the large arteries issuing from the ventricles, the isovolumetric stage ends as the SL valves are forced open and blood is expelled from the ventricles into the aorta and pulmonary trunk. During this **ventricular ejection phase**, the pressure in the aorta normally reaches about 120 mm Hg.

③ **Isovolumetric relaxation: early diastole.** During this brief phase following the T wave, the ventricles relax. Because the blood remaining in their chambers, referred to as the *end systolic volume* (*ESV*), is no longer compressed, ven-

tricular pressure drops rapidly and blood in the aorta and pulmonary trunk flows back toward the heart, closing the SL valves. Closure of the aortic valve causes a brief rise in aortic pressure as backflowing blood rebounds off the closed valve cusps, an event beginning at the **dicrotic notch** shown on the pressure graph. Once again the ventricles are totally closed chambers.

All during ventricular systole, the atria have been in diastole. They have been filling with blood and the intra-atrial pressure has been rising. When blood pressure on the atrial side of the AV valves exceeds that in the ventricles, the AV valves are forced open and ventricular filling, phase ① , begins again. Atrial pressure drops to its lowest point and ventricular pressure begins to rise, completing the cycle.

Assuming the average heart beats 75 times each minute, the length of the cardiac cycle is about 0.8 s, with atrial systole accounting for 0.1 s and ventricular systole 0.3 s. The remaining 0.4 s is a period of total heart relaxation, the **quiescent period**.

Notice two important points: (1) Blood flow through the heart is controlled entirely by pressure changes and (2) blood flows down a pressure gradient through any available opening. The pressure changes, in turn, reflect the alternating contraction and relaxation of the myocardium and cause the heart valves to open, which keeps blood flowing in the forward direction.

The situation in the right side of the heart is essentially the same as in the left side *except* for pressure. The pulmonary circulation is a low-pressure circulation as evidenced by the much thinner myocardium of its right ventricle. So, typical systolic and diastolic pressures for the pulmonary artery are 24 and 8 mm Hg as compared to systemic aortic pressures of 120 and 80 mm Hg, respectively. However, the two sides of the heart eject the same blood volume with each heartbeat.

CHECK YOUR UNDERSTANDING

12. The second heart sound is associated with the closing of which valve(s)?

13. If the mitral valve were insufficient, would you expect to hear the murmur (of blood flowing through the valve that should be closed) during ventricular systole or diastole?

14. During the cardiac cycle, there are two periods when all four valves are closed. Name these two periods.

For answers, see Appendix G.

Cardiac Output

▶ Name and explain the effects of various factors regulating stroke volume and heart rate.

▶ Explain the role of the autonomic nervous system in regulating cardiac output.

Cardiac output (CO) is the amount of blood pumped out by *each* ventricle in 1 minute. It is the product of heart rate (HR) and stroke volume (SV). **Stroke volume** is defined as the volume of blood pumped out by one ventricle with each beat. In general, stroke volume is correlated with the force of ventricular contraction.

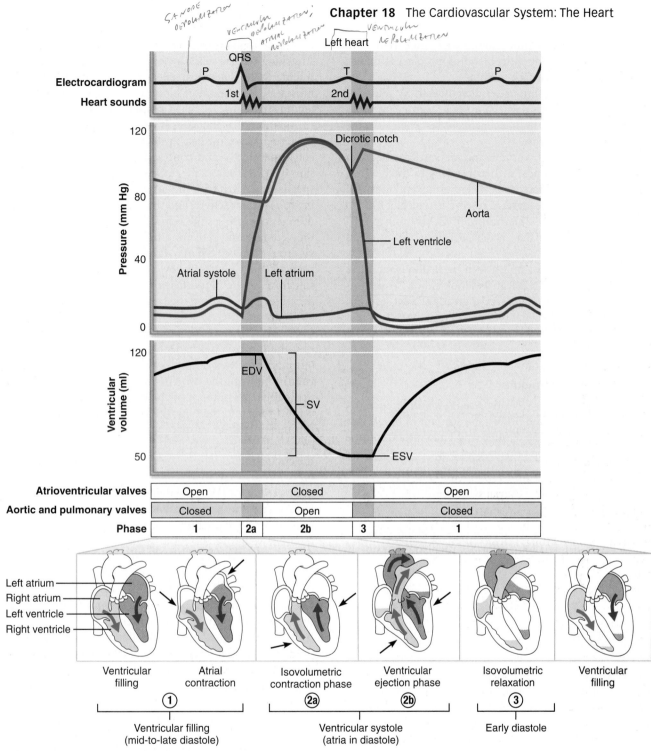

Figure 18.20 Summary of events during the cardiac cycle. An ECG tracing (*top*) correlated with graphs of pressure and volume changes (*center*) in the left side of the heart. Pressures are lower in the right side of the heart. Timing of heart sounds is also indicated. (*Bottom*) Events of phases 1 through 3 of the cardiac cycle.

Using normal resting values for heart rate (75 beats/min) and stroke volume (70 ml/beat), the average adult cardiac output can be computed:

$$CO = HR \times SV = \frac{75 \text{ beats}}{\text{min}} \times \frac{70 \text{ ml}}{\text{beat}}$$

$$= \frac{5250 \text{ ml}}{\text{min}} = \frac{5.25 \text{ L}}{\text{min}}$$

The normal adult blood volume is about 5 L (a little more than 1 gallon). As you can see, the entire blood supply passes through each side of the heart once each minute.

Notice that cardiac output varies directly with SV and HR. This means that CO increases when the stroke volume increases or the heart beats faster or both, and it decreases when either or both of these factors decrease.

Cardiac output is highly variable and increases markedly in response to special demands, such as running to catch a bus. **Cardiac reserve** is the difference between resting and maximal CO. In nonathletic people, cardiac reserve is typically four to five times resting CO (20–25 L/min), but CO in trained athletes during competition may reach 35 L/min (seven times resting).

How does the heart accomplish such tremendous increases in output? To understand this feat, let's look at how stroke volume and heart rate are regulated. As you read the next sections, refer to Figure 18.22 on p. 686 for an overview of the factors that affect stroke volume and heart rate, and consequently, cardiac output.

Regulation of Stroke Volume

Essentially, stroke volume (SV) represents the difference between **end diastolic volume (EDV)**, the amount of blood that collects in a ventricle during diastole, and **end systolic volume (ESV)**, the volume of blood remaining in a ventricle *after* it has contracted. The EDV, determined by how long ventricular diastole lasts and by venous pressure, is normally about 120 ml. (An increase in either factor *raises* EDV.) The ESV, determined by arterial blood pressure and the force of ventricular contraction, is approximately 50 ml. (The higher the arterial blood pressure, the higher the ESV.) To figure normal stroke volume, simply plug these values into this equation:

$$SV = EDV - ESV = \frac{120 \text{ ml}}{\text{beat}} - \frac{50 \text{ ml}}{\text{beat}} = \frac{70 \text{ ml}}{\text{beat}}$$

As you can see, each ventricle pumps out about 70 ml of blood with each beat, which is about 60% of the blood in its chambers.

So what is important here—how do we make sense out of this alphabet soup (SV, ESV, EDV)? Although many factors affect SV by causing changes in EDV or ESV, the three most important are *preload, contractility,* and *afterload.* As we describe in detail next, preload affects EDV, whereas contractility and afterload affect the ESV.

Preload: Degree of Stretch of Heart Muscle   According to the **Frank-Starling law of the heart**, the critical factor controlling SV is the **preload**, which is the degree to which cardiac muscle cells are stretched just before they contract. Recall that at an *optimal length* of muscle fibers (and sarcomeres) (1) the maximum number of active cross bridge attachments is possible between actin and myosin, and (2) the force of contraction is maximal. Cardiac muscle, like skeletal muscle, exhibits a *length-tension relationship.*

Resting skeletal muscle fibers are kept at or near optimal length for developing maximal tension while resting cardiac cells are normally *shorter* than optimal length. As a result, stretching cardiac cells can produce dramatic increases in contractile force. The most important factor stretching cardiac muscle is the amount of blood returning to the heart and distending its ventricles, called **venous return**.

Anything that increases the volume or speed of venous return, such as a slow heart rate or exercise, increases EDV and, consequently, SV and contraction force (see Figure 18.22). A slow heartbeat allows more time for ventricular filling. Exercise speeds venous return because both increased sympathetic nervous system activity and the squeezing action of the skeletal muscles compresses the veins, decreasing the volume of blood they contain and returning more blood to the heart. During vigorous exercise, SV may double as a result of increased venous return. Conversely, low venous return, such as might result from severe blood loss or an extremely rapid heart rate, decreases EDV, causing the heart to beat less forcefully and the SV to drop.

Because the systemic and pulmonary circulations are in series, the intrinsic mechanism we just described ensures equal outputs of the two ventricles and proper distribution of blood volume between the two circuits. If one side of the heart suddenly begins to pump more blood than the other, the increased venous return to the opposite ventricle forces that ventricle—through increased cardiac muscle stretch—to pump out an equal volume, preventing backup or accumulation of blood in the circulation.

Contractility   EDV is the major *intrinsic factor* influencing SV, but SV can also be enhanced by *extrinsic factors* that increase heart muscle contractility. **Contractility** is defined as the contractile strength achieved at a given muscle length. Note in Figure 18.22 that contractility is *independent* of muscle stretch and EDV. An increase in contractility is due to a greater Ca^{2+} influx into the cytoplasm from the extracellular fluid and the SR. Enhanced contractility results in ejection of more blood from the heart (greater SV), hence a lower ESV.

Increased sympathetic stimulation increases contractility of the heart. As noted on p. 679, sympathetic fibers serve not only the intrinsic conduction system but the entire heart. One effect of norepinephrine or epinephrine binding is to initiate a cyclic AMP second-messenger system that increases Ca^{2+} entry, which in turn promotes more cross bridge binding and enhances ventricular contractility **(Figure 18.21)**.

A battery of other chemicals also influence contractility. For example, contractility is enhanced by the hormones glucagon, thyroxine, and epinephrine, by the drug digitalis, and by high levels of extracellular Ca^{2+}. Factors that increase contractility are called *positive inotropic agents* (*ino* = muscle, fiber). Those that impair or decrease contractility are called *negative inotropic agents,* and include acidosis (excess H^+), rising extracellular K^+ levels, and drugs called calcium channel blockers.

Afterload: Back Pressure Exerted by Arterial Blood   The pressure that must be overcome for the ventricles to eject blood is called **afterload**. It is essentially the back pressure exerted on the aortic and pulmonary valves by arterial blood,

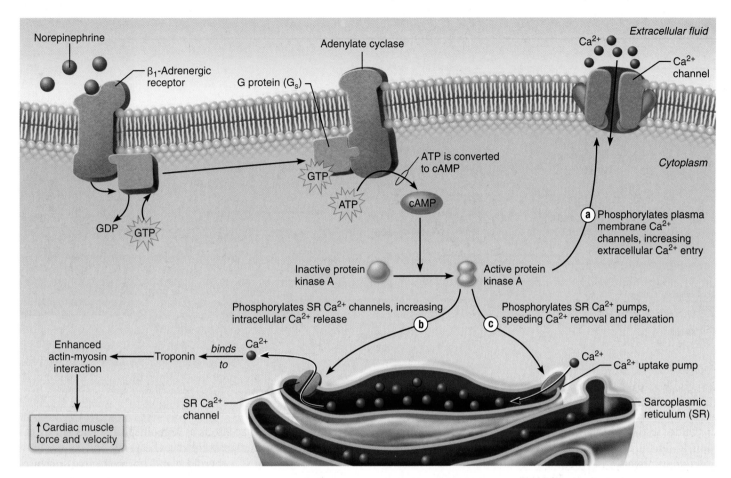

Figure 18.21 Norepinephrine increases heart contractility via a cyclic AMP second-messenger system. Cyclic AMP activates protein kinases that phosphorylate ⓐ Ca^{2+} channels in the plasma membrane, promoting entry of more Ca^{2+} from the extracellular space; ⓑ SR Ca^{2+} channels, causing the SR to release more Ca^{2+}; and ⓒ SR calcium uptake pumps, causing them to remove Ca^{2+} more rapidly from the sarcoplasm, thereby speeding relaxation and making more Ca^{2+} available for release on the next beat.

about 80 mm Hg in the aorta and 8 mm Hg in the pulmonary trunk. In healthy individuals, afterload is not a major determinant of stroke volume because it is relatively constant. However, in people with hypertension (high blood pressure), afterload is important indeed because it reduces the ability of the ventricles to eject blood. Consequently, more blood remains in the heart after systole, resulting in increased ESV and reduced stroke volume.

Regulation of Heart Rate

Given a healthy cardiovascular system, SV tends to be relatively constant. However, when blood volume drops sharply or when the heart is seriously weakened, SV declines and CO is maintained by increasing HR and contractility. Temporary stressors can also influence HR—and consequently CO—by acting through homeostatic mechanisms induced neurally, chemically, and physically. Factors that increase HR are called *positive chronotropic* (*chrono* = time) factors, and those decreasing HR are *negative chronotropic* factors.

Autonomic Nervous System Regulation The most important extrinsic controls affecting heart rate are exerted by the autonomic nervous system, as shown on the right side of **Figure 18.22**. When the sympathetic nervous system is activated by emotional or physical stressors, such as fright, anxiety, or exercise, sympathetic nerve fibers release norepinephrine at their cardiac synapses. Norepinephrine binds to β_1-adrenergic receptors in the heart, causing threshold to be reached more quickly. As a result, the pacemaker fires more rapidly and the heart responds by beating faster.

Sympathetic stimulation also enhances contractility and speeds relaxation. It does this by enhancing Ca^{2+} movements in the contractile cells as we described above and in Figure 18.21. ESV falls as a result of this increased contractility, so SV does not decline, as it would if only heart *rate* were increased. (Remember, when the heart beats faster, there is less time for ventricular filling and so a lower EDV.)

The parasympathetic division opposes sympathetic effects and effectively reduces heart rate when a stressful situation has passed. Parasympathetic-initiated cardiac responses are mediated by acetylcholine, which hyperpolarizes the membranes of its effector cells by *opening* K^+ channels. Because vagal innervation of the ventricles is sparse, parasympathetic activity has little or no effect on cardiac contractility.

18

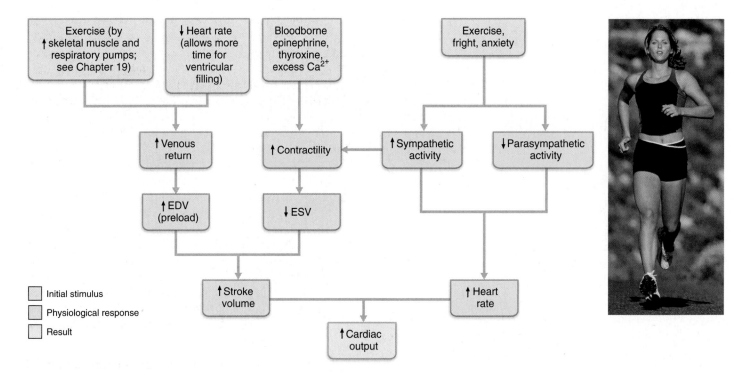

Figure 18.22 Factors involved in regulation of cardiac output.

Under resting conditions, both autonomic divisions continuously send impulses to the SA node of the heart, but the *dominant* influence is inhibitory. For this reason, the heart is said to exhibit **vagal tone**, and heart rate is generally slower than it would be if the vagal nerves were not innervating it. Cutting the vagal nerves results in an almost immediate increase in heart rate of about 25 beats/min, reflecting the inherent rate (100 beats/min) of the pacemaking SA node.

When either division of the autonomic nervous system is stimulated more strongly by sensory inputs relayed from various parts of the cardiovascular system, the other division is temporarily inhibited. Most such sensory input is generated by *baroreceptors* which respond to changes in systemic blood pressure, as we will discuss in Chapter 19. Another example, the **atrial (Bainbridge) reflex**, is a sympathetic reflex initiated by increased venous return and increased atrial filling. Stretching the atrial walls increases heart rate by stimulating both the SA node and the atrial stretch receptors, which trigger reflexive adjustments that result in increased sympathetic stimulation of the heart.

Increased or decreased CO results in corresponding changes to systemic blood pressure, so blood pressure regulation often involves reflexive controls of heart rate. In Chapter 19 we describe in more detail neural mechanisms that regulate blood pressure.

Chemical Regulation Chemicals normally present in the blood and other body fluids may influence heart rate, particularly if they become excessive or deficient.

1. **Hormones.** *Epinephrine*, liberated by the adrenal medulla during sympathetic nervous system activation, produces the same cardiac effects as norepinephrine released by the sympathetic nerves: It enhances heart rate and contractility.

Thyroxine is a thyroid gland hormone that increases metabolic rate and body heat production. When released in large quantities, it causes a slower but more sustained increase in heart rate than that caused by epinephrine. Thyroxine also *enhances* the effects of epinephrine and norepinephrine on the heart, so chronically hyperthyroid individuals may develop a weakened heart.

2. **Ions.** Physiological relationships between intracellular and extracellular ions must be maintained for normal heart function. Plasma electrolyte imbalances pose real dangers to the heart.

HOMEOSTATIC IMBALANCE

Reduced Ca^{2+} blood levels (*hypocalcemia*) depress the heart. Conversely, above-normal levels (*hypercalcemia*) tightly couple the excitation-contraction mechanism and prolong the plateau phase of the action potential. These events dramatically increase heart irritability, which can lead to spastic heart contractions that permit the heart little rest. Many drugs used to treat heart conditions focus on calcium transport into cardiac cells.

High or low blood K^+ levels are particularly dangerous and arise in a number of clinical conditions. Excessive K^+ (*hyperkalemia*) interferes with depolarization by lowering the resting potential, and may lead to heart block and cardiac arrest. *Hypokalemia* is also life threatening, in that the heart beats feebly and arrhythmically. ■

Other Factors Age, gender, exercise, and body temperature also influence HR, although they are less important than neural factors. Resting heart rate is fastest in the fetus

(140–160 beats/min) and gradually declines throughout life. Average heart rate is faster in females (72–80 beats/min) than in males (64–72 beats/min).

Exercise raises HR by acting through the sympathetic nervous system (Figure 18.22). Exercise also increases systemic blood pressure and routes more blood to the working muscles. However, resting HR in the physically fit tends to be substantially lower than in those who are out of condition, and in trained athletes it may be as slow as 40 beats/min. We explain this apparent paradox below.

Heat increases HR by enhancing the metabolic rate of cardiac cells. This explains the rapid, pounding heartbeat you feel when you have a high fever and also accounts, in part, for the effect of exercise on HR (remember, working muscles generate heat). Cold directly decreases heart rate.

HOMEOSTATIC IMBALANCE

HR varies with changes in activity, but marked and persistent rate changes usually signal cardiovascular disease. **Tachycardia** (tak″e-kar′de-ah; "heart hurry") is an abnormally fast heart rate (more than 100 beats/min) that may result from elevated body temperature, stress, certain drugs, or heart disease. Persistent tachycardia is considered pathological because tachycardia occasionally promotes fibrillation.

Bradycardia (brad″e-kar′de-ah; *brady* = slow) is a heart rate slower than 60 beats/min. It may result from low body temperature, certain drugs, or parasympathetic nervous activation. It is a known, and desirable, consequence of endurance training. As physical and cardiovascular conditioning increases, the heart hypertrophies and SV increases, and so resting heart rate can be lower and still provide the same cardiac output. However, persistent bradycardia in poorly conditioned people may result in grossly inadequate blood circulation to body tissues, and bradycardia is often a warning of brain edema after head trauma. ■

Homeostatic Imbalance of Cardiac Output

The heart's pumping action ordinarily maintains a balance between cardiac output and venous return. Were this not so, a dangerous damming up of blood (blood congestion) would occur in the veins returning blood to the heart.

When the pumping efficiency (CO) of the heart is so low that blood circulation is inadequate to meet tissue needs, the heart is said to be in **congestive heart failure (CHF)**. This progressively worsening condition reflects weakening of the myocardium by various conditions which damage it in different ways. Let's take a look.

1. **Coronary atherosclerosis.** This condition, essentially a clogging of the coronary vessels with fatty buildup, impairs blood and oxygen delivery to the cardiac cells. The heart becomes increasingly hypoxic and begins to contract ineffectively.
2. **Persistent high blood pressure.** Normally, pressure in the aorta during diastole is 80 mm Hg, and the left ventricle exerts only slightly over that amount of force to eject blood from its chamber. When aortic diastolic blood pressure rises to 90 mm Hg or more, the myocardium must ex-

ert more force to open the aortic valve and pump out the same amount of blood. If this situation of enhanced afterload becomes chronic, the ESV rises and the myocardium hypertrophies. Eventually, the stress takes its toll and the myocardium becomes progressively weaker.
3. **Multiple myocardial infarcts.** A succession of MIs depresses pumping efficiency because the dead heart cells are replaced by noncontractile fibrous (scar) tissue.
4. **Dilated cardiomyopathy (DCM)** (kar″de-o-my-ah′path-e). The cause of this condition, in which the ventricles stretch and become flabby and the myocardium deteriorates, is often unknown. Drug toxicity (alcohol, cocaine, excess catecholamines, chemotherapeutic agents), hyperthyroidism, and inflammation of the heart following an infection are implicated in some cases. The heart's attempts to work harder result in increasing levels of Ca^{2+} in the cardiac cells. The Ca^{2+} activates calcineurin, a calcium-sensitive enzyme that initiates a cascade which switches on genes that cause heart enlargement. CO is poor because ventricular contractility is impaired, and the condition progressively worsens.

Because the heart is a double pump, each side can initially fail independently of the other. If the left side fails, **pulmonary congestion** occurs. The right side continues to propel blood to the lungs, but the left side does not adequately eject the returning blood into the systemic circulation. Blood vessels in the lungs become engorged with blood, the pressure in them increases, and fluid leaks from the circulation into the lung tissue, causing pulmonary edema. If the congestion is untreated, the person suffocates.

If the right side of the heart fails, **peripheral congestion** occurs. Blood stagnates in body organs, and pooled fluids in the tissue spaces impair the ability of body cells to obtain adequate amounts of nutrients and oxygen and to rid themselves of wastes. The resulting edema is most noticeable in the extremities (feet, ankles, and fingers).

Failure of one side of the heart puts a greater strain on the other side, and ultimately the whole heart fails. A seriously weakened, or *decompensated*, heart is irreparable. Treatment is directed primarily toward (1) removing the excess leaked fluid with *diuretics* (drugs that increase excretion of Na^+ and water by the kidneys), (2) reducing afterload with drugs that drive down blood pressure, and (3) increasing contractility with digitalis derivatives. However, heart transplants and other surgical or mechanical remedies to replace damaged heart muscle are providing additional hope for some cardiac patients.

CHECK YOUR UNDERSTANDING

15. After running to catch a bus, Josh noticed that his heart was beating faster than normally and was pounding forcefully in his chest. How did his faster HR and increased SV come about?
16. What problem of cardiac output might ensue if the heart beats far too rapidly for an extended period, that is, if tachycardia occurs? Why?

For answers, see Appendix G.

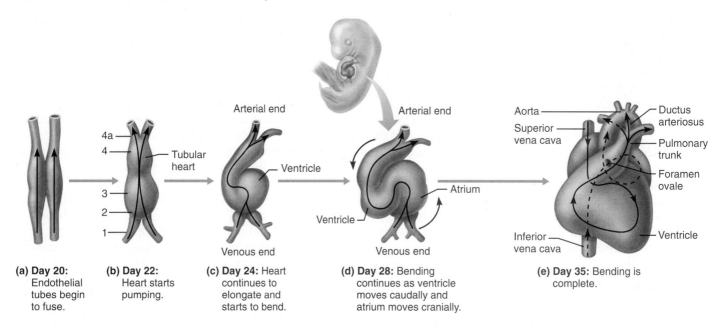

Figure 18.23 Development of the human heart. Ventral view, with the cranial direction toward the top of the figures. Arrows show the direction of blood flow. Days are approximate. In **(b)**: 1 is the sinus venosus; 2, the atrium; 3, the ventricle; 4, the bulbus cordis; and 4a, the truncus arteriosus.

Developmental Aspects of the Heart

▶ Describe fetal heart formation, and indicate how the fetal heart differs from the adult heart.

▶ Provide examples of age-related changes in heart function.

The human heart, derived from mesoderm and guided by powerful signaling molecules, begins as two simple endothelial tubes that quickly fuse to form a single chamber or heart tube that is busily pumping blood by the 22nd day of gestation (Figure 18.23). The tube develops four slightly bulged areas that represent the earliest heart chambers. From tail to head, following the direction of blood flow, the four primitive chambers are the following (Figure 18.23b):

1. **Sinus venosus** (ven-o′sus). This chamber initially receives all the venous blood of the embryo. It will become the smooth-walled part of the right atrium and the coronary sinus. It also gives rise to the sinoatrial node, which "takes the baton" and sets heart rate early in embryonic development.

2. **Atrium.** This embryonic chamber eventually becomes the pectinate muscle–ridged parts of the atria.

3. **Ventricle.** The strongest pumping chamber of the early heart, the ventricle gives rise to the *left* ventricle.

4. **Bulbus cordis.** This chamber, plus its cranial extension, the *truncus arteriosus* (labeled 4a in the figure), give rise to the pulmonary trunk, the first part of the aorta, and most of the *right* ventricle.

During the next three weeks, the heart "tube" exhibits dramatic contortions as it undergoes rightward looping, and major structural changes convert it into a four-chambered organ capable of acting as a double pump—all without missing a beat! The ventricle moves caudally and the atrium cranially, assuming their adult positions. The heart divides into its four definitive chambers (via a number of stages), the midline septum forms, and the bulbus cordis splits into the pulmonary trunk and ascending aorta. After the second month, few changes other than growth occur until birth.

The interatrial septum of the fetal heart is incomplete. The **foramen ovale** (literally, "oval door") connects the two atria and allows blood entering the right heart to bypass the pulmonary circuit and the collapsed, nonfunctional fetal lungs (Figure 18.23e). Another lung bypass, the **ductus arteriosus**, exists between the pulmonary trunk and the aorta. At or shortly after birth, these shunts close, completing the separation between the right and left sides of the heart. In the adult heart, the position of the foramen ovale is revealed by the fossa ovalis, and the **ligamentum arteriosum** is the fibrous remnant of the ductus arteriosus (see Figure 18.4b). We give a more complete description of the fetal and newborn circulation in Chapter 28 (see Figure 28.14).

⚖ HOMEOSTATIC IMBALANCE

Building a perfect heart is difficult. Each year about 30,000 infants are born in the U.S. with one or more of 30 different **congenital heart defects**, making them the most common of all birth defects. Most congenital heart problems are traceable to environmental influences, such as maternal infection or drug intake during month 2 when the major events of heart formation occur.

The most prevalent abnormalities produce two basic kinds of disorders in the newborn. They either (1) lead to mixing of

Narrowed aorta

Occurs in about 1 in every 500 births

Occurs in about 1 in every 1500 births

Occurs in about 1 in every 2000 births

(a) Ventricular septal defect.
The superior part of the inter-ventricular septum fails to form; thus, blood mixes between the two ventricles. More blood is shunted from left to right because the left ventricle is stronger.

(b) Coarctation of the aorta.
A part of the aorta is narrowed, increasing the workload of the left ventricle.

(c) Tetralogy of Fallot. Multiple defects (*tetra* = four): (1) Pulmonary trunk too narrow and pulmonary valve stenosed, resulting in (2) hypertrophied right ventricle; (3) ventricular septal defect; (4) aorta opens from both ventricles.

Figure 18.24 Three examples of congenital heart defects. Tan areas indicate the locations of the defects.

oxygen-poor systemic blood with oxygenated pulmonary blood (so that inadequately oxygenated blood reaches the body tissues) or (2) involve narrowed valves or vessels that greatly increase the workload on the heart. Examples of the first type of defect are *septal defects* (**Figure 18.24a**) and *patent ductus arteriosus*, in which the connection between the aorta and pulmonary trunk remains open. *Coarctation of the aorta* (Figure 18.24b) is an example of the second type of problem. *Tetralogy of Fallot* (te-tral′o-je ov fal-o′), a serious condition in which the baby becomes cyanotic within minutes of birth, encompasses both types of disorders (Figure 18.24c). Modern surgical techniques can correct most of these heart defects. ■

In the absence of congenital heart problems, the heart functions admirably throughout a long lifetime for most people. Homeostatic mechanisms are normally so efficient that people rarely notice when the heart is working harder. In people who exercise regularly and vigorously, the heart gradually adapts to the increased demand by increasing in size and becoming a more efficient and more powerful pump. Consequently, SV increases and resting heart rate declines. Aerobic exercise also helps to clear fatty deposits from blood vessel walls throughout the body, retarding atherosclerosis and coronary heart disease. Barring some chronic illnesses, this beneficial cardiac response to exercise persists into ripe old age.

The key word on benefiting from exercise is *regularity*. Regular exercise gradually enhances the myocardial endurance and strength. For example, 30 minutes a day of moderately vigorous exercise (brisk walking, biking, or yard work) offers significant health benefits to most adults. However, intermittent vigorous exercise, enjoyed by weekend athletes, may push an unconditioned heart beyond its ability to respond to the unexpected demands and bring on a myocardial infarct.

Because of the incredible amount of work the heart does over the course of a lifetime, certain structural changes are inevitable. These age-related changes affecting the heart include

1. **Sclerosis and thickening of valve flaps.** This change occurs particularly where the stress of blood flow is greatest (mitral valve). For this reason, heart murmurs are more common in elderly people.
2. **Decline in cardiac reserve.** Although the passing years seem to cause few changes in resting heart rate, the aged heart is less able to respond to both sudden and prolonged stressors that demand increased output. Sympathetic control of the heart becomes less efficient (in part because the amount of cAMP produced on stimulation decreases with age). HR gradually becomes more variable and there is a decline in maximum HR. These changes are less of a problem in physically active seniors.
3. **Fibrosis of cardiac muscle.** As a person ages, more and more cardiac cells die and are replaced with fibrous tissue. As a result, the heart stiffens and its filling in preparation for the next heartbeat is less efficient, resulting in reduced stroke volume. Additionally, the nodes of the heart's conduction system sometimes become fibrosed (scarred) with age, which increases the incidence of arrhythmias and other conduction problems.
4. **Atherosclerosis.** The insidious progress of atherosclerosis begins in childhood, but inactivity, smoking, and stress accelerate it. The most serious consequences to the heart are hypertensive heart disease and coronary artery occlusion, both of which increase the risk of heart attack and stroke. Although the aging process itself leads to changes in blood vessel walls that result in atherosclerosis, many investigators feel that diet, not aging, is the single most important contributor to cardiovascular disease. There is some agreement that risk is lowered if people consume less animal fat, cholesterol, and salt.

18

18

CHECK YOUR UNDERSTANDING

17. Name the two components of the fetal heart that allow blood to bypass the lungs.
18. In the past decade, many people over 70 have competed in the Ironman World Championships in Hawaii. In what way might age-related changes of the heart limit the performance of these athletes?

For answers, see Appendix G.

The heart is an exquisitely engineered double pump that operates with precision to propel blood into the large arteries leaving its chambers. However, continuous circulation of blood also depends critically on the pressure dynamics in the blood vessels. Chapter 19 considers the structure and function of these vessels and relates this information to the work of the heart to provide a complete picture of cardiovascular functioning.

RELATED CLINICAL TERMS

Asystole (a-sis′to-le) Situation in which the heart fails to contract.

Cardiac catheterization Diagnostic procedure involving passage of a fine catheter (tubing) through a blood vessel into the heart; blood samples are withdrawn, allowing oxygen content, blood flow, and pressures within the heart to be measured. Findings help to detect valve problems, heart deformities, and other heart malfunctions.

Commotio cordis ("concussion of the heart") Situation in which a relatively mild blow to the chest causes heart failure and sudden death because it occurs during a vulnerable interval (2 ms) when the heart is repolarizing. Explains those rare instances when youngsters drop dead on the playing field after being hit in the chest by a ball.

Cor pulmonale (kor pul-mun-nă-′le; *cor* = heart, *pulmo* = lung) A condition of right-sided heart failure resulting from elevated blood pressure in the pulmonary circuit (pulmonary hypertension). Acute cases may develop suddenly due to a pulmonary embolism; chronic cases are usually associated with chronic lung disorders such as emphysema.

Endocarditis (en″do-kar-di′tis) Inflammation of the endocardium, usually confined to the endocardium of the heart valves. Endocarditis often results from infection by bacteria that have entered the bloodstream but may result from fungal infection or an autoimmune response. Drug addicts may develop endocarditis by injecting themselves with contaminated needles.

Heart palpitation A heartbeat that is unusually strong, fast, or irregular so that the person becomes aware of it; may be caused by certain drugs, emotional pressures ("nervous heart"), or heart disorders.

Hypertrophic cardiomyopathy (HCM) The leading cause of sudden death in young athletes, this condition, which is usually inherited, causes the cardiac muscle cells to enlarge, thickening the heart wall. The heart pumps strongly but doesn't relax well during diastole when the heart is filling.

Mitral valve prolapse Valve disorder affecting up to 1% of the population; most often seen in young women. It appears to have a genetic basis resulting in abnormal chordae tendineae or a malfunction of the papillary muscles; one or more of the flaps of the mitral valve become incompetent and billow into the left atrium during ventricular systole, allowing blood regurgitation. Occasionally requires valve replacement surgery.

Myocarditis (mi″o-kar-di′tis; *myo* = muscle, *card* = heart, *itis* = inflammation) Inflammation of the cardiac muscle layer (myocardium) of the heart; sometimes follows an untreated streptococcal infection in children. May weaken the heart and impair its ability to act as an effective pump.

Paroxysmal atrial tachycardia (PAT) Bursts of atrial contractions with little pause between them.

Ventricular tachycardia (VT or V-tac) Rapid ventricular contractions that are not coordinated with atrial activity.

CHAPTER SUMMARY

Media study tools that could provide you additional help in reviewing specific key topics of Chapter 18 are referenced below.

iP = *Interactive Physiology*

Heart Anatomy (pp. 662–672)

Size, Location, and Orientation (p. 663)

1. The human heart, about the size of a clenched fist, is located obliquely within the mediastinum of the thorax.

Coverings of the Heart (p. 663)

2. The heart is enclosed within a double sac made up of the outer fibrous pericardium and the inner serous pericardium (parietal and visceral layers). The pericardial cavity between the serous layers contains lubricating serous fluid.

Layers of the Heart Wall (pp. 663–664)

3. Layers of the heart wall, from the interior out, are the endocardium, the myocardium (reinforced by a fibrous skeleton), and the epicardium (visceral layer of the serous pericardium).

Chambers and Associated Great Vessels (pp. 664–668)

4. The heart has two superior atria and two inferior ventricles. Functionally, the heart is a double pump.

5. Entering the right atrium are the superior vena cava, the inferior vena cava, and the coronary sinus. Four pulmonary veins enter the left atrium.

6. The right ventricle discharges blood into the pulmonary trunk; the left ventricle pumps blood into the aorta.

Pathway of Blood Through the Heart (pp. 668–669)

7. The right heart is the pulmonary circuit pump. Oxygen-poor systemic blood enters the right atrium, passes into the right ventricle, through the pulmonary trunk to the lungs, and back to the left atrium via the pulmonary veins.

8. The left heart is the systemic circuit pump. Oxygen-laden blood entering the left atrium from the lungs flows into the left ventricle and then into the aorta, which provides the functional supply of all body organs. Systemic veins return the oxygen-depleted blood to the right atrium.

Coronary Circulation (pp. 669–670)

9. The right and left coronary arteries branch from the aorta and via their main branches (anterior and posterior interventricular, right marginal, and circumflex arteries) supply the heart itself. Venous blood, collected by the cardiac veins (great, middle, and small), is emptied into the coronary sinus.

10. Blood delivery to the myocardium occurs during heart relaxation.

Heart Valves (pp. 670–672)

11. The atrioventricular valves (tricuspid and mitral) prevent backflow into the atria when the ventricles are contracting; the pulmonary and aortic valves (semilunar valves) prevent backflow into the ventricles when the ventricles are relaxing.

iP Cardiovascular System; Topic: Anatomy Review: The Heart, pp. 1–8.

Cardiac Muscle Fibers (pp. 672–676)

Microscopic Anatomy (pp. 672–673)

1. Cardiac muscle cells are branching, striated, generally uninucleate cells. They contain myofibrils consisting of typical sarcomeres.

2. Adjacent cardiac cells are connected by intercalated discs containing desmosomes and gap junctions. The myocardium behaves as a functional syncytium because of electrical coupling provided by gap junctions.

Mechanism and Events of Contraction (pp. 673–675)

3. As in skeletal muscle, the membrane depolarization of contractile myocytes causes opening of sodium channels and sodium entry, which is responsible for the rising phase of the action potential curve. Depolarization also opens slow Ca^{2+} channels; Ca^{2+} entry prolongs the period of depolarization (creates the plateau). The action potential is coupled to sliding of the myofilaments by Ca^{2+} released by the SR and entering from the extracellular space. Compared to skeletal muscle, cardiac muscle has a prolonged refractory period that prevents tetany.

iP Cardiovascular System; Topic: Cardiac Action Potential, pp. 11–18.

Energy Requirements (pp. 675–676)

4. Cardiac muscle has abundant mitochondria and depends almost entirely on aerobic respiration to form ATP.

Heart Physiology (pp. 676–687)

Electrical Events (pp. 676–680)

1. Certain noncontractile cardiac muscle cells exhibit automaticity and rhythmicity and can independently initiate action potentials. Such cells have an unstable resting potential called a pacemaker potential that gradually depolarizes, drifting toward threshold for firing. These cells compose the intrinsic conduction system of the heart.

2. The conduction system of the heart consists of the SA and AV nodes, the AV bundle and bundle branches, and the Purkinje fibers. This system coordinates the depolarization of the heart and ensures that the heart beats as a unit. The SA node has the fastest rate of spontaneous depolarization and acts as the heart's pacemaker; it sets the sinus rhythm.

3. Defects in the intrinsic conduction system can cause arrhythmias, fibrillation, and heart block.

4. The heart is innervated by the autonomic nervous system. Cardiac centers in the medulla include the cardioacceleratory center, which projects to the T_1–T_5 region of the spinal cord, which in turn projects to the cervical and upper thoracic sympathetic trunk. Postganglionic fibers innervate the SA and AV nodes and the cardiac muscle fibers. The cardioinhibitory center exerts its influence via the parasympathetic vagus nerves (X), which project to the heart wall. Most parasympathetic fibers serve the SA and AV nodes.

5. An electrocardiogram is a graphic representation of the cardiac conduction cycle. The P wave reflects atrial depolarization. The QRS complex indicates ventricular depolarization; the T wave represents ventricular repolarization.

iP Cardiovascular System; Topic: Intrinsic Conduction System, pp. 1–7; Topic: Cardiac Action Potential, pp. 1–10.

Heart Sounds (p. 681)

6. Normal heart sounds arise chiefly from turbulent blood flow during the closing of heart valves. Abnormal heart sounds, called murmurs, usually reflect valve problems.

Mechanical Events: The Cardiac Cycle (p. 682)

7. A cardiac cycle consists of the events occurring during one heartbeat. During mid-to-late diastole, the ventricles fill and the atria contract. Ventricular systole consists of the isovolumetric contraction phase and the ventricular ejection phase. During early diastole, the ventricles are relaxed and are closed chambers until the atrial pressure exceeds the ventricular pressure, forcing the AV valves open. Then the cycle begins again. At a normal heart rate of 75 beats/min, a cardiac cycle lasts 0.8 s.

8. Pressure changes promote blood flow and valve opening and closing.

iP Cardiovascular System; Topic: Cardiac Cycle, pp. 1–19.

Cardiac Output (pp. 682–687)

9. Cardiac output, typically 5 L/min, is the amount of blood pumped out by each ventricle in 1 minute. Stroke volume is the amount of blood pumped out by a ventricle with each contraction. Cardiac output = heart rate × stroke volume.

10. Stroke volume depends to a large extent on the degree of stretch of cardiac muscle by venous return. Approximately 70 ml, it is the difference between end diastolic volume (EDV) and end systolic volume (ESV). Anything that influences heart rate or blood volume influences venous return, hence stroke volume.

11. Activation of the sympathetic nervous system increases heart rate and contractility; parasympathetic activation decreases heart rate but has little effect on contractility. Ordinarily, the heart exhibits vagal tone.

12. Chemical regulation of the heart is effected by hormones (epinephrine and thyroxine) and ions (particularly potassium and calcium). Imbalances in ions severely impair heart activity.

13. Other factors influencing heart rate are age, sex, exercise, and body temperature.

18

14. Congestive heart failure occurs when the pumping ability of the heart is inadequate to provide normal circulation to meet body needs. Right heart failure leads to systemic edema; left heart failure results in pulmonary edema.

iP Cardiovascular System; Topic: Cardiac Output, pp. 1–11.

Developmental Aspects of the Heart (pp. 688–690)

1. The heart begins as a simple (mesodermal) tube that is pumping blood by the fourth week of gestation. The fetal heart has two lung bypasses: the foramen ovale and the ductus arteriosus.

2. Congenital heart defects are the most common of all birth defects. The most common of these disorders lead to inadequate oxygenation of blood or increase the workload of the heart.

3. Age-related changes include sclerosis and thickening of the valve flaps, declines in cardiac reserve, fibrosis of cardiac muscle, and atherosclerosis.

4. Risk factors for cardiac disease include dietary factors, excessive stress, cigarette smoking, and lack of exercise.

REVIEW QUESTIONS

Multiple Choice/Matching

(Some questions have more than one correct answer. Select the best answer or answers from the choices given.)

1. When the semilunar valves are open, which of the following are occurring? **(a)** 2, 3, 5, 6, **(b)** 1, 2, 3, 7, **(c)** 1, 3, 5, 6, **(d)** 2, 4, 5, 7.
   (1) coronary arteries fill
   (2) AV valves are closed
   (3) ventricles are in systole
   (4) ventricles are in diastole
   (5) blood enters aorta
   (6) blood enters pulmonary arteries
   (7) atria contract

2. The portion of the intrinsic conduction system located in the interventricular septum is the **(a)** AV node, **(b)** SA node, **(c)** AV bundle, **(d)** Purkinje fibers.

3. An ECG provides information about **(a)** cardiac output, **(b)** movement of the excitation wave across the heart, **(c)** coronary circulation, **(d)** valve impairment.

4. The sequence of contraction of the heart chambers is **(a)** random, **(b)** left chambers followed by right chambers, **(c)** both atria followed by both ventricles, **(d)** right atrium, right ventricle, left atrium, left ventricle.

5. The fact that the left ventricular wall is thicker than the right reveals that it **(a)** pumps a greater volume of blood, **(b)** pumps blood against greater resistance, **(c)** expands the thoracic cage, **(d)** pumps blood through a smaller valve.

6. The chordae tendineae **(a)** close the atrioventricular valves, **(b)** prevent the AV valve flaps from everting, **(c)** contract the papillary muscles, **(d)** open the semilunar valves.

7. In the heart, which of the following apply? **(1)** Action potentials are conducted from cell to cell across the myocardium via gap junctions, **(2)** the SA node sets the pace for the heart as a whole, **(3)** spontaneous depolarization of cardiac cells can occur in the absence of nerve stimulation, **(4)** cardiac muscle can continue to contract for long periods in the absence of oxygen. **(a)** all of the above, **(b)** 1, 3, 4, **(c)** 1, 2, 3, **(d)** 2, 3.

8. The activity of the heart depends on intrinsic properties of cardiac muscle and on neural factors. Thus, **(a)** vagus nerve stimulation of the heart reduces heart rate, **(b)** sympathetic nerve stimulation of the heart decreases time available for ventricular filling, **(c)** sympathetic stimulation of the heart increases its force of contraction, **(d)** all of the above.

9. Freshly oxygenated blood is first received by the **(a)** right atrium, **(b)** left atrium, **(c)** right ventricle, **(d)** left ventricle.

Short Answer Essay Questions

10. Describe the location and position of the heart in the body.

11. Describe the pericardium and distinguish between the fibrous and the serous pericardia relative to histological structure and location.

12. Trace one drop of blood from the time it enters the right atrium until it enters the left atrium. What is this circuit called?

13. **(a)** Describe how heart contraction and relaxation influence coronary blood flow. **(b)** Name the major branches of the coronary arteries, and note the heart regions served by each.

14. The refractory period of cardiac muscle is much longer than that of skeletal muscle. Why is this a desirable functional property?

15. **(a)** Name the elements of the intrinsic conduction system of the heart in order, beginning with the pacemaker. **(b)** What is the important function of this conduction system?

16. Draw a normal ECG pattern. Label and explain the significance of its deflection waves.

17. Define cardiac cycle, and follow the events of one cycle.

18. What is cardiac output, and how is it calculated?

19. Discuss how the Frank-Starling law of the heart helps to explain the influence of venous return on stroke volume.

20. **(a)** Describe the common function of the foramen ovale and the ductus arteriosus in a fetus. **(b)** What problems result if these shunts remain patent (open) after birth?

Critical Thinking and Clinical Application Questions

1. A gang member was stabbed in the chest during a street fight. He was cyanotic and unconscious from lack of blood delivery to the brain. The diagnosis was cardiac tamponade. What is cardiac tamponade and how does it cause the observed symptoms?

2. You have been called upon to demonstrate the technique for listening to valve sounds. **(a)** Explain where you would position your stethoscope to auscultate **(1)** the aortic valve of a patient with severe aortic valve insufficiency and **(2)** a stenotic mitral valve. **(b)** During which period(s) would you hear these abnormal valve sounds most clearly? (During atrial diastole, ventricular systole, ventricular diastole, or atrial systole?) **(c)** What cues would you use to differentiate between an insufficient and a stenosed valve?

3. Florita Santos, a middle-aged woman, is admitted to the coronary care unit with a diagnosis of left ventricular failure resulting from a myocardial infarction. Her history indicated that she was aroused in the middle of the night by severe chest pain. Her skin is pale and cold, and moist sounds are heard over the lower regions of both lungs. Explain how failure of the left ventricle can cause these signs and symptoms.

4. Heather, a newborn baby, needs surgery because she was born with an aorta that arises from the right ventricle and a pulmonary trunk that issues from the left ventricle, a condition called transposition of the great vessels. What are the physiological consequences of this defect?

5. Gabriel, a heroin addict, feels tired, is weak and feverish, and has vague aches and pains. Terrified that he has AIDS, he goes to a doctor and is informed that he is suffering not from AIDS, but from a heart murmur accompanied by endocarditis. What is the most likely way that Gabriel contracted endocarditis?

6. As Cara worked at her dissection, she became frustrated that several of the structures she had to learn about had more than one common name. Provide another name for each of these structures:

(a) atrioventricular groove, (b) tricuspid valve, (c) bicuspid valve (give two synonyms), and (d) atrioventricular bundle.

Access everything you need to practice, review, and self-assess for both your A&P lecture and lab courses at **myA&P** (www.myaandp.com). There, you'll find powerful online resources including chapter quizzes and tests, games, A&P Flix animations with quizzes, *Interactive Physiology*® with quizzes, MP3 Tutor Sessions, Practice Anatomy Lab™, and more to help you get a better grade in your course.

19

The Cardiovascular System: Blood Vessels

Blood vessels are sometimes compared to a system of pipes with blood circulating in them, but this analogy is only a starting point. Unlike rigid pipes, blood vessels are dynamic structures that pulsate, constrict, relax, and even proliferate. In this chapter we examine the structure and function of these important circulatory passageways.

The **blood vessels** of the body form a closed delivery system that begins and ends at the heart. The idea that blood circulates in the body dates back to the 1620s with the inspired experiments of William Harvey, an English physician. Prior to that time, people thought, as proposed by the ancient Greek physician Galen, that blood moved through the body like an ocean tide, first moving out from the heart and then ebbing back in the same vessels.

PART **1**

OVERVIEW OF BLOOD VESSEL STRUCTURE AND FUNCTION

The three major types of blood vessels are *arteries, capillaries,* and *veins.* As the heart contracts, it forces blood into the large arteries leaving the ventricles. The blood then moves into successively smaller arteries, finally reaching their smallest branches, the *arterioles* (ar-te′re-ōlz; "little arteries"), which feed into the capillary beds of body organs and tissues. Blood drains from the capillaries into *venules* (ven′ūlz), the smallest veins, and then on into larger and larger veins that merge to form the large veins that ultimately empty into the heart. Altogether, the blood vessels in the adult human stretch for about 100,000 km (60,000 miles) through the internal body landscape!

Arteries carry blood *away from* the heart, so they are said to "branch," "diverge," or "fork" as they form smaller and smaller divisions. **Veins**, by contrast, carry blood *toward* the heart and so are said to "join," "merge," and "converge" into the successively larger vessels approaching the heart. In the systemic circulation, arteries always carry oxygenated blood and veins always carry oxygen-poor blood. The opposite is true in the pulmonary circulation, where the arteries, still defined as the vessels leading away from the heart, carry oxygen-poor blood to the lungs, and the veins carry oxygen-rich blood from the lungs to the heart. The special umbilical vessels of a fetus also differ in the roles of veins and arteries.

Of all the blood vessels, only the capillaries have intimate contact with tissue cells and directly serve cellular needs. Exchanges between the blood and tissue cells occur primarily through the gossamer-thin capillary walls.

Structure of Blood Vessel Walls

▶ Describe the three layers that typically form the wall of a blood vessel, and state the function of each.

▶ Define vasoconstriction and vasodilation.

The walls of all blood vessels, except the very smallest, have three distinct layers, or *tunics* ("coverings"), that surround a central blood-containing space, the vessel **lumen** (Figure 19.1).

The innermost tunic is the **tunica intima** (in′tĭ-mah). The name is easy to remember once you know that this tunic is in *intimate* contact with the blood in the lumen. This tunic contains the **endothelium**, the simple squamous epithelium that lines the lumen of all vessels. The endothelium is continuous with the endocardial lining of the heart, and its flat cells fit closely together, forming a slick surface that minimizes friction as blood moves through the lumen. In vessels larger than 1 mm in diameter, a *subendothelial layer*, consisting of a basement membrane and loose connective tissue, supports the endothelium.

The middle tunic, the **tunica media** (me′de-ah), is mostly circularly arranged smooth muscle cells and sheets of elastin. The activity of the smooth muscle is regulated by sympathetic *vasomotor nerve fibers* of the autonomic nervous system and a whole battery of chemicals. Depending on the body's needs at any given moment, either **vasoconstriction** (reduction in lumen diameter as the smooth muscle contracts) or **vasodilation** (increase in lumen diameter as the smooth muscle relaxes) can be effected. The activities of the tunica media are critical in regulating circulatory dynamics because small changes in vessel diameter greatly influence blood flow and blood pressure. Generally, the tunica media is the bulkiest layer in arteries, which bear the chief responsibility for maintaining blood pressure and continuous blood circulation.

The outermost layer of a blood vessel wall, the **tunica externa** (formerly called the *tunica adventitia*; ad″ven-tish′e-ah; "coming from outside"), is composed largely of loosely woven collagen fibers that protect and reinforce the vessel, and anchor it to surrounding structures. The tunica externa is infiltrated with nerve fibers, lymphatic vessels, and, in larger veins, a network of elastin fibers. In larger vessels, the tunica externa contains a system of tiny blood vessels, the **vasa vasorum** (va′sah va-sor′um)—literally, "vessels of the vessels" that nourish the more external tissues of the blood vessel wall. The innermost or luminal portion of the vessel obtains its nutrients directly from blood in the lumen.

The three vessel types vary in length, diameter, relative wall thickness, and tissue makeup (Table 19.1). The relationship of the various blood vascular channels to one another and to vessels of the lymphatic system (which recovers fluids that leak from the circulation) is summarized in Figure 19.2.

CHECK YOUR UNDERSTANDING

1. Which branch of the autonomic nervous system innervates blood vessels? Which layer of the blood vessel wall do these nerves innervate? What are the effectors (cells that carry out the response)?
2. When vascular smooth muscle contracts, what happens to the diameter of the blood vessel? What is this called?

For answers, see Appendix G.

Arterial System

▶ Compare and contrast the structure and function of the three types of arteries.

In terms of relative size and function, arteries can be divided into three groups—elastic arteries, muscular arteries, and arterioles.

Vein

Artery

(a)

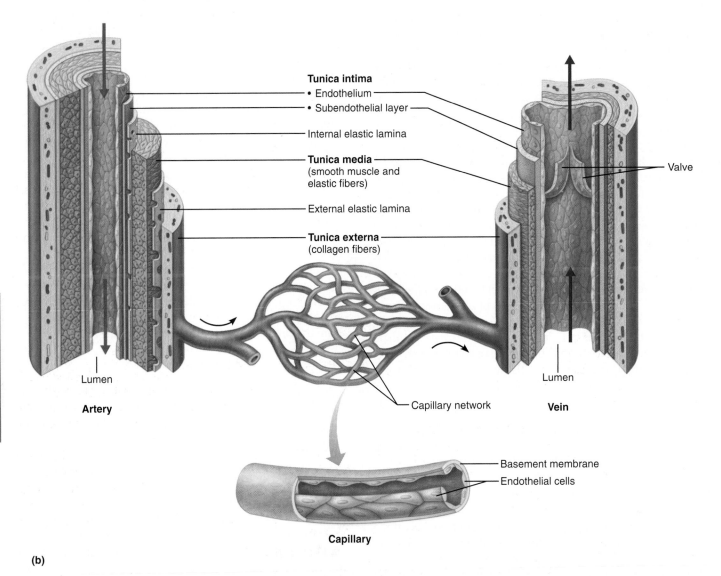

Tunica intima
• Endothelium
• Subendothelial layer

Internal elastic lamina

Tunica media
(smooth muscle and
elastic fibers)

External elastic lamina

Tunica externa
(collagen fibers)

Valve

Lumen

Artery

Capillary network

Lumen

Vein

Basement membrane
Endothelial cells

Capillary

(b)

19

Figure 19.1 Generalized structure of arteries, veins, and capillaries. (a) Light photomicrograph of a muscular artery and the corresponding vein in cross section (70×). **(b)** Comparison of wall structure of arteries, veins, and capillaries. Note that the tunica media is thick in arteries and thin in veins, while the tunica externa is thin in arteries and relatively thicker in veins.

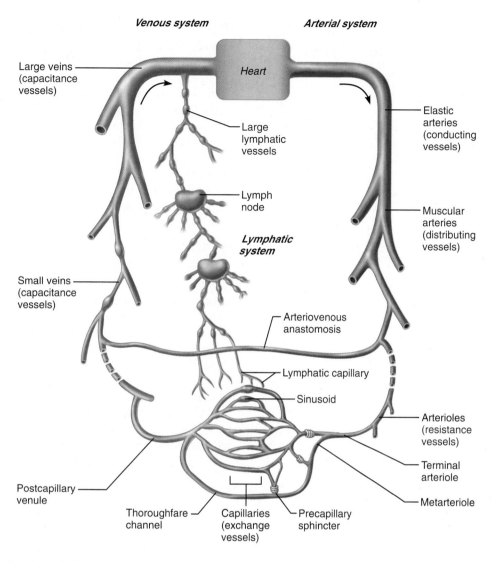

Figure 19.2 The relationship of blood vessels to each other and to the lymphatic vessels. Lymphatic vessels recover excess tissue fluid and return it to the blood.

Elastic (Conducting) Arteries

Elastic arteries are the thick-walled arteries near the heart—the aorta and its major branches. These arteries are the largest in diameter, ranging from 2.5 cm to 1 cm, and the most elastic (Table 19.1). Because their large lumens make them low-resistance pathways that conduct blood from the heart to medium-sized arteries, elastic arteries are sometimes referred to as **conducting arteries** (Figure 19.2).

Elastic arteries contain more elastin than any other vessel type. It is present in all three tunics, but the tunica media contains the most. There the elastin constructs concentric "holey" laminae (sheets) of elastic connective tissue that look like slices of Swiss cheese interspersed between the layers of smooth muscle cells. Although elastic arteries also contain substantial amounts of smooth muscle, they are relatively inactive in vasoconstriction. Thus, in terms of function, they can be visualized as simple elastic tubes.

Elastic arteries are pressure reservoirs, expanding and recoiling as blood is ejected from the heart. Consequently, blood flows fairly continuously rather than starting and stopping with the pulsating rhythm of the heartbeat. If the blood vessels become hard and unyielding, as in arteriosclerosis, blood flows more intermittently, similar to the way water flows through a hard rubber garden hose attached to a faucet. When the faucet is on, the high pressure makes the water gush out of the hose. But when the faucet is shut off, the water flow abruptly becomes a trickle and then stops, because the hose walls cannot recoil to keep the water under pressure. Also, without the pressure-smoothing effect of the elastic arteries, the walls of arteries throughout the body experience higher pressures. Battered by high pressures, the arteries eventually weaken and may balloon out or even burst. (These problems are discussed in *A Closer Look* on pp. 702–703.)

19

TABLE 19.1	Summary of Blood Vessel Anatomy	
VESSEL TYPE/ ILLUSTRATION*	**AVERAGE LUMEN DIAMETER (D) AND WALL THICKNESS (T)**	**RELATIVE TISSUE MAKEUP** Endothelium / Elastic Tissues / Smooth Muscles / Fibrous (Collagenous) Tissues
Elastic artery	D : 1.5 cm T : 1.0 mm	
Muscular artery	D : 6.0 mm T : 1.0 mm	
Arteriole	D : 37.0 μm T : 6.0 μm	
Capillary	D : 9.0 μm T : 0.5 μm	
Venule	D : 20.0 μm T : 1.0 μm	
Vein	D : 5.0 mm T : 0.5 mm	

*Size relationships are not proportional. Smaller vessels are drawn relatively larger so detail can be seen. See column 2 for actual dimensions.

Muscular (Distributing) Arteries

Distally the elastic arteries give way to the **muscular**, or **distributing**, **arteries**, which deliver blood to specific body organs and account for most of the named arteries studied in the anatomy laboratory. Their internal diameter ranges from that of a little finger (1 cm) to that of a pencil lead (about 0.3 mm).

Proportionately, muscular arteries have the thickest tunica media of all vessels. Their tunica media contains relatively more smooth muscle and less elastic tissue than do elastic arteries (Table 19.1). For this reason, they are more active in vasoconstriction and less distensible. In muscular arteries, however, there *is* an *elastic lamina* on each face of the tunica media.

Arterioles

The smallest of the arteries, **arterioles** have a lumen diameter ranging from 0.3 mm down to 10 μm. Larger arterioles have all three tunics, but their tunica media is chiefly smooth muscle with a few scattered elastic fibers. Smaller arterioles, which lead into the capillary beds, are little more than a single layer of smooth muscle cells spiraling around the endothelial lining.

As we will describe shortly, minute-to-minute blood flow into the capillary beds is determined by arteriole diameter, which varies in response to changing neural, hormonal, and local chemical influences. When arterioles constrict, the tissues served are largely bypassed. When arterioles dilate, blood flow into the local capillaries increases dramatically.

Capillaries

▶ Describe the structure and function of a capillary bed.

The microscopic **capillaries** are the smallest blood vessels. Their exceedingly thin walls consist of just a thin tunica intima (see Figure 19.1b). In some cases, one endothelial cell forms the entire circumference of the capillary wall. At strategic locations along the outer surface of some capillaries are spider-shaped *pericytes*, smooth muscle–like cells that stabilize the capillary wall and help control capillary permeability (Figure 19.3a).

Average capillary length is 1 mm and average lumen diameter is 8–10 μm, just large enough for red blood cells to slip through in single file. Most tissues have a rich capillary supply, but there are exceptions. Tendons and ligaments are poorly vascularized. Cartilage and epithelia lack capillaries, but receive nutrients from blood vessels in nearby connective tissues, and the avascular cornea and lens of the eye receive nutrients from the aqueous humor.

If blood vessels are compared to a system of expressways and roads, the capillaries are the back alleys and driveways that provide direct access to nearly every cell in the body. Given their location and the thinness of their walls, capillaries are ideally suited for their role—exchange of materials (gases, nutrients, hormones, and so on) between the blood and the interstitial fluid (Figure 19.2 and Table 19.1). We describe these exchanges later in this chapter. Here, we focus on capillary structure.

Types of Capillaries

Structurally, there are three types of capillaries—*continuous*, *fenestrated*, and *sinusoidal*. **Continuous capillaries**, abundant in the skin and muscles, are most common (Figure 19.3a). They are continuous in the sense that their endothelial cells provide an uninterrupted lining, adjacent cells being joined laterally by *tight junctions*. However, these junctions are usually incomplete and leave gaps of unjoined membrane called **intercellular clefts**, which are just large enough to allow limited passage of fluids and small solutes. Typically, the endothelial cell cytoplasm contains numerous pinocytotic vesicles that ferry fluids across the capillary wall.

Brain capillaries, however, are unique. There the tight junctions of the continuous capillaries are complete and extend around the entire perimeter of the endothelial cells, constituting the structural basis of the *blood-brain barrier* that we described in Chapter 12.

Fenestrated capillaries (fen′es-tra-tid) are similar to the continuous variety except that some of the endothelial cells in fenestrated capillaries are riddled with oval *pores*, or *fenestrations* (*fenestra* = window) (Figure 19.3b). The fenestrations are usually covered by a delicate membrane, or diaphragm (probably condensed basal lamina material), but even so, fenestrated capillaries are much more permeable to fluids and small solutes than continuous capillaries are.

Fenestrated capillaries are found wherever active capillary absorption or filtrate formation occurs. For example, fenestrated capillaries in the small intestine receive nutrients from digested food, and those in endocrine organs allow hormones rapid entry into the blood. Fenestrated capillaries with perpetually open pores occur in the kidneys, where rapid filtration of blood plasma is essential.

Sinusoids (si′nŭ-soyds), or **sinusoidal capillaries**, are highly modified, leaky capillaries found only in the liver, bone marrow, spleen, and adrenal medulla. Sinusoids have large, irregularly shaped lumens and are usually fenestrated. Their endothelial lining has fewer tight junctions and larger intercellular clefts than ordinary capillaries (Figure 19.3c).

These structural adaptations allow large molecules and even blood cells to pass between the blood and surrounding tissues. In the liver, the endothelium of the sinusoids is *discontinuous* and its lining includes large **hepatic macrophages** (Kupffer cells), which remove and destroy any contained bacteria. In other organs, such as the spleen, phagocytes located just outside the sinusoids stick cytoplasmic extensions through the intercellular clefts into the sinusoidal lumen to get at their "prey." Blood flows sluggishly through the tortuous sinusoid channels, allowing time for it to be modified in various ways.

Capillary Beds

Capillaries do not function independently. Instead they tend to form interweaving networks called **capillary beds**. The flow of blood from an arteriole to a venule—that is, through a capillary bed—is called the **microcirculation**. In most body regions, a capillary bed consists of two types of vessels: (1) a *vascular shunt*

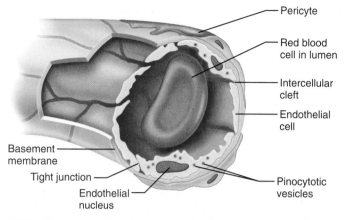

(a) Continuous capillary. Least permeable, and most common (e.g., skin, muscle).

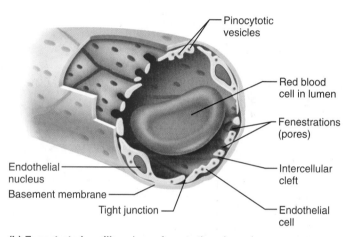

(b) Fenestrated capillary. Large fenestrations (pores) increase permeability. Occurs in special locations (e.g., kidney, small intestine).

(c) Sinusoidal capillary. Most permeable. Occurs in special locations (e.g., liver, bone marrow, spleen).

Figure 19.3 Capillary structure. Note that the basement membrane is incomplete only in **(c)** and that pericytes most often occur on continuous capillaries.

19

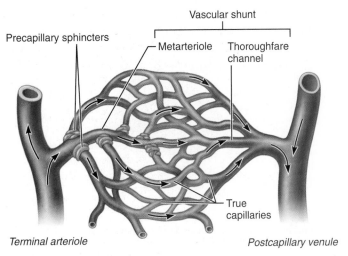

(a) Sphincters open—blood flows through true capillaries.

(b) Sphincters closed—blood flows through metarteriole–thoroughfare channel and bypasses true capillaries.

Figure 19.4 Anatomy of a capillary bed.

(metarteriole–thoroughfare channel), a short vessel that directly connects the arteriole and venule at opposite ends of the bed, and (2) *true capillaries*, the actual *exchange vessels* (Figure 19.4).

The **terminal arteriole** feeding the bed leads into a **metarteriole** (a vessel structurally intermediate between an arteriole and a capillary), which is continuous with the **thoroughfare channel** (intermediate between a capillary and a venule). The thoroughfare channel, in turn, joins the **postcapillary venule** that drains the bed.

The **true capillaries** number 10 to 100 per capillary bed, depending on the organ or tissues served. They usually branch off the metarteriole (proximal end of the shunt) and return to the thoroughfare channel (the distal end), but occasionally they spring from the terminal arteriole and empty directly into the venule. A cuff of smooth muscle fibers, called a **precapillary sphincter**, surrounds the root of each true capillary at the metarteriole and acts as a valve to regulate blood flow into the capillary.

Blood flowing through a terminal arteriole may go either through the true capillaries or through the shunt. When the precapillary sphincters are relaxed (open), as in Figure 19.4a, blood flows through the true capillaries and takes part in ex-

changes with tissue cells. When the sphincters are contracted (closed), as in Figure 19.4b, blood flows through the shunts and bypasses the tissue cells.

The relative amount of blood entering a capillary bed is regulated by local chemical conditions and arteriolar vasomotor nerve fibers. A bed may be flooded with blood or almost completely bypassed, depending on conditions in the body or in that specific organ. For example, suppose you have just eaten and are sitting relaxed, listening to your favorite musical group. Food digestion is going on, and blood is circulating freely through the true capillaries of your gastrointestinal organs to receive the breakdown products of digestion. Between meals, however, most of these same capillary pathways are closed.

To take another example, when you are exercising vigorously blood is rerouted from the digestive organs (food or no food) to the capillary beds of your skeletal muscles where it is more immediately needed. This rerouting helps explain why vigorous exercise right after a meal can cause indigestion or abdominal cramps.

Venous System

▶ Describe the structure and function of veins, and explain how veins differ from arteries.

Blood is carried from the capillary beds toward the heart by veins. Along the route, the diameter of successive venous vessels increases, and their walls gradually thicken as they progress from venules to the larger and larger veins.

Venules

Ranging from 8 to 100 μm in diameter, **venules** are formed when capillaries unite. The smallest venules, the *postcapillary venules*, consist entirely of endothelium around which pericytes congregate. They are extremely porous (more like capillaries than veins in this way), and fluid and white blood cells move easily from the bloodstream through their walls. Indeed, a well-recognized sign of an inflamed area is adhesion of white blood cells to the postcapillary venule endothelium, followed by their migration through the wall into the inflamed tissue. The larger venules have one or two layers of smooth muscle cells (a scanty tunica media) and thin externa as well.

Veins

Venules join to form *veins*. Veins usually have three distinct tunics, but their walls are always thinner and their lumens larger than those of corresponding arteries (Figure 19.1 and Table 19.1). Consequently, in the view seen in routine histological preparations, veins are usually collapsed and their lumens appear slitlike.

There is relatively little smooth muscle or elastin in the tunica media, which is poorly developed and tends to be thin even in the largest veins. The tunica externa is the heaviest wall layer. Consisting of thick longitudinal bundles of collagen fibers and elastic networks, it is often several times thicker than the tunica media. In the largest veins—the venae cavae, which return

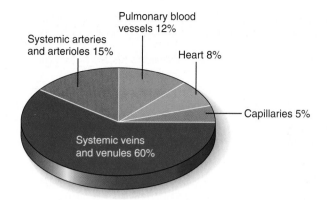

Systemic arteries
and arterioles 15%

Pulmonary blood
vessels 12%

Heart 8%

Capillaries 5%

Systemic veins
and venules 60%

Figure 19.5 Relative proportion of blood volume throughout the cardiovascular system. The systemic veins are called capacitance vessels because they are distensible and contain a large proportion of the blood volume. Pulmonary blood vessels supply the lungs; systemic blood vessels supply the rest of the body.

blood directly to the heart—the tunica externa is further thickened by longitudinal bands of smooth muscle.

With their large lumens and thin walls, veins can accommodate a fairly large blood volume. Veins are called **capacitance vessels** and **blood reservoirs** because up to 65% of the body's blood supply is found in the veins at any time (Figure 19.5). Even so, they are normally only partially filled.

The walls of veins can be much thinner than arterial walls without danger of bursting because the blood pressure in veins is low. However, the low-pressure condition demands some adaptations to ensure that blood is returned to the heart at the same rate it was pumped into the circulation. The large-diameter lumens of veins (which offer relatively little resistance to blood flow) are one structural adaptation.

Another adaptation is valves that prevent blood from flowing backward. **Venous valves** are formed from folds of the tunica intima, and resemble the semilunar valves of the heart in both structure and function (see Figure 19.1). Venous valves are most abundant in the veins of the limbs, where the upward flow of blood is opposed by gravity. They are absent in veins of the thoracic and abdominal body cavities.

A simple experiment demonstrates the effectiveness of venous valves. Hang one hand by your side until the blood vessels on its dorsal aspect distend with blood. Next place two fingertips against one of the distended veins, and pressing firmly, move the superior finger proximally along the vein and then release that finger. The vein will remain flattened and collapsed, despite the pull of gravity. Finally, remove the distal fingertip and watch the vein refill with blood.

HOMEOSTATIC IMBALANCE

Varicose veins are veins that have become tortuous and dilated because of incompetent (leaky) valves. More than 15% of adults suffer from varicose veins, usually in the lower limbs. Several factors contribute, including heredity and conditions that hinder venous return, such as prolonged standing in one position, obesity, or pregnancy. Both the "potbelly" of an overweight

person and the enlarged uterus of a pregnant woman exert downward pressure on vessels of the groin, restricting return of blood to the heart. Consequently, blood pools in the lower limbs, and with time, the valves weaken and the venous walls stretch and become floppy. Superficial veins, which receive little support from surrounding tissues, are especially susceptible.

Another cause of varicose veins is elevated venous pressure. For example, straining to deliver a baby or have a bowel movement raises intra-abdominal pressure, preventing blood from draining from the veins of the anal canal. The resulting varicosities in the anal veins are called *hemorrhoids* (hem′ŏ-roidz). ■

Venous sinuses, such as the *coronary sinus* of the heart and the *dural venous sinuses* of the brain, are highly specialized, flattened veins with extremely thin walls composed only of endothelium. They are supported by the tissues that surround them, rather than by any additional tunics. The dural venous sinuses, which receive cerebrospinal fluid and blood draining from the brain, are reinforced by the tough dura mater that covers the brain surface.

Vascular Anastomoses

Where vascular channels unite, they form interconnections called **vascular anastomoses** (ah-nas″to-mo′sēz; "coming together"). Most organs receive blood from more than one arterial branch, and arteries supplying the same territory often merge, forming **arterial anastomoses**. These anastomoses provide alternate pathways, called **collateral channels**, for blood to reach a given body region. If one branch is cut or blocked by a clot, the collateral channel can often provide the area with an adequate blood supply.

Arterial anastomoses occur around joints, where active movement may hinder blood flow through one channel. They are also common in abdominal organs, the brain, and the heart. Arteries that do not anastomose or that have a poorly developed collateral circulation supply the retina, kidneys, and spleen. If their blood flow is interrupted, cells supplied by such vessels die.

The metarteriole–thoroughfare channel shunts of capillary beds that connect arterioles and venules are examples of **arteriovenous anastomoses**. Veins interconnect much more freely than arteries, and **venous anastomoses** are common. (You may be able to see venous anastomoses through the skin on the dorsum of your hand.) Because venous anastomoses are abundant, occlusion of a vein rarely blocks blood flow or leads to tissue death.

CHECK YOUR UNDERSTANDING

3. Name the type of artery that matches each description: major role in dampening the pulsatile pressure of heart contractions; vasodilation or constriction determines blood flow to individual capillary beds; have the thickest tunica media relative to their lumen size.

(Text continues on p. 703.)

19

A CLOSER LOOK

Atherosclerosis? Get Out the Cardiovascular Drāno

When pipes get clogged, it is usually because we've dumped something down the drain that shouldn't be there—a greasy mass or a hairball. Sometimes, pipes get blocked when something is growing inside them (tree roots, for example), trapping the normal sludge coming through (see top photo). In **arteriosclerosis**, the walls of our arteries become thicker and stiffer, and hypertension results. In **atherosclerosis**, the most common form of arteriosclerosis, small, patchy thickenings called *atheromas* form that can intrude into the vessel lumen, making it easy for arterial spasms or a roaming blood clot to close the vessel completely.

Although all arteries are susceptible to atherosclerosis, those most often affected are the aorta and the coronary and carotid arteries.

Onset and Stages

How does this scourge of blood vessels that indirectly causes half of the deaths in the Western world come about? The development of a full-blown atheroma is believed to occur in several stages.

1. **The endothelium is injured.** According to the *response to injury hypothesis*, the initial event is damage to the tunica intima caused by bloodborne chemicals, hypertension, components of cigarette smoke, or viral or bacterial infections. Researchers suspect that almost any type of chronic infection—even periodontal problems—could set the stage for atherosclerosis. How a bacterium such as *Chlamydophila pneumoniae* (found in some plaques) triggers atheroma development is not completely understood, but we know that any injury to the endothelium sets off the alarm summoning the immune system and the inflammatory process to repair the damage.

2. **Lipids accumulate and oxidize in the tunica intima.** Injured endothelial cells release chemotactic agents and growth (mitosis-inducing) factors, and begin to transport and modify lipids picked up from the blood, particularly low-density lipoproteins (LDLs) that deliver cholesterol to tissue cells via the bloodstream. This accumulated

Top A pipe clogged by accumulated deposits. *Bottom* Atherosclerotic plaques nearly close a human artery.

LDL oxidizes in the hostile inflammatory environment. This not only damages neighboring cells, but also acts as a chemotactic agent, attracting macrophages. Some of these macrophages become so engorged with LDLs that they are transformed into lipid-laden *foam cells*. The accumulation of foam cells forms a **fatty streak**, the first visible sign of atheroma development.

3. **Smooth muscle cells proliferate and a fibrous cap forms.** Smooth muscle cells migrate from the tunica media and deposit collagen and elastin fibers, thickening the intima and producing fibrous lesions with a core of dead and dying foam cells called **fibrous** or **atherosclerotic plaques**. At first the vessel walls accommodate the growing plaque by expanding outward, but eventually these fatty mounds be-

gin to protrude into the vessel lumen, producing full-blown atherosclerosis (see bottom photo).

4. **The plaque becomes unstable.** As the plaque continues to enlarge, the cells at its center die. Calcium is deposited, and collagen fiber production by smooth muscle cells declines. Now called a **complicated plaque**, it constricts the vessel and causes the arterial walls to fray and ulcerate, conditions that encourage blood sludging and backup, platelet adhesion, and thrombus formation. The vessels' increased rigidity leads to hypertension. Together, these events increase the risk of myocardial infarcts, strokes, and aneurysms, and are responsible for the pain (angina) that occurs when heart muscle is ischemic.

Additionally, impaired endothelial cells release less nitric oxide and prostacyclin—chemicals that promote vasodilation and inhibit platelet aggregation. This may be one cause of the increased thrombus formation in those with atherosclerosis. In some individuals, increased thrombus formation may be due to an altered form of LDL called *lipoprotein (a)*, which inhibits fibrinolysis by competing with plasminogen.

We often think of large complicated plaques as being the culprits for heart attacks and strokes, but plaques of any size may rupture and form a clot. At least one-third of all heart attacks are caused by plaques too small to be seen on traditional arteriograms. They cause no warning symptoms, and the victim appears perfectly healthy until he or she drops dead! One goal of current research is to find ways to identify these vulnerable plaques.

Risk Factors

Why are some of us so troubled by atherosclerosis while others of us are seemingly immune to its ravages? A large number of interacting risk factors determine the progress of atheroma development. Risk factors include increasing age, male sex, a family history of atherosclerosis, high blood cholesterol, hypertension, cigarette smoking, lack of exercise, diabetes, obesity, stress, and intake of trans fats.

Prevention and Treatment

Some risk factors are under our control. We can quit smoking, lose weight, exercise regularly to increase blood levels of high-density lipoprotein (HDL), the "good" lipoprotein that removes cholesterol from vessel walls and carries it to the liver, and eat a healthy diet low in saturated and trans fats.

But for many of us, these measures are not enough and a pharmaceutical approach is needed. Cholesterol-lowering drugs called statins were at first hoped to act as cadiovascular Drāno and wash the fatty plaques off the walls. They do lower LDL, but have been shown to decrease plaque size by only a small amount. A significant part of their action, though, is their unexpected side benefit—anti-inflammatory activity, which appears to help stabilize existing plaques and keep them from rupturing. The humble aspirin has also gained new respect—the American Heart Association recommends that people at high risk

for heart attack or stroke take one baby aspirin (81 mg) daily to prevent clot formation when plaques do rupture.

Larger plaques that partially block arteries are treated in much the same way we would treat a blocked sewer pipe—dig it up and replace it or call Roto-Rooter to drill through the obstruction. In *coronary bypass surgery*, veins removed from the legs or small arteries removed from the thoracic cavity are implanted in the heart to restore myocardial circulation. In *balloon angioplasty*, a catheter with a balloon tightly packed into its tip is threaded through the vessels. When the catheter reaches the obstruction, the balloon is inflated to compress the fatty mass against the vessel wall. Angioplasty temporarily clears the path, but *restenoses* (new blockages) often occur. *Stents*, short metal-mesh tubes that look much like a ziti noodle, are inserted into the newly dilated vessels in order to hold the vessel open, but these

often become clogged as well. Treating the area with bursts of radiation (*brachytherapy*) or using stents that slowly release drugs that inhibit smooth muscle proliferation help reduce restenosis.

When an atheroma ruptures and induces clot formation, *thrombolytic (clot-dissolving) agents* are used. A genetically engineered form of the naturally occuring *tissue plasminogen activator* (*tPA*) is injected directly into the blocked vessel. tPA restores blood flow quickly and puts an early end to many heart attacks and strokes in progress.

Of course, it's best to prevent atherosclerosis from progressing in the first place by changing our lifestyles. Americans like their burgers and butter. But if heart disease can be prevented by reversing atherosclerosis, many people with diseased arteries may be willing to trade lifelong habits for a healthy old age!

---

4. Look at Figure 19.4 on p. 700 and assume that the capillary bed depicted is in your calf muscle. Which condition—(a) or (b)—would the bed be in if you were doing calf raises at the gym?

5. What is the function of valves in veins? What forms the valves?

6. In the systemic circuit, which contains more blood—arteries or veins—or is it the same?

For answers, see Appendix G.

For answers, see Appendix G.

PART 2

PHYSIOLOGY OF CIRCULATION

Have you ever climbed a mountain? Well, get ready to climb a hypothetical mountain as you learn about circulatory dynamics. Like scaling a mountain, tackling blood pressure regulation and other topics of cardiovascular physiology is challenging while you're doing it, and exhilarating when you succeed. Let's begin the climb.

To sustain life, blood must be kept circulating. By now, you are aware that the heart is the pump, the arteries are pressure reservoirs and conduits, the arterioles are resistance vessels that control distribution, the capillaries are exchange sites, and the veins are conduits and blood reservoirs. Now for the dynamics of this system.

Introduction to Blood Flow, Blood Pressure, and Resistance

▶ Define blood flow, blood pressure, and resistance, and explain the relationships between these factors.

First we need to define three physiologically important terms—blood flow, blood pressure, and resistance—and examine how these factors relate to the physiology of blood circulation.

Definition of Terms

1. **Blood flow** is the volume of blood flowing through a vessel, an organ, or the entire circulation in a given period (ml/min). If we consider the entire vascular system, blood flow is equivalent to cardiac output (CO), and under resting conditions, it is relatively constant. At any given moment, however, blood flow through *individual* body organs may vary widely and is intimately related to their immediate needs.

2. **Blood pressure (BP)**, the force per unit area exerted on a vessel wall by the contained blood, is expressed in millimeters of mercury (mm Hg). For example, a blood pressure of 120 mm Hg is equal to the pressure exerted by a column of mercury 120 mm high. Unless stated otherwise, the term *blood pressure* means systemic arterial blood pressure in the largest arteries near the heart. It is the pressure gradient—the *differences* in blood pressure within the vascular system—that provides the driving force that keeps blood moving, always from an area of higher pressure to an area of lower pressure, through the body.

3. **Resistance** is opposition to flow and is a measure of the amount of friction blood encounters as it passes through the vessels. Because most friction is encountered in the peripheral (systemic) circulation, well away from the heart, we generally use the term **peripheral resistance**. There are three important sources of resistance: blood viscosity, vessel length, and vessel diameter.

- *Blood viscosity.* The internal resistance to flow that exists in all fluids is *viscosity* (vis-kos′ĭ-te) and is related to the thickness or "stickiness" of a fluid. The greater the viscosity, the less easily molecules slide past one another and the more difficult it is to get and keep the fluid moving. Blood is much more viscous than water because it contains formed elements and plasma proteins. Consequently, it flows more slowly under the same conditions. Blood viscosity is fairly constant, but infrequent conditions such as polycythemia (excessive numbers of red blood cells) can increase blood viscosity and, hence, resistance. On the other hand, if the red blood cell count is low, as in some anemias, blood is less viscous and peripheral resistance declines.
- *Total blood vessel length.* The relationship between total blood vessel length and resistance is straightforward: the longer the vessel, the greater the resistance. For example, an infant's blood vessels lengthen as he or she grows to adulthood, and so both peripheral resistance and blood pressure increase.
- *Blood vessel diameter.* Because blood viscosity and vessel length are normally unchanging, the influence of these factors can be considered constant in healthy people. Changes in blood vessel diameter are frequent, however, and significantly alter peripheral resistance.

   How so? The answer lies in principles of fluid flow. Fluid close to the wall of a tube or channel is slowed by friction as it passes along the wall, whereas fluid in the center of the tube flows more freely and faster. You can verify this by watching the flow of water in a river. Water close to the bank hardly seems to move, while that in the middle of the river flows quite rapidly.

   In a tube of a given size, the relative speed and position of fluid in the different regions of the tube's cross section remain constant, a phenomenon called *laminar flow* or *streamlining*. The smaller the tube, the greater the friction, because relatively more of the fluid contacts the tube wall, where its movement is impeded.

   Resistance varies *inversely* with the *fourth power* of the vessel radius (one-half the diameter). This means, for example, that if the radius of a vessel is doubled, the resistance drops to one-sixteenth of its original value ($r^4 = 2 \times 2 \times 2 \times 2 = 16$ and $1/r^4 = 1/16$). For this reason, the large arteries close to the heart, which do not change dramatically in diameter, contribute little to peripheral resistance. Instead, the small-diameter arterioles, which can enlarge or constrict in response to neural and chemical controls, are the major determinants of peripheral resistance.

When blood encounters either an abrupt change in the tube size or rough or protruding areas of the tube wall (such as the fatty plaques of atherosclerosis), the smooth laminar blood flow is replaced by *turbulent flow*, that is, irregular fluid motion where blood from the different laminae mixes. Turbulence dramatically increases resistance.

Relationship Between Flow, Pressure, and Resistance

Now that we have defined these terms, let us summarize briefly the relationships between them. Blood flow (*F*) is *directly* proportional to the difference in blood pressure (ΔP) between two points in the circulation, that is, the blood pressure, or hydrostatic pressure, gradient. Thus, when ΔP increases, blood flow speeds up, and when ΔP decreases, blood flow declines. Blood flow is *inversely* proportional to the peripheral resistance (*R*) in the systemic circulation; if *R* increases, blood flow decreases. These relationships are expressed by the formula

$$F = \frac{\Delta P}{R}$$

Of these two factors influencing blood flow, *R* is far more important than ΔP in influencing local blood flow because *R* can easily be changed by altering blood vessel diameter. For example, when the arterioles serving a particular tissue dilate (thus decreasing the resistance), blood flow to that tissue increases, even though the systemic pressure is unchanged or may actually be falling.

CHECK YOUR UNDERSTANDING

7. List three factors that determine resistance in a vessel. Which of these factors is physiologically most important?
8. Suppose vasoconstriction decreases the diameter of a vessel to one-third its size. What happens to the rate of flow through that vessel? (Calculate the expected size of the change.)

For answers, see Appendix G.

Systemic Blood Pressure

▶ List and explain the factors that influence blood pressure, and describe how blood pressure is regulated.

▶ Define hypertension. Describe its manifestations and consequences.

Any fluid driven by a pump through a circuit of closed channels operates under pressure, and the nearer the fluid is to the pump, the greater the pressure exerted on the fluid. The dynamics of blood flow in blood vessels is no exception, and blood flows through the blood vessels along a pressure gradient, always moving from higher- to lower-pressure areas. Fundamentally, *the pumping action of the heart generates blood flow. Pressure results when flow is opposed by resistance.*

19

As illustrated in **Figure 19.6**, systemic blood pressure is highest in the aorta and declines throughout the pathway to finally reach 0 mm Hg in the right atrium. The steepest drop in blood pressure occurs in the arterioles, which offer the greatest resistance to blood flow. However, as long as a pressure gradient exists, no matter how small, blood continues to flow until it completes the circuit back to the heart.

Arterial Blood Pressure

Arterial blood pressure reflects two factors: (1) how much the elastic arteries close to the heart can be stretched (their *compliance* or *distensibility*) and (2) the volume of blood forced into them at any time. If the amounts of blood entering and leaving the elastic arteries in a given period were equal, arterial pressure would be constant. Instead, as Figure 19.6 reveals, blood pressure rises and falls in a regular fashion in the elastic arteries near the heart. In other words, it is obviously *pulsatile*.

As the left ventricle contracts and expels blood into the aorta, it imparts kinetic energy to the blood, which stretches the elastic aorta as aortic pressure reaches its peak. Indeed, if the aorta were opened during this period, blood would spurt upward 5 or 6 feet! This pressure peak, called the **systolic pressure** (sis-tah′lik), averages 120 mm Hg in healthy adults. Blood moves forward into the arterial bed because the pressure in the aorta is higher than the pressure in the more distal vessels.

During diastole, the aortic valve closes, preventing blood from flowing back into the heart, and the walls of the aorta (and other elastic arteries) recoil, maintaining sufficient pressure to keep the blood flowing forward into the smaller vessels. During this time, aortic pressure drops to its lowest level (approximately 70 to 80 mm Hg in healthy adults), called the **diastolic pressure** (di-as-tah′lik). You can picture the elastic arteries as pressure reservoirs that operate as auxiliary pumps to keep blood circulating throughout the period of diastole, when the heart is relaxing. Essentially, the volume and energy of blood stored in the elastic arteries during systole are given back during diastole.

The difference between the systolic and diastolic pressures is called the **pulse pressure**. It is felt as a throbbing pulsation in an artery (a *pulse*) during systole, as the elastic arteries are expanded by the blood being forced into them by ventricular contraction. Increased stroke volume and faster blood ejection from the heart (a result of increased contractility) cause *temporary* increases in the pulse pressure. Pulse pressure is chronically increased by arteriosclerosis because the elastic arteries become less stretchy.

Because aortic pressure fluctuates up and down with each heartbeat, the important pressure figure to consider is the **mean arterial pressure (MAP)**—the pressure that propels the blood to the tissues. Diastole usually lasts longer than systole, so the MAP is not simply the value halfway between systolic and diastolic pressures. Instead, it is roughly equal to the diastolic pressure plus one-third of the pulse pressure.

$$\text{MAP} = \text{diastolic pressure} + \frac{\text{pulse pressure}}{3}$$

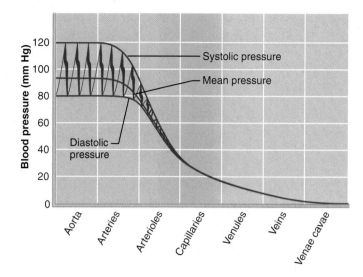

Figure 19.6 Blood pressure in various blood vessels of the systemic circulation.

For a person with a systolic blood pressure of 120 mm Hg and a diastolic pressure of 80 mm Hg:

$$\text{MAP} = 80 \text{ mm Hg} + \frac{40 \text{ mm Hg}}{3} = 93 \text{ mm Hg}$$

MAP and pulse pressure both decline with increasing distance from the heart. The MAP loses ground to the never-ending friction between the blood and the vessel walls, and the pulse pressure is gradually phased out in the less elastic muscular arteries, where elastic rebound of the vessels ceases to occur. At the end of the arterial tree, blood flow is steady and the pulse pressure has disappeared.

Capillary Blood Pressure

As Figure 19.6 shows, by the time blood reaches the capillaries, blood pressure has dropped to approximately 35 mm Hg and by the end of the capillary beds is only around 15 mm Hg. Such low capillary pressures are desirable because (1) capillaries are fragile and high pressures would rupture them, and (2) most capillaries are extremely permeable and thus even the low capillary pressure forces solute-containing fluids (filtrate) out of the bloodstream into the interstitial space. As we describe later in this chapter, these fluid flows are important for continuously refreshing the interstitial fluid.

Venous Blood Pressure

Unlike arterial pressure, which pulsates with each contraction of the left ventricle, venous blood pressure is steady and changes very little during the cardiac cycle. The pressure gradient in the veins, from venules to the termini of the venae cavae, is only about 15 mm Hg (that from the aorta to the ends of the arterioles is about 60 mm Hg). This pressure difference between arteries and veins becomes very clear when the vessels are cut. If a vein is cut, the blood flows evenly from the wound, but a lacerated

19

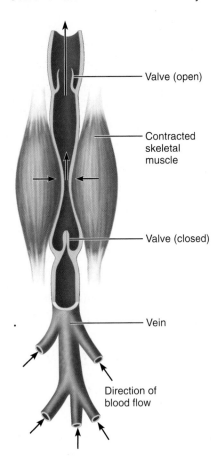

Figure 19.7 The muscular pump. When contracting skeletal muscles press against a vein, the valves proximal to the area of contraction are forced open and blood is propelled toward the heart. The valves distal to the area of contraction are closed by the backflowing blood.

artery spurts blood. The very low pressure in the venous system reflects the cumulative effects of peripheral resistance, which dissipates most of the energy of blood pressure (as heat) during each circuit.

Despite the structural modifications of veins (large lumens and valves), venous pressure is normally too low to promote adequate venous return. For this reason, three functional adaptations are critically important to venous return. The first is the **respiratory "pump."** Pressure changes occurring in the ventral body cavity during breathing create the respiratory pump that moves blood up toward the heart. As we inhale, abdominal pressure increases, squeezing the local veins and forcing blood toward the heart. At the same time, the pressure in the chest decreases, allowing thoracic veins to expand and speeding blood entry into the right atrium.

The second and most important adaptation is the **muscular "pump,"** consisting of skeletal muscle activity. As the skeletal muscles surrounding the deep veins contract and relax, they "milk" blood toward the heart, and once blood passes each successive valve, it cannot flow back **(Figure 19.7)**. People who earn their living in "standing professions," such as hairdressers and dentists, often have swollen ankles because blood pools in

the feet and legs during prolonged periods of skeletal muscle inactivity.

The third adaptation is the layer of smooth muscle around the veins that constricts under sympathetic control, increasing venous return. This is yet another way in which the sympathetic nervous system increases cardiac output.

Maintaining Blood Pressure

Maintaining a steady flow of blood from the heart to the toes is vital for organs to function properly. But making sure a person jumping out of bed in the morning does not keel over from inadequate blood flow to the brain requires the finely tuned cooperation of the heart, blood vessels, and kidneys—all supervised by the brain.

Central among the homeostatic mechanisms that regulate cardiovascular dynamics are those that maintain blood pressure, principally *cardiac output, peripheral resistance,* and *blood volume.* If we rearrange the formula pertaining to blood flow presented on p. 704, we can see how cardiac output (blood flow of the entire circulation) and peripheral resistance relate to blood pressure.

$$F = \Delta P/R \quad \text{or} \quad CO = \Delta P/R \quad \text{or} \quad \Delta P = CO \times R$$

Clearly, blood pressure varies *directly* with CO and R. Additionally, blood pressure varies directly with blood volume because CO depends on blood volume (the heart can't pump out what doesn't enter its chambers). So in theory, a change (increase or decrease) in any of these variables would cause a corresponding change in blood pressure. However, what *really* happens in the body is that changes in one variable that threaten blood pressure homeostasis are quickly compensated for by changes in the other variables.

As we described in Chapter 18, CO is equal to *stroke volume* (ml/beat) times *heart rate* (beats/min), and normal CO is 5.0 to 5.5 L/min. **Figure 19.8** shows the main factors determining cardiac output—venous return and the neural and hormonal controls. Remember that the cardioinhibitory center in the medulla is "in charge" of heart rate most of the time and, via the parasympathetic vagus nerves, maintains the *resting heart rate.* During "resting" periods, stroke volume is controlled mainly by venous return (end diastolic volume). During stress, the cardioacceleratory center takes over, activating the sympathetic nervous system and increasing both heart rate (by acting on the SA node) and stroke volume (by enhancing cardiac muscle contractility, which decreases end systolic volume). The enhanced CO, in turn, results in an increase in MAP.

In the following discussion we focus on factors that regulate blood pressure by altering peripheral resistance and blood volume, but a flowchart showing the influence of nearly all other important factors is provided in Figure 19.11 (p. 711).

Short-Term Mechanisms: Neural Controls

The *short-term controls* of blood pressure, mediated by the nervous system and bloodborne chemicals, counteract moment-to-moment fluctuations in blood pressure by altering peripheral resistance (and CO).

Figure 19.8 **Major factors enhancing cardiac output.** BP = blood pressure, EDV = end diastolic volume, ESV = end systolic volume.

Neural controls of peripheral resistance are directed at two main goals: (1) Maintaining adequate MAP by altering blood vessel diameter. (Remember, very small changes in blood vessel diameter cause substantial changes in peripheral resistance, and hence in systemic blood pressure.) Under conditions of low blood volume, all vessels except those supplying the heart and brain are constricted to allow as much blood as possible to flow to those two vital organs. (2) Altering blood distribution to respond to specific demands of various organs. For example, during exercise blood is shunted temporarily from the digestive organs to the skeletal muscles.

Most neural controls operate via reflex arcs involving *baroreceptors* and associated afferent fibers, the vasomotor center of the medulla, vasomotor fibers, and vascular smooth muscle. Occasionally, inputs from *chemoreceptors* and higher brain centers also influence the neural control mechanism.

Role of the Vasomotor Center

The neural center that oversees changes in the diameter of blood vessels is the **vasomotor center**, a cluster of neurons in the medulla. This center plus the cardiac centers described earlier make up the **cardiovascular center** that integrates blood pressure control by altering cardiac output and blood vessel diameter. The vasomotor center transmits impulses at a fairly steady rate along sympathetic efferents called **vasomotor fibers**,

which exit from the T_1 through L_2 levels of the spinal cord and run to innervate the smooth muscle of blood vessels, mainly arterioles. As a result, the arterioles are almost always in a state of moderate constriction, called **vasomotor tone**.

The degree of vasomotor tone varies from organ to organ. Generally, arterioles of the skin and digestive viscera receive vasomotor impulses more frequently and tend to be more strongly constricted than those of skeletal muscles. Any increase in sympathetic activity produces generalized vasoconstriction and a rise in blood pressure. Decreased sympathetic activity allows the vascular muscle to relax somewhat and causes blood pressure to decline to basal levels.

Vasomotor activity is modified by inputs from (1) baroreceptors (pressure-sensitive mechanoreceptors that respond to changes in arterial pressure and stretch), (2) chemoreceptors (receptors that respond to changes in blood levels of carbon dioxide, H^+, and oxygen), and (3) higher brain centers. Let's take a look.

Baroreceptor-Initiated Reflexes

When arterial blood pressure rises, it stretches **baroreceptors**, neural receptors located in the *carotid sinuses* (dilations in the internal carotid arteries, which provide the major blood supply to the brain), in the *aortic arch*, and in the walls of nearly every large artery of the neck and thorax. When stretched, baroreceptors

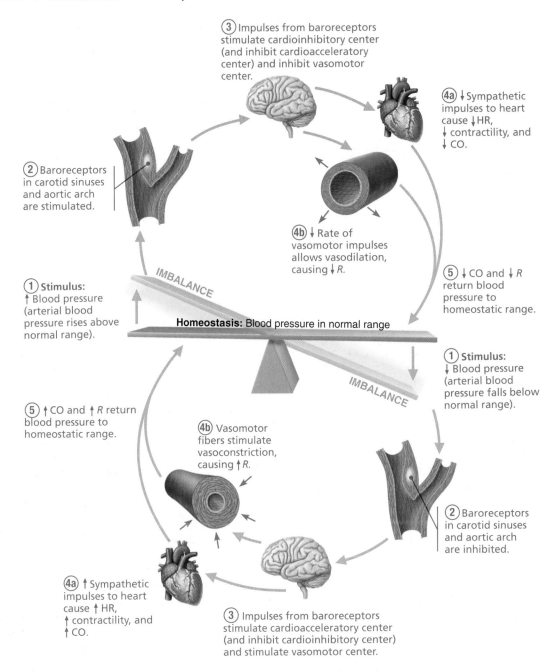

(3) Impulses from baroreceptors stimulate cardioinhibitory center (and inhibit cardioaccelleratory center) and inhibit vasomotor center.

(4a) ↓Sympathetic impulses to heart cause ↓HR, ↓ contractility, and ↓ CO.

(2) Baroreceptors in carotid sinuses and aortic arch are stimulated.

(4b) ↓ Rate of vasomotor impulses allows vasodilation, causing ↓R.

(5) ↓ CO and ↓ R return blood pressure to homeostatic range.

IMBALANCE

(1) **Stimulus:** ↑ Blood pressure (arterial blood pressure rises above normal range).

Homeostasis: Blood pressure in normal range

(1) **Stimulus:** ↓ Blood pressure (arterial blood pressure falls below normal range).

IMBALANCE

(5) ↑CO and ↑R return blood pressure to homeostatic range.

(4b) Vasomotor fibers stimulate vasoconstriction, causing ↑R.

(2) Baroreceptors in carotid sinuses and aortic arch are inhibited.

(4a) ↑Sympathetic impulses to heart cause ↑ HR, ↑ contractility, and ↑ CO.

(3) Impulses from baroreceptors stimulate cardioaccelleratory center (and inhibit cardioinhibitory center) and stimulate vasomotor center.

Figure 19.9 Baroreceptor reflexes that help maintain blood pressure homeostasis.
CO = cardiac output; *R* = peripheral resistance; HR = heart rate; BP = blood pressure.

send a rapid stream of impulses to the vasomotor center. This input inhibits the vasomotor center, resulting in vasodilation of not only arterioles but also veins, and a decline in blood pressure (Figure 19.9).

While dilation of the arterioles substantially reduces peripheral resistance, venodilation shifts blood to the venous reservoirs, causing a decline in both venous return and cardiac output. Afferent impulses from the baroreceptors also reach the cardiac centers, where the impulses stimulate parasympathetic activity and inhibit the cardioaccelleratory center, reducing heart rate and contractile force.

A decline in MAP initiates reflex vasoconstriction and increases cardiac output, causing blood pressure to rise. In this

way, peripheral resistance and cardiac output are regulated in tandem so that changes in blood pressure are minimized.

The function of rapidly responding baroreceptors is to protect the circulation against short-term (acute) changes in blood pressure, such as those occurring when you change your posture. For example, blood pressure falls (particularly in the head) when a person stands up after reclining. Baroreceptors taking part in the **carotid sinus reflex** protect the blood supply to the brain, whereas those activated in the **aortic reflex** help maintain adequate blood pressure in the systemic circuit as a whole.

Baroreceptors are relatively *ineffective* in protecting us against sustained pressure changes, as evidenced by the fact that many people develop chronic hypertension. In such cases, the

TABLE 19.2	Influence of Selected Hormones on Variables Affecting Blood Pressure		
HORMONE	**EFFECT ON BP**	**EFFECT ON VARIABLE**	**SITE OF ACTION**
Epinephrine and norepinephrine (NE)	↑	↑ CO (HR and contractility)	Heart (β_1 receptors)
		↑ Peripheral resistance (vasoconstriction)	Arterioles (α receptors)
Angiotensin II	↑	↑ Peripheral resistance (vasoconstriction)	Arterioles
Atrial natriuretic peptide (ANP)	↓	↓ Peripheral resistance (vasodilation)	Arterioles
Antidiuretic hormone (ADH)	↑	↑ Peripheral resistance (vasoconstriction)	Arterioles
		↑ Blood volume (↓ water loss)	Kidney tubule cells
Aldosterone	↑	↑ Blood volume (↓ water and salt loss)	Kidney tubule cells
Cortisol	↑	↑ Blood volume (↓ water and salt loss)	Kidney tubule cells

baroreceptors are "reprogrammed" (adapt) to monitor pressure changes at a higher set point.

Chemoreceptor-Initiated Reflexes

When the carbon dioxide levels rise, or the pH falls, or oxygen content of the blood drops sharply, **chemoreceptors** in the aortic arch and large arteries of the neck transmit impulses to the cardioacceleratory center, which then increases cardiac output, and to the vasomotor center, which causes reflex vasoconstriction. The rise in blood pressure that follows speeds the return of blood to the heart and lungs.

The most prominent chemoreceptors are the *carotid* and *aortic bodies* located close by the baroreceptors in the carotid sinuses and aortic arch. Chemoreceptors are more important in regulating respiratory rate than blood pressure, so we consider their function in Chapter 22.

Influence of Higher Brain Centers

Reflexes that regulate blood pressure are integrated in the medulla oblongata of the brain stem. Although the cerebral cortex and hypothalamus are not involved in routine controls of blood pressure, these higher brain centers can modify arterial pressure via relays to the medullary centers. For example, the fight-or-flight response mediated by the hypothalamus has profound effects on blood pressure. (Even the simple act of speaking can make your blood pressure jump if the person you are talking to makes you anxious.) The hypothalamus also mediates the redistribution of blood flow and other cardiovascular responses that occur during exercise and changes in body temperature.

Short-Term Mechanisms: Hormonal Controls

As we have seen, changing levels of carbon dioxide and oxygen help regulate blood pressure via the chemoreceptor reflexes. Hormones, too, help regulate blood pressure, both in the short term via changes in peripheral resistance and in the long term via changes in blood volume **(Table 19.2)**. Paracrines (local

chemicals), on the other hand, primarily serve to match the amount of blood flow to the metabolic need of a particular tissue. In rare instances, massive release of paracrines can affect blood pressure. We will discuss these paracrines later—here we will examine the short-term effects of hormones.

- **Adrenal medulla hormones.** During periods of stress, the adrenal gland releases **norepinephrine** (**NE**) and **epinephrine** to the blood, and both hormones enhance the sympathetic fight-or-flight response. As noted earlier, NE has a vasoconstrictive action. Epinephrine increases cardiac output and promotes generalized vasoconstriction (except in skeletal and cardiac muscle, where it generally causes vasodilation).

    It is interesting to note that *nicotine,* an important chemical in tobacco and one of the strongest toxins known, causes intense vasoconstriction not only by directly stimulating ganglionic sympathetic neurons but also by prompting release of large amounts of epinephrine and NE.
- **Angiotensin II.** When blood pressure or blood volume are low, the kidneys release the hormone renin. Renin acts as an enzyme, ultimately generating **angiotensin II** (an″je-o-ten′sin), which stimulates intense vasoconstriction, promoting a rapid rise in systemic blood pressure. It also stimulates release of aldosterone and ADH, which act in long-term regulation of blood pressure by enhancing blood volume.
- **Atrial natriuretic peptide.** The atria of the heart produce the hormone **atrial natriuretic peptide** (**ANP**), which causes blood volume and blood pressure to decline. As noted in Chapter 16, ANP antagonizes aldosterone and prods the kidneys to excrete more sodium and water from the body, causing blood volume to drop. It also causes generalized vasodilation.
- **Antidiuretic hormone.** Produced by the hypothalamus, **antidiuretic hormone** (**ADH**, also called **vasopressin**) stimulates the kidneys to conserve water. It is not usually important in short-term blood pressure regulation, but when blood pressure falls to dangerously low levels (as during severe hemorrhage), much more ADH is released and helps restore arterial pressure by causing intense vasoconstriction.

19

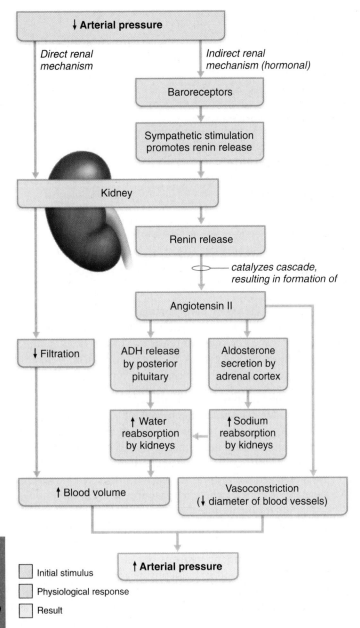

Figure 19.10 Direct and indirect (hormonal) mechanisms for renal control of blood pressure. The sympathetic nervous system acts to increase blood pressure in the long term by triggering renin release, but also acts by other mechanisms in the short term (not shown).

Long-Term Mechanisms: Renal Regulation

The long-term controls of blood pressure, mediated by renal mechanisms, counteract fluctuations in blood pressure not by altering peripheral resistance (as in short-term controls) but rather by altering blood volume.

Although baroreceptors respond to short-term changes in blood pressure, they quickly adapt to prolonged or chronic episodes of high or low pressure. This is where the kidneys step in to restore and maintain blood pressure homeostasis by regulating blood volume. Although blood volume varies with age, body size, and sex, renal mechanisms usually maintain it at close to 5 L.

As we noted earlier, blood volume is a major determinant of cardiac output (via its influence on venous return, EDV, and stroke volume). An increase in blood volume is followed by a rise in blood pressure, and anything that increases blood volume—such as excessive salt intake, which promotes water retention—raises MAP because of the greater fluid load in the vascular tree. By the same token, decreased blood volume translates to a fall in blood pressure. Blood loss and the garden-variety dehydration that occurs during vigorous exercise are common causes of reduced blood volume. A sudden drop in blood pressure often signals internal bleeding and blood volume too low to support normal circulation.

However, these assertions—increased blood volume increases BP and decreased blood volume decreases BP—do not tell the whole story because we are dealing with a dynamic system. Increases in blood volume that cause a rise in blood pressure also stimulate the kidneys to eliminate water, which reduces blood volume and consequently blood pressure. Likewise, falling blood volume triggers renal mechanisms that increase blood volume and blood pressure. As you can see, blood pressure can be stabilized or maintained within normal limits only when blood volume is stable.

The kidneys act both directly and indirectly to regulate arterial pressure and provide the major long-term mechanism of blood pressure control. The *direct renal mechanism* alters blood volume independently of hormones. When either blood volume or blood pressure rises, the rate at which fluid filters from the bloodstream into the kidney tubules is speeded up. In such situations, the kidneys cannot process the filtrate rapidly enough, and more of it leaves the body in urine. As a result, blood volume and blood pressure fall. When blood pressure or blood volume is low, water is conserved and returned to the bloodstream, and blood pressure rises **(Figures 19.10 and 19.11)**. As blood volume goes, so goes the arterial blood pressure.

The *indirect renal mechanism* is the **renin-angiotensin mechanism**. When arterial blood pressure declines, the kidneys release the enzymatic hormone *renin* into the blood. Renin triggers a series of reactions that produce angiotensin II, as mentioned previously. *Angiotensin II* increases blood pressure in three main ways (Figure 19.10). (1) It is a potent vasoconstrictor, increasing blood pressure by increasing peripheral resistance. (2) It stimulates the adrenal cortex to secrete **aldosterone**, a hormone that enhances renal reabsorption of sodium. As sodium moves into the bloodstream, water follows, and as a result, blood volume is conserved. (3) It prods the posterior pituitary to release ADH, which promotes more water reabsorption. As we will see in Chapter 26, angiotensin II also triggers the sensation of thirst, which enhances water consumption, ultimately restoring blood volume and so blood pressure.

Monitoring Circulatory Efficiency

The efficiency of a person's circulation can be assessed by taking pulse and blood pressure measurements. These measurements, along with measurements of respiratory rate and body temperature, are referred to collectively as the body's **vital signs**. Let's examine how vital signs are determined or measured.

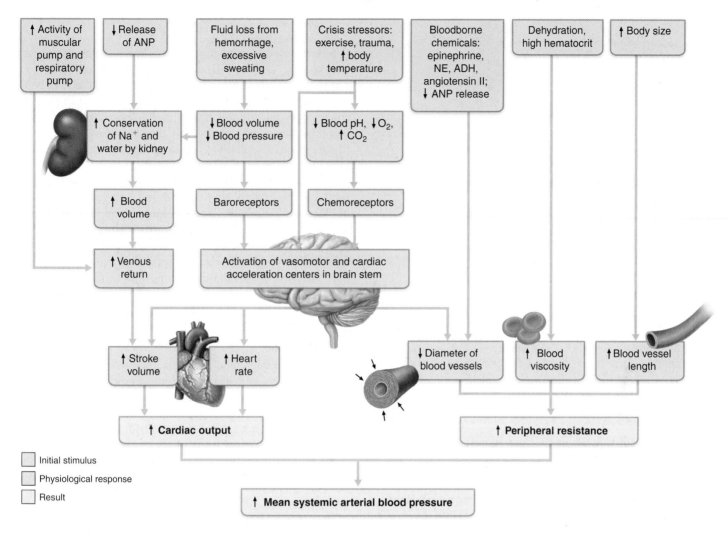

Figure 19.11 Factors causing an increase in MAP.

Taking a Pulse

The alternating expansion and recoil of arteries during each cardiac cycle allow us to feel a pressure wave—a **pulse**—that is transmitted through the arterial tree. You can feel a pulse in any artery that lies close to the body surface by compressing the artery against firm tissue, and this provides an easy way to count heart rate. Because it is so accessible, the point where the radial artery surfaces at the wrist, the *radial pulse*, is routinely used to take a pulse measurement, but there are several other clinically important arterial pulse points **(Figure 19.12)**.

These same points are also called **pressure points** because they are compressed to stop blood flow into distal tissues during hemorrhage. For example, if you seriously lacerate your hand, you can slow or stop the bleeding by compressing the radial or the brachial artery.

Monitoring pulse rate is an easy way to assess the effects of activity, postural changes, and emotions on heart rate. For example, the pulse of a healthy man may be around 66 beats per minute when he is lying down, rise to 70 when he sits up, and rise to 80 when he suddenly stands. During vigorous exercise or emotional upset, pulse rates between 140 and 180 are

not unusual because of sympathetic nervous system effects on the heart.

Measuring Blood Pressure

Most often, systemic arterial blood pressure is measured indirectly in the brachial artery of the arm by the **auscultatory method** (aw-skul′tah-to″re). The *blood pressure cuff*, or *sphygmomanometer* (sfig″mo-mah-nom′ĕ-ter; *sphygmo* = pulse), is wrapped snugly around the arm just superior to the elbow and inflated until the cuff pressure exceeds systolic pressure. At this point, blood flow into the arm is stopped and a brachial pulse cannot be felt or heard. As the cuff pressure is gradually reduced, the examiner listens (auscultates) with a stethoscope for sounds in the brachial artery.

The pressure read when the first soft tapping sounds are heard (the first point at which a small amount of blood is spurting through the constricted artery) is systolic pressure. As the cuff pressure is reduced further, these sounds, called the *sounds of Korotkoff*, become louder and more distinct, but when the artery is no longer constricted and blood flows freely, the sounds

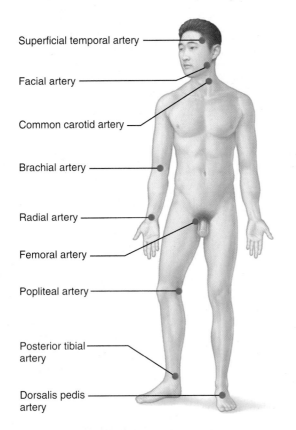

Superficial temporal artery

Facial artery

Common carotid artery

Brachial artery

Radial artery

Femoral artery

Popliteal artery

Posterior tibial artery

Dorsalis pedis artery

Figure 19.12 Body sites where the pulse is most easily palpated. (The specific arteries indicated are discussed on pp. 726–735.)

can no longer be heard. The pressure at which the sounds disappear is the diastolic pressure.

In normal adults at rest, systolic pressure varies between 110 and 140 mm Hg, and diastolic pressure between 70 and 80 mm Hg. Blood pressure also cycles over a 24-hour period, peaking in the morning in response to waxing and waning levels of various hormones (epinephrine, glucocorticoids, and melatonin). These hormones can either bind directly to receptors that control vasoconstriction or increase the number of receptors available.

Extrinsic factors also play a role: Blood pressure varies with age, sex, weight, race, mood, physical activity, posture, and socioeconomic status. What is "normal" for you may not be normal for your grandfather or your neighbor. Nearly all of these variations can be explained in terms of the factors affecting blood pressure discussed earlier.

Alterations in Blood Pressure

Hypotension

Hypotension, or low blood pressure, is a systolic pressure below 100 mm Hg. In many cases, hypotension simply reflects individual variations and is no cause for concern. In fact, low blood pressure is often associated with long life and an old age free of cardiovascular illness.

HOMEOSTATIC IMBALANCE

Elderly people are prone to *orthostatic hypotension*—temporary low blood pressure and dizziness when they rise suddenly from a reclining or sitting position. The aging sympathetic nervous system does not respond as quickly as it once did to postural changes, so blood pools briefly in the lower limbs, reducing blood pressure and consequently blood delivery to the brain. Making postural changes slowly to give the nervous system time to adjust usually prevents this problem.

Chronic hypotension may hint at poor nutrition. Poorly nourished people are often anemic and have inadequate levels of blood proteins, both of which reduce blood viscosity, and so their blood pressure is lower than normal. Chronic hypotension also warns of Addison's disease (inadequate adrenal cortex function), hypothyroidism, or severe tissue wasting. *Acute hypotension* is one of the most important signs of circulatory shock (p. 719) and a threat to patients undergoing surgery and those in intensive care units. ■

Hypertension

Hypertension, high blood pressure, may be transient or persistent. Transient elevations in systolic pressure occur as normal adaptations during fever, physical exertion, and emotional upset. Persistent hypertension is common in obese people for a variety of reasons that are not completely understood. It appears that hormones released from adipocytes both increase sympathetic tone and interfere with the ability of endothelial cells to induce vasodilation.

HOMEOSTATIC IMBALANCE

Chronic hypertension is a common and dangerous disease. An estimated 30% of people over the age of 50 years are hypertensive. Although this "silent killer" is usually asymptomatic for the first 10 to 20 years, it slowly but surely strains the heart and damages the arteries. Prolonged hypertension is the major cause of heart failure, vascular disease, renal failure, and stroke. Because the heart is forced to pump against greater resistance, it must work harder, and in time the myocardium enlarges. When finally strained beyond its capacity to respond, the heart weakens and its walls become flabby. Hypertension also ravages the blood vessels, accelerating the progress of atherosclerosis (see *A Closer Look* on pp. 702–703). As the vessels become increasingly blocked, blood flow to the tissues becomes inadequate and vascular complications appear in the brain, heart, kidneys, and retinas of the eyes.

Although hypertension and atherosclerosis are often linked, it is often difficult to blame hypertension on any distinct anatomical pathology. Hypertension is defined physiologically as a condition of sustained arterial pressure of 140/90 or higher, and the higher the pressure, the greater the risk for serious cardiovascular problems. Until recently, elevated diastolic pressures were considered to be more significant medically, but new studies suggest that systolic pressure is a better predictor of the likelihood of future problems in those older than 50.

19

About 90% of hypertensive people have **primary**, or **essential**, **hypertension**, in which no underlying cause has been identified. This is because primary hypertension is due to a rich interplay between hereditary predispositions and a variety of environmental factors:

1. Heredity. Hypertension runs in families. Children of hypertensive parents are twice as likely to develop hypertension as are children of normotensive parents, and more blacks than whites are hypertensive. Many of the factors listed here require a genetic predisposition, and the course of the disease varies in different population groups.
2. Diet. Dietary factors that contribute to hypertension include high intakes of salt (NaCl), saturated fat, and cholesterol and deficiencies in certain metal ions (K^+, Ca^{2+}, and Mg^{2+}).
3. Obesity.
4. Age. Clinical signs of the disease usually appear after age 40.
5. Diabetes mellitus.
6. Stress. Particularly at risk are "hot reactors," people whose blood pressure zooms upward during every stressful event.
7. Smoking. Nicotine enhances the sympathetic nervous system's vasoconstrictor effects.

Primary hypertension cannot be cured, but most cases can be controlled by restricting salt, fat, and cholesterol intake, losing weight, stopping smoking, managing stress, and taking antihypertensive drugs. Drugs commonly used are diuretics, beta-blockers, calcium channel blockers, angiotensin-converting enzyme (ACE) inhibitors, and angiotensin II receptor blockers. Inhibiting ACE or blocking receptors for angiotensin II suppresses the renin-angiotensin mechanism.

Secondary hypertension, which accounts for 10% of cases, is due to identifiable disorders, such as obstruction of the renal arteries, kidney disease, and endocrine disorders such as hyperthyroidism and Cushing's syndrome. Treatment for secondary hypertension is directed toward correcting the causative problem. ■

CHECK YOUR UNDERSTANDING

9. Describe the baroreceptor-initiated reflex changes that occur to maintain blood pressure when you rise from a lying-down to a standing position.
10. The kidneys play an important role in maintaining MAP by influencing which variable? Explain how renal artery obstruction could cause secondary hypertension.

For answers, see Appendix G.

Blood Flow Through Body Tissues: Tissue Perfusion

▶ Explain how blood flow is regulated in the body in general and in its specific organs.

Blood flow through body tissues, or **tissue perfusion**, is involved in (1) delivery of oxygen and nutrients to, and removal of

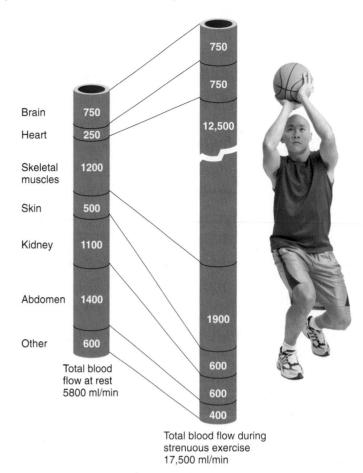

Figure 19.13 Distribution of blood flow at rest and during strenuous exercise.

wastes from, tissue cells, (2) gas exchange in the lungs, (3) absorption of nutrients from the digestive tract, and (4) urine formation in the kidneys. The rate of blood flow to each tissue and organ is almost exactly the right amount to provide for proper function—no more, no less.

When the body is at rest, the brain receives about 13% of total blood flow, the heart 4%, kidneys 20%, and abdominal organs 24%. Skeletal muscles, which make up almost half of body mass, normally receive about 20% of total blood flow. During exercise, however, nearly all of the increased cardiac output flushes into the skeletal muscles and blood flow to the kidneys and digestive organs is reduced **(Figure 19.13)**.

Velocity of Blood Flow

Have you ever watched a swift river emptying into a large lake? The water's speed decreases as it enters the lake until it becomes almost imperceptible. This is because the total cross-sectional area of the lake is much larger than that of the river. Velocity in this case is *inversely* related to cross-sectional area. The same thing happens with blood flow inside our blood vessels.

As shown in **Figure 19.14**, the speed or velocity of blood flow changes as blood travels through the systemic circulation. It is

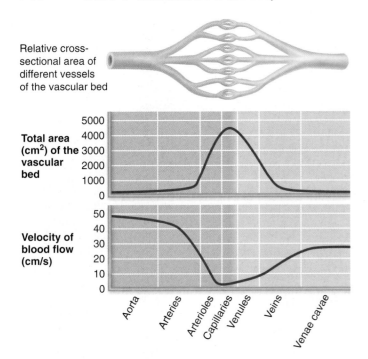

Relative cross-sectional area of different vessels of the vascular bed

Total area (cm²) of the vascular bed

Velocity of blood flow (cm/s)

Aorta — Arteries — Arterioles — Capillaries — Venules — Veins — Venae cavae

Figure 19.14 Relationship between blood flow velocity and total cross-sectional area in various blood vessels of the systemic circulation.

fastest in the aorta and other large arteries (the river), slowest in the capillaries (whose large total cross-sectional area make them analogous to the lake), and then picks up speed again in the veins (the river again).

Just as in our analogy of the river and lake, blood flows fastest where the total cross-sectional area is least. As the arterial system branches, the total cross-sectional area of the vascular bed increases, and the velocity of blood flow declines proportionately. Even though the individual branches have smaller lumens, their *combined* cross-sectional areas and thus the volume of blood they can hold are much greater than that of the aorta. For example, the cross-sectional area of the aorta is 2.5 cm² but that of all the capillaries is 4500 cm². This difference in cross-sectional area results in a fast blood flow in the aorta (40–50 cm/s) and a slow blood flow in the capillaries (about 0.03 cm/s). Slow capillary flow is beneficial because it allows adequate time for exchanges between the blood and tissue cells.

As capillaries combine to form first venules and then veins, total cross-sectional area declines and velocity increases. The cross-sectional area of the venae cavae is 8 cm², and the velocity of blood flow varies from 10 to 30 cm/s in those vessels, depending on the activity of the skeletal muscle pump.

Autoregulation: Local Regulation of Blood Flow

How does each organ or tissue manage to get the blood flow that it needs as our activities change throughout the day? The answer is **autoregulation**, the automatic adjustment of blood flow to each tissue in proportion to the tissue's requirements at any instant. This process is regulated by local conditions and is largely independent of systemic factors. The MAP is the same everywhere in the body and homeostatic mechanisms adjust cardiac output as needed to maintain that constant pressure. Changes in blood flow through individual organs are controlled *intrinsically* by modifying the diameter of local arterioles feeding the capillaries.

You can compare blood flow autoregulation to water use in your home. To get water in a sink, or a garden hose, you have to turn on a faucet. Whether you have several taps open or none, the pressure in the main water pipe in the street remains relatively constant, as it does in the even larger water lines closer to the pumping station. Similarly, what is happening in the arterioles feeding the capillary beds of a given organ has little effect on pressure in the muscular artery feeding the organ, or in the large elastic arteries. The pumping station is, of course, the heart. The beauty of this system is that as long as the water company (circulatory feedback mechanisms) maintains a relatively constant water pressure (MAP), local demand regulates the amount of fluid (blood) delivered to various areas.

In summary, organs regulate their own blood flows by varying the resistance of their arterioles. As we describe next, these intrinsic control mechanisms may be classed as *metabolic* (chemical) or *myogenic* (physical).

Metabolic Controls

In most tissues, declining levels of oxygen and accumulation of other substances released by metabolically active tissues serve as autoregulation stimuli. These substances include H^+ (from CO_2 and lactic acid), K^+, adenosine, and prostaglandins. The relative importance of these factors is not clear. Many of them act directly to relax vascular smooth muscle, but some may act by causing the release of nitric oxide from vascular endothelial cells.

Nitric oxide (NO) is a powerful vasodilator which acts via a cyclic GMP second-messenger system. NO is quickly destroyed and its potent vasodilator effects are very brief. However, some researchers believe that NO can be transported over longer distances by being bound to chemical buffers in the blood and that it is released where vasodilation is needed. Until recently the sympathetic nervous system was thought to rule blood vessel diameter, but we now know that its primary vascular role is to produce vasoconstriction, and that NO plays the major role in causing vasodilation. The endothelium also releases potent vasoconstrictors, including the family of peptides called **endothelins**, which are among the most potent vasoconstrictors known.

The net result of metabolically controlled autoregulation is immediate vasodilation of the arterioles serving the capillary beds of the "needy" tissues and dilation of their precapillary sphincters. This creates a temporary increase in blood flow to the area, allowing blood to surge through the true capillaries and become available to the tissue cells. Inflammatory chemicals (such as histamine, kinins, and prostaglandins) released in injury, infection, or allergic reactions also cause vasodilation.

Intrinsic mechanisms (autoregulation)
- Distribute blood flow to individual organs and tissues as needed

Extrinsic mechanisms
- Maintain mean arterial pressure (MAP)
- Redistribute blood during exercise and thermoregulation

Metabolic controls

↓ *Amounts of:*
pH
O_2

↑ *Amounts of:*
CO_2
K^+
Prostaglandins
Adenosine
Nitric oxide
Endothelins

Myogenic controls
Stretch

Sympathetic — Nerves

α Receptors
β Receptors
Epinephrine, norepinephrine

Angiotensin II — Hormones

Antidiuretic hormone (ADH)

Atrial natriuretic peptide (ANP)

Dilates
Constricts

Figure 19.15 Summary of intrinsic and extrinsic control of arteriolar smooth muscle in the systemic circulation. α-Adrenergic receptors (smooth muscle contraction, arteriolar constriction) are located in arterioles supplying most tissues, whereas β-adrenergic receptors (smooth muscle relaxation, arteriolar dilation) are located primarily in arterioles supplying skeletal and heart muscle.

Inflammatory vasodilation helps the defense mechanisms clear microorganisms and toxins, and promotes healing.

Myogenic Controls

Fluctuations in systemic blood pressure would cause problems for individual organs were it not for the **myogenic responses** (*myo* = muscle; *gen* = origin) of vascular smooth muscle. Inadequate blood perfusion through an organ is quickly followed by a decline in the organ's metabolic rate and, if prolonged, organ death. Likewise, excessively high arterial pressure and tissue perfusion can be dangerous because the combination may rupture more fragile blood vessels.

Fortunately, vascular smooth muscle prevents these problems by responding directly to passive stretch (caused by increased intravascular pressure) with increased tone, which resists the stretch and causes vasoconstriction. Reduced stretch promotes vasodilation and increases blood flow into the tissue. These myogenic responses keep tissue perfusion fairly constant despite most variations in systemic pressure.

Generally, both metabolic and myogenic factors determine the final autoregulatory response of a tissue. For example, **reactive hyperemia** (hi″per-e′me-ah) refers to the dramatically increased blood flow into a tissue that occurs after the blood supply to the area has been temporarily blocked. It results both from the myogenic response and from an accumulation of metabolic wastes in the area during occlusion. The various intrinsic (local) and extrinsic controls of arteriolar diameter are summarized in Figure 19.15, with colored arrows indicating their effects—green for dilation and red for constriction.

Long-Term Autoregulation

If the nutrient requirements of a tissue are greater than the short-term autoregulatory mechanism can easily supply, a long-term autoregulatory mechanism may develop over a period of weeks or months to enrich the local blood flow still more. The number of blood vessels in the region increases, and existing vessels enlarge. This phenomenon, called *angiogenesis*, is particularly common in the heart when a coronary vessel is partially occluded. It occurs throughout the body in people who live in high-altitude areas, where the air contains less oxygen.

Blood Flow in Special Areas

Each organ has special requirements and functions that are revealed in its pattern of autoregulation. Autoregulation in the brain, heart, and kidneys is extraordinarily efficient. In those organs, adequate perfusion is maintained even when MAP is fluctuating.

19

Skeletal Muscles

Blood flow in skeletal muscle varies with fiber type and muscle activity. Generally speaking, capillary density and blood flow are greater in red (slow oxidative) fibers than in white (fast glycolytic) fibers. Resting skeletal muscles receive about 1 L of blood per minute, and only about 25% of their capillaries are open. During such periods, myogenic and general neural mechanisms predominate. When muscles become active, blood flow increases (*hyperemia*) in direct proportion to their greater *metabolic* activity, a phenomenon called **active** or **exercise hyperemia**.

This form of autoregulation occurs almost entirely in response to the decreased oxygen concentration and accumulation of metabolic factors that result from the "revved-up" metabolism of working muscles. However, systemic adjustments mediated by the vasomotor center must also occur to ensure that blood delivery to the muscles is both faster and more abundant. During exercise, sympathetic nervous system activity increases. Norepinephrine released from sympathetic nerve endings causes vasoconstriction of the vessels of blood reservoirs such as those of the digestive viscera and skin, diverting blood away from these regions temporarily and ensuring that more blood reaches the muscles. In skeletal muscles, the sympathetic nervous system and local metabolic controls have opposing effects on arteriolar diameter. During exercise, local controls override sympathetic vasoconstriction. Consequently, blood flow to skeletal muscles can increase tenfold or more during physical activity, as you saw in Figure 19.13, and virtually all capillaries in the active muscles open to accommodate the increased flow.

Epinephrine acting at beta (β) adrenergic receptors and acetylcholine acting at cholinergic receptors were once thought to contribute to arteriolar dilation during exercise. However, these appear to have little physiological importance in the control of human skeletal muscle blood flow. Without question, strenuous exercise is one of the most demanding conditions the cardiovascular system faces. Ultimately, the major factor determining how long muscles can continue to contract vigorously is the ability of the cardiovascular system to deliver adequate oxygen and nutrients and remove waste products.

The Brain

Blood flow to the brain averages 750 ml/min and is maintained at a relatively constant level. Constant cerebral blood flow is necessary because neurons are totally intolerant of ischemia.

Although the brain is the most metabolically active organ in the body, it is the least able to store essential nutrients. Cerebral blood flow is regulated by one of the body's most precise autoregulatory systems and is tailored to local neuronal need. For example, when you make a fist with your right hand, the neurons in the left cerebral motor cortex controlling that movement receive a more abundant blood supply than the adjoining neurons. Brain tissue is exceptionally sensitive to declining pH, and increased blood carbon dioxide levels (resulting in acidic conditions in brain tissue) cause marked vasodilation. Oxygen deficit is a much less potent stimulus for autoregulation. How-

ever, very high carbon dioxide levels abolish autoregulatory mechanisms and severely depress brain activity.

Besides metabolic controls, the brain also has a myogenic mechanism that protects it from possibly damaging changes in blood pressure. When MAP declines, cerebral vessels dilate to ensure adequate brain perfusion. When MAP rises, cerebral vessels constrict, protecting the small, more fragile vessels farther along the pathway from rupture due to excessive pressure. Under certain circumstances, such as brain ischemia caused by rising intracranial pressure (as with a brain tumor), the brain (via the medullary cardiovascular centers) regulates its own blood flow by triggering a rise in systemic blood pressure. However, when systemic pressure changes are extreme, the brain becomes vulnerable. Fainting, or *syncope* (sin'cuh-pe; "cutting short"), occurs when MAP falls below 60 mm Hg. Cerebral edema is the usual result of pressures over 160 mm Hg, which dramatically increase brain capillary permeability.

The Skin

Blood flow through the skin (1) supplies nutrients to the cells, (2) aids in body temperature regulation, and (3) provides a blood reservoir. The first function is served by autoregulation in response to the need for oxygen, but the second and third require neural intervention. The primary function of the cutaneous circulation is to help maintain body temperature, so we will concentrate on the skin's temperature regulation function here.

Below the skin surface are extensive venous plexuses. The blood flow through these plexuses can change from 50 ml/min to as much as 2500 ml/min, depending on body temperature. This capability reflects neural adjustments of blood flow through arterioles and through unique coiled arteriovenous anastomoses. These tiny A-V shunts are located mainly in the fingertips, palms of the hands, toes, soles of the feet, ears, nose, and lips. They are richly supplied with sympathetic nerve endings (a characteristic that sets them apart from the shunts of most other capillary beds), and are controlled by reflexes initiated by temperature receptors or signals from higher CNS centers. The arterioles, in addition, are responsive to metabolic autoregulatory stimuli.

When the skin surface is exposed to heat, or body temperature rises for other reasons (such as vigorous exercise), the hypothalamic "thermostat" signals for reduced vasomotor stimulation of the skin vessels. As a result, warm blood flushes into the capillary beds and heat radiates from the skin surface. Vasodilation of the arterioles is enhanced even more when we sweat, because an enzyme in perspiration acts on a protein present in tissue fluid to produce *bradykinin*, which stimulates the vessel's endothelial cells to release the potent vasodilator NO.

When the ambient temperature is cold and body temperature drops, superficial skin vessels are strongly constricted. Hence, blood almost entirely bypasses the capillaries associated with the arteriovenous anastomoses, diverting the warm blood to the deeper, more vital organs. Paradoxically, the skin may stay quite rosy because some blood gets "trapped" in the superficial capillary loops as the shunts swing into operation. The trapped blood remains red because the chilled skin cells take up less O_2.

The Lungs

Blood flow through the pulmonary circuit to and from the lungs is unusual in many ways. The pathway is relatively short, and pulmonary arteries and arterioles are structurally like veins and venules. That is, they have thin walls and large lumens. Because resistance to blood flow is low in the pulmonary arterial system, less pressure is needed to propel blood through those vessels. Consequently, arterial pressure in the pulmonary circulation is much lower than in the systemic circulation (24/8 versus 120/80 mm Hg).

Another unusual feature of the pulmonary circulation is that the autoregulatory mechanism is the *opposite* of what is seen in most tissues: Low pulmonary oxygen levels cause local vasoconstriction, and high levels promote vasodilation. While this may seem odd, it is perfectly consistent with the gas exchange role of this circulation. When the air sacs of the lungs are flooded with oxygen-rich air, the pulmonary capillaries become flushed with blood and ready to receive the oxygen load. If the air sacs are collapsed or blocked with mucus, the oxygen content in those areas is low, and blood largely bypasses those nonfunctional areas.

The Heart

Movement of blood through the smaller vessels of the coronary circulation is influenced by aortic pressure and by the pumping activity of the ventricles. When the ventricles contract and compress the coronary vessels, blood flow through the myocardium stops. As the heart relaxes, the high aortic pressure forces blood through the coronary circulation. Under normal circumstances, the myoglobin in cardiac cells stores sufficient oxygen to satisfy the cells' oxygen needs during systole. However, an abnormally rapid heartbeat seriously reduces the ability of the myocardium to receive adequate oxygen and nutrients during diastole.

Under resting conditions, blood flow through the heart is about 250 ml/min and is probably controlled by a myogenic mechanism. Consequently, blood flow remains fairly constant despite wide variations (50 to 140 mm Hg) in coronary perfusion pressure. During strenuous exercise, the coronary vessels dilate in response to local accumulation of vasodilators (particularly adenosine), and blood flow may increase three to four times (see Figure 19.13). Additionally, any event that decreases the oxygen content of the blood releases vasodilators that adjust the O_2 supply to the O_2 demand.

This enhanced blood flow during increased heart activity is important because under resting conditions, cardiac cells use as much as 65% of the oxygen carried to them in blood. (Most other tissue cells use about 25% of the delivered oxygen.) Consequently, increasing the blood flow is the only way to make sufficient additional oxygen available to a more vigorously working heart.

11. Suppose you are in a bicycle race. What happens to the smooth muscle in the arterioles supplying your leg muscles? What is the key mechanism in this case?

12. If many arterioles in your body dilated at once, you would expect MAP to plummet. What prevents MAP from decreasing during your bicycle race?

For answers, see Appendix G.

Blood Flow Through Capillaries and Capillary Dynamics

▶ Outline factors involved in capillary dynamics, and explain the significance of each.

Blood flow through capillary networks is slow and intermittent. This phenomenon, called **vasomotion**, reflects the on/off opening and closing of precapillary sphincters in response to local autoregulatory controls.

Capillary Exchange of Respiratory Gases and Nutrients

Oxygen, carbon dioxide, most nutrients, and metabolic wastes pass between the blood and interstitial fluid by diffusion. Recall that in **diffusion**, movement always occurs along a concentration gradient—each substance moving from an area of its higher concentration to an area of its lower concentration. Hence, oxygen and nutrients pass from the blood, where their concentration is fairly high, through the interstitial fluid to the tissue cells. Carbon dioxide and metabolic wastes leave the cells, where their content is higher, and diffuse into the capillary blood.

There are four different routes across capillaries for different types of molecules, as **Figure 19.16** shows. ① Lipid-soluble molecules, such as respiratory gases, diffuse through the lipid bilayer of the endothelial cell plasma membranes. Small water-soluble solutes, such as amino acids and sugars, pass through ② fluid-filled intercellular capillary clefts or ③ fenestrations. ④ Some larger molecules, such as proteins, are actively transported in pinocytotic vesicles or caveolae. As we mentioned earlier, capillaries differ in their "leakiness," or permeability. Liver capillaries, for instance, have large fenestrations that allow even proteins to pass freely, whereas brain capillaries are impermeable to most substances.

Fluid Movements: Bulk Flow

While nutrient and gas exchanges are occurring across the capillary walls by diffusion, bulk fluid flows are also going on. Fluid is forced out of the capillaries through the clefts at the arterial end of the bed, but most of it returns to the bloodstream at the venous end. Though relatively unimportant to capillary exchange, bulk flow is extremely important in determining the relative fluid volumes in the bloodstream and the interstitial space. (Approximately 20 L of fluid are filtered out of the capillaries each day before being returned to the blood—almost seven times the total plasma volume!) As we describe next, the

Figure 19.16 Capillary transport mechanisms. The four possible pathways or routes of transport across the endothelial cell wall of a fenestrated capillary.

direction and amount of fluid that flows across the capillary walls reflect the balance between two dynamic and opposing forces—hydrostatic and colloid osmotic pressures.

Hydrostatic Pressures   **Hydrostatic pressure** is the force exerted by a fluid pressing against a wall. In capillaries, hydrostatic pressure is the same as *capillary blood pressure*—the pressure exerted by blood on the capillary walls. **Capillary hydrostatic pressure (HP$_c$)** tends to force fluids through the capillary walls (a process called *filtration*), leaving behind cells and most proteins. Blood pressure drops as blood flows along the length of a capillary bed, so HP$_c$ is higher at the arterial end of the bed (35 mm Hg) than at the venous end (17 mm Hg).

In theory, blood pressure—which forces fluid out of the capillaries—is opposed by the **interstitial fluid hydrostatic pressure (HP$_{if}$)** acting outside the capillaries and pushing fluid in. For this reason, the *net* hydrostatic pressure acting on the capillaries at any point is the difference between HP$_c$ and HP$_{if}$. However, there is usually very little fluid in the interstitial space, because the lymphatic vessels constantly withdraw it. HP$_{if}$ may vary from slightly negative to slightly positive, but traditionally it is assumed to be zero. For simplicity, that is the value we use here.

The *net effective hydrostatic pressures* at the arterial and venous ends of the capillary bed are essentially equal to HP$_c$ (in other words, to blood pressure) at those locations. This information is summarized in **Figure 19.17**.

Colloid Osmotic Pressures   **Colloid osmotic pressure**, the force opposing hydrostatic pressure, is created by the presence in a fluid of large nondiffusible molecules, such as plasma proteins, that are unable to cross the capillary wall. Such molecules draw water toward themselves. In other words, they encourage osmosis because the water concentration in their vicinity is lower than it is on the opposite side of the capillary wall. A quick and dirty way to remember this is "hydrostatic pressure pushes and osmotic pressure sucks."

The abundant plasma proteins in capillary blood (primarily albumin molecules) develop a **capillary colloid osmotic pressure (OP$_c$)**, also called *oncotic pressure*, of approximately 26 mm Hg. Interstitial fluid contains few proteins, so its colloid osmotic pressure (**OP$_{if}$**) is substantially lower—from 0.1 to 5 mm Hg. We use a value of 1 mm Hg for the OP$_{if}$ in Figure 19.17.

Unlike HP, OP does not vary significantly from one end of the capillary bed to the other. In our example, the *net osmotic pressure* that pulls fluid back into the capillary blood is OP$_c$ − OP$_{if}$ = 26 mm Hg − 1 mm Hg = 25 mm Hg.

Hydrostatic-Osmotic Pressure Interactions   To determine whether there is a net gain or net loss of fluid from the blood, we have to calculate the **net filtration pressure (NFP)**, which considers all the forces acting at the capillary bed. At any point along a capillary, fluids will leave the capillary if net HP is greater than net OP, and fluids will enter the capillary if net OP exceeds net HP. As shown in Figure 19.17, hydrostatic forces dominate at the arterial end (all values are in mm Hg):

$$NFP = (HP_c - HP_{if}) - (OP_c - OP_{if})$$
$$= (35 - 0) - (26 - 1)$$
$$= (35 - 25) = 10 \text{ mm Hg}$$

As you can see in this example, a pressure of 10 mm Hg (net excess of HP) is forcing fluid out of the capillary. At the other, venous end, osmotic forces dominate:

$$NFP = (17 - 0) - (26 - 1)$$
$$= 17 - 25 = -8 \text{ mm Hg}$$

The negative pressure value we see here indicates that the NFP (due to net excess of OP) is driving fluid *into* the capillary bed (a process called *reabsorption*). As a result, net fluid flow is *out of* the circulation at the arterial ends of capillary beds and *into* the circulation at the venous ends.

19

Figure 19.17 Fluid flows at capillaries.

However, more fluid enters the tissue spaces than is returned to the blood, resulting in a net loss of fluid from the circulation of about 1.5 ml/min. This fluid and any leaked proteins are picked up by the lymphatic vessels and returned to the vascular system, which accounts for the relatively low levels of both fluid and proteins in the interstitial space. Were this not so, this "insignificant" fluid loss would empty your blood vessels of plasma in about 24 hours!

CHECK YOUR UNDERSTANDING

13. Suppose that the OP of the interstitial fluid (OP_{if}) rose dramatically—say because of a severe bacterial infection in the surrounding tissue. (a) Predict how fluid flow would change in this situation. (b) Now calculate the NFP at the venous end of the capillary in Figure 19.17 if OP_{if} increased to 10 mm Hg. (c) In which direction does fluid flow at the venous end of the capillary now—in or out?

For answers, see Appendix G.

Circulatory Shock

▶ Define circulatory shock. List several possible causes.

Circulatory shock is any condition in which blood vessels are inadequately filled and blood cannot circulate normally. This results in inadequate blood flow to meet tissue needs. If the condition persists, cells die and organ damage follows.

The most common form of shock is **hypovolemic shock** (hi″po-vo-le′mik; *hypo* = low, deficient; *volemia* = blood volume), which results from large-scale loss of blood, as might follow acute hemorrhage, severe vomiting or diarrhea, or extensive burns. If blood volume drops rapidly, heart rate increases in an attempt to correct the problem. Thus, a weak, "thready" pulse is often the first sign of hypovolemic shock. Intense vasoconstriction also occurs, which shifts blood from the various blood reservoirs into the major circulatory channels and enhances venous return. Blood pressure is stable at first, but eventually drops if blood loss continues. A sharp drop in blood pressure is a serious, and late, sign of hypovolemic shock. The key to managing hypovolemic shock is to replace fluid volume as quickly as possible.

Although you have not yet explored all of the body systems that respond to hypovolemic shock, acute bleeding is such a threat to life that it seems important to have a comprehensive flowchart of its recognizable signs and symptoms and an accounting of the body's attempt to restore homeostasis. **Figure 19.18** provides such a resource. Study it in part now, and in more detail later once you have studied the remaining body systems.

In **vascular shock**, blood volume is normal, but circulation is poor as a result of an abnormal expansion of the vascular bed caused by extreme vasodilation. The huge drop in peripheral resistance that follows is revealed by rapidly falling blood pressure. A common cause of vascular shock is loss of vasomotor tone due to anaphylaxis (anaphylactic shock), a systemic allergic reaction in which bodywide vasodilation is triggered by the

19

Figure 19.18 Events and signs of compensated (nonprogressive) hypovolemic shock.

massive release of histamine. Two other common causes are failure of autonomic nervous system regulation (also referred to as *neurogenic shock*), and septicemia (*septic shock*), a severe systemic bacterial infection (bacterial toxins are notorious vasodilators).

Transient vascular shock may occur when you sunbathe for a prolonged time. The heat of the sun on your skin causes cutaneous blood vessels to dilate. Then, if you stand up abruptly, blood pools briefly (because of gravity) in the dilated vessels of

your lower limbs rather than returning promptly to the heart. Consequently, your blood pressure falls. The dizziness you feel at this point is a signal that your brain is not receiving enough oxygen.

Cardiogenic shock, or pump failure, occurs when the heart is so inefficient that it cannot sustain adequate circulation. Its usual cause is myocardial damage, as might follow numerous myocardial infarcts.

14. Your neighbor, Bob, calls you because he thinks he is having an allergic reaction to a medication. You find Bob on the verge of losing consciousness and having trouble breathing. When paramedics arrive, they note his blood pressure is 63/38 and he has a rapid, thready pulse. Explain Bob's low blood pressure and his rapid heart rate.

For answers, see Appendix G.

PART **3**

CIRCULATORY PATHWAYS: BLOOD VESSELS OF THE BODY

The Two Main Circulations of the Body

▶ Trace the pathway of blood through the pulmonary circuit, and state the importance of this special circulation.

▶ Describe the general functions of the systemic circuit.

When referring to the body's complex network of blood vessels, the term **vascular system** is often used. However, the heart is actually a double pump that serves two distinct circulations, each with its own set of arteries, capillaries, and veins. The *pulmonary circulation* is the short loop that runs from the heart to the lungs and back to the heart. The *systemic circulation* routes blood through a long loop to all parts of the body before returning it to the heart. Both circuits are shown schematically in **Table 19.3** on pp. 722–723.

Systemic Arteries and Veins: Differences in Pathways and Courses

As we saw in Chapter 18, the heart pumps all of its blood into a single systemic artery—the aorta. In contrast, blood returning to the heart is delivered largely by two terminal systemic veins, the superior and inferior venae cavae. The single exception to this is the blood draining from the myocardium of the heart, which is collected by the cardiac veins and reenters the right atrium via the coronary sinus.

In addition to these differences between arteries and veins connecting to the heart, there are three important differences between systemic arteries and veins:

1. **Arteries run deep while veins are both deep and superficial.** Deep veins parallel the course of the systemic arteries and both are protected by body tissues along most of their course. With a few exceptions, the naming of these veins is identical to that of their companion arteries. Superficial veins run just beneath the skin and are readily seen, especially in the limbs, face, and neck. Because there are no superficial arteries, the names of the superficial veins do not correspond to the names of any of the arteries.
2. **Venous pathways are more interconnected.** Unlike the fairly distinct arterial pathways, venous pathways tend to have numerous interconnections, and many veins are represented by not one but two similarly named vessels. As a result, venous pathways are more difficult to follow.
3. **The brain and digestive systems have unique venous drainage systems.** Most body regions have a similar pattern for their arterial supply and venous drainage. However, the venous drainage pattern in at least two important body areas is unique. First, venous blood draining from the brain enters large *dural venous sinuses* rather than typical veins. Second, blood draining from the digestive organs enters a special subcirculation, the *hepatic portal system*, and perfuses through the liver before it reenters the general systemic circulation (see Table 19.12).

Principal Vessels of the Systemic Circulation

▶ Name and give the location of the major arteries and veins in the systemic circulation.

▶ Describe the structure and special function of the hepatic portal system.

Except for special vessels and shunts of the fetal circulation (described in Chapter 28), the principal arteries and veins of the systemic circulation are described in **Tables 19.4** through **19.13**.

Notice that by convention, oxygen-rich blood is shown red, while blood that is relatively oxygen-poor is depicted blue, regardless of vessel types. A unique convention used in the schematic flowcharts (pipe diagrams) that accompany each table is that the vessels that would be closer to the viewer are shown in brighter, more intense colors than those deeper or farther from the viewer—for example, for veins, the darker blue vessels would be closer to the viewer in the body region shown.

19

TABLE 19.3 Pulmonary and Systemic Circulations

Pulmonary Circulation

The pulmonary circulation (Figure 19.19a) functions only to bring blood into close contact with the alveoli (air sacs) of the lungs so that gases can be exchanged. It does not directly serve the metabolic needs of body tissues.

Oxygen-poor, dark red blood enters the pulmonary circulation as it is pumped from the right ventricle into the large **pulmonary trunk** (Figure 19.19b), which runs diagonally upward for about 8 cm and then divides abruptly to form the **right** and **left pulmonary arteries**. In the lungs, the pulmonary arteries subdivide into the **lobar arteries** (lo′bar) (three in the right lung and two in the left lung), each of which serves one lung lobe. The lobar arteries accompany the main bronchi into the lungs and then branch profusely, forming first arterioles and then the dense networks of **pulmonary capillaries** that surround and cling to the delicate air sacs. It is here that oxygen moves from the alveolar air to the blood and carbon dioxide moves from the blood to the alveolar air. As gases are exchanged and the oxygen content of the blood rises, the blood becomes bright red. The pulmonary capillary beds drain into venules, which join to form the two **pulmonary veins** exiting from each lung. The four pulmonary veins complete the circuit by unloading their precious cargo into the left atrium of the heart. Note that any vessel with the term *pulmonary* or *lobar* in its name is part of the pulmonary circulation. All others are part of the systemic circulation.

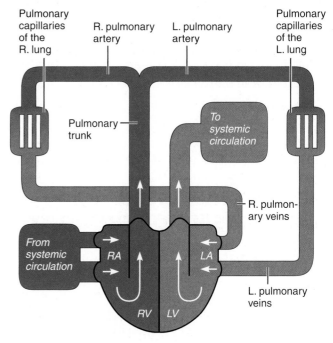

(a) Schematic flowchart.

Figure 19.19 **Pulmonary circulation.**

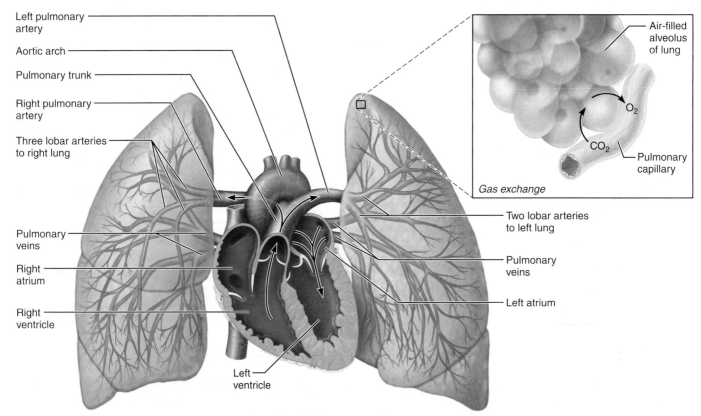

(b) Illustration. The pulmonary arterial system is shown in blue to indicate that the blood carried is oxygen-poor. The pulmonary venous drainage is shown in red to indicate that the blood transported is oxygen-rich.

19

TABLE 19.3   *(continued)*

Pulmonary arteries carry oxygen-poor, carbon dioxide–rich blood, and pulmonary veins carry oxygen-rich blood.* This is opposite the situation in the systemic circulation, where arteries carry oxygen-rich blood and veins carry carbon dioxide–rich, relatively oxygen-poor blood.

Systemic Circulation

The systemic circulation provides the *functional blood supply* to all body tissues; that is, it delivers oxygen, nutrients, and other needed substances while carrying away carbon dioxide and other metabolic wastes. Freshly oxygenated blood* returning from the pulmonary circuit is pumped out of the left ventricle into the aorta (**Figure 19.20**). From the aorta, blood can take various routes, because essentially all systemic arteries branch from this single great vessel. The aorta arches upward from the heart and then curves and runs downward along the body midline to its terminus in the pelvis, where it splits to form the two large arteries serving the lower extremities. The branches of the aorta continue to subdivide to produce the arterioles and, finally, the capillaries that ramify through the organs. Venous blood draining from organs inferior to the diaphragm ultimately enters the inferior vena cava.[†] Except for some coronary and thoracic venous drainage (which enters the azygos system of veins), body regions above the diaphragm are drained by the superior vena cava. The venae cavae empty the carbon dioxide–laden blood into the right atrium of the heart.

Two points concerning the two major circulations must be emphasized: (1) Blood passes from systemic veins to systemic arteries only after first moving through the pulmonary circuit (Figure 19.19a), and (2) although the entire cardiac output of the right ventricle passes through the pulmonary circulation, only a small fraction of the output of the left ventricle flows through any single organ (Figure 19.20). The systemic circulation can be viewed as multiple circulatory channels functioning in parallel to distribute blood to all body organs.

As you examine the tables that follow and locate the various systemic arteries and veins in the illustrations, be aware of cues that make your memorization task easier. In many cases, the name of a vessel reflects the body region traversed (axillary, brachial, femoral, etc.), the organ served (renal, hepatic, gonadal), or the bone followed (vertebral, radial, tibial). Also, notice that arteries and veins tend to run side by side and, in many places, they also run with nerves. Finally, be alert to the fact that the systemic vessels do not always match on the right and left sides of the body. Thus, while almost all vessels in the head and limbs are bilaterally symmetrical, some of the large, deep vessels of the trunk region are asymmetrical or unpaired.

*By convention, oxygen-rich blood is shown *red* and oxygen-poor blood is shown *blue*.
[†]Venous blood from the digestive viscera passes through the hepatic portal circulation (liver and associated veins) before entering the inferior vena cava.

Figure 19.20 Schematic flowchart showing an overview of the systemic circulation. The pulmonary circulation is shown in gray for comparison.

The distribution of the aorta and major arteries of the systemic circulation is diagrammed in flowchart form in **Figure 19.21a** and illustrated in Figure 19.21b. Fine points about the various vessels arising from the aorta are provided in Tables 19.5 through 19.8.

The **aorta** is the largest artery in the body. In adults, the aorta (a-or′ tah) is approximately the size of a garden hose where it issues from the left ventricle of the heart. Its internal diameter is 2.5 cm, and its wall is about 2 mm thick. It decreases in size slightly as it runs to its terminus. The aortic valve guards the base of the aorta and prevents backflow of blood during diastole. Opposite each aortic valve cusp is an *aortic sinus*, which contains baroreceptors important in reflex regulation of blood pressure.

Different portions of the aorta are named according to shape or location. The first portion, the **ascending aorta**, runs posteriorly and to the right of the pulmonary trunk. It persists for only about 5 cm before curving to the left as the aortic arch. The only branches of the ascending aorta are the **right** and **left coro-**nary arteries, which supply the myocardium. The **aortic arch**, deep to the sternum, begins and ends at the sternal angle (T₄ level). Its three major branches (R to L) are: (1) the **brachiocephalic trunk** (bra′ke-o-sĕ-fal″ik; "armhead"), which passes superiorly under the right sternoclavicular joint and branches into the **right common carotid artery** (kah-rot′id) and the **right subclavian artery**, (2) the **left common carotid artery**, and (3) the **left subclavian artery**. These three vessels provide the arterial supply of the head, neck, upper limbs, and part of the thorax wall. The **thoracic**, or **descending**, **aorta** runs along the anterior spine from T₅ to T₁₂, sending off numerous small arteries to the thorax wall and viscera before piercing the diaphragm. As it enters the abdominal cavity, it becomes the **abdominal aorta**. This portion supplies the abdominal walls and viscera and ends at the L₄ level, where it splits into the **right** and **left common iliac arteries**, which supply the pelvis and lower limbs.

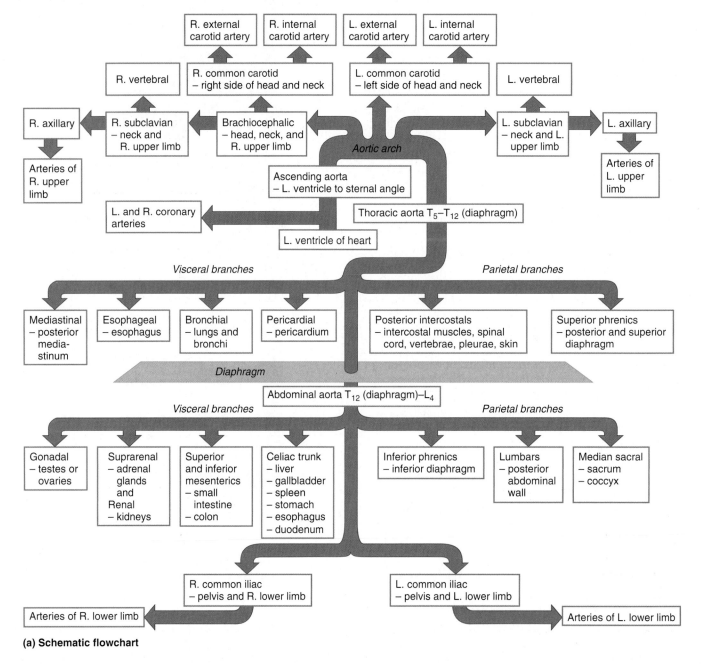

(a) Schematic flowchart

TABLE 19.4   *(continued)*

Arteries of the head and trunk
- Internal carotid artery
- External carotid artery
- Common carotid arteries
- Vertebral artery
- Subclavian artery
- Brachiocephalic trunk
- Aortic arch
- Ascending aorta
- Coronary artery

- Celiac trunk
- Abdominal aorta
- Superior mesenteric artery
- Renal artery
- Gonadal artery
- Inferior mesenteric artery
- Common iliac artery
- Internal iliac artery

Arteries that supply the upper limb
- Subclavian artery
- Axillary artery
- Brachial artery
- Radial artery
- Ulnar artery
- Deep palmar arch
- Superficial palmar arch
- Digital arteries

Arteries that supply the lower limb
- External iliac artery
- Femoral artery
- Popliteal artery
- Anterior tibial artery
- Posterior tibial artery
- Arcuate artery

Figure 19.21 **Major arteries of the systemic circulation.**

(b) Illustration, anterior view

19

TABLE 19.5	Arteries of the Head and Neck

Four paired arteries supply the head and neck. These are the common carotid arteries, plus three branches from each subclavian artery: the vertebral arteries, the thyrocervical trunks, and the costocervical trunks (Figure 19.22b). Of these, the common carotid arteries have the broadest distribution (Figure 19.22a).

Each common carotid divides into two major branches (the internal and external carotid arteries). At the division point, each internal carotid artery has a slight dilation, the **carotid sinus**, that contains baroreceptors that assist in reflex blood pressure control. The **carotid bodies**, chemoreceptors involved in the control of respiratory rate, are located close by. Pressing on the neck in the area of the carotid sinuses can cause unconsciousness (*carot* = stupor) because the pressure created mimics high blood pressure, eliciting vasodilation, which interferes with blood delivery to the brain.

Description and Distribution

Common carotid arteries.   The origins of these two arteries differ: The right common carotid artery arises from the brachiocephalic trunk; the left is the second branch of the aortic arch. The common carotid arteries ascend through the lateral neck, and at the superior border of the larynx (the level of the "Adam's apple"), each divides into its two major branches, the *external* and *internal carotid arteries*.

The **external carotid arteries** supply most tissues of the head except for the brain and orbit. As each artery runs superiorly, it sends branches to the thyroid gland and larynx (**superior thyroid artery**), the tongue (**lingual artery**), the skin and muscles of the anterior face (**facial artery**), and the posterior scalp (**occipital artery**). Each external carotid artery terminates by splitting into a **superficial temporal artery**, which supplies the parotid salivary gland and most of the scalp, and a **maxillary artery**, which supplies the upper and lower jaws and chewing muscles, the teeth, and the nasal cavity. A clinically important branch of the maxillary artery is the *middle meningeal artery* (not illustrated). It enters the skull through the foramen spinosum and supplies the inner surface of the parietal bone, squamous region of the temporal bone, and the underlying dura mater.

The larger **internal carotid arteries** supply the orbits and more than 80% of the cerebrum. They assume a deep course and enter the skull through the carotid canals of the temporal bones. Once inside the cranium, each artery gives off one main branch, the ophthalmic artery, and then divides into the anterior and middle cerebral arteries. The **ophthalmic arteries** (of-thal'mik) supply the eyes, orbits, forehead, and nose. Each **anterior cerebral artery** supplies the medial surface of the frontal and parietal lobes of the cerebral hemisphere on its side and also anastomoses with its partner on the opposite side via a short arterial shunt called the **anterior communicating artery** (Figure 19.22d). The **middle cerebral arteries** run in the lateral sulci of their respective cerebral hemispheres and supply the lateral parts of the temporal, parietal, and frontal lobes.

Vertebral arteries.   These vessels spring from the subclavian arteries at the root of the neck and ascend through foramina in the transverse processes of the cervical vertebrae to enter the skull through the foramen magnum. En route, they send branches to the vertebrae and cervical spinal cord and to some deep structures of the neck. Within the cranium, the right and left vertebral arteries join to form the **basilar artery** (bas'ĭ-lar), which ascends along the anterior aspect of the brain stem, giving off branches to the cerebellum, pons, and inner ear (Figure 19.22b and d). At the pons-midbrain border, the basilar artery divides into a pair of **posterior cerebral arteries**, which supply the occipital lobes and the inferior parts of the temporal lobes.

(a) Schematic flowchart

TABLE 19.5 (continued)

Arterial shunts called **posterior communicating arteries** connect the posterior cerebral arteries to the middle cerebral arteries anteriorly. The two posterior and single anterior communicating arteries complete the formation of an arterial anastomosis called the **cerebral arterial circle (circle of Willis)**. This structure encircles the pituitary gland and optic chiasma and unites the brain's anterior and posterior blood supplies. It also equalizes blood pressure in the two brain areas and pro-vides alternate routes for blood to reach the brain tissue if a carotid or vertebral artery becomes occluded.

Thyrocervical and costocervical trunks. These short vessels arise from the subclavian artery just lateral to the vertebral arteries on each side (Figures 19.22b and Figure 19.23). The thyrocervical trunk mainly supplies the thyroid gland, portions of the cervical vertebrae and spinal cord, and some scapular muscles. The costocervical trunk serves deep neck and superior intercostal muscles.

Figure 19.22 Arteries of the head, neck, and brain.

Ophthalmic artery

Basilar artery

Vertebral artery

Internal carotid artery

External carotid artery

Common carotid artery

Thyrocervical trunk

Costocervical trunk

Subclavian artery

Axillary artery

Branches of the external carotid artery

• Superficial temporal artery

• Maxillary artery

• Occipital artery

• Facial artery

• Lingual artery

• Superior thyroid artery

Larynx

Thyroid gland (overlying trachea)

Clavicle (cut)

Brachiocephalic trunk

Internal thoracic artery

(b) Arteries of the head and neck, right aspect

(c) Colorized arteriograph of the arterial supply of the brain

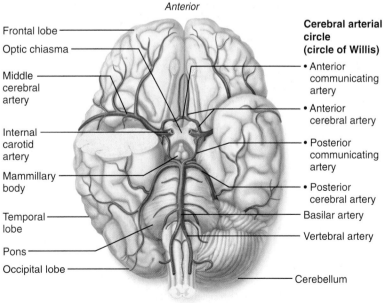

Anterior

Frontal lobe

Optic chiasma

Middle cerebral artery

Internal carotid artery

Mammillary body

Temporal lobe

Pons

Occipital lobe

Cerebral arterial circle (circle of Willis)

• Anterior communicating artery

• Anterior cerebral artery

• Posterior communicating artery

• Posterior cerebral artery

Basilar artery

Vertebral artery

Cerebellum

Posterior

(d) Major arteries serving the brain (inferior view, right side of cerebellum and part of right temporal lobe removed)

19

TABLE 19.6 **Arteries of the Upper Limbs and Thorax**

The upper limbs are supplied entirely by arteries arising from the **subclavian arteries (Figure 19.23a)**. After giving off branches to the neck, each subclavian artery courses laterally between the clavicle and first rib to enter the axilla, where its name changes to axillary artery. The thorax wall is supplied by an array of vessels that arise either directly from the thoracic aorta or from branches of the subclavian arteries. Most visceral organs of the thorax receive their functional blood supply from small branches issuing from the thoracic aorta. Because these vessels are so small and tend to vary in number (except for the bronchial arteries), they are not illustrated in Figures 19.23a and b, but several of them are listed at the end of this table.

Description and Distribution

Arteries of the Upper Limb

Axillary artery. As it runs through the axilla accompanied by cords of the brachial plexus, each axillary artery gives off branches to the axilla, chest wall, and shoulder girdle. These branches include the **thoracoacromial artery** (tho"rah-ko-ah-kro'me-al), which supplies the deltoid muscle and pectoral region; the **lateral thoracic artery**, which serves the lateral chest wall and breast; the **subscapular artery** to the scapula, dorsal thorax wall, and part of the latissimus dorsi muscle; and the **anterior** and **posterior circumflex humeral arteries**, which wrap around the humeral neck and help supply the shoulder joint and the deltoid muscle. As the axillary artery emerges from the axilla, it becomes the brachial artery.

Brachial artery. The brachial artery runs down the medial aspect of the humerus and supplies the anterior flexor muscles of the arm. One major branch, the **deep artery of the arm**, serves the posterior triceps brachii muscle. As it nears the elbow, the brachial artery gives off several small branches that contribute to an anastomosis serving the elbow joint and connecting it to the arteries of the forearm. As the brachial artery crosses the anterior midline aspect of the elbow, it provides an easily palpated pulse point (brachial pulse) (see Figure 19.12). Immediately beyond the elbow, the brachial artery splits to form the radial and ulnar arteries, which more or less follow the course of similarly named bones down the length of the anterior forearm.

Radial artery. The radial artery runs from the median line of the cubital fossa to the styloid process of the radius. It supplies the lateral muscles of the forearm, the wrist, and the thumb and index finger. At the root of the thumb, the radial artery provides a convenient site for taking the radial pulse.

Ulnar artery. The ulnar artery supplies the medial aspect of the forearm, fingers 3–5, and the medial aspect of the index finger. Proximally, the ulnar artery gives off a short branch, the **common interosseous artery** (in"ter-os'e-us), which runs between the radius and ulna to serve the deep flexors and extensors of the forearm.

Palmar arches. In the palm, branches of the radial and ulnar arteries anastomose to form the **superficial** and **deep palmar arches**. The **metacarpal arteries** and the **digital arteries** that supply the fingers arise from these palmar arches.

Arteries of the Thorax Wall

Internal thoracic arteries. The internal thoracic arteries (formerly called the internal mammary arteries) arise

(a) Schematic flowchart

TABLE 19.6 (continued)

Vertebral artery
Thyrocervical trunk
Costocervical trunk
Suprascapular artery
Thoracoacromial artery
Axillary artery
Subscapular artery
Posterior circumflex humeral artery
Anterior circumflex humeral artery
Brachial artery
Deep artery of arm
Common interosseous artery
Radial artery
Ulnar artery
Deep palmar arch
Superficial palmar arch
Digital arteries

Common carotid arteries
Right subclavian artery
Left subclavian artery
Brachiocephalic trunk
Posterior intercostal arteries
Anterior intercostal artery
Internal thoracic artery
Lateral thoracic artery
Descending aorta

(b) Illustration, anterior view

Figure 19.23 **Arteries of the right upper limb and thorax.**

from the subclavian arteries and supply blood to most of the anterior thorax wall. Each of these arteries descends lateral to the sternum and gives off **anterior intercostal arteries**, which supply the intercostal spaces anteriorly. The internal thoracic artery also sends superficial branches to the skin and mammary glands and terminates in twiglike branches to the anterior abdominal wall and diaphragm.

Posterior intercostal arteries. The superior two pairs of posterior intercostal arteries are derived from the **costocervical trunk**. The next nine pairs issue from the thoracic aorta and course around the rib cage to anastomose anteriorly with the anterior intercostal arteries. Inferior to the 12th rib, a pair of **subcostal arteries** emerges from the thoracic aorta (not illustrated). The posterior intercostal arteries supply the posterior intercostal spaces, deep muscles of the back, vertebrae, and spinal cord. Together, the posterior and anterior intercostal arteries supply the intercostal muscles.

Superior phrenic arteries. One or more paired superior phrenic arteries serve the posterior superior aspect of the diaphragm surface.

Arteries of the Thoracic Viscera
Pericardial arteries. Several tiny branches supply the posterior pericardium.

Bronchial arteries. Two left and one right bronchial arteries supply systemic (oxygen-rich) blood to the lungs, bronchi, and pleurae.

Esophageal arteries. Four to five esophageal arteries supply the esophagus.

Mediastinal arteries. Many small mediastinal arteries serve the posterior mediastinum.

19

TABLE 19.7 **Arteries of the Abdomen**

The arterial supply to the abdominal organs arises from the abdominal aorta (Figure 19.24a). Under resting conditions, about half of the entire arterial flow is found in these vessels. Except for the celiac trunk, the superior and inferior mesenteric arteries, and the median sacral artery, all are paired vessels. These arteries supply the abdominal wall, diaphragm, and visceral organs of the abdominopelvic cavity. The branches are given here in order of their issue.

(a) Schematic flowchart.

Figure 19.24 **Arteries of the abdomen.**

TABLE 19.7 *(continued)*

Description and Distribution

Inferior phrenic arteries. The inferior phrenics emerge from the aorta at T$_{12}$, just inferior to the diaphragm. They serve the inferior diaphragm surface.

Celiac trunk. This very large unpaired branch of the abdominal aorta divides almost immediately into three branches: the common hepatic, splenic, and left gastric arteries (Figure 19.24b). The **common hepatic artery** (hĕ-pat′ik) gives off branches to the stomach, duodenum, and pancreas. Where the **gastroduodenal artery** branches off, it becomes the **hepatic artery proper**, which splits into right and left branches that serve the liver. As the **splenic artery** (splen′ik) passes deep to the stomach, it sends branches to the pancreas and stomach and terminates in branches to the spleen. The **left gastric artery** (*gaster* = stomach) supplies part of the stomach and the inferior esophagus. The **right** and **left gastroepiploic arteries** (gas″ tro-ep″ĭ-plo′ik), branches of the gastroduodenal and splenic arteries, respectively, serve the greater curvature of the stomach. A **right gastric artery**, which supplies the stomach's lesser curvature, may arise from the common hepatic artery or from the hepatic artery proper.

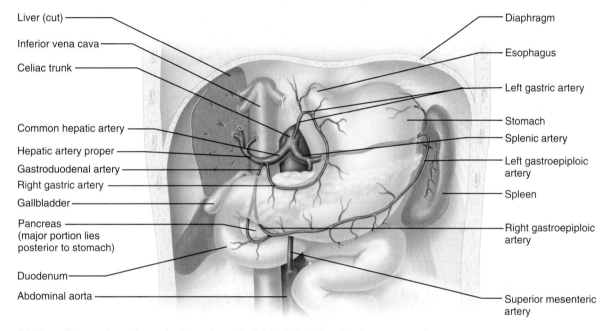

(b) The celiac trunk and its major branches. The left half of the liver has been removed.

Figure 19.24 *(continued)*

19

TABLE 19.7	Arteries of the Abdomen *(continued)*

Superior mesenteric artery (mes-en-ter′ik).   This large, un-paired artery arises from the abdominal aorta at the L_1 level immediately below the celiac trunk (Figure 19.24d). It runs deep to the pancreas and then enters the mesentery, where its numerous anastomosing branches serve virtually all of the small intestine via the **intestinal arteries**, and most of the large intestine—the appendix, cecum, ascending colon (via the **ileocolic** and **right colic arteries**), and part of the transverse colon (via the **middle colic artery**).

Suprarenal arteries (soo″prah-re′nal).   The **middle suprarenal arteries** flank the origin of the superior mesenteric artery as they emerge from the abdominal aorta (Figure 19.24c). They supply blood to the adrenal (suprarenal) glands overlying the kidneys. The adrenal glands also receive two sets of branches not illustrated: *superior suprarenal* branches from the nearby inferior phrenic arteries, and *inferior suprarenal* branches from the nearby renal arteries.

Renal arteries.   The short but wide renal arteries, right and left, issue from the lateral surfaces of the aorta slightly below the superior mesenteric artery (between L_1 and L_2). Each serves the kidney on its side.

Gonadal arteries (go-nă′dul).   The paired gonadal arteries are called the **testicular arteries** in males and the **ovarian arteries** in females. The ovarian arteries extend into the pelvis to serve the ovaries and part of the uterine tubes. The much longer testicular arteries descend through the pelvis and inguinal canals to enter the scrotum, where they serve the testes.

Inferior mesenteric artery.   This final major branch of the abdominal aorta is unpaired and arises from the anterior aortic surface at the L_3 level. It serves the distal part of the large intestine—from the midpart of the transverse colon to the midrectum—via its **left colic**, **sigmoidal**, and **superior rectal branches** (Figure 19.24d). Looping anastomoses between the superior and inferior mesenteric arteries help ensure that blood will continue to reach the digestive viscera in cases of trauma to one of these abdominal arteries.

Lumbar arteries.   Four pairs of lumbar arteries arise from the posterolateral surface of the aorta in the lumbar region. These segmental arteries supply the posterior abdominal wall.

Median sacral artery.   The unpaired median sacral artery issues from the posterior surface of the abdominal aorta at its terminus. This tiny artery supplies the sacrum and coccyx.

Common iliac arteries.   At the L_4 level, the aorta splits into the right and left common iliac arteries, which supply blood to the lower abdominal wall, pelvic organs, and lower limbs (Figure 19.24c).

CHECK YOUR UNDERSTANDING

15. Which paired artery supplies most of the tissues of the head except for the brain and orbits?
16. Name the arterial anastomosis at the base of the brain.
17. Name the four unpaired arteries that emerge from the abdominal aorta.

For answers, see Appendix G.

19

TABLE 19.7   (continued)

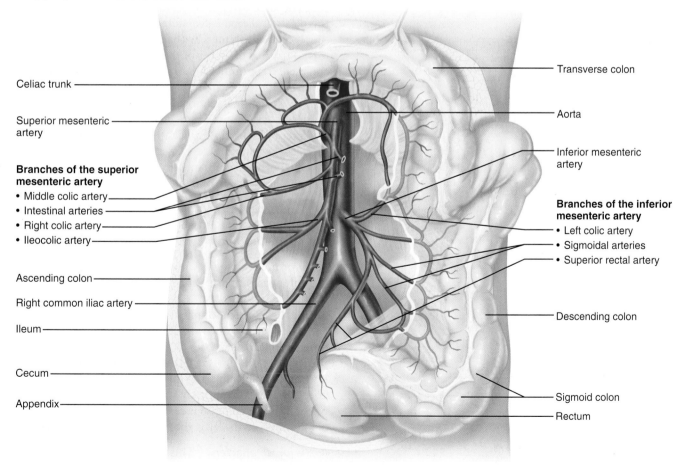

(c) **Major branches of the abdominal aorta.**

Labels (top figure):
- Hiatus (opening) for inferior vena cava
- Hiatus (opening) for esophagus
- Adrenal (suprarenal) gland
- Celiac trunk
- Kidney
- Abdominal aorta
- Lumbar arteries
- Ureter
- Median sacral artery
- Diaphragm
- Inferior phrenic artery
- Middle suprarenal artery
- Renal artery
- Superior mesenteric artery
- Gonadal (testicular or ovarian) artery
- Inferior mesenteric artery
- Common iliac artery

Labels (bottom figure):
- Celiac trunk
- Superior mesenteric artery
- **Branches of the superior mesenteric artery**
  - Middle colic artery
  - Intestinal arteries
  - Right colic artery
  - Ileocolic artery
- Ascending colon
- Right common iliac artery
- Ileum
- Cecum
- Appendix
- Transverse colon
- Aorta
- Inferior mesenteric artery
- **Branches of the inferior mesenteric artery**
  - Left colic artery
  - Sigmoidal arteries
  - Superior rectal artery
- Descending colon
- Sigmoid colon
- Rectum

(d) **Distribution of the superior and inferior mesenteric arteries.** The transverse colon has been pulled superiorly.

Figure 19.24 *(continued)* **Arteries of the abdomen.**

19

TABLE 19.8   Arteries of the Pelvis and Lower Limbs

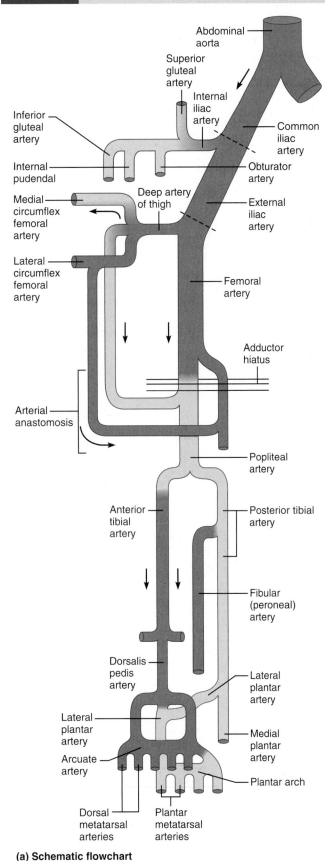

(a) Schematic flowchart

Figure 19.25 **Arteries of the right pelvis and lower limb.**

At the level of the sacroiliac joints, the **common iliac arteries** divide into two major branches, the internal and external iliac arteries (Figure 19.25a). The internal iliacs distribute blood mainly to the pelvic region. The external iliacs primarily serve the lower limbs but also send some branches to the abdominal wall.

Description and Distribution

Internal iliac arteries.   These paired arteries run into the pelvis and distribute blood to the pelvic walls and viscera (bladder, rectum, uterus, and vagina in the female and prostate and ductus deferens in the male). Additionally they serve the gluteal muscles via the **superior** and **inferior gluteal arteries**, adductor muscles of the medial thigh via the **obturator artery**, and external genitalia and perineum via the **internal pudendal artery** (not illustrated).

External iliac arteries.   These arteries supply the lower limbs (Figure 19.25b). As they course through the pelvis, they give off branches to the anterior abdominal wall. After passing under the inguinal ligaments to enter the thigh, they become the femoral arteries.

Femoral arteries.   As each of these arteries passes down the anteromedial thigh, it gives off several branches to the thigh muscles. The largest of the deep branches is the **deep artery of the thigh** (also called the **deep femoral artery**), which is the main supply to the thigh muscles (hamstrings, quadriceps, and adductors). Proximal branches of the deep femoral artery, the **lateral** and **medial circumflex femoral arteries**, encircle the neck of the femur. The medial circumflex artery is the major vessel to the head of the femur. If it is torn in a hip fracture, the bone tissue of the head of the femur dies. A long descending branch of the lateral circumflex artery supplies the vastus lateralis muscle. Near the knee the femoral artery passes posteriorly and through a gap in the adductor magnus muscle, the *adductor hiatus,* to enter the popliteal fossa, where its name changes to popliteal artery.

Popliteal artery.   This posterior vessel contributes to an arterial anastomosis that supplies the knee region and then splits into the anterior and posterior tibial arteries of the leg.

Anterior tibial artery.   The anterior tibial artery runs through the anterior compartment of the leg, supplying the extensor muscles along the way. At the ankle, it becomes the **dorsalis pedis artery**, which supplies the ankle and dorsum of the foot, and gives off a branch, the **arcuate artery**, which issues the **dorsal metatarsal arteries** to the metatarsus of the foot. The superficial dorsalis pedis ends by penetrating into the sole where it forms the medial part of the **plantar arch**. The dorsalis pedis artery provides a clinically important pulse point, the pedal pulse. If the pedal pulse is easily felt, it is fairly certain that the blood supply to the leg is good.

Posterior tibial artery.   This large artery courses through the posteromedial part of the leg and supplies the flexor muscles. Proximally, it gives off a large branch, the **fibular (peroneal) artery**, which supplies the lateral fibularis muscles of the leg. On

TABLE 19.8 (continued)

the medial side of the foot, the posterior tibial artery divides into **lateral** and **medial plantar arteries** that serve the plantar surface of the foot. The lateral plantar artery forms the lateral end of the plantar arch. **Plantar metatarsal arteries** and **digital arteries** to the toes arise from the plantar arch.

(c) **Posterior view**

(b) **Anterior view**

Figure 19.25 (continued)

CHECK YOUR UNDERSTANDING

18. You are assessing the circulation in the leg of a diabetic patient at the clinic. Name the artery you palpate in each of these three locations: behind the knee, behind the medial malleolus of the tibia, on the dorsum of the foot.

For answers, see Appendix G.

In our survey of the systemic veins, the major tributaries (branches) of the venae cavae are noted first in Figure 19.26, followed by a description in Tables 19.10 through 19.13 of the venous pattern of the various body regions. Because veins run toward the heart, the most distal veins are named first and those closest to the heart last. Deep veins generally drain the same areas served by their companion arteries, so they are not described in detail.

Description and Areas Drained

Superior vena cava.   This great vein receives systemic blood draining from all areas superior to the diaphragm, except the heart wall. It is formed by the union of the **right** and **left**

brachiocephalic veins and empties into the right atrium (Figure 19.26b). Notice that there are two brachiocephalic veins, but only one brachiocephalic artery (trunk). Each brachiocephalic vein is formed by the joining of the **internal jugular** and **subclavian veins** on its side. In most of the flowcharts that follow, only the vessels draining blood from the right side of the body are shown (except for the azygos circulation of the thorax).

Inferior vena cava.   The widest blood vessel in the body, this vein returns blood to the heart from all body regions below the diaphragm. The abdominal aorta lies directly to its left. The distal end of the inferior vena cava is formed by the junction of the paired **common iliac veins** at L_5. From this point, it courses superiorly along the anterior aspect of the spine, receiving venous blood draining from the abdominal walls, gonads, and kidneys. Immediately above the diaphragm, the inferior vena cava ends as it enters the inferior aspect of the right atrium.

Figure 19.26 Major veins of the systemic circulation.

(a) Schematic flowchart

19

TABLE 19.9   *(continued)*

Figure 19.26 *(continued)*

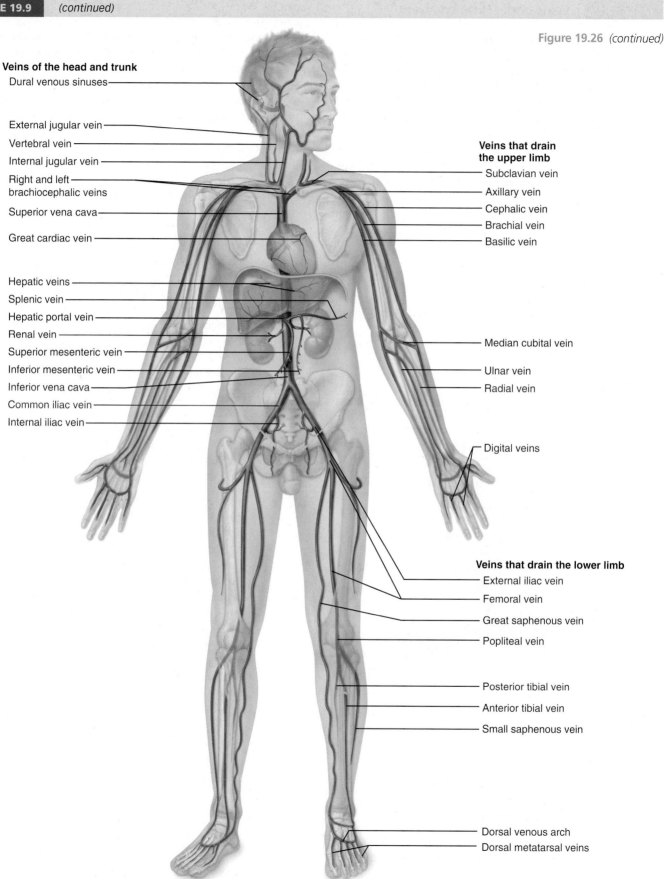

Veins of the head and trunk
- Dural venous sinuses
- External jugular vein
- Vertebral vein
- Internal jugular vein
- Right and left brachiocephalic veins
- Superior vena cava
- Great cardiac vein
- Hepatic veins
- Splenic vein
- Hepatic portal vein
- Renal vein
- Superior mesenteric vein
- Inferior mesenteric vein
- Inferior vena cava
- Common iliac vein
- Internal iliac vein

Veins that drain the upper limb
- Subclavian vein
- Axillary vein
- Cephalic vein
- Brachial vein
- Basilic vein
- Median cubital vein
- Ulnar vein
- Radial vein
- Digital veins

Veins that drain the lower limb
- External iliac vein
- Femoral vein
- Great saphenous vein
- Popliteal vein
- Posterior tibial vein
- Anterior tibial vein
- Small saphenous vein
- Dorsal venous arch
- Dorsal metatarsal veins

(b) Illustration, anterior view. The vessels of the pulmonary circulation are not shown.

TABLE 19.10   **Veins of the Head and Neck**

Most blood draining from the head and neck is collected by three pairs of veins: the external jugular veins, which empty into the subclavians; the internal jugular veins; and the vertebral veins, which drain into the brachiocephalic vein **(Figure 19.27a)**. Although most extracranial veins have the same names as the extracranial arteries, their courses and interconnections differ substantially.

Most veins of the brain drain into the **dural venous sinuses**, an interconnected series of enlarged chambers located between the dura mater layers. The **superior** and **inferior sagittal sinuses** are in the falx cerebri, which dips down between the cerebral hemispheres. The inferior sagittal sinus drains into the **straight**

sinus posteriorly (Figure 19.27a and c). The superior sagittal and straight sinuses then empty into the **transverse sinuses**, which run in shallow grooves on the internal surface of the occipital bone. These drain into the S-shaped **sigmoid sinuses**, which become the *internal jugular veins* as they leave the skull through the jugular foramen. The **cavernous sinuses**, which flank the sphenoid body, receive venous blood from the **ophthalmic veins** of the orbits and the facial veins, which drain the nose and upper lip area. The internal carotid artery and cranial nerves III, IV, VI, and part of V, all run *through* the cavernous sinus on their way to the orbit and face.

Description and Area Drained

External jugular veins.   The right and left external jugular veins drain superficial scalp and face structures served by the external carotid arteries. However, their tributaries anastomose frequently, and some of the superficial drainage from these regions enters the internal jugular veins as well. As the external jugular veins descend through the lateral neck, they pass obliquely over the sternocleidomastoid muscles and then empty into the subclavian veins.

Vertebral veins.   Unlike the vertebral arteries, the vertebral veins do not serve much of the brain. Instead they drain the cervical vertebrae, the spinal cord, and some small neck muscles. They run inferiorly through the transverse foramina of the cervical vertebrae and join the brachiocephalic veins at the root of the neck.

Internal jugular veins.   The paired internal jugular veins, which receive the bulk of blood draining from the brain, are the largest of the paired veins draining the head and neck. They arise from the dural venous sinuses, exit the skull via the *jugular foramina*, and then descend through the neck alongside the internal carotid arteries. As they move inferiorly, they receive blood from some of the deep veins of the face and neck—branches of the **facial** and **superficial temporal veins** (Figure 19.27b). At the base of the neck, each internal jugular vein joins the subclavian vein on its own side to form a brachiocephalic vein. As already noted, the two brachiocephalic veins unite to form the superior vena cava.

(a) Schematic flowchart

Figure 19.27 Venous drainage of the head, neck, and brain.

CHECK YOUR UNDERSTANDING

19. In what important way does the area drained by the vertebral veins differ from the area served by the vertebral arteries?

20. Which veins drain the dural venous sinuses and where do these veins terminate?

For answers, see Appendix G.

TABLE 19.10 *(continued)*

Ophthalmic vein

Superficial temporal vein

Facial vein

Occipital vein

Posterior auricular vein

External jugular vein

Vertebral vein

Internal jugular vein

Superior and middle thyroid veins

Brachiocephalic vein

Subclavian vein

Superior vena cava

(b) Veins of the head and neck, right superficial aspect

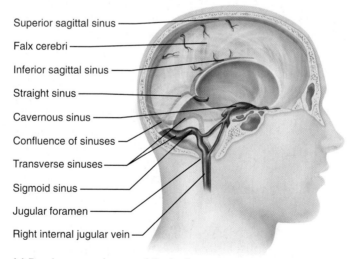

Superior sagittal sinus

Falx cerebri

Inferior sagittal sinus

Straight sinus

Cavernous sinus

Confluence of sinuses

Transverse sinuses

Sigmoid sinus

Jugular foramen

Right internal jugular vein

(c) Dural venous sinuses of the brain

Figure 19.27 *(continued)*

19

TABLE 19.11   Veins of the Upper Limbs and Thorax

The deep veins of the upper limbs follow the paths of their companion arteries and have the same names (Figure 19.28a). However, except for the largest, most are paired veins that flank their

(a) Schematic flowchart

artery. The superficial veins of the upper limbs are larger than the deep veins and are easily seen just beneath the skin. The median cubital vein, crossing the anterior aspect of the elbow, is commonly used to obtain blood samples or administer intravenous medications.

Blood draining from the mammary glands and the first two to three intercostal spaces enters the **brachiocephalic veins**. However, the vast majority of thoracic tissues and the thorax wall are drained by a complex network of veins called the **azygos system** (az′ĭ-gos). The branching nature of the azygos system provides a collateral circulation for draining the abdominal wall and other areas served by the inferior vena cava, and there are numerous anastomoses between the azygos system and the inferior vena cava.

Description and Areas Drained

Deep Veins of the Upper Limbs

The most distal deep veins of the upper limb are the radial and ulnar veins. The deep and superficial **palmar venous arches** of the hand empty into the **radial** and **ulnar veins** of the forearm, which then unite to form the **brachial vein** of the arm. As the brachial vein enters the axilla, it becomes the **axillary vein**, which becomes the **subclavian vein** at the level of the first rib.

Superficial Veins of the Upper Limbs

The superficial venous system begins with the **dorsal venous arch** (not illustrated), a plexus of superficial veins in the dorsum of the hand. In the distal forearm, this plexus drains into three major superficial veins—the cephalic and basilic veins and the median antebrachial vein—which anastomose frequently as they course upward (Figure 19.28b). The **cephalic vein** bends around the radius as it travels superiorly and then continues up the lateral superficial aspect of the arm to the shoulder, where it runs in the groove between the deltoid and pectoralis muscles to join the axillary vein. The **basilic vein** courses along the posteromedial aspect of the forearm, crosses the elbow, and then takes a deep course. In the axilla, it joins the brachial vein, forming the axillary vein. At the anterior aspect of the elbow, the **median cubital vein** connects the basilic and cephalic veins. The **median antebrachial vein** lies between the radial and ulnar veins in the forearm and terminates (variably) at the elbow by entering either the basilic or the cephalic vein.

The Azygos System

The azygos system consists of the following vessels, which flank the vertebral column laterally.

Azygos vein. Located against the right side of the vertebral column, the **azygos vein** (*azygos* = unpaired) originates in the abdomen, from the **right ascending lumbar vein** that drains most of the right abdominal cavity wall and from the **right posterior intercostal veins** (except the first) that drain the chest muscles. At the T₄ level, it arches over the great vessels that run to the right lung and empties into the superior vena cava.

TABLE 19.11 (continued)

Hemiazygos vein (hĕ′me-a-zi′gus; "half the azygos"). This vessel ascends on the left side of the vertebral column. Its origin, from the **left ascending lumbar vein** and the lower (9th–11th) **posterior intercostal veins**, mirrors that of the inferior portion of the azygos vein on the right. About midthorax, the hemiazygos vein passes in front of the vertebral column and joins the azygos vein.

Accessory hemiazygos vein. The accessory hemiazygos completes the venous drainage of the left (middle) thorax and can be thought of as a superior continuation of the hemiazygos vein. It receives blood from the 4th–8th posterior intercostal veins and then crosses to the right to empty into the azygos vein. Like the azygos, it receives oxygen-poor systemic blood from the bronchi of the lungs (*bronchial veins*).

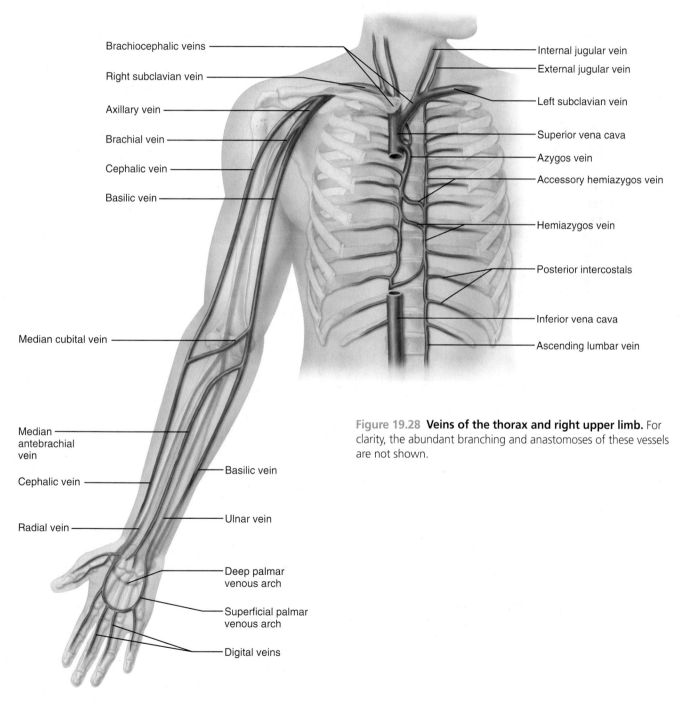

Figure 19.28 **Veins of the thorax and right upper limb.** For clarity, the abundant branching and anastomoses of these vessels are not shown.

(b) Anterior view

TABLE 19.12 **Veins of the Abdomen**

Blood draining from the abdominopelvic viscera and abdominal walls is returned to the heart by the **inferior vena cava** (Figure 19.29a). Most of its venous tributaries have names that correspond to the arteries serving the abdominal organs.

Veins draining the digestive viscera empty into a common vessel, the *hepatic portal vein,* which transports this venous blood into the liver before it is allowed to enter the major systemic circulation via the hepatic veins (Figure 19.29b). Such a venous system—veins connecting two capillary beds together—is called a *portal system* and always serves very specific needs. The **hepatic portal system** carries nutrient-rich blood (which may also contain toxins and microorganisms) from the digestive organs to the liver; where it can be "treated" before it reaches the rest of the body. As the blood percolates slowly through the liver sinusoidal capillaries, hepatocytes process nutrients and toxins, and phagocytic cells rid the blood of bacteria and other foreign matter. The veins of the abdomen are listed in inferior to superior order.

Description and Areas Drained

Lumbar veins. Several pairs of lumbar veins drain the posterior abdominal wall. They empty both directly into the inferior vena cava and into the ascending lumbar veins of the azygos system of the thorax.

Gonadal (testicular or ovarian) veins. The right gonadal vein drains the ovary or testis on the right side of the body and empties into the inferior vena cava. The left member drains into the left renal vein superiorly.

Renal veins. The right and left renal veins drain the kidneys.

Suprarenal veins. The right suprarenal vein drains the adrenal gland on the right and empties into the inferior vena cava. The left suprarenal vein drains into the left renal vein.

Hepatic portal system. Like all portal systems, the hepatic portal system is a series of vessels in which two separate capillary beds lie between the arterial supply and the final venous drainage. In this case, the first capillary beds are in the stomach and intestines and drain into tributaries of the **hepatic portal vein**, which brings them to the second capillary bed in the liver. The short hepatic portal vein begins at the L_2 level. Numerous tributaries from the stomach and pancreas contribute to the hepatic portal system (Figure 19.29c), but the major vessels are as follows:

- **Superior mesenteric vein:** Drains the entire small intestine, part of the large intestine (ascending and transverse regions), and stomach.
- **Splenic vein:** Collects blood from the spleen, parts of the stomach and pancreas, and then joins the superior mesenteric vein to form the hepatic portal vein.
- **Inferior mesenteric vein:** Drains the distal portions of the large intestine and rectum and joins the splenic vein just before that vessel unites with the superior mesenteric vein to form the hepatic portal vein.

Hepatic veins. The right, left, and middle hepatic veins carry venous blood from the liver to the inferior vena cava.

Cystic veins. The cystic veins drain the gallbladder and join the portal veins in the liver.

Inferior phrenic veins. The inferior phrenic veins drain the inferior surface of the diaphragm.

(a) Schematic flowchart.

Figure 19.29 **Veins of the abdomen.**

TABLE 19.12   *(continued)*

Hepatic veins

Inferior vena cava

Right suprarenal vein

Right gonadal vein

External iliac vein

Inferior phrenic vein

Left suprarenal vein

Renal veins

Left ascending lumbar vein

Lumbar veins

Left gonadal vein

Common iliac vein

Internal iliac vein

(b) Tributaries of the inferior vena cava. Venous drainage of abdominal organs not drained by the hepatic portal vein.

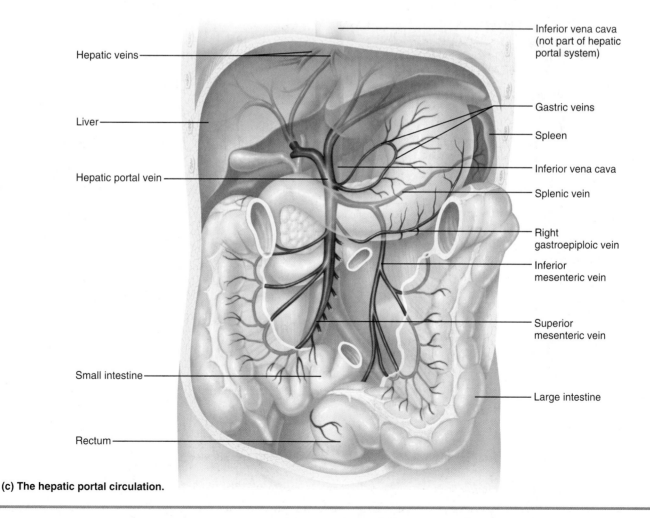

Hepatic veins

Liver

Hepatic portal vein

Small intestine

Rectum

Inferior vena cava (not part of hepatic portal system)

Gastric veins

Spleen

Inferior vena cava

Splenic vein

Right gastroepiploic vein

Inferior mesenteric vein

Superior mesenteric vein

Large intestine

19

(c) The hepatic portal circulation.

TABLE 19.13 **Veins of the Pelvis and Lower Limbs**

As in the upper limbs, most deep veins of the lower limbs have the same names as the arteries they accompany and many are double. The two superficial saphenous veins (great and small) are poorly supported by surrounding tissues, and are common sites of varicosities. The great saphenous (*saphenous* = obvious) vein is frequently excised and used as a coronary bypass vessel.

Description and Areas Drained

Deep veins. After being formed by the union of the **medial** and **lateral plantar veins**, the **posterior tibial vein** ascends deep in the calf muscle and receives the **fibular (peroneal) vein** (Figure 19.30). The **anterior tibial vein**, which is the superior continuation of the **dorsalis pedis vein** of the foot, unites at the knee with the posterior tibial vein to form the **popliteal vein**, which crosses the back of the knee. As the popliteal vein emerges from the knee, it becomes the **femoral vein**, which drains the deep structures of the thigh. The femoral vein becomes the **external iliac vein** as it enters the pelvis. In the pelvis, the external iliac vein unites with the **internal iliac vein** to form the **common iliac vein**. The distribution of the internal iliac veins parallels that of the internal iliac arteries.

Superficial veins. The **great** and **small saphenous veins** (sah-fe′nus) issue from the **dorsal venous arch** of the foot (Figure 19.30b and c). These veins anastomose frequently with each other and with the deep veins along their course. The great saphenous vein is the longest vein in the body. It travels superiorly along the medial aspect of the leg to the thigh, where it empties into the femoral vein just distal to the inguinal ligament. The small saphenous vein runs along the lateral aspect of the foot and then through the deep fascia of the calf muscles, which it drains. At the knee, it empties into the popliteal vein.

(b) Anterior view **(c) Posterior view**

(a) Schematic flowchart of the anterior and posterior veins

Figure 19.30 **Veins of the right lower limb.**

21. What is a portal system? What is the function of the hepatic portal system?

22. Name the leg veins that often become varicosed.

For answers, see Appendix G.

Developmental Aspects of Blood Vessels

▶ Explain how blood vessels develop in the fetus.

▶ Provide examples of changes that often occur in blood vessels as a person ages.

The endothelial lining of blood vessels is formed by mesodermal cells, which collect in little masses called **blood islands** throughout the microscopic embryo. These then form fragile sprouting extensions that reach toward one another and toward the forming heart to lay down the rudimentary vascular tubes. Meanwhile, adjacent mesenchymal cells, stimulated by platelet-derived growth factor, surround the endothelial tubes, forming the stabilizing muscular and fibrous coats of the vessel walls.

How do blood vessels "know" where to grow? Many blood vessels simply follow the same guidance cues that nerves follow, which is why forming vessels often snuggle closely to nerves. Whether a vessel becomes an artery or a vein depends upon the local concentration of a differentiation factor called vascular endothelial growth factor. As noted in Chapter 18, the heart is pumping blood through the rudimentary vascular system by the fourth week of development.

In addition to the fetal shunts that bypass the nonfunctional lungs (the *foramen ovale* and *ductus arteriosus*), other vascular modifications are found in the fetus. A special vessel, the *ductus venosus*, largely bypasses the liver. Also important are the *umbilical vein* and *arteries*, large vessels that circulate blood between the fetal circulation and the placenta where gas and nutrient exchanges occur with the mother's blood (see Chapter 28). Once the fetal circulatory pattern is laid down, few vascular changes occur until birth, when the umbilical vessels and shunts are occluded.

In contrast to congenital heart diseases, congenital vascular problems are rare, and blood vessels are remarkably trouble-free during youth. Vessel formation occurs as needed to support body growth, wound healing, and to rebuild vessels lost each month during a woman's menstrual cycle. As we age, signs of vascular disease begin to appear. In some, the venous valves weaken, and purple, snakelike varicose veins appear. In others, more insidious signs of inefficient circulation appear: tingling in the fingers and toes and cramping of muscles.

Although the degenerative process of atherosclerosis begins in youth, its consequences are rarely apparent until middle to old age, when it may precipitate a myocardial infarct or stroke. Until puberty, the blood vessels of boys and girls look alike, but from puberty to about age 45, women have strikingly less atherosclerosis than men because of the protective effects of estrogen, the beneficial effects of which are well documented. By enhancing nitric oxide production, inhibiting endothelin release, and blocking voltage-gated Ca^{2+} channels, estrogen's effect on blood vessels is to reduce resistance to blood flow. Estrogen also stimulates the liver to produce enzymes that speed up catabolism of LDLs and increase the production of HDLs, thus reducing the risk of atherosclerosis (see *A Closer Look*).

Between the ages of 45 and 65, when estrogen production wanes in women, this "gap" between the sexes closes, and males and females above age 65 are equally at risk for cardiovascular disease. You might expect that giving postmenopausal women supplementary estrogen would maintain this protective effect. Surprisingly, clinical trials have shown that this is not the case.

Blood pressure changes with age. In a newborn baby, arterial pressure is about 90/55. Blood pressure rises steadily during childhood to finally reach the adult value (120/80). In old age, normal blood pressure averages 150/90, which is hypertensive in younger people. After age 40, the incidence of hypertension increases dramatically. Unlike atherosclerosis, which is increasingly important in old age, hypertension claims many youthful victims and is the single most important cause of sudden cardiovascular death in men in their early 40s and 50s.

At least some vascular disease is a product of our modern technological culture. "Blessed" with high-protein, lipid-rich diets, empty-calorie snacks, energy-saving devices, and high-stress jobs, many of us are struck down prematurely. Cardiovascular disease can be prevented somewhat by diet modifications, regular aerobic exercise, and eliminating cigarette smoking. Poor diet, lack of exercise, and smoking are probably more detrimental to your blood vessels than aging itself could ever be!

23. List three differences between systemic arteries and veins with respect to their general pathways and courses.

24. Name three fetal shunts that are occluded shortly after birth. Which structure is bypassed by each shunt?

25. List three common age-related vascular problems.

For answers, see Appendix G.

19

Now that we have described the structure and function of blood vessels, our survey of the cardiovascular system is complete. The pump, the plumbing, and the circulating fluid form a dynamic organ system that ceaselessly services every other organ system of the body, as summarized in *Making Connections* on pp. 746–747. However, our study of the circulatory system is still unfinished because we have yet to examine the lymphatic system, which acts with the cardiovascular system to ensure continuous circulation and to provide sites from which lymphocytes can police the body and provide for immunity. These are the topics of Chapter 20.

System Connections

Homeostatic Interrelationships Between the Cardiovascular System and Other Body Systems

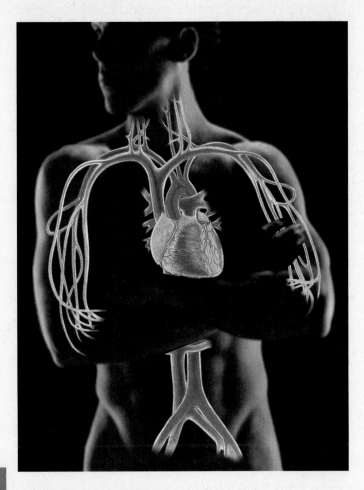

Nervous System

- The cardiovascular system delivers oxygen and nutrients; carries away wastes
- The ANS regulates cardiac rate and force; sympathetic division maintains blood pressure and controls blood flow to skin for thermoregulation

Endocrine System

- The cardiovascular system delivers oxygen and nutrients; carries away wastes; blood serves as a transport vehicle for hormones
- Various hormones influence blood pressure (epinephrine, ANP, angiotensin II, thyroxine, ADH); estrogen maintains vascular health in women

Lymphatic System/Immunity

- The cardiovascular system delivers oxygen and nutrients to lymphatic organs, which house immune cells; provides transport medium for lymphocytes and antibodies; carries away wastes
- The lymphatic system picks up leaked fluid and plasma proteins and returns them to the cardiovascular system; immune cells protect cardiovascular organs from specific pathogens

Respiratory System

- The cardiovascular system delivers oxygen and nutrients; carries away wastes
- The respiratory system carries out gas exchange: loads oxygen and unloads carbon dioxide from the blood; respiratory "pump" aids venous return

Digestive System

- The cardiovascular system delivers oxygen and nutrients; carries away wastes
- The digestive system provides nutrients to the blood including iron and B vitamins essential for RBC (and hemoglobin) formation

Integumentary System

- The cardiovascular system delivers oxygen and nutrients; carries away wastes
- The skin vasculature is an important blood reservoir and provides a site for heat loss from the body

Skeletal System

- The cardiovascular system delivers oxygen and nutrients; carries away wastes
- Bones are the sites of hematopoiesis; protect cardiovascular organs by enclosure; and provide a calcium depot

Muscular System

- The cardiovascular system delivers oxygen and nutrients; carries away wastes
- The muscle "pump" aids venous return; aerobic exercise enhances cardiovascular efficiency and helps prevent atherosclerosis

Urinary System

- The cardiovascular system delivers oxygen and nutrients; carries away wastes; blood pressure allows filtration in the kidneys
- The urinary system helps regulate blood volume and pressure by altering urine volume and releasing renin

Reproductive System

- The cardiovascular system delivers oxygen and nutrients; carries away wastes
- Estrogen maintains vascular and osseous health in women

19

The Cardiovascular System and Interrelationships With the Muscular, Nervous, and Urinary Systems

The cardiovascular system is the "king of systems." No body system can live without the blood that surges ceaselessly through cardiovascular channels. Likewise, it is nearly impossible to find a system that does not influence the cardiovascular system in some way. The respiratory and digestive systems enrich blood with oxygen and nutrients, respectively, and in turn take a share of the various riches the blood has to offer. By returning leaked plasma fluid to the vascular system, the lymphatic system helps to keep those vessels filled with blood so that circulation is possible. However, the three cardiovascular system partnerships that we will look at more closely here are those it has with the muscular, nervous, and urinary systems.

Muscular System

Talk about one hand washing the other—that's a pretty fair analogy for the interaction between the cardiovascular and muscular systems. Muscles cramp and become nonfunctional when deprived of an adequate supply of oxygen-rich blood, and their capillary supply expands (or atrophies) along with changes in muscle mass. The arterioles of skeletal muscle even have special beta-adrenergic receptors so that they can be dilated by circulating epinephrine when most other body arterioles are responding to vasoconstrictor "orders." When muscles are active and healthy, so too is the cardiovascular system. Without exercise, the heart weakens and loses mass; but when we exercise aerobically, the heart increases in size and strength. Heart rate goes down as stroke volume rises, and a lower HR means that the heart relaxes more and beats hundreds of thousands times less in a lifetime. Aerobic exercise also enhances HDL blood levels and reduces LDL levels—helping to clear fatty deposits from the vascular walls and deferring atherosclerosis, hypertension, and heart disease. Not a bad trade!

Nervous System

The brain must have absolutely continuous oxygen and glucose delivery; thus it should come as no surprise that the brain has the body's most precise autoregulatory circulation mechanism. Acting on acutely sensitive arterioles, this mechanism protects the brain. For this we can be profoundly thankful, for when neurons die, an important part of us dies as well. The cardiovascular system is just as dependent on the nervous system. Although an intrinsic pacemaker sets sinus rhythm, it does not even begin to adapt to stimuli that mobilize the cardiovascular system to peak efficiency in maintaining blood pressure during position changes and delivering blood faster during times of stress. This is the job of the autonomic nervous system, which initiates reflexes as necessary to increase or decrease cardiac output and peripheral resistance, and to redirect blood from one organ to others to serve specific needs and protect vital organs.

Urinary System

Like the lymphatic system, the urinary system (primarily the kidneys) helps maintain blood volume and circulatory dynamics, but in a much more complicated way. The kidneys use blood pressure (courtesy of the cardiovascular system) to form the filtrate which the kidney tubule cells then process. Essentially this processing involves reclaiming needed nutrients and water while allowing metabolic waste and excess ions (including H^+) to leave the body in urine. As a result, blood is continually refreshed and blood composition and volume are carefully regulated. So dedicated are the kidneys to preserving blood volume that urine output stops entirely when blood volume is severely depressed. On the other hand, the kidneys can increase systemic BP by releasing renin when the blood pressure becomes inadequate.

Clinical Connections

Cardiovascular System

Case study: Mr. Hutchinson, another middle-aged victim of the collision on Route 91, has a tourniquet around his thigh when admitted in an unconscious state to Noble Hospital. The emergency technician who brings him in states that his right lower limb was pinned beneath the bus for at least 30 minutes. He is immediately scheduled for surgery. Admission notes include the following:

- Multiple contusions of lower limbs
- Compound fracture of the right tibia; bone ends covered with sterile gauze
- Right leg blanched and cold, no pulse
- Blood pressure 90/48; pulse 140/min and thready; patient diaphoretic (sweaty)

1. Relative to what you have learned about tissue requirements for oxygen, what is the condition of the tissues in the right lower limb?

2. Will the fracture be attended to, or will Mr. Hutchinson's other homeostatic needs take precedence? Explain your answer choice and predict his surgical treatment.

3. What do you conclude regarding Mr. Hutchinson's cardiovascular measurements (pulse and BP), and what measures do you expect will be taken to remedy the situation before commencing surgery?

(Answers in Appendix G)

RELATED CLINICAL TERMS

Aneurysm (an′u-rizm; *aneurysm* = a widening) A balloonlike out-pocketing of an artery wall that places the artery at risk for rupture; most often reflects gradual weakening of the artery by chronic hypertension or arteriosclerosis. The most common sites of aneurysm formation are the abdominal aorta and arteries feeding the brain and kidneys.

Angiogram (an′je-o-gram″; *angio* = a vessel; *gram* = writing) Diagnostic technique involving the infusion of a radiopaque substance into the circulation for X-ray examination of specific blood vessels. The major technique for diagnosing coronary artery occlusion and risk of a heart attack.

Diuretic (*diure* = urinate) A chemical that promotes urine formation, thus reducing blood volume. Diuretic drugs are frequently prescribed to manage hypertension.

Phlebitis (flĕ-bi′tis; *phleb* = vein; *itis* = inflammation) Inflammation of a vein accompanied by painful throbbing and redness of the skin over the inflamed vessel. It is most often caused by bacterial infection or local physical trauma.

Phlebotomy (flĕ-bot′o-me; *tomy* = cut) A venous incision or puncture made for the purpose of withdrawing blood or bloodletting.

Sclerotherapy Procedure used for removing varicose or spider veins. Tiny needles are used to inject hardening agents into the abnormal vein. The vein scars, closes down, and is absorbed by the body.

Thrombophlebitis Condition of undesirable intravascular clotting initiated by a roughening of a venous lining; often follows severe episodes of phlebitis. An ever-present danger is that the clot may detach and form an embolus.

CHAPTER SUMMARY

Media study tools that could provide you additional help in reviewing specific key topics of Chapter 19 are referenced below.

iP = *Interactive Physiology*

PART 1: OVERVIEW OF BLOOD VESSEL STRUCTURE AND FUNCTION

1. Blood is transported throughout the body via a continuous system of blood vessels. Arteries transport blood away from the heart; veins carry blood back to the heart. Capillaries carry blood to tissue cells and are exchange sites.

Structure of Blood Vessel Walls   (p. 695)

1. All blood vessels except capillaries have three layers: tunica intima, tunica media, and tunica externa. Capillary walls are composed of the tunica intima only.

Arterial System   (pp. 695–698)

1. Elastic (conducting) arteries are the large arteries close to the heart that expand during systole, acting as pressure reservoirs, and then recoil during diastole to keep blood moving. Muscular (distributing) arteries carry blood to specific organs; they are less stretchy and more active in vasoconstriction. Arterioles regulate blood flow into capillary beds.
2. Arteriosclerosis is a degenerative vascular disease that decreases the elasticity of arteries. Atherosclerosis is the formation of fatty subendothelial lesions.

Capillaries   (pp. 698–700)

1. Capillaries are microscopic vessels with very thin walls. Most exhibit intercellular clefts, which aid in the exchange between the blood and interstitial fluid.
2. The most permeable capillaries are sinusoids (wide, tortuous channels). Fenestrated capillaries with pores are next most permeable. Least permeable are continuous capillaries, which lack pores.
3. Vascular shunts (metarteriole–thoroughfare channels) connect the terminal arteriole and postcapillary venule at opposite ends of a capillary bed. Most true capillaries arise from and rejoin the shunt channels. The amount of blood flowing into the true capillaries is regulated by precapillary sphincters.

Venous System   (pp. 700–701)

1. Veins have comparatively larger lumens than arteries, and a system of valves prevents backflow of blood.
2. Normally most veins are only partially filled; for this reason, they can serve as blood reservoirs.

Vascular Anastomoses   (pp. 701–703)

1. The joining together of arteries to provide alternate channels for blood to reach the same organ is called an anastomosis. Vascular anastomoses also form between veins and between arterioles and venules.

iP Cardiovascular System; Topic: Anatomy Review: Blood Vessel Structure and Function, pp. 1–27.

PART 2: PHYSIOLOGY OF CIRCULATION

Introduction to Blood Flow, Blood Pressure, and Resistance   (pp. 703–704)

1. Blood flow is the amount of blood flowing through a vessel, an organ, or the entire circulation in a given period of time. Blood pressure is the force per unit area exerted on a vessel wall by the contained blood. Resistance is opposition to blood flow; blood viscosity and blood vessel length and diameter contribute to resistance.
2. Blood flow is directly proportional to blood pressure and inversely proportional to resistance.

iP Cardiovascular System; Topic: Factors that Affect Blood Pressure, pp. 1–15.

Systemic Blood Pressure   (pp. 704–706)

1. Systemic blood pressure is highest in the aorta and lowest in the venae cavae. The steepest drop in BP occurs in the arterioles, where resistance is greatest.

19

2. Arterial BP depends on compliance of the elastic arteries and on how much blood is forced into them. Arterial blood pressure is pulsatile, and peaks during systole; this is measured as systolic pressure. During diastole, as blood is forced distally in the circulation by the rebound of elastic arteries, arterial BP drops to its lowest value, called the diastolic pressure.

3. Pulse pressure is systolic pressure minus diastolic pressure. The mean arterial pressure (MAP) = diastolic pressure plus one-third of pulse pressure and is the pressure that keeps blood moving throughout the cardiac cycle.

4. Low capillary pressure (35 to 15 mm Hg) protects the delicate capillaries from rupture while still allowing adequate exchange across the capillary walls.

5. Venous pressure is nonpulsatile and low (declining to zero) because of the cumulative effects of resistance. Venous valves, large lumens, functional adaptations (muscular and respiratory pumps), and sympathetic nervous system activity promote venous return.

Maintaining Blood Pressure (pp. 706–713)

1. Blood pressure varies directly with CO, peripheral resistance (R), and blood volume. Vessel diameter is the major factor determining resistance, and small changes in the diameter of vessels (chiefly arterioles) significantly affect blood pressure.

iP Cardiovascular System; Topic: Measuring Blood Pressure, pp. 1–13.

2. BP is regulated by autonomic neural reflexes involving baroreceptors or chemoreceptors, the vasomotor center (a medullary center that regulates blood vessel diameter), and sympathetic vasomotor fibers, which act on vascular smooth muscle.

3. Activation of the receptors by falling BP (and to a lesser extent by a rise in blood CO_2, or falling blood pH or O_2 levels) stimulates the vasomotor center to increase vasoconstriction and the cardioaccelerator center to increase heart rate and contractility. Rising BP inhibits the vasomotor center (permitting vasodilation) and activates the cardioinhibitory center.

4. Higher brain centers (cerebrum and hypothalamus) may modify neural controls of BP via medullary centers.

5. Hormones that increase BP by promoting vasoconstriction include epinephrine and NE (these also increase heart rate and contractility), ADH, and angiotensin II (generated in response to renin release by kidney cells). Hormones that reduce BP by promoting vasodilation include atrial natriuretic peptide, which also causes a decline in blood volume.

6. The kidneys regulate blood pressure by regulating blood volume. Rising BP directly enhances filtrate formation and fluid losses in urine; falling BP causes the kidneys to retain more water, increasing blood volume.

7. Indirect renal regulation of blood volume involves the renin-angiotensin mechanism, a hormonal mechanism. When BP falls, the kidneys release renin, which triggers the formation of angiotensin II (a vasoconstrictor) and release of aldosterone, which causes salt and water retention.

iP Cardiovascular System; Topic: Blood Pressure Regulation, pp. 1–31.

8. Pulse and blood pressure measurements are used to assess cardiovascular efficiency.

9. The pulse is the alternating expansion and recoil of arterial walls with each heartbeat. Pulse points are also pressure points.

10. Blood pressure is routinely measured by the auscultatory method. Normal blood pressure in adults is 120/80 (systolic/diastolic).

11. Hypotension, or low blood pressure (systolic pressure below 100 mm Hg), is rarely a problem. It is a sign of health in the well conditioned. In other individuals it warns of poor nutrition, disease, or circulatory shock.

12. Chronic hypertension (high blood pressure) is persistent BP readings of 140/90 or higher. It indicates increased peripheral resistance, which strains the heart and promotes vascular complications of other organs, particularly the eyes and kidneys. It is a major cause of myocardial infarct, stroke, and renal disease. Risk factors are high-fat, high-salt diet, obesity, diabetes mellitus, advanced age, smoking, stress, and being a member of the black race or a family with a history of hypertension.

iP Cardiovascular System; Topic: Measuring Blood Pressure, pp. 11 and 12.

Blood Flow Through Body Tissues: Tissue Perfusion (pp. 713–721)

1. Blood flow is involved in delivering nutrients and wastes to and from cells, gas exchange, absorbing nutrients, and forming urine.

2. Blood flows fastest where the cross-sectional area of the vascular bed is least (aorta), and slowest where the total cross-sectional area is greatest (capillaries). The slow flow in capillaries allows time for nutrient-waste exchanges.

3. Autoregulation is the local adjustment of blood flow to individual organs based on their immediate requirements. It involves myogenic controls that maintain flow despite changes in blood pressure, and local chemical factors. Vasodilators include increased CO_2, H^+, and nitric oxide. Decreased O_2 concentrations also cause vasodilation. Other factors, including endothelins, decrease blood flow.

iP Cardiovascular; Topic: Autoregulation and Capillary Dynamics, pp. 1–13.

4. In most instances, autoregulation is controlled by oxygen deficits and accumulation of local metabolites. However, autoregulation in the brain is controlled primarily by a drop in pH and by myogenic mechanisms; and vasodilation of pulmonary circuit vessels occurs in response to high levels of oxygen.

5. Nutrients, gases, and other solutes smaller than plasma proteins cross the capillary wall by diffusion. Water-soluble substances move through the clefts or fenestrations; fat-soluble substances pass through the lipid portion of the endothelial cell membrane; larger molecules are actively transported via pinocytotic vesicles or caveolae.

6. Bulk flow of fluids at capillary beds determines the distribution of fluids between the bloodstream and the interstitial space. It reflects the relative effect of outward (net hydrostatic pressure) forces minus the effect of inward (net osmotic pressure) forces. In general, fluid flows out of the capillary bed at the arterial end and reenters the capillary blood at the venule end.

iP Cardiovascular; Topic: Autoregulation and Capillary Dynamics, pp. 14–38.

7. The small net loss of fluid and protein into the interstitial space is collected by lymphatic vessels and returned to the cardiovascular system.

8. Circulatory shock occurs when blood perfusion of body tissues is inadequate. Most cases of shock reflect low blood volume (hypovolemic shock), abnormal vasodilation (vascular shock), or pump failure (cardiogenic shock).

19

PART 3: CIRCULATORY PATHWAYS: BLOOD VESSELS OF THE BODY

The Two Main Circulations of the Body (p. 721)

1. The pulmonary circulation transports O_2-poor, CO_2-laden blood to the lungs for oxygenation and carbon dioxide unloading. Blood returning to the right atrium of the heart is pumped by the right ventricle to the lungs via the pulmonary trunk. Blood issuing from the lungs is returned to the left atrium by the pulmonary veins. (See Table 19.3 and Figure 19.19.)
2. The systemic circulation transports oxygenated blood from the left ventricle to all body tissues via the aorta and its branches. Venous blood returning from the systemic circuit is delivered to the right atrium via the venae cavae.

Systemic Arteries and Veins: Differences in Pathways and Courses (p. 721)

1. All arteries are deep while veins are both deep and superficial. Superficial veins tend to have numerous interconnections. Dural venous sinuses and the hepatic portal circulation are unique venous drainage patterns.

Principal Vessels of the Systemic Circulation (pp. 721–745)

1. Tables 19.3 to 19.13 and Figures 19.20 to 19.30 illustrate and describe vessels of the systemic circulation.

Developmental Aspects of Blood Vessels (p. 745)

1. The fetal vasculature develops from embryonic blood islands and mesenchyme and is functioning in blood delivery by the fourth week.
2. Fetal circulation differs from circulation after birth. The pulmonary and hepatic shunts and special umbilical vessels are normally occluded shortly after birth.
3. Blood pressure is low in infants and rises to adult values. Age-related vascular problems include varicose veins, hypertension, and atherosclerosis. Hypertension is the most important cause of sudden cardiovascular death in middle-aged men. Atherosclerosis is the most important cause of cardiovascular disease in the aged.

REVIEW QUESTIONS

Multiple Choice/Matching

(Some questions have more than one correct answer. Select the best answer or answers from the choices given.)

1. Which statement does not accurately describe veins? (a) They have less elastic tissue and smooth muscle than arteries, (b) they contain more fibrous tissue than arteries, (c) most veins in the extremities have valves, (d) they always carry deoxygenated blood.
2. Smooth muscle in the blood vessel wall (a) is found primarily in the tunica intima, (b) is mostly circularly arranged, (c) is most abundant in veins, (d) is usually innervated by the parasympathetic nervous system.
3. Peripheral resistance (a) is inversely proportional to the length of the vascular bed, (b) increases in anemia, (c) decreases in polycythemia, (d) is inversely related to the diameter of the arterioles.
4. Which of the following can lead to decreased venous return of blood to the heart? (a) an increase in blood volume, (b) an increase in venous pressure, (c) damage to the venous valves, (d) increased muscular activity.
5. Arterial blood pressure increases in response to (a) increasing stroke volume, (b) increasing heart rate, (c) arteriosclerosis, (d) rising blood volume, (e) all of these.
6. Which of the following would *not* result in the dilation of the feeder arterioles and opening of the precapillary sphincters in systemic capillary beds? (a) a decrease in local tissue O_2 content, (b) an increase in local tissue CO_2, (c) a local increase in histamine, (d) a local increase in pH.
7. The structure of a capillary wall differs from that of a vein or an artery because (a) it has two tunics instead of three, (b) there is less smooth muscle, (c) it has a single tunic—only the tunica intima, (d) none of these.
8. The baroreceptors in the carotid sinus and aortic arch are sensitive to (a) a decrease in CO_2, (b) changes in arterial pressure, (c) a decrease in O_2, (d) all of these.
9. The myocardium receives its blood supply directly from the (a) aorta, (b) coronary arteries, (c) coronary sinus, (d) pulmonary arteries.

10. Blood flow in the capillaries is steady despite the rhythmic pumping of the heart because of the (a) elasticity of the large arteries, (b) small diameter of capillaries, (c) thin walls of the veins, (d) venous valves.
11. Tracing the blood from the heart to the right hand, we find that blood leaves the heart and passes through the aorta, the right subclavian artery, the axillary and brachial arteries, and through either the radial or ulnar artery to arrive at the hand. Which artery is missing from this sequence? (a) coronary, (b) brachiocephalic, (c) cephalic, (d) right common carotid.
12. Which of the following do not drain directly into the inferior vena cava? (a) inferior phrenic veins, (b) hepatic veins, (c) inferior mesenteric vein, (d) renal veins.
13. In atherosclerosis, which layer of the vessel wall thickens most? (a) tunica media, (b) tunica intima, (c) tunica adventitia, (d) tunica externa.
14. Suppose that at a given point along a capillary, the following forces exist: capillary hydrostatic pressure (HP_c) = 30 mm Hg, interstitial fluid hydrostatic pressure (HP_{if}) = 0 mm Hg, capillary colloid osmotic pressure (OP_c) = 25 mm Hg, and interstitial fluid colloid osmotic pressure (OP_{if}) = 2 mm Hg. The net filtration pressure at this point in the capillary is (a) 3 mm Hg, (b) −3 mm Hg, (c) −7 mm Hg, (d) 7 mm Hg.
15. Using the letters from column B, match the artery descriptions in column A. (Note that some require more than a single choice.)

Column A	Column B
____ (1) unpaired branch of abdominal aorta	(a) right common carotid
____ (2) second branch of aortic arch	(b) superior mesenteric
	(c) left common carotid
____ (3) branch of internal carotid	(d) external iliac
	(e) inferior mesenteric
____ (4) branch of external carotid	(f) superficial temporal
	(g) celiac trunk
____ (5) origin of femoral arteries	(h) facial
	(i) ophthalmic
	(j) internal iliac

Short Answer Essay Questions

16. How is the anatomy of capillaries and capillary beds well suited to their function?

17. Distinguish between elastic arteries, muscular arteries, and arterioles relative to location, histology, and functional adaptations.

18. Write an equation showing the relationship between peripheral resistance, blood flow, and blood pressure.

19. **(a)** Define blood pressure. Differentiate between systolic and diastolic blood pressure. **(b)** What is the normal blood pressure value for a young adult?

20. Describe the neural mechanisms responsible for controlling blood pressure.

21. Explain the reasons for the observed changes in blood flow velocity in the different regions of the circulation.

22. How does the control of blood flow to the skin for the purpose of regulating body temperature differ from the control of nutrient blood flow to skin cells?

23. Describe neural and chemical (both systemic and local) effects exerted on the blood vessels when one is fleeing from a mugger. (Be careful, this is more involved than it appears at first glance.)

24. How are nutrients, wastes, and respiratory gases transported to and from the blood and tissue spaces?

25. **(a)** What blood vessels contribute to the formation of the hepatic portal circulation? **(b)** Why is a portal circulation a "strange" circulation?

26. Physiologists often consider capillaries and postcapillary venules together. **(a)** What functions do these vessels share? **(b)** Structurally, how do they differ?

Critical Thinking and Clinical Application Questions

1. Mrs. Johnson is brought to the emergency room after being involved in an auto accident. She is hemorrhaging and has a rapid, thready pulse, but her blood pressure is still within normal limits. Describe the compensatory mechanisms that are acting to maintain her blood pressure in the face of blood loss.

2. A 60-year-old man is unable to walk more than 100 yards without experiencing severe pain in his left leg; the pain is relieved by resting for 5–10 minutes. He is told that the arteries of his leg are becoming occluded with fatty material and is advised to have the sympathetic nerves serving that body region severed. Explain how such surgery might help to relieve this man's problem.

3. Your friend Joanie, who knows little about science, is reading a magazine article about a patient who had an "aneurysm at the base of his brain that suddenly grew much larger." The surgeons' first goal was to "keep it from rupturing," and the second goal was to "relieve the pressure on the brain stem and cranial nerves." The surgeons were able to "replace the aneurysm with a section of plastic tubing," so the patient recovered. Joanie asks you what all this means. Explain. (Hint: Check this chapter's Related Clinical Terms, p. 748.)

4. The Agawam High School band is playing some lively marches while the coaches are giving pep talks to their respective football squads. Although it is September, it is unseasonably hot (88°F/31°C) and the band uniforms are wool. Suddenly, Harry the tuba player becomes light-headed and faints. Explain his fainting in terms of vascular events.

5. When one is cold or the external temperature is low, most venous blood returning from the distal part of the arm travels in the deep veins where it picks up heat (by countercurrent exchange) from the nearby brachial artery en route. However, when one is hot, and especially during exercise, venous return from the distal arm travels in the superficial veins and those veins tend to bulge superficially in a person who is working out. Explain why venous return takes a different route in the second situation.

6. Edema (swelling due to an increase in interstitial fluid) is a common clinical problem. On one of your first days of an introductory clinical experience, you encounter four patients who all have severe edema for different reasons. Your challenge is to explain the cause of the edema. In each case, try to explain the edema in terms of either an increase or a decrease in one of the four pressures that causes bulk flow at capillaries (see Figure 19.17).

   (1) First you encounter Mrs. Taylor in the medical ward awaiting a liver transplant. What is the connection between liver failure and her edema? (Hint: Think about the liver's role in producing plasma proteins.)

   (2) Next you follow a resident to the obstetric ward, where Mrs. So is experiencing premature labor. Which of the pressures that drive bulk flow might be altered here? (Hint: What might the expanded uterus be pressing on?)

   (3) Then you are called to emergency, where Mr. Herrera is in anaphylactic shock. In anaphylactic shock, the capillaries become leaky, allowing plasma proteins that are normally kept inside the blood vessels to escape into the interstitial fluid. Which of the pressures driving bulk flow is altered in this case and in what direction is the change?

   (4) Finally, you go to the oncology ward where Mrs. O'Leary is recovering from surgery for advanced breast cancer that had infiltrated her right breast and axillary lymph nodes. All of her axillary lymph nodes were removed and unfortunately, this severed most of the lymphatic vessels draining her right arm. You notice that her right arm is quite edematous. Why? Mrs. O'Leary is given a compression sleeve to wear on this arm to help relieve the edema. Which of the pressures driving bulk flow at the capillaries will be altered by the compression sleeve?

19

20

The Lymphatic System and Lymphoid Organs and Tissues

They can't all be superstars! When we mentally tick off the names of the body's organ systems, the lymphatic (lim-fat′ik) system and the lymphoid organs and tissues are probably not the first to come to mind. Yet if they failed their quiet background work, our cardiovascular system would stop working and our immune system would be hopelessly impaired.

The **lymphatic system** actually consists of three parts: (1) a meandering network of *lymphatic vessels*, (2) *lymph*, the fluid contained in those vessels, and (3) *lymph nodes* that cleanse the lymph as it passes through them. Inasmuch as the lymph nodes also form part of the *lymphoid organs and tissues*, the structures and functions of the lymphatic system overlap with those of the lymphoid organs and tissues. In addition to lymph nodes, the lymphoid organs and tissues include the spleen, thymus, tonsils, and other lymphoid tissues scattered throughout the body. The lymphoid organs house phagocytic cells and lymphocytes, which play essential roles in the body's defense mechanisms and its resistance to disease. Together, the lymphatic system and the lymphoid organs and tissues provide the structural basis of the immune system.

Lymphatic Vessels

► List the functions of the lymphatic vessels.

► Describe the structure and distribution of lymphatic vessels.

► Describe the source of lymph and mechanism(s) of lymph transport.

As blood circulates through the body, nutrients, wastes, and gases are exchanged between the blood and the interstitial fluid. As we explained in Chapter 19, the hydrostatic and colloid osmotic pressures operating at capillary beds force fluid out of the blood at the arterial ends of the beds ("upstream") and cause most of it to be reabsorbed at the venous ends ("downstream"). The fluid that remains behind in the tissue spaces, as much as 3 L daily, becomes part of the interstitial fluid.

This leaked fluid, plus any plasma proteins that escape from the bloodstream, must be carried back to the blood to ensure that the cardiovascular system has sufficient blood volume to operate properly. This problem of circulatory dynamics is resolved by the **lymphatic vessels**, or **lymphatics**, an elaborate system of drainage vessels that collect the excess protein-containing interstitial fluid and return it to the bloodstream. Once interstitial fluid enters the lymphatics, it is called **lymph** (*lymph* = clear water).

Distribution and Structure of Lymphatic Vessels

The lymphatic vessels form a one-way system in which lymph flows only toward the heart. This transport system begins in microscopic blind-ended **lymphatic capillaries** (Figure 20.1a). These capillaries weave between the tissue cells and blood capillaries in the loose connective tissues of the body. Lymphatic

(a) Structural relationship between a capillary bed of the blood vascular system and lymphatic capillaries.

(b) Lymphatic capillaries are blind-ended tubes in which adjacent endothelial cells overlap each other, forming flaplike minivalves.

Figure 20.1 Distribution and special structural features of lymphatic capillaries. Arrows in **(a)** indicate direction of fluid movement.

capillaries are widespread, but they are absent from bones and teeth, bone marrow, and the entire central nervous system (where the excess tissue fluid drains into the cerebrospinal fluid).

Although similar to blood capillaries, lymphatic capillaries are so remarkably permeable that they were once thought to be open at one end like a straw. We now know that they owe their permeability to two unique structural modifications:

1. The endothelial cells forming the walls of lymphatic capillaries are not tightly joined. Instead, the edges of adjacent cells overlap each other loosely, forming easily opened, flaplike *minivalves* (Figure 20.1b).
2. Collagen filaments anchor the endothelial cells to surrounding structures so that any increase in interstitial fluid volume opens the minivalves, rather than causing the lymphatic capillaries to collapse.

So, what we have is a system analogous to one-way swinging doors in the lymphatic capillary wall. When fluid pressure in the interstitial space is greater than the pressure in the lymphatic capillary, the minivalve flaps gape open, allowing fluid to enter the lymphatic capillary. However, when the pressure is greater *inside* the lymphatic capillary, the endothelial minivalve flaps are forced closed, preventing lymph from leaking back out as the pressure moves it along the vessel.

Proteins in the interstitial space are unable to enter blood capillaries, but they enter lymphatic capillaries easily. In addition, when tissues are inflamed, lymphatic capillaries develop openings that permit uptake of even larger particles such as cell debris, pathogens (disease-causing microorganisms such as bacteria and viruses), and cancer cells. The pathogens can then use the lymphatics to travel throughout the body. This threat to the body is partly resolved by the fact that the lymph takes "detours" through the lymph nodes, where it is cleansed of debris and "examined" by cells of the immune system.

Highly specialized lymphatic capillaries called **lacteals** (lak′te-alz) are present in the fingerlike villi of the intestinal mucosa. The lymph draining from the digestive viscera is milky white (*lacte* = milk) rather than clear because the lacteals play a major role in absorbing digested fats from the intestine. This fatty lymph, called **chyle** ("juice"), is also delivered to the blood via the lymphatic stream.

From the lymphatic capillaries, lymph flows through successively larger and thicker-walled channels—first collecting vessels, then trunks, and finally the largest of all, the ducts (Figure 20.1). The **lymphatic collecting vessels** have the same three tunics as veins, but the collecting vessels are thinner walled, have more internal valves, and anastomose more. In general, lymphatics in the skin travel along with superficial *veins*, while the deep lymphatic vessels of the trunk and digestive viscera travel with deep *arteries*. The exact anatomical distribution of lymphatic vessels varies greatly between individuals, even more so than it does for veins.

The **lymphatic trunks** are formed by the union of the largest collecting vessels, and drain fairly large areas of the body. The major trunks, named mostly for the regions from which they collect lymph, are the paired **lumbar, bronchomediastinal**,

subclavian, and **jugular trunks**, and the single **intestinal trunk** (Figure 20.2b).

Lymph is eventually delivered to one of two large *ducts* in the thoracic region. The **right lymphatic duct** drains lymph from the right upper limb and the right side of the head and thorax (Figure 20.2a). The much larger **thoracic duct** receives lymph from the rest of the body. It arises anterior to the first two lumbar vertebrae as an enlarged sac, the **cisterna chyli** (sis-ter′nah ki′li), that collects lymph from the two large lumbar trunks that drain the lower limbs and from the intestinal trunk that drains the digestive organs. As the thoracic duct runs superiorly, it receives lymphatic drainage from the left side of the thorax, left upper limb, and the head region. Each terminal duct empties its lymph into the venous circulation at the junction of the internal jugular vein and subclavian vein on its own side of the body (Figure 20.2b).

HOMEOSTATIC IMBALANCE

Like the larger blood vessels, the larger lymphatics receive their nutrient blood supply from a branching vasa vasorum. When lymphatic vessels are severely inflamed, the related vessels of the vasa vasorum become congested with blood. As a result, the pathway of the associated superficial lymphatics becomes visible through the skin as red lines that are tender to the touch. This unpleasant condition is called *lymphangitis* (lim″fan-ji′tis; *angi* = vessel). ∎

Lymph Transport

The lymphatic system lacks an organ that acts as a pump. Under normal conditions, lymphatic vessels are low-pressure conduits, and the same mechanisms that promote venous return in blood vessels act here as well—the milking action of active skeletal muscles, pressure changes in the thorax during breathing, and valves to prevent backflow. Lymphatics are usually bundled together in connective tissue sheaths along with blood vessels, and pulsations of nearby arteries also promote lymph flow. In addition to these mechanisms, smooth muscle in the walls of the lymphatic trunks and thoracic duct contracts rhythmically, helping to pump the lymph along.

Even so, lymph transport is sporadic and slow. About 3 L of lymph enters the bloodstream every 24 hours, a volume almost exactly equal to the amount of fluid lost to the tissue spaces from the bloodstream in the same time period. Movement of adjacent tissues is extremely important in propelling lymph through the lymphatics. When physical activity or passive movements increase, lymph flows much more rapidly (balancing the greater rate of fluid loss from the blood in such situations). For this reason, it is a good idea to immobilize a badly infected body part to hinder flow of inflammatory material from that region.

HOMEOSTATIC IMBALANCE

Anything that prevents the normal return of lymph to the blood, such as blockage of the lymphatics by tumors or removal of lymphatics during cancer surgery, results in short-term but

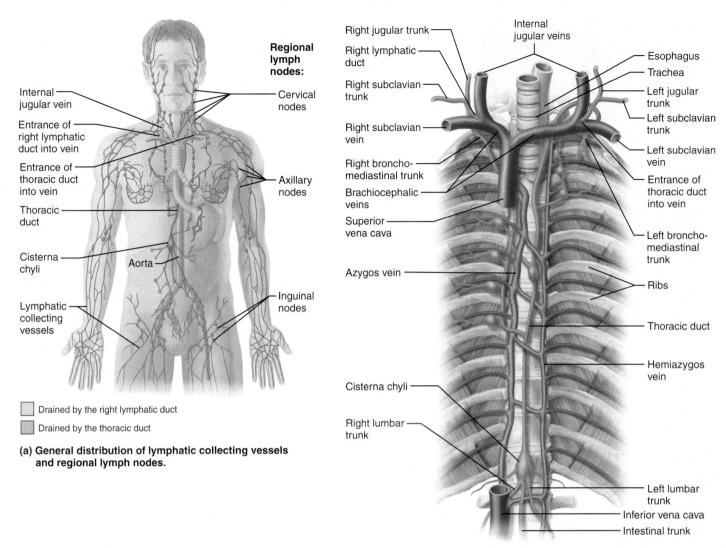

(a) **General distribution of lymphatic collecting vessels and regional lymph nodes.**

☐ Drained by the right lymphatic duct
☐ Drained by the thoracic duct

(b) **Major lymphatic trunks and ducts in relation to veins and surrounding structures.** Anterior view.

Figure 20.2 **The lymphatic system.**

severe localized edema *(lymphedema).* Usually, however, lymphatic drainage is eventually reestablished by regrowth from the vessels remaining in the area. ■

This completes the description of the lymphatic vessels. To summarize their functions, they (1) return excess tissue fluid to the bloodstream, (2) return leaked proteins to the blood, and (3) carry absorbed fat from the intestine to the blood (through lacteals).

CHECK YOUR UNDERSTANDING

1. What is lymph? Where does it come from?
2. Name two lymphatic ducts and indicate the body regions usually drained by each.
3. What is the driving force for lymph movement?

For answers, see Appendix G.

Lymphoid Cells and Tissues

▶ Describe the basic structure and cellular population of lymphoid tissue. Differentiate between diffuse and follicular lymphoid tissues.

In order to understand the basic aspects of the role of the lymphoid organs in the body, we investigate their components—lymphoid cells and lymphoid tissues—before considering the organs themselves.

Lymphoid Cells

Infectious microorganisms that manage to penetrate the body's epithelial barriers quickly proliferate in the underlying loose connective tissues. These invaders are fought off by the inflammatory response, by phagocytes (macrophages and neutrophils), and by lymphocytes.

20

- Macrophage
- Reticular cells on reticular fibers
- Lymphocytes
- Medullary sinus
- Reticular fiber

Figure 20.3 Reticular tissue in a human lymph node. Scanning electron micrograph (690×).

Lymphocytes, the main warriors of the immune system, arise in red bone marrow (along with other formed elements). They then mature into one of the two main varieties of immunocompetent cells—**T cells (T lymphocytes)** or **B cells (B lymphocytes)**—that protect the body against antigens. (*Antigens* are anything the body perceives as foreign, such as bacteria and their toxins, viruses, mismatched RBCs, or cancer cells.) Activated T cells manage the immune response, and some of them directly attack and destroy infected cells. B cells protect the body by producing **plasma cells**, daughter cells that secrete antibodies into the blood (or other body fluids). Antibodies mark antigens for destruction by phagocytes or other means. The precise roles of the lymphocytes in immunity are explored in Chapter 21.

Lymphoid **macrophages** play a crucial role in body protection and in the immune response by phagocytizing foreign substances and by helping to activate T cells. So, too, do the spiny-looking **dendritic cells** that capture antigens and bring them back to the lymph nodes. Last but not least are the **reticular cells**, fibroblast-like cells that produce the reticular fiber **stroma** (stro′mah), which is the network that supports the other cell types in the lymphoid organs and tissues (**Figure 20.3**).

Lymphoid Tissue

Lymphoid (lymphatic) tissue is an important component of the immune system, mainly because it (1) houses and provides a proliferation site for lymphocytes and (2) furnishes an ideal surveillance vantage point for lymphocytes and macrophages.

Lymphoid tissue, largely composed of a type of loose connective tissue called **reticular connective tissue**, dominates all the lymphoid organs except the thymus. Macrophages live on the fibers of the reticular network. Huge numbers of lymphocytes that have squeezed through the walls of postcapillary venules coursing through this tissue temporarily occupy the spaces of this network (Figure 20.3). Then, they leave to patrol the body again. The cycling of lymphocytes between the circulatory vessels, lymphoid tissues, and loose connective tissues of the body ensures that lymphocytes reach infected or damaged sites quickly.

Lymphoid tissue comes in various "packages." **Diffuse lymphatic tissue**, consisting of a few scattered reticular tissue elements, is found in virtually every body organ, but larger collections appear in the lamina propria of mucous membranes and in lymphoid organs. **Lymphoid follicles (nodules)** represent another way lymphoid tissue is organized. Like diffuse lymphatic tissue, they lack a capsule, but follicles are solid, spherical bodies consisting of tightly packed reticular elements and cells. Follicles often have lighter-staining centers, called **germinal centers**. Proliferating B cells predominate in germinal centers, and these centers enlarge dramatically when the B cells are dividing rapidly and producing plasma cells. In many cases, the follicles form part of larger lymphoid organs, such as lymph nodes. However, isolated aggregations of lymphoid follicles occur in the intestinal wall as Peyer's patches and in the appendix.

Lymph Nodes

▶ Describe the general location, histological structure, and functions of lymph nodes.

The principal lymphoid organs in the body are the **lymph nodes**, which cluster along the lymphatic vessels of the body. There are hundreds of these small organs, but because they are usually embedded in connective tissue, they are not ordinarily seen. Large clusters of lymph nodes occur near the body surface in the inguinal, axillary, and cervical regions, places where the lymphatic collecting vessels converge to form trunks (see Figure 20.2a).

Lymph nodes have two basic functions, both concerned with body protection. (1) As lymph is transported back to the bloodstream, the lymph nodes act as lymph "filters." Macrophages in the nodes remove and destroy microorganisms and other debris that enter the lymph from the loose connective tissues, effectively preventing them from being delivered to the blood and spreading to other parts of the body. (2) They help activate the immune system. Lymph nodes and other lymphoid organs are strategically located sites where lymphocytes encounter antigens and are activated to mount an attack against them. Let's look at how the structure of a lymph node supports these defensive functions.

Structure of a Lymph Node

Lymph nodes vary in shape and size, but most are bean shaped and less than 2.5 cm (1 inch) in length. Each node is surrounded by a dense fibrous **capsule** from which connective tissue strands

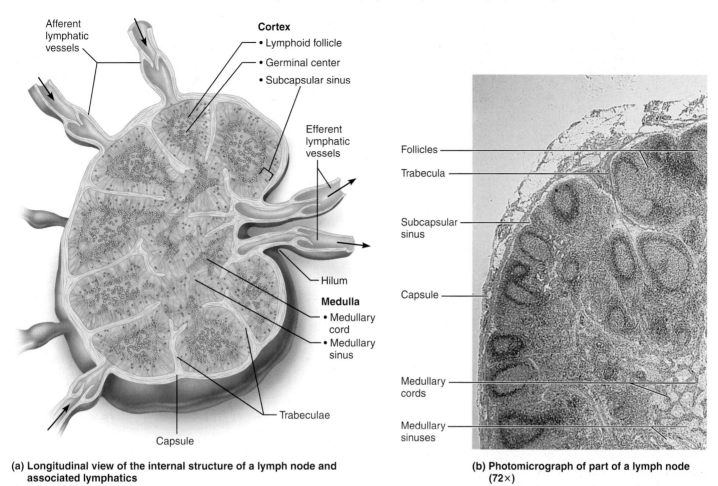

(a) **Longitudinal view of the internal structure of a lymph node and associated lymphatics**

(b) **Photomicrograph of part of a lymph node (72×)**

Figure 20.4 **Lymph node.** In **(a)**, notice that several afferent lymphatics converge on its convex side, whereas fewer efferent lymphatics exit at its hilum.

called **trabeculae** extend inward to divide the node into a number of compartments **(Figure 20.4)**. The node's internal framework, or stroma, of reticular fibers physically supports the ever-changing population of lymphocytes.

A lymph node has two histologically distinct regions, the **cortex** and the **medulla**. The superficial part of the cortex contains densely packed follicles, many with germinal centers heavy with dividing B cells. Dendritic cells nearly encapsulate the follicles and abut the deeper part of the cortex, which primarily houses T cells in transit. The T cells circulate continuously between the blood, lymph nodes, and lymph, performing their surveillance role.

Medullary cords are thin inward extensions from the cortical lymphoid tissue, and contain both types of lymphocytes plus plasma cells. Throughout the node are **lymph sinuses**, large lymph capillaries spanned by crisscrossing reticular fibers. Numerous macrophages reside on these reticular fibers and phagocytize foreign matter in the lymph as it flows by in the sinuses. Additionally, some of the lymph-borne antigens in the percolating lymph leak into the surrounding lymphoid tissue, where they activate lymphocytes to mount an immune attack against them.

Circulation in the Lymph Nodes

Lymph enters the convex side of a lymph node through a number of **afferent lymphatic vessels**. It then moves through a large, baglike sinus, the **subcapsular sinus**, into a number of smaller sinuses that cut through the cortex and enter the medulla. The lymph meanders through these sinuses and finally exits the node at its **hilum** (hi′lum), the indented region on the concave side, via **efferent lymphatic vessels**. There are fewer efferent vessels draining the node than afferent vessels feeding it, so the flow of lymph through the node stagnates somewhat, allowing time for the lymphocytes and macrophages to carry out their protective functions. Lymph passes through several nodes before it is completely cleansed.

HOMEOSTATIC IMBALANCE

Sometimes lymph nodes are overwhelmed by the agents they are trying to destroy. For example, when large numbers of bacteria are trapped in the nodes, the nodes become inflamed, swollen, and tender to the touch, a condition often referred to (erroneously) as swollen "glands." Such infected lymph nodes are called *buboes* (bu′bōz). (Buboes are the most obvious symptom of bubonic plague, the "Black Death" that killed much of Europe's population in the late Middle Ages.)

20

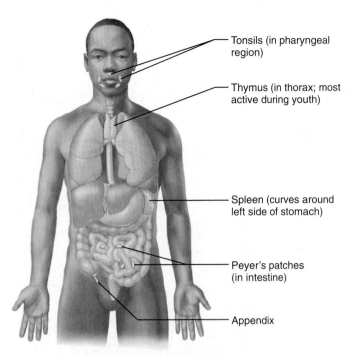

Tonsils (in pharyngeal region)

Thymus (in thorax; most active during youth)

Spleen (curves around left side of stomach)

Peyer's patches (in intestine)

Appendix

Figure 20.5 Lymphoid organs. Locations of the tonsils, spleen, thymus, Peyer's patches, and appendix.

Lymph nodes can also become secondary cancer sites, particularly in the case of metastasizing cancers that enter lymphatic vessels and become trapped there. The fact that cancer-infiltrated lymph nodes are swollen but usually not painful helps distinguish cancerous lymph nodes from those infected by microorganisms. ■

CHECK YOUR UNDERSTANDING

4. What is a lymphoid follicle? What type of lymphocyte predominates in follicles, especially in their germinal centers?
5. What is the benefit of having fewer efferent than afferent lymphatics in lymph nodes?

For answers, see Appendix G.

Other Lymphoid Organs

▶ Name and describe the other lymphoid organs of the body. Compare and contrast them with lymph nodes, structurally and functionally.

Lymph nodes are just one example of the many types of **lymphoid organs** or aggregates of lymphatic tissue in the body. Others are the spleen, thymus, tonsils, and Peyer's patches of the intestine (**Figure 20.5**), as well as bits of lymphatic tissue scattered in the connective tissues. Except for the thymus, the common feature of all these organs is their tissue makeup: All are composed of *reticular connective tissue*. Although all lymphoid organs help protect the body, only the lymph nodes filter lymph. The other lymphoid organs and tissues typically have efferent lymphatics draining them, but lack afferent lymphatics.

Spleen

The soft, blood-rich **spleen** is about the size of a fist and is the largest lymphoid organ. Located in the left side of the abdominal cavity just beneath the diaphragm, it curls around the anterior aspect of the stomach (Figure 20.5 and Figure 20.6). It is served by the large *splenic artery* and *vein*, which enter and exit the *hilum* on its slightly concave anterior surface.

The spleen provides a site for lymphocyte proliferation and immune surveillance and response. But perhaps even more important are its blood-cleansing functions. Besides extracting aged and defective blood cells and platelets from the blood, its macrophages remove debris and foreign matter from blood flowing through its sinuses. The spleen also performs three additional, and related, functions.

1. It stores some of the breakdown products of red blood cells for later reuse (for example, it salvages iron for making hemoglobin) and releases others to the blood for processing by the liver.
2. It stores blood platelets.
3. It is thought to be a site of erythrocyte production in the fetus (a capability that normally ceases after birth).

Like lymph nodes, the spleen is surrounded by a fibrous capsule, has trabeculae that extend inward, and contains both lymphocytes and macrophages. Consistent with its blood-processing functions, it also contains huge numbers of erythrocytes. Areas composed mostly of lymphocytes suspended on reticular fibers are called **white pulp**. The white pulp clusters or forms "cuffs" around the *central arteries* (small branches of the splenic artery) in the organ and forms what appear to be islands in a sea of red pulp. **Red pulp** is essentially all remaining splenic tissue, that is, the venous sinuses (blood sinusoids) and the **splenic cords**, regions of reticular connective tissue exceptionally rich in macrophages. Red pulp is most concerned with disposing of worn-out red blood cells and bloodborne pathogens, whereas white pulp is involved with the immune functions of the spleen.

The naming of the pulp regions reflects their appearance in fresh spleen tissue rather than their staining properties. Indeed, as you can see in the photomicrograph in Figure 20.6d, the white pulp sometimes appears darker than the red pulp due to the darkly staining nuclei of the densely packed lymphocytes.

HOMEOSTATIC IMBALANCE

Because the spleen's capsule is relatively thin, a direct blow or severe infection may cause it to rupture, spilling blood into the peritoneal cavity. Once, removal of the ruptured spleen (a procedure called a *splenectomy*) was the standard treatment and thought necessary to prevent life-threatening hemorrhage and shock. However, surgeons have discovered that, if left alone, the spleen can often repair itself. At major trauma centers, the frequency of emergency splenectomies has decreased from 70% to 40%. If the spleen is removed, the liver and bone marrow take over most of its functions. In children younger than 12, the spleen will regenerate if a small part of it is left in the body. ■

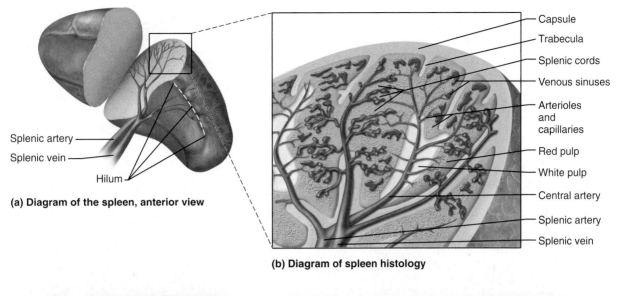

(a) Diagram of the spleen, anterior view

(b) Diagram of spleen histology

(c) Photograph of the spleen in its normal position in the abdominal cavity, anterior view.

(d) Photomicrograph of spleen tissue (30×). The white pulp, a lymphoid tissue with many lymphocytes, is surrounded by red pulp containing abundant erythrocytes.

Figure 20.6 **The spleen.** (See *A Brief Atlas of the Human Body*, Plate 39.)

Thymus

The bilobed **thymus** (thi′mus) has important functions primarily during the early years of life. It is found in the inferior neck and extends into the superior thorax, where it partially overlies the heart deep to the sternum (see Figure 20.5 and Figure 20.7). The thymus is the site where T lymphocyte precursors mature to become immunocomptetent lymphocytes. In other words, the thymus is where T lymphocytes become able to defend us against specific pathogens in the immune response.

Prominent in newborns, the thymus continues to increase in size during the first year, when it is highly active. After puberty, it starts to atrophy gradually and by old age it has been replaced almost entirely by fibrous and fatty tissue and is difficult to distinguish from surrounding connective tissue.

To understand thymic histology, it helps to compare the thymus to a cauliflower head—the flowerets represent *thymic lobules*, each containing an outer cortex and an inner medulla (Figure 20.7). Most thymic cells are lymphocytes. In the cortical regions the rapidly dividing lymphocytes are densely packed, but a few macrophages are scattered among them. The thymus has no follicles, because it lacks B cells. The lighter-staining medullary areas contain fewer lymphocytes plus some bizarre structures called **thymic (Hassall's) corpuscles**. Consisting of concentric whorls of keratinized epithelial cells, they were thought to be sites of T cell destruction. Recent evidence suggests that Hassall's corpuscles are involved in the development of a class of T lymphocytes called regulatory T cells, which are important for preventing autoimmune responses.

In addition to its lack of follicles, the thymus differs from other lymphoid organs in two other important ways. First, it functions strictly in maturation of T lymphocyte precursors and thus is the only lymphoid organ that does not *directly* fight antigens. In fact, the so-called *blood-thymus barrier* keeps bloodborne antigens from leaking into the cortical regions to prevent premature activation of the immature lymphocytes. Second, the stroma of the thymus consists of epithelial cells

20

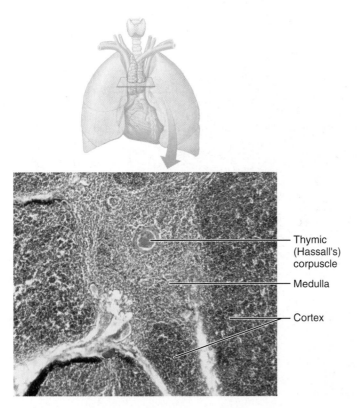

Figure 20.7 **The thymus.** The photomicrograph of a portion of the thymus shows part of a lobule with cortical and medullary regions (70×).

Figure 20.8 **Histology of the palatine tonsil.** The exterior surface of the tonsil is covered by squamous epithelium, which invaginates deeply to form tonsillar crypts (20×).

rather than reticular fibers. These epithelial cells provide the physical and chemical environment in which T lymphocytes can become immunocompetent.

Tonsils

The **tonsils** are the simplest lymphoid organs. They form a ring of lymphatic tissue around the entrance to the pharynx (throat), where they appear as swellings of the mucosa (**Figures 20.8** and 22.3). The tonsils are named according to location. The paired **palatine tonsils** are located on either side at the posterior end of the oral cavity. These are the largest of the tonsils and the ones most often infected. A lumpy collection of lymphoid follicles at the base of the tongue is referred to collectively as the **lingual tonsil**. The **pharyngeal tonsil** (referred to as the *adenoids* if enlarged) is in the posterior wall of the nasopharynx. The tiny **tubal tonsils** surround the openings of the auditory tubes into the pharynx. The tonsils gather and remove many of the pathogens entering the pharynx in food or in inhaled air.

The lymphoid tissue of the tonsils contains follicles with obvious germinal centers surrounded by diffusely scattered lymphocytes. The tonsils are not fully encapsulated, and the epithelium overlying them invaginates deep into their interior, forming blind-ended **tonsillar crypts** (Figure 20.8). The crypts trap bacteria and particulate matter, and the bacteria work their way through the mucosal epithelium into the lymphoid tissue,

where most are destroyed. It seems a bit dangerous to "invite" infection this way, but this strategy produces a wide variety of immune cells that have a "memory" for the trapped pathogens. In other words, the body takes a calculated risk early on (during childhood) for the benefits of heightened immunity and better health later.

Aggregates of Lymphoid Follicles

Peyer's patches (pi′erz), or *aggregated lymphoid nodules*, are large clusters of lymphoid follicles, structurally similar to the tonsils. They are located in the wall of the distal portion of the small intestine (Figure 20.5 and **Figure 20.9**). Lymphoid follicles are also heavily concentrated in the wall of the **appendix**, a tubular offshoot of the first part of the large intestine. Peyer's patches and the appendix are in an ideal position (1) to destroy bacteria (which are present in large numbers in the intestine) before these pathogens can breach the intestinal wall, and (2) to generate many "memory" lymphocytes for long-term immunity.

Peyer's patches, the appendix, and the tonsils—all located in the digestive tract—and lymphoid follicles in the walls of the bronchi (organs of the respiratory tract) and in the mucosa of genitourinary organs are part of the collection of small lymphoid tissues referred to as **mucosa-associated lymphatic tissue (MALT)**. MALT protects passages that are open to the exterior from the never-ending onslaughts of foreign matter entering them.

Developmental Aspects of the Lymphatic System and Lymphoid Organs and Tissues

▶ Outline the development of the lymphatic system and the lymphoid organs and tissues.

By the fifth week of embryonic development, the beginnings of the lymphatic vessels and the main clusters of lymph nodes are apparent. These arise from the budding of **lymph sacs** from developing veins. The first of these, the *jugular lymph sacs*, arise at the junctions of the internal jugular and subclavian veins and form a branching system of lymphatic vessels throughout the thorax, upper extremities, and head. The two main connections of the jugular lymph sacs to the venous system are retained and become the right lymphatic duct and, on the left, the superior part of the thoracic duct. Caudally the elaborate system of abdominal lymphatics buds largely from the primitive inferior vena cava. The lymphatics of the pelvic region and lower extremities form from sacs on the iliac veins.

Except for the thymus, which is an endodermal derivative, the lymphoid organs develop from mesodermal mesenchymal cells that migrate to particular body sites and develop into reticular tissue. The thymus, the first lymphoid organ to appear, forms as an outgrowth of the lining of the primitive pharynx. It then detaches and migrates caudally to the thorax where it becomes infiltrated with immature lymphocytes derived from hematopoietic tissues elsewhere in the embryo's body. Except for the spleen and tonsils, the lymphoid organs are poorly developed before birth. Shortly after birth, they become heavily populated by lymphocytes, and their development parallels the maturation of the immune system.

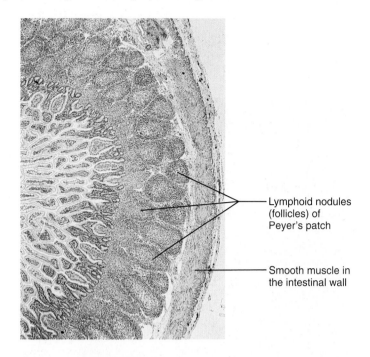

Figure 20.9 Peyer's patch. Histological structure of aggregated lymphoid nodules—a Peyer's patch—in the wall of the ileum of the small intestine (20×).

Lymphoid nodules (follicles) of Peyer's patch

Smooth muscle in the intestinal wall

CHECK YOUR UNDERSTANDING

6. What is MALT? List several components of MALT.
7. List several functions of the spleen.
8. Which lymphoid organ develops first?

For answers, see Appendix G.

Although the functions of the lymphatic vessels and lymphoid organs overlap, each helps maintain body homeostasis in unique ways, as summarized in *Making Connections* (pp. 762–763). The lymphatic vessels help maintain blood volume. The macrophages of lymphoid organs remove and destroy foreign matter in lymph and blood. Additionally, lymphoid organs and tissues provide sites from which the immune system can be mobilized. In Chapter 21, we continue this story as we examine the inflammatory and immune responses that allow us to resist a constant barrage of pathogens.

RELATED CLINICAL TERMS

Elephantiasis (el″lĕ-fan-ti′ah-sis) Typically a tropical disease in which the lymphatics (particularly those of the lower limbs and scrotum) become clogged with parasitic roundworms, an infectious condition called filariasis. Swelling (due to edema) reaches enormous proportions.

Hodgkin's disease A malignancy of lymphoid tissue; symptoms include swollen, nonpainful lymph nodes, fatigue, and often intermittent fever and night sweats. Characterized by presence of giant malignantly transformed B cells called Reed-Sternberg cells. Infection with Epstein-Barr virus (see mononucleosis below) and genetic susceptibility appear to be predisposing factors. Treated with chemotherapy and radiation; high cure rate.

Lymphadenopathy (lim-fad″ĕ-nop′ah-the; *adeno* = a gland; *pathy* = disease) Any disease of the lymph nodes.

Lymphangiography (lim-fan″je-og′rah-fe) Diagnostic procedure in which the lymphatic vessels are injected with radiopaque dye and then visualized with X rays.

Lymphoma Any neoplasm (tumor) of the lymphoid tissue, whether benign or malignant.

System Connections

System Connections: Homeostatic Interrelationships Between the Lymphatic System/Immunity and Other Body Systems

Nervous System

- Lymphatic vessels pick up leaked plasma fluid and proteins in PNS structures; immune cells protect PNS structures from specific pathogens
- The nervous system innervates larger lymphatics; opiate neuropeptides influence immune functions; the brain helps regulate immune response

Endocrine System

- Lymphatic vessels pick up leaked fluids and proteins; lymph helps distribute hormones; immune cells protect endocrine organs
- The thymus produces hormones that are thought to be involved in the maturation of T cells; stress hormones depress immune activity

Cardiovascular System

- Lymphatic vessels pick up leaked plasma and proteins; spleen removes and destroys aged RBCs and debris, and stores iron and platelets; immune cells protect cardiovascular organs from specific pathogens
- Blood is the source of lymph; lymphatics develop from veins; blood circulates immune elements

Respiratory System

- Lymphatic vessels pick up leaked fluids and proteins from respiratory organs; immune cells protect respiratory organs from specific pathogens; the tonsils and plasma cells in the respiratory mucosa (which secrete the antibody IgA) prevent pathogen invasion
- The lungs provide O_2 needed by lymphoid/immune cells and eliminate CO_2; the pharynx houses the tonsils; respiratory "pump" aids lymph flow

Digestive System

- Lymphatic vessels pick up leaked fluids and proteins from digestive organs; lymph transports some products of fat digestion to the blood; lymphoid follicles in the intestinal wall prevent invasion of pathogens
- The digestive system digests and absorbs nutrients needed by cells of lymphoid organs; gastric acidity inhibits pathogens' entry into blood

Urinary System

- Lymphatic vessels pick up leaked fluid and proteins from urinary organs; immune cells protect urinary organs from specific pathogens
- Urinary system eliminates wastes and maintains homeostatic balances of water, pH, and electrolytes in the blood for lymphoid/immune cell functioning; urine flushes some pathogens out of the urinary tract

Reproductive System

- Lymphatic vessels pick up leaked fluid and proteins; immune cells protect against pathogens
- Reproductive organs' hormones may influence immune functioning; acidity of vaginal secretions is bacteriostatic

Integumentary System

- Lymphatic vessels pick up leaked plasma fluid and proteins from the dermis; lymphocytes in lymphoid organs and tissues enhance the skin's protective role by defending against specific pathogens via the immune response
- The skin's keratinized epithelium provides a mechanical barrier to pathogens; epithelial dendritic cells and dermal macrophages act as antigen presenters in the immune response; acid pH of skin secretions inhibits growth of bacteria on the skin

Skeletal System

- Lymphatic vessels pick up leaked plasma fluid and proteins from the periostea; immune cells protect bones from pathogens
- The bones house hematopoietic tissue which produces the lymphocytes (and macrophages) that populate lymphoid organs and provide immunity

Muscular System

- Lymphatic vessels pick up leaked fluids and proteins; immune cells protect muscles from pathogens
- The skeletal muscle "pump" aids the flow of lymph; heat produced during muscle activity initiates feverlike effects

20

The Lymphatic System/Immunity and Interrelationships with the Cardiovascular System

All living body cells are bathed by lymph. Nonetheless, the lymphatic system with its ghostly vessels is elusive and hard to pin down. Like a ground mole that tunnels throughout your yard, you know it's there, but you never see it as it quietly goes about its business. Since hormones made by endocrine organs are released into the extracellular space, and lymphatic vessels take up the fluid containing them, there is little question that lymph is an important medium for delivering hormones throughout the body. Lymph plays a similar delivery role as it delivers fats absorbed by the digestive organs.

Our immune system, charged with protecting the body from specific pathogens, is often considered a separate and independent functional system. However, it is impossible to divorce the immune system from the lymphatic system because the lymph nodes belong to both systems. The lymphoid organs and tissues, including the lymph nodes, are the anatomical underpinnings of the immune system. The lymphoid organs are the programming sites and seedbeds for the immune cells. The lymph nodes and spleen provide crucial vantage points for monitoring blood and lymph for the presence of foreign substances. Less understood are the intimate interactions between the immune cells that populate the lymphoid tissues and the nervous and endocrine systems, but we defer this interesting topic to Chapter 21 to give you the opportunity to consider the immune system in detail.

Although the lymphatic system serves the entire body, its chief "master" is the cardiovascular system. The immune system is also intimately tied to the cardiovascular system. It is these relationships that we will explore further here.

Cardiovascular System

By now you are probably fairly comfortable with the fact that the lymphatic system picks up and returns leaked fluid and proteins to the blood vascular system. So, what's the big deal? We ingest water in virtually everything we eat and drink—lost water is replaceable in a few minutes, right? The answer, of course, is "true." But what would still be missing is the leaked proteins, and these plasma proteins (most made by the liver) take time and energy to make. Since plasma proteins play a major role in keeping fluid in blood vessels (or encouraging its return), without them our blood vessels would contain too little fluid to support blood circulation. And without blood circulation, the whole body would die for lack of oxygen and nutrients and drown in its own wastes. Lymphoid organs also help to maintain the health and purity of blood—lymph nodes filter microorganisms and other debris from lymph before it is allowed to reenter the blood, and the spleen performs the same cleansing service for blood. In addition, the spleen disposes of inefficient, deformed, or aged erythrocytes.

The benefits are not entirely one-way. Lymphatic vessels spring from veins of the cardiovascular system, and blood delivers oxygen and nutrients to all body organs, including lymphoid ones. Blood also provides a means for (1) rapid transport of lymphocytes (immune cells) that continuously patrol the body for foreign substances and (2) broad distribution of antibodies (made by descendants of B cells called plasma cells), which mark foreign substances for destruction by phagocytosis or other means. Furthermore, the endothelial cells of capillaries express surface protein "signals" (integrins/adhesion molecules) that lymphocytes can recognize when the surrounding area is injured or infected. Hence, capillaries guide immune cells to the sites where their protective services are needed, and the extremely porous walls of the postcapillary venules allow them to slip through the vessel wall to get there.

Lymphatic System/Immunity

Case study: Back to following the progress of Mr. Hutchinson, we learn that the routine complete blood count (CBC) performed on admission revealed that his leukocyte count is dangerously low and follow-up lab tests show that his lymphocytes are deficient. One day postsurgery, he complains of pain in his right ring finger (that hand had a crush injury). When examined, the affected finger and the dorsum of the right hand were edematous, and red streaks radiated superiorly on his right forearm. Higher-than-normal doses of antibiotics are prescribed, and a sling is applied to the affected arm. Nurses are instructed to wear gloves and gown when giving Mr. Hutchinson his care.

Relative to these observations:

1. What do the red streaks emanating from the bruised finger indicate? What would you conclude his problem was if there were no red streaks but the right arm was very edematous?

2. Why is it important that Mr. Hutchinson not move the affected arm excessively (i.e., why was the sling ordered)?

3. How might the low lymphocyte count, megadoses of antibiotics, and orders for additional clinical staff protection be related?

4. Do you predict that Mr. Hutchinson's recovery will be uneventful or problematic? Why?

(Answers in Appendix G)

Mononucleosis A viral disease common in adolescents and young adults; symptoms include fatigue, fever, sore throat, and swollen lymph nodes. Caused by the Epstein-Barr virus, which is transmitted in saliva ("kissing disease") and specifically attacks B lymphocytes. This attack leads to a massive activation of T lymphocytes, which in turn attack the virus-infected B cells. Large numbers of oversized T lymphocytes circulate in the bloodstream. (These lymphocytes were originally misidentified as monocytes: *mononucleosis* = a condition of monocytes.) Usually lasts four to six weeks.

Non-Hodgkin's lymphoma Includes all cancers of lymphoid tissues except Hodgkin's disease. Involves uncontrolled multiplication and metastasis of undifferentiated lymphocytes, with swelling of the lymph nodes, spleen, and Peyer's patches; other organs may eventually become involved. The fifth most common cancer. A high-grade type, which primarily affects young people, grows quickly but is responsive to chemotherapy; up to a 75% remission rate. A low-grade type, which affects the elderly, is resistant to chemotherapy and so is often fatal.

Sentinel node The first node that receives lymph drainage from a body area suspected of being cancerous. When examined for presence of cancer cells, this node gives the best indication of whether metastasis through the lymphatic vessels has occurred.

Splenomegaly (sple″no-meg′ah-le; *mega* = big) Enlargement of the spleen due to accumulation of infectious microorganisms; typically caused by septicemia, mononucleosis, malaria, or leukemia.

Tonsillitis (ton″sĭ-li′tis; *itis* = inflammation) Inflammation of the tonsils, typically due to bacterial infection; they become red, swollen, and sore.

CHAPTER SUMMARY

Media study tools that could provide you additional help in reviewing specific key topics of Chapter 20 are referenced below.

iP = *Interactive Physiology*

1. Lymphatic vessels, lymph nodes, and lymph make up the lymphatic system. Lymphatic vessels return fluids that have leaked from the blood vascular system back to the blood. Lymphoid organs and tissues protect the body by removing foreign material from the lymph and blood streams, and provide a site for immune surveillance.

Lymphatic Vessels (pp. 753–755)

Distribution and Structure of Lymphatic Vessels (pp. 753–754)

1. Lymphatic vessels form a one-way network—lymphatic capillaries, collecting vessels, trunks, and ducts—in which fluid flows only toward the heart. The right lymphatic duct drains lymph from the right arm and right side of the upper body; the thoracic duct receives lymph from the rest of the body. These ducts empty into the blood vascular system at the junction of the internal jugular and subclavian veins in the neck.
2. Lymphatic capillaries are exceptionally permeable, admitting proteins and particulate matter from the interstitial space.
3. Pathogens and cancer cells may spread through the body via the lymphatic stream.

Lymph Transport (pp. 754–755)

4. The flow of lymphatic fluid is slow; it is maintained by skeletal muscle contraction, pressure changes in the thorax, and contractions of the lymphatic vessels. Backflow is prevented by valves.

iP Immune System; Topic: Anatomy Review, pp. 7–9.

Lymphoid Cells and Tissues (pp. 755–756)

Lymphoid Cells (pp. 755–756)

1. The cells in lymphoid tissues include lymphocytes (immunocompetent cells called T cells or B cells), plasma cells (antibody-producing offspring of B cells), macrophages and dendritic cells (cells that capture antigens and initiate an immune response), and reticular cells that form the lymphoid tissue stroma.

Lymphoid Tissue (p. 756)

2. Lymphoid tissue is reticular connective tissue. It houses macrophages and a continuously changing population of lymphocytes. It is an important element of the immune system.
3. Lymphoid tissue may be diffuse or packaged into dense follicles. Follicles often display germinal centers (areas where B cells are proliferating).

iP Immune System; Topic: Anatomy Review, pp. 4–5.

Lymph Nodes (pp. 756–758)

1. Lymph nodes, the principal lymphoid organs, are discrete encapsulated structures containing both diffusely arranged and dense reticular tissue. Clustered along lymphatic vessels, lymph nodes filter lymph and help activate the immune system.

Structure of a Lymph Node (pp. 756–757)

2. Each lymph node has a fibrous capsule, a cortex, and a medulla. The cortex contains mostly lymphocytes, which act in immune responses; the medulla contains macrophages, which engulf and destroy viruses, bacteria, and other foreign debris, as well as lymphocytes and plasma cells.

Circulation in the Lymph Nodes (pp. 757–758)

3. Lymph enters the lymph nodes via afferent lymphatic vessels and exits via efferent vessels. There are fewer efferent vessels; therefore, lymph flow stagnates within the lymph node, allowing time for its cleansing.

iP Immune System; Topic: Anatomy Review, pp. 10–12.

Other Lymphoid Organs (pp. 758–763)

1. Unlike lymph nodes, the spleen, thymus, tonsils, and Peyer's patches do not filter lymph. However, most lymphoid organs contain both macrophages and lymphocytes.

Spleen (p. 758)

2. The spleen provides a site for lymphocyte proliferation and immune function, and destroys aged or defective red blood cells and bloodborne pathogens. It also stores and releases the breakdown products of hemoglobin as necessary, stores platelets, and acts as a hematopoietic site in the fetus.

Thymus (pp. 759–760)

3. The thymus is most functional during youth. The thymus provides the environment in which T lymphocytes mature and become immunocompetent.

Tonsils and Aggregates of Lymphoid Follicles (pp. 760–761)

4. Peyer's patches of the intestinal wall, lymphoid follicles of the appendix, tonsils of the pharynx and oral cavity, and follicles in the genitourinary and respiratory tract mucosae are known as MALT (mucosa-associated lymphatic tissue). They prevent pathogens in these passages from penetrating the mucous membrane lining.

 Immune System; Topic: Anatomy Review, pp. 13–14, 16–20.

Developmental Aspects of the Lymphatic System and Lymphoid Organs and Tissues (p. 761)

1. Lymphatics develop as outpocketings of developing veins. The thymus develops from endoderm; the other lymphoid organs derive from mesenchymal cells of mesoderm.
2. The thymus is the first lymphoid organ to develop.
3. Lymphoid organs are populated by lymphocytes, which arise from hematopoietic tissue.

REVIEW QUESTIONS

Multiple Choice/Matching

(Some questions have more than one correct answer. Select the best answer or answers from the choices given.)

1. Lymphatic vessels (a) serve as sites for immune surveillance, (b) filter lymph, (c) transport leaked plasma proteins and fluids to the cardiovascular system, (d) are represented by vessels that resemble arteries, capillaries, and veins.

2. The saclike initial portion of the thoracic duct is the (a) lacteal, (b) right lymphatic duct, (c) cisterna chyli, (d) lymph sac.

3. Entry of lymph into the lymphatic capillaries is promoted by which of the following? (a) one-way minivalves formed by overlapping endothelial cells, (b) the respiratory pump, (c) the skeletal muscle pump, (d) greater fluid pressure in the interstitial space.

4. The structural framework of lymphoid organs is (a) areolar connective tissue, (b) hematopoietic tissue, (c) reticular tissue, (d) adipose tissue.

5. Lymph nodes are densely clustered in all of the following body areas *except* (a) the brain, (b) the axillae, (c) the groin, (d) the cervical region.

6. The germinal centers in lymph nodes are largely sites of (a) macrophages, (b) proliferating B lymphocytes, (c) T lymphocytes, (d) all of these.

7. The red pulp areas of the spleen are sites of (a) venous sinuses, macrophages, and red blood cells, (b) clustered lymphocytes, (c) connective tissue septa.

8. The lymphoid organ that functions primarily during youth and then begins to atrophy is the (a) spleen, (b) thymus, (c) palatine tonsils, (d) bone marrow.

9. Collections of lymphoid tissue (MALT) that guard mucosal surfaces include all of the following except (a) appendix follicles, (b) the tonsils, (c) Peyer's patches, (d) the thymus.

Short Answer Essay Questions

10. Compare and contrast blood, interstitial fluid, and lymph.
11. Compare the structure and functions of a lymph node to those of the spleen.

12. (a) What anatomical characteristic ensures that the flow of lymph through a lymph node is slow? (b) Why is this desirable?
13. Why doesn't the absence of lymphatic arteries represent a problem?

Critical Thinking and Clinical Application Questions

1. Mrs. Jackson, a 59-year-old woman, has undergone a left radical mastectomy (removal of the left breast and left axillary lymph nodes and vessels). Her left arm is severely swollen and painful, and she is unable to raise it to more than shoulder height. (a) Explain her signs and symptoms. (b) Can she expect to have relief from these symptoms in time? How so?

2. A friend tells you that she has tender, swollen "glands" along the left side of the front of her neck. You notice that she has a bandage on her left cheek that is not fully hiding a large infected cut there. Exactly what are her swollen "glands," and how did they become swollen?

3. Once almost a rite of childhood, tonsillectomy (surgical removal of the tonsils) is now rarely performed. Similarly, while ruptured spleens were once routinely removed, they are now conserved whenever possible. Why should these lymphoid organs be preserved when possible

 myA&P place

Access everything you need to practice, review, and self-assess for both your A&P lecture and lab courses at **myA&P** (www.myaandp.com). There, you'll find powerful online resources, including chapter quizzes and tests, games, A&P Flix animations with quizzes, *Interactive Physiology*® with quizzes, MP3 Tutor Sessions, Practice Anatomy Lab™, and more to help you get a better grade in your course.

20

21

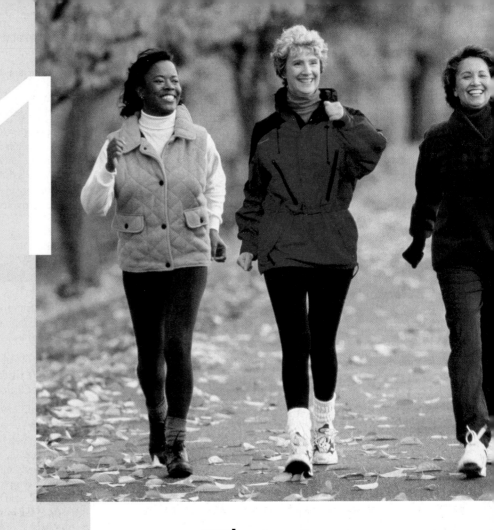

The Immune System: Innate and Adaptive Body Defenses

Every second of every day, armies of hostile bacteria, fungi, and viruses swarm on our skin and yet we stay amazingly healthy most of the time. The body seems to have evolved a single-minded approach to such foes—if you're not with us, you're against us! To implement that stance, it relies heavily on two intrinsic defense systems that act both independently and cooperatively to provide resistance to disease, or **immunity** (*immun* = free).

1. The **innate (nonspecific) defense system**, like a lowly foot soldier, is always prepared, responding within minutes to protect the body from all foreign substances. This system has two "barricades." The *first line of defense* is the external body membranes—intact skin and mucosae. The *second line of defense*, called into action whenever the first line has been penetrated, uses antimicrobial proteins, phagocytes, and other cells to inhibit the invaders' spread throughout the body. The hallmark of the second line of defense is inflammation.

2. The **adaptive** (or **specific**) **defense system** is more like an elite fighting force equipped with high-tech weapons that attacks *particular* foreign substances and provides the body's *third line of defense*. This defensive response takes considerably more time to mount than the innate response. Although we consider them separately, the adaptive and innate systems always work hand in hand. An overview of these two systems is shown in **Figure 21.1**. Small portions of this diagram will reappear in subsequent figures to let you know which part of the immune system we're dealing with.

Although certain organs of the body (notably lymphoid organs) are intimately involved in the immune response, the **immune system** is a *functional system* rather than an organ system in an anatomical sense. Its "structures" are a diverse array of molecules plus trillions of immune cells (especially lymphocytes) that inhabit lymphoid tissues and circulate in body fluids.

Once, the term *immune system* was equated with the adaptive defense system only. However, we now know that the innate and adaptive defenses are deeply intertwined. Specifically, (1) many defensive molecules are released and recognized by both the innate and adaptive arms; (2) the innate responses are not as nonspecific as once thought and have specific pathways to target certain foreign substances; and (3) proteins released during innate responses alert cells of the adaptive system to the presence of specific foreign molecules in the body.

When the immune system is operating effectively, it protects the body from most infectious microorganisms, cancer cells, and transplanted organs or grafts. It does this both directly, by cell attack, and indirectly, by releasing mobilizing chemicals and protective antibody molecules.

PART 1

INNATE DEFENSES

Because they are part and parcel of our anatomy, you could say we come fully equipped with innate defenses. The mechanical barriers that cover body surfaces and the cells and chemicals

Figure 21.1 Overview of innate and adaptive defenses. Humoral immunity (primarily involving B lymphocytes) and cellular immunity (involving T lymphocytes) are distinct but overlapping areas of adaptive immunity. For simplicity, the many interactions between innate and adaptive defenses are not shown here.

that act on the initial internal battlefronts are in place at birth, ready to ward off invading **pathogens** (harmful or disease-causing microorganisms) and infection.

Many times, our innate defenses alone are able to destroy pathogens and ward off infection. In other cases, the adaptive immune system is called into action to reinforce and enhance the innate defenses. Either way, the innate defenses reduce the workload of the adaptive system by preventing the entry and spread of microorganisms in the body.

Surface Barriers: Skin and Mucosae

▶ Describe surface membrane barriers and their protective functions.

The body's first line of defense—the *skin* and the *mucous membranes*, along with the secretions these membranes produce—is highly effective. As long as the epidermis is unbroken, this heavily keratinized epithelial membrane presents a formidable physical barrier to most microorganisms that swarm on the skin. Keratin is also resistant to most weak acids and bases and to bacterial enzymes and toxins. Intact mucosae provide similar mechanical barriers within the body. Recall that mucous membranes line all body cavities that open to the exterior: the digestive, respiratory, urinary, and reproductive tracts. Besides serving as physical barriers, these epithelial membranes produce a variety of protective chemicals:

1. The acidity of skin secretions (pH 3 to 5) inhibits bacterial growth. In addition, lipids in sebum and dermcidin in

eccrine sweat are toxic to bacteria. Vaginal secretions of adult females are also very acidic.

2. The stomach mucosa secretes a concentrated hydrochloric acid solution and protein-digesting enzymes. Both kill microorganisms.

3. Saliva, which cleanses the oral cavity and teeth, and lacrimal fluid of the eye contain **lysozyme**, an enzyme that destroys bacteria.

4. Sticky mucus traps many microorganisms that enter the digestive and respiratory passageways.

The respiratory tract mucosae also have structural modifications that counteract potential invaders. Tiny mucus-coated hairs inside the nose trap inhaled particles, and cilia on the mucosa of the upper respiratory tract sweep dust- and bacteria-laden mucus toward the mouth, preventing it from entering the lower respiratory passages, where the warm, moist environment provides an ideal site for bacterial growth.

Although the surface barriers are quite effective, they are breached occasionally by small nicks and cuts resulting, for example, from brushing your teeth or shaving. When this happens and microorganisms invade deeper tissues, the *internal* innate defenses come into play.

CHECK YOUR UNDERSTANDING

1. What distinguishes the innate defense system from the adaptive defense system?
2. What is the first line of defense against disease?

For answers, see Appendix G.

Internal Defenses: Cells and Chemicals

▶ Explain the importance of phagocytosis and natural killer cells in innate body defense.

The body uses an enormous number of nonspecific cellular and chemical devices to protect itself, including phagocytes, natural killer cells, antimicrobial proteins, and fever. The inflammatory response enlists macrophages, mast cells, all types of white blood cells, and dozens of chemicals that kill pathogens and help repair tissue. All these protective ploys identify potentially harmful substances by recognizing surface carbohydrates unique to infectious organisms (bacteria, viruses, and fungi).

Phagocytes

Pathogens that get through the skin and mucosae into the underlying connective tissue are confronted by *phagocytes* (*phago* = eat). The chief phagocytes are **macrophages** ("big eaters"), which derive from white blood cells called **monocytes** that leave the bloodstream, enter the tissues, and develop into macrophages.

Free macrophages, like the alveolar macrophages of the lungs, wander throughout the tissue spaces in search of cellular debris or "foreign invaders." *Fixed macrophages* like *Kupffer cells* in the liver and microglia of the brain are permanent residents of particular organs. Whatever their mobility, all macrophages are similar structurally and functionally.

Neutrophils, the most abundant type of white blood cell, become phagocytic on encountering infectious material in the tissues.

Phagocytosis

A phagocyte engulfs particulate matter much the way an amoeba ingests a food particle. Flowing cytoplasmic extensions bind to the particle and then pull it inside, enclosed within a membrane-lined vesicle (**Figure 21.2a**). The resulting **phagosome** is then fused with a *lysosome* to form a **phagolysosome** (steps ①–③ in Figure 21.2b).

Phagocytic attempts are not always successful. In order for a phagocyte to accomplish ingestion, **adherence** must occur. The phagocyte must first *adhere* or cling to the pathogen, a feat made possible by recognizing the pathogen's carbohydrate "signature." Recognition is particularly difficult with microorganisms such as pneumococcus, which have an external capsule made of complex sugars. These pathogens can sometimes elude capture because phagocytes cannot bind to their capsules. Adherence is both more probable and more efficient when complement proteins or antibodies coat foreign particles, a process called **opsonization** ("to make tasty"), because the coating provides "handles" to which phagocyte receptors can bind.

Sometimes the way neutrophils and macrophages kill ingested prey is more than simple acidification and digestion by lysosomal enzymes. For example, pathogens such as the tuberculosis bacillus and certain parasites are resistant to lysosomal enzymes and can even multiply within the phagolysosome. However, when the macrophage is stimulated by chemicals released by other immune cells called helper T cells, additional enzymes are activated that produce the **respiratory burst**. This event liberates a deluge of free radicals (including nitric oxide and superoxide) that have potent cell-killing abilities. More widespread cell killing is caused by oxidizing chemicals (H_2O_2 and a substance identical to household bleach). The respiratory burst also increases the pH and osmolarity in the phagolysosome, which activates other protein-digesting enzymes that digest the invader. Neutrophils also produce antimicrobial chemicals, called *defensins*, that pierce the pathogen's membrane.

When phagocytes are unable to ingest their targets (because of size, for example), they can release their toxic chemicals into the extracellular fluid. Whether killing ingested or extracellular targets, neutrophils rapidly destroy themselves in the process, whereas macrophages are more robust and can go on to kill another day.

Natural Killer Cells

Natural killer (NK) cells, which "police" the body in blood and lymph, are a unique group of defensive cells that can lyse and kill cancer cells and virus-infected body cells before the adaptive immune system is activated. Sometimes called the "pit bulls" of the defense system, NK cells are part of a small group of *large*

Innate defenses ——▶ Internal defenses

(a) A macrophage (purple) uses its cytoplasmic extensions to pull spherical bacteria (green) toward it. Scanning electron micrograph (1750×).

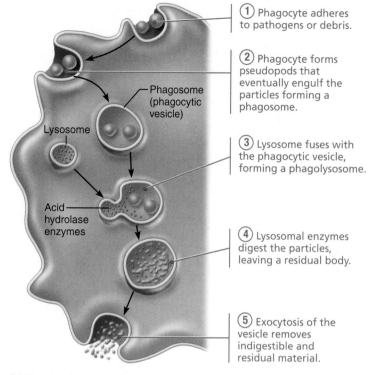

① Phagocyte adheres to pathogens or debris.

② Phagocyte forms pseudopods that eventually engulf the particles forming a phagosome.

③ Lysosome fuses with the phagocytic vesicle, forming a phagolysosome.

④ Lysosomal enzymes digest the particles, leaving a residual body.

⑤ Exocytosis of the vesicle removes indigestible and residual material.

Phagosome (phagocytic vesicle)

Lysosome

Acid hydrolase enzymes

(b) Events of phagocytosis.

Figure 21.2 **Phagocytosis.**

granular lymphocytes. Unlike lymphocytes of the adaptive immune system, which recognize and react only against *specific* virus-infected or tumor cells, NK cells are far less picky. They can eliminate a variety of infected or cancerous cells by detecting the lack of "self" cell-surface receptors and by recognizing certain surface sugars on the target cell. The name "natural" killer cells reflects this nonspecificity of NK cells.

NK cells are not phagocytic. Their mode of killing, which involves direct contact and induces the target cell to undergo apoptosis (programmed cell death), uses the same killing mechanisms used by cytotoxic T cells (described fully on p. 792). NK cells also secrete potent chemicals that enhance the inflammatory response.

Inflammation: Tissue Response to Injury

▶ Describe the inflammatory process. Identify several inflammatory chemicals and indicate their specific roles.

The **inflammatory response** is triggered whenever body tissues are injured by physical trauma (a blow), intense heat, irritating chemicals, or infection by viruses, fungi, or bacteria. The inflammatory response has several beneficial effects:

1. Prevents the spread of damaging agents to nearby tissues
2. Disposes of cell debris and pathogens
3. Sets the stage for repair

The four *cardinal signs* of short-term, or acute, inflammation are *redness, heat* (*inflam* = set on fire), *swelling*, and *pain*. If the

inflamed area is a joint, joint movement may be hampered temporarily. This forces the injured part to rest, which aids healing. Some authorities consider *impairment of function* to be the fifth cardinal sign of acute inflammation. **Figure 21.3** presents an overview of the inflammatory process, and shows how these cardinal signs come about.

Vasodilation and Increased Vascular Permeability

The inflammatory process begins with a chemical "alarm" as a flood of inflammatory chemicals are released into the extracellular fluid. Macrophages (and cells of certain boundary tissues such as epithelial cells lining the gastrointestinal and respiratory tracts) bear surface membrane receptors, called **Toll-like receptors (TLRs)**, that play a central role in triggering immune responses. So far 11 types of human TLRs have been identified, each recognizing a specific class of attacking microbe. For example, one type responds to a glycolipid in cell walls of the tuberculosis bacterium and another to a component of gram-negative bacteria such as *Salmonella*. Once activated, a TLR triggers the release of chemicals called *cytokines* that promote inflammation and attract WBCs to the scene.

Macrophages are not the only sort of recognition "tool" in the innate system. **Mast cells**, a key component of the inflammatory response, release the potent inflammatory chemical **histamine** (his'tah-mēn). In addition, injured and stressed tissue cells, phagocytes, lymphocytes, basophils, and blood proteins are all sources of inflammatory mediators. These chemicals include not only histamine and cytokines, but **kinins** (ki'ninz), **prostaglandins** (pros"tah-glan'dinz), **leukotrienes**,

21

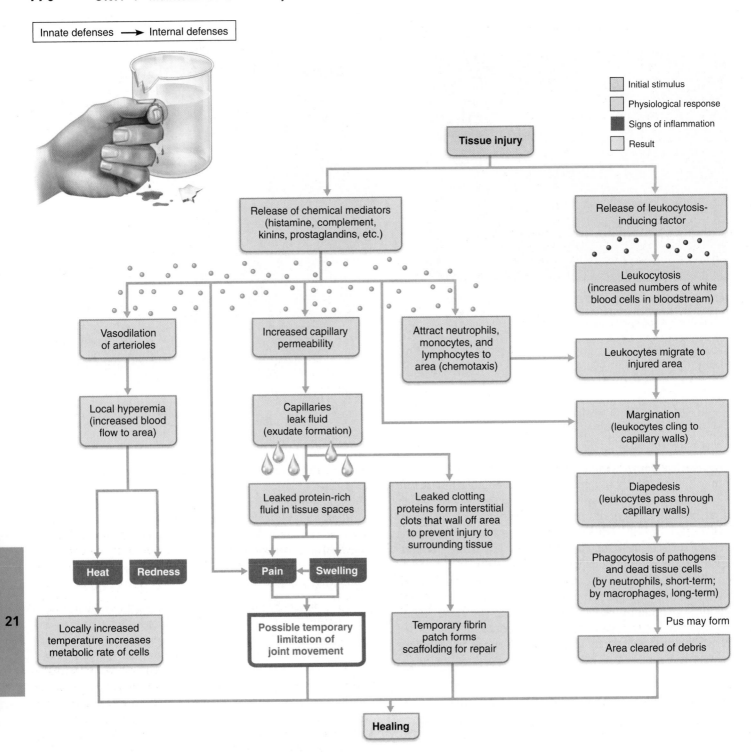

Figure 21.3 Inflammation: flowchart of events. The four cardinal signs of acute inflammation are shown in red boxes, as is limitation of joint movement, which in some cases constitutes a fifth cardinal sign (impairment of function).

and **complement**. They all cause arterioles in the injured area to dilate, although some of these mediators have individual inflammatory roles as well **(Table 21.1).** As more blood flows into the area, local **hyperemia** (congestion with blood) occurs, accounting for the *redness* and *heat* of an inflamed region.

The liberated chemicals also increase the permeability of local capillaries. Consequently, **exudate**—fluid containing clotting fac-

tors and antibodies—seeps from the blood into the tissue spaces. This exudate causes the local *swelling*, also called edema, that presses on adjacent nerve endings, contributing to a sensation of *pain*. Pain also results from the release of bacterial toxins, and the sensitizing effects of released prostaglandins and kinins. Aspirin and some other anti-inflammatory drugs produce their analgesic (pain-reducing) effects by inhibiting prostaglandin synthesis.

Innate defenses → Internal defenses

Inflammatory chemicals diffusing from the inflamed site act as chemotactic agents.

④ **Chemotaxis.** Neutrophils follow chemical trail.

Capillary wall
— Basement membrane
— Endothelium

① **Leukocytosis.** Neutrophils enter blood from bone marrow.

② **Margination.** Neutrophils cling to capillary wall.

③ **Diapedesis.** Neutrophils flatten and squeeze out of capillaries.

Figure 21.4 Phagocyte mobilization.

Although edema may seem detrimental, it isn't. The surge of protein-rich fluids into the tissue spaces sweeps any foreign material into the lymphatic vessels for processing in the lymph nodes. It also delivers important proteins such as complement and clotting factors to the interstitial fluid (Figure 21.3). The clotting proteins form a gel-like fibrin mesh that forms a scaffold for permanent repair. This isolates the injured area and prevents the spread of bacteria and other harmful agents into surrounding tissues. Walling off the injured area is such an important defense strategy that some bacteria (such as *Streptococcus*) have evolved enzymes that break down the clot, allowing the bacteria to spread rapidly into adjacent tissues.

At inflammatory sites where an epithelial barrier has been breached, additional chemicals enter the battle—β-defensins. These broad-spectrum antimicrobial chemicals are continuously present in epithelial mucosal cells in small amounts and help maintain the sterile environment of the body's internal passageways (urinary tract, respiratory bronchi, etc.). However, when the mucosal surface is abraded or penetrated and the underlying connective tissue becomes inflamed, β-defensin output increases dramatically, helping to control bacterial and fungal colonization in the exposed area.

Phagocyte Mobilization

Soon after inflammation begins, the damaged area is flooded with phagocytes. Neutrophils lead, followed by macrophages. If the inflammation was provoked by pathogens, a group of plasma proteins known as complement (to be discussed shortly) is activated and elements of adaptive immunity (lymphocytes and antibodies) also migrate to the injured site. The process by which phagocytes are mobilized to infiltrate the injured site consists of the four steps illustrated in **Figure 21.4**.

① **Leukocytosis.** Neutrophils enter blood from red bone marrow in response to chemicals called **leukocytosis-inducing factors** released by injured cells. Within a few hours, the number of neutrophils in blood increases four- to fivefold, resulting in **leukocytosis** (an increase in WBCs that is a characteristic of inflammation).

② **Margination.** Inflamed endothelial cells sprout cell adhesion molecules (CAMs) that signal "this is the place." As neutrophils encounter these CAMs, they slow and roll along the surface, achieving an initial foothold. When activated by inflammatory chemicals, CAMs on neutrophils bind tightly to endothelial cells. This clinging of phagocytes to the inner walls of the capillaries and postcapillary venules is called **margination**.

21

TABLE 21.1   Inflammatory Chemicals

CHEMICAL	SOURCE	PHYSIOLOGICAL EFFECTS
Histamine	Granules of mast cells and basophils. Released in response to mechanical injury, presence of certain microorganisms, and chemicals released by neutrophils.	Promotes vasodilation of local arterioles. Increases permeability of local capillaries, promoting exudate formation.
Kinins (bradykinin and others)	A plasma protein, kininogen, is cleaved by the enzyme kallikrein found in plasma, urine, saliva, and in lysosomes of neutrophils and other types of cells. Cleavage releases active kinin peptides.	Same as for histamine. Also induce chemotaxis of leukocytes and prompt neutrophils to release lysosomal enzymes, thereby enhancing generation of more kinins. Induce pain.
Prostaglandins	Fatty acid molecules produced from arachidonic acid found in all cell membranes; generated by enzymes of neutrophils, basophils, mast cells, and others.	Same as for histamine. Also induce neutrophil chemotaxis. Induce pain.
Platelet-derived growth factor (PDGF)	Secreted by platelets and endothelial cells.	Stimulates fibroblast activity and repair of damaged tissues.
Complement	See Table 21.2 (below).	
Cytokines	See Table 21.4 (p. 790).	

TABLE 21.2   Summary of Innate Body Defenses

CATEGORY/ASSOCIATED ELEMENTS	PROTECTIVE MECHANISM
First Line of Defense: Surface Membrane Barriers	
Intact skin epidermis	Forms mechanical barrier that prevents entry of pathogens and other harmful substances into body
▪ Acid mantle	Skin secretions (sweat and sebum) make epidermal surface acidic, which inhibits bacterial growth; also contain various bactericidal chemicals
▪ Keratin	Provides resistance against acids, alkalis, and bacterial enzymes
Intact mucous membranes	Form mechanical barrier that prevents entry of pathogens
▪ Mucus	Traps microorganisms in respiratory and digestive tracts
▪ Nasal hairs	Filter and trap microorganisms in nasal passages
▪ Cilia	Propel debris-laden mucus away from nasal cavity and lower respiratory passages
▪ Gastric juice	Contains concentrated hydrochloric acid and protein-digesting enzymes that destroy pathogens in stomach
▪ Acid mantle of vagina	Inhibits growth of most bacteria and fungi in female reproductive tract
▪ Lacrimal secretion (tears); saliva	Continuously lubricate and cleanse eyes (tears) and oral cavity (saliva); contain lysozyme, an enzyme that destroys microorganisms
▪ Urine	Normally acid pH inhibits bacterial growth; cleanses the lower urinary tract as it flushes from the body
Second Line of Defense: Innate Cellular and Chemical Defenses	
Phagocytes	Engulf and destroy pathogens that breach surface membrane barriers; macrophages also contribute to adaptive immune responses
Natural killer (NK) cells	Promote apoptosis (cell suicide) by direct cell attack against virus-infected or cancerous body cells; do not require specific antigen recognition; do not exhibit a memory response
Inflammatory response	Prevents spread of injurious agents to adjacent tissues, disposes of pathogens and dead tissue cells, and promotes tissue repair; chemical mediators released attract phagocytes (and other immune cells) to the area
Antimicrobial proteins ▪ Interferons (α, β, γ)	Proteins released by virus-infected cells and certain lymphocytes that protect uninfected tissue cells from viral takeover; mobilize immune system
▪ Complement	Lyses microorganisms, enhances phagocytosis by opsonization, and intensifies inflammatory and immune responses
Fever	Systemic response initiated by pyrogens; high body temperature inhibits microbial multiplication and enhances body repair processes

21

③ **Diapedesis.** Continued chemical signaling prompts the neutrophils to flatten and squeeze through the capillary walls—**diapedesis**.

④ **Chemotaxis.** Inflammatory chemicals act as homing devices, or more precisely **chemotactic agents**. Neutrophils and other WBCs migrate up the gradient of chemotactic agents to the site of injury (positive **chemotaxis**). Within an hour after the inflammatory response has begun, neutrophils have collected at the site and are devouring any foreign material present.

As the body's counterattack continues, monocytes follow neutrophils into the injured area. Monocytes are fairly poor phagocytes, but within 12 hours of leaving the blood and entering the tissues, they swell and develop large numbers of lysosomes, becoming macrophages with insatiable appetites. These late-arriving macrophages replace the neutrophils on the battlefield.

Macrophages are the central actors in the final disposal of cell debris as an acute inflammation subsides, and they predominate at sites of prolonged, or *chronic*, inflammation. The ultimate goal of an inflammatory response is to clear the injured area of pathogens, dead tissue cells, and any other debris so that tissue can be repaired. Once this is accomplished, healing usually occurs quickly.

HOMEOSTATIC IMBALANCE

In severely infected areas, the battle takes a considerable toll on both sides, and creamy yellow **pus** (a mixture of dead or dying neutrophils, broken-down tissue cells, and living and dead pathogens) may accumulate in the wound. If the inflammatory mechanism fails to clear the area of debris, the sac of pus may be walled off by collagen fibers, forming an *abscess*. Surgical drainage of abscesses is often necessary before healing can occur.

Some bacteria, such as tuberculosis bacilli, are resistant to digestion by the macrophages that engulf them. They escape the effects of prescription antibiotics by remaining snugly enclosed within their macrophage hosts. In such cases, *infectious granulomas* form. These tumorlike growths contain a central region of infected macrophages surrounded by uninfected macrophages and an outer fibrous capsule. A person may harbor pathogens walled off in granulomas for years without displaying any symptoms. However, if the person's resistance to infection is ever compromised, the bacteria may be activated and break out, leading to clinical disease symptoms. ■

Antimicrobial Proteins

▶ Name the body's antimicrobial substances and describe their function.

A variety of **antimicrobial proteins** enhance the innate defenses by attacking microorganisms directly or by hindering their ability to reproduce. The most important of these are interferons and complement proteins **(Table 21.2)**.

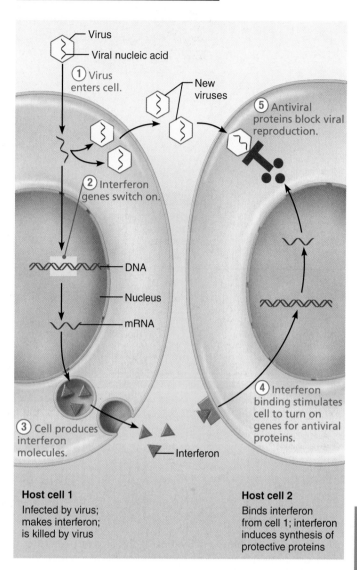

Figure 21.5 The interferon mechanism against viruses.

Interferons

Viruses—essentially nucleic acids surrounded by a protein coat—lack the cellular machinery to generate ATP or synthesize proteins. They do their "dirty work," or damage, in the body by invading tissue cells and taking over the cellular metabolic machinery needed to reproduce themselves. The infected cells can do little to save themselves, but some can secrete small proteins called **interferons (IFNs)** (in″ter-fēr′onz) to help protect cells that have not yet been infected. The IFNs diffuse to nearby cells, where they stimulate synthesis of proteins which then "interfere" with viral replication in the still-healthy cells by blocking protein synthesis and degrading viral RNA **(Figure 21.5)**. Because IFN protection is not *virus-specific*, IFNs produced against a particular virus protect against a variety of other viruses.

The IFNs are a family of related proteins produced by a variety of body cells, each having a slightly different physiological effect. Lymphocytes secrete gamma (γ), or immune, interferon,

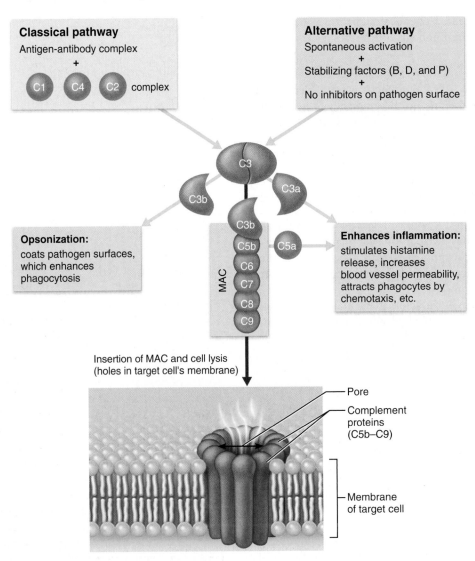

Figure 21.6 Complement activation. In the classical pathway of complement activation, antibodies coating the surface of a pathogen activate complement proteins C1, C4, and C2, which in turn activate C3. In the alternative pathway of complement activation, C3 spontaneously activates and attaches to pathogen membranes. (Unlike our own membranes, pathogen membranes do not have inhibitors of complement activation.) Factors B, D, and P stabilize spontaneously activated C3. The two pathways converge at C3, which splits into two active pieces: C3a and C3b. C3a promotes inflammation (with the help of C5a). C3b enhances phagocytosis by acting as an opsonin. In certain target cells (mostly bacteria), C3b also activates other complement proteins that can form a membrane attack complex (MAC). MACs form from activated complement components (C5b and C6 to C9) that insert into the target cell membrane, creating funnel-shaped pores that can lyse the target cell.

but most other leukocytes secrete alpha (α) interferon. Beta (β) interferon is secreted by fibroblasts. IFN-β and -α reduce inflammation, keeping it in control. Besides their antiviral effects, interferons activate macrophages and mobilize NK cells. Because both macrophages and NK cells can act directly against malignant cells, the interferons play some anticancer role.

Genetically engineered IFNs have found a niche as antiviral agents. For example, *IFN-α* is used to treat genital warts and hepatitis C. *IFN-β* is used to treat patients with multiple sclerosis, a devastating demyelinating disease.

Complement

The term **complement system**, or simply **complement**, refers to a group of at least 20 plasma proteins that normally circulate in the blood in an inactive state. These proteins include C1 through C9, factors B, D, and P, plus several regulatory proteins. Complement provides a major mechanism for destroying foreign substances in the body. Its activation unleashes chemical mediators that amplify virtually all aspects of the inflammatory process. Another effect of complement activation is that certain bacteria and other cell types are killed by cell lysis. (Luckily our own cells are equipped with proteins that inactivate complement.) Although complement is a nonspecific defensive mechanism, it "complements" (enhances) the effectiveness of *both* innate and adaptive defenses.

Complement can be activated by the two pathways outlined in **Figure 21.6**. The **classical pathway** involves *antibodies*, water-soluble protein molecules that the adaptive immune system produces to fight off foreign invaders. The classical pathway depends on the binding of antibodies to the invading organisms and the subsequent binding of C1 to the microorganism-antibody complexes, a step called *complement fixation*, which we will describe on p. 785. The **alternative pathway** is triggered when spontaneously activated C3 and factors B, D, and P interact on the surface of certain microorganisms.

Like the blood clotting cascade, complement activation by either pathway involves a cascade in which proteins are activated in an orderly sequence—each step catalyzing the next. The two pathways converge at C3, which cleaves into C3a and C3b. This event initiates a common terminal pathway that enhances inflammation, promotes phagocytosis, and can cause cell lysis.

The lytic events begin when C3b binds to the target cell's surface, triggering the insertion of a group of complement proteins called **MAC (membrane attack complex)** into the cell's membrane. MAC forms and stabilizes a hole in the membrane that ensures lysis of the target cell by inducing a massive influx of water.

The C3b molecules that coat the microorganism provide "handles" that receptors on macrophages and neutrophils can adhere to, allowing them to engulf the particle more rapidly. As noted earlier, this process is called *opsonization*. C3a and other cleavage products formed during complement fixation amplify the inflammatory response by stimulating mast cells and basophils to release histamine and by attracting neutrophils and other inflammatory cells to the area.

Fever

▶ Explain how fever helps protect the body.

Inflammation is a localized response to infection, but sometimes the body's response to the invasion of microorganisms is more widespread. **Fever**, or abnormally high body temperature, is a systemic response to invading microorganisms. As we will describe further in Chapter 24, body temperature is regulated by a cluster of neurons in the hypothalamus, commonly referred to as the body's thermostat. Normally set at approximately 37°C (98.6°F), the thermostat is reset upward in response to chemicals called **pyrogens** (*pyro* = fire), secreted by leukocytes and macrophages exposed to foreign substances in the body.

High fevers are dangerous because excess heat denatures enzymes. Mild or moderate fever, however, is an adaptive response that seems to benefit the body. In order to multiply, bacteria require large amounts of iron and zinc, but during a fever the liver and spleen sequester these nutrients, making them less available. Fever also increases the metabolic rate of tissue cells in general, speeding up repair processes.

CHECK YOUR UNDERSTANDING

3. What is opsonization and how does it help phagocytes? Give an example of a molecule that acts as an opsonin.
4. Under what circumstances are our own cells killed by NK cells?
5. What are the cardinal signs of inflammation and what causes them?

For answers, see Appendix G.

PART 2

ADAPTIVE DEFENSES

Most of us would find it wonderfully convenient if we could walk into a single clothing store and buy a complete wardrobe—hat to shoes—that fit perfectly regardless of any special figure problems. We know that such a service would be next to impossible to find. And yet, we take for granted our **adaptive immune system**, the body's built-in *specific defensive system* that stalks and eliminates with nearly equal precision almost any type of pathogen that intrudes into the body.

When it operates effectively, the adaptive immune system protects us from a wide variety of infectious agents, as well as from abnormal body cells. When it fails, or is disabled, the result is such devastating diseases as cancer and AIDS. The activity of the adaptive immune system tremendously amplifies the inflammatory response and is responsible for most complement activation.

At first glance, the adaptive system seems to have a major shortcoming. Unlike the innate system, which is always ready and able to react, the adaptive system must "meet" or be primed by an initial exposure to a specific foreign substance (antigen). Only then can it protect the body against that substance, and this priming takes precious time.

The basis of this specific immunity was revealed in the late 1800s. Researchers demonstrated that animals surviving a serious bacterial infection have in their blood protective factors (the proteins we now call *antibodies*) that defend against future attacks by the same pathogen. Furthermore, researchers found that if antibody-containing serum from the surviving animals was injected into animals that had not been exposed to the pathogen, those injected animals would also be protected. These landmark experiments were exciting because they revealed three important aspects of the adaptive immune response:

1. **It is specific.** It recognizes and is directed against *particular* pathogens or foreign substances that initiate the immune response.
2. **It is systemic.** Immunity is not restricted to the initial infection site.
3. **It has "memory."** After an initial exposure, it recognizes and mounts even stronger attacks on the previously encountered pathogens.

21

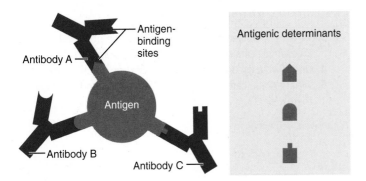

Figure 21.7 Most antigens have several different antigenic determinants. Antibodies (and related receptors on lymphocytes) bind to small areas on the antigen surface called antigenic determinants. In this example, three types of antibodies react with different antigenic determinants on the same antigen molecule.

At first antibodies were thought to be the sole artillery of the adaptive immune system, but in the mid-1900s it was discovered that injection of antibody-containing serum did *not* always protect the recipient from diseases the serum donor had survived. In such cases, however, injection of the donor's lymphocytes *did* provide immunity. As the pieces fell into place, researchers recognized two separate but overlapping arms of adaptive immunity, each using a variety of attack mechanisms that vary with the intruder.

Humoral immunity (hu′mor-ul), also called **antibody-mediated immunity**, is provided by antibodies present in the body's "humors," or fluids (blood, lymph, etc.). Though they are produced by lymphocytes (or their offspring), antibodies circulate freely in the blood and lymph, where they bind primarily to bacteria, to bacterial toxins, and to free viruses, inactivating them temporarily and marking them for destruction by phagocytes or complement.

When lymphocytes themselves rather than antibodies defend the body, the immunity is called **cellular** or **cell-mediated immunity** because the protective factor is living cells. Cellular immunity also has cellular targets—virus-infected or parasite-infected tissue cells, cancer cells, and cells of foreign grafts. The lymphocytes act against such targets either *directly*, by killing the foreign cells, or *indirectly*, by releasing chemical mediators that enhance the inflammatory response or activate other lymphocytes or macrophages. As you can see, both arms of the adaptive immune system respond to virtually the same foreign substances, but they do it in very different ways.

Before we describe the humoral and cell-mediated responses, let's first consider the *antigens* that trigger the activity of the remarkable cells involved in these immune responses.

Antigens

▶ Define antigen and describe how antigens affect the adaptive defenses.

▶ Define complete antigen, hapten, and antigenic determinant.

Antigens (an′tĭ-jenz) are substances that can mobilize the adaptive defenses and provoke an immune response. They are the ultimate targets of all adaptive immune responses. Most antigens are large, complex molecules (both natural and synthetic) that are not normally present in the body. Consequently, as far as our immune system is concerned, they are intruders, or **nonself**.

Complete Antigens and Haptens

Antigens can be *complete* or *incomplete*. **Complete antigens** have two important functional properties:

1. **Immunogenicity**, which is the ability to stimulate proliferation of specific lymphocytes and antibodies. (*Antigen* is a contraction of "*anti*body *gen*erating," which refers to this particular antigenic property.)
2. **Reactivity**, which is the ability to react with the activated lymphocytes and the antibodies released by immunogenic reactions.

An almost limitless variety of foreign molecules can act as complete antigens, including virtually all foreign proteins, many large polysaccharides, and some lipids and nucleic acids. Of these, proteins are the strongest antigens. Pollen grains and microorganisms—such as bacteria, fungi, and virus particles—are all immunogenic because their surfaces bear many different foreign macromolecules.

As a rule, small molecules—such as peptides, nucleotides, and many hormones—are not immunogenic. But, if they link up with the body's own proteins, the adaptive immune system may recognize the *combination* as foreign and mount an attack that is harmful rather than protective. (We describe these reactions, called *hypersensitivities*, later in the chapter.) In such cases, the troublesome small molecule is called a **hapten** (hap′ten; *haptein* = grasp) or **incomplete antigen**. Unless attached to protein carriers, haptens have reactivity but not immunogenicity. Besides certain drugs (particularly penicillin), chemicals that act as haptens are found in poison ivy, animal dander, detergents, cosmetics, and a number of common household and industrial products.

Antigenic Determinants

The ability of a molecule to act as an antigen depends on both its size and its complexity. Only certain parts of an entire antigen, called **antigenic determinants**, are immunogenic. Free antibodies or lymphocyte receptors bind to these sites in much the same manner an enzyme binds to a substrate.

Most naturally occurring antigens have a variety of antigenic determinants on their surfaces, some more potent than others in provoking an immune response (**Figure 21.7**). Different antigenic determinants are "recognized" by different lymphocytes, so a single antigen may mobilize several lymphocyte populations and may stimulate formation of many kinds of antibodies. Large proteins have hundreds of chemically different antigenic determinants, which accounts for their high immunogenicity and reactivity. However, large simple molecules such as plastics, which have many identical, regularly repeating units (and so are not chemically complex), have little or no immunogenicity. Such substances are used to make artificial implants because the substances are not seen as foreign and rejected by the body.

Self-Antigens: MHC Proteins

The external surfaces of all our cells are dotted with a huge variety of protein molecules. Assuming your immune system has been properly "programmed," your **self-antigens** are not foreign or antigenic to you, but they are strongly antigenic to other individuals. (This is the basis of transfusion reactions and graft rejection.)

Among the cell surface proteins that mark a cell as *self* is a group of glycoproteins called **MHC proteins**. Genes of the **major histocompatibility complex (MHC)** code for these proteins. Because millions of combinations of these genes are possible, it is unlikely that any two people except identical twins have the same MHC proteins.

There are two major groups of MHC proteins, distinguished by location. Class I MHC proteins are found on virtually *all* body cells, but class II MHC proteins are found *only on certain cells* that act in the immune response.

Each MHC molecule has a deep groove that typically displays a peptide. In healthy cells, peptides displayed by class I MHC come from the breakdown of cellular proteins during normal protein recycling and tend to be quite diverse, but are nevertheless all self-antigens. However, in infected cells, class I MHC also binds fragments of *foreign* antigens that come from within the infected cell. Peptides displayed by class II MHC come from outside the cell. As we will describe shortly, these displayed peptides play a crucial role in mobilizing the adaptive defenses.

CHECK YOUR UNDERSTANDING

> **6.** Name three key characteristics of adaptive immunity.
> **7.** What is the difference between a complete antigen and a hapten?
> **8.** What marks a cell as "self" as opposed to "nonself"?

For answers, see Appendix G.

Cells of the Adaptive Immune System: An Overview

▶ Compare and contrast the origin, maturation process, and general function of B and T lymphocytes.

▶ Define immunocompetence and self-tolerance, and describe their development in B and T lymphocytes.

▶ Name several antigen-presenting cells and describe their roles in adaptive defenses.

The three crucial cell types of the adaptive immune system are two distinct populations of lymphocytes, plus *antigen-presenting cells (APCs)*. **B lymphocytes** or **B cells** oversee humoral immu-

nity. **T lymphocytes** or **T cells** are non-antibody-producing lymphocytes that constitute the cell-mediated arm of adaptive immunity. Unlike the lymphocytes, APCs do not respond to specific antigens but instead play essential auxiliary roles.

Lymphocytes

Like all other blood cells, lymphocytes originate in red bone marrow from hematopoietic stem cells. During development, lymphocytes are "educated." The aim of this education is twofold:

1. **Immunocompetence.** Each lymphocyte must become able (competent) to recognize its one specific antigen by binding to it. This ability is called **immunocompetence**.
2. **Self-tolerance.** Each lymphocyte must be relatively unresponsive to self-antigens so that it does not attack the body's own cells. This is called **self-tolerance**.

B and T cells are educated in different parts of the body. T cells undergo this two- to three-day maturation process in the thymus. B cells become immunocompetent and self-tolerant in the bone marrow. The lymphoid organs where the lymphocytes become immunocompetent—thymus and bone marrow—are called **primary lymphoid organs**. All other lymphoid organs are referred to as **secondary lymphoid organs**.

Immunocompetent B and T cells that have not yet been exposed to antigen are called *naive*. Naive B cells and T cells are exported to the lymph nodes, spleen, and other secondary lymphoid organs, where encounters with antigens may occur. Then, when the lymphocytes bind with recognized antigens, the lymphocytes are activated to complete their differentiation into effector and memory B or T cells. **Figure 21.8** summarizes lymphocyte development.

Development of Immunocompetence and Self-Tolerance

When B or T cells become immunocompetent, they display a unique type of receptor on their surface. These receptors (some 10^5 per cell) enable the lymphocyte to recognize and bind a specific antigen. Once these receptors appear, the lymphocyte is committed to react to one distinct antigenic determinant, and one only, because *all* of its antigen receptors are the same.

The receptors on B cells are in fact membrane-bound antibodies, while the receptors on T cells are not antibodies but are products of the same gene superfamily. These similar structures have similar functions, and both cell types are capable of responding to the same antigens.

For T cells, the education in the thymus ensures that they meet two essential criteria for life as a successful T cell. First, the T cell must be able to bind MHC molecules, since it is on these molecules that antigens are presented to the T cell for recognition. Second, the T cell must *not* react strongly to self-antigens that are normally found in the body.

In order to ensure that all T cells meet these criteria, their education consists of positive and negative selection **(Figure 21.9)**. **Positive selection**, which occurs in the thymic cortex, is essentially an **MHC restriction** process. It identifies T cells whose

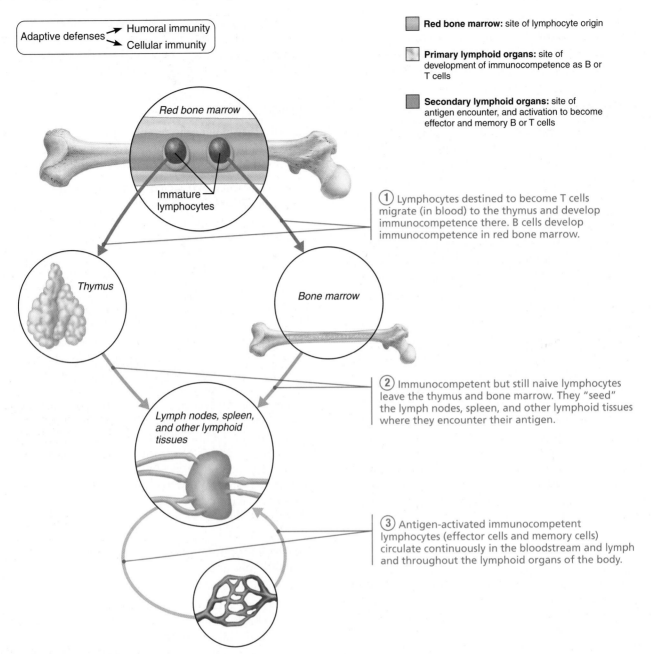

Adaptive defenses → Humoral immunity
→ Cellular immunity

Red bone marrow: site of lymphocyte origin

Primary lymphoid organs: site of development of immunocompetence as B or T cells

Secondary lymphoid organs: site of antigen encounter, and activation to become effector and memory B or T cells

Red bone marrow

Immature lymphocytes

① Lymphocytes destined to become T cells migrate (in blood) to the thymus and develop immunocompetence there. B cells develop immunocompetence in red bone marrow.

Thymus

Bone marrow

② Immunocompetent but still naive lymphocytes leave the thymus and bone marrow. They "seed" the lymph nodes, spleen, and other lymphoid tissues where they encounter their antigen.

Lymph nodes, spleen, and other lymphoid tissues

③ Antigen-activated immunocompetent lymphocytes (effector cells and memory cells) circulate continuously in the bloodstream and lymph and throughout the lymphoid organs of the body.

Figure 21.8 Lymphocyte traffic. Immature lymphocytes arise in red bone marrow. (Note that red marrow is not found in the medullary cavity of the diaphysis of long bones in adults.) Plasma cells (antibody-secreting effector B cells) usually do not circulate.

receptors are capable of recognizing (binding) self-MHC molecules and eliminates all others. In this way positive selection produces an army of self-MHC-restricted T cells.

T cells that make it through positive selection are then tested to make sure that they do not recognize (bind tightly) self-antigens displayed on self-MHC. If they do, they are eliminated by apoptosis (programmed cell death). This is **negative selection**, and it occurs in the inner edge of the thymic cortex. Negative selection ensures immunologic self-tolerance, making sure that T cells don't attack the body's own cells, which would cause autoimmune disorders. This education of T cells

is expensive indeed—only about 2% of T cells survive it and continue on to become successful immunocompetent, self-tolerant T cells.

Less is known about the factors that control B cell maturation in humans. In the bone marrow, self-reactive B cells are either eliminated by apoptosis (*clonal deletion*), or are given a chance to change their self-reactive antigen receptor by *receptor editing*, in which there is another rearrangement of the antigen-binding part of the receptor. Nevertheless, some self-reacting B cells do leave the bone marrow. In the periphery, these self-reactive B cells are inactivated (a phenomenon called *anergy*).

21

Generation of Antigen Receptor Diversity in Lymphocytes

We know that lymphocytes become immunocompetent *before* meeting the antigens they may later attack. *It is our genes, not antigens, that determine what specific foreign substances our immune system will be able to recognize and resist.* In other words, the immune cell receptors represent our genetically acquired knowledge of the microbes that are likely to be in our environment.

An antigen simply determines which existing T or B cells will proliferate and mount the attack against it. Only some of the antigens our lymphocytes are programmed to resist will ever invade our bodies. Consequently, only some members of our army of immunocompetent cells are mobilized in our lifetime. The others are forever idle.

Our lymphocytes make up to a billion different types of antigen receptors. These receptors, like all other proteins, are specified by genes, so you might think that an individual must have billions of genes. Not so; each body cell only contains about 25,000 genes that code for all the proteins the cell must make.

How can a limited number of genes generate a seemingly limitless number of different antigen receptors? Molecular genetic studies have shown that the genes that dictate the structure of each antigen receptor are not present as such in embryonic cells. Instead of a complete set of "antigen receptor genes," embryonic cells contain a few hundred genetic bits and pieces that can be thought of as a "Lego set" for antigen receptor genes. As each lymphocyte becomes immunocompetent, these gene segments are shuffled and combined in different ways in a process called **somatic recombination**. The information of the newly assembled genes is then expressed as the surface receptors of B and T cells and as the antibodies later released by the B cell's "offspring."

Antigen-Presenting Cells

The major role of **antigen-presenting cells (APCs)** in immunity is to engulf antigens and then present fragments of them, like signal flags, on their own surfaces where they can be recognized by T cells. In other words, they *present antigens* to the cells that will deal with the antigens. The major types of cells acting as APCs are *dendritic cells* (present in connective tissues and in the epidermis, where they are also called *Langerhans cells*), *macrophages*, and *B lymphocytes*.

Notice that all these cell types are in sites that make it easy to encounter and process antigens. Dendritic cells are at the body's frontiers, best situated to act as mobile sentinels. Macrophages are widely distributed throughout the lymphoid organs and connective tissues. When they present antigens, dendritic cells and macrophages activate T cells. Activated T cells, in turn, release chemicals that prod macrophages to become *activated macrophages*, true "killers" that are insatiable phagocytes and secrete bactericidal chemicals. As you will see, interactions between various lymphocytes, and between lymphocytes and APCs, underlie virtually all phases of the immune response.

Macrophages tend to remain fixed in the lymphoid organs, as if waiting for antigens to come to them. But lymphocytes, es-

Figure 21.9 **T cell education in the thymus.**

pecially the T cells (which account for 65–85% of bloodborne lymphocytes), circulate continuously throughout the body. This circulation greatly increases a lymphocyte's chance of coming into contact with antigens located in different parts of the body, as well as with huge numbers of macrophages and other lymphocytes. Although lymphocyte recirculation appears to be random, the lymphocyte emigration to the tissues where their protective services are needed is highly specific, regulated by homing signals (CAMs) displayed on vascular endothelial cells.

Immune cells in lymph nodes are in a strategic position to encounter a large variety of antigens because lymphatic capillaries pick up proteins and pathogens from nearly all body tissues. Lymphocytes and APCs in the tonsils act primarily against microorganisms that invade the oral and nasal cavities, and the spleen acts as a filter to trap bloodborne antigens.

In addition to T cell recirculation and passive delivery of antigens to lymphoid organs by lymphatics, a third delivery

Figure 21.10 Dendritic cell. Scanning electron micrograph (1050×).

mechanism—migration of dendritic cells to secondary lymphoid organs—is now recognized as the most important way of ensuring that the immune cells encounter invading antigens. With their long, wispy extensions, dendritic cells are very efficient antigen catchers (Figure 21.10). Once they have internalized antigens by phagocytosis, they enter nearby lymphatics to get to the lymphoid organ where they will present the antigens to T cells. Indeed, dendritic cells are the most effective antigen presenters known—it's their only job. Dendritic cells are a key link between innate and adaptive immunity. They initiate adaptive immune responses particularly tailored to the type of pathogen that they have encountered.

In summary, the two-fisted adaptive immune system uses lymphocytes, APCs, and specific molecules to identify and destroy all substances—both living and nonliving—that are in the body but not recognized as self. The system's response to such threats depends on the ability of its cells (1) to recognize antigens in the body by binding to them and (2) to communicate with one another so that the whole system mounts a response specific to those antigens.

CHECK YOUR UNDERSTANDING

9. What event (or observation) signals that a B or T cell has achieved immunocompetence?

10. Which of the following T cells would survive education in the thymus? (a) one that recognizes neither MHC nor self-antigen, (b) one that recognizes both MHC and self-antigen, (c) one that recognizes MHC but not self-antigen, (d) one that recognizes self-antigen but not MHC.

11. Name three different APCs. Which is most important for T lymphocyte activation?

For answers, see Appendix G.

Humoral Immune Response

▶ Define humoral immunity.

▶ Describe the process of clonal selection of a B cell.

▶ Recount the roles of plasma cells and memory cells in humoral immunity.

The **antigen challenge**, the first encounter between an immunocompetent but naive lymphocyte and an invading antigen, usually takes place in the spleen or in a lymph node, but it may happen in any secondary lymphoid organ. If the lymphocyte is a B cell, the challenging antigen provokes the *humoral immune response*, in which antibodies are produced against the challenger.

Clonal Selection and Differentiation of B Cells

An immunocompetent but naive B lymphocyte is *activated*—stimulated to complete its differentiation—when matching antigens bind to its surface receptors and cross-link adjacent receptors together. Antigen binding is quickly followed by receptor-mediated endocytosis of the cross-linked antigen-receptor complexes. This sequence of steps triggers **clonal selection** (klo'nul) because it stimulates the B cell to grow and then multiply rapidly to form an army of cells all exactly like itself and bearing the same antigen-specific receptors (Figure 21.11). The resulting family of identical cells, all descended from the *same* ancestor cell, is called a **clone**. The antigen does the selecting in clonal selection by "choosing" a lymphocyte with complementary receptors. (As we will see shortly, interactions with T cells are usually required to help B cells achieve full activation.)

Most cells of the clone differentiate into **plasma cells**, the antibody-secreting *effector cells* of the humoral response. Although B cells secrete limited amounts of antibodies, plasma cells develop the elaborate internal machinery (largely rough endoplasmic reticulum) needed to secrete antibodies at the unbelievable rate of about 2000 molecules per second. Each plasma cell functions at this breakneck pace for 4 to 5 days and then dies. The secreted antibodies, each with the same antigen-binding properties as the receptor molecules on the surface of the parent B cell, circulate in the blood or lymph. There they bind to free antigens and mark them for destruction by other innate or adaptive mechanisms.

Clone cells that do not become plasma cells become long-lived **memory cells.** They can mount an almost immediate humoral response if they encounter the same antigen again at some future time (Figure 21.11, bottom).

Immunological Memory

The cellular proliferation and differentiation we have just described constitute the **primary immune response**, which occurs on first exposure to a particular antigen. The primary response typically has a lag period of 3 to 6 days after the antigen challenge. This lag period mirrors the time required for the few B cells specific for that antigen to proliferate (about 12 generations) and

Adaptive defenses → Humoral immunity

Figure 21.11 Clonal selection of a B cell.

for their offspring to differentiate into plasma cells. After the mobilization period, plasma antibody levels rise, reach peak levels in about 10 days, and then decline **(Figure 21.12)**.

If (and when) someone is reexposed to the same antigen, whether it's the second or the twenty-second time, a **secondary immune response** occurs. Secondary immune responses are faster, more prolonged, and more effective, because the immune system has already been primed to the antigen, and sensitized memory cells are already in place "on alert." These memory cells provide what is commonly called **immunological memory**.

Within hours after recognition of the "old enemy" antigen, a new army of plasma cells is being generated. Within 2 to 3 days the antibody concentration in the blood, called the *antibody titer*, rises steeply to reach much higher levels than were achieved in the primary response. Secondary response antibodies not only bind with greater affinity (more tightly), but their blood levels remain high for weeks to months. (When the appropriate chemical signals are present, plasma cells can keep functioning for much

longer than the 4 to 5 days seen in primary responses.) Memory cells persist for long periods in humans and many retain their capacity to produce powerful secondary humoral responses for life.

The same general phenomena occur in the cellular immune response: A primary response sets up a pool of effector cells (in this case, T cells) and generates memory cells that can then mount secondary responses.

Active and Passive Humoral Immunity

▶ Compare and contrast active and passive humoral immunity.

When your B cells encounter antigens and produce antibodies against them, you are exhibiting **active humoral immunity**. Active immunity is acquired in two ways **(Figure 21.13)**. It is (1) *naturally acquired* when you get a bacterial or viral infection, during which time you may develop symptoms of the disease and suffer a little (or a lot), and (2) *artificially acquired*

21

Figure 21.12 Primary and secondary humoral responses. The primary response to antigen A generates memory cells that give rise to the enhanced secondary response to antigen A. The response to antigen B is independent of the response to antigen A.

when you receive **vaccines**. Indeed, once researchers realized that secondary responses are so much more vigorous than primary responses, the race was on to develop vaccines to "prime" the immune response by providing a first meeting with the antigen.

Most vaccines contain pathogens that are dead or *attenuated* (living, but extremely weakened), or their components. Vaccines provide two benefits:

1. They spare us most of the symptoms and discomfort of the disease that would otherwise occur during the primary response.
2. Their weakened antigens provide functional antigenic determinants that are both immunogenic and reactive.

Vaccine *booster shots*, which may intensify the immune response at later meetings with the same antigen, are also available.

Vaccines have wiped out smallpox and have substantially lessened the illness caused by such former childhood killers as whooping cough, polio, and measles. Although vaccines have dramatically reduced hepatitis B, tetanus, and pneumonia in adults, immunization of adults in the U.S. has a much lower priority than that of children and as a result more than 65,000 Americans die each year from vaccine-preventable infections (pneumonia, influenza, and hepatitis).

Conventional vaccines have shortcomings. Although it was originally believed that the immune response was about the same regardless of how an antigen got into the body (under its own power or via a vaccine), that has proved not to be the case.

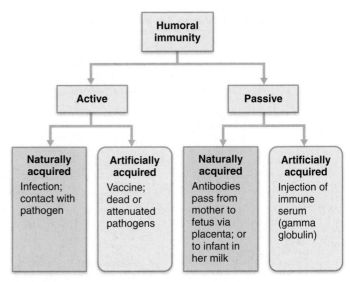

Figure 21.13 Active and passive humoral immunity. Immunological memory is established via active immunity, never via passive immunity.

Apparently vaccines mainly target the type of helper T cell that revs up B cell defenses and antibody formation (the T_H2 cell, described shortly) as opposed to the type that generates strong cell-mediated responses (T_H1). As a result, lots of antibodies are formed that provide immediate protection, but cellular immunological memory is only poorly established. (The immune system is deprived of the learning experience that comes with clearing an infection via a T_H1-mediated response.)

In extremely rare cases, vaccines cause the very disease they are trying to prevent because the attenuated virus isn't weakened enough. In other cases, contaminating proteins (for example, egg albumin) cause allergic responses to the vaccine. The new "naked DNA" antiviral vaccines, blasted into the skin with a gene gun, and *edible* vaccines taken orally appear to circumvent these problems.

Passive humoral immunity differs from active immunity, both in the antibody source and in the degree of protection it provides (Figure 21.13). Instead of being made by your plasma cells, the antibodies are harvested from the serum of an immune human or animal donor. As a result, your B cells are *not* challenged by antigens, immunological memory does *not* occur, and the protection provided by the "borrowed" antibodies ends when they naturally degrade in the body.

Passive immunity is conferred *naturally* on a fetus or infant when the mother's antibodies cross the placenta or are ingested with the mother's milk. For several months after birth, the baby is protected from all the antigens to which the mother has been exposed. Passive immunity is *artificially* conferred via a serum such as *gamma globulin*, which is administered after exposure to hepatitis. Other immune sera are used to treat poisonous snake bites (antivenom), botulism, rabies, and tetanus (antitoxin) because these rapidly fatal diseases would kill a person before active immunity could be established. The donated antibodies provide immediate protection, but their effect is short-lived (two to three weeks).

Adaptive defenses ➝ Humoral immunity

Figure 21.14 Antibody structure. (a) Schematic antibody structure (based on IgG) consists of four polypeptides—two short *light chains* and two long *heavy chains* joined together by disulfide bonds (S–S). Each chain has a V (variable) region (which differs in antibodies from different cells) and a C (constant) region (essentially identical in different antibodies of the same class). Together, the variable regions form the antigen-binding sites—two per antibody monomer. **(b)** Computer-generated image of antibody structure.

CHECK YOUR UNDERSTANDING

12. In clonal selection, "who" does the selecting? What is being selected?

13. Why is the secondary response to an antigen so much faster than the primary response?

14. How do vaccinations protect against common childhood illnesses such as chicken pox, measles, and mumps?

For answers, see Appendix G.

Antibodies

▶ Describe the structure of an antibody monomer, and name the five classes of antibodies.

▶ Explain the function(s) of antibodies and describe clinical uses of monoclonal antibodies.

Antibodies, also called **immunoglobulins (Igs)** (im″u-no-glob′u-linz), constitute the **gamma globulin** part of blood proteins. As we mentioned earlier, antibodies are proteins secreted in response to an antigen by effector B cells called plasma cells, and they are capable of binding specifically with that antigen. They are formed in response to an incredible number of different antigens.

Despite their variety, all antibodies can be grouped into one of five Ig classes, each slightly different in structure and function. Before seeing how these Ig classes differ from one another, let's take a look at how all antibodies are alike.

Basic Antibody Structure

Regardless of its class, each antibody has a basic structure consisting of four looping polypeptide chains linked together by disulfide (sulfur-to-sulfur) bonds. The four chains combined form a molecule, called an **antibody monomer** (mon′o-mer), with two identical halves. The molecule as a whole is T or Y shaped **(Figure 21.14)**.

Two of the chains, called the **heavy (H) chains**, are identical to each other and contain more than 400 amino acids each (blue chains in Figure 21.14a). The other two chains, called the **light (L) chains** (pink), are also identical to each other, but they are only about half as long as each H chain. The heavy chains have a flexible *hinge* region at their approximate "middles." The "loops" on each chain are created by disulfide bonds between amino acids that are in the same chain but about 60–70 amino acids apart. These bonds cause the intervening parts of the polypeptide chains to loop out.

Each chain forming an antibody has a **variable (V) region** at one end and a much larger **constant (C) region** at the other end. Antibodies responding to different antigens have very different V regions, but their C regions are the same (or nearly so) in all antibodies of a given class. In each arm of the monomer, the V regions of the heavy and light chains combine to form an **antigen-binding site** shaped to "fit" a specific antigenic determinant. Consequently, each antibody monomer has two such antigen-binding regions.

The C regions that form the *stem* of the antibody monomer determine the antibody class and serve common functions in

21

TABLE 21.3   **Immunoglobulin Classes**

IgM
(pentamer)

IgM exists in monomer and pentamer (five united monomers) forms. The monomer, which is attached to the B cell surface, serves as an antigen receptor. The pentamer (illustrated) circulates in blood plasma and is the first Ig class released by plasma cells during the primary response. (This fact is diagnostically useful because presence of IgM in plasma usually indicates current infection by the pathogen eliciting IgM's formation.) Its numerous antigen-binding sites make IgM a potent agglutinating agent, and it readily fixes and activates complement.

IgA
(dimer)

IgA monomer exists in limited amounts in plasma. The dimer (illustrated), referred to as secretory IgA, is found in body secretions such as saliva, sweat, intestinal juice, and milk, and helps prevent attachment of pathogens to epithelial cell surfaces (including mucous membranes and the epidermis).

IgD
(monomer)

IgD is virtually always attached to the external surface of a B cell, where it functions as an antigen receptor of the B cell.

IgG
(monomer)

IgG is the most abundant and diverse antibody in plasma, accounting for 75–85% of circulating antibodies. It protects against bacteria, viruses, and toxins circulating in blood and lymph, readily fixes complement, and is the main antibody of both secondary and late primary responses. It crosses the placenta and confers passive immunity from the mother to the fetus.

IgE
(monomer)

IgE is slightly larger than the IgG antibody. It is secreted by plasma cells in skin, mucosae of the gastrointestinal and respiratory tracts, and tonsils. Its stem region becomes bound to mast cells and basophils, and when its receptor ends are triggered by an antigen, it causes the cells to release histamine and other chemicals that mediate inflammation and an allergic reaction. Typically only traces of IgE are found in plasma, but levels rise during severe allergic attacks or chronic parasitic infections of the gastrointestinal tract.

all antibodies: These are the *effector regions* of the antibody that dictate (1) the cells and chemicals of the body the antibody can bind to, and (2) how the antibody class functions in antigen elimination. For example, some antibodies can fix complement, some circulate in blood and others are found primarily in body secretions, some cross the placental barrier, and so on.

Antibody Classes

The five major immunoglobulin classes are designated IgM, IgA, IgD, IgG, and IgE, on the basis of the C regions in their heavy chains. (Remember the name MADGE to recall the five Ig types.) Compared to the other antibodies, IgM is a huge antibody. It is constructed from five Y-shaped units, or *monomers*, linked together to form a *pentamer* (*penta* = five), as illustrated in **Table 21.3**. IgA occurs in both monomer and *dimer* (two linked monomers) forms. (Only the dimer is shown in the table.) IgD, IgG, and IgE are monomers and have the same basic Y-shaped structure.

The antibodies of each class have different biological roles and locations in the body. IgM is the first antibody class *released* to the blood by plasma cells. It readily fixes complement. The IgA dimer, also called **secretory IgA**, is found primarily in mucus and other secretions that bathe body surfaces. It plays a major role in preventing pathogens from gaining entry into the body. IgD is always bound to a B cell surface, where it acts as a B cell receptor. IgG is the most abundant antibody in plasma and the only Ig class that crosses the placental barrier. For this reason, the passive immunity that a mother transfers to her fetus is courtesy of her IgG antibodies. Like IgM, IgG can fix complement, and *only* these two antibody classes can do so. IgE antibodies, found in minute quantities in blood, are the "troublemaker" antibodies involved in some allergies. These and other characteristics unique to each immunoglobulin class are summarized in Table 21.3.

Generating Antibody Diversity

Recall from p. 779 that the billions of different kinds of antibodies produced by plasma cells come about as the result of somatic recombination of a limited number of gene segments. The random mixing of gene segments that code for the antigen-binding site (variable regions) accounts for only part of the huge variability seen in antibody specificity. Certain areas of one gene segment in activated B cells contain *hypervariable regions* that are "hot spots" for somatic mutations, and that enormously increase antibody variation.

A single plasma cell can switch from making one kind of H chain to making another kind, thereby producing two or more different antibody classes having the same antigen specificity. For example, the first antibody released in the primary response is IgM, and then the plasma cell begins to secrete IgG. During secondary responses, almost all of the Ig protein is IgG.

Antibody Targets and Functions

Though antibodies themselves cannot destroy antigens, they can inactivate them and tag them for destruction (**Figure 21.15**). The common event in all antibody-antigen interactions is formation of **antigen-antibody** (or **immune**) **complexes**. Defensive mechanisms used by antibodies include neutralization,

Adaptive defenses ➞ Humoral immunity

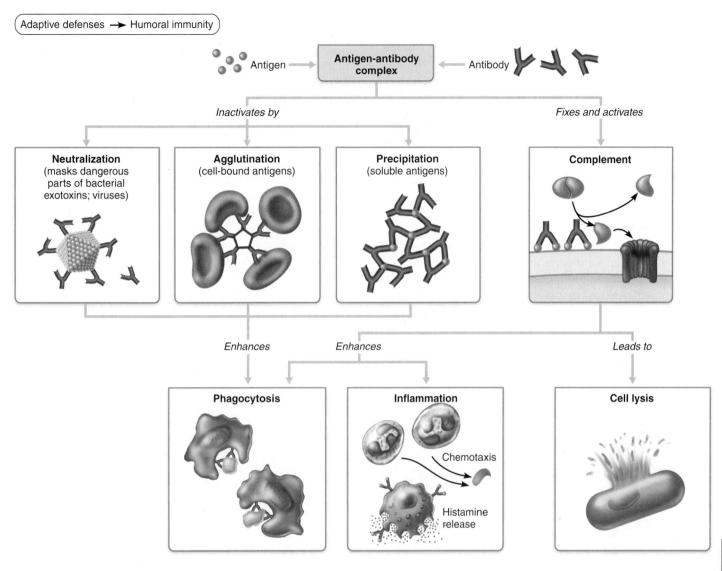

Figure 21.15 Mechanisms of antibody action. Antibodies act against free viruses, red blood cell antigens, bacterial toxins, intact bacteria, fungi, and parasitic worms.

agglutination, precipitation, and complement fixation, with the first two most important.

Neutralization, the simplest defensive mechanism, occurs when antibodies block specific sites on viruses or bacterial exotoxins (toxic chemicals secreted by bacteria). As a result, the virus or exotoxin loses its toxic effect because it cannot bind to receptors on tissue cells to cause injury. The antigen-antibody complexes are eventually destroyed by phagocytes.

Because antibodies have more than one antigen-binding site, they can bind to the same determinant on more than one antigen at a time. Consequently, antigen-antibody complexes can be cross-linked into large lattices. When cell-bound antigens are cross-linked, the process causes clumping, or **agglutination**, of the foreign cells. IgM, with 10 antigen-binding sites, is an especially potent agglutinating agent (see Table 21.3). Recall from Chapter 17 that this type of reaction occurs when mismatched blood is transfused (the foreign red blood cells are clumped) and is the basis of tests used for blood typing.

In **precipitation**, soluble molecules (instead of cells) are cross-linked into large complexes that settle out of solution. Like agglutinated bacteria, precipitated antigen molecules are much easier for phagocytes to capture and engulf than are freely moving antigens.

Complement fixation and activation is the chief antibody defense used against cellular antigens, such as bacteria or mismatched red blood cells. When several antibodies bind together on the same cell, the complement-binding sites on their stem regions align. This triggers complement fixation into the antigenic cell's surface, followed by cell lysis. Additionally, as we described earlier, molecules released during complement activation tremendously amplify the inflammatory response and promote phagocytosis via opsonization. In this way, a positive feedback cycle that enlists more and more defensive elements is set into motion.

A quick and dirty way to remember how antibodies work is to remember they have a PLAN of action—precipitation, lysis (by complement), agglutination, and neutralization.

⚖ HOMEOSTATIC IMBALANCE

Around the world, billions of people are infected by parasitic worms such as *Ascaris* and *Schistosoma*. These large pathogens are difficult for our immune systems to deal with and "PLAN" is insufficient. Nevertheless, antibodies still play a critical role in the worm's destruction. IgE antibodies coat the surface of parasitic worms, marking them for destruction by eosinophils. When eosinophils encounter antibody-coated worms, they bind to the exposed stems of the IgE. This triggers the eosinophils to release the toxic contents of their large cytoplasmic granules all over their prey. ▪

Monoclonal Antibodies

In addition to their role in providing passive immunity, commercially prepared antibodies are used in research, clinical testing, and treatment. **Monoclonal antibodies**, used for such purposes, are produced by descendants of a single cell. They are pure antibody preparations specific for a single antigenic determinant.

Monoclonal antibodies are made by fusing tumor cells and B lymphocytes. The resulting cell hybrids, called **hybridomas** (hi″brĭ-do′mahz), have desirable traits of both parent cells. Like tumor cells, hybridomas proliferate indefinitely in culture, and like B cells, they produce a single type of antibody.

Monoclonal antibodies are used to diagnose pregnancy, certain sexually transmitted diseases, some types of cancer, hepatitis, and rabies. These monoclonal antibody tests are more specific, more sensitive, and faster than their conventional counterparts. Monoclonal antibodies are also being used to treat leukemia and lymphomas, cancers that are present in the circulation and so are easily accessible to injected antibodies. They also serve as "guided missiles" to deliver anticancer drugs only to cancerous tissue, and to treat certain autoimmune diseases (as we will discuss later).

CHECK YOUR UNDERSTANDING

15. Which class of antibody is most abundant in blood? Which is secreted first in a primary immune response? Which is most abundant in secretions?

16. List four ways in which antibodies can bring about destruction of a pathogen.

For answers, see Appendix G.

Cell-Mediated Immune Response

▶ Follow antigen processing in the body.

▶ Define cell-mediated immunity and describe the process of activation and clonal selection of T cells.

Despite their immense versatility, antibodies provide only partial immunity. Their prey is the *obvious* pathogen. They are fairly useless against infectious microorganisms like viruses and the tuberculosis bacillus that quickly slip inside body cells to multiply there. In these cases, the cell-mediated arm of adaptive immunity comes into play.

The T cells that mediate cellular immunity are a diverse lot, much more complex than B cells in both classification and function. There are two major populations of T cells based on which of a pair of structurally related *cell differentiation glycoproteins*—CD4 or CD8—is displayed by a mature T cell. These glycoproteins are surface receptors but are distinct from the T cell antigen receptors. They play a role in interactions between T cells and other cells.

When activated, CD4 and CD8 cells differentiate into the two major kinds of *effector cells* of cellular immunity (as well as memory cells). **CD4 cells** usually become **helper T cells** (T_H). On the other hand, **CD8 cells** become **cytotoxic T cells** (T_C) whose role is to destroy any cells in the body that harbor anything foreign **(Figure 21.16)**. In addition to these two major groups of effector T cells, there are regulatory T cells (T_{Reg}), memory T cells, and some fairly rare subgroups. We will provide details of T cells' roles shortly.

Before going into the details of the cell-mediated immune response, let's recap and compare the relative importance of the humoral and cellular responses in adaptive immunity. Antibodies, produced by plasma cells, are in many ways the simplest ammunition of the immune response. They are specialized to latch onto intact bacteria and soluble foreign molecules *in extracellular environments*—in other words, free in body secretions and tissue fluid and circulating in blood and lymph. Antibodies never invade solid tissues unless a lesion is present.

At the most basic level, the race between antibody production and pathogen multiplication determines whether or not you become sick. Remember, however, that forming antibody-antigen complexes does *not* destroy the antigens. Instead, it prepares them for destruction by innate defenses.

In contrast to B cells and antibodies, T cells cannot "see" either free antigens or antigens that are in their natural state. T cells can recognize and respond only to *processed* fragments of protein antigens displayed on surfaces of body cells (APCs and others). Consequently, T cells are best suited for cell-to-cell interactions. Their direct attacks on antigens (mediated by the cytotoxic T cells) target body cells infected by viruses or bacteria; abnormal or cancerous body cells; and cells of infused or transplanted foreign tissues.

Clonal Selection and Differentiation of T Cells

The stimulus for clonal selection and differentiation is the same in B cells and T cells—binding of antigen. However, the mechanism by which T cells recognize "their" antigen is very different than that in B cells and has some unique restrictions.

MHC Proteins and Antigen Presentation

Like B cells, immunocompetent T cells are activated when the variable regions of their surface receptors bind to a "recognized" antigen. However, T cells must accomplish *double recognition*: They must simultaneously recognize nonself (the antigen) and self (an MHC protein of a body cell).

Two types of MHC proteins are important to T cell activation. **Class I MHC proteins** are displayed by virtually all body cells except red blood cells and are recognized by cytotoxic (CD8)

21

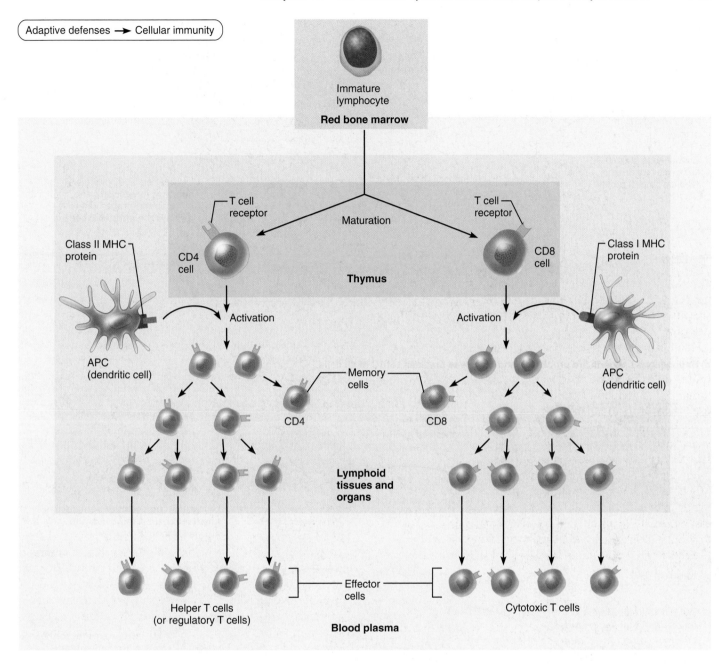

Figure 21.16 Major types of T cells based on displayed cell differentiation glycoproteins (CD4, CD8).

T cells. A class I MHC protein is synthesized at the endoplasmic reticulum and then binds with a protein fragment 8 or 9 amino acids long that is ferried into the ER from the cytosol by special transport proteins. The "loaded" class I MHC protein then migrates to the plasma membrane to display its attached protein fragment.

The attached fragment is always part of some protein synthesized *in the cell*—either a bit of a cellular (self) protein or a peptide derived from a foreign protein synthesized in a body cell. Both are called an **endogenous antigen**. The endogenous antigens are broken down to peptides within a proteasome before they are loaded onto MHCs. Two examples of endogenous foreign antigens are the viral proteins produced by virus-infected cells and alien (mutated) proteins made by a body cell that has become cancerous. **Figure 21.17a** summarizes the processing and display of endogenous antigens on class I MHC proteins.

The role of class I MHC proteins in the immune response is crucially important because they provide the means for signaling to cytotoxic T cells that infectious microorganisms are hiding in body cells. Without such means, viruses and certain bacteria that thrive in cells could multiply unnoticed and unbothered. When class I MHC proteins display fragments of our own proteins (self-antigens), cytotoxic T cells passing by get the signal "Leave this cell alone, it's ours!" and ignore them. But when class I MHC proteins display foreign antigens, they betray the invaders and "sound a molecular alarm" that signals invasion.

21

(a) Endogenous antigens are processed and displayed on class I MHC of all cells.

(b) Exogenous antigens are processed and displayed on class II MHC of antigen-presenting cells (APCs).

Figure 21.17 **MHC proteins, and antigen processing and display.**

21

In this signaling, the class I MHC proteins both (1) act as antigen holders and (2) form the self part of the self-nonself complexes that cytotoxic T cells must recognize in order to kill.

Unlike the widely distributed class I MHC proteins, the second type of MHC protein is less widespread. **Class II MHC proteins** are typically found only on the surfaces of cells that present antigens to CD4 cells: dendritic cells, macrophages, and B cells. Like their class I MHC counterparts, class II MHC proteins are synthesized at the ER and bind to peptide fragments. However, the peptides they bind are longer (14–17 amino acids) and come from **exogenous antigens** (antigens from *outside* the cell) that have been engulfed and broken down in the phagolysosome.

Figure 21.17b summarizes how exogenous antigens are processed and displayed. While still in the ER, each class II MHC molecule binds a protein called an *invariant chain*. This coupling prevents the MHC molecule from binding to a peptide while in the ER. The class II MHC protein then moves from the ER through the Golgi apparatus and into a phagolysosome. There the invariant chain loosens its hold on the MHC molecule, allowing the "jaws" of MHC to close around a degraded exogenous protein fragment. The vesicle is then recycled to the cell surface, where the class II MHC protein displays its booty for CD4 cells to recognize.

T Cell Activation

T cell activation is actually a two-step process involving antigen binding and co-stimulation. Both steps usually occur on the surface of the same antigen-presenting cell (APC). As we described earlier, dendritic cells are the most potent APCs, displaying very small parts of antigens attached to their surface MHC proteins for recognition. In addition, dendritic cells migrate to the lymph nodes and other lymphoid tissues to present their antigens to T cells. As a result of this early alert, the body is spared a good deal of tissue damage that might otherwise occur.

Antigen Binding This first step mostly entails what we have already described: T cell antigen receptors (**TCRs**) bind to an antigen-MHC complex on the surface of an APC. Like B cell receptors, a TCR has variable and constant regions, but it consists of two rather than four polypeptide chains.

CD4 and CD8 cells have different requirements for the class of MHC protein that helps deliver the activation signal. This constraint, acquired during the education process in the thymus, is called *MHC restriction*. CD4 cells (that usually become helper T cells) can bind only to antigens linked to class II MHC proteins, which are typically displayed on APC surfaces **(Figure 21.18)**. CD8 cells (that become cytotoxic T cells) are activated by antigen fragments complexed with class I MHC proteins, also found on the surface of APCs.

The MHC restriction that we've just described presents a problem for APCs. As a rule, class I MHC proteins display endogenous antigens—those that originate inside that cell. How do APCs obtain endogenous antigens from another cell and display them on class I MHCs in order to activate CD8 cells? Dendritic cells have the special ability to do this. They obtain other cells' endogenous antigens by either engulfing dying virus-infected or tumor cells, or by importing antigens through

Figure 21.18 Clonal selection of T cells involves simultaneous recognition of self and nonself. Activation of CD4 cells is shown here, but activation of CD8 cells is similar. Co-stimulation (also essential for activation) is not shown.

temporary gap junctions with infected cells. Dendritic cells then display these antigens on *both* class I and class II MHCs.

The TCR that recognizes the nonself-self complex is linked to multiple intracellular signaling pathways. Besides the TCR, other T cell surface proteins are involved in this first step. For example, the CD4 and CD8 proteins used to identify the two major T cell groups are adhesion molecules that help maintain the coupling during antigen recognition. Additionally, the CD4 and CD8 proteins are associated with kinase enzymes located inside the T cells that phosphorylate cell proteins, activating some and inactivating others when antigen binding occurs. Once antigen binding has occurred, the T cell is stimulated but is still "idling," like a car that has been started but not put into gear.

Co-stimulation The story isn't over yet because step 2 comes next. Before a T cell can proliferate and form a clone, it must recognize one or more **co-stimulatory signals**. This requires T cell binding to still other surface receptors on an APC. For example, dendritic cells and macrophages begin to sprout *B7 proteins* on their surfaces when the innate defenses are being mobilized. B7 binding to the CD28 receptor on a T cell is a crucial co-stimulatory signal.

TABLE 21.4	Selected Cytokines
CYTOKINE	**FUNCTION IN IMMUNE RESPONSE**
Interferons (IFNs)	
▪ Alpha (α) and beta (β)	Secreted by many cells. Have antiviral effects; activate NK cells.
▪ Gamma (γ)	Secreted by lymphocytes. Activates macrophages; stimulates synthesis and expression of more class I and II MHC proteins; promotes differentiation of T_H cells into T_H1.
Interleukins (ILs)	
▪ IL-1	Secreted by activated macrophages. Promotes inflammation and T cell activation; causes fever (a pyrogen that resets the thermostat of the hypothalamus).
▪ IL-2	Secreted by T_H cells. Stimulates proliferation of T and B cells; activates NK cells.
▪ IL-4	Secreted by some T_H cells. Promotes differentiation to T_H2; promotes B cell activation; switches antibody production to IgE.
▪ IL-5	Secreted by some T_H cells and mast cells. Attracts and activates eosinophils; causes plasma cells to secrete IgA antibodies.
▪ IL-10	Secreted by macrophages and T_{Reg} cells. Inhibits macrophages and dendritic cells; turns down cellular and innate immune response.
▪ IL-12	Secreted by dendritic cells and macrophages. Stimulates T_C and NK cell activity; promotes T_H1 differentiation.
▪ IL-17	Secreted by T_H17 cells. Important in innate and adaptive immunity and recruitment of neutrophils. Involved in inflammation in some autoimmune diseases.
Suppressor factors	A generic term for a number of cytokines that suppress the immune system, for example TGF-β and IL-10.
Transforming growth factor beta (TGF-β)	A suppressor factor similar to IL-10.
Tumor necrosis factors (TNFs)	Produced by lymphocytes and in large amounts by macrophages. Promote inflammation; enhance phagocyte chemotaxis and nonspecific killing; slow tumor growth by selectively damaging tumor blood vessels; promote cell death by apoptosis.

21

After co-stimulation, cytokine chemicals such as interleukin 1 and 2 released by APCs or T cells themselves nudge the activated T cells to proliferate and differentiate. As you might guess, there are several types of cytokines, each type promoting a different response in the activated T cells.

What happens if a T cell binds to antigen without receiving the co-stimulatory signal? In this case, the T cell becomes tolerant to that antigen and is unable to divide or to secrete cytokines. This state of unresponsiveness to antigen is called **anergy**.

The two-signal sequence acts as a safeguard to prevent the immune system from destroying healthy cells. Without this safeguard, class I MHC proteins, which occur on all body cells and which display peptides from within the cell, could activate cytotoxic T cells, leading to widespread damage of healthy cells. The important thing to understand is that along with antigen binding, co-stimulation is crucial for T cell activation. To go back to our idling car analogy, the car will not go anywhere unless the car has both (1) been started and (2) put into gear.

Once activated, a T cell enlarges and proliferates to form a clone of cells that differentiate and perform functions according to their T cell class. This primary response peaks within a week of exposure to the triggering antigen. A period of apoptosis then occurs between days 7 and 30, during which time the activated T cells die off and effector activity wanes as the amount of antigen declines.

This wholesale disposal of T cells has a critical protective role because activated T cells are potential hazards. They produce huge amounts of inflammatory cytokines, which contribute to infection-driven hyperplasia, and may promote malignancies in chronically inflamed tissue. Additionally, once they've done their job, the effector T cells are unnecessary and thus disposable. Thousands of clone members become memory T cells, persisting perhaps for life, and providing a reservoir of T cells that can later mediate secondary responses to the same antigen.

Cytokines

The chemical messengers involved in cellular immunity belong to a group of molecules called **cytokines**, a general term for mediators that influence cell development, differentiation, and responses in the immune system. Cytokines include interferons and interleukins. In **Table 21.4**, you can see the large variety of these molecules and their myriad effects on target cells.

The cytokines include hormone-like or paracrine-like glycoproteins released by a variety of cells. As we mentioned previously, some cytokines act to promote T cell proliferation. For example, **interleukin 1 (IL-1)**, released by macrophages, stimulates bound T cells to liberate **interleukin 2 (IL-2)** and to synthesize more IL-2 receptors. IL-2 is a key growth factor. Acting on the cells that release it (as well as other T cells), it sets up a positive feedback cycle that encourages activated T cells to divide even more rapidly. (Therapeutically, IL-2 is used to treat melanoma and kidney cancers.)

Additionally, all activated T cells secrete one or more other cytokines that help amplify and regulate a variety of adaptive and innate immune responses. Some (such as *tumor necrosis factor*) are cell toxins. Others (e.g., *gamma interferon*) enhance the killing power of macrophages; and still others are inflammatory factors.

CHECK YOUR UNDERSTANDING

17. Class II MHC proteins display what kind of antigens? What class of T cell recognizes antigens bound to class II MHC? What types of cells display these proteins?

18. What happens when antigens are bound in the absence of co-stimulators?

For answers, see Appendix G.

Specific Effector T Cell Roles

▶ Describe T cell functions in the body.

When immunocompetent CD4 cells are activated, their offspring become effector cells (cells that carry out T cell functions) or memory cells (cells that cause faster, more prolonged responses upon a second encounter with an antigen). As we mentioned earlier, effector CD4 cells are helper or regulatory T cells, and effector CD8 cells are cytotoxic T cells. There are other minor "oddball" populations of effector T cells, but here we will focus on the three major groups.

Helper T Cells

Helper T cells play a central role in adaptive immunity, mobilizing both its cellular and its humoral arms, as the examples in **Figure 21.19** show. Once T_H cells have been primed by APC presentation of antigen, they help activate B and T cells, and induce B and T cell proliferation. In fact, without the "director" T_H cells, there is *no* adaptive immune response. They also activate macrophages to become more potent killers, and their cytokines furnish the chemical help needed to recruit other immune cells to fight off intruders.

Helper T cells interact directly with B cells displaying antigen fragments bound to class II MHC receptors (Figure 21.19a). They prod the B cells into more rapid division and then, like the boss of an assembly line, signal for antibody formation to begin. Whenever a T_H cell binds to a B cell, the T cell releases interleukin 4 and other cytokines. B cells may be activated solely by binding to certain antigens called **T cell–independent antigens**, but most antigens require T cell help to activate the B cells to which they bind. These more common antigens are called **T cell–dependent antigens**. In general, T cell–independent antigen responses are weak and short-lived. B cell division continues as long as it is stimulated by the T_H cell. In this way, helper T cells help unleash the protective potential of B cells.

Similarly, activating CD8 cells into destructive cytotoxic T cells usually requires help from T_H cells. As shown in Figure 21.19b, T_H cells cause dendritic cells to express on their surfaces the co-stimulatory molecules required for CD8 cell activation.

T_H cell help in humoral immunity

① T_H cell binds with the self-nonself complexes of a B cell that has encountered its antigen and is displaying it on MHC II on its surface.

② T_H cell releases interleukins as co-stimulatory signals to complete B cell activation.

Labels: Activated helper T cell; T cell receptor (TCR); Helper T cell CD4 protein; MHC II protein of B cell displaying processed antigen; IL-4 and other cytokines; B cell (being activated)

(a)

T_H cell help in cell-mediated immunity

① Previously activated T_H cell binds dendritic cell.

② T_H cell stimulates dendritic cell to express co-stimulatory molecules (not shown) needed to activate CD8 cell.

③ Dendritic cell can now activate CD8 cell with the help of interleukin 2 secreted by T_H cell.

Labels: CD4 protein; Class II MHC protein; APC (dendritic cell); Helper T cell; IL-2; Class I MHC protein; CD8 protein; CD8 T cell

(b)

Figure 21.19 The central role of helper T cells in mobilizing both humoral and cellular immunity. (a) T_H and B cells usually must interact directly for full B cell activation. **(b)** Co-stimulatory molecules required for CD8 T cell activation are expressed by dendritic cells in response to T_H cell binding. (Some types of antigens induce these co-stimulatory molecules themselves, in which case T_H cell help may not be needed.) The T_H cell also produces interleukin 2, which causes the CD8 cell to proliferate and differentiate.

Cytokines released by T_H cells not only mobilize lymphocytes and macrophages but also attract other types of white blood cells into the area and tremendously amplify innate defenses. As the released chemicals summon more and more cells into the battle, the immune response gains momentum, and the antigens are overwhelmed by the sheer numbers of immune elements acting against them.

It is interesting, but not surprising, that different subsets of helper T cells exist. The subset that develops during T_H cell

Adaptive defenses → Humoral immunity / Cellular immunity

21

differentiation depends on the type of antigen and the site at which it is encountered as well as the cytokine exposure of the differentiating T_H cell. For example, IL-12 induces T_H1 differentiation, while IL-4 drives T_H2 differentiation. Generally speaking, the T_H1 cells stimulate inflammation, activate macrophages, and promote differentiation of cytotoxic T cells. In other words, they mediate classical cell-mediated immunity. By contrast, T_H2 cells mainly promote defense against extracellular pathogens. In particular, they mobilize eosinophils to the battlefield and activate immune responses that depend on B cells and antibody formation. A third type of T_H cell, T_H17, links together adaptive and innate immunity by releasing IL-17, which promotes inflammatory responses and may underlie some autoimmune diseases.

Cytotoxic T Cells

Cytotoxic T cells are the only T cells that can directly attack and kill other cells. Activated T_C cells roam the body, circulating in and out of the blood and lymph and through lymphoid organs in search of body cells displaying antigens that the T_C cells recognize. Their main targets are virus-infected cells, but they also attack tissue cells infected by certain intracellular bacteria or parasites, cancer cells, and foreign cells introduced into the body by blood transfusions or organ transplants.

Before the onslaught can begin, the cytotoxic T cell must "dock" on the target cell by binding to a self-nonself complex. Remember, all body cells display class I MHC antigens, so all infected or abnormal body cells can be destroyed by these T cells. The attack on foreign human cells, such as those of a graft, is more difficult to explain because here *all* of the antigens are nonself. However, apparently the T_C cells sometimes "see" the foreign class I MHC antigens as a combination of self class I MHC protein bound to foreign antigen.

Once cytotoxic T cells recognize their targets, how do they deliver a **lethal hit**? There are two major mechanisms. One involves **perforins** and **granzymes** and is illustrated in Figure 21.20a. Another mechanism of killing by cytotoxic cells involves binding to a specific membrane receptor (a **Fas receptor**) on the target cell, an event that stimulates the target cell to undergo apoptosis.

NK cells use the same key mechanisms for killing their target cells. NK cells, however, do not look for foreign antigen displayed on class I MHC proteins. Instead they search for other signs of abnormality, including the *lack* of class I MHC or the presence of antibody coating the target cell. Stressed cells also often express different surface markers (such as some belonging to a family called MIC), which can activate NK cells. In short, NK cells stalk abnormal or foreign cells in the body that T_C cells can't "see."

NK and T_C lymphocytes roam the body, adhering to and crawling over the surfaces of other cells, examining them for markers they might recognize, a process called **immune surveillance**. NK cells check to make sure each cell has "identity flags" (class I MHC proteins *inhibit* NK cell attack), whereas T_C cells check the "identity flags" to see if they look the way they are supposed to (foreign antigens *stimulate* T_C cell attack).

Regulatory T Cells

In contrast to the role of T_H cells in activating adaptive immunity, related T cells called **regulatory T (T_{Reg}) cells** dampen the immune response. They act either by direct contact or by releasing inhibitory cytokines such as IL-10 and TGF-β. T_{Reg} cells are important in preventing autoimmune reactions because they suppress self-reactive lymphocytes in the periphery—that is, outside the lymphoid organs. The function and development of these cells and their subpopulations is currently a hot research topic. For example, researchers hope to use T_{Reg} cells to induce tolerance to transplanted tissue and to lessen the severity of autoimmune diseases.

■ ■ ■

In summary, each type of T cell has unique roles to play in the immune response, yet is heavily enmeshed in interactions with other immune cells and elements as summarized in **Table 21.5** and in the overview of the entire primary immune response in **Figure 21.21**. The lesson to take away with you is that without helper T cells, *there is no adaptive immune response* because the helper cells direct or help complete the activation of *both* B cells and T cells. Their crucial role in immunity is painfully evident when they are destroyed, as in AIDS (see p. 796).

Organ Transplants and Prevention of Rejection

▶ Indicate the tests ordered before an organ transplant is done, and methods used to prevent transplant rejection.

Organ transplants, a viable treatment option for many patients with end-stage cardiac or renal disease, have been done with mixed success for over 50 years. Immune rejection presents a particular problem when the goal is to provide such patients with functional organs from a living or recently deceased donor.

Essentially, there are four major varieties of grafts:

1. **Autografts** are tissue grafts transplanted from one body site to another in the *same person*.
2. **Isografts** are grafts donated to a patient by a *genetically identical individual*, the only example being identical twins.
3. **Allografts** are grafts transplanted from individuals that are *not genetically identical* but belong to the *same species*.
4. **Xenografts** are grafts *taken from another animal species*, such as transplanting a baboon heart into a human being.

Transplant success depends on the similarity of the tissues because T cells, NK cells, macrophages, and antibodies act vigorously to destroy any foreign tissue in the body. Autografts and isografts are the ideal donor tissues. Given an adequate blood supply and no infection, they are always successful because the MHC proteins are identical.

Successful xenografts from genetically engineered animals are still just a promise on the horizon. Consequently, the problematic graft type, and also the type most frequently used, is the allograft. The organ is usually obtained from a living human donor (in the case of kidney, liver, bone marrow) or harvested from a human donor who has just died (heart or lung).

Before an allograft is attempted, the ABO and other blood group antigens of donor and recipient must be determined, because these antigens are also present on most body cells. Next, recipient and donor tissues are typed to determine their MHC

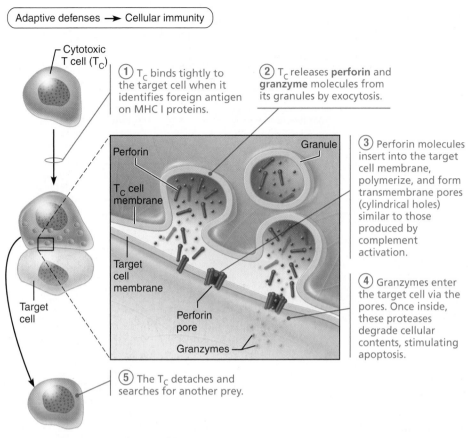

Adaptive defenses → Cellular immunity

Cytotoxic T cell (T$_C$)

① T$_C$ binds tightly to the target cell when it identifies foreign antigen on MHC I proteins.

② T$_C$ releases **perforin** and **granzyme** molecules from its granules by exocytosis.

Perforin

Granule

T$_C$ cell membrane

Target cell membrane

Target cell

Perforin pore

Granzymes

③ Perforin molecules insert into the target cell membrane, polymerize, and form transmembrane pores (cylindrical holes) similar to those produced by complement activation.

④ Granzymes enter the target cell via the pores. Once inside, these proteases degrade cellular contents, stimulating apoptosis.

⑤ The T$_C$ detaches and searches for another prey.

(a) A mechanism of target cell killing by T$_C$ cells.

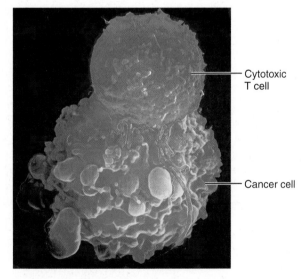

Cytotoxic T cell

Cancer cell

(b) Scanning electron micrograph of a T$_C$ cell killing a cancer cell (2100×).

Figure 21.20 Cytotoxic T cells attack infected and cancerous cells.

antigen match. MHC variation among human tissues is tremendous, so matching for all MHC antigens is impossible. In general, however, the closer the match the less likely is rejection.

Following surgery the patient is treated with *immuno-suppressive therapy.* It involves drugs of the following categories: (1) corticosteroid drugs to suppress inflammation; (2) antipro-

liferative drugs, and (3) immunosuppressant drugs. Many of these drugs kill rapidly dividing cells (such as activated lymphocytes), and all of them have severe side effects.

The major problem with immunosuppressive therapy is that the patient's suppressed immune system cannot protect the body against other foreign agents. As a result, overwhelming

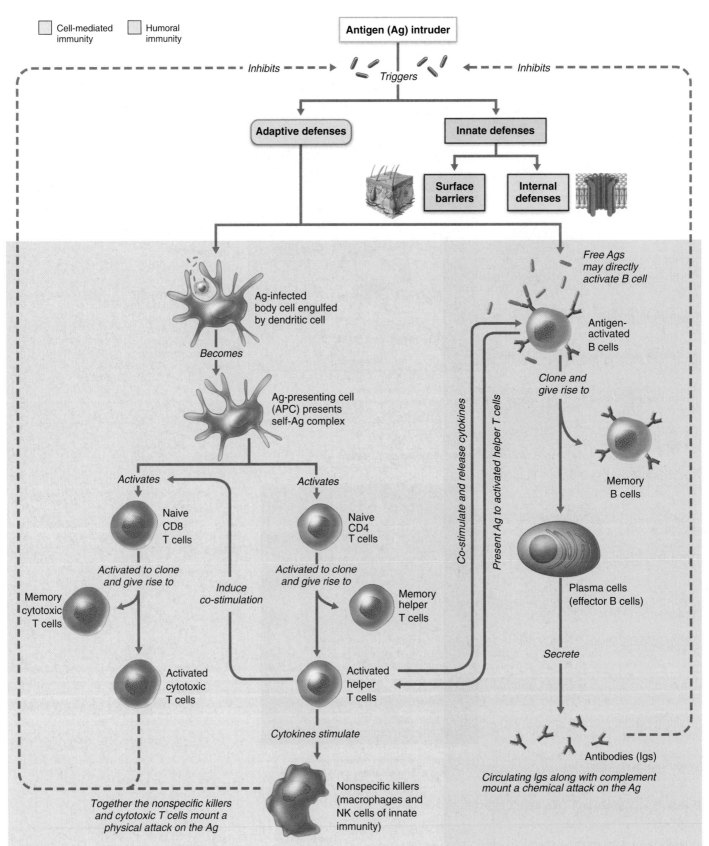

Figure 21.21 Simplified summary of the primary immune response. Co-stimulation usually requires direct cell-cell interactions; cytokines enhance these and many other events. Although complement, NK cells, and phagocytes are innate defenses, they are enlisted in the fight by cytokines. (For simplicity, only B cell receptors are illustrated.)

TABLE 21.5	Cells and Molecules of the Adaptive Immune Response
ELEMENT	**FUNCTION IN IMMUNE RESPONSE**
Cells	
B cell	Lymphocyte that matures in bone marrow. Induced to replicate by antigen binding, usually followed by helper T cell interactions in lymphoid tissues. Its progeny (clone members) form memory cells and plasma cells.
Plasma cell	Antibody-producing "machine"; produces huge numbers of antibodies (immunoglobulins) with the same antigen specificity. An effector B cell.
Helper T cell (T_H)	An effector CD4 T cell central to both humoral and cellular immunity. After binding with a specific antigen presented by an APC, it stimulates production of cytotoxic T cells and plasma cells to help fight invader, activates macrophages, and acts both directly and indirectly by releasing cytokines.
Cytotoxic T cell (T_C)	An effector CD8 cell. Activated by antigen presented by an APC, often with helper T cell involvement. Its specialty is killing virus-invaded body cells and cancer cells; also involved in rejection of foreign tissue grafts.
Regulatory T cell (T_{Reg})	Slows or stops activity of immune system. Important in controlling autoimmune diseases; several different populations probably exist.
Memory cell	Descendant of activated B cell or any class of T cell; generated during initial immune response (primary response). May exist in body for years after, enabling it to respond quickly and efficiently to subsequent infections or meetings with same antigen.
Antigen-presenting cell (APC)	Any of several cell types (dendritic cell, macrophage, B cell) that engulfs and digests antigens that it encounters, presenting parts of them on its plasma membrane (bound to an MHC protein) for recognition by T cells bearing receptors for same antigen. This function, antigen presentation, is essential for normal cell-mediated responses. Macrophages and dendritic cells also release chemicals (cytokines) that activate many other immune cells.
Molecules	
Antigen	Substance capable of provoking an immune response. Typically a large complex molecule (e.g., protein or modified protein) not normally present in the body.
Antibody (immunoglobulin)	Protein produced by B cell or by plasma cell. Antibodies produced by plasma cells are released into body fluids (blood, lymph, saliva, mucus, etc.), where they attach to antigens, causing complement fixation, neutralization, precipitation, or agglutination, which "mark" the antigens for destruction by phagocytes or complement.
Perforins, granzymes	Released by T_C cells. Perforins create large pores in the target cell's membrane, allowing entry of apoptosis-inducing granzymes.
Complement	Group of bloodborne proteins activated after binding to antibody-covered antigens or certain molecules on the surface of microorganisms; enhances inflammatory response and causes lysis of some microorganisms.
Cytokines	Small proteins that act as chemical messengers between various parts of the immune system. See Table 21.4.

bacterial and viral infection remains the most frequent cause of death in transplant patients. The key to successful graft survival is to provide enough immunosuppression to prevent graft rejection but not enough to be toxic, and to use antibiotics to keep infection under control. Even with the best conditions, by ten years after receiving a transplant, roughly 50% of patients have rejected the donor organ.

In rare cases, transplant patients have naturally achieved a state of immune tolerance and have been able to "ditch the drugs." Finding a way to induce tolerance is the goal of many research projects. One approach is to create a **chimeric immune system** (*chimer* = monster) by temporarily suppressing the recipient's bone marrow and then dousing it with bone marrow from the same donor as the new organ in the hope that this combined immune system will treat the transplanted organ as self. Another approach tries to harness the body's own tolerance-inducing cells, the regulatory T cells, to suppress only those immune reactions that lead to transplant rejection.

CHECK YOUR UNDERSTANDING

19. Which type of T cell is the most important in both cell-mediated and humoral immunity? Why?
20. Describe the killing mechanism of cytotoxic T cells that involves perforins.
21. Which proteins must be carefully matched before an organ transplant?

For answers, see Appendix G.

Homeostatic Imbalances of Immunity

▶ Give examples of immune deficiency diseases and of hypersensitivity states.

▶ Cite factors involved in autoimmune disease.

21

Certain circumstances can cause the immune system to become depressed, to fail, or to act in a way that damages the body. Most such problems can be classified as immunodeficiencies, autoimmune diseases, or hypersensitivities.

Immunodeficiencies

Any congenital or acquired condition that causes immune cells, phagocytes, or complement to behave abnormally is called an **immunodeficiency**.

The most devastating *congenital conditions* are a group of related disorders called **severe combined immunodeficiency (SCID) syndromes**, which result from various genetic defects that produce a marked deficit of B and T cells. One SCID defect causes abnormalities in a subunit common to the receptors for several interleukins. Another results in a defective *adenosine deaminase (ADA)* enzyme. In the absence of normal ADA, metabolites that are lethal to T cells accumulate in the body.

Children afflicted with SCID have little or no protection against disease-causing organisms of any type. Interventions must begin in the first months of life because minor infections easily shrugged off by most children cause SCID victims to become deathly ill and wasted. Untreated, this condition is fatal, but successful transplants of matched donor hematopoietic stem cells dramatically improve survival rates. Recent genetic engineering techniques using viruses as vectors to transfer corrected genes to the victim's own hematopoietic stem cells have shown promise.

There are various *acquired immunodeficiencies*. For example, *Hodgkin's disease*, a cancer of the B cells, can lead to immunodeficiency by depressing lymph node cells. Immunosuppressive drugs used in transplantation and certain drugs used to treat cancer also suppress the immune system. But the most devastating of the acquired immunodeficiencies is **acquired immune deficiency syndrome (AIDS)**, which cripples the immune system by interfering with the activity of helper T cells.

First identified in the United States in 1981 among homosexual men and intravenous drug users, AIDS is characterized by severe weight loss, night sweats, swollen lymph nodes, and increasingly frequent opportunistic infections, including a rare type of pneumonia called *pneumocystis pneumonia*, and the bizarre malignancy *Kaposi's sarcoma*, a cancer of the blood vessels evidenced by purple skin lesions. Some AIDS victims develop severe dementia. The course of AIDS is often grim, finally ending in complete debilitation and death from cancer or overwhelming infection.

AIDS is caused by a virus transmitted in body secretions—especially blood, semen, and vaginal secretions. The virus commonly enters the body via blood transfusions or blood-contaminated needles and during sexual intercourse. It is also present in saliva and tears, and there are documented cases of transmission by oral sex. Early in the epidemic, hemophiliacs were also at particular risk because the blood factors they need were isolated from pooled blood donations. Manufacturers began taking measures to kill the virus in 1984 and new genetically engineered factors became available, but an estimated 60% of the hemophiliacs in the U.S. were already infected.

The virus, **HIV (human immunodeficiency virus)**, destroys T_H cells, depressing cell-mediated immunity. Although B cells and T_C cells initially mount a vigorous response to viral exposure, in time a profound deficit of B cell and cytotoxic T cell function develops. The whole immune system is turned topsy-turvy.

The virus multiplies steadily in the lymph nodes throughout most of the asymptomatic period, which averages ten years in the absence of treatment. Symptoms appear when the lymph nodes can no longer contain the virus and the immune system collapses. The virus also invades the brain (which accounts for the dementia of some AIDS patients).

The infectious specificity of HIV reflects the fact that CD4 proteins provide the avenue of attack. Researchers have identified an HIV coat glycoprotein complex (gp120/gp41) that fits into the CD4 receptor like a plug fits into a socket. However, HIV also needs a *second* receptor (e.g., CXCR4) on the target cell. Once all these proteins have connected, gp41 fuses the virus to the target cell. Once inside, HIV "sets up housekeeping," using the viral enzyme *reverse transcriptase* to produce DNA from the information encoded in its (viral) RNA. This DNA copy, now called a *provirus*, then inserts itself into the target cell's DNA and directs the cell to crank out new copies of viral RNA and proteins so that the virus can multiply and infect other cells.

Although T_H cells are the main HIV targets, other body cells displaying CD4 proteins (macrophages, monocytes, and dendritic cells) are also at risk. The HIV reverse transcriptase enzyme is not very accurate and produces errors rather frequently, causing HIV's relatively high mutation rate and its changing resistance to drugs.

The years since 1981 have witnessed a global AIDS epidemic. By the end of 2007, 33 million people had died of AIDS since it was first identified, and about 33 million people were living with HIV worldwide, almost 90% of them in the developing countries of Asia and sub-Saharan Africa. Half of the victims are women, a case distribution indicating that in the most heavily hit countries, most HIV transmission occurs via heterosexual contacts. The virus can also be transmitted from an infected mother to her fetus.

The estimated number of Americans infected with HIV is now over 1 million. Of these, a quarter don't yet know that they are infected, either because anti-HIV antibodies are not yet detectable in the blood (this may take as long as six months after infection), or because (for one reason or another) they have not yet been tested. The "face of AIDS" is changing too. Homosexual men still account for the bulk of cases transmitted by sexual contact in the U.S., but more and more heterosexuals are contracting this disease. Particularly disturbing is the number of diagnosed cases among teenagers and young adults, with AIDS now the sixth leading killer of all Americans ages 25 to 44.

No cure for AIDS has yet been found. Over 40 clinical trials of HIV vaccines are under way around the world. Disappointingly, several large trials testing the effectiveness of vaccines have failed to show any effect in blocking HIV infection, and it is unlikely that an approved vaccine will be available soon.

Fortunately, a number of antiviral drugs are available, and these fall into three broad classes. *Reverse transcriptase inhibitors*, such as AZT and ddC, were early on the scene, followed by *protease inhibitors* (saquinavir, ritonavir, and others). These first two classes of drugs inhibit important viral enzymes after the virus has gained entry into the target cell. New to the scene are *fusion inhibitors* (such as enfuvirtide) that block gp41, preventing the virus from entering the cell in the first place. Combination therapy using three drugs at once delivers a one-two punch to the virus. It postpones drug resistance and causes the *viral load* (amount of HIV virus per milliliter of blood) to plummet while boosting the number of T_H cells.

Sadly, even combination drug therapies fail as the virus becomes resistant. New hope comes from a class of drugs now being developed that blocks integrase, the viral enzyme, responsible for integration of the HIV provirus into the target cell's DNA. However, drug research is slow and laborious and the clock is ticking.

Autoimmune Diseases

Occasionally the immune system loses its ability to distinguish friend (self) from foe (foreign antigens). When this happens, the artillery of the immune system, like friendly fire, turns against itself. The body produces antibodies (*autoantibodies*) and cytotoxic T cells that destroy its own tissues. This puzzling phenomenon is called **autoimmunity**. If a disease state results, it is referred to as **autoimmune disease**.

Some 5% of adults in North America—two-thirds of them women—are afflicted with autoimmune disease. Most common are

- *Multiple sclerosis*, which destroys the myelin of the white matter of the brain and spinal cord (see p. 405)
- *Myasthenia gravis*, which impairs communication between nerves and skeletal muscles (see p. 285)
- *Graves' disease*, which prompts the thyroid gland to produce excessive amounts of thyroxine (see p. 611)
- *Type 1 (insulin-dependent) diabetes mellitus*, which destroys pancreatic beta cells, resulting in a deficit of insulin and inability to use carbohydrates (see p. 622)
- *Systemic lupus erythematosus* (*SLE*), a systemic disease that particularly affects the kidneys, heart, lungs, and skin (see Related Clinical Terms)
- *Glomerulonephritis*, a severe impairment of renal function
- *Rheumatoid arthritis*, which systematically destroys joints (see pp. 270–271)

The most widely used treatments of autoimmune diseases suppress the entire immune system, relying, for example, on anti-inflammatory drugs such as corticosteroids. Newer treatments seek to target specific aspects of the immune response. For example, antibodies against TNF-α have provided dramatic results in the treatment of rheumatoid arthritis. *Thalidomide*, used in the 1950s to alleviate morning sickness in pregnancy until it was found to cause tragic birth defects, has been given a second chance in treating autoimmune disease because it blocks TNF production. Another therapeutic approach uses antibodies against cell adhesion molecules, preventing lymphocytes from exiting blood vessels into target areas. This approach shows promise in helping victims of a variety of autoimmune disorders, and has been used to treat multiple sclerosis. Another novel treatment for multiple sclerosis involves injecting a DNA vaccine that induces tolerance to the myelin antigen targeted by the autoimmune reaction.

How do autoimmune diseases arise? As you recall, lymphocytes undergo an extensive education in the bone marrow and thymus that weeds out self-reactive cells. This weeding is thorough, but not too thorough, since there are pathogens that look somewhat like self. Weakly self-reactive lymphocytes that can detect these kinds of pathogens are allowed into the periphery, where they may cause autoimmune disease if they become activated.

Recall that activation of a T cell requires a co-stimulatory signal on an APC (see p. 789), and that these co-stimulatory signals are only present if the APC has received "danger" signals alerting it to the presence of damage or invaders. This is an important safety check that generally keeps both humoral and cellular immunity under control. In addition, regulatory T (T_{Reg}) cells also inhibit autoimmune reactions.

Normally, these mechanisms are sufficient, but sometimes self-reactive lymphocytes slip out of control. It appears that one of the following events may trigger this:

1. **Foreign antigens resemble self-antigens.** If the determinants on a self-antigen resemble those on a foreign antigen, antibodies made against the foreign antigen can cross-react with the self-antigen. For instance, antibodies produced during a streptococcal infection react with heart antigens, causing lasting damage to the heart muscle and valves, as well as to joints and kidneys. This age-old disease is called *rheumatic fever*.
2. **New self-antigens appear.** Self-proteins not previously exposed to the immune system may appear in the circulation. They may be generated by (1) gene mutations that cause new proteins to appear at the external cell surface, (2) changes in the structure of self-antigens by hapten attachment or as a result of infectious damage, or (3) release by trauma of novel self-antigens normally hidden behind barriers such as the blood-brain barrier. These newly generated proteins then become immune system targets.

Hypersensitivities

At first, the immune response was thought to be purely protective. However, it was not long before its dangerous potentials were discovered. **Hypersensitivities** result when the immune system causes tissue damage as it fights off a perceived threat (such as pollen or animal dander) that would otherwise be harmless to the body. People rarely die of hypersensitivities. They are just miserable with them.

The different types of hypersensitivity reactions are distinguished by (1) their time course, and (2) whether antibodies or T cells are involved. Hypersensitivities mediated by antibodies are the *immediate* and *subacute hypersensitivities*. T cells cause *delayed hypersensitivity*.

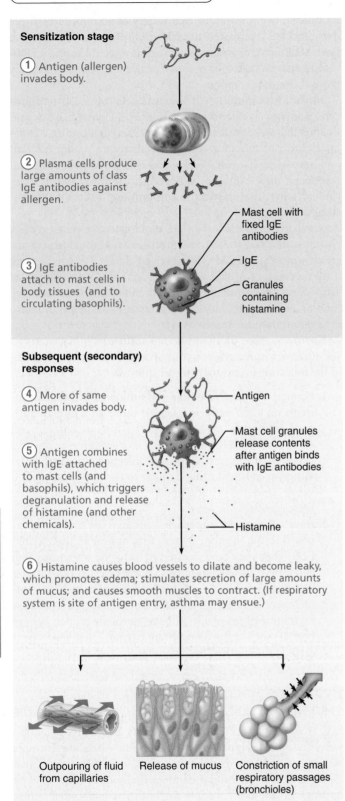

Adaptive defenses → Humoral immunity

Sensitization stage

1 Antigen (allergen) invades body.

2 Plasma cells produce large amounts of class IgE antibodies against allergen.

Mast cell with fixed IgE antibodies

IgE

3 IgE antibodies attach to mast cells in body tissues (and to circulating basophils).

Granules containing histamine

Subsequent (secondary) responses

4 More of same antigen invades body.

Antigen

5 Antigen combines with IgE attached to mast cells (and basophils), which triggers degranulation and release of histamine (and other chemicals).

Mast cell granules release contents after antigen binds with IgE antibodies

Histamine

6 Histamine causes blood vessels to dilate and become leaky, which promotes edema; stimulates secretion of large amounts of mucus; and causes smooth muscles to contract. (If respiratory system is site of antigen entry, asthma may ensue.)

Outpouring of fluid from capillaries

Release of mucus

Constriction of small respiratory passages (bronchioles)

Figure 21.22 Mechanism of an acute allergic (immediate hypersensitivity) response.

Immediate Hypersensitivities

The **immediate hypersensitivities**, also called **acute** or **type I hypersensitivities**, are simply what most of us would call **allergies** (*allo* = altered; *erg* = reaction). An **allergen** is an antigen that causes an allergic reaction. Allergic reactions begin within seconds after contact with the allergen and last about half an hour.

The initial meeting with an allergen produces no symptoms but it sensitizes the person. APCs digest the allergen and present its fragments to T_H cells as usual. In susceptible individuals, an abnormally large number of these T_H cells differentiate into IL-4-secreting T_H2 cells. IL-4 stimulates B cells to mature into IgE-secreting plasma cells, which spew out huge amounts of antibody specific for the allergen. When the IgE molecules attach to *mast cells* and *basophils*, sensitization is complete.

An allergic reaction is triggered by later encounters with the same allergen, which promptly binds and cross-links the IgE antibodies on the surfaces of the mast cells and basophils. This event induces an enzymatic cascade that causes the mast cells and basophils to degranulate, releasing a flood of *histamine* and other inflammatory chemicals that together induce the inflammatory response typical of allergy **(Figure 21.22)**.

Allergic reactions may be local or systemic. Mast cells are abundant in connective tissues of the skin and beneath the mucosa of respiratory passages and the gastrointestinal tract, and these areas are common sites of local allergic reactions. Histamine causes blood vessels to become dilated and leaky, and is largely to blame for the best recognized symptoms of allergy: runny nose, itching reddened skin (hives), and watery eyes. When the allergen is inhaled, symptoms of *asthma* appear because smooth muscle in the walls of the bronchioles contracts, constricting those small passages and restricting air flow. When the allergen is ingested in food or via drugs, gastrointestinal discomfort (cramping, vomiting, or diarrhea) occurs. Over-the-counter antiallergy drugs contain antihistamines that counteract these effects.

The bodywide or systemic response known as **anaphylactic shock** is fairly rare. It typically occurs when the allergen directly enters the blood and circulates rapidly through the body, as might happen with certain bee stings or spider bites. It may also follow injection of a foreign substance (such as penicillin or other drugs which act as haptens).

The mechanism of anaphylactic shock is essentially the same as that of local responses, but when mast cells and basophils are enlisted throughout the entire body, the outcome is life threatening. The bronchioles constrict (and the tongue may swell), making it difficult to breathe, and the sudden vasodilation and fluid loss from the bloodstream may cause circulatory collapse (hypotensive shock) and death within minutes. Epinephrine is the drug of choice to reverse these histamine-mediated effects.

Subacute Hypersensitivities

Like the immediate types, **subacute hypersensitivities** are caused by antibodies (IgG and IgM rather than IgE) and can be transferred via blood plasma or serum. However, their onset is slower (1–3 hours after antigen exposure) and the duration of the reaction is longer (10–15 hours).

Cytotoxic (type II) reactions occur when antibodies bind to antigens on specific body cells and subsequently stimulate phagocytosis and complement-mediated lysis of the cellular antigens. Type II hypersensitivity may occur after a patient has received a transfusion of mismatched blood and the foreign red blood cells are lysed by complement.

Immune-complex (type III) hypersensitivity results when antigens are widely distributed through the body or blood and the insoluble antigen-antibody complexes formed cannot be cleared from a particular area. (This may reflect a persistent infection or a situation in which huge amounts of antigen-antibody complexes are formed.) An intense inflammatory reaction occurs, complete with complement-mediated cell lysis and cell killing by neutrophils that severely damages local tissues. One example of type III hypersensitivity is *farmer's lung* (induced by inhaling moldy hay). Additionally, many immune-complex responses are involved in autoimmune disorders, such as glomerulonephritis, systemic lupus erythematosus, and rheumatoid arthritis.

Delayed Hypersensitivities

Delayed hypersensitivity (type IV) reactions are slower to appear (1–3 days) than antibody-mediated hypersensitivity reactions. The mechanism is basically that of a cell-mediated immune response, which depends on helper T cells. Inflammation and tissue damage comes about through the action of cytokine-activated macrophages, and sometimes cytotoxic T cells.

The most familiar examples of delayed hypersensitivity reactions are those classified as **allergic contact dermatitis** which follow skin contact with poison ivy, some metals (nickel in jewelry), and certain cosmetic and deodorant chemicals. These agents act as haptens, and after diffusing through the skin and attaching to self-proteins, they are perceived as foreign by the immune system. The *Mantoux* and *tine tests*, two skin tests for tuberculosis, depend on delayed hypersensitivity reactions. When the tubercle antigens are introduced just under the skin, a small hard lesion forms that persists for days if the person has been sensitized to the antigen.

CHECK YOUR UNDERSTANDING

22. What makes HIV particularly hard for the immune system to defeat?

23. What event triggers the release of histamine from mast cells in an allergic response?

For answers, see Appendix G.

Developmental Aspects of the Immune System

▶ Describe changes in immunity that occur with aging.

▶ Briefly describe the role of the nervous system in regulating the immune response.

Stem cells of the immune system originate in the liver and spleen during weeks 1–9 of embryonic development. Later the bone marrow becomes the predominant source of stem cells, and it persists in this role into adult life. In late fetal life and shortly after birth, the young lymphocytes develop self-tolerance and immunocompetence in their "programming organs" (thymus and bone marrow) and then populate the other lymphoid tissues. When challenged by an antigen, the naive T and B cells further differentiate into effector cells and memory cells.

The newborn's immune system depends primarily on antibodies, and hence on T_H2 lymphocytes. The T_H1 system is educated and gets stronger as a result of encounters with microbes—both harmful and harmless. If such "exercise" does not occur, immune balance is upset and the T_H2 system flourishes, causing the immune system to teeter toward allergies. Unhappily, our desire to keep our children squeaky clean with antibiotics that kill off both harmful and harmless bacteria may derail normal immune development.

The ability of the immune system to recognize foreign substances is controlled by genes. However, the nervous system also plays a role in the immune response, and studies of psychoneuroimmunology—a brain-twisting term coined to describe links between the brain and the immune system—have begun to reveal some answers. For example, the immune response is definitely impaired in individuals who are depressed or under severe stress, such as those mourning the death of a beloved family member or friend.

Our immune system normally serves us very well until late in life. Then its efficiency begins to wane, and its ability to fight infection declines. Old age is also accompanied by greater susceptibility to both immune deficiency and autoimmune diseases. The greater incidence of cancer in the elderly is assumed to be an example of the progressive failure of the immune system. We do not know why the immune system begins to fail, but we do know that the thymus begins to atrophy after puberty and the production of naive T and B cells declines with age, possibly because progenitor cells reach the limits of their ability to further divide.

■ ■ ■

The adaptive immune system provides remarkable defenses against disease. These amazingly diverse defenses are regulated by cellular interactions and a flood of chemicals. T cells and antibodies make perfect partners. Antibodies respond swiftly to toxins and molecules on the outer surfaces of foreign organisms, and T cells destroy foreign antigens hidden inside cells and our own cells that have become mutinous (cancer cells). The innate immune system exhibits a different arsenal for body defense, an arsenal that is simpler perhaps and more easily understood. The innate and adaptive defenses are tightly interlocked, each providing what the other cannot and amplifying each other's effects.

21

RELATED CLINICAL TERMS

Congenital thymic aplasia An immune deficiency disease in which the thymus fails to develop. Affected individuals have no T cells, hence little or no immune protection; fetal thymic and bone marrow transplants have been helpful in some cases.

Eczema (ek′zĕ-mah) A clinical term for several conditions that cause "weeping" skin lesions and intense itching. One common cause, *atopic dermatitis*, has a strong familial predisposition, has features of immediate hypersensitivity, and usually begins in the first five years of life. Recent research suggests the underlying defect may be increased leakiness of the skin.

Hashimoto's thyroiditis An autoimmune disease in which the thyroid gland is attacked by both B and T lymphocytes. It is the most common cause of hypothyroidism, affecting mostly middle-aged and elderly women. Genetic factors associated with this autoimmune disease (certain MHC variants) make individuals susceptible to environmental triggers (possibly iodine, irradiation, or trauma).

Immunization The process of rendering a subject immune (by vaccination or injection of antiserum).

Immunology The study of immunity.

Immunopathology Disease of the immune system.

Septic shock (sepsis) A dangerous condition in which the inflammatory response goes out of control. Kills 175,000 people a year in the U.S. Results from especially severe bacterial infections or more ordinary infections that grow rapidly worse in patients with weakened defenses, such as the hospitalized elderly recovering from surgery. In an inflammatory response, neutrophils and other white blood cells leave the capillaries and enter the infected connective tissue, secreting cytokines that increase capillary permeability. Secretion of cytokines is normally moderate, but in sepsis, continued cytokine release makes capillaries so leaky that the bloodstream is depleted of fluid. Blood pressure falls and the body organs shut down, causing death in 50% of all cases. Sepsis has proven difficult to control and its incidence remains high.

Systemic lupus erythematosus (SLE) (er″ĭ-the′mah-to′sus) A systemic autoimmune disorder that occurs mainly in young females. Diagnosis is helped by finding antinuclear (anti-DNA) antibodies in the patient's serum. DNA–anti-DNA complexes (typical of type III hypersensitivity) localize in the kidneys (the capillary filters, or glomeruli), in blood vessels, in the brain, and in the synovial membranes of joints, resulting in glomerulonephritis, vascular problems, loss of memory and mental sharpness, and painful arthritis. Reddened skin lesions, particularly a "butterfly rash" (the sign of the wolf, or *lupus*) on the face, are common.

CHAPTER SUMMARY

Media study tools that could provide you additional help in reviewing specific key topics of Chapter 21 are referenced below.

iP = *Interactive Physiology*

PART 1: INNATE DEFENSES

Surface Barriers: Skin and Mucosae   (pp. 767–768)

1. Skin and mucous membranes constitute the first line of defense. Their role is to prevent pathogens from entering the body. Protective membranes line all body cavities and organs exposed to the exterior.
2. Surface membranes provide mechanical barriers to pathogens. Some have structural modifications and produce secretions that enhance their defensive effects: The skin's acidity, lysozyme, mucus, keratin, and ciliated cells are examples.

iP IP Immune System; Topic: Innate Host Defenses, pp. 3–5.

Internal Defenses: Cells and Chemicals   (pp. 768–775)

1. The innate cellular and chemical defenses provide the body's second line of defense.

Phagocytes   (p. 768)

2. Phagocytes (macrophages, neutrophils, and the like) engulf and destroy pathogens that breach epithelial barriers. This process is facilitated when antibodies or complement to which the phagocyte's receptors can bind attach to the pathogen's surface. Cell killing is enhanced by the respiratory burst.

Natural Killer Cells   (pp. 768–769)

3. Natural killer cells are large granular lymphocytes that act nonspecifically to kill virus-infected and malignant cells.

Inflammation: Tissue Response to Injury   (pp. 769–773)

4. The inflammatory response prevents the spread of harmful agents, disposes of pathogens and dead tissue cells, and promotes healing. Exudate is formed; protective leukocytes enter the area; the area is walled off by fibrin; and tissue repair occurs.
5. The cardinal signs of inflammation are swelling, redness, heat, and pain. These result from vasodilation and increased permeability of blood vessels induced by inflammatory chemicals. If the inflamed area is a joint, movement may be impaired.

Antimicrobial Proteins   (pp. 773–775)

6. Interferons are a group of related proteins synthesized by virus-infected cells and certain immune cells that prevent viruses from multiplying in other body cells.
7. Activation of complement (a group of plasma proteins) on the membrane of a foreign cell promotes phagocytosis of that cell, enhances the inflammation, and sometimes causes lysis of the target cell.

Fever   (p. 775)

8. Fever enhances the body's fight against pathogens by increasing metabolism, which speeds up defensive actions and repair processes, and by prompting the liver and spleen to sequester iron and zinc needed for bacterial multiplication.

iP Immune System; Topic: Innate Host Defenses, pp. 6–23.

PART 2: ADAPTIVE DEFENSES

1. The adaptive immune system recognizes something as foreign and acts to immobilize, neutralize, or remove it. The adaptive immune response is antigen-specific, systemic, and has memory. It provides the body's third line of defense.

iP Immune System; Topic: Immune System Overview, p. 7.

Antigens (pp. 776–777)

1. Antigens are substances capable of generating an immune response.

Complete Antigens and Haptens (p. 776)

2. Complete antigens have both immunogenicity and reactivity. Incomplete antigens or haptens must combine with a body protein before becoming immunogenic.

Antigenic Determinants (pp. 776–777)

3. Antigenic determinants are the portions of antigen molecules that are recognized as foreign. Most antigens have many such sites.

Self-Antigens: MHC Proteins (p. 777)

4. Major histocompatibility complex (MHC) proteins are membrane-bound glycoproteins that mark our cells as "self." Class I MHC proteins are found on the surfaces of all body cells (except RBCs); the class II variety is found on certain cells that function in adaptive immune responses (dendritic cells, macrophages, and B cells).

iP Immune System; Topic: Immune System Overview, p. 8; Topic: Cellular Immunity, pp. 5–8.

Cells of the Adaptive Immune System: An Overview (pp. 777–780)

Lymphocytes (pp. 777–779)

1. Lymphocytes arise from hematopoietic stem cells of the bone marrow and are educated to develop immunocompetence and self-tolerance. T cells are educated in the thymus and confer cell-mediated immunity. B cells are educated in the bone marrow and provide humoral immunity. Immunocompetence is signaled by the appearance of antigen-specific receptors on the surface of the lymphocyte. Immunocompetent lymphocytes seed the secondary lymphoid organs, where the antigen challenge occurs, and circulate between the blood, lymph, and lymphoid organs.

2. In both B and T lymphocytes, antigen receptor diversity is generated by shuffling gene fragments.

Antigen-Presenting Cells (pp. 779–780)

3. Antigen-presenting cells (APCs) include dendritic cells, macrophages, and B lymphocytes. They internalize antigens and present antigenic determinants on their surfaces for recognition by T cells.

iP Immune System; Topic: Common Characteristics of B and T Lymphocytes, pp. 8–13.

Humoral Immune Response (pp. 780–786)

Clonal Selection and Differentiation of B Cells (p. 780)

1. Clonal selection and differentiation of B cells occur when antigens bind to their receptors, causing them to proliferate. Most of the clone members become effector cells called plasma cells, which secrete antibodies. This is the primary adaptive immune response.

Immunological Memory (pp. 780–781)

2. Other clone members become memory B cells, capable of mounting a rapid attack against the same antigen in subsequent encounters (secondary immune responses). The memory cells provide humoral immunological memory.

Active and Passive Humoral Immunity (pp. 781–783)

3. Active humoral immunity is acquired during an infection or via vaccination and provides immunological memory. Passive immunity is conferred when a donor's antibodies are injected into the bloodstream, or when the mother's antibodies cross the placenta. Its protection is short-lived; immunological memory is not established.

Antibodies (pp. 783–786)

4. The antibody monomer consists of four polypeptide chains, two heavy and two light, connected by disulfide bonds. Each chain has both a constant and a variable region. Constant regions determine antibody function and class. Variable regions enable the antibody to recognize its specific antigen.

5. Five classes of antibodies exist: IgM, IgA, IgD, IgG, and IgE. They differ structurally and functionally.

6. Antibody functions include complement fixation and antigen neutralization, precipitation, and agglutination.

7. Monoclonal antibodies are pure preparations of a single antibody type useful in diagnostic tests and in treatment for some types of cancer. They are prepared by fusing B cells with tumor cells to produce hybridomas.

iP Immune System; Topic: Common Characteristics of B and T Lymphocytes, pp. 14–15; Topic: Humoral Immunity, pp. 3–14.

Cell-Mediated Immune Response (pp. 786–795)

Clonal Selection and Differentiation of T Cells (pp. 786–791)

1. Immunocompetent CD4 and CD8 T cells are activated by binding to an antigen-containing MHC protein displayed on the surface of an APC. A co-stimulatory signal is also essential. Clonal selection occurs and the clone members differentiate into the appropriate effector T cells that mount the primary immune response (e.g., helper and cytotoxic T cells). Some clone members become memory T cells.

Specific Effector T Cell Roles (pp. 791–792)

2. Helper T cells are required for full activation of most B and T cells, activate macrophages, and release essential cytokines. Cytotoxic T cells directly attack and kill infected cells and cancer cells. Regulatory (T_{Reg}) T cells help to maintain tolerance in the periphery.

3. The immune response is enhanced by cytokines such as interleukin 1 released by macrophages, and interleukin 2, gamma interferon, and others released by activated T cells.

Organ Transplants and Prevention of Rejection (pp. 792–795)

4. Grafts or foreign organ transplants are rejected by cell-mediated responses unless the patient is immunosuppressed. Infections are major complications in such patients.

iP Immune System; Topic: Cellular Immunity, pp. 3–4, 9, 11–14.

Homeostatic Imbalances of Immunity (pp. 795–799)

Immunodeficiencies (pp. 796–797)

1. Immunodeficiency diseases include severe combined immunodeficiency (SCID) syndromes and acquired immune deficiency syndrome (AIDS). Overwhelming infections are fatal because the immune system is unable to combat them.

21

Autoimmune Diseases (p. 797)

2. Autoimmune disease occurs when the body regards its own tissues as foreign and mounts an immune attack against them. Examples include rheumatoid arthritis and multiple sclerosis.

Hypersensitivities (pp. 797–799)

3. Hypersensitivity is an abnormally intense reaction to an otherwise harmless antigen. Immediate hypersensitivities (allergies) are mounted by IgE antibodies. Subacute hypersensitivities, involving both antibodies and complement, include antibody-mediated cytotoxic and immune-complex hypersensitivities. Cell-mediated hypersensitivity is called delayed hypersensitivity.

Developmental Aspects of the Immune System (p. 799)

1. Development of the immune response occurs around the time of birth. The ability of the immune system to recognize foreign substances is genetically determined.

2. The nervous system plays an important role in regulating immune responses, possibly through common mediators. Depression impairs immune function.

3. With aging, the immune system becomes less responsive. The elderly more often suffer from immune deficiency, autoimmune diseases, and cancer.

REVIEW QUESTIONS

Multiple Choice/Matching

(Some questions have more than one correct answer. Select the best answer or answers from the choices given.)

1. All of the following are considered innate body defenses *except* (a) complement, (b) phagocytosis, (c) antibodies, (d) lysozyme, (e) inflammation.

2. The process by which neutrophils squeeze through capillary walls in response to inflammatory signals is called (a) diapedesis, (b) chemotaxis, (c) margination, (d) opsonization.

3. Antibodies released by plasma cells are involved in (a) humoral immunity, (b) immediate hypersensitivity reactions, (c) autoimmune disorders, (d) all of the above.

4. Which of the following antibodies can fix complement? (a) IgA, (b) IgD, (c) IgE, (d) IgG, (e) IgM.

5. Which antibody class is abundant in body secretions? (Use the choices from question 4.)

6. Small molecules that must combine with large proteins to become immunogenic are called (a) complete antigens, (b) kinins, (c) antigenic determinants, (d) haptens.

7. Lymphocytes that develop immunocompetence in the bone marrow are (a) T lymphocytes, (b) B lymphocytes, (c) NK cells, (d) B and T lymphocytes.

8. Cells that can directly attack target cells include all of the following *except* (a) macrophages, (b) cytotoxic T cells, (c) helper T cells, (d) natural killer cells.

9. Which of the following is involved in the activation of a B cell? (a) antigen, (b) helper T cell, (c) cytokine, (d) all of the above.

10. The cell type most often invaded by HIV is a(n) (a) eosinophil, (b) cytotoxic T cell, (c) natural killer cell, (d) helper T cell, (e) B cell.

11. Complement fixation promotes all of the following except (a) cell lysis, (b) inflammation, (c) opsonization, (d) interferon release, (e) chemotaxis of neutrophils and other cells.

12. Using the letters from column B, match the cell description in column A. (Note that all require more than a single choice.)

Column A	Column B
_____ (1) phagocyte	(a) natural killer cells
_____ (2) releases histamine	(b) neutrophil
_____ (3) releases perforins	(c) dendritic cells
_____ (4) lymphocyte	(d) mast cell
_____ (5) effector cells of adaptive immunity	(e) cytotoxic T cell
_____ (6) antigen-presenting cell	(f) B cell
	(g) macrophage
	(h) helper T cell
	(i) basophil

Short Answer Essay Questions

13. Besides acting as mechanical barriers, the skin epidermis and mucosae of the body have other attributes that contribute to their protective roles. Cite the common body locations and the importance of mucus, lysozyme, keratin, acid pH, and cilia.

14. Explain why attempts at phagocytosis are not always successful; cite factors that increase the likelihood of success.

15. What is complement? How does it cause bacterial lysis? What are some of the other roles of complement?

16. Interferons are referred to as antiviral proteins. What stimulates their production, and how do they protect uninfected cells? What cells of the body secrete interferons?

17. Differentiate between humoral and cell-mediated adaptive immunity.

18. Although the adaptive immune system has two arms, it has been said, "no T cells, no immunity." Explain.

19. Define immunocompetence and self-tolerance. How is self-tolerance achieved?

20. Differentiate between a primary and a secondary immune response. Which is more rapid and why?

21. Define antibody. Using an appropriately labeled diagram, describe the structure of an antibody monomer. Indicate and label variable and constant regions, heavy and light chains.

22. What is the role of the variable regions of an antibody? Of the constant regions?

23. Name the five antibody classes and describe where each is most likely to be found in the body.

24. How do antibodies help defend the body?

25. Do vaccines produce active or passive humoral immunity? Explain your answer. Why is passive immunity less satisfactory?

26. Describe the process of activation of a CD4 T cell.

27. Describe the specific roles of helper, regulatory, and cytotoxic T cells in normal cell-mediated immunity.

28. Name several cytokines and describe their role in the immune response.

29. Define hypersensitivity. List three types of hypersensitivity reactions. For each, note whether antibodies or T cells are involved and provide two examples.

30. What events can result in autoimmune disease?

31. What accounts for the declining efficiency of the immune system with age?

Critical Thinking and Clinical Application Questions

1. Jenny, a 6-year-old child who has been raised in a germ-free environment from birth, is a victim of one of the most severe examples of an abnormal immune system. Jenny also suffers from cancer caused by the Epstein-Barr virus. Relative to this case: (**a**) What is the usual fate of children with Jenny's condition and similar circumstances if no treatment is attempted? (**b**) Why is Jenny's brother chosen as the hematopoietic stem cell donor? (**c**) Why is her physician planning to use umbilical cord blood as a source of stem cells for transplant if her brother's stem cells fail (what are the hoped-for results)? (**d**) Attempt to explain Jenny's cancer. (**e**) What similarities and dissimilarities exist between Jenny's illness and AIDS?

2. Some people with a deficit of IgA exhibit recurrent respiratory tract infections. Explain this observation.

3. Capillary permeability increases and plasma proteins leak into the interstitial fluid as part of the inflammatory process. Why is this desirable?

4. Costanza was picking grapes in her father's arbor when she felt a short prickling pain in her finger. She ran crying to her father, who removed an insect stinger and calmed her with a glass of lemonade. Twenty minutes later Costanza's finger was red, swollen, and throbbing where she had been stung. What type of immune response was she exhibiting? What treatment would relieve her discomfort?

5. Caroline, a pregnant 29-year-old, has been HIV-positive for at least 10 years, dating back to when she was homeless and injecting heroin on a regular basis. While she currently has no symptoms of AIDS, she is taking several medications and is worried about the possibility that her baby might be infected. How do you think the HIV virus might be transferred from a mother to her offspring? Which of Caroline's cells are infected by the virus and why is the viral attack on these cells so devastating? Why is Caroline taking medication even though she has no symptoms? What types of medications might she be taking and how do they affect the virus and its replication?

21

22

The Respiratory System

Far from self-sustaining, the body depends on the external environment, both as a source of substances the body needs to survive and as a catch basin for its wastes. The trillions of cells making up the body require a continuous supply of oxygen to carry out their vital functions. We cannot do without oxygen for even a little while, as we can without food or water.

As cells use oxygen, they give off carbon dioxide, a waste product the body must get rid of. They also generate dangerous free radicals, the inescapable by-products of living in a world full of oxygen. But let's get to the topic of this chapter, the respiratory system.

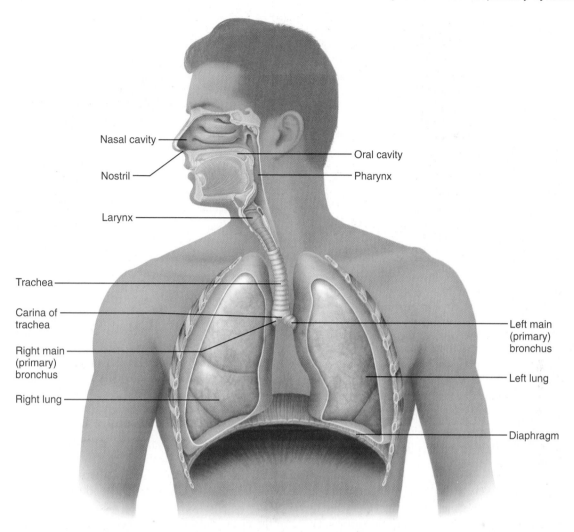

Nasal cavity

Nostril

Larynx

Trachea

Carina of trachea

Right main (primary) bronchus

Right lung

Oral cavity

Pharynx

Left main (primary) bronchus

Left lung

Diaphragm

Figure 22.1 The major respiratory organs in relation to surrounding structures.

The major function of the **respiratory system** is to supply the body with oxygen and dispose of carbon dioxide. To accomplish this function, at least four processes, collectively called **respiration**, must happen:

1. **Pulmonary ventilation**: movement of air into and out of the lungs so that the gases there are continuously changed and refreshed (commonly called breathing).
2. **External respiration**: movement of oxygen from the lungs to the blood and of carbon dioxide from the blood to the lungs.
3. **Transport of respiratory gases**: transport of oxygen from the lungs to the tissue cells of the body, and of carbon dioxide from the tissue cells to the lungs. This transport is accomplished by the cardiovascular system using blood as the transporting fluid.
4. **Internal respiration**: movement of oxygen from blood to the tissue cells and of carbon dioxide from tissue cells to blood.

Only the first two processes are the special responsibility of the respiratory system **(Figure 22.1)**, but it cannot accomplish its primary goal of obtaining oxygen and eliminating carbon

dioxide unless the third and fourth processes also occur. As you can see, the respiratory and circulatory systems are closely coupled, and if either system fails, the body's cells begin to die from oxygen starvation.

The actual use of oxygen and production of carbon dioxide by tissue cells, known as *cellular respiration,* is the cornerstone of all energy-producing chemical reactions in the body. We discuss cellular respiration, which is not a function of the respiratory system, in the metabolism section of Chapter 24.

Because it moves air, the respiratory system is also involved with the sense of smell and with speech.

Functional Anatomy of the Respiratory System

▶ Identify the organs forming the respiratory passageway(s) in descending order until the alveoli are reached.

▶ Describe the location, structure, and function of each of the following: nose, paranasal sinuses, pharynx, and larynx.

▶ List and describe several protective mechanisms of the respiratory system.

22

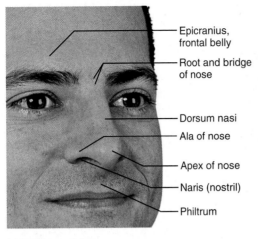

Epicranius, frontal belly

Root and bridge of nose

Dorsum nasi

Ala of nose

Apex of nose

Naris (nostril)

Philtrum

(a) Surface anatomy

Frontal bone

Nasal bone

Septal cartilage

Maxillary bone (frontal process)

Lateral process of septal cartilage

Minor alar cartilages

Dense fibrous connective tissue

Major alar cartilages

(b) External skeletal framework

Figure 22.2 The external nose.

The respiratory system includes the *nose, nasal cavity,* and *paranasal sinuses;* the *pharynx;* the *larynx;* the *trachea;* the *bronchi* and their smaller branches; and the *lungs,* which contain the terminal air sacs, or *alveoli* (Figure 22.1). Functionally, the system consists of two zones. The **respiratory zone**, the actual site of gas exchange, is composed of the respiratory bronchioles, alveolar ducts, and alveoli, all microscopic structures. The **conducting zone** includes all other respiratory passageways, which provide fairly rigid conduits for air to reach the gas exchange sites. The conducting zone organs also cleanse, humidify, and warm incoming air. As a result, air reaching the lungs has fewer irritants (dust, bacteria, etc.) than when it entered the system, and it is warm and damp, like the air of the tropics. The functions of the major organs of the respiratory system are summarized in **Table 22.1**.

In addition to these organs, some authorities also include the respiratory muscles (diaphragm, etc.) as part of this system. Although we will consider how these skeletal muscles bring about the volume changes that promote ventilation, we continue to classify them as part of the *muscular system.*

The Nose and Paranasal Sinuses

The nose is the only externally visible part of the respiratory system. Unlike the eyes and lips, facial features often referred to poetically, the nose is usually an irreverent target. We are urged to keep our nose to the grindstone and to keep it out of other people's business. Considering its important functions, however, it deserves more esteem. The nose (1) provides an airway for respiration, (2) moistens and warms entering air, (3) filters and cleans inspired air, (4) serves as a resonating chamber for speech, and (5) houses the olfactory (smell) receptors.

The structures of the nose are divided into the *external nose* and the internal *nasal cavity* for ease of consideration. The surface features of the external nose include the *root* (area between the eyebrows), *bridge,* and *dorsum nasi* (anterior

margin), the latter terminating in the *apex* (tip of the nose) **(Figure 22.2a)**. Just inferior to the apex is a shallow vertical groove called the *philtrum* (fil′trum). The external openings of the nose, the *nostrils* or *nares* (na′rēz), are bounded laterally by the flared *alae*.

The skeletal framework of the external nose is fashioned by the nasal and frontal bones superiorly (forming the bridge and root, respectively), the maxillary bones laterally, and flexible plates of hyaline cartilage (the alar and septal cartilages, and the lateral processes of the septal cartilage) inferiorly (Figure 22.2b). Noses vary a great deal in size and shape, largely because of differences in the nasal cartilages. The skin covering the nose's dorsal and lateral aspects is thin and contains many sebaceous glands.

The internal **nasal cavity** lies in and posterior to the external nose. During breathing, air enters the cavity by passing through the **nostrils**, or **nares** (Figure 22.2a and **Figure 22.3c**). The nasal cavity is divided by a midline **nasal septum**, formed anteriorly by the septal cartilage and posteriorly by the vomer bone and perpendicular plate of the ethmoid bone (see Figure 7.14b, p. 213). The nasal cavity is continuous posteriorly with the nasal portion of the pharynx through the **posterior nasal apertures**, also called the *choanae* (ko-a′ne; "funnels").

The roof of the nasal cavity is formed by the ethmoid and sphenoid bones of the skull. The floor is formed by the *palate,* which separates the nasal cavity from the oral cavity below. Anteriorly, where the palate is supported by the palatine bones and processes of the maxillary bones, it is called the **hard palate**. The unsupported posterior portion is the muscular **soft palate**.

The part of the nasal cavity just superior to the nostrils, called the **nasal vestibule**, is lined with skin containing sebaceous and sweat glands and numerous hair follicles. The hairs, or **vibrissae** (vi-bris′e; *vibro* = to quiver), filter coarse particles (dust, pollen) from inspired air. The rest of the nasal cavity is lined with two types of mucous membrane. The **olfactory epithelium (mucosa)**, lining the slitlike superior region of the

22

TABLE 22.1	Principal Organs of the Respiratory System	
STRUCTURE	**DESCRIPTION, GENERAL AND DISTINCTIVE FEATURES**	**FUNCTION**
Nose	Jutting external portion is supported by bone and cartilage. Internal nasal cavity is divided by midline nasal septum and lined with mucosa.	Produces mucus; filters, warms, and moistens incoming air; resonance chamber for speech
	Roof of nasal cavity contains olfactory epithelium.	Receptors for sense of smell
Paranasal sinuses	Mucosa-lined, air-filled cavities in cranial bones surrounding nasal cavity.	Same as for nasal cavity; also lighten skull
Pharynx	Passageway connecting nasal cavity to larynx and oral cavity to esophagus. Three subdivisions: nasopharynx, oropharynx, and laryngopharynx.	Passageway for air and food
	Houses tonsils (lymphoid tissue masses involved in protection against pathogens).	Facilitates exposure of immune system to inhaled antigens
Larynx	Connects pharynx to trachea. Has framework of cartilage and dense connective tissue. Opening (glottis) can be closed by epiglottis or vocal folds.	Air passageway; prevents food from entering lower respiratory tract
	Houses vocal folds (true vocal cords).	Voice production
Trachea	Flexible tube running from larynx and dividing inferiorly into two main bronchi. Walls contain C-shaped cartilages that are incomplete posteriorly where connected by trachealis muscle.	Air passageway; cleans, warms, and moistens incoming air
Bronchial tree	Consists of right and left main bronchi, which subdivide within the lungs to form lobar and segmental bronchi and bronchioles. Bronchiolar walls lack cartilage but contain complete layer of smooth muscle. Constriction of this muscle impedes expiration.	Air passageways connecting trachea with alveoli; cleans, warms, and moistens incoming air
Alveoli	Microscopic chambers at termini of bronchial tree. Walls of simple squamous epithelium are underlain by thin basement membrane. External surfaces are intimately associated with pulmonary capillaries.	Main sites of gas exchange
	Special alveolar cells produce surfactant.	Reduces surface tension; helps prevent lung collapse
Lungs	Paired composite organs that flank mediastinum in thorax. Composed primarily of alveoli and respiratory passageways. Stroma is fibrous elastic connective tissue, allowing lungs to recoil passively during expiration.	House respiratory passages smaller than the main bronchi
Pleurae	Serous membranes. Parietal pleura lines thoracic cavity; visceral pleura covers external lung surfaces.	Produce lubricating fluid and compartmentalize lungs

nasal cavity, contains smell receptors. The balance of the nasal cavity mucosa, the **respiratory mucosa**, is a pseudostratified ciliated columnar epithelium, containing scattered *goblet cells*, that rests on a lamina propria richly supplied with *mucous* and *serous glands*. (Mucous cells secrete mucus, and serous cells secrete a watery fluid containing enzymes.)

Each day, these glands secrete about a quart (or a liter) of mucus containing *lysozyme*, an antibacterial enzyme. The sticky mucus traps inspired dust, bacteria, and other debris, while lysozyme attacks and destroys bacteria chemically. The epithelial cells of the respiratory mucosa also secrete *defensins*, natural antibiotics that help get rid of invading microbes. Additionally, the high water content of the mucus film acts to humidify the inhaled air.

The ciliated cells of the respiratory mucosa create a gentle current that moves the sheet of contaminated mucus posteriorly toward the throat, where it is swallowed and digested by stomach juices. We are usually unaware of this important action of our nasal cilia, but when exposed to cold air they become sluggish, allowing mucus to accumulate in the nasal cavity and

then dribble out the nostrils. This along with the fact that water vapor in expired air tends to condense at these lower temperatures helps explain why you might have a "runny" nose on a crisp, wintry day.

The nasal mucosa is richly supplied with sensory nerve endings, and contact with irritating particles (dust, pollen, and the like) triggers a sneeze reflex. The sneeze forces air outward in a violent burst—a somewhat crude way of expelling irritants from the nose.

Rich plexuses of capillaries and thin-walled veins underlie the nasal epithelium and warm incoming air as it flows across the mucosal surface. When the inspired air is cold, the vascular plexus becomes engorged with blood, thereby intensifying the air-heating process. Because of the abundance and superficial location of these blood vessels, nosebleeds are common and often profuse.

Protruding medially from each lateral wall of the nasal cavity are three scroll-like mucosa-covered projections, the *superior, middle,* and *inferior nasal conchae* (kong′ke) (Figure 22.3). The groove inferior to each concha is a *nasal meatus* (me-a′tus). The

22

Olfactory epithelium

Mucosa of pharynx

Tubal tonsil

Pharyngotympanic (auditory) tube

Nasopharynx

Olfactory nerves

Superior nasal concha and superior nasal meatus

Middle nasal concha and middle nasal meatus

Inferior nasal concha and inferior nasal meatus

Hard palate

Soft palate

Uvula

(a) Photograph

Pharynx
Nasopharynx
Oropharynx
Laryngopharynx

(b) Regions of the pharynx

Cribriform plate of ethmoid bone

Sphenoid sinus

Posterior nasal aperture

Nasopharynx
Pharyngeal tonsil

Opening of pharyngotympanic tube

Uvula

Oropharynx
Palatine tonsil

Isthmus of the fauces

Laryngopharynx

Esophagus

Trachea

Frontal sinus

Nasal cavity
Nasal conchae (superior, middle and inferior)

Nasal meatuses (superior, middle, and inferior)

Nasal vestibule

Nostril

Hard palate

Soft palate

Tongue

Lingual tonsil

Hyoid bone

Larynx
Epiglottis

Vestibular fold

Thyroid cartilage

Vocal fold

Cricoid cartilage

Thyroid gland

(c) Illustration

Figure 22.3 The upper respiratory tract. Midsagittal section of the head and neck. (See also *A Brief Atlas of the Human Body*, Figure 47.)

22

curved conchae greatly increase the mucosal surface area exposed to the air and enhance air turbulence in the cavity. The gases in inhaled air swirl through the twists and turns, but heavier, nongaseous particles tend to be deflected onto the mucus-coated surfaces, where they become trapped. As a result, few particles larger than 6 μm make it past the nasal cavity.

The conchae and nasal mucosa not only function during inhalation to filter, heat, and moisten the air, but also act during exhalation to reclaim this heat and moisture. In other words, the inhaled air cools the conchae, then during exhalation these cooled conchae precipitate moisture and extract heat from the humid air flowing over them. This reclamation process minimizes the amount of moisture and heat lost from the body through breathing, helping us to survive in dry and cold climates.

The nasal cavity is surrounded by a ring of **paranasal sinuses** (Figure 22.3c). They are located in the frontal, sphenoid, ethmoid, and maxillary bones (see Figure 7.15, p. 216). The sinuses lighten the skull, and together with the nasal cavity they warm and moisten the air. The mucus they produce ultimately flows into the nasal cavity, and the suctioning effect created by nose blowing helps drain the sinuses.

HOMEOSTATIC IMBALANCE

Cold viruses, streptococcal bacteria, and various allergens can cause *rhinitis* (ri-ni′tis), inflammation of the nasal mucosa accompanied by excessive mucus production, nasal congestion, and postnasal drip. The nasal mucosa is continuous with that of the rest of the respiratory tract, explaining the typical nose to throat to chest progression of colds. Because the mucosa extends tentacle-like into the nasolacrimal (tear) ducts and paranasal sinuses, nasal cavity infections often spread to those regions, causing **sinusitis** (inflamed sinuses). When the passageways connecting the sinuses to the nasal cavity are blocked with mucus or infectious material, the air in the sinus cavities is absorbed. The result is a partial vacuum and a *sinus headache* localized over the inflamed areas. ■

The Pharynx

The funnel-shaped **pharynx** (far′ingks) connects the nasal cavity and mouth superiorly to the larynx and esophagus inferiorly. Commonly called the *throat*, the pharynx vaguely resembles a short length of garden hose as it extends for about 13 cm (5 inches) from the base of the skull to the level of the sixth cervical vertebra (Figure 22.1).

From superior to inferior, the pharynx is divided into three regions—the *nasopharynx*, *oropharynx*, and *laryngopharynx* (Figure 22.3b). The muscular pharynx wall is composed of skeletal muscle throughout its length (see Table 10.3, pp. 334–335). However, the cellular composition of its mucosa varies from one pharyngeal region to another.

The Nasopharynx

The **nasopharynx** is posterior to the nasal cavity, inferior to the sphenoid bone, and superior to the level of the soft palate. Because it lies above the point where food enters the body, it serves *only* as an air passageway. During swallowing, the soft palate and its pendulous *uvula* (u′vu-lah; "little grape") move superiorly, an action that closes off the nasopharynx and prevents food from entering the nasal cavity. (When we giggle, this sealing action fails and fluids being swallowed can end up spraying out the nose.)

The nasopharynx is continuous with the nasal cavity through the posterior nasal apertures (Figure 22.3c). Its pseudostratified ciliated epithelium takes over the job of propelling mucus where the nasal mucosa leaves off. High on its posterior wall is the **pharyngeal tonsil** (far-rin′je-al) (or *adenoids*), which traps and destroys pathogens entering the nasopharynx in air.

HOMEOSTATIC IMBALANCE

Infected and swollen adenoids block air passage in the nasopharynx, making it necessary to breathe through the mouth. As a result, the air is not properly moistened, warmed, or filtered before reaching the lungs. When the adenoids are chronically enlarged, both speech and sleep may be disturbed. ■

The *pharyngotympanic* (*auditory*) *tubes*, which drain the middle ear cavities and allow middle ear pressure to equalize with atmospheric pressure, open into the lateral walls of the nasopharynx (Figure 22.3a). A ridge of pharyngeal mucosa, referred to as a *tubal tonsil*, arches over each of these openings. Because of their strategic location, the tubal tonsils help protect the middle ear against infections likely to spread from the nasopharynx. The pharyngeal tonsil, superoposterior and medial to the tubal tonsils, also plays this protective role.

The Oropharynx

The **oropharynx** lies posterior to the oral cavity and is continuous with it through an archway called the **isthmus of the fauces** (faw′sēz; "throat") (Figure 22.3c). Because the oropharynx extends inferiorly from the level of the soft palate to the epiglottis, both swallowed food and inhaled air pass through it.

As the nasopharynx blends into the oropharynx, the epithelium changes from pseudostratified columnar to a more protective stratified squamous epithelium. This structural adaptation accommodates the increased friction and greater chemical trauma accompanying food passage.

The paired **palatine tonsils** lie embedded in the oropharyngeal mucosa of the lateral walls of the fauces. The **lingual tonsil** covers the posterior surface of the tongue.

The Laryngopharynx

Like the oropharynx above it, the **laryngopharynx** (lah-ring″go-far′ingks) serves as a passageway for food and air and is lined with a stratified squamous epithelium. It lies directly posterior to the upright epiglottis and extends to the larynx, where the respiratory and digestive pathways diverge. At that point the laryngopharynx is continuous with the esophagus posteriorly. The esophagus conducts food and fluids to the stomach; air enters the larynx anteriorly. During swallowing, food has the "right of way," and air passage temporarily stops.

22

(a) Anterior superficial view

(b) Sagittal view; anterior surface to the right

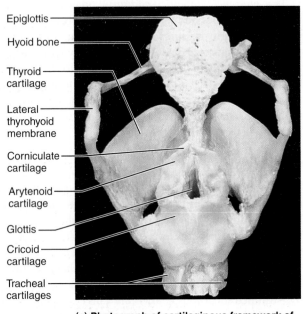

(c) Photograph of cartilaginous framework of the larynx, posterior view

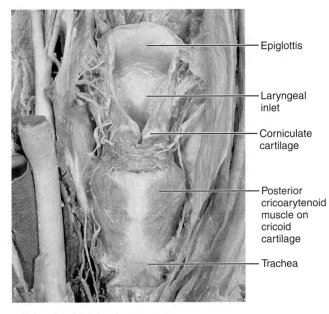

(d) Photograph of posterior aspect

Figure 22.4 **The larynx.**

The Larynx

Basic Anatomy

The **larynx** (lar′ingks), or voice box, extends for about 5 cm (2 inches) from the level of the third to the sixth cervical vertebra. Superiorly it attaches to the hyoid bone and opens into the laryngopharynx. Inferiorly it is continuous with the trachea (Figure 22.3c).

The larynx has three functions. Its two main tasks are to provide a *patent* (open) airway and to act as a switching mechanism to route air and food into the proper channels. Because it houses the vocal folds (vocal cords), the third function of the larynx is voice production.

The framework of the larynx is an intricate arrangement of nine cartilages connected by membranes and ligaments (Figure 22.4). Except for the epiglottis, all laryngeal cartilages are hyaline cartilages. The large, shield-shaped **thyroid cartilage** is formed by the fusion of two cartilage plates. The midline **laryngeal prominence** (lah-rin′je-al), which marks the fusion point, is obvious externally as the *Adam's apple*. The thyroid cartilage is typically larger in males than in females because male sex hormones stimulate its growth during puberty. Inferior to the thyroid cartilage is the ring-shaped

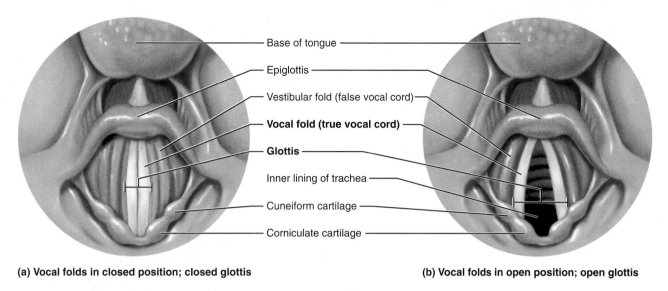

(a) Vocal folds in closed position; closed glottis   (b) Vocal folds in open position; open glottis

Figure 22.5 Movements of the vocal folds. Drawings of superior views of the larynx and vocal folds, as if seen through a laryngoscope.

cricoid cartilage (kri′koid), perched atop and anchored to the trachea inferiorly.

Three pairs of small cartilages, **arytenoid** (ar″ĭ-te′noid), **cuneiform** (ku-ne′ĭ-form), and **corniculate cartilages**, form part of the lateral and posterior walls of the larynx. The most important of these are the pyramid-shaped arytenoid cartilages, which anchor the vocal folds.

The ninth cartilage, the flexible, spoon-shaped **epiglottis** (ep″ĭ-glot′is; "above the glottis"), is composed of elastic cartilage and is almost entirely covered by a taste bud–containing mucosa. The epiglottis extends from the posterior aspect of the tongue to its anchoring point on the anterior rim of the thyroid cartilage (Figure 22.4b and c).

When only air is flowing into the larynx, the inlet to the larynx is open wide and the free edge of the epiglottis projects upward. During swallowing, the larynx is pulled superiorly and the epiglottis tips to cover the laryngeal inlet. Because this action keeps food out of the lower respiratory passages, the epiglottis has been called the guardian of the airways. Anything other than air entering the larynx initiates the cough reflex, which acts to expel the substance. This protective reflex does not work when we are unconscious, so it is never a good idea to administer liquids when attempting to revive an unconscious person.

Lying under the laryngeal mucosa on each side are the **vocal ligaments**, which attach the arytenoid cartilages to the thyroid cartilage. These ligaments, composed largely of elastic fibers, form the core of mucosal folds called the **vocal folds**, or **true vocal cords**, which appear pearly white because they lack blood vessels (Figure 22.5).

The vocal folds vibrate, producing sounds as air rushes up from the lungs. The vocal folds and the medial opening between them through which air passes are called the **glottis**. Superior to the vocal folds is a similar pair of mucosal folds called the **vestibular folds**, or **false vocal cords**. These play no direct part in sound production but help to close the glottis when we swallow.

The superior portion of the larynx, an area subject to food contact, is lined by stratified squamous epithelium. Below the vocal folds the epithelium is a pseudostratified ciliated columnar type that acts as a dust filter. The power stroke of its cilia is directed upward toward the pharynx so that mucus is continually moved *away* from the lungs. We help to move mucus up and out of the larynx when we "clear our throat."

Voice Production

Speech involves the intermittent release of expired air and the opening and closing of the glottis. The length of the vocal folds and the size of the glottis change with the action of the intrinsic laryngeal muscles that clothe the cartilages. Most of these muscles move the arytenoid cartilages. As the length and tension of the vocal folds change, the pitch of the sound varies. Generally, the tenser the vocal folds, the faster they vibrate and the higher the pitch.

As a boy's larynx enlarges during puberty, his vocal folds become longer and thicker. Because this causes them to vibrate more slowly, his voice becomes deeper. Until the young man learns to control his newly enlarged vocal folds, his voice "cracks."

Loudness of the voice depends on the force with which the airstream rushes across the vocal folds. The greater the force, the stronger the vibration and the louder the sound. The vocal folds do not move at all when we whisper, but they vibrate vigorously when we yell. The power source for creating the airstream is the muscles of the chest, abdomen, and back.

The vocal folds actually produce buzzing sounds. The perceived quality of the voice depends on the coordinated activity of many structures above the glottis. For example, the entire length of the pharynx acts as a resonating chamber, to amplify and enhance the sound quality. The oral, nasal, and sinus cavities also contribute to vocal resonance. In addition, good enunciation depends on the "shaping" of sound into recognizable consonants and vowels by muscles in the pharynx, tongue, soft palate, and lips.

22

(b) Photomicrograph of the tracheal wall (320×)

(c) Scanning electron micrograph of cilia in the trachea (2500×)

Figure 22.6 Tissue composition of the tracheal wall. In the scannig electron micrograh in **(c)**, the cilia appear as yellow, grasslike projections. Mucus-secreting goblet cells (orange) with short microvilli are interspersed between the ciliated cells.

22

HOMEOSTATIC IMBALANCE

Inflammation of the vocal folds, or **laryngitis**, causes the vocal folds to swell, interfering with their vibration. This produces a change in the voice tone, hoarseness, or in severe cases inability to speak above a whisper. Laryngitis is also caused by overuse of the voice, very dry air, bacterial infections, tumors on the vocal folds, and inhalation of irritating chemicals. ■

Sphincter Functions of the Larynx

Under certain conditions, the vocal folds act as a sphincter that prevents air passage. During abdominal straining associated with defecation, the glottis closes to prevent exhalation and the abdominal muscles contract, causing the intra-abdominal pressure to rise. These events, collectively known as **Valsalva's maneuver**, help empty the rectum and can also splint (stabilize) the body trunk when one lifts a heavy load.

The Trachea

The **trachea** (tra′ke-ah), or *windpipe*, descends from the larynx through the neck and into the mediastinum. It ends by dividing into the two main bronchi at midthorax (see Figure 22.1). In humans, it is 10–12 cm (about 4 inches) long and 2 cm (3/4 inch) in diameter, and very flexible and mobile. Interestingly, early anatomists mistook the trachea for a rough-walled artery (*trachea* = rough).

The tracheal wall consists of several layers that are common to many tubular body organs—the *mucosa, submucosa,* and *adventitia*—plus a layer of hyaline cartilage **(Figure 22.6)**. The **mucosa** has the same goblet cell–containing pseudostratified epithelium that occurs throughout most of the respiratory tract. Its cilia continually propel debris-laden mucus toward the pharynx. This epithelium rests on a fairly thick lamina propria that has a rich supply of elastic fibers.

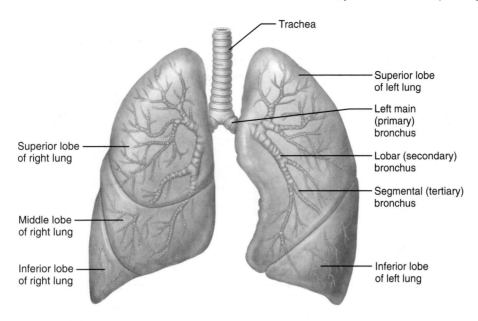

Figure 22.7 Conducting zone passages. The air pathway inferior to the larynx consists of the trachea and the main, lobar, and segmental bronchi, which branch into the smaller bronchi and bronchioles until the terminal bronchioles of the lungs are reached.

HOMEOSTATIC IMBALANCE

Smoking inhibits and ultimately destroys cilia, after which coughing is the only means of preventing mucus from accumulating in the lungs. For this reason, smokers with respiratory congestion should avoid medications that inhibit the cough reflex. ■

The **submucosa**, a connective tissue layer deep to the mucosa, contains seromucous glands that help produce the mucus "sheets" within the trachea. The submucosa is supported by 16 to 20 C-shaped rings of hyaline cartilage encased by the **adventitia**, the outermost layer of connective tissue (Figure 22.6).

The trachea's elastic elements make it flexible enough to stretch and move inferiorly during inspiration and recoil during expiration, but the cartilage rings prevent it from collapsing and keep the airway patent despite the pressure changes that occur during breathing. The open posterior parts of the cartilage rings, which abut the esophagus (Figure 22.6a), are connected by smooth muscle fibers of the **trachealis muscle** and by soft connective tissue. Because this portion of the tracheal wall is not rigid, the esophagus can expand anteriorly as swallowed food passes through it. Contraction of the trachealis muscle decreases the trachea's diameter, causing expired air to rush upward from the lungs with greater force. This action helps to expel mucus from the trachea when we cough by accelerating the exhaled air to speeds of 100 mph!

The last tracheal cartilage is expanded, and a spar of cartilage, called the **carina** (kar-ri′nah; "keel"), projects posteriorly from its inner face, marking the point where the trachea branches into the two *main bronchi*. The mucosa of the carina is highly sensitive and violent coughing is triggered when a foreign object makes contact with it.

By the time incoming air reaches the end of the trachea, it is warm, cleansed of most impurities, and saturated with water vapor.

HOMEOSTATIC IMBALANCE

Tracheal obstruction is life threatening. Many people have suffocated after choking on a piece of food that suddenly closed off their trachea. The **Heimlich maneuver**, a procedure in which air in the victim's lungs is used to "pop out," or expel, an obstructing piece of food, has saved many people from becoming victims of "café coronaries." The maneuver is simple to learn and easy to do. However, it is best learned by demonstration because cracked ribs are a distinct possibility when it is done incorrectly. ■

CHECK YOUR UNDERSTANDING

1. Air moving from the nose to the trachea passes by a number of structures. List (in order) as many of these structures as you can.
2. Which structure seals the larynx when we swallow?
3. Which structural features of the trachea allow it to expand and contract, yet keep it from collapsing?

For answers, see Appendix G.

The Bronchi and Subdivisions

▶ Distinguish between conducting and respiratory zone structures.

▶ Describe the makeup of the respiratory membrane, and relate structure to function.

The air passageways in the lungs branch and branch again, about 23 times overall. This branching pattern of airways is often called the **bronchial** or **respiratory tree** (Figure 22.7). The

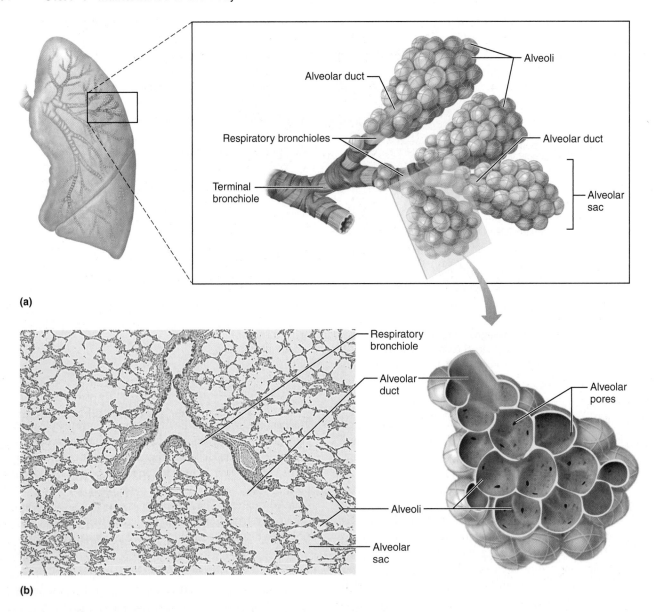

(a)

(b)

Figure 22.8 Respiratory zone structures. (a) Diagrammatic view of respiratory bronchioles, alveolar ducts, alveolar sacs, and alveoli. **(b)** Photomicrograph of a section of human lung, showing the respiratory structures that form the final divisions of the bronchial tree (70x). Notice the thinness of the alveolar walls.

bronchial tree is the site where conducting zone structures give way to respiratory zone structures **(Figure 22.8)**.

Conducting Zone Structures

The trachea divides to form the **right** and **left main (primary) bronchi** (brong′ki) approximately at the level of T$_7$ in an erect (standing) person. Each bronchus runs obliquely in the mediastinum before plunging into the medial depression (hilum) of the lung on its own side (Figure 22.7). The right main bronchus is wider, shorter, and more vertical than the left. Consequently, it is the more common site for an inhaled foreign object to become lodged.

Once inside the lungs, each main bronchus subdivides into **lobar (secondary) bronchi**—three on the right and two on the left—each supplying one lung lobe. The lobar bronchi branch into third-order **segmental (tertiary) bronchi**, which divide repeatedly into smaller and smaller bronchi (fourth-order, fifth-order, etc.). Passages smaller than 1 mm in diameter are called **bronchioles** ("little bronchi"), and the tiniest of these, the **terminal bronchioles**, are less than 0.5 mm in diameter.

The tissue composition of the walls of the main bronchi mimics that of the trachea, but as the conducting tubes become smaller, the following structural changes occur:

1. **Support structures change.** The cartilage rings are replaced by irregular *plates* of cartilage, and by the time the bronchioles are reached, supportive cartilage is no longer present in the tube walls. However, elastic fibers are found in the tube walls throughout the bronchial tree.

2. **Epithelium type changes.** The mucosal epithelium thins as it changes from pseudostratified columnar to columnar and then to cuboidal in the terminal bronchioles. Cilia are sparse, and mucus-producing cells are absent in the bronchioles. For this reason, most airborne debris found at or below the level of the bronchioles must be removed by macrophages in the alveoli.

3. **Amount of smooth muscle increases.** The relative amount of smooth muscle in the tube walls increases as the passageways become smaller. A complete layer of circular smooth muscle in the bronchioles and the lack of supporting cartilage (which would hinder constriction) allows the bronchioles to provide substantial resistance to air passage under certain conditions (as we will describe later).

Respiratory Zone Structures

Defined by the presence of thin-walled air sacs called **alveoli** (al-ve′o-li; *alveol* = small cavity), the respiratory zone begins as the terminal bronchioles feed into **respiratory bronchioles** within the lung (Figure 22.8). Protruding from these smallest bronchioles are scattered alveoli. The respiratory bronchioles lead into winding **alveolar ducts**, whose walls consist of diffusely arranged rings of smooth muscle cells, connective tissue fibers, and outpocketing alveoli. The alveolar ducts lead into terminal clusters of alveoli called **alveolar sacs**.

Many people mistakenly equate alveoli, the site of gas exchange, with alveolar sacs, but they are not the same thing. The alveolar sac is analogous to a bunch of grapes, and the alveoli are the individual grapes. The 300 million or so gas-filled alveoli in the lungs account for most of the lung volume and provide a tremendous surface area for gas exchange.

The Respiratory Membrane   The walls of the alveoli are composed primarily of a single layer of squamous epithelial cells, called **type I cells**, surrounded by a flimsy basement membrane. The thinness of their walls is hard to imagine, but a sheet of tissue paper is 15 times thicker. The external surfaces of the alveoli are densely covered with a "cobweb" of pulmonary capillaries **(Figure 22.9)**. Together, the alveolar and capillary walls and their fused basement membranes form the **respiratory membrane**, a 0.5-μm-thick *air-blood barrier* that has gas on one side and blood flowing past on the other (Figure 22.9c). Gas exchanges occur readily by simple diffusion across the respiratory membrane—O_2 passes from the alveolus into the blood, and CO_2 leaves the blood to enter the gas-filled alveolus.

Scattered amid the type I squamous cells that form the major part of the alveolar walls are cuboidal **type II cells** (Figure 22.9c). The type II cells secrete a fluid containing a detergent-like substance called *surfactant* that coats the gas-exposed alveolar surfaces. (We describe surfactant's role in reducing the surface tension of the alveolar fluid later in this chapter.) Recently, type II cells have been shown to secrete a number of antimicrobial proteins that are important elements of innate immunity.

The alveoli have three other significant features: (1) They are surrounded by fine elastic fibers of the same type that surround the entire bronchial tree. (2) Open **alveolar pores** connecting adjacent alveoli allow air pressure throughout the lung to be equalized and provide alternate air routes to any alveoli whose bronchi have collapsed due to disease. (3) Remarkably efficient **alveolar macrophages** crawl freely along the internal alveolar surfaces.

Although huge numbers of infectious microorganisms are continuously carried into the alveoli, alveolar surfaces are usually sterile. Because the alveoli are "dead ends," aged and dead macrophages must be prevented from accumulating in them. Most macrophages simply get swept up by the ciliary current of superior regions and carried passively to the pharynx. In this manner, we clear and swallow over 2 million alveolar macrophages per hour!

The Lungs and Pleurae

▶ Describe the gross structure of the lungs and pleurae.

The paired **lungs** occupy all of the thoracic cavity except the mediastinum, which houses the heart, great blood vessels, bronchi, esophagus, and other organs **(Figure 22.10)**.

Gross Anatomy of the Lungs

Each cone-shaped lung is surrounded by pleurae and connected to the mediastinum by vascular and bronchial attachments, collectively called the lung **root**. The anterior, lateral, and posterior lung surfaces lie in close contact with the ribs and form the continuously curving **costal surface**. Just deep to the clavicle is the **apex**, the narrow superior tip of the lung. The concave, inferior surface that rests on the diaphragm is the **base**.

On the mediastinal surface of each lung is an indentation, the **hilum**, through which pulmonary and systemic blood vessels, bronchi, lymphatic vessels, and nerves enter and leave the lungs. Each main bronchus plunges into the hilum on its own side and begins to branch almost immediately. All conducting and respiratory passageways distal to the main bronchi are found in the lungs.

The two lungs differ slightly in shape and size because the apex of the heart is slightly to the left of the median plane. The left lung is smaller than the right, and the **cardiac notch**—a concavity in its medial aspect—is molded to and accommodates the heart (Figure 22.10a). The left lung is subdivided into superior and inferior **lobes** by the *oblique fissure*, whereas the right lung is partitioned into superior, middle, and inferior lobes by the *oblique* and *horizontal fissures*.

Each lobe contains a number of pyramid-shaped **bronchopulmonary segments** separated from one another by connective tissue septa. Each segment is served by its own artery and vein and receives air from an individual segmental (tertiary) bronchus. Initially each lung contains ten bronchopulmonary segments arranged in similar (but not identical) patterns **(Figure 22.11)**. Subsequent fusion of adjacent segmental arteries reduces the number in the left lung to eight or nine segments.

The bronchopulmonary segments are clinically important because pulmonary disease is often confined to one or a few

22

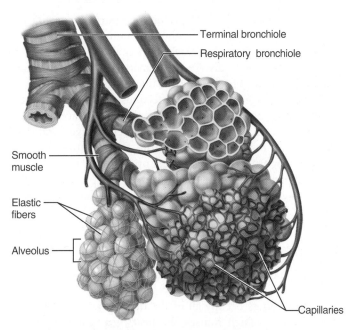

Terminal bronchiole

Respiratory bronchiole

Smooth muscle

Elastic fibers

Alveolus

Capillaries

(a) Diagrammatic view of capillary-alveoli relationships

(b) Scanning electron micrograph of casts of alveoli and associated pulmonary capillaries (300x)

Nucleus of type I (squamous epithelial) cell

Alveolar pores

Capillary

Macrophage

Endothelial cell nucleus

Respiratory membrane

Red blood cell

O_2

CO_2

Capillary

Alveolus

Alveolar epithelium

Fused basement membranes of the alveolar epithelium and the capillary endothelium

Capillary endothelium

Alveoli (gas-filled air spaces)   Red blood cell in capillary   Type II (surfactant-secreting) cell   Type I cell of alveolar wall

(c) Detailed anatomy of the respiratory membrane

Figure 22.9 Alveoli and the respiratory membrane. Elastic fibers and capillaries surround all alveoli, but for clarity they are shown only on some alveoli in **(a)**.
SOURCE: (b) Kessel and Kardon/Visuals Unlimited.

segments. Their connective tissue partitions allow diseased segments to be surgically removed without damaging neighboring healthy segments or impairing their blood supply.

The smallest subdivisions of the lung visible with the naked eye are the **lobules**, which appear at the lung surface as hexa-

gons ranging from the size of a pencil eraser to the size of a penny (Figure 22.10b). Each lobule is served by a large bronchiole and its branches. In most city dwellers and in smokers, the connective tissue that separates the individual lobules is blackened with carbon.

22

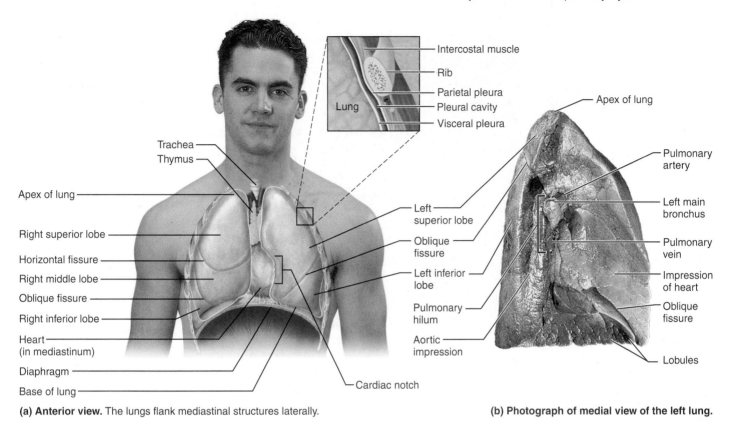

Intercostal muscle
Rib
Parietal pleura
Pleural cavity
Visceral pleura
Lung

Trachea
Thymus
Apex of lung
Right superior lobe
Horizontal fissure
Right middle lobe
Oblique fissure
Right inferior lobe
Heart (in mediastinum)
Diaphragm
Base of lung

Left superior lobe
Oblique fissure
Left inferior lobe
Pulmonary hilum
Aortic impression
Cardiac notch

Apex of lung
Pulmonary artery
Left main bronchus
Pulmonary vein
Impression of heart
Oblique fissure
Lobules

(a) Anterior view. The lungs flank mediastinal structures laterally.

(b) Photograph of medial view of the left lung.

Posterior

Vertebra
Esophagus (in mediastinum)
Root of lung at hilum
• Left main bronchus
• Left pulmonary artery
• Left pulmonary vein

Right lung
Parietal pleura
Visceral pleura
Pleural cavity

Left lung
Thoracic wall
Pulmonary trunk
Heart (in mediastinum)
Anterior mediastinum

Pericardial membranes
Sternum

Anterior

(c) Transverse section through the thorax, viewed from above. Lungs, pleural membranes, and major organs in the mediastinum are shown.

Figure 22.10 Anatomical relationships of organs in the thoracic cavity. In **(c)**, the size of the pleural cavity is exaggerated for clarity.

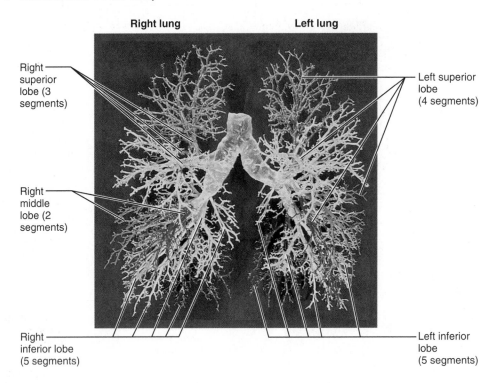

Right lung   **Left lung**

Right superior lobe (3 segments)

Left superior lobe (4 segments)

Right middle lobe (2 segments)

Right inferior lobe (5 segments)

Left inferior lobe (5 segments)

Figure 22.11 A cast of the bronchial tree. The individual bronchopulmonary segments have been painted different colors.

As we mentioned earlier, the lungs consist largely of air spaces. The balance of lung tissue, or its **stroma** (literally "mattress" or "bed"), is mostly elastic connective tissue. As a result, the lungs are soft, spongy, elastic organs that together weigh just over 1 kg (2.2 lb). The elasticity of healthy lungs helps to reduce the work of breathing, as we will describe shortly.

Blood Supply and Innervation of the Lungs

The lungs are perfused by two circulations, the pulmonary and the bronchial, which differ in size, origin, and function. Systemic venous blood that is to be oxygenated in the lungs is delivered by the **pulmonary arteries**, which lie anterior to the main bronchi (Figure 22.10c). In the lungs, the pulmonary arteries branch profusely along with the bronchi and finally feed into the **pulmonary capillary networks** surrounding the alveoli (see Figure 22.9a).

Freshly oxygenated blood is conveyed from the respiratory zones of the lungs to the heart by the **pulmonary veins**. Their tributaries course back to the hilum both with the corresponding bronchi and in the connective tissue septa separating the bronchopulmonary segments.

In contrast to the pulmonary circulation, the **bronchial arteries** provide oxygenated systemic blood to lung tissue. They arise from the aorta, enter the lungs at the hilum, and then run along the branching bronchi. They provide a high-pressure, low-volume supply of oxygenated blood to all lung tissues except the alveoli, which receive blood from the low-pressure, high-volume pulmonary circulation. Some systemic venous blood is drained from the lungs by the tiny bronchial veins, but there are multiple anastomoses between the two circulations, and most venous blood returns to the heart via the pulmonary veins.

Because *all* of the body's blood passes through the lungs about once each minute, the lung capillary endothelium is an ideal location for enzymes that act on materials in the blood. Examples include *angiotensin converting enzyme*, which activates an important blood pressure hormone, and enzymes that inactivate certain prostaglandins.

The lungs are innervated by parasympathetic and sympathetic motor fibers, and visceral sensory fibers. These nerve fibers enter each lung through the **pulmonary plexus** on the lung root and run along the bronchial tubes and blood vessels in the lungs. Parasympathetic fibers constrict the air tubes, whereas the sympathetic nervous system dilates them.

The Pleurae

The **pleurae** (ploo're; "sides") form a thin, double-layered serosa. The layer called the **parietal pleura** covers the thoracic wall and superior face of the diaphragm (Figure 22.10a, c). It continues around the heart and between the lungs, forming the lateral walls of the mediastinal enclosure and snugly enclosing the lung root. From here, the pleura extends as the layer called the **visceral pleura** to cover the external lung surface, dipping into and lining its fissures.

The pleurae produce **pleural fluid**, which fills the slitlike **pleural cavity** between them. This lubricating secretion allows the lungs to glide easily over the thorax wall during our breathing movements. Although the pleurae slide easily across each other, their separation is strongly resisted by the surface tension of the pleural fluid. Consequently, the lungs cling tightly to the thorax wall and are forced to expand and recoil passively as the volume of the thoracic cavity alternately increases and decreases during breathing.

22

The pleurae also help divide the thoracic cavity into three chambers—the central mediastinum and the two lateral pleural compartments, each containing a lung. This compartmentalization helps prevent one mobile organ (for example, the lung or heart) from interfering with another. It also limits the spread of local infections.

HOMEOSTATIC IMBALANCE

Pleurisy (ploo′rĭ-se), inflammation of the pleurae, often results from pneumonia. Inflamed pleurae become rough, resulting in friction and stabbing pain with each breath. As the disease progresses, the pleurae may produce an excessive amount of fluid. This increased fluid relieves the pain caused by pleural surfaces rubbing together, but may exert pressure on the lungs and hinder breathing movements.

Other fluids that may accumulate in the pleural cavity include blood (leaked from damaged blood vessels) and blood filtrate (the watery fluid that oozes from the lung capillaries when left-sided heart failure occurs). The general term for fluid accumulation in the pleural cavity is *pleural effusion*. ■

CHECK YOUR UNDERSTANDING

4. What features of the alveoli and their respiratory membranes suit them to their function of exchanging gases by diffusion?
5. A 3-year-old boy is brought to the emergency department after aspirating (inhaling) a peanut. Bronchoscopy confirms the suspicion that the peanut is lodged in a bronchus and then it is successfully extracted. Which main bronchus was the peanut most likely to be in? Why?
6. The lungs are perfused by two different circulations. Name these circulations and indicate their roles in the lungs.

For answers, see Appendix G.

Mechanics of Breathing

Breathing, or **pulmonary ventilation**, consists of two phases: **inspiration**, the period when air flows into the lungs, and **expiration**, the period when gases exit the lungs.

Pressure Relationships in the Thoracic Cavity

▶ Explain the functional importance of the partial vacuum that exists in the intrapleural space.

Before we can begin to describe the breathing process, it is important to understand that *respiratory pressures are always described relative to* **atmospheric pressure** (P_{atm}), which is the pressure exerted by the air (gases) surrounding the body. At sea level, atmospheric pressure is 760 mm Hg (the pressure exerted by a column of mercury 760 mm high). This pressure can also be expressed in atmosphere units: atmospheric pressure = 760 mm Hg = 1 atm.

A negative respiratory pressure in any respiratory area, such as −4 mm Hg, indicates that the pressure in that area is lower than atmospheric pressure by 4 mm Hg (760 − 4 = 756 mm Hg).

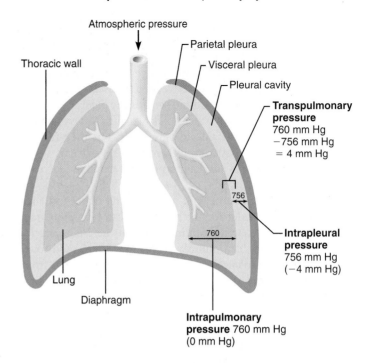

Figure 22.12 Intrapulmonary and intrapleural pressure relationships. Differences in pressure relative to atmospheric pressure (760 mm Hg) are given in parentheses. Values shown are at the end of a normal expiration. For illustration, the size of the pleural cavity has been greatly exaggerated.

A positive respiratory pressure is higher than atmospheric pressure, and zero respiratory pressure is equal to atmospheric pressure. Now we are ready to examine the pressure relationships that normally exist in the thoracic cavity.

Intrapulmonary Pressure

The **intrapulmonary** (intra-alveolar) **pressure** (P_{pul}) is the pressure in the alveoli. Intrapulmonary pressure rises and falls with the phases of breathing, but it *always* eventually equalizes with the atmospheric pressure (Figure 22.12).

Intrapleural Pressure

The pressure in the pleural cavity, the **intrapleural pressure** (P_{ip}), also fluctuates with breathing phases, but is always about 4 mm Hg less than P_{pul}. That is, P_{ip} is *always* negative relative to P_{pul}.

How is this negative intrapleural pressure established? In other words, what causes it? Let's examine the forces that exist in the thorax to see if we can answer these questions. First of all, we know there are opposing forces. Two forces act to pull the lungs (visceral pleura) away from the thorax wall (parietal pleura) and cause lung collapse:

1. **The lungs' natural tendency to recoil.** Because of their elasticity, lungs always assume the smallest size possible.
2. **The surface tension of the alveolar fluid.** The molecules of the fluid lining the alveoli attract each other and this produces *surface tension* that constantly acts to draw the alveoli to their smallest possible dimension.

However, these lung-collapsing forces are opposed by the natural elasticity of the chest wall, a force that tends to pull the thorax outward and to enlarge the lungs.

So which force wins? The answer is neither in a healthy person, because of the strong adhesive force between the parietal and visceral pleurae. Pleural fluid secures the pleurae together in the same way a drop of water holds two glass slides together. The pleurae slide from side to side easily, but they remain closely apposed, and separating them requires extreme force. The net result of the dynamic interplay between these forces is a negative P_{ip}.

The amount of pleural fluid in the pleural cavity must remain minimal in order for the negative P_{ip} to be maintained. The pleural fluid is actively pumped out of the pleural cavity into the lymphatics continuously. If it wasn't, fluid would accumulate in the intrapleural space (remember, fluids move from high to low pressure), producing a positive pressure in the pleural cavity.

We cannot overemphasize the importance of negative pressure in the intrapleural space and the tight coupling of the lungs to the thorax wall. Any condition that equalizes P_{ip} with the intrapulmonary (or atmospheric) pressure causes *immediate lung collapse*. It is the **transpulmonary pressure**—the difference between the intrapulmonary and intrapleural pressures ($P_{pul} - P_{ip}$)—that keeps the air spaces of the lungs open or, phrased another way, keeps the lungs from collapsing. Moreover, *the size of the transpulmonary pressure determines the size of the lungs* at any time—the greater the transpulmonary pressure, the larger the lungs.

HOMEOSTATIC IMBALANCE

Atelectasis (at″ĕ-lik′tah-sis), or lung collapse, occurs when a bronchiole becomes plugged (as may follow pneumonia). Its associated alveoli then absorb all of their air and collapse. Atelectasis can also occur when air enters the pleural cavity either through a chest wound, or due to rupture of the visceral pleura, which allows air to enter the pleural cavity from the respiratory tract. The presence of air in the pleural cavity is referred to as a **pneumothorax** (nu″mo-tho′raks; "air thorax"). The condition is reversed by drawing air out of the intrapleural space with chest tubes, which allows the pleurae to heal and the lung to reinflate and resume its normal function. Note that because the lungs are in separate cavities, one lung can collapse without interfering with the function of the other. ■

Pulmonary Ventilation

▶ Relate Boyle's law to events of inspiration and expiration.

▶ Explain the relative roles of the respiratory muscles and lung elasticity in producing the volume changes that cause air to flow into and out of the lungs.

Pulmonary ventilation, consisting of inspiration and expiration, is a mechanical process that depends on volume changes in the thoracic cavity. A rule to keep in mind throughout the following discussion is that *volume changes* lead to *pressure changes*, and pressure changes lead to the *flow of gases* to equalize the pressure.

The relationship between the pressure and volume of a gas is given by **Boyle's law**: At constant temperature, the pressure of a gas varies inversely with its volume. That is,

$$P_1V_1 = P_2V_2$$

where P is the pressure of the gas, V is its volume, and subscripts 1 and 2 represent the initial and resulting conditions respectively.

Gases always *fill* their container. Consequently, in a large container, the molecules in a given amount of gas will be far apart and the pressure will be low. But if the volume of the container is reduced, the gas molecules will be forced closer together and the pressure will rise. A good example is an inflated automobile tire. The tire is hard and strong enough to bear the weight of the car because air is compressed to about one-third of its atmospheric volume in the tire, providing the high pressure. Now let's see how this relates to inspiration and expiration.

Inspiration

Visualize the thoracic cavity as a gas-filled box with a single entrance at the top, the tubelike trachea. The volume of this box is changeable and can be increased by enlarging all of its dimensions, thereby decreasing the gas pressure inside it. This drop in pressure causes air to rush into the box from the atmosphere, because gases always flow down their pressure gradients.

The same thing happens during normal quiet inspiration, when the **inspiratory muscles**—the diaphragm and external intercostal muscles—are activated. Here's how quiet inspiration works:

1. **Action of the diaphragm.** When the dome-shaped diaphragm contracts, it moves inferiorly and flattens out (**Figure 22.13**, top). As a result, the superior-inferior dimension (height) of the thoracic cavity increases.

2. **Action of the intercostal muscles.** Contraction of the external intercostal muscles lifts the rib cage and pulls the sternum superiorly (Figure 22.13, top). Because the ribs curve downward as well as forward around the chest wall, the broadest lateral and anteroposterior dimensions of the rib cage are normally directed obliquely downward. But when the ribs are raised and drawn together, they swing outward, expanding the diameter of the thorax both laterally and in the anteroposterior plane. This is much like the action that occurs when a curved bucket handle is raised—it moves outward as it moves upward.

Although these actions expand the thoracic dimensions by only a few millimeters along each plane, this is enough to increase thoracic volume by almost 500 ml—the usual volume of air that enters the lungs during a normal quiet inspiration. Of the two types of inspiratory muscles, the diaphragm is far more important in producing the volume changes that lead to normal quiet inspiration.

As the thoracic dimensions increase during inspiration, the lungs are stretched and the intrapulmonary volume increases. As

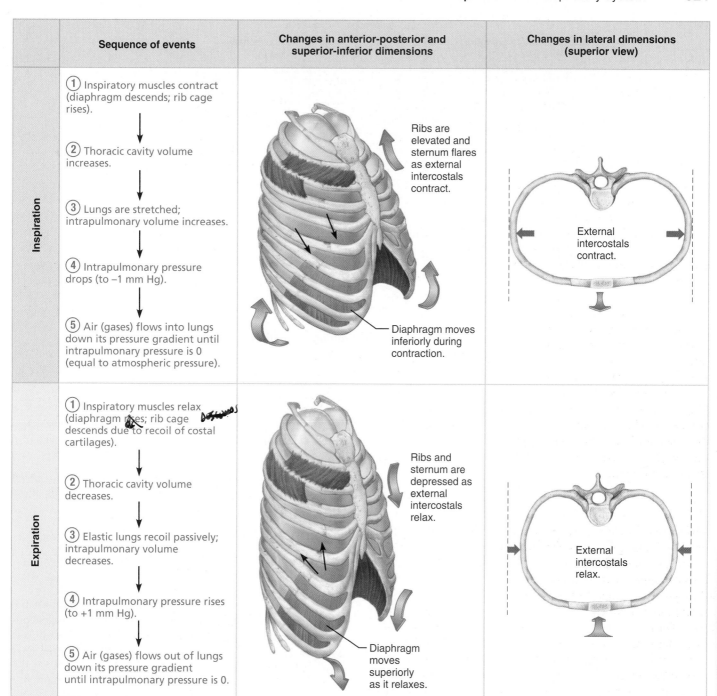

	Sequence of events	Changes in anterior-posterior and superior-inferior dimensions	Changes in lateral dimensions (superior view)
Inspiration	① Inspiratory muscles contract (diaphragm descends; rib cage rises). ② Thoracic cavity volume increases. ③ Lungs are stretched; intrapulmonary volume increases. ④ Intrapulmonary pressure drops (to –1 mm Hg). ⑤ Air (gases) flows into lungs down its pressure gradient until intrapulmonary pressure is 0 (equal to atmospheric pressure).	Ribs are elevated and sternum flares as external intercostals contract. Diaphragm moves inferiorly during contraction.	External intercostals contract.
Expiration	① Inspiratory muscles relax (diaphragm rises; rib cage descends due to recoil of costal cartilages). ② Thoracic cavity volume decreases. ③ Elastic lungs recoil passively; intrapulmonary volume decreases. ④ Intrapulmonary pressure rises (to +1 mm Hg). ⑤ Air (gases) flows out of lungs down its pressure gradient until intrapulmonary pressure is 0.	Ribs and sternum are depressed as external intercostals relax. Diaphragm moves superiorly as it relaxes.	External intercostals relax.

Figure 22.13 Changes in thoracic volume and sequence of events during inspiration and expiration. The sequence of events in the left column includes volume changes during inspiration (top) and expiration (bottom). The lateral views in the middle column show changes in the superior-inferior dimension (as the diaphragm alternately contracts and relaxes) and in the anterior-posterior dimension (as the external intercostal muscles alternately contract and relax). The superior views of transverse thoracic sections in the right column show lateral dimension changes resulting from alternate contraction and relaxation of the external intercostal muscles.

a result, P_{pul} drops about 1 mm Hg relative to P_{atm}. Anytime the intrapulmonary pressure is less than the atmospheric pressure ($P_{pul} < P_{atm}$), air rushes into the lungs along the pressure gradient. Inspiration ends when $P_{pul} = P_{atm}$. During the same period, P_{ip} declines to about –6 mm Hg relative to P_{atm} **(Figure 22.14)**.

During the *deep* or *forced inspirations* that occur during vigorous exercise and in some chronic obstructive pulmonary diseases, the thoracic volume is further increased by activity of accessory muscles. Several muscles, including the scalenes and sternocleidomastoid muscles of the neck and the pectoralis

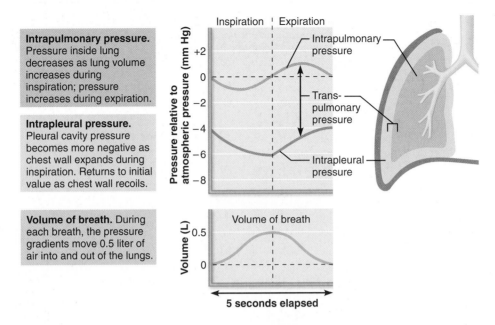

Figure 22.14 Changes in intrapulmonary and intrapleural pressures during inspiration and expiration. Notice that normal atmospheric pressure (760 mm Hg) is given a value of 0 on the scale.

minor of the chest, raise the ribs even more than occurs during quiet inspiration. Additionally, the back extends as the thoracic curvature is straightened by the erector spinae muscles.

Expiration

Quiet expiration in healthy individuals is a passive process that depends more on lung elasticity than on muscle contraction. As the inspiratory muscles relax and resume their resting length, the rib cage descends and the lungs recoil (Figure 22.13, bottom). As a result, both the thoracic and intrapulmonary volumes decrease. This volume decrease compresses the alveoli, and P_{pul} rises to about 1 mm Hg above atmospheric pressure (Figure 22.14). When $P_{pul} > P_{atm}$, the pressure gradient forces gases to flow out of the lungs.

Forced expiration is an active process produced by contraction of abdominal wall muscles, primarily the oblique and transversus muscles. These contractions (1) increase the intra-abdominal pressure, which forces the abdominal organs superiorly against the diaphragm, and (2) depress the rib cage. The internal intercostal muscles also help to depress the rib cage and decrease thoracic volume.

Control of accessory muscles of expiration is important when precise regulation of air flow from the lungs is desired. For instance, the ability of a trained vocalist to hold a musical note depends on the coordinated activity of several muscles normally used in forced expiration.

CHECK YOUR UNDERSTANDING

7. What is the driving force for ventilation?

8. What causes the intrapulmonary pressure to decrease during inspiration?

9. What causes the partial vacuum (negative pressure) inside the pleural cavity? What happens to a lung if air enters the pleural cavity? What is the clinical name for this condition?

For answers, see Appendix G.

Physical Factors Influencing Pulmonary Ventilation

▶ List several physical factors that influence pulmonary ventilation.

As we have seen, the lungs are stretched during inspiration and recoil passively during expiration. The inspiratory muscles consume energy to enlarge the thorax. Energy is also used to overcome various factors that hinder air passage and pulmonary ventilation. We examine these factors next.

Airway Resistance

The major *nonelastic* source of resistance to gas flow is friction, or drag, encountered in the respiratory passageways. The relationship between gas flow (F), pressure (P), and resistance (R) is given by the following equation:

$$F = \frac{\Delta P}{R}$$

Notice that the factors determining gas flow in the respiratory passages and blood flow in the cardiovascular system are equivalent. The amount of gas flowing into and out of the alveoli is directly proportional to ΔP, the *difference* in pressure, or the pressure gradient, between the external atmosphere and the alveoli. Normally, very small differences in pressure produce large changes in the volume of gas flow. The average pressure gradient during normal quiet breathing is 2 mm Hg or less, and yet it is sufficient to move 500 ml of air in and out of the lungs with each breath.

But, as the equation also indicates, gas flow changes *inversely* with resistance. In other words, gas flow decreases as resistance increases. As in the cardiovascular system, resistance in the respiratory tree is determined mostly by the diameters of the conducting tubes. However, as a rule, airway resistance is insignificant for two reasons:

1. Airway diameters in the first part of the conducting zone are huge, relative to the low viscosity of air.
2. As the airways get progressively smaller, there are progressively more branches. As a result, although individual bronchioles are tiny, there are an enormous number of them in parallel, so the total cross-sectional area is huge.

Consequently, the greatest resistance to gas flow occurs in the medium-sized bronchi (Figure 22.15). At the terminal bronchioles, gas flow stops and diffusion takes over as the main force driving gas movement, so resistance is no longer an issue.

HOMEOSTATIC IMBALANCE

Smooth muscle of the bronchiolar walls is exquisitely sensitive to neural controls and certain chemicals. For example, inhaled irritants activate a reflex of the parasympathetic division of the nervous system that causes vigorous constriction of the bronchioles and dramatically reduces air passage. During an *acute asthma attack*, histamine and other inflammatory chemicals can cause such strong bronchoconstriction that pulmonary ventilation almost completely stops, regardless of the pressure gradient. Conversely, epinephrine released during sympathetic nervous system activation or administered as a drug dilates bronchioles and reduces airway resistance. Local accumulations of mucus, infectious material, or solid tumors in the passageways are important sources of airway resistance in those with respiratory disease.

Whenever airway resistance rises, breathing movements become more strenuous, but such compensation has its limits. When the bronchioles are severely constricted or obstructed, even the most magnificent respiratory efforts cannot restore ventilation to life-sustaining levels. ■

Alveolar Surface Tension

At any gas-liquid boundary, the molecules of the liquid are more strongly attracted to each other than to the gas molecules. This unequal attraction produces a state of tension at the liquid surface, called **surface tension**, that (1) draws the liquid molecules closer together and reduces their contact with the dissimilar gas molecules, and (2) resists any force that tends to increase the surface area of the liquid.

Water is composed of highly polar molecules and has a very high surface tension. As the major component of the liquid film that coats the alveolar walls, water is always acting to reduce the alveoli to their smallest possible size, as we noted earlier. If the film were pure water, the alveoli would collapse between breaths. But the alveolar film contains **surfactant** (ser-fak′tant),

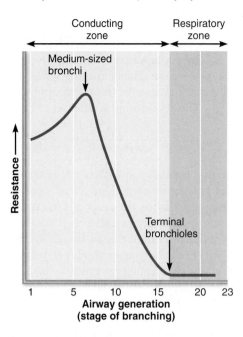

Figure 22.15 Resistance in respiratory passageways. Airway resistance peaks in the medium-sized bronchi and then declines sharply as the total cross-sectional area of the airways increases rapidly.

a detergent-like complex of lipids and proteins produced by the type II alveolar cells. Surfactant decreases the cohesiveness of water molecules, much the way a laundry detergent reduces the attraction of water for water, allowing water to interact with and pass through fabric. As a result, the surface tension of alveolar fluid is reduced, and less energy is needed to overcome those forces to expand the lungs and discourage alveolar collapse. Breaths that are deeper than normal stimulate type II cells to secrete more surfactant.

HOMEOSTATIC IMBALANCE

When too little surfactant is present, surface tension forces can collapse the alveoli. Once this happens, the alveoli must be completely reinflated during each inspiration, an effort that uses tremendous amounts of energy. This is the problem faced by newborns with **infant respiratory distress syndrome (IRDS)**, a condition peculiar to premature babies. Since inadequate pulmonary surfactant is produced until the last two months of fetal development, babies born prematurely often are unable to keep their alveoli inflated between breaths. IRDS is treated by spraying natural or synthetic surfactant into the newborn's respiratory passageways. In addition, devices that maintain a positive airway pressure throughout the respiratory cycle are often used to keep the alveoli open between breaths. In severe cases, mechanical ventilators are required.

Many IRDS survivors suffer from *bronchopulmonary dysplasia*, a chronic lung disease, during childhood and beyond. This condition is believed to result from inflammatory injury to respiratory zone structures caused by mechanical ventilation of the premature newborn's delicate lungs. ■

22

Lung Compliance

Healthy lungs are unbelievably stretchy, and this distensibility is referred to as **lung compliance**. Specifically, lung compliance (C_L) is a measure of the change in lung volume (ΔV_L) that occurs with a given change in the transpulmonary pressure [$\Delta(P_{pul} - P_{ip})$]. This relationship is stated as

$$C_L = \frac{\Delta V_L}{\Delta(P_{pul} - P_{ip})}$$

The more a lung expands for a given rise in transpulmonary pressure, the greater its compliance. Said another way, the higher the lung compliance, the easier it is to expand the lungs at any given transpulmonary pressure.

Lung compliance is determined largely by two factors: (1) distensibility of the lung tissue and (2) alveolar surface tension. Because lung distensibility is generally high and alveolar surface tension is kept low by surfactant, the lungs of healthy people tend to have high compliance, which favors efficient ventilation.

Lung compliance is diminished by a decrease in the natural resilience of the lungs. Chronic inflammation, or infections such as tuberculosis, can cause nonelastic scar tissue to replace normal lung tissue (*fibrosis*). Another factor that can decrease lung compliance is a decrease in production of surfactant. The lower the lung compliance, the more energy is needed just to breathe.

Since the lungs are contained within the thoracic cavity, we also need to consider the compliance (distensibility) of the thoracic wall. Factors that decrease the compliance of the thoracic wall hinder the expansion of the lungs. The total compliance of the respiratory system is comprised of lung compliance and thoracic wall compliance.

HOMEOSTATIC IMBALANCE

Deformities of the thorax, ossification of the costal cartilages (common during old age), and paralysis of the intercostal muscles all reduce total respiratory compliance by hindering thoracic expansion. ■

Respiratory Volumes and Pulmonary Function Tests

▶ Explain and compare the various lung volumes and capacities.

▶ Define dead space.

▶ Indicate types of information that can be gained from pulmonary function tests.

The amount of air flushed in and out of the lungs depends on the conditions of inspiration and expiration. Consequently, several respiratory volumes can be described. Specific combinations of these respiratory volumes, called *respiratory capacities*, are measured to gain information about a person's respiratory status.

Respiratory Volumes

The four **respiratory volumes** of interest are tidal, inspiratory reserve, expiratory reserve, and residual. The values recorded in **Figure 22.16a** (and used in the following text) represent normal values for a healthy 20-year-old male weighing about 70 kg (155 lb). Figure 22.16b provides average values for males and females.

During normal quiet breathing, about 500 ml of air moves into and then out of the lungs with each breath. This respiratory volume is the **tidal volume (TV)**. The amount of air that can be inspired forcibly beyond the tidal volume (2100 to 3200 ml) is called the **inspiratory reserve volume (IRV)**.

The **expiratory reserve volume (ERV)** is the amount of air—normally 1000 to 1200 ml—that can be evacuated from the lungs after a tidal expiration. Even after the most strenuous expiration, about 1200 ml of air remains in the lungs; this is the **residual volume (RV)**, which helps to keep the alveoli patent (open) and to prevent lung collapse.

Respiratory Capacities

The **respiratory capacities** include inspiratory capacity, functional residual capacity, vital capacity, and total lung capacity (Figure 22.16). As noted, the respiratory capacities always consist of two or more lung volumes.

The **inspiratory capacity (IC)** is the total amount of air that can be inspired after a tidal expiration, so it is the sum of TV and IRV. The **functional residual capacity (FRC)** represents the amount of air remaining in the lungs after a tidal expiration and is the combined RV and ERV.

Vital capacity (VC) is the total amount of exchangeable air. It is the sum of TV, IRV, and ERV. In healthy young males, VC is approximately 4800 ml. The **total lung capacity (TLC)** is the sum of all lung volumes and is normally around 6000 ml. As indicated in Figure 22.16b, lung volumes and capacities (with the possible exception of TV) tend to be smaller in women than in men because of women's smaller size.

Dead Space

Some of the inspired air fills the conducting respiratory passageways and never contributes to gas exchange in the alveoli. The volume of these conducting zone conduits, which make up the **anatomical dead space**, typically amounts to about 150 ml. (The rule of thumb is that the anatomical dead space volume in a healthy young adult is equal to 1 ml per pound of ideal body weight.) This means that if TV is 500 ml, only 350 ml of it is involved in alveolar ventilation. The remaining 150 ml of the tidal breath is in the anatomical dead space.

If some alveoli cease to act in gas exchange (due to alveolar collapse or obstruction by mucus, for example), the **alveolar dead space** is added to the anatomical dead space, and the sum of the nonuseful volumes is referred to as **total dead space**.

Pulmonary Function Tests

Because the various lung volumes and capacities are often abnormal in people with pulmonary disorders, they are routinely measured in such patients. The original clinical measuring

22

(a) Spirographic record for a male

	Measurement	Adult male average value	Adult female average value	Description
Respiratory volumes	Tidal volume (TV)	500 ml	500 ml	Amount of air inhaled or exhaled with each breath under resting conditions
	Inspiratory reserve volume (IRV)	3100 ml	1900 ml	Amount of air that can be forcefully inhaled after a normal tidal volume inhalation
	Expiratory reserve volume (ERV)	1200 ml	700 ml	Amount of air that can be forcefully exhaled after a normal tidal volume exhalation
	Residual volume (RV)	1200 ml	1100 ml	Amount of air remaining in the lungs after a forced exhalation
Respiratory capacities	Total lung capacity (TLC)	6000 ml	4200 ml	Maximum amount of air contained in lungs after a maximum inspiratory effort: TLC = TV + IRV + ERV + RV
	Vital capacity (VC)	4800 ml	3100 ml	Maximum amount of air that can be expired after a maximum inspiratory effort: VC = TV + IRV + ERV
	Inspiratory capacity (IC)	3600 ml	2400 ml	Maximum amount of air that can be inspired after a normal expiration: IC = TV + IRV
	Functional residual capacity (FRC)	2400 ml	1800 ml	Volume of air remaining in the lungs after a normal tidal volume expiration: FRC = ERV + RV

(b) Summary of respiratory volumes and capacities for males and females

Figure 22.16 Respiratory volumes and capacities. Idealized spirographic record of respiratory volumes in **(a)** is for a healthy young 70-kg adult male.

device, a **spirometer** (spi-rom′ĕ-ter), was a simple but cumbersome instrument utilizing a hollow bell inverted over water. Now patients simply blow into a small electronic measuring device.

Spirometry is most useful for evaluating losses in respiratory function and for following the course of certain respiratory diseases. It cannot provide a specific diagnosis, but it can distinguish between *obstructive pulmonary disease* involving increased airway resistance (such as chronic bronchitis) and *restrictive disorders* involving a reduction in total lung capacity resulting from structural or functional changes in the lungs. (These changes might be due to diseases such as tuberculosis, or to fibrosis due to exposure to certain environmental agents such as asbestos). Increases in TLC, FRC, and RV may occur as a result

of hyperinflation of the lungs in obstructive disease, whereas VC, TLC, FRC, and RV are reduced in restrictive diseases, which limit lung expansion.

More information can be obtained about a patient's ventilation status by assessing the rate at which gas moves into and out of the lungs. The **minute ventilation** is the total amount of gas that flows into or out of the respiratory tract in 1 minute. During normal quiet breathing, the minute ventilation in healthy people is about 6 L/min (500 ml per breath multiplied by 12 breaths per minute). During vigorous exercise, the minute ventilation may reach 200 L/min.

Two other useful tests are FVC and FEV. **FVC**, or **forced vital capacity**, measures the amount of gas expelled when a subject takes a deep breath and then forcefully exhales maximally and as

TABLE 22.2	Effects of Breathing Rate and Depth on Alveolar Ventilation of Three Hypothetical Patients						
BREATHING PATTERN OF HYPOTHETICAL PATIENT	**DEAD SPACE VOLUME (DSV)**	**TIDAL VOLUME (TV)**	**RESPIRATORY RATE***	**MINUTE VENTILATION (MVR)**	**ALVEOLAR VENTILATION (AVR)**	**% EFFECTIVE VENTILATION (AVR/MVR)**
I—Normal rate and depth	150 ml	500 ml	20/min	10,000 ml/min	7000 ml/min	70%
II—Slow, deep breathing	150 ml	1000 ml	10/min	10,000 ml/min	8500 ml/min	85%
III—Rapid, shallow breathing	150 ml	250 ml	40/min	10,000 ml/min	4000 ml/min	40%

* Respiratory rate values are artificially adjusted to provide equivalent minute ventilation as a baseline for comparison of alveolar ventilation.

rapidly as possible. **FEV,** or **forced expiratory volume,** determines the amount of air expelled during specific time intervals of the FVC test. For example, the volume exhaled during the first second is FEV_1. Those with healthy lungs can exhale about 80% of the FVC within 1 second. Those with obstructive pulmonary disease exhale considerably less than 80% of the FVC within 1 second, while those with restrictive disease can exhale 80% or more of FVC in 1 second even though their FVC is reduced.

Alveolar Ventilation

Minute ventilation values provide a rough yardstick for assessing respiratory efficiency, but the **alveolar ventilation rate (AVR)** is a better index of effective ventilation. The AVR takes into account the volume of air wasted in the dead space and measures the flow of fresh gases in and out of the alveoli during a particular time interval. AVR is computed with this equation:

$$\underset{\text{(ml/min)}}{\text{AVR}} = \underset{\text{(breaths/min)}}{\text{frequency}} \times \underset{\text{(ml/breath)}}{(\text{TV} - \text{dead space})}$$

In healthy people, AVR is usually about 12 breaths per minute times the difference of 500 – 150 ml per breath, or 4200 ml/min.

Because anatomical dead space is constant in a particular individual, increasing the volume of each inspiration (breathing depth) enhances AVR and gas exchange more than raising the respiratory rate. AVR drops dramatically during rapid shallow breathing because most of the inspired air never reaches the exchange sites. Furthermore, as tidal volume approaches the dead space value, effective ventilation approaches zero, regardless of how fast a person is breathing. The effects of breathing rate and breathing depth on alveolar ventilation are summarized for three hypothetical patients in Table 22.2.

Nonrespiratory Air Movements

Many processes other than breathing move air into or out of the lungs, and these processes may modify the normal respiratory rhythm. Most of these **nonrespiratory air movements** result from reflex activity, but some are produced voluntarily. The most common of these movements are described in Table 22.3.

CHECK YOUR UNDERSTANDING

10. Resistance in the airways is typically low. Why? (Give at least two reasons.)

11. Premature infants often lack adequate surfactant. How does this affect their ability to breathe?

12. Explain why slow, deep breaths ventilate the alveoli more effectively than do rapid, shallow breaths.

For answers, see Appendix G.

22

TABLE 22.3	Nonrespiratory Air (Gas) Movements
MOVEMENT	**MECHANISM AND RESULT**
Cough	Taking a deep breath, closing glottis, and forcing air superiorly from lungs against glottis; glottis opens suddenly and a blast of air rushes upward. Can dislodge foreign particles or mucus from lower respiratory tract and propel such substances superiorly.
Sneeze	Similar to a cough, except that expelled air is directed through nasal cavities as well as through oral cavity; depressed uvula routes air upward through nasal cavities. Sneezes clear upper respiratory passages.
Crying	Inspiration followed by release of air in a number of short expirations. Primarily an emotionally induced mechanism.
Laughing	Essentially same as crying in terms of air movements produced. Also an emotionally induced response.
Hiccups	Sudden inspirations resulting from spasms of diaphragm; believed to be initiated by irritation of diaphragm or phrenic nerves, which serve diaphragm. Sound occurs when inspired air hits vocal folds of closing glottis.
Yawn	Very deep inspiration, taken with jaws wide open; not believed to be triggered by levels of oxygen or carbon dioxide in blood. Ventilates all alveoli (not the case in normal quiet breathing).

Gas Exchanges Between the Blood, Lungs, and Tissues

▶ State Dalton's law of partial pressures and Henry's law.

▶ Describe how atmospheric and alveolar air differ in composition, and explain these differences.

▶ Relate Dalton's and Henry's laws to events of external and internal respiration.

As you've discovered, during *external respiration* oxygen enters and carbon dioxide leaves the blood in the lungs by diffusion. At the body tissues, where the process is called *internal respiration*, the same gases move in opposite directions, also by diffusion. To understand these processes, let's examine some of the physical properties of gases and consider the composition of alveolar gas.

Basic Properties of Gases

Two more gas laws provide most of the information we need—*Dalton's law of partial pressures* reveals how a gas behaves when it is part of a mixture of gases, and *Henry's law* will help us understand movement of gases into and out of solution.

Dalton's Law of Partial Pressures

Dalton's law of partial pressures states that the total pressure exerted by a mixture of gases is the sum of the pressures exerted independently by each gas in the mixture. Further, the pressure exerted by each gas—its **partial pressure**—is directly proportional to the percentage of that gas in the gas mixture.

As indicated in **Table 22.4**, nitrogen makes up about 79% of air, and the partial pressure of nitrogen (P_{N_2}) is 78.6% × 760 mm Hg, or 597 mm Hg. Oxygen, which accounts for nearly 21% of the atmosphere, has a partial pressure (P_{O_2}) of 159 mm Hg (20.9 % × 760 mm Hg). Together nitrogen and oxygen contribute about 99% of the total atmospheric pressure. Air also contains 0.04% carbon dioxide, up to 0.5% water vapor, and insignificant amounts of inert gases (such as argon and helium).

At high altitudes, where the atmosphere is less influenced by gravity, partial pressures decline in direct proportion to the decrease in atmospheric pressure. For example, at 10,000 feet above sea level where the atmospheric pressure is 523 mm Hg, P_{O_2} is 110 mm Hg. Moving in the opposite direction, atmospheric pressure increases by 1 atm (760 mm Hg) for each 33 feet of descent (in water) below sea level. At 99 feet below sea level, the total pressure exerted on the body is equivalent to 4 atm, or 3040 mm Hg, and the partial pressure exerted by each component gas is also quadrupled.

Henry's Law

According to **Henry's law**, when a gas is in contact with a liquid, that gas will dissolve in the liquid in proportion to its partial pressure. Accordingly, the greater the concentration of a particular gas in the gas phase, the more and the faster that gas will go into solution in the liquid. At equilibrium, the gas partial pressures in the two phases are the same. If, however, the partial pressure of the gas later becomes greater in the liquid than in the adjacent gas phase, some of the dissolved gas molecules will reenter the gaseous phase. So the direction and amount of movement of a gas is determined by its partial pressure in the two phases. This flexible situation is exactly what occurs when gases are exchanged in the lungs and tissues.

How much of a gas will dissolve in a liquid at any given partial pressure also depends on the *solubility* of the gas in the liquid and on the *temperature* of the liquid. The gases in air have very different solubilities in water (and in plasma). Carbon dioxide is most soluble. Oxygen is only 1/20 as soluble as CO_2, and N_2 is only half as soluble as O_2. For this reason, at a given partial pressure, much more CO_2 than O_2 dissolves in water, and practically no N_2 goes into solution.

The effect of increasing the liquid's temperature is to decrease gas solubility. Think of club soda, which is produced by forcing CO_2 gas to dissolve in water under high pressure. If you take the cap off a refrigerated bottle of club soda and allow it to stand at room temperature, in just a few minutes you will have plain water—all the CO_2 gas will have escaped from solution.

TABLE 22.4	Comparison of Gas Partial Pressures and Approximate Percentages in the Atmosphere and in the Alveoli				
	ATMOSPHERE (SEA LEVEL)			ALVEOLI	
GAS	APPROXIMATE PERCENTAGE	PARTIAL PRESSURE (mm Hg)		APPROXIMATE PERCENTAGE	PARTIAL PRESSURE (mm Hg)
N_2	78.6	597		74.9	569
O_2	20.9	159		13.7	104
CO_2	0.04	0.3		5.2	40
H_2O	0.46	3.7		6.2	47
	100.0%	760		100.0%	760

Inspired air:
P_{O_2} 160 mm Hg
P_{CO_2} 0.3 mm Hg

O_2 CO_2

Alveoli of lungs:
P_{O_2} 104 mm Hg
P_{CO_2} 40 mm Hg

O_2 CO_2

External respiration

Pulmonary arteries

Pulmonary veins (P_{O_2} 100 mm Hg)

Blood leaving tissues and entering lungs:
P_{O_2} 40 mm Hg
P_{CO_2} 45 mm Hg

O_2 CO_2

Blood leaving lungs and entering tissue capillaries:
P_{O_2} 100 mm Hg
P_{CO_2} 40 mm Hg

O_2 CO_2

Heart

Systemic veins

Systemic arteries

Internal respiration

CO_2 O_2

O_2 CO_2

Tissues:
P_{O_2} less than 40 mm Hg
P_{CO_2} greater than 45 mm Hg

Figure 22.17 Partial pressure gradients promoting gas movements in the body. Top: Gradients promoting O_2 and CO_2 exchange across the respiratory membrane in the lungs. Bottom: Gradients promoting gas movements across systemic capillary membranes in body tissues. (Note that the small decrease in P_{O_2} in blood leaving lungs is due to partial dilution of pulmonary capillary blood with less oxygenated blood.)

Hyperbaric oxygen chambers provide clinical applications of Henry's law. These chambers contain O_2 gas at pressures higher than 1 atm and are used to force greater-than-normal amounts of O_2 into the blood of patients suffering from carbon monoxide poisoning or tissue damage following radiation therapy. Hyper-

baric therapy is also used to treat individuals with gas gangrene, because the anaerobic bacteria causing this infection cannot live in the presence of high O_2 levels. Scuba diving provides another illustration of Henry's law—if divers rise rapidly from the depths, dissolved nitrogen forms bubbles in their blood, causing "the bends."

HOMEOSTATIC IMBALANCE

Although breathing O_2 gas at 2 atm is not a problem for short periods, **oxygen toxicity** develops rapidly when P_{O_2} is greater than 2.5–3 atm. Excessively high O_2 concentrations generate huge amounts of harmful free radicals, resulting in profound CNS disturbances, coma, and death. ■

Composition of Alveolar Gas

As shown in Table 22.4, the gaseous makeup of the atmosphere is quite different from that in the alveoli. The atmosphere is almost entirely O_2 and N_2; the alveoli contain more CO_2 and water vapor and much less O_2. These differences reflect the effects of (1) gas exchanges occurring in the lungs (O_2 diffuses from the alveoli into the pulmonary blood and CO_2 diffuses in the opposite direction), (2) humidification of air by conducting passages, and (3) the mixing of alveolar gas that occurs with each breath. Because only 500 ml of air is inspired with each tidal inspiration, gas in the alveoli is actually a mixture of newly inspired gases and gases remaining in the respiratory passageways between breaths.

The alveolar partial pressures of O_2 and CO_2 are easily changed by increasing breathing depth and rate. A high AVR brings more O_2 into the alveoli, increasing alveolar P_{O_2} and rapidly eliminating CO_2 from the lungs.

External Respiration

During external respiration (pulmonary gas exchange) dark red blood flowing through the pulmonary circuit is transformed into the scarlet river that is returned to the heart for distribution by systemic arteries to all body tissues. This color change is due to O_2 uptake and binding to hemoglobin in red blood cells (RBCs), but CO_2 exchange (unloading) is occurring equally fast.

The following three factors influence the movement of oxygen and carbon dioxide across the respiratory membrane:

1. Partial pressure gradients and gas solubilities
2. Matching of alveolar ventilation and pulmonary blood perfusion
3. Structural characteristics of the respiratory membrane

Let's look at these factors one by one in the sections that follow.

Partial Pressure Gradients and Gas Solubilities

Partial pressure gradients of O_2 and CO_2 drive the diffusion of these gases across the respiratory membrane. A steep oxygen partial pressure gradient exists across the respiratory membrane because the P_{O_2} of deoxygenated blood in the pulmonary arteries is only 40 mm Hg, as opposed to a P_{O_2} of approximately 104 mm Hg in the alveoli. As a result, O_2 diffuses rapidly from the alveoli into the pulmonary capillary blood **(Figure 22.17)**. Equilibrium—that is, a P_{O_2} of 104 mm Hg on both sides of the respiratory membrane—

Figure 22.18 Oxygenation of blood in the pulmonary capillaries at rest. Note that the time from blood entering the pulmonary capillaries (indicated by 0) until the P_{O_2} is 104 mm Hg is approximately 0.25 second.

usually occurs in 0.25 second, which is about one-third the time a red blood cell is in a pulmonary capillary (**Figure 22.18**). The lesson here is that the blood can flow through the pulmonary capillaries three times as quickly and still be adequately oxygenated.

Carbon dioxide diffuses in the opposite direction along a much gentler partial pressure gradient of about 5 mm Hg (45 mm Hg to 40 mm Hg) until equilibrium occurs at 40 mm Hg. Carbon dioxide is then expelled gradually from the alveoli during expiration.

Even though the O_2 pressure gradient for oxygen diffusion is much steeper than the CO_2 gradient, equal amounts of these gases are exchanged. Why? The reason is because CO_2 is 20 times more soluble in plasma and alveolar fluid than O_2.

Ventilation-Perfusion Coupling

For gas exchange to be efficient, there must be a close match, or coupling, between the amount of gas reaching the alveoli, known as *ventilation*, and the blood flow in pulmonary capillaries, known as *perfusion*. As we explained in Chapter 19, local autoregulatory mechanisms continuously respond to alveolar conditions.

Specifically, in alveoli where ventilation is inadequate, P_{O_2} is low, as **Figure 22.19a** shows. As a result, the terminal arterioles constrict, and blood is redirected to respiratory areas where P_{O_2} is high and oxygen pickup may be more efficient.

In alveoli where ventilation is maximal, pulmonary arterioles dilate, increasing blood flow into the associated pulmonary capillaries, as Figure 22.19b shows. Notice that the autoregulatory mechanism controlling pulmonary vascular muscle is the

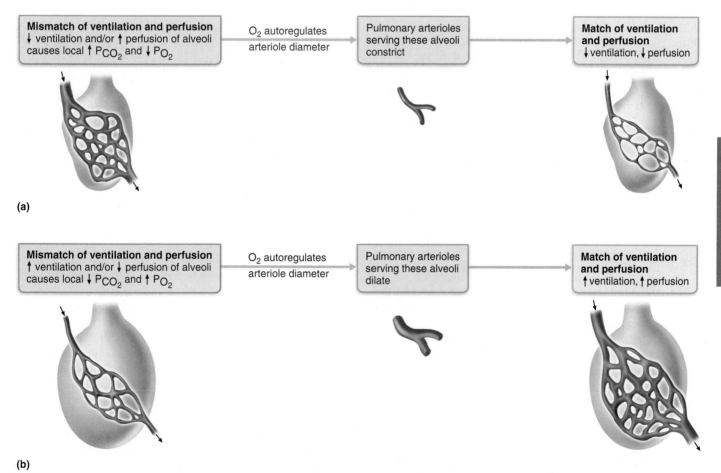

Figure 22.19 Ventilation-perfusion coupling. Autoregulatory events result in local matching of blood flow (perfusion) through the pulmonary capillaries with the amount of alveolar ventilation.

opposite of the mechanism controlling most arterioles in the systemic circulation.

While changes in alveolar P_{O_2} affect the diameter of pulmonary blood vessels (arterioles), changes in alveolar P_{CO_2} cause changes in the diameters of the *bronchioles*. Bronchioles servicing areas where alveolar CO_2 levels are high dilate, allowing CO_2 to be eliminated from the body more rapidly. Bronchioles serving areas where P_{CO_2} is low constrict.

As a result of changing the diameter of local bronchioles and arterioles, alveolar ventilation and pulmonary perfusion are synchronized. Poor alveolar ventilation results in low oxygen and high carbon dioxide levels in the alveoli. Consequently, the pulmonary arterioles constrict and the airways dilate, bringing blood flow and air flow into closer physiological match. High P_{O_2} and low P_{CO_2} in the alveoli cause bronchioles serving the alveoli to constrict, and promote flushing of blood into the pulmonary capillaries.

Although these homeostatic mechanisms provide appropriate conditions for efficient gas exchange, they never completely balance ventilation and perfusion in every alveolus due to other factors. In particular, (1) gravity causes regional variations in both blood and air flow in the lungs, and (2) the occasional alveolar duct plugged with mucus creates unventilated areas. These factors, together with the shunting of blood from bronchial veins, account for the slight drop in P_{O_2} from alveolar air (104 mm Hg) to pulmonary venous blood (100 mm Hg), as shown in Figure 22.17.

Thickness and Surface Area of the Respiratory Membrane

In healthy lungs, the respiratory membrane is only 0.5 to 1 μm thick, and gas exchange is usually very efficient.

HOMEOSTATIC IMBALANCE

The effective thickness of the respiratory membrane increases dramatically if the lungs become waterlogged and edematous, as in pneumonia or left heart failure (see p. 687). Under such conditions, even the total time (0.75 s) that red blood cells are in transit through the pulmonary capillaries may not be enough for adequate gas exchange, and body tissues begin to suffer from oxygen deprivation. ■

The greater the surface area of the respiratory membrane, the more gas can diffuse across it in a given time period. The alveolar surface area is enormous in healthy lungs. Spread flat, the total gas exchange surface of these tiny sacs in an adult male's lungs is about 90 m^2, approximately 40 times greater than the surface area of his skin!

HOMEOSTATIC IMBALANCE

In certain pulmonary diseases, the alveolar surface area actually functioning in gas exchange is drastically reduced. This reduction occurs in emphysema, when the walls of adjacent alveoli break down and the alveolar chambers become larger. It also occurs when tumors, mucus, or inflammatory material blocks gas flow into the alveoli. ■

Internal Respiration

In internal respiration, involving capillary gas exchange in body tissues, the partial pressure and diffusion gradients are reversed from the situation we have just described for external respiration and pulmonary gas exchange. However, the factors promoting gas exchanges between the systemic capillaries and the tissue cells are essentially identical to those acting in the lungs (see Figure 22.17). Tissue cells continuously use O_2 for their metabolic activities and produce CO_2. Because P_{O_2} in the tissues is always lower than that in the systemic arterial blood (40 mm Hg versus 100 mm Hg), O_2 moves rapidly from the blood into the tissues until equilibrium is reached. At the same time, CO_2 moves quickly along its pressure gradient into the blood. As a result, venous blood draining the tissue capillary beds and returning to the heart has a P_{O_2} of 40 mm Hg and a P_{CO_2} of 45 mm Hg.

In summary, the gas exchanges that occur between the blood and the alveoli and between the blood and the tissue cells take place by simple diffusion driven by the partial pressure gradients of O_2 and CO_2 that exist on the opposite sides of the exchange membranes.

CHECK YOUR UNDERSTANDING

13. You are given a sealed container of water and air. The P_{CO_2} and P_{O_2} in the air are both 100 mm Hg. What are the P_{CO_2} and P_{O_2} in the water? Which gas has more molecules dissolved in the water? Why?

14. P_{O_2} in the alveoli is about 56 mm Hg lower than in the inspired air. Explain this difference.

15. Suppose a patient is receiving oxygen by mask. Are the arterioles leading into the O_2-enriched alveoli dilated or constricted? What is the advantage of this response?

For answers, see Appendix G.

Transport of Respiratory Gases by Blood

We have considered external and internal respiration consecutively to emphasize their similarities, but keep in mind that it is the blood that transports O_2 and CO_2 between these two exchange sites.

Oxygen Transport

▶ Describe how oxygen is transported in the blood, and explain how oxygen loading and unloading is affected by temperature, pH, BPG, and P_{CO_2}.

Molecular oxygen is carried in blood in two ways: bound to hemoglobin within red blood cells and dissolved in plasma. Oxygen is poorly soluble in water, so only about 1.5% of the oxygen transported is carried in the dissolved form. Indeed, if this were the *only* means of oxygen transport, a P_{O_2} of 3 atm or a cardiac output of 15 times normal would be required to provide the oxygen levels needed by body tissues! This problem, of course,

22

has been solved by hemoglobin, and 98.5% of the oxygen ferried from the lungs to the tissues is carried in a loose chemical combination with hemoglobin.

Association of Oxygen and Hemoglobin

As we described in Chapter 17, hemoglobin (Hb) is composed of four polypeptide chains, each bound to an iron-containing heme group (see Figure 17.4). Because the iron atoms bind oxygen, each hemoglobin molecule can combine with four molecules of O_2, and oxygen loading is rapid and reversible.

The hemoglobin-oxygen combination, called **oxyhemoglobin** (ok″sĭ-he″mo-glo′bin), is written **HbO$_2$.** Hemoglobin that has released oxygen is called **reduced hemoglobin**, or **deoxyhemoglobin**, and is written **HHb**. Loading and unloading of O_2 can be indicated by a single reversible equation:

$$HHb + O_2 \underset{\text{Tissues}}{\overset{\text{Lungs}}{\rightleftharpoons}} HbO_2 + H^+$$

After the first O_2 molecule binds to iron, the Hb molecule changes shape. As a result, it more readily takes up two more O_2 molecules, and uptake of the fourth is even more facilitated. When all four heme groups are bound to O_2, a hemoglobin molecule is said to be *fully saturated*. When one, two, or three oxygen molecules are bound, hemoglobin is *partially saturated*. By the same token, unloading of one oxygen molecule enhances the unloading of the next, and so on. In this way, the *affinity* (binding strength) of hemoglobin for oxygen changes with the extent of oxygen saturation, and both loading and unloading of oxygen are very efficient.

The rate at which Hb reversibly binds or releases O_2 is regulated by P_{O_2}, temperature, blood pH, P_{CO_2}, and blood concentration of an organic chemical called BPG. These factors interact to ensure adequate deliveries of O_2 to tissue cells.

Influence of P_{O_2} on Hemoglobin Saturation   The relationship between the degree of hemoglobin saturation and the P_{O_2} of blood is not linear, because the affinity of hemoglobin for O_2 changes with O_2 binding, as we just described. The **oxygen-hemoglobin dissociation curve** shows this relationship **(Figure 22.20)**. This S-shaped curve has a steep slope for P_{O_2} values between 10 and 50 mm Hg and then flattens out (plateaus) between 70 and 100 mm Hg.

Under normal resting conditions (P_{O_2} = 100 mm Hg), arterial blood hemoglobin is 98% saturated, and 100 ml of systemic arterial blood contains about 20 ml of O_2. This *oxygen content* of arterial blood is written as 20 vol % (volume percent). As arterial blood flows through the systemic capillaries, about 5 ml of O_2 per 100 ml of blood is released, yielding an Hb saturation of 75% and an O_2 content of 15 vol % in venous blood.

The nearly complete saturation of Hb in arterial blood explains why breathing deeply increases both the alveolar and arterial blood P_{O_2} but causes very little increase in the O_2 saturation of hemoglobin. Remember, P_{O_2} measurements indicate only the amount of O_2 dissolved in plasma, not the amount bound to hemoglobin. However, P_{O_2} values are a good index of lung function, and when arterial P_{O_2} is significantly less than alveolar P_{O_2} some degree of respiratory impairment exists.

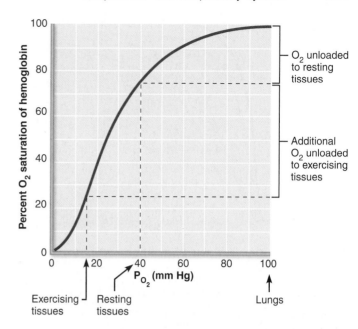

Figure 22.20 Oxygen-hemoglobin dissociation curve. Hb saturation changes as blood P_{O_2} changes. Notice that hemoglobin is almost completely saturated at a P_{O_2} of 70 mm Hg. Rapid loading and unloading of O_2 to and from hemoglobin occur at P_{O_2} values in the steep portion of the curve. In the systemic circuit, approximately 25% of Hb-bound O_2 is unloaded to resting tissues. Thus, hemoglobin of venous blood from resting tissue is still about 75% saturated with oxygen after one round through the body. During exercise, P_{O_2} can drop as low as 15 mm Hg, causing an additional 50% unloading and leaving the Hb only 25% saturated.

The oxygen-hemoglobin dissociation curve in Figure 22.20 reveals two other important facts. First, Hb is almost completely saturated at a P_{O_2} of 70 mm Hg, and further increases in P_{O_2} produce only small increases in O_2 binding. The adaptive value of this is that O_2 loading and delivery to the tissues can still be adequate when the P_{O_2} of inspired air is well below its usual levels, a situation common at higher altitudes and in people with cardiopulmonary disease.

Second, because most O_2 *unloading* occurs on the steep portion of the curve, a small drop in P_{O_2} will cause a large increase in unloading. Normally, only 20–25% of bound oxygen is unloaded during one systemic circuit, and substantial amounts of O_2 are still available in venous blood (the *venous reserve*). Consequently, if O_2 drops to very low levels in the tissues, as might occur during vigorous exercise, much more O_2 will dissociate from hemoglobin to be used by the tissue cells without any increase in respiratory rate or cardiac output.

Influence of Other Factors on Hemoglobin Saturation   Temperature, blood pH, P_{CO_2}, and the amount of BPG in the blood all influence hemoglobin saturation at a given P_{O_2}. BPG (2,3-bisphosphoglycerate), which binds reversibly with hemoglobin, is produced by red blood cells (RBCs) as they break down glucose by the anaerobic process called glycolysis.

All of these factors influence Hb saturation by modifying hemoglobin's three-dimensional structure, and thereby changing its affinity for O_2. Generally speaking, an *increase* in

(a)

(b)

Figure 22.21 Effect of temperature, P_{CO_2}, and blood pH on the oxygen-hemoglobin dissociation curve. Oxygen unloading is enhanced at conditions of **(a)** increased temperature, **(b)** increased P_{CO_2}, and/or hydrogen ion concentration (decreased pH), causing the dissociation curve to shift to the right. This response is called the Bohr effect.

temperature, P_{CO_2}, H^+, or BPG levels in blood decreases Hb's affinity for O_2, enhancing oxygen unloading from the blood. This is shown by the rightward shift of the oxygen-hemoglobin dissociation curve in **Figure 22.21**. (The purple lines represent normal body conditions, and the red lines show the shift to the right.)

Conversely, a *decrease* in any of these factors increases hemoglobin's affinity for oxygen, decreasing oxygen unloading. This change shifts the dissociation curve to the left (as the blue lines show in Figure 22.21).

If you give a little thought to how these factors might be related, you'll realize that they all tend to be at their highest levels in the systemic capillaries where oxygen unloading is the goal. As cells metabolize glucose and use O_2, they release CO_2, which increases the P_{CO_2} and H^+ levels in the capillary blood. Both declining blood pH (acidosis) and increasing P_{CO_2}

weaken the Hb-O_2 bond, a phenomenon called the **Bohr effect**. As a result, oxygen unloading is enhanced where it is most needed.

Additionally, heat is a by-product of metabolic activity, and active tissues are usually warmer than less active ones. A rise in temperature affects hemoglobin's affinity for O_2 both directly and indirectly (via its influence on RBC metabolism and BPG synthesis). Collectively, these factors see to it that Hb unloads much more O_2 in the vicinity of hard-working tissue cells.

HOMEOSTATIC IMBALANCE

Whatever the cause, inadequate oxygen delivery to body tissues is called **hypoxia** (hi-pok′se-ah). This condition is observed more easily in fair-skinned people because their skin and mucosae take on a bluish cast (become *cyanotic*) when Hb saturation falls below 75%. In dark-skinned individuals, this color change can be observed only in the mucosae and nail beds.

Classification of hypoxia based on cause is as follows:

- **Anemic hypoxia** reflects poor O_2 delivery resulting from too few RBCs or from RBCs that contain abnormal or too little Hb.
- **Ischemic (stagnant) hypoxia** results when blood circulation is impaired or blocked. Congestive heart failure may cause bodywide ischemic hypoxia, whereas emboli or thrombi block oxygen delivery only to tissues distal to the obstruction.
- **Histotoxic hypoxia** occurs when body cells are unable to use O_2 even though adequate amounts are delivered. This variety of hypoxia is the consequence of metabolic poisons, such as cyanide.
- **Hypoxemic hypoxia** is indicated by reduced arterial P_{O_2}. Possible causes include disordered or abnormal ventilation-perfusion coupling, pulmonary diseases that impair ventilation, and breathing air containing scant amounts of O_2.

Carbon monoxide poisoning is a unique type of hypoxemic hypoxia, and a leading cause of death from fire. Carbon monoxide (CO) is an odorless, colorless gas that competes vigorously with O_2 for heme binding sites. Moreover, because Hb's affinity for CO is more than 200 times greater than its affinity for oxygen, CO is a highly successful competitor. Even at minuscule partial pressures, carbon monoxide can displace oxygen.

CO poisoning is particularly dangerous because it does not produce the characteristic signs of hypoxia—cyanosis and respiratory distress. Instead the victim is confused and has a throbbing headache. In rare cases, fair skin becomes cherry red (the color of the Hb-CO complex), which the eye of the beholder interprets as a healthy "blush." Patients with CO poisoning are given hyperbaric therapy (if available) or 100% O_2 until the CO has been cleared from the body. ■

Carbon Dioxide Transport

▶ Describe carbon dioxide transport in the blood.

Normally active body cells produce about 200 ml of CO_2 each minute—exactly the amount excreted by the lungs. Blood

(a) Oxygen release and carbon dioxide pickup at the tissues

(b) Oxygen pickup and carbon dioxide release in the lungs

Figure 22.22 Transport and exchange of CO₂ and O₂. Relative sizes of the transport arrows indicate the proportionate amounts of O_2 and CO_2 moved by each method. (Reduced hemoglobin is HHb.)

transports CO_2 from the tissue cells to the lungs in three forms (Figure 22.22):

1. **Dissolved in plasma** (7–10%). The smallest amount of CO_2 is transported simply dissolved in plasma.
2. **Chemically bound to hemoglobin** (just over 20%). In this form, dissolved CO_2 is bound and carried in the

RBCs as **carbaminohemoglobin** (kar-bam″ĭ-no-he″mo-glo′bin):

$$CO_2 + Hb \rightleftharpoons HbCO_2$$
carbaminohemoglobin

This reaction is rapid and does not require a catalyst. Carbon dioxide transport in RBCs does not compete with oxyhemoglobin transport because carbon dioxide binds directly to the amino acids of *globin* (and not to the heme).

CO_2 loading and unloading to and from Hb are directly influenced by the P_{CO_2} and the degree of Hb oxygenation. Carbon dioxide rapidly dissociates from hemoglobin in the lungs, where the P_{CO_2} of alveolar air is lower than that in blood. Carbon dioxide is loaded in the tissues, where the P_{CO_2} is higher than that in the blood. Deoxygenated hemoglobin combines more readily with carbon dioxide than does oxygenated hemoglobin, as we will see in the discussion of the Haldane effect below.

3. **As bicarbonate ion in plasma** (about 70%). Most carbon dioxide molecules entering the plasma quickly enter the RBCs, where most of the reactions that prepare carbon dioxide for transport as **bicarbonate ions (HCO_3^-)** in plasma occur. As illustrated in Figure 22.22a, when dissolved CO_2 diffuses into the RBCs, it combines with water, forming carbonic acid (H_2CO_3). H_2CO_3 is unstable and dissociates into hydrogen ions and bicarbonate ions:

$$CO_2 + H_2O \rightleftharpoons H_2CO_3 \rightleftharpoons H^+ + HCO_3^-$$

carbon   water   carbonic   hydrogen   bicarbonate
dioxide   acid   ion   ion

Although this reaction also occurs in plasma, it is thousands of times faster in RBCs because they (and not plasma) contain **carbonic anhydrase** (kar-bon′ik an-hi′drās), an enzyme that reversibly catalyzes the conversion of carbon dioxide and water to carbonic acid. Hydrogen ions released during the reaction (as well as CO_2 itself) bind to Hb, triggering the Bohr effect. In this way CO_2 loading enhances O_2 release. Because of the buffering effect of Hb, the liberated H^+ causes little change in pH under resting conditions. As a result, blood becomes only slightly more acidic (the pH declines from 7.4 to 7.34) as it passes through the tissues.

Once generated, HCO_3^- moves quickly from the RBCs into the plasma, where it is carried to the lungs. To counterbalance the rapid outrush of these anions from the RBCs, chloride ions (Cl^-) move from the plasma into the RBCs. This ion exchange process, called the **chloride shift**, occurs via facilitated diffusion through a RBC membrane protein.

In the lungs, the process is reversed (Figure 22.22b). As blood moves through the pulmonary capillaries, its P_{CO_2} declines from 45 mm Hg to 40 mm Hg. For this to occur, CO_2 must first be freed from its "bicarbonate housing." HCO_3^- reenters the RBCs (and Cl^- moves into the plasma) and binds with H^+ to form carbonic acid, which is then split by carbonic anhydrase to release CO_2 and water. This CO_2, along with that released from hemoglobin and from solution in plasma, then diffuses along its partial pressure gradient from the blood into the alveoli.

The Haldane Effect

The amount of carbon dioxide transported in blood is markedly affected by the degree of oxygenation of the blood. The lower the P_{O_2} and the lower the extent of Hb saturation with oxygen, the more CO_2 that can be carried in the blood.

This phenomenon, called the **Haldane effect**, reflects the greater ability of reduced hemoglobin to form carbaminohemoglobin and to buffer H^+ by combining with it. As CO_2 enters the systemic bloodstream, it causes more oxygen to dissociate from Hb (Bohr effect). The dissociation of O_2 allows more CO_2 to combine with Hb (Haldane effect).

The Haldane effect encourages CO_2 exchange in both the tissues and lungs. In the pulmonary circulation, the situation that we just described is reversed—uptake of O_2 facilitates release of CO_2 (Figure 22.22b). As Hb becomes saturated with O_2, the H^+ released combines with HCO_3^-, helping to unload CO_2 from the pulmonary blood.

Influence of CO_2 on Blood pH

Typically, the H^+ released during carbonic acid dissociation is buffered by Hb or other proteins within the RBCs or in plasma. The HCO_3^- generated in the red blood cells diffuses into the plasma, where it acts as the *alkaline reserve* part of the blood's carbonic acid–bicarbonate buffer system.

The **carbonic acid–bicarbonate buffer system** is very important in resisting shifts in blood pH, as shown in the equation in point 3 concerning CO_2 transport. For example, if the hydrogen ion concentration in blood begins to rise, excess H^+ is removed by combining with HCO_3^- to form carbonic acid (a weak acid). If H^+ concentration drops below desirable levels in blood, carbonic acid dissociates, releasing hydrogen ions and lowering the pH again.

Changes in respiratory rate or depth can produce dramatic changes in blood pH by altering the amount of carbonic acid in the blood. Slow, shallow breathing allows CO_2 to accumulate in the blood. As a result, carbonic acid levels increase and blood pH drops. Conversely, rapid, deep breathing quickly flushes CO_2 out of the blood, reducing carbonic acid levels and increasing blood pH. In this way, respiratory ventilation can provide a fast-acting system to adjust blood pH (and P_{CO_2}) when it is disturbed by metabolic factors. Respiratory adjustments play a major role in the acid-base balance of the blood, as we will discuss in Chapter 26.

CHECK YOUR UNDERSTANDING

16. Rapidly metabolizing tissues generate large amounts of CO_2 and H^+. How does this affect O_2 unloading? What is this effect called?

17. List the three ways CO_2 is transported in blood and state approximate percentages of each.

18. What is the relationship between CO_2 and pH in the blood? Explain.

For answers, see Appendix G.

Control of Respiration

Although our tidelike breathing seems so beautifully simple, its control is more complex than you might think. Higher brain centers, chemoreceptors, and other reflexes all modify the basic respiratory rhythms generated in the brain stem.

22

Neural Mechanisms

▶ Describe the neural controls of respiration.

The control of respiration primarily involves neurons in the reticular formation of the medulla and pons. Because the medulla sets the respiratory rhythm, we will begin there.

Medullary Respiratory Centers

Clustered neurons in two areas of the medulla oblongata appear to be critically important in respiration. These are (1) the **dorsal respiratory group (DRG)**, located dorsally near the root of cranial nerve IX, and (2) the **ventral respiratory group (VRG)**, a network of neurons that extends in the ventral brain stem from the spinal cord to the pons-medulla junction (**Figure 22.23**).

The VRG appears to be a rhythm-generating and integrative center. It contains groups of neurons that fire during inspiration and others that fire during expiration in a dance of mutual inhibition. When its inspiratory neurons fire, a burst of impulses travels along the **phrenic** and **intercostal nerves** to excite the diaphragm and external intercostal muscles, respectively (Figure 22.23). As a result, the thorax expands and air rushes into the lungs. When the VRG's expiratory neurons fire, the output stops, and expiration occurs passively as the inspiratory muscles relax and the lungs recoil.

This cyclic on/off activity of the inspiratory and expiratory neurons repeats continuously and produces a respiratory rate of 12–15 breaths per minute, with inspiratory phases lasting about 2 seconds followed by expiratory phases lasting about 3 seconds. This normal respiratory rate and rhythm is referred to as **eupnea** (ūp-ne′ah; *eu* = good, *pne* = breath). During severe hypoxia, VRG networks generate gasping (perhaps in a last-ditch effort to restore O$_2$ to the brain). Respiration stops completely when a certain cluster of VRG neurons is completely suppressed, as by an overdose of morphine or alcohol.

Until recently, it was thought that the DRG acts as an inspiratory center, performing many of the tasks now known to be performed by the VRG. We now know that in almost all mammals including humans, the DRG integrates input from peripheral stretch and chemoreceptors (which we will describe shortly) and communicates this information to the VRG. It may seem surprising, but many of the details of this system so essential to life are still being worked out.

Pontine Respiratory Centers

Although the VRG generates the basic respiratory rhythm, the pontine respiratory centers influence and modify the activity of medullary neurons. For example, pontine centers appear to smooth out the transitions from inspiration to expiration, and vice versa. When lesions are made in its superior region, inspirations become very prolonged, a phenomenon called *apneustic breathing*.

The **pontine respiratory group**, formerly called the *pneumotaxic center* (noo″mo-tak′sik), and other pontine centers transmit impulses to the VRG of the medulla (Figure 22.23). This input modifies and fine-tunes the breathing rhythms generated by the VRG during certain activities such as vocalization, sleep,

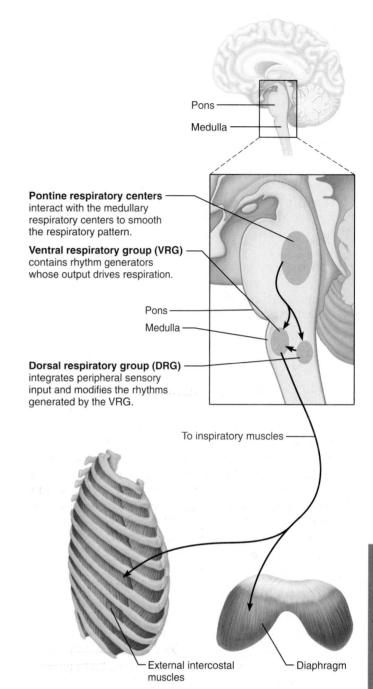

Pons
Medulla

Pontine respiratory centers interact with the medullary respiratory centers to smooth the respiratory pattern.

Ventral respiratory group (VRG) contains rhythm generators whose output drives respiration.

Pons
Medulla

Dorsal respiratory group (DRG) integrates peripheral sensory input and modifies the rhythms generated by the VRG.

To inspiratory muscles

External intercostal muscles

Diaphragm

Figure 22.23 Locations of respiratory centers and their postulated connections. The efferent pathway shown here is incomplete. Medullary neurons communicate with lower motor neurons in the spinal cord, but these are omitted for simplicity.

and exercise. As you would expect from these functions, the pontine respiratory centers, like the DRG, receive input from higher brain centers and from various sensory receptors in the periphery.

Genesis of the Respiratory Rhythm

There is little question that breathing is rhythmic, but we still cannot fully explain the origin of its rhythm. One hypothesis is that there are *pacemaker neurons*, which have intrinsic (automatic)

Figure 22.24 Neural and chemical influences on brain stem respiratory centers.
Excitatory influences (+) increase the frequency of impulses sent to the muscles of respiration and recruit additional motor units, resulting in deeper, faster breathing. Inhibitory influences (−) have the reverse effect. In some cases, the impulses may be excitatory or inhibitory (±), depending on which receptors or brain regions are activated. The cerebral cortex also directly innervates respiratory muscle motor neurons (not shown).

rhythmicity like the pacemaker cells found in the heart. Pacemaker-like activity has been demonstrated in certain VRG neurons, but suppressing their activity does not abolish breathing. This leads us to the second (and more widely accepted) hypothesis: Normal respiratory rhythm is a result of reciprocal inhibition of interconnected neuronal networks in the medulla. Rather than a single set of pacemaker neurons, there are two sets that inhibit each other and so cycle their activity to generate the rhythm.

Factors Influencing Breathing Rate and Depth

▶ Compare and contrast the influences of arterial pH, arterial partial pressures of oxygen and carbon dioxide, lung reflexes, volition, and emotions on respiratory rate and depth.

Inspiratory depth is determined by how actively the respiratory center stimulates the motor neurons serving the respiratory muscles. The greater the stimulation, the greater the number of motor units excited and the greater the force of respiratory muscle contractions. Respiratory rate is determined by how long the inspiratory center is active or how quickly it is switched off.

Depth and rate of breathing can be modified in response to changing body demands. The respiratory centers in the medulla and pons are sensitive to both excitatory and inhibitory stimuli. We describe these stimuli next and they are summarized in **Figure 22.24**.

Chemical Factors

Among the factors that influence breathing rate and depth, the most important are changing levels of CO_2, O_2, and H^+ in arterial blood. Sensors responding to such chemical fluctuations, called **chemoreceptors**, are found in two major body locations. The **central chemoreceptors** are located throughout the brain stem, including the ventrolateral medulla. The **peripheral chemoreceptors** are found in the aortic arch and carotid arteries.

Influence of P_{CO_2}   Of all the chemicals influencing respiration, CO_2 is the most potent and the most closely controlled. Normally, arterial P_{CO_2} is 40 mm Hg and is maintained within ±3 mm Hg of this level by an exquisitely sensitive homeostatic mechanism that is mediated mainly by the effect that rising CO_2 levels have on the central chemoreceptors of the brain stem **(Figure 22.25)**.

As P_{CO_2} levels rise in the blood, a condition referred to as **hypercapnia** (hi″per-kap′ne-ah), CO_2 accumulates in the brain. As CO_2 accumulates, it is hydrated to form carbonic acid. The acid dissociates, H^+ is liberated, and the pH drops. This is the same reaction that occurs when CO_2 enters RBCs (see p. 834). The increase in H^+ excites the central chemoreceptors, which make abundant synapses with the respiratory regulatory centers. As a result, the depth and rate of breathing are increased. This enhanced alveolar ventilation quickly flushes CO_2 out of the blood, increasing blood pH.

An elevation of only 5 mm Hg in arterial P_{CO_2} results in a doubling of alveolar ventilation, even when arterial O_2 levels and pH are unchanged. When P_{O_2} and pH are below normal, the response to elevated P_{CO_2} is even greater. Increased ventilation is normally self-limiting, ending when homeostatic blood P_{CO_2} levels are restored.

Notice that while rising blood CO_2 levels act as the initial stimulus, it is rising levels of H^+ generated within the brain that prod the *central* chemoreceptors into increased activity. (CO_2 readily diffuses across the blood-brain barrier between the brain and the blood, but H^+ does not.) In the final analysis, control of breathing during rest is aimed primarily at *regulating the H^+ concentration in the brain.*

HOMEOSTATIC IMBALANCE

Hyperventilation is an increase in the rate and depth of breathing that exceeds the body's need to remove CO_2. A person experiencing an anxiety attack may hyperventilate involuntarily to the point where he or she becomes dizzy or faints. This happens because low CO_2 levels in the blood (**hypocapnia**) cause cerebral blood vessels to constrict, reducing brain perfusion and producing cerebral ischemia. Earlier symptoms of hyperventilation are tingling and involuntary muscle spasms (tetany) in the hands and face caused by blood Ca^{2+} levels falling as pH rises. Such attacks may be averted by breathing into a paper bag because then the air being inspired is expired air, rich in carbon dioxide, which causes carbon dioxide to be retained in the blood. ■

When P_{CO_2} is abnormally low, respiration is inhibited and becomes slow and shallow. In fact, periods of **apnea** (breathing cessation) may occur until arterial P_{CO_2} rises and again stimulates respiration.

Sometimes swimmers voluntarily hyperventilate so that they can hold their breath longer during swim meets. This is incredibly dangerous for the following reasons. Blood O_2 content rarely drops much below 60% of normal during regular breath-holding, because as P_{O_2} drops, P_{CO_2} rises enough to make breathing unavoidable. However, strenuous hyperventilation can lower P_{CO_2} so much that a lag period occurs before it rebounds enough to stimulate respiration again. This lag may allow oxygen levels to fall well below 50 mm Hg, causing the swimmer to black out (and perhaps drown) before he or she has the urge to breathe.

Influence of P_{O_2} Cells sensitive to arterial O_2 levels are found in the peripheral chemoreceptors, that is, in the **aortic bodies** of

Figure 22.25 Negative feedback mechanism by which changes in P_{CO_2} and blood pH regulate ventilation.

Legend:
- Initial stimulus
- Physiological response
- Result

the aortic arch and in the **carotid bodies** at the bifurcation of the common carotid arteries (Figure 22.26). Those in the carotid bodies are the main oxygen sensors.

Under normal conditions, the effect of declining P_{O_2} on ventilation is slight and mostly limited to enhancing the sensitivity of peripheral receptors to increased P_{CO_2}. Arterial P_{O_2} must drop *substantially*, to at least 60 mm Hg, before O_2 levels become a major stimulus for increased ventilation. This is not as strange as it may appear. Remember, there is a huge reservoir of O_2 bound to Hb, and Hb remains almost entirely saturated unless or until the P_{O_2} of alveolar gas and arterial blood falls below 60 mm Hg. The brain stem centers then begin to suffer from O_2 starvation, and their activity is depressed. At the same time, the peripheral chemoreceptors become excited and stimulate the respiratory centers to increase ventilation, even if P_{CO_2} is normal.

22

— Brain

— Sensory nerve fiber in cranial nerve IX (pharyngeal branch of glossopharyngeal)

— External carotid artery

— Internal carotid artery

— **Carotid body**

— Common carotid artery

— Cranial nerve X (vagus nerve)

— Sensory nerve fiber in cranial nerve X

— **Aortic bodies** in aortic arch

— Aorta

— Heart

Figure 22.26 Location and innervation of the peripheral chemoreceptors in the carotid and aortic bodies.

In this way, the peripheral chemoreceptor system can maintain ventilation when alveolar O_2 levels are low even though brain stem centers are depressed by hypoxia.

Influence of Arterial pH Changes in arterial pH can modify respiratory rate and rhythm even when CO_2 and O_2 levels are normal. Because little H^+ diffuses from the blood into the brain, the direct effect of arterial H^+ concentration on central chemoreceptors is insignificant compared to the effect of H^+ generated by elevations in P_{CO_2}. The increased ventilation that occurs in response to falling arterial pH is mediated through the peripheral chemoreceptors.

Although changes in P_{CO_2} and H^+ concentration are interrelated, they are distinct stimuli. A drop in blood pH may reflect CO_2 retention, but it may also result from metabolic causes, such as accumulation of lactic acid during exercise or of fatty

acid metabolites (ketone bodies) in patients with poorly controlled diabetes mellitus. Regardless of cause, as arterial pH declines, respiratory system controls attempt to compensate and raise the pH by eliminating CO_2 (and carbonic acid) from the blood by increasing respiratory rate and depth.

Summary of Interactions of P_{CO_2}, P_{O_2}, and Arterial pH
Although every cell in the body must have O_2 to live, the body's need to rid itself of CO_2 is the most important stimulus for breathing in a healthy person. However, CO_2 does not act in isolation, and various chemical factors enforce or inhibit one another's effects. These interactions are summarized here:

1. *Rising CO_2 levels are the most powerful respiratory stimulant.* As CO_2 is hydrated in brain tissue, liberated H^+ acts directly on the central chemoreceptors, causing a reflexive increase in breathing rate and depth. Low P_{CO_2} levels depress respiration.
2. *Under normal conditions, blood P_{O_2} affects breathing only indirectly by influencing peripheral chemoreceptor sensitivity to changes in P_{CO_2}.* Low P_{O_2} augments P_{CO_2} effects, and high P_{O_2} levels diminish the effectiveness of CO_2 stimulation.
3. *When arterial P_{O_2} falls below 60 mm Hg, it becomes the major stimulus for respiration, and ventilation is increased via reflexes initiated by the peripheral chemoreceptors.* This may increase O_2 loading into the blood, but it also causes hypocapnia (low P_{CO_2} blood levels) and an increase in blood pH, both of which inhibit respiration.
4. *Changes in arterial pH resulting from CO_2 retention or metabolic factors act indirectly through the peripheral chemoreceptors to promote changes in ventilation, which in turn modify arterial P_{CO_2} and pH.* Arterial pH does not influence the central chemoreceptors directly.

Influence of Higher Brain Centers

Hypothalamic Controls Acting through the hypothalamus and the rest of the limbic system, strong emotions and pain send signals to the respiratory centers, modifying respiratory rate and depth. For example, have you ever touched something cold and clammy and gasped? That response was mediated through the hypothalamus. So too is the breath holding that occurs when we are angry and the increased respiratory rate that occurs when we are excited. A rise in body temperature acts to increase the respiratory rate, while a drop in body temperature produces the opposite effect. Sudden chilling of the body (a dip in the North Atlantic Ocean in late October) can cause cessation of breathing (apnea)—or at the very least, leave you gasping.

Cortical Controls Although the brain stem respiratory centers normally regulate breathing involuntarily, we can also exert conscious (volitional) control over the rate and depth of our breathing. We can choose to hold our breath or to take an extra-deep breath, for example. During voluntary control, the cerebral motor cortex sends signals to the motor neurons that stimulate the respiratory muscles, bypassing the medullary centers.

Our ability to voluntarily hold our breath is limited, however, because the brain stem respiratory centers automatically reinitiate breathing when the blood concentration of CO_2 reaches critical levels. That explains why drowning victims typically have water in their lungs.

Pulmonary Irritant Reflexes

The lungs contain receptors that respond to an enormous variety of irritants. When activated, these receptors communicate with the respiratory centers via vagal nerve afferents. Accumulated mucus, inhaled debris such as dust, or noxious fumes stimulate receptors in the bronchioles that promote reflex constriction of those air passages. The same irritants stimulate a cough when present in the trachea or bronchi, and a sneeze when present in the nasal cavity.

The Inflation Reflex

The visceral pleurae and conducting passages in the lungs contain numerous stretch receptors that are vigorously stimulated when the lungs are inflated. These receptors signal the medullary respiratory centers via afferent fibers of the vagus nerves, sending inhibitory impulses that end inspiration and allow expiration to occur. As the lungs recoil, the stretch receptors become quiet, and inspiration is initiated once again. This reflex, called the **inflation reflex**, or **Hering-Breuer reflex** (her′ing broy′er), is thought to be more a protective response (to prevent excessive stretching of the lungs) than a normal regulatory mechanism.

CHECK YOUR UNDERSTANDING

19. Which brain stem respiratory area is thought to generate the respiratory rhythm?
20. Which chemical factor in blood normally provides the most powerful stimulus to breathe? Which chemoreceptors are most important for this response?

For answers, see Appendix G.

Respiratory Adjustments

▶ Compare and contrast the hyperpnea of exercise with hyperventilation.

▶ Describe the process and effects of acclimatization to high altitude.

Exercise

Respiratory adjustments during exercise are geared both to intensity and duration of the exercise. Working muscles consume tremendous amounts of O_2 and produce large amounts of CO_2, and so ventilation can increase 10- to 20-fold during vigorous exercise. This increase in ventilation in response to metabolic needs is called **hyperpnea** (hi″perp-ne′ah).

How does it differ from hyperventilation? The respiratory changes in hyperpnea do not lead to significant changes in

blood O_2 and CO_2 levels. By contrast, hyperventilation is excessive ventilation, and is characterized by low P_{CO_2} and alkalosis.

Exercise-enhanced ventilation does *not* appear to be prompted by rising P_{CO_2} and declining P_{O_2} and pH in the blood for two reasons. First, ventilation increases abruptly as exercise begins, followed by a gradual increase, and then a steady state of ventilation. When exercise stops, there is an initial small but abrupt decline in ventilation rate, followed by a gradual decrease to the pre-exercise value. Second, although venous levels change, arterial P_{CO_2} and P_{O_2} levels remain surprisingly constant during exercise. In fact, P_{CO_2} may decline to below normal and P_{O_2} may rise slightly because of the efficiency of the respiratory adjustments. Our present understanding of the mechanisms that produce these observations is sketchy, but the most accepted explanation is as follows.

The abrupt increase in ventilation that occurs as exercise begins reflects interaction of three neural factors:

1. Psychological stimuli (our conscious anticipation of exercise)
2. Simultaneous cortical motor activation of skeletal muscles and respiratory centers
3. Excitatory impulses reaching respiratory centers from proprioceptors in moving muscles, tendons, and joints

The subsequent gradual increase and then plateauing of respiration probably reflect the rate of CO_2 delivery to the lungs (the "CO_2 flow"). The small but abrupt decrease in ventilation that occurs as exercise ends reflects the shutting off of the three neural factors listed above. The subsequent gradual decline to baseline ventilation likely reflects a decline in the CO_2 flow that occurs as the oxygen deficit is being repaid. The rise in lactic acid levels that contributes to O_2 deficit is *not* a result of inadequate respiratory function, because alveolar ventilation and pulmonary perfusion are as well matched during exercise as during rest (hemoglobin remains fully saturated). Rather, it reflects cardiac output limitations or inability of the skeletal muscles to further increase their oxygen consumption.

In light of this fact, the practice of inhaling pure O_2 by mask, used by some football players to replenish their "oxygen-starved" bodies as quickly as possible, is useless. The panting athlete *does* have an O_2 deficit, but inspiring extra oxygen will not help, because the shortage is in the muscles—not the lungs.

High Altitude

Most people live between sea level and an altitude of approximately 2400 m (8000 feet). In this range, differences in atmospheric pressure are not great enough to cause healthy people any problems when they spend brief periods in the higher-altitude areas. However, when you travel quickly from sea level to elevations above 8000 ft, where atmospheric pressure and P_{O_2} are lower, your body responds with symptoms of *acute mountain sickness (AMS)*—headaches, shortness of breath, nausea, and dizziness. AMS is common in travelers to ski resorts such as Vail, Colorado (8120 ft), and Brian Head, Utah (a heart-pounding 9600 ft). In severe cases of AMS, lethal pulmonary and cerebral edema may occur.

22

When you move on a *long-term* basis from sea level to the mountains, your body begins to make respiratory and hematopoietic adjustments via an adaptive response called **acclimatization**. As we have already explained, decreases in arterial P_{O_2} cause the peripheral chemoreceptors to become more responsive to increases in P_{CO_2}, and a substantial decline in P_{O_2} directly stimulates the peripheral chemoreceptors. As a result, ventilation increases as the brain attempts to restore gas exchange to previous levels. Within a few days, the minute ventilation stabilizes at a level 2–3 L/min higher than the sea level rate. Increased ventilation also reduces arterial CO_2 levels, so the P_{CO_2} of individuals living at high altitudes is typically below 40 mm Hg (its value at sea level).

High-altitude conditions always result in lower-than-normal hemoglobin saturation levels because less O_2 is available to be loaded. For example, at about 19,000 ft above sea level, O_2 saturation of arterial blood is only 67% (compared to nearly 98% at sea level). But Hb unloads only 20–25% of its oxygen at sea level, which means that even at the reduced saturations at high altitudes, the O_2 needs of the tissues are still met adequately under resting conditions. Additionally, at high altitudes hemoglobin's affinity for O_2 is reduced because of increases in BPG concentration, with the result that more O_2 is released to the tissues during each circulatory round.

Although the tissues in a person at high altitude receive adequate oxygen under normal conditions, problems arise when all-out efforts are demanded of the cardiovascular and respiratory systems (as discovered by athletes competing in the 1968 Summer Olympics on the high mesa of Mexico City, at 7370 ft). Unless a person is fully acclimatized, such conditions almost guarantee that body tissues will become severely hypoxic.

When blood O_2 levels decline, the kidneys accelerate production of erythropoietin, which stimulates bone marrow production of RBCs (see Chapter 17, p. 639). This phase of acclimatization, which occurs slowly, provides long-term compensation for living at high altitudes.

CHECK YOUR UNDERSTANDING

21. An injured soccer player arrives by ambulance in the emergency room. She is in obvious distress, breathing rapidly. Her blood P_{CO_2} is 26 mm Hg and pH is 7.5. Is she suffering from hyperventilation or hyperpnea? Explain.

22. What long-term adjustments does the body make when living at high altitude?

For answers, see Appendix G.

Homeostatic Imbalances of the Respiratory System

▶ Compare the causes and consequences of chronic bronchitis, emphysema, asthma, tuberculosis, and lung cancer.

The respiratory system is particularly vulnerable to infectious diseases because it is wide open to airborne pathogens. Many of these inflammatory conditions, such as rhinitis and laryngitis, were considered earlier in the chapter. Here we turn our attention to the most disabling disorders: *chronic obstructive pulmonary disease* (*COPD*), *asthma, tuberculosis,* and *lung cancer.* COPD and lung cancer are living proof of the devastating effects of cigarette smoking on the body. Long known to promote cardiovascular disease, cigarettes are perhaps even more effective at destroying the lungs.

Chronic Obstructive Pulmonary Disease

The **chronic obstructive pulmonary diseases (COPD)**, exemplified best by emphysema and chronic bronchitis, are a major cause of death and disability in North America. The key physiological feature of these diseases is an irreversible decrease in the ability to force air out of the lungs. These diseases also share other common features (**Figure 22.27**):

1. More than 80% of patients have a history of smoking.
2. **Dyspnea** (disp-ne′ah), difficult or labored breathing often referred to as "air hunger," occurs and gets progressively more severe.
3. Coughing and frequent pulmonary infections are common.
4. Most COPD victims develop respiratory failure manifested as **hypoventilation** (insufficient ventilation in relation to metabolic needs, causing CO_2 retention), respiratory acidosis, and hypoxemia.

Emphysema is distinguished by permanent enlargement of the alveoli, accompanied by destruction of the alveolar walls. Invariably the lungs lose their elasticity. This has three important consequences: (1) Accessory muscles must be enlisted to breathe, and victims are perpetually exhausted because breathing requires 15–20% of their total body energy supply (as opposed to 5% in healthy individuals). (2) For complex reasons, the bronchioles open during inspiration but collapse during expiration, trapping huge volumes of air in the alveoli. This hyperinflation leads to development of a permanently expanded "barrel chest" and flattens the diaphragm, thus reducing ventilation efficiency. (3) Damage to the pulmonary capillaries as the alveolar walls disintegrate increases resistance in the pulmonary circuit, forcing the right ventricle to overwork and consequently become enlarged. In addition to cigarette smoking, hereditary factors (e.g., alpha-1 antitrypsin deficiency) cause emphysema in some patients.

In **chronic bronchitis**, inhaled irritants lead to chronic excessive mucus production by the mucosa of the lower respiratory passageways and to inflammation and fibrosis of that mucosa. These responses obstruct the airways and severely impair lung ventilation and gas exchange. Pulmonary infections are frequent because bacteria thrive in the stagnant pools of mucus. However, the degree of dyspnea is usually moderate compared to that of emphysema sufferers. In addition to the major factor of cigarette smoking, environmental pollution may contribute to the development of chronic bronchitis.

In the clinical setting you might see two very different patterns that represent the extremes of patients with COPD. One pattern has traditionally been called the "pink puffer": these patients work so hard maintaining adequate ventilation that they

Figure 22.27 The pathogenesis of COPD.

chemoreceptor responses to CO_2 adapt to chronically high P_{CO_2} (essentially becoming nonfunctional), leaving only oxygen starvation to trigger adequate ventilation. However, this doesn't seem to be the case—oxygen administration barely changes ventilation. Instead, two other factors provide an explanation. First, oxygen dilates pulmonary arterioles, increasing perfusion and worsening an already poor ventilation-perfusion mismatch. Second, oxygen drives more CO_2 off of hemoglobin (the Haldane effect), dumping it into alveoli from which it cannot be removed because of the underlying disease. This whole problem can be avoided simply by using the minimum concentration of oxygen that relieves the patient's hypoxia.

Asthma

Asthma is characterized by episodes of coughing, dyspnea, wheezing, and chest tightness—alone or in combination. Most acute attacks are accompanied by a sense of panic. Although sometimes classed with COPD because it is an obstructive disorder, asthma is marked by acute exacerbations followed by symptom-free periods—that is, the obstruction is *reversible*.

The cause of asthma has been hard to pin down. Initially it was viewed as a consequence of bronchospasm triggered by various factors such as cold air, exercise, or allergens. However, when it was discovered that bronchoconstriction has relatively little effect on air flow through normal lungs, researchers probed more deeply and found that in asthma, active inflammation of the airways comes first. The airway inflammation is an immune response under the control of T_H2 cells, a subset of T lymphocytes that, by secreting certain interleukins, stimulate the production of IgE and recruit inflammatory cells (notably eosinophils) to the site.

Once someone has allergic asthma, the inflammation persists even during symptom-free periods and makes the airways hypersensitive to almost any irritant. (The most common triggers are in the home—the allergens from dust mites, cockroaches, cats, dogs, and fungi.) Once the airway walls are thickened with inflammatory exudate, the effect of bronchospasm is vastly magnified and can dramatically reduce air flow.

About one in ten people in North America suffer from asthma—children more than adults. Over the past 20 years, the number of cases of asthma has risen dramatically, an increase which may now be plateauing. While asthma remains a major health problem, better treatment options have begun to reduce the number of deaths due to asthma. Instead of merely treating the symptoms of asthma with fast-acting bronchodilators, we now treat the underlying inflammation using inhaled corticosteroids. New approaches to limiting the airway inflammation include antileukotrienes and antibodies against the patient's own IgE class of antibodies.

Tuberculosis

Tuberculosis (TB), the infectious disease caused by the bacterium *Mycobacterium tuberculosis*, is spread by coughing and primarily enters the body in inhaled air. TB mostly affects the

lose weight, becoming thin but still having nearly normal blood gases. In contrast, "blue bloaters," commonly of stocky build, become sufficiently hypoxic that they are obviously cyanotic. The hypoxia causes constriction of pulmonary blood vessels, which leads to pulmonary hypertension and right-sided heart failure. Traditionally, "pink puffers" were associated with emphysema while "blue bloaters" were associated with chronic bronchitis.

As usual, things are not that clear-cut. It turns out that patients with the same underlying disease can display either one of these two clinical patterns, and this may depend on a third factor—the strength of their innate respiratory drive. Most COPD patients fall in between these two clinical extremes.

COPD is routinely treated with bronchodilators and corticosteroids in aerosol form (inhalers). Severe dyspnea and hypoxia mandate oxygen use. For a few patients, surgical treatment for COPD, called *lung volume reduction surgery*, may be beneficial. In this procedure, part of the grossly enlarged lungs is removed to give the remaining lung tissue room to expand. While this surgery does not prolong life, it can offer certain COPD patients increased exercise capability and a higher quality of life, although at a high cost.

COPD patients in acute respiratory distress are commonly given oxygen. This oxygen must be administered with care, however. In some of these patients, giving pure oxygen can increase the blood P_{CO_2} (and lower blood pH) to life-threatening levels. It was once thought that this was due to the sudden loss of a hypoxic drive. The *hypoxic drive* hypothesis proposed that

22

lungs but can spread through the lymphatics to affect other organs. One-third of the world's population is infected, but most people never develop active TB because a massive inflammatory and immune response usually contains the primary infection in fibrous, or calcified, nodules (tubercles) in the lungs. However, the bacteria survive in the nodules and when the person's immunity is weakened, they may break out and cause symptomatic TB, involving fever, night sweats, weight loss, a racking cough, and coughing up blood.

Until the 1930s, TB was responsible for one-third of all deaths among 20- to 45-year-old adults in the U.S. With the advent of antibiotics in the 1940s, this killer was put into retreat and its prevalence declined dramatically. During the mid-1980s, there was an alarming increase in TB due to TB-infected HIV patients. This trend has now been brought under control and TB rates in the U.S. are again decreasing.

Of potential concern are deadly strains of drug-resistant (even multidrug-resistant) TB that develop when treatment is incomplete or inadequate. Such strains are found elsewhere in the world and have appeared in North America. Ideal breeding grounds for such strains are shelters for the homeless with their densely packed populations. The TB bacterium grows very slowly and drug therapy entails a 12-month course of antibiotics. The transient nature of shelter populations makes it difficult to track TB patients and ensure they take their medications for the full 12 months. The threat of TB epidemics is so real that health centers in some cities are detaining such patients in sanatoriums against their will for as long as it takes to complete a cure.

Lung Cancer

Lung cancer is the leading cause of cancer death for both men and women in North America, causing more deaths than breast, prostate, and colorectal cancer combined. This is tragic, because lung cancer is largely preventable—nearly 90% of lung cancers are the result of smoking. The cure rate for lung cancer is notoriously low, with most victims dying within one year of diagnosis. The overall five-year survival of those with lung cancer is about 17%. Because lung cancer is aggressive and metastasizes rapidly and widely, most cases are not diagnosed until they are well advanced.

Lung cancer appears to follow closely the oncogene-activating steps outlined in *A Closer Look* in Chapter 4. Ordinarily, nasal hairs, sticky mucus, and cilia do a fine job of protecting the lungs from chemical and biological irritants, but when a person smokes, these defenses are overwhelmed and eventually stop functioning. In particular, smoking paralyzes the cilia that clear mucus from the airways, allowing irritants and pathogens to accumulate. The "cocktail" of free radicals and other carcinogens in tobacco smoke eventually translates into lung cancer.

The three most common types of lung cancer are (1) **squamous cell carcinoma** (25–30% of cases), which arises in the epithelium of the bronchi or their larger subdivisions and tends to form masses that may cavitate (hollow out) and bleed, (2) **adenocarcinoma** (about 40%), which originates in peripheral lung areas as solitary nodules that develop from bronchial

glands and alveolar cells, and (3) **small cell carcinoma** (about 20%), which contains round lymphocyte-sized cells that originate in the main bronchi and grow aggressively in small grapelike clusters within the mediastinum. Subsequent metastasis from the mediastinum is especially rapid. Some small cell carcinomas cause problems beyond their effects on the lungs because they become ectopic sites of hormone production. For example, some secrete ACTH (leading to Cushing's syndrome) or ADH (which results in the syndrome of inappropriate ADH secretion, or SIADH; see p. 608).

Complete removal of the diseased lung has the greatest potential for prolonging life and providing a cure. However, this choice is open to few lung cancer patients because the cancer has often metastasized before it is discovered. In most cases, radiation therapy and chemotherapy are the only options, but these have low success rates.

Fortunately, there are several new therapies on the horizon. These include (1) antibodies that target specific growth factors or other molecules required by the tumor or that deliver toxic agents directly to the tumor, (2) cancer vaccines to stimulate the immune system to fight the tumor, and (3) various forms of gene therapy to replace the defective genes that make tumor cells divide continuously. As clinical trials progress, we will learn which of these approaches is most effective.

Developmental Aspects of the Respiratory System

▶ Trace the embryonic development of the respiratory system.

▶ Describe normal changes that occur in the respiratory system from infancy to old age.

Because embryos develop in a cephalocaudal (head-to-tail) direction, the upper respiratory structures appear first. By the fourth week of development, two thickened plates of ectoderm, the **olfactory placodes** (plak′ōds), are present on the anterior aspect of the head (Figure 22.28). These quickly invaginate to form **olfactory pits** that form the nasal cavities. The olfactory pits then extend posteriorly to connect with the developing pharynx, which forms at the same time from the endodermal germ layer.

The epithelium of the lower respiratory organs develops as an outpocketing of the foregut endoderm, which becomes the pharyngeal mucosa. This protrusion, called the **laryngotracheal bud**, is present by the fifth week of development. The proximal part of the bud forms the tracheal lining, and its distal end splits and forms the mucosae of the bronchi and all their subdivisions, including (eventually) the lung alveoli. Mesoderm covers these endoderm-derived linings and forms the walls of the respiratory passageways and the stroma of the lungs.

By 28 weeks, the respiratory system has developed sufficiently to allow a baby born prematurely to breathe on its own. As we noted earlier, infants born before this time tend to exhibit infant respiratory distress syndrome resulting from inadequate surfactant production.

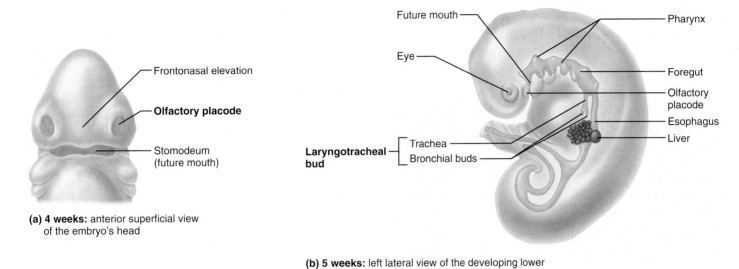

Figure 22.28 **Embryonic development of the respiratory system.**

During fetal life, the lungs are filled with fluid and all respiratory exchanges are made by the placenta. Vascular shunts cause circulating blood to largely bypass the lungs (see Chapter 28). At birth, the fluid-filled pathway empties, and the respiratory passageways fill with air. As the P_{CO_2} in the baby's blood rises, the respiratory centers are excited, causing the baby to take its first breath. The alveoli inflate and begin to function in gas exchange, but it is nearly two weeks before the lungs are fully inflated.

HOMEOSTATIC IMBALANCE

Important birth defects of the respiratory system include *cleft palate* (described in Chapter 7) and *cystic fibrosis.* **Cystic fibrosis (CF)**, the most common lethal genetic disease in North America, strikes in one out of every 2400 births. CF causes secretion of abnormally viscous mucus that clogs the respiratory passages, providing a breeding ground for airborne bacteria that predisposes the child to respiratory infections. It appears that infection of CF victims' lungs with the bacterium *Pseudomonas aeruginosa* trips a genetic switch that causes the disabled cells to churn out oceans of abnormal mucin (the primary component of mucus). The bacteria then feed on the stagnant pools of mucus and keep sending signals to the cells to make more. Toxins released by the bacteria and the local inflammatory reaction set up by the immune response both damage the lungs. Unable to reach the bacteria embedded in the mucus, the immune cells begin to attack the lung tissue, turning the air sacs into bloated cysts.

Repeated cycles of infection, chronic inflammation, and resulting tissue damage eventually result in such extensive damage that it can be treated only by a lung transplant. The disease also impairs food digestion by clogging ducts that deliver pancreatic enzymes and bile to the small intestine, and sweat glands of CF patients produce an extremely salty perspiration.

At the root of CF is a faulty gene that codes for the *CFTR* (cystic fibrosis transmembrane conductance regulator) *protein.* The normal CFTR protein works as a membrane channel to control Cl^- flow in and out of cells. In those with the mutated gene, CFTR lacks an essential amino acid and so it gets "stuck" in the endoplasmic reticulum, unable to reach the membrane and perform its normal role. Consequently, less Cl^- is secreted and less water follows, resulting in the thick mucus typical of CF.

Conventional therapy for CF has been mucus-dissolving drugs, "clapping" the chest to loosen the thick mucus, and antibiotics to prevent infection. The basic goal of CF research is to restore normal salt and water movements by (1) introducing normal CFTR genes into respiratory tract mucosa cells, (2) prodding another channel protein to take over the duties of transporting Cl^-, and (3) developing techniques to free the CFTR protein from the ER. Suppressing the inflammatory response in the lungs is another goal. Among anti-inflammatory agents being tested is a fatty acid found in fish oils, docosahexaenoic acid (DHA). A novel and surprisingly simple approach involves inhaling hypertonic saline droplets. This draws water into the mucus, making it more liquid. Alone or in combination, these therapies provide new hope to patients with CF. ■

The respiratory rate is highest in newborn infants (40–80 respirations per minute). At five years of age it is around 25 per minute, and in adults it is between 12 and 18 per minute. In old age, the rate often increases again. At birth, only about one-sixth of the final number of alveoli are present. The lungs continue to mature and more alveoli are formed until young adulthood. However, if a person begins smoking in the early teens, the lungs never completely mature, and those additional alveoli are lost forever.

In infants, the ribs take a nearly horizontal course. For this reason, infants rely almost entirely on descent of the diaphragm to increase thoracic volume for inspiration. By the second year, the ribs are positioned more obliquely, and the adult form of breathing is established.

22

System Connections

Homeostatic Interrelationships Between the Respiratory System and Other Body Systems

Nervous System

- Respiratory system provides oxygen needed for normal neuronal activity and disposes of carbon dioxide
- Medullary and pontine centers regulate respiratory rate and depth; stretch receptors in lungs and chemoreceptors provide feedback

Endocrine System

- Respiratory system provides oxygen and disposes of carbon dioxide; angiotensin converting enzyme in lungs converts angiotensin I to angiotensin II
- Epinephrine dilates the bronchioles; testosterone promotes laryngeal enlargement in pubertal males; glucocorticoids promote surfactant production

Cardiovascular System

- Respiratory system provides oxygen and disposes of carbon dioxide; carbon dioxide present in blood as HCO_3^- and H_2CO_3 contributes to blood buffering
- Blood is the transport medium for respiratory gases

Lymphatic System/Immunity

- Respiratory system provides oxygen and disposes of carbon dioxide; tonsils in pharynx house immune cells
- Lymphatic system helps to maintain blood volume required for respiratory gas transport; immune system protects respiratory organs from bacteria, bacterial toxins, viruses, protozoa, fungi, and cancer

Digestive System

- Respiratory system provides oxygen and disposes of carbon dioxide
- Digestive system provides nutrients needed by respiratory system organs

Urinary System

- Respiratory system provides oxygen and disposes of carbon dioxide to provide short-term pH homeostasis
- Kidneys dispose of metabolic wastes of respiratory system organs (other than carbon dioxide) and maintain long-term pH homeostasis

Reproductive System

- Respiratory system provides oxygen and disposes of carbon dioxide

Integumentary System

- Respiratory system provides oxygen and disposes of carbon dioxide
- Skin protects respiratory system organs by forming surface barriers

Skeletal System

- Respiratory system provides oxygen and disposes of carbon dioxide
- Bones protect lungs and bronchi by enclosure

Muscular System

- Respiratory system provides oxygen needed for muscle activity and disposes of carbon dioxide
- Activity of the diaphragm and intercostal muscles essential for producing volume changes that lead to pulmonary ventilation; regular exercise increases respiratory efficiency

22

The Respiratory System and Interrelationships with the Cardiovascular, Lymphatic/Immune, and Muscular Systems

Every day we inhale and exhale nearly 10,000 L of air. This accomplishes two things—it supplies the body with the oxygen it needs to oxidize food and release energy, and it expels carbon dioxide, the major waste product of that process. As crucial as breathing is, most of us don't think very often about the importance of having fresh air on call. But the phenomenon of gasping for air is familiar to every athlete. Indeed, the respiratory rate of a competitive swimmer may jump to over 40 breaths/min and the amount of air inhaled per breath may soar from the usual 500 ml to as much as 6 to 7 L.

The respiratory system is beautifully engineered for its function. Its alveoli are flushed with new air more than 15,000 times each day and the alveolar walls are so indescribably thin that red blood cells moving single-file through the pulmonary capillaries can make the gaseous "swaps" with the air-filled alveoli within a fraction of a second. Although every cell in the body depends on this system for the oxygen it needs to live, the respiratory system interactions that we will consider here are those it has with the cardiovascular, lymphatic/immune, and muscular systems.

Cardiovascular System

The interaction between the respiratory and cardiovascular systems is so intimate that these two systems are inseparable. Respiratory system organs, as important as they are, can make only the external gas exchanges, those that occur in the lungs. Although all body cells depend on the respiratory system to provide needed oxygen, they pick up that oxygen not from the lungs but from the blood. Thus, without blood to act as the intermediary and the heart and blood vessels to act as the hardware to pump the blood around the body, all the efforts of the respiratory system would be useless.

In turn, angiotensin converting enzyme on lung capillary endothelium plays an important role in blood pressure regulation.

Lymphatic System/Immunity

Of all body systems, only the respiratory system is completely exposed to the external environment (yes, the skin is exposed but its exposed parts are all dead). Because air contains a rich mix of potentially dangerous inhabitants (bacteria, viruses, fungi, asbestos fibers, etc.), the respiratory system is continuously at risk for infection or damage from external agents. Lymphoid outposts help protect the respiratory tract and enhance the defenses (cilia, mucus) that the respiratory system itself erects. Particularly well situated to apprehend intruders at the oral-nasal-pharynx junction are the palatine, pharyngeal, lingual, and tubal tonsils. Their macrophages engulf foreign antigens and they provide sites where lymphocytes are sensitized to mount immune responses.

Muscular System

Skeletal muscle cells, like other body cells, need oxygen to live. The notable part of this interaction is that most respiratory compensations that occur service increased muscular activity. (It is difficult to think of incidents where this is not the case—the exceptions concern disease conditions.) When we are at rest, the respiratory system operates at basal levels, but any time physical activity becomes more vigorous, the respiratory rhythm picks up the beat to match supply with need and to maintain the acid-base balance of the blood.

Respiratory System

Case study: Barbara Joley was in the bus that was hit broadside. When she was freed from the wreckage, she was deeply cyanotic and her respiration had stopped. Her heart was still beating, but her pulse was fast and thready. The emergency medical technician reported that when Barbara was found, her head was cocked at a peculiar angle and it looked like she had a fracture at the level of the C_2 vertebra. The following questions refer to these observations.

1. How might the "peculiar" head position explain Barbara's cessation of breathing?

2. What procedures (do you think) should have been initiated immediately by the emergency personnel?

3. Why is Barbara cyanotic? Explain cyanosis.

4. Assuming that Barbara survives, how will her accident affect her lifestyle in the future?

Barbara survived transport to the hospital and notes recorded at admission included the following observations.

- Right thorax compressed; ribs 7 to 9 fractured
- Right lung atelectasis

Relative to these notes:

5. What is atelectasis and why is only the right lung affected?

6. How do the recorded injuries relate to the atelectasis?

7. What treatment will be done to reverse the atelectasis? What is the rationale for this treatment?

(Answers in Appendix G)

HOMEOSTATIC IMBALANCE

Most respiratory system problems are the result of external factors—for example, viral or bacterial infections or obstruction of the trachea by a piece of food. For many years, bacterial pneumonia was one of the worst killers in North America. Antibiotics have greatly decreased its lethality, but it is still a dangerous disease, particularly in the elderly. By far the most problematic diseases *at present* are those described earlier: COPD, asthma, lung cancer, and multidrug-resistant tuberculosis. ■

The maximum amount of oxygen we can use during aerobic metabolism, $\dot{V}_{O_2max}$, declines about 9% per decade in inactive people beginning in their mid-20s. In those that remain active, $\dot{V}_{O_2max}$ still declines but much less. As we age, the thoracic wall becomes more rigid and the lungs gradually lose their elasticity, resulting in a decreasing ability to ventilate the lungs. Vital capacity declines by about one-third by the age of 70. Blood O_2 levels decline slightly, and many old people tend to become hypoxic during sleep and exhibit *sleep apnea* (temporary cessation of breathing during sleep).

The number of glands in the nasal mucosa decreases as does blood flow to this mucosa. For this reason, the nose dries and produces a thick mucus that makes us want to clear our throat.

Additionally, many of the respiratory system's protective mechanisms become less effective with age. Ciliary activity of the mucosa decreases, and the macrophages in the lungs become sluggish. The net result is that the elderly are more at risk for respiratory tract infections, particularly pneumonia and influenza.

CHECK YOUR UNDERSTANDING

23. What distinguishes the obstruction in asthma from that in chronic bronchitis?

24. What is the underlying defect in cystic fibrosis?

25. List two reasons for the decline in vital capacity seen with age.

For answers, see Appendix G.

Lungs, bronchial tree, heart, and connecting blood vessels—together, these organs fashion a remarkable system that ensures that blood is oxygenated and relieved of carbon dioxide and that all tissue cells have access to these services. Although the cooperation of the respiratory and cardiovascular systems is obvious, all organ systems of the body depend on the functioning of the respiratory system, as summarized in *Making Connections* on pp. 844–845.

RELATED CLINICAL TERMS

Adult respiratory distress syndrome (ARDS) A dangerous lung condition that can develop after severe illness or injury to the body. Neutrophils leave the body's capillaries in large numbers and then secrete chemicals that increase capillary permeability. The capillary-rich lungs are heavily affected. As the lungs fill with the fluids of edema, the patient suffocates. Even with mechanical ventilation, ARDS is hard to control and often lethal.

Adenoidectomy (adenotonsillectomy) Surgical removal of an infected pharyngeal tonsil (adenoids).

Aspiration (as″pĭ-ra′shun) (1) The act of inhaling or drawing something into the lungs or respiratory passages. Pathological aspiration in which vomit or excessive mucus is drawn into the lungs may occur when a person is unconscious or anesthetized; turning the head to one side is preventive. (2) Withdrawal of fluid by suction (use of an aspirator); done during surgery to keep an area free of blood or other body fluids; mucus is aspirated from the trachea of tracheotomy patients.

Bronchoscopy (*scopy* = viewing) Use of a viewing tube inserted through the nose or mouth to examine the internal surface of the main bronchi in the lung. Forceps attached to the tip of the tube can remove trapped objects or take samples of mucus for examination.

Cheyne-Stokes breathing (chān′stōks) Abnormal breathing pattern sometimes seen just before death (the "death rattle") and in people with combined neurological and cardiac disorders. It consists of bursts of tidal volume breaths (increasing and then decreasing in depth) alternating with periods of apnea. Trauma and hypoxia of the brain stem centers, as well as P_{CO_2} imbalances between arterial blood and brain, may be causative factors.

Deviated septum Condition in which the nasal septum takes a more lateral course than usual and may obstruct breathing; often manifests in old age or from nose trauma.

Endotracheal tube A thin plastic tube threaded into the trachea through the nose or mouth; used to deliver oxygen to patients who are breathing inadequately, in a coma, or under anesthesia.

Epistaxis (ep″ĭ-stak′sis; *epistazo* = to bleed at the nose) Nosebleed; commonly follows trauma to the nose or excessive nose blowing. Most nasal bleeding is from the highly vascularized anterior septum and can be stopped by pinching the nostrils closed or packing them with cotton.

Nasal polyps Mushroomlike benign neoplasms of the nasal mucosa; sometimes caused by infections, but most often cause is unknown; may block air flow.

Orthopnea (or″thop-ne′ah; *ortho* = straight, upright) Inability to breathe in the horizontal (lying down) position.

Otorhinolaryngology (o″to-ri″no-lar″in-gol′o-je; *oto* = ear; *rhino* = nose) Branch of medicine that deals with diagnosis and treatment of diseases of the ears, nose, and throat.

Pneumonia Infectious inflammation of the lungs, in which fluid accumulates in the alveoli; the eighth most common cause of death in the United States. Most of the more than 50 different varieties of pneumonia are viral or bacterial.

Pulmonary embolism Obstruction of the pulmonary artery or one of its branches by an embolus (most often a blood clot that has been carried from the lower limbs and through the right side of the heart into the pulmonary circulation). Symptoms are chest pain, productive bloody cough, tachycardia, and rapid, shallow breathing. Can cause sudden death unless treated quickly; usual treatment is oxygen by mask, pain relievers, and anticoagulant

22

drugs. For severe cases, clot busters (thrombolytic drugs) are also used.

Stuttering A problem of voice production in which the first syllable of words is repeated in "machine-gun" fashion. Primarily a problem with neural control of the larynx and other voice-producing structures. Many stutterers become fluent when whispering or singing, both of which involve a change in the manner of vocalization.

Sudden infant death syndrome (SIDS) Unexpected death of an apparently healthy infant during sleep. Commonly called crib death, SIDS is one of the most frequent causes of death in infants under 1 year old. Believed to be a problem of immaturity of the respiratory control centers. Most cases occur in infants placed in a prone position (on their abdomen) to sleep—a position that may result in hypoxia and hypercapnia due to rebreathing exhaled (CO_2-rich) air. Since 1992, a campaign recommending placing infants on their back to sleep has led to a decline of 40% or more in the incidence of SIDS in the U.S.

Tracheotomy (tra″ke-ot′o-me) Surgical opening of the trachea; done to provide an alternate route for air to reach the lungs when more superior respiratory passageways are obstructed (as by food or a crushed larynx).

CHAPTER SUMMARY

Media study tools that could provide you additional help in reviewing specific key topics of Chapter 22 are referenced below.

iP = *Interactive Physiology*

1. Respiration involves four processes: pulmonary ventilation, external respiration, transport of respiratory gases in the blood, and internal respiration. Both the respiratory system and the cardiovascular system are involved in respiration.

Functional Anatomy of the Respiratory System (pp. 805–819)

2. Respiratory system organs are divided functionally into conducting zone structures (nose to bronchioles), which filter, warm, and moisten incoming air; and respiratory zone structures (respiratory bronchioles to alveoli), where gas exchanges occur.

The Nose and Paranasal Sinuses (pp. 806–809)

3. The nose provides an airway for respiration; warms, moistens, and cleanses incoming air; and houses the olfactory receptors.

4. The external nose is shaped by bone and cartilage plates. The nasal cavity, which opens to the exterior, is divided by the nasal septum. Paranasal sinuses and nasolacrimal ducts drain into the nasal cavities.

The Pharynx (p. 809)

5. The pharynx extends from the base of the skull to the level of C_6. The nasopharynx is an air conduit; the oropharynx and laryngopharynx are common passageways for food and air. Tonsils are found in the oropharynx and nasopharynx.

The Larynx (pp. 810–812)

6. The larynx, or voice box, contains the vocal folds (cords). It also provides a patent airway and serves as a switching mechanism to route food and air into the proper channels.

7. The epiglottis prevents food or liquids from entering the respiratory channels during swallowing.

The Trachea (pp. 812–813)

8. The trachea extends from the larynx to the main bronchi. The trachea is reinforced by C-shaped cartilage rings, which keep the trachea patent, and its mucosa is ciliated.

The Bronchi and Subdivisions (pp. 813–815)

9. The right and left main bronchi run into their respective lungs, within which they continue to subdivide into smaller and smaller passageways.

10. The terminal bronchioles lead into respiratory zone structures: respiratory bronchioles, alveolar ducts, alveolar sacs, and finally alveoli. Gas exchange occurs in the alveoli, across the respiratory membrane.

11. As the respiratory conduits become smaller, cartilage is reduced in amount and finally lost; the mucosa thins, and smooth muscle in the walls increases.

iP Respiratory System; Topic: Anatomy Review: Respiratory Structures, p. 6.

The Lungs and Pleurae (pp. 815–819)

12. The lungs, the paired organs of gas exchange, flank the mediastinum in the thoracic cavity. Each is suspended in pleurae via its root and has a base, an apex, and medial and costal surfaces. The right lung has three lobes; the left has two.

13. The lungs are primarily air passageways/chambers, supported by an elastic connective tissue stroma.

14. The pulmonary arteries carry blood returned from the systemic circulation to the lungs, where gas exchange occurs. The pulmonary veins return newly oxygenated (and most bronchial venous) blood back to the heart to be distributed throughout the body. The bronchial arteries provide the nutrient blood supply of the lungs.

15. The parietal pleura lines the thoracic wall and mediastinum; the visceral pleura covers external lung surfaces. Pleural fluid reduces friction during breathing movements.

iP Respiratory System; Topic: Anatomy Review: Respiratory Structures, pp. 1–5.

Mechanics of Breathing (pp. 819–826)
Pressure Relationships in the Thoracic Cavity (pp. 819–820)

1. Intrapulmonary pressure is the pressure within the alveoli. Intrapleural pressure is the pressure within the pleural cavity; normally it is negative relative to intrapulmonary pressures.

iP Respiratory System; Topic: Pulmonary Ventilation, pp. 7–9.

Pulmonary Ventilation (pp. 820–822)

2. Gases travel from an area of higher pressure to an area of lower pressure.

3. Inspiration occurs when the diaphragm and external intercostal muscles contract, increasing the dimensions (and volume) of the thorax. As the intrapulmonary pressure drops, air rushes into the lungs until the intrapulmonary and atmospheric pressures are equalized.

4. Expiration is largely passive, occurring as the inspiratory muscles relax and the lungs recoil. When intrapulmonary pressure exceeds atmospheric pressure, gases flow from the lungs.

iP Respiratory System; Topic: Pulmonary Ventilation, pp. 3–6, 11–13.

Physical Factors Influencing Pulmonary Ventilation (pp. 822–824)

5. Friction in the air passageways causes resistance, which decreases air passage and causes breathing movements to become more strenuous. The greatest resistance to air flow occurs in the mid-size bronchi.

6. Surface tension of alveolar fluid acts to reduce alveolar size and collapse the alveoli. This tendency is resisted in part by surfactant.

7. Premature infants have problems keeping their lungs inflated owing to the lack of surfactant in their alveoli, resulting in infant respiratory distress syndrome (IRDS). Surfactant formation begins late in fetal development.

8. Total respiratory compliance depends on elasticity of lung tissue and flexibility of the bony thorax. When compliance is impaired, inspiration becomes more difficult.

iP Respiratory System; Topic: Pulmonary Ventilation, pp. 14–18.

Respiratory Volumes and Pulmonary Function Tests (pp. 824–826)

9. The four respiratory volumes are tidal, inspiratory reserve, expiratory reserve, and residual. The four respiratory capacities are vital, functional residual, inspiratory, and total lung. Respiratory volumes and capacities may be measured by spirometry.

10. Anatomical dead space is the air-filled volume (about 150 ml) of the conducting passageways. If alveoli become nonfunctional in gas exchange, their volume is added to the anatomical dead space, and the sum is the total dead space.

11. Alveolar ventilation is the best index of ventilation efficiency because it accounts for anatomical dead space.

$$AVR = (TV - \text{dead space}) \times \text{respiratory rate}$$

12. The FVC and FEV tests, which determine the rate at which VC air can be expelled, are particularly valuable in distinguishing between obstructive and restrictive disease.

Nonrespiratory Air Movements (p. 826)

13. Nonrespiratory air movements are voluntary or reflex actions that clear the respiratory passageways or express emotions.

Gas Exchanges Between the Blood, Lungs, and Tissues (pp. 827–830)

Basic Properties of Gases (pp. 827–828)

1. Dalton's law states that each gas in a mixture of gases exerts pressure in proportion to its percentage in the total mixture.

2. Henry's law states that the amount of gas that will dissolve in a liquid is proportional to the partial pressure of the gas. Solubility of the gas in the liquid and the temperature are other important factors.

iP Respiratory System; Topic: Gas Exchange, pp. 1–6.

Composition of Alveolar Gas (p. 828)

3. Alveolar gas contains more carbon dioxide and water vapor and considerably less oxygen than atmospheric air.

External Respiration (pp. 828–830)

4. External respiration is the process of gas exchange that occurs in the lungs. Oxygen enters the pulmonary capillaries; carbon dioxide leaves the blood and enters the alveoli. Factors influencing this process include the partial pressure gradients, the thickness of the respiratory membrane, surface area available, and the matching of alveolar ventilation and pulmonary perfusion.

Internal Respiration: (p. 830)

5. Internal respiration is the gas exchange that occurs between the systemic capillaries and the tissues. Carbon dioxide enters the blood, and oxygen leaves the blood and enters the tissues.

iP Respiratory System; Topic: Gas Exchange, pp. 6–11, 15–16.

Transport of Respiratory Gases by Blood (pp. 830–834)

Oxygen Transport (pp. 830–832)

1. Molecular oxygen is carried bound to hemoglobin in the red blood cells. The amount of oxygen bound to hemoglobin depends on the P_{O_2} and P_{CO_2} of blood, blood pH, the presence of BPG, and temperature. A small amount of oxygen gas is transported dissolved in plasma.

2. Hypoxia occurs when inadequate amounts of oxygen are delivered to body tissues. When this occurs, the skin and mucosae may become cyanotic.

Carbon Dioxide Transport (pp. 832–834)

3. CO_2 is transported in the blood dissolved in plasma, chemically bound to hemoglobin, and (primarily) as bicarbonate ion in plasma. Loading and unloading of O_2 and CO_2 are mutually beneficial.

4. Accumulation of CO_2 leads to decreased pH; depletion of CO_2 from blood leads to increased blood pH.

iP Respiratory System; Topic: Gas Transport, pp. 1–15.

Control of Respiration (pp. 834–839)

Neural Mechanisms (pp. 835–836)

1. Medullary respiratory centers are the dorsal and ventral respiratory groups. The ventral respiratory group is likely responsible for the rhythmicity of breathing.

2. The pontine respiratory centers influence the activity of the medullary respiratory centers.

Factors Influencing Breathing Rate and Depth (pp. 836–839)

3. Important chemical factors modifying baseline respiratory rate and depth are arterial levels of CO_2, H^+, and O_2.

4. An increasing arterial P_{CO_2} level (hypercapnia) is the most powerful respiratory stimulant. It acts (via release of H^+ in brain tissue) on the central chemoreceptors to cause a reflexive increase in the rate and depth of breathing.

5. Hypocapnia depresses respiration and results in decreased ventilation and, possibly, apnea.

6. Arterial P_{O_2} levels below 60 mm Hg strongly stimulate peripheral chemoreceptors.

7. Decreased pH and a decline in blood P_{O_2} act on peripheral chemoreceptors and enhance the response to CO_2.

8. Emotions, pain, body temperature changes, and other stressors can alter respiration by acting through hypothalamic centers. Respiration can also be controlled voluntarily for short periods.

9. Pulmonary irritant reflexes are initiated by dust, mucus, fumes, and pollutants.

10. The inflation (Hering-Breuer) reflex is a protective reflex initiated by extreme overinflation of the lungs; it acts to terminate inspiration.

iP Respiratory System; Topic: Control of Respiration, pp. 6–14.

Respiratory Adjustments   (pp. 839–840)

Exercise   (p. 839)

1. As exercise begins, there is an abrupt increase in ventilation (hyperpnea) followed by a more gradual increase. When exercise stops, there is an abrupt decrease in ventilation followed by a gradual decline to baseline values.
2. P_{O_2}, P_{CO_2}, and blood pH remain quite constant during exercise and hence do not appear to account for changes in ventilation. Inputs from higher centers and proprioceptors may contribute.

High Altitude   (pp. 839–840)

3. At high altitudes, there is a decrease in arterial P_{O_2} and hemoglobin saturation levels because of the decrease in atmospheric pressure compared to sea level. Increased ventilation helps restore P_{O_2} to physiological levels.
4. Long-term acclimatization involves increased erythropoiesis.

Homeostatic Imbalances of the Respiratory System (pp. 840–842)

1. Two major respiratory disorders are COPD (emphysema and chronic bronchitis) and lung cancer; a significant cause is cigarette smoking. A third major disorder is asthma. Multidrug-resistant tuberculosis may become a major health problem.

Chronic Obstructive Pulmonary Disease   (pp. 840–841)

2. COPD is characterized by an irreversible decrease in the ability to force air out of the lungs. Patients may become cyanotic as a result of chronic hypoxia.
3. Emphysema is characterized by permanent enlargement and destruction of alveoli. The lungs lose their elasticity, and expiration becomes an active process.
4. Chronic bronchitis is characterized by excessive mucus production in the lower respiratory passageways, which severely impairs ventilation and gas exchange.

Asthma   (p. 841)

5. Asthma is a reversible obstructive condition caused by an immune response that causes its victims to wheeze and gasp for air as their inflamed respiratory passages constrict. It is marked by exacerbations and periods of relief from symptoms.

Tuberculosis   (pp. 841–842)

6. Tuberculosis (TB), an infectious disease caused by an airborne bacterium, mainly affects the lungs. Although most infected individuals remain asymptomatic by walling off the bacteria in nodules (tubercles), disease symptoms ensue when immunity is depressed. Some patients' failure to complete drug therapy have produced multidrug-resistant TB strains.

Lung Cancer   (p. 842)

7. Lung cancer, promoted by free radicals and other carcinogens, is extremely aggressive and metastasizes rapidly.

Developmental Aspects of the Respiratory System (pp. 842–843, 846)

1. The superior respiratory system mucosa develops from the invagination of the ectodermal olfactory placodes; that of the inferior passageways develops from an outpocketing of the endodermal foregut lining. Mesoderm forms the walls of the respiratory conduits and the lung stroma.
2. Cystic fibrosis (CF), the most common fatal hereditary disease in North America, results from an abnormal CFTR protein that fails to form a chloride channel. The result is thick mucus which clogs respiratory passages and invites infection.
3. With age, the thorax becomes more rigid, the lungs become less elastic, and vital capacity declines. In addition, sleep apnea becomes more common, and respiratory system protective mechanisms are less effective.

REVIEW QUESTIONS

Multiple Choice/Matching

(Some questions have more than one correct answer. Select the best answer or answers from the choices given.)

1. Cutting the phrenic nerves will result in (a) air entering the pleural cavity, (b) paralysis of the diaphragm, (c) stimulation of the diaphragmatic reflex, (d) paralysis of the epiglottis.
2. Which of the following laryngeal cartilages is/are not paired? (a) epiglottis, (b) arytenoid, (c) cricoid, (d) cuneiform, (e) corniculate.
3. Under ordinary circumstances, the inflation reflex is initiated by (a) noxious chemicals, (b) the ventral respiratory group, (c) overinflation of the alveoli and bronchioles, (d) the pontine respiratory centers.
4. The detergent-like substance that keeps the alveoli from collapsing between breaths because it reduces the surface tension of the water film in the alveoli is called (a) lecithin, (b) bile, (c) surfactant, (d) reluctant.
5. Which of the following determines the *direction* of gas movement? (a) solubility in water, (b) partial pressure gradient, (c) temperature, (d) molecular weight and size of the gas molecule.
6. When the inspiratory muscles contract, (a) the size of the thoracic cavity is increased in diameter, (b) the size of the thoracic cavity is increased in length, (c) the volume of the thoracic cavity is decreased, (d) the size of the thoracic cavity is increased in both length and diameter.
7. The nutrient blood supply of the lungs is provided by (a) the pulmonary arteries, (b) the aorta, (c) the pulmonary veins, (d) the bronchial arteries.
8. Oxygen and carbon dioxide are exchanged in the lungs and through all cell membranes by (a) active transport, (b) diffusion, (c) filtration, (d) osmosis.
9. Which of the following would not normally be treated by 100% oxygen therapy? (Choose all that apply.) (a) anoxia, (b) carbon monoxide poisoning, (c) respiratory crisis in an emphysema patient, (d) eupnea.
10. Most oxygen carried in the blood is (a) in solution in the plasma, (b) combined with plasma proteins, (c) chemically combined with the heme in red blood cells, (d) in solution in the red blood cells.
11. Which of the following has the greatest stimulating effect on the respiratory centers in the brain? (a) oxygen, (b) carbon dioxide, (c) calcium, (d) willpower.

12. In mouth-to-mouth artificial respiration, the rescuer blows air from his or her own respiratory system into that of the victim. Which of the following statements are correct? (**1**) Expansion of the victim's lungs is brought about by blowing air in at higher than atmospheric pressure (positive-pressure breathing). (**2**) During inflation of the lungs, the intrapleural pressure increases. (**3**) This technique will not work if the victim has a hole in the chest wall, even if the lungs are intact. (**4**) Expiration during this procedure depends on the elasticity of the alveolar and thoracic walls. (**a**) all of these, (**b**) 1, 2, 4, (**c**) 1, 2, 3, (**d**) 1, 4.

13. A baby holding its breath will (**a**) have brain cells damaged because of low blood oxygen levels, (**b**) automatically start to breathe again when the carbon dioxide levels in the blood reach a high enough value, (**c**) suffer heart damage because of increased pressure in the carotid sinus and aortic arch areas, (**d**) be called a "blue baby."

14. Under ordinary circumstances, which of the following blood components is of no physiological significance? (**a**) bicarbonate ions, (**b**) carbaminohemoglobin, (**c**) nitrogen, (**d**) chloride.

15. Damage to which of the following would most likely result in cessation of breathing? (**a**) the pontine respiratory group, (**b**) the ventral respiratory group of the medulla, (**c**) the stretch receptors in the lungs, (**d**) the dorsal respiratory group of the medulla.

16. The bulk of carbon dioxide is carried (**a**) chemically combined with the amino acids of hemoglobin as carbaminohemoglobin in the red blood cells, (**b**) as the ion HCO_3^- in the plasma after first entering the red blood cell, (**c**) as carbonic acid in the plasma, (**d**) chemically combined with the heme portion of Hb.

Short Answer Essay Questions

17. Trace the route of air from the nares to an alveolus. Name subdivisions of organs where applicable, and differentiate between conducting and respiratory zone structures.

18. (**a**) Why is it important that the trachea is reinforced with cartilage rings? (**b**) Of what advantage is it that the rings are incomplete posteriorly?

19. Briefly explain the anatomical "reason" why most men have deeper voices than boys or women.

20. The lungs are mostly passageways and elastic tissue. (**a**) What is the role of the elastic tissue? (**b**) Of the passageways?

21. Describe the functional relationships between volume changes and gas flow into and out of the lungs.

22. Discuss how airway resistance, lung compliance, and alveolar surface tension influence pulmonary ventilation.

23. (**a**) Differentiate clearly between minute respiratory volume and alveolar ventilation rate. (**b**) Which provides a more accurate measure of ventilatory efficiency, and why?

24. State Dalton's law of partial pressures and Henry's law.

25. (**a**) Define hyperventilation. (**b**) If you hyperventilate, do you retain or expel more carbon dioxide? (**c**) What effect does hyperventilation have on blood pH?

26. Describe age-related changes in respiratory function.

Critical Thinking and Clinical Application Questions

1. Harry, the swimmer with the fastest time on the Springfield College swim team, routinely hyperventilates before a meet, as he says, "to sock some more oxygen into my lungs so I can swim longer without having to breathe." First of all, what basic fact about oxygen loading has Harry forgotten (a lapse leading to false thinking)? Second, how is Harry jeopardizing not only his time but his life?

2. A member of the "Blues" gang was rushed into an emergency room after receiving a knife wound in the left side of his thorax. The diagnosis was pneumothorax and a collapsed lung. Explain exactly (**a**) why the lung collapsed, and (**b**) why only one lung (not both) collapsed.

3. A surgeon removed three adjacent bronchopulmonary segments from the left lung of a patient with TB. Almost half of the lung was removed, yet there was no severe bleeding, and relatively few blood vessels had to be cauterized (closed off). Why was the surgery so easy to perform?

4. After a week of scuba diving in the Bahamas, Mary Ann boards an airplane. During her flight home, she develops aching joints, nausea, and dyspnea, which resolve upon landing. During the flight, the cabin pressure was equivalent to an altitude of 8000 feet. Explain her problems.

23

The Digestive System

Children are fascinated by the workings of the digestive system. They relish crunching a potato chip, delight in making "mustaches" with milk, and giggle when their stomach "growls." As adults, we know that a healthy digestive system is essential to maintaining life, because it converts foods into the raw materials that build and fuel our body's cells. Specifically, the **digestive system** takes in food, breaks it down into nutrient molecules, absorbs these molecules into the bloodstream, and then rids the body of the indigestible remains.

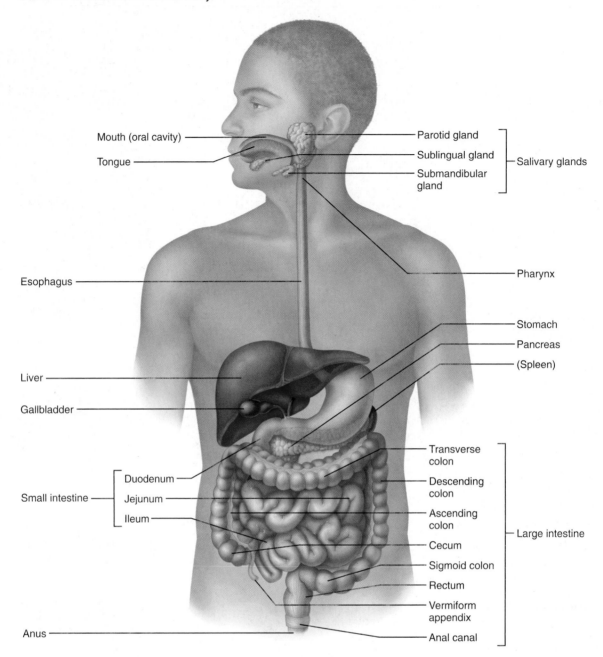

Figure 23.1 Alimentary canal and related accessory digestive organs. (See *A Brief Atlas of the Human Body*, Figure 64a.)

PART 1

OVERVIEW OF THE DIGESTIVE SYSTEM

▶ Describe the function of the digestive system, and differentiate between organs of the alimentary canal and accessory digestive organs.

The organs of the digestive system fall into two main groups: (1) those of the *alimentary canal* (al″ĭ-men′tar-e; *aliment* = nourish) and (2) *accessory digestive organs* **(Figure 23.1).**

The **alimentary canal**, also called the **gastrointestinal (GI) tract** or **gut**, is the continuous, muscular digestive tube that winds through the body. It **digests** food—breaks it down into smaller fragments (*digest* = dissolved)—and **absorbs** the digested fragments through its lining into the blood. The organs of the alimentary canal are the *mouth, pharynx, esophagus, stomach, small intestine,* and *large intestine.* The large intestine leads to the terminal opening, or *anus.* In a cadaver, the alimentary canal is approximately 9 m (about 30 ft) long, but in a living person, it is considerably shorter because of its muscle tone. Food material in this tube is technically outside the body because the canal is open to the external environment at both ends.

The **accessory digestive organs** are the *teeth, tongue, gallbladder,* and a number of large digestive glands—the *salivary*

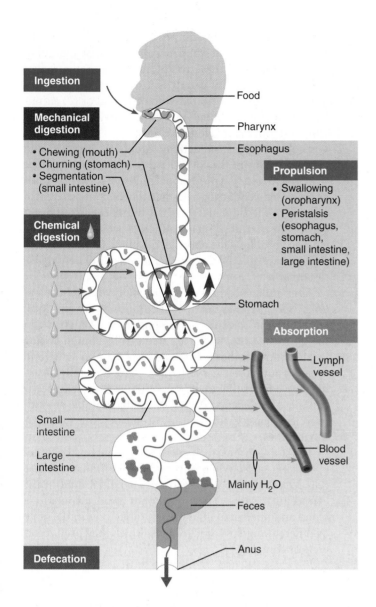

Figure 23.2 Gastrointestinal tract activities. Note that sites of chemical digestion produce enzymes or receive enzymes or other secretions made by accessory organs outside the alimentary canal.

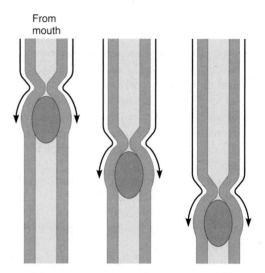

(a) Peristalsis: Adjacent segments of alimentary tract organs alternately contract and relax, which moves food along the tract distally.

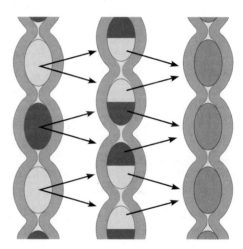

(b) Segmentation: Nonadjacent segments of alimentary tract organs alternately contract and relax, moving the food forward then backward. Food mixing and slow food propulsion occurs.

Figure 23.3 Peristalsis and segmentation.

glands, liver, and *pancreas.* The teeth and tongue are in the mouth, or oral cavity, while the digestive glands and gallbladder lie outside the GI tract and connect to it by ducts. The accessory digestive glands produce a variety of secretions that contribute to the breakdown of foodstuffs.

Digestive Processes

▶ List and define the major processes occurring during digestive system activity.

We can view the digestive tract as a "disassembly line" in which food becomes less complex at each step of processing and its nutrients become available to the body. The processing of food by the digestive system involves six essential activities: ingestion, propulsion, mechanical digestion, chemical digestion, absorption, and defecation **(Figure 23.2)**.

1. **Ingestion** is simply taking food into the digestive tract, usually via the mouth.
2. **Propulsion**, which moves food through the alimentary canal, includes *swallowing*, which is initiated voluntarily, and *peristalsis* (per″ĭ-stal′sis), an involuntary process. **Peristalsis** (*peri* = around; *stalsis* = constriction), the major means of propulsion, involves alternate waves of contraction and relaxation of muscles in the organ walls **(Figure 23.3a)**. Its main effect is to squeeze food along the tract, but some mixing occurs as well. In fact, peristaltic waves are so powerful that, once swallowed, food and fluids will reach your stomach even if you stand on your head.
3. **Mechanical digestion** physically prepares food for chemical digestion by enzymes. Mechanical processes include chewing, mixing of food with saliva by the tongue, churning food in the stomach, and **segmentation**, or rhythmic

local constrictions of the small intestine (Figure 23.3b). Segmentation mixes food with digestive juices and increases the efficiency of absorption by repeatedly moving different parts of the food mass over the intestinal wall.

4. **Chemical digestion** is a series of catabolic steps in which complex food molecules are broken down to their chemical building blocks by enzymes secreted into the lumen of the alimentary canal. Chemical digestion of foodstuffs begins in the mouth and is essentially complete in the small intestine.

5. **Absorption** is the passage of digested end products (plus vitamins, minerals, and water) from the lumen of the GI tract through the mucosal cells by active or passive transport into the blood or lymph. The small intestine is the major absorptive site.

6. **Defecation** eliminates indigestible substances from the body via the anus in the form of feces.

Some of these processes are the job of a single organ. For example, only the mouth ingests and only the large intestine defecates. But most digestive system activities require the cooperation of several organs and occur bit by bit as food moves along the tract. Later, we will consider which of these specific processes each GI tract organ performs and the neural or hormonal factors that regulate these processes.

CHECK YOUR UNDERSTANDING

1. Name one organ of the alimentary canal found in the thorax. Name three organs located in the abdominal cavity.
2. What is the usual site of ingestion?
3. Which essential digestive activity actually moves nutrients from the outside to the inside of the body?

For answers, see Appendix G.

Basic Functional Concepts

▶ Describe stimuli and controls of digestive activity.

A theme we have stressed in this book is the body's efforts to maintain the constancy of its internal environment. Most organ systems respond to changes in that environment either by attempting to restore some plasma variable to its former levels or by changing their own function. The digestive system, however, creates an optimal environment for its functioning in the lumen (cavity) of the GI tract, an area that is actually *outside* the body, and essentially all digestive tract regulatory mechanisms act to control luminal conditions so that digestion and absorption can occur there as effectively as possible.

Two facts apply to these regulatory mechanisms:

1. **Digestive activity is provoked by a range of mechanical and chemical stimuli.** Sensors (mechanoreceptors and chemoreceptors) involved in controls of GI tract activity are located in the walls of the tract organs. These sensors respond to several stimuli. The most important are stretching of the organ by food in the lumen, osmolarity

(solute concentration) and pH of the contents, and the presence of substrates and end products of digestion. When stimulated, these receptors initiate reflexes that (1) activate or inhibit glands that secrete digestive juices into the lumen or hormones into the blood or (2) stimulate smooth muscle of the GI tract walls to mix lumen contents and move them along the tract.

2. **Controls of digestive activity are both intrinsic and extrinsic.** Many of the controlling systems of the digestive tract are *intrinsic*—a product of "in-house" nerve plexuses or hormone-producing cells. Between the muscle layers in the wall of the alimentary canal is the so-called **gut brain** consisting of enteric nerve plexuses which spread like chicken wire along the entire length of the GI tract and influence each other both in the same and in different digestive organs.

As a result, two kinds of reflex activity occur, short and long. *Short reflexes* are mediated entirely by the local *enteric* or "gut" plexuses in response to stimuli arising in the GI tract. *Long reflexes* are initiated by stimuli arising inside or outside the GI tract and involve CNS centers and extrinsic autonomic nerves (Figure 23.4). Generally speaking, nerve fibers that excite smooth muscle secrete acetylcholine or substance P, and those that inhibit smooth muscle release vasoactive intestinal peptide (VIP) or nitric oxide.

The stomach and small intestine also contain hormone-producing cells. When appropriately stimulated, these cells release their products to the interstitial fluid in the extracellular space. Their hormones are distributed via blood and interstitial fluid to their target cells in the same or different digestive tract organs, which they prod to secrete or contract.

CHECK YOUR UNDERSTANDING

4. When sensors in the GI tract are stimulated, they respond via reflexes. What types of digestive activity may be put into motion via those reflexes?
5. The term "gut brain" does not really mean there is a brain in the digestive system. What does it refer to?

For answers, see Appendix G.

Digestive System Organs: Relationships

Relationship of the Digestive Organs to the Peritoneum

▶ Describe the location and function of the peritoneum.

▶ Define retroperitoneal and name the retroperitoneal organs.

Most digestive system organs reside in the abdominopelvic cavity. Recall from Chapter 1 that all ventral body cavities contain

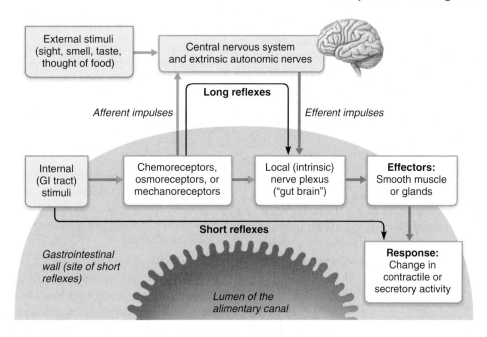

Figure 23.4 Neural reflex pathways initiated by stimuli inside or outside the gastrointestinal tract.

slippery *serous membranes*. The **peritoneum** of the abdominopelvic cavity is the most extensive of these membranes (Figure 23.5a). The **visceral peritoneum** covers the external surfaces of most digestive organs and is continuous with the **parietal peritoneum** that lines the body wall. Between the two peritoneums is the **peritoneal cavity**, a slitlike potential space containing a slippery fluid secreted by the serous membranes. The serous fluid lubricates the mobile digestive organs, allowing them to glide easily across one another and along the body wall as they carry out their digestive activities.

A **mesentery** (mes′en-ter″e) is a double layer of peritoneum—a sheet of two serous membranes fused back to back—that

extends to the digestive organs from the body wall. Mesenteries provide routes for blood vessels, lymphatics, and nerves to reach the digestive viscera; hold organs in place; and store fat. In most places the mesentery is *dorsal* and attaches to the posterior abdominal wall, but there are *ventral* mesenteries as well, such as the one that extends from the liver to the anterior abdominal wall (Figure 23.5a). As you read about the digestive organ mesenteries, you will see that some of them are given specific names (such as the *omenta*), or are called "ligaments" (even though these peritoneal folds are nothing like the fibrous ligaments that connect bones).

Not all alimentary canal organs are suspended by a mesentery. For example, during development, some parts of the small

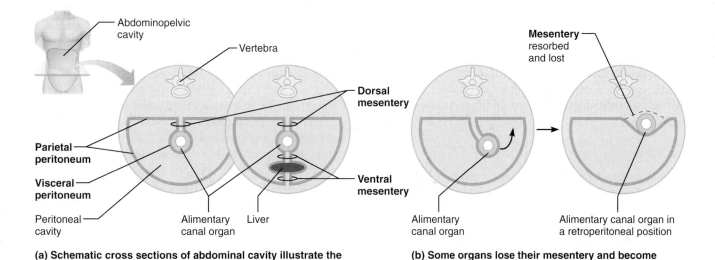

(a) Schematic cross sections of abdominal cavity illustrate the peritoneums and mesenteries.

(b) Some organs lose their mesentery and become retroperitoneal during development.

Figure 23.5 The peritoneum and the peritoneal cavity. Note that the peritoneal cavity is much smaller than depicted here.

intestine adhere to the dorsal abdominal wall (Figure 23.5b). In so doing, they lose their mesentery and come to lie posterior to the peritoneum. These organs, which include most of the pancreas and parts of the large intestine, are called **retroperitoneal organs** (*retro* = behind). By contrast, digestive organs (like the stomach) that keep their mesentery and remain in the peritoneal cavity are called **intraperitoneal** or **peritoneal organs**.

HOMEOSTATIC IMBALANCE

Peritonitis is inflammation of the peritoneum. It can arise from a piercing abdominal wound, from a perforating ulcer that leaks stomach juices into the peritoneal cavity, or from poor sterile technique during abdominal surgery, but most commonly it results from a burst appendix (that sprays bacteria-containing feces all over the peritoneum). In peritonitis, the peritoneal coverings tend to stick together around the infection site. This localizes the infection, providing time for macrophages to attack to prevent the inflammation from spreading. If peritonitis becomes widespread within the peritoneal cavity, it is dangerous and often lethal. Treatment includes removing as much infectious debris as possible from the peritoneal cavity and administering megadoses of antibiotics. ■

Blood Supply: The Splanchnic Circulation

▶ Define splanchnic circulation.

▶ Indicate the importance of the hepatic portal system.

The **splanchnic circulation** includes those arteries that branch off the abdominal aorta to serve the digestive organs and the *hepatic portal circulation*. The arterial supply—the hepatic, splenic, and left gastric branches of the celiac trunk that serve the spleen, liver, and stomach, and the mesenteric arteries (superior and inferior) that serve the small and large intestines (see pp. 730 and 731)—normally receives one-quarter of the cardiac output. This blood volume percentage increases after a meal has been eaten. The hepatic portal circulation (described on pp. 742–743) collects nutrient-rich venous blood draining from the digestive viscera and delivers it to the liver. The liver collects the absorbed nutrients for metabolic processing or for storage before releasing them back to the bloodstream for general cellular use.

CHECK YOUR UNDERSTANDING

6. How does the location of the visceral peritoneum differ from that of the parietal peritoneum?
7. Of the following organs, which is/are retroperitoneal? Stomach, pancreas, liver.
8. What name is given to the venous portion of the splanchnic circulation?

For answers, see Appendix G.

Histology of the Alimentary Canal

▶ Describe the tissue composition and the general function of each of the four layers of the alimentary canal.

Each digestive organ has only a share of the work of digestion. Consequently, it helps to consider structural characteristics that promote similar functions in all parts of the alimentary canal before we consider the functional anatomy of the digestive system.

From the esophagus to the anal canal, the walls of the alimentary canal have the same four basic layers, or *tunics—mucosa, submucosa, muscularis externa*, and *serosa* (Figure 23.6). Each layer contains a predominant tissue type that plays a specific role in food breakdown.

The Mucosa

The **mucosa**, or **mucous membrane**—the innermost layer—is a moist epithelial membrane that lines the alimentary canal lumen from mouth to anus. Its major functions are (1) to *secrete* mucus, digestive enzymes, and hormones, (2) to *absorb* the end products of digestion into the blood, and (3) to *protect* against infectious disease. The mucosa in a particular region of the GI tract may express one or all three of these capabilities.

More complex than most other mucosae in the body, the typical digestive mucosa consists of three sublayers: (1) a lining epithelium, (2) a lamina propria, and (3) a muscularis mucosae. Typically, the **epithelium** of the mucosa is a *simple columnar epithelium* rich in mucus-secreting cells. The slippery mucus it produces protects certain digestive organs from being digested themselves by enzymes working within their cavities and eases food passage along the tract. In the stomach and small intestine, the mucosa also contains both enzyme-synthesizing and hormone-secreting cells. For this reason, in such sites, the mucosa is a diffuse kind of endocrine organ as well as part of the digestive organ.

The **lamina propria** (*proprius* = one's own), which underlies the epithelium, is loose areolar connective tissue. Its capillaries nourish the epithelium and absorb digested nutrients. Its isolated lymphoid follicles, part of **MALT**, the mucosa-associated lymphatic tissue described on p. 761, help defend us against bacteria and other pathogens, which have rather free access to our digestive tract. Particularly large collections of lymphoid follicles occur within the pharynx (as the tonsils) and in the appendix.

External to the lamina propria is the **muscularis mucosae**, a scant layer of smooth muscle cells that produces local movements of the mucosa. For example, twitching of this muscle layer dislodges food particles that have adhered to the mucosa. In the small intestine, this muscle layer's tone throws the mucosa into a series of small folds that immensely increase its surface area.

The Submucosa

The **submucosa**, just external to the mucosa, is areolar connective tissue containing a rich supply of blood and lymphatic vessels, lymphoid follicles, and nerve fibers. Its abundant elastic

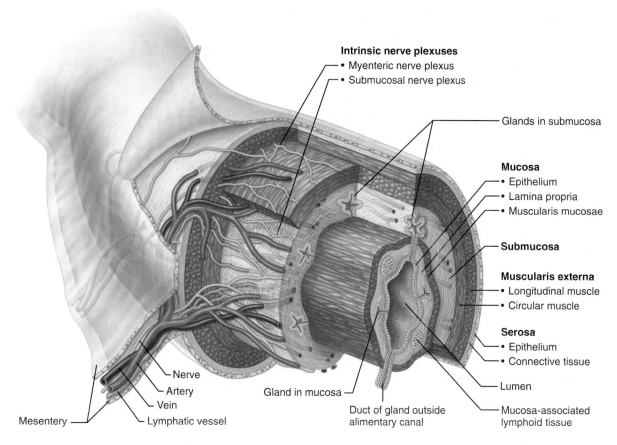

Intrinsic nerve plexuses
- Myenteric nerve plexus
- Submucosal nerve plexus

Glands in submucosa

Mucosa
- Epithelium
- Lamina propria
- Muscularis mucosae

Submucosa

Muscularis externa
- Longitudinal muscle
- Circular muscle

Serosa
- Epithelium
- Connective tissue

Lumen

Mucosa-associated lymphoid tissue

Duct of gland outside alimentary canal

Gland in mucosa

Nerve
Artery
Vein
Lymphatic vessel

Mesentery

Figure 23.6 Basic structure of the alimentary canal. Its four basic layers are the mucosa, submucosa, muscularis externa, and serosa.

fibers enable the stomach to regain its normal shape after temporarily storing a large meal. Its extensive vascular network supplies surrounding tissues of the GI tract wall.

The Muscularis Externa

Surrounding the submucosa is the **muscularis externa**, also simply called the **muscularis**. This layer is responsible for segmentation and peristalsis. It typically has an inner *circular layer* and an outer *longitudinal layer* of smooth muscle cells (see Figures 4.10c and 23.6). In several places along the tract, the circular layer thickens, forming *sphincters* that act as valves to prevent backflow and control food passage from one organ to the next.

The Serosa

The **serosa**, the protective outermost layer of the intraperitoneal organs, is the *visceral peritoneum*. It is formed of areolar connective tissue covered with *mesothelium*, a single layer of squamous epithelial cells (see Figures 4.8a and 4.3a, respectively).

In the esophagus, which is located in the thoracic instead of the abdominopelvic cavity, the serosa is replaced by an **adventitia** (ad″ven-tish′e-ah). The adventitia is ordinary fibrous connective tissue that binds the esophagus to surrounding structures. Retroperitoneal organs have *both* a serosa (on the side facing the peritoneal cavity) and an adventitia (on the side abutting the dorsal body wall).

Enteric Nervous System of the Alimentary Canal

As we noted earlier, the alimentary canal has its own in-house nerve supply, staffed by the so-called **enteric neurons** (*enter* = gut), which communicate widely with one another to regulate digestive system activity. These semiautonomous enteric neurons constitute the bulk of the two major *intrinsic nerve plexuses* (ganglia interconnected by unmyelinated fiber tracts) found in the walls of the alimentary canal: the submucosal and myenteric nerve plexuses (Figure 23.6).

The **submucosal nerve plexus** occupies the submucosa. It includes sensory as well as motor neurons, and it chiefly regulates the activity of glands and smooth muscle in the mucosa.

The large **myenteric nerve plexus** (mi-en′ter-ik; "intestinal muscle") lies between the circular and longitudinal muscle layers of the muscularis externa. Enteric neurons of this plexus provide the major nerve supply to the GI tract wall and control GI tract motility. Control of the patterns of segmentation and peristalsis is largely automatic, involving pacemaker cells and local reflex arcs between enteric neurons in the same or different plexuses or (even) organs.

The enteric nervous system is also linked to the central nervous system by afferent visceral fibers and by sympathetic and parasympathetic branches (motor fibers) of the autonomic nervous system that enter the intestinal wall and synapse with neurons in the intrinsic plexuses. Hence, digestive activity is also subject to extrinsic controls exerted by autonomic fibers via long reflex arcs (see Figure 23.4). Generally speaking, parasympathetic inputs enhance secretory activity and motility, whereas sympathetic impulses inhibit digestive activities.

But the largely independent enteric ganglia are much more than just way stations for the autonomic nervous system as is the case in other organ systems. Indeed, the enteric nervous system contains over 100 million neurons, more than the entire spinal cord.

CHECK YOUR UNDERSTANDING

9. Name the layers of the alimentary canal from the inside out.
10. Jerry has been given a drug that inhibits parasympathetic stimulation of his digestive tract. Should he "eat hearty" or temporarily refrain from eating, and why?

For answers, see Appendix G.

PART 2

FUNCTIONAL ANATOMY OF THE DIGESTIVE SYSTEM

Now that we have summarized some points that unify the digestive system organs, let's consider the special structural and functional capabilities of each organ of this system. Most of the digestive organs are shown in their normal body positions in Figure 23.1, so you may find it helpful to refer back to that illustration from time to time as you read the following sections.

The Mouth and Associated Organs

▶ Describe the gross and microscopic anatomy and the basic functions of the mouth, pharynx, and esophagus.

▶ Describe the composition and functions of saliva, and explain how salivation is regulated.

▶ Explain the dental formula and differentiate clearly between deciduous and permanent teeth.

The mouth is the only part of the alimentary canal involved in ingestion. However, most digestive functions associated with the mouth reflect the activity of the related accessory organs, such as the teeth, salivary glands, and tongue, because in the mouth food is chewed and mixed with saliva containing enzymes that begin the process of chemical digestion. The mouth also begins the propulsive process of swallowing, which carries food through the pharynx and esophagus to the stomach.

The Mouth

The **mouth**, a mucosa-lined cavity, is also called the **oral cavity**, or *buccal cavity* (buk′al). Its boundaries are the lips anteriorly, cheeks laterally, palate superiorly, and tongue inferiorly (Figure 23.7). Its anterior opening is the **oral orifice**. Posteriorly, the oral cavity is continuous with the *oropharynx*.

The walls of the mouth are lined with a thick stratified squamous epithelium (see Figure 4.3e) which can withstand considerable friction. The epithelium on the gums, hard palate, and dorsum of the tongue is slightly keratinized for extra protection against abrasion during eating. Like all moist surface linings, the oral mucosa responds to injury by producing antimicrobial peptides called *defensins*, which helps to explain how the mouth, a site teeming with disease-causing microbes, remains so remarkably healthy.

The Lips and Cheeks

The **lips (labia)** and the **cheeks**, which help keep food between the teeth when we chew, are composed of a core of skeletal muscle covered externally by skin. The *orbicularis oris muscle* forms the fleshy lips; the cheeks are formed largely by the *buccinators*. The recess bounded externally by the lips and cheeks and internally by the gums and teeth is called the **vestibule** ("porch"). The area that lies within the teeth and gums is the **oral cavity proper**.

The lips are much larger than most people think. Anatomically they extend from the inferior margin of the nose to the superior boundary of the chin. The reddened area where a person applies lipstick or lands a kiss is called the **red margin**. This transitional zone, where keratinized skin meets the oral mucosa, is poorly keratinized and translucent, allowing the red color of blood in the underlying capillaries to show through. Because the red margin lacks sweat or sebaceous glands, it must be moistened with saliva periodically to prevent it from becoming dry and cracked (chapped lips). The **labial frenulum** (fren′u-lum) is a median fold that joins the internal aspect of each lip to the gum (Figure 23.7b).

The Palate

The **palate**, forming the roof of the mouth, has two distinct parts: the hard palate anteriorly and the soft palate posteriorly (Figure 23.7). The **hard palate** is underlain by the palatine bones and the palatine processes of the maxillae, and it forms a rigid surface against which the tongue forces food during chewing. The mucosa on either side of its *raphe* (ra′fe), a midline ridge, is slightly corrugated, which helps to create friction.

The **soft palate** is a mobile fold formed mostly of skeletal muscle that rises reflexively to close off the nasopharynx when we swallow.

■ To demonstrate this action, try to breathe and swallow at the same time.

Laterally, the soft palate is anchored to the tongue by the **palatoglossal arches** and to the wall of the oropharynx by the more posterior **palatopharyngeal arches**. These two paired folds form the boundaries of the **fauces** (faw′sēz; *fauc* = throat), the arched area of the oropharynx that contains the palatine tonsils. Projecting downward from the free edge of the soft palate is the fingerlike **uvula** (u′vu-lah).

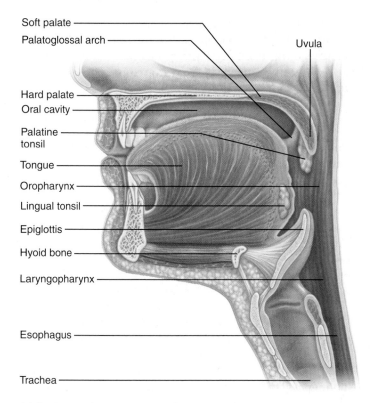

Soft palate
Palatoglossal arch
Uvula
Hard palate
Oral cavity
Palatine tonsil
Tongue
Oropharynx
Lingual tonsil
Epiglottis
Hyoid bone
Laryngopharynx
Esophagus
Trachea

(a) Sagittal section of the oral cavity and pharynx

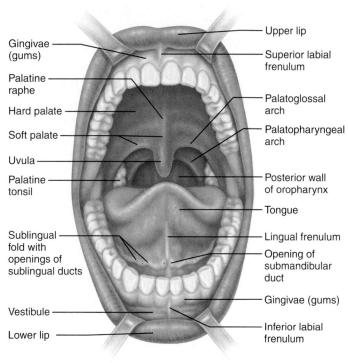

Gingivae (gums)
Palatine raphe
Hard palate
Soft palate
Uvula
Palatine tonsil
Sublingual fold with openings of sublingual ducts
Vestibule
Lower lip
Upper lip
Superior labial frenulum
Palatoglossal arch
Palatopharyngeal arch
Posterior wall of oropharynx
Tongue
Lingual frenulum
Opening of submandibular duct
Gingivae (gums)
Inferior labial frenulum

(b) Anterior view

Figure 23.7 Anatomy of the oral cavity (mouth).

The Tongue

The **tongue** occupies the floor of the mouth and fills most of the oral cavity when the mouth is closed (Figure 23.7). The tongue is composed of interlacing bundles of skeletal muscle fibers, and during chewing, it grips the food and constantly repositions it between the teeth. The tongue also mixes food with saliva forming it into a compact mass called a **bolus** (bo'lus; "a lump"), and then initiates swallowing by pushing the bolus posteriorly into the pharynx. The versatile tongue also helps us form consonants (k, d, t, and so on) when we speak.

The tongue has both intrinsic and extrinsic skeletal muscle fibers. The **intrinsic muscles** are confined in the tongue and are not attached to bone. Their muscle fibers, which run in several different planes, allow the tongue to change its shape (but not its position), becoming thicker, thinner, longer, or shorter as needed for speech and swallowing.

The **extrinsic muscles** extend to the tongue from their points of origin on bones of the skull or the soft palate, as described in Chapter 10 (see Table 10.2 and Figure 10.7). The extrinsic muscles alter the tongue's position. They protrude it, retract it, and move it from side to side. The tongue has a median septum of connective tissue, and each half contains identical muscle groups. A fold of mucosa called the **lingual frenulum** secures the tongue to the floor of the mouth and limits its posterior movements of the tongue.

HOMEOSTATIC IMBALANCE

Children born with an extremely short lingual frenulum are often referred to as "tongue-tied" because when tongue movement is restricted, speech is distorted. This congenital condition, called *ankyloglossia* ("fused tongue"), is corrected surgically by snipping the frenulum. ∎

The superior tongue surface bears papillae, peglike projections of the underlying mucosa (Figure 23.8). The conical **filiform papillae** give the tongue surface a roughness that aids in licking semisolid foods (such as ice cream) and provide friction for manipulating foods in the mouth. These papillae, the smallest and most numerous type, align in parallel rows on the tongue dorsum. They contain keratin, which stiffens them and gives the tongue its whitish appearance.

The mushroom-shaped **fungiform papillae** are scattered widely over the tongue surface. Each has a vascular core that gives it a reddish hue. Ten to twelve large **circumvallate**, or **vallate**, **papillae** are located in a V-shaped row at the back of the tongue. They resemble the fungiform papillae but have an additional surrounding furrow. Pleatlike **foliate papillae** are located on the lateral aspects of the posterior tongue. The fungiform, circumvallate, and foliate papillae house taste buds, but those on the foliate papillae function in taste primarily in infancy and early childhood.

Immediately posterior to the circumvallate papillae is the **terminal sulcus**, a groove that distinguishes the portion of the

23

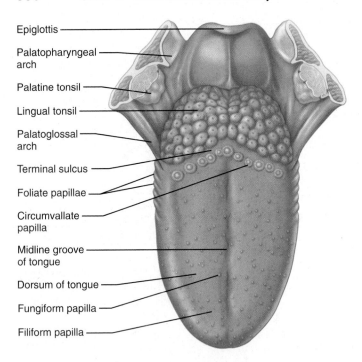

Epiglottis

Palatopharyngeal arch

Palatine tonsil

Lingual tonsil

Palatoglossal arch

Terminal sulcus

Foliate papillae

Circumvallate papilla

Midline groove of tongue

Dorsum of tongue

Fungiform papilla

Filiform papilla

Figure 23.8 Dorsal surface of the tongue, and the tonsils.

tongue that lies in the oral cavity (its *body*) from its posterior portion in the oropharynx (its *root*). The mucosa covering the root of the tongue lacks papillae, but it is still bumpy because of the nodular *lingual tonsil*, which lies just deep to its mucosa (Figure 23.8).

CHECK YOUR UNDERSTANDING

11. How does the vestibule of the mouth differ from the oral cavity proper?
12. What structure forms the roof of the mouth?
13. Besides preparing food for swallowing, the tongue has another role. What is it?

For answers, see Appendix G.

The Salivary Glands

A number of glands associated with the oral cavity secrete **saliva**. Saliva (1) cleanses the mouth, (2) dissolves food chemicals so that they can be tasted, (3) moistens food and aids in compacting it into a bolus, and (4) contains enzymes that begin the chemical breakdown of starchy foods.

Most saliva is produced by **extrinsic salivary glands** that lie outside the oral cavity and empty their secretions into it. Their output is augmented slightly by small **intrinsic salivary glands**, also called **buccal glands**, scattered throughout the oral cavity mucosa.

The extrinsic salivary glands are paired compound tubuloalveolar glands that develop from the oral mucosa and remain connected to it by ducts **(Figure 23.9a)**. The large **parotid gland** (pah-rot′id; *par* = near, *otid* = the ear) lies anterior to the ear between the masseter muscle and the skin. The prominent parotid

duct parallels the zygomatic arch, pierces the buccinator muscle, and opens into the vestibule next to the second upper molar. Branches of the facial nerve run through the parotid gland on their way to the muscles of facial expression. For this reason, surgery on this gland can result in facial paralysis.

HOMEOSTATIC IMBALANCE

Mumps, a common children's disease, is an inflammation of the parotid glands caused by the mumps virus (*myxovirus*), which spreads from person to person in saliva. If you check the location of the parotid glands in Figure 23.9a, you can understand why people with mumps complain that it hurts to open their mouth or chew. Besides that discomfort, other signs and symptoms of mumps include moderate fever and pain when swallowing acid foods (sour pickles, grapefruit juice, etc.). Mumps viral infections in adult males carry a 25% risk that the testes may become infected as well, leading to sterility. ■

About the size of a walnut, the **submandibular gland** lies along the medial aspect of the mandibular body. Its duct runs beneath the mucosa of the oral cavity floor and opens at the base of the lingual frenulum (see Figure 23.7b). The small **sublingual gland** lies anterior to the submandibular gland under the tongue and opens via 10–12 ducts into the floor of the mouth (Figure 23.9a).

To a greater or lesser degree, the salivary glands are composed of two types of secretory cells: mucous and serous (Figure 23.9b). **Serous cells** produce a watery secretion containing enzymes, ions, and a tiny bit of mucin, whereas the **mucous cells** produce **mucus**, a stringy, viscous solution. The parotid glands contain only serous cells. Submandibular and buccal glands have approximately equal numbers of serous and mucous cells. The sublingual glands contain mostly mucous cells.

Composition of Saliva

Saliva is largely water—97 to 99.5%—and therefore is hypoosmotic. Its osmolarity depends on the precise glands that are active and the nature of the stimulus for salivation. As a rule, saliva is slightly acidic (pH 6.75 to 7.00), but its pH may vary. Its solutes include electrolytes ($Na^+, K^+, Cl^-, PO_4^{3-}$, and HCO_3^-); the digestive enzymes salivary amylase and lingual lipase (both optimally active at an acid pH); the proteins mucin (mu′sin), lysozyme, and IgA; and metabolic wastes (urea and uric acid). When dissolved in water, the glycoprotein *mucin* forms thick mucus that lubricates the oral cavity and hydrates foodstuffs.

Protection against microorganisms is provided by (1) *IgA antibodies*; (2) *lysozyme*, a bactericidal enzyme that inhibits bacterial growth in the mouth and may help to prevent tooth decay; (3) a cyanide compound; and (4) *defensins* (see p. 644). Besides acting as a local antibiotic, defensins function as cytokines to call defensive cells (lymphocytes, neutrophils, etc.) into the mouth for battle.

In addition to these four protectors, the friendly bacteria that live on the back of the tongue convert food-derived nitrates in saliva into nitrites which, in turn, are converted into *nitric oxide* in an acid environment. This transformation occurs around the

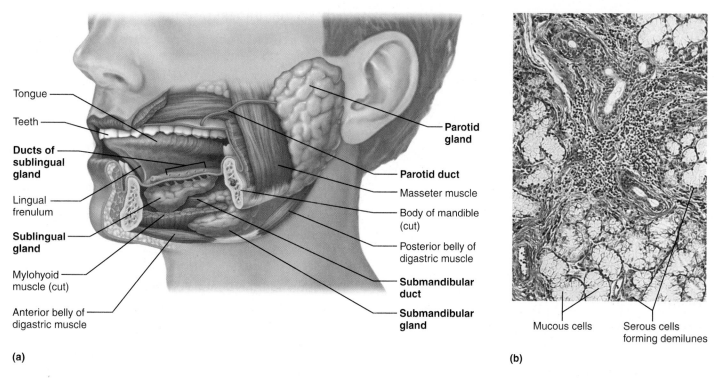

Tongue

Teeth

Ducts of sublingual gland

Lingual frenulum

Sublingual gland

Mylohyoid muscle (cut)

Anterior belly of digastric muscle

Parotid gland

Parotid duct

Masseter muscle

Body of mandible (cut)

Posterior belly of digastric muscle

Submandibular duct

Submandibular gland

(a)

Mucous cells   Serous cells forming demilunes

(b)

Figure 23.9 **The salivary glands. (a)** The parotid, submandibular, and sublingual glands associated with the left aspect of the oral cavity. **(b)** Photomicrograph of the sublingual gland (150×), which is a mixed salivary gland. Mucus-producing cells stain light blue and serous-secreting units stain purple. The serous cells sometimes form demilunes (caps) around the bases of the mucous cells.

gums, where acid-producing bacteria tend to cluster, and in the hydrochloric acid–rich secretions of the stomach. The highly toxic nitric oxide is believed to act as a bactericidal agent in these locations.

Saliva also serves as a clinical medium that can be used to detect and monitor certain diseases. For example, saliva tests for HIV antibodies, oral cancer, and diabetes are available. Additionally, quick assessments of body hormone levels may be done using saliva.

Control of Salivation

The intrinsic salivary glands secrete saliva continuously in amounts just sufficient to keep the mouth moist. But when food enters the mouth, the extrinsic glands are activated and copious amounts of saliva pour out. The average output of saliva is 1000–1500 ml per day.

Salivation is controlled primarily by the parasympathetic division of the autonomic nervous system. When we ingest food, chemoreceptors and mechanoreceptors in the mouth send signals to the **salivatory nuclei** in the brain stem (pons and medulla). As a result, parasympathetic nervous system activity increases and impulses sent via motor fibers in the *facial* (*VII*) and *glossopharyngeal* (*IX*) *nerves* trigger a dramatically increased output of watery (serous), enzyme-rich saliva. The chemoreceptors are activated most strongly by acidic substances such as vinegar and citrus juice. The mechanoreceptors are activated by virtually any mechanical stimulus in the mouth—even rubber bands.

Sometimes just the sight or smell of food is enough to get the juices flowing. The mere thought of hot fudge sauce on peppermint stick ice cream will make many a mouth water! Irritation of the lower regions of the GI tract by bacterial toxins, spicy foods, or hyperacidity—particularly when accompanied by a feeling of nausea—also increases salivation. This response may help wash away or neutralize the irritants.

In contrast to parasympathetic controls, the sympathetic division (specifically fibers in T_1–T_3) causes release of a thick, mucin-rich saliva. Extremely strong activation of the sympathetic division constricts blood vessels serving the salivary glands and almost completely inhibits saliva release, causing a dry mouth (*xerostomia*). Dehydration also inhibits salivation because low blood volume results in reduced filtration pressure at capillary beds.

HOMEOSTATIC IMBALANCE

Any disease process that inhibits saliva secretion causes a marked increase in dental caries (cavities) and difficulty in talking, swallowing, and eating. Because decomposing food particles are allowed to accumulate and bacteria flourish, *halitosis* (hal″ĭ-to′sis; "bad breath") can result. The odor is caused mainly by the metabolic activity of anaerobic protein-digesting bacteria at the back of the tongue that yields hydrogen sulfide (rotten egg smell), and methyl mercaptan (also in feces), cadaverine (associated with rotting corpses), and others. ■

23

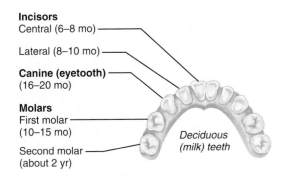

Incisors
Central (6–8 mo)
Lateral (8–10 mo)
Canine (eyetooth)
(16–20 mo)
Molars
First molar
(10–15 mo)
Second molar
(about 2 yr)

*Deciduous
(milk) teeth*

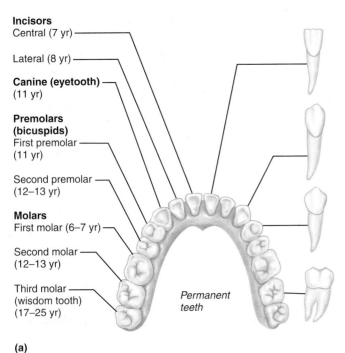

Incisors
Central (7 yr)
Lateral (8 yr)
Canine (eyetooth)
(11 yr)
**Premolars
(bicuspids)**
First premolar
(11 yr)
Second premolar
(12–13 yr)
Molars
First molar (6–7 yr)
Second molar
(12–13 yr)
Third molar
(wisdom tooth)
(17–25 yr)

*Permanent
teeth*

(a)

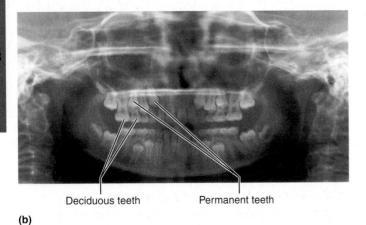

Deciduous teeth   Permanent teeth

(b)

Figure 23.10 Human dentition. (a) Teeth of the lower jaw: the deciduous and permanent sets. Approximate age at which tooth erupts is shown in parentheses. The shapes of individual teeth are shown on the right. **(b)** X ray of the mouth of a child of 7 years showing permanent teeth forming deep to the deciduous teeth.

14. What is the importance of the serous portion of saliva?
15. Name four antimicrobial substances found in saliva.

For answers, see Appendix G.

The Teeth

The **teeth** lie in sockets (alveoli) in the gum-covered margins of the mandible and maxilla. The role of the teeth in food processing needs little introduction. We *masticate*, or chew, by opening and closing our jaws and moving them from side to side while continually using our tongue to move the food between our teeth. In the process, the teeth tear and grind the food, breaking it down into smaller fragments.

Dentition and the Dental Formula

Ordinarily by age 21, two sets of teeth, the **primary** and **permanent dentitions**, have formed **(Figure 23.10a)**. The primary dentition consists of the **deciduous teeth** (de-sid′u-us; *decid* = falling off), also called **milk** or **baby teeth**. The first teeth to appear, at about age 6 months, are the lower central incisors. Additional pairs of teeth erupt at one- to two-month intervals until about 24 months, when all 20 milk teeth have emerged.

As the deep-lying **permanent teeth** enlarge and develop, the roots of the milk teeth are resorbed from below (Figure 23.10b), causing them to loosen and fall out between the ages of 6 and 12 years. Generally, all the teeth of the permanent dentition but the third molars have erupted by the end of adolescence. The third molars, also called *wisdom teeth*, emerge between the ages of 17 and 25 years. There are usually 32 permanent teeth in a full set, but sometimes the wisdom teeth never erupt or are completely absent.

HOMEOSTATIC IMBALANCE

When a tooth remains embedded in the jawbone, it is said to be *impacted*. Impacted teeth can cause a good deal of pressure and pain and must be removed surgically. Wisdom teeth are most commonly impacted. ■

Teeth are classified according to their shape and function as incisors, canines, premolars, and molars (Figure 23.10a). The chisel-shaped **incisors** are adapted for cutting or nipping off pieces of food. The conical or fanglike **canines** (cuspids or eyeteeth) tear and pierce. The **premolars** (bicuspids) and **molars** have broad crowns with rounded cusps (tips) and are best suited for grinding or crushing. The molars (literally, "millstones"), with four or five cusps, are the best grinders. During chewing, the upper and lower molars repeatedly lock together, an action that generates tremendous crushing forces.

The **dental formula** is a shorthand way of indicating the numbers and relative positions of the different types of teeth in the mouth. This formula is written as a ratio, uppers over lowers, for *one-half* of the mouth. Since the other side is a mirror image, the total dentition is obtained by multiplying the dental formula by 2. The primary dentition consists of two incisors (I), one canine (C), and two molars (M) on each side of each jaw, and its dental formula is written as

$$\frac{\text{2I, 1C, 2M (upper jaw)}}{\text{2I, 1C, 2M (lower jaw)}} \times 2 \ (20 \text{ teeth})$$

Similarly, the permanent dentition [two incisors, one canine, two premolars (PM), and three molars] is

$$\frac{\text{2I, 1C, 2PM, 3M}}{\text{2I, 1C, 2PM, 3M}} \times 2 \ (32 \text{ teeth})$$

Tooth Structure

Each tooth has two major regions: the crown and the root (Figure 23.11). The enamel-covered **crown** is the exposed part of the tooth above the **gingiva** (jin′jĭ-vah), or **gum**, which surrounds the tooth like a tight collar. **Enamel**, a brittle ceramic-like material thick as a dime, directly bears the force of chewing. The hardest substance in the body, it is heavily mineralized with calcium salts, and its densely packed hydroxyapatite (mineral) crystals are oriented in force-resisting columns perpendicular to the tooth's surface. The cells that produce enamel degenerate when the tooth erupts; consequently, any decayed or cracked areas of the enamel will not heal and must be artificially filled.

The portion of the tooth embedded in the jawbone is the **root**. Canine teeth, incisors, and premolars have one root, although the first upper premolars commonly have two. The first two upper molars have three roots, while the corresponding lower molars have two. The root pattern of the third molar varies, but a fused single root is most common.

The crown and root are connected by a constricted tooth region called the **neck**. The outer surface of the root is covered by **cementum**, a calcified connective tissue, which attaches the tooth to the thin **periodontal ligament** (per″e-o-don′tal; "around the tooth"). This ligament anchors the tooth in the bony alveolus of the jaw, forming a fibrous joint called a *gomphosis*. Where the gingiva borders on a tooth, it dips downward to form a shallow groove called the *gingival sulcus*.

In youth, the gingiva adheres tenaciously to the enamel covering the crown. But as the gums begin to recede with age, the gingiva adheres to the more sensitive cementum covering the superior region of the root. As a result, the teeth *appear* to get longer in old age—hence the expression "long in the tooth" sometimes applied to elderly people.

Dentin, a protein-rich bonelike material, underlies the enamel cap and forms the bulk of a tooth. More resilient than enamel, dentin acts as a shock absorber for forces acting on the enamel during biting and chewing. Dentin surrounds a central **pulp cavity** containing a number of soft tissue structures (connective tissue, blood vessels, and nerve fibers) collectively called **pulp**. Pulp supplies nutrients to the tooth tissues and provides for tooth sensation. Where the pulp cavity extends into the root, it becomes the **root canal**. At the proximal end of each root canal is an **apical foramen** that allows blood vessels, nerves, and other structures to enter the pulp cavity.

The teeth are served by the superior and inferior alveolar nerves, branches of the trigeminal nerve (see Table 13.2, p. 497).

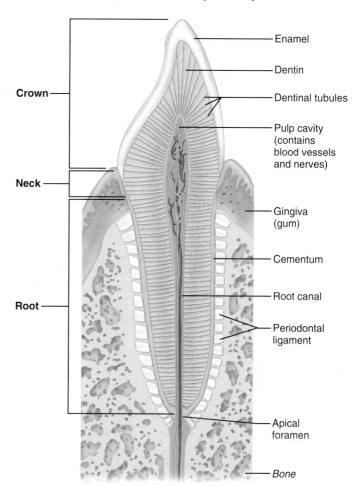

Figure 23.11 Longitudinal section of a canine tooth within its bony alveolus.

Labels: Crown; Neck; Root; Enamel; Dentin; Dentinal tubules; Pulp cavity (contains blood vessels and nerves); Gingiva (gum); Cementum; Root canal; Periodontal ligament; Apical foramen; Bone

Blood is supplied by the superior and inferior alveolar arteries, branches of the maxillary artery (see Figure 19.22b, p. 727).

Dentin contains unique radial striations called *dentinal tubules* (Figure 23.11). Each tubule contains an elongated process of an **odontoblast** (o-don′to-blast; "tooth former"), the cell type that secretes and maintains the dentin. The cell bodies of odontoblasts line the pulp cavity just deep to the dentin. Dentin is formed throughout adult life and gradually encroaches on the pulp cavity. New dentin can also be laid down fairly rapidly to compensate for tooth damage or decay.

Enamel, dentin, and cementum are all calcified and resemble bone (to differing extents), but they differ from bone in that they are avascular. Enamel also differs from cementum and dentin because it lacks collagen as its main organic component and it is almost entirely mineral.

HOMEOSTATIC IMBALANCE

Death of a tooth's nerve and consequent darkening of the tooth is commonly caused by a blow to the jaw. Local swelling pinches off the blood supply to the tooth and the nerve dies. Typically the pulp becomes infected by bacteria sometime later and must be removed by *root canal therapy*. After the cavity is sterilized

23

and filled with an inert material, the tooth is capped (covered with an artificial crown). ■

Tooth and Gum Disease

Dental caries (kār′ēz; "rottenness"), or **cavities**, result from gradual demineralization of enamel and underlying dentin by bacterial action. Decay begins when **dental plaque** (a film of sugar, bacteria, and other mouth debris) adheres to the teeth. Bacterial metabolism of the trapped sugars produces acids, which can dissolve the calcium salts of the teeth. Once the salts are leached out, the remaining organic matrix of the tooth is readily digested by protein-digesting enzymes released by the bacteria. Frequent brushing and flossing daily help prevent damage by removing forming plaque.

More serious than tooth decay is the effect of unremoved plaque on the gums. As dental plaque accumulates, it calcifies, forming **calculus** (kal′ku-lus; "stone") or tartar. These stony-hard deposits disrupt the seals between the gingivae and the teeth, deepening the sulcus and putting the gums at risk for infection by pathogenic anaerobic bacteria. In the early stages of such an infection, called **gingivitis** (jin″jĭ-vi′tis), the gums are red, sore, swollen, and may bleed.

Gingivitis is reversible if the calculus is removed, but if it is neglected the bacteria eventually form pockets of infection which become inflamed. Neutrophils and immune system cells (lymphocytes and macrophages) attack not only the intruders but also body tissues, carving deep pockets around the teeth, destroying the periodontal ligament, and activating osteoclasts which dissolve the bone away. This more serious condition, called **periodontal disease**, or **periodontitis**, affects up to 95% of all people over the age of 35 and accounts for 80–90% of tooth loss in adults. While periodontitis is widely thought to be a bacterial disease, a 14-year study of young adults indicates that those who regularly smoke marijuana are three to five times as likely as nonusers to have areas of severe gum detachment.

Regardless of its cause, tooth loss from periodontitis is not inevitable. Even advanced periodontitis can be treated by scraping the teeth, cleaning the infected pockets, then cutting the gums to shrink the pockets, and following up with anti-inflammatory and antibiotic therapy. Together, these treatments alleviate the bacterial infestations and encourage reattachment of the surrounding tissues to the teeth and bone.

Much less painful are (1) a new laser approach for destroying the diseased tissues and (2) a nonsurgical therapy now in clinical trials in which an antibiotic-impregnated film is temporarily glued to the exposed root surface. Clinical treatment is followed up by a home regimen to remove plaque by consistent frequent brushing and flossing and hydrogen peroxide rinses.

There may be more at risk than teeth in people with periodontal disease. Some contend that it increases the risk of heart disease and stroke in at least two ways: (1) the chronic inflammation promotes atherosclerotic plaque formation, and (2) bacteria entering the blood from infected gums stimulate clot formation that helps to clog coronary and cerebral arteries. Risk factors for periodontal disease include smoking, diabetes mellitus, and oral (tongue or lip) piercing.

CHECK YOUR UNDERSTANDING

16. Seven-year-old Tina ran to her daddy to show him her lower central incisor which she had wiggled until it "fell out." Is this a primary or secondary tooth? What name is given to teeth that (according to Tina) fall out?
17. What tooth substance is harder than bone? Which tooth part includes nervous tissue and blood vessels?
18. Which teeth are the "grinders"?

For answers, see Appendix G.

The Pharynx

From the mouth, food passes posteriorly into the **oropharynx** and then the **laryngopharynx** (see Figure 23.7a), both common passageways for food, fluids, and air. (The nasopharynx has no digestive role.)

The histology of the pharyngeal wall resembles that of the oral cavity. The mucosa contains a friction-resistant stratified squamous epithelium well supplied with mucus-producing glands. The external muscle layer consists of two *skeletal muscle* layers. The cells of the inner layer run longitudinally. Those of the outer layer, the *pharyngeal constrictor* muscles, encircle the wall like three stacked fists (see Figure 10.8b). Contractions of these muscles propel food into the esophagus below.

The Esophagus

The **esophagus** (ĕ-sof′ah-gus; "carry food"), a muscular tube about 25 cm (10 inches) long, is collapsed when not involved in food propulsion **(Figure 23.12)**. After food moves through the laryngopharynx, it is routed into the esophagus posteriorly as the epiglottis closes off the larynx to food entry.

As shown in Figure 23.1, the esophagus takes a fairly straight course through the mediastinum of the thorax. It pierces the diaphragm at the **esophageal hiatus** (hi-a′tus; "gap") to enter the abdomen. It joins the stomach at the **cardiac orifice** within the abdominal cavity. The cardiac orifice is surrounded by the **gastroesophageal** or **cardiac sphincter** (gas″tro-ĕ-sof″ah-je′al), which is a *physiological* sphincter (see Figure 23.13). That is, it acts as a valve, but the only structural evidence of this sphincter is a slight thickening of the circular smooth muscle at that point. The muscular diaphragm, which surrounds this sphincter, helps keep it closed when food is not being swallowed.

⚖ HOMEOSTATIC IMBALANCE

Heartburn, the first symptom of *gastroesophageal reflux disease* (*GERD*), is the burning, radiating substernal pain that occurs when the acidic gastric juice regurgitates into the esophagus. Symptoms are so similar to those of a heart attack that many first-time sufferers of heartburn are rushed to the hospital emergency room. Heartburn is most likely to happen when a person has eaten or drunk to excess, and in conditions that force abdominal contents superiorly, such as extreme obesity,

23

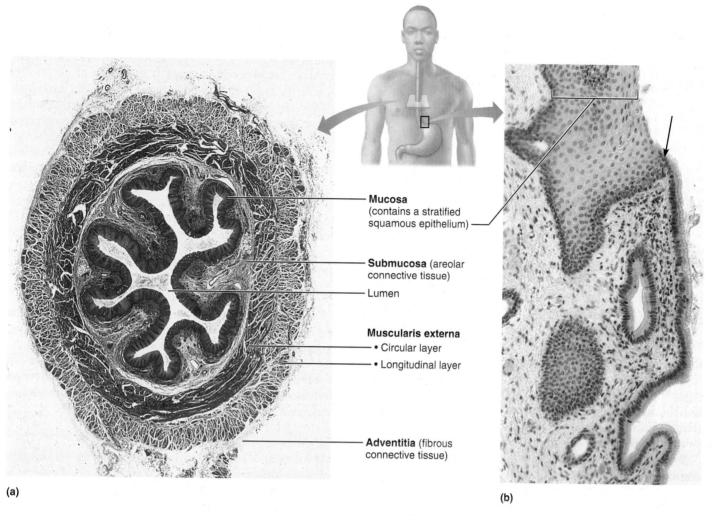

Mucosa (contains a stratified squamous epithelium)

Submucosa (areolar connective tissue)

Lumen

Muscularis externa
• Circular layer
• Longitudinal layer

Adventitia (fibrous connective tissue)

(a)

(b)

Figure 23.12 Microscopic structure of the esophagus. (a) Cross-sectional view of the esophagus taken from the region close to the stomach junction (10×). The muscularis is composed of smooth muscle. **(b)** Longitudinal section through the esophagus-stomach junction (120×). Arrow shows the point of abrupt transition from the stratified squamous epithelium of the esophagus (top) to the simple columnar epithelium of the stomach (bottom).

pregnancy, and running, which causes stomach contents to splash upward with each step (runner's reflux).

Heartburn is also common in those with a **hiatal hernia**, a structural abnormality (most often due to an abnormal relaxation or weakening of the gastroesophageal sphincter) in which the superior part of the stomach protrudes slightly above the diaphragm. Since the diaphragm no longer reinforces the sphincter, gastric juice may enter the esophagus, particularly when lying down. If the episodes are frequent and prolonged, *esophagitis* (inflammation of the esophagus) and *esophageal ulcers* may result. An even more threatening sequel is esophageal cancer. These consequences can usually be prevented or managed by avoiding late-night snacks and by using antacid preparations. ∎

Unlike the mouth and pharynx, the esophagus wall has all four of the basic alimentary canal layers described earlier. Some features of interest:

1. The esophageal mucosa contains a nonkeratinized stratified squamous epithelium. At the esophagus-stomach junction, that abrasion-resistant epithelium changes abruptly to the simple columnar epithelium of the stomach, which is specialized for secretion (Figure 23.12b).

2. When the esophagus is empty, its mucosa and submucosa are thrown into longitudinal folds (Figure 23.12a). When food is in transit in the esophagus, these folds flatten out.

3. The submucosa contains mucus-secreting *esophageal glands*. As a bolus moves through the esophagus, it compresses these glands, causing them to secrete mucus that "greases" the esophageal walls and aids food passage.

4. The muscularis externa is skeletal muscle in its superior third, a mixture of skeletal and smooth muscle in its middle third, and entirely smooth muscle in its inferior third.

5. Instead of a serosa, the esophagus has a fibrous adventitia composed entirely of connective tissue, which blends with surrounding structures along its route.

19. To what two organ systems does the pharynx belong?

20. How is the muscularis externa of the esophagus unique in the body?

21. What is the functional significance of the epithelial change seen at the esophagus-stomach junction?

For answers, see Appendix G.

Digestive Processes: Mouth to Esophagus

▶ Describe the mechanisms of chewing and swallowing.

The mouth and its accessory digestive organs are involved in most digestive processes. The mouth (1) ingests, (2) begins mechanical digestion by chewing, (3) initiates propulsion by swallowing, and (4) starts the chemical breakdown of polysaccharides. Salivary amylase, the main enzyme in saliva, digests starch and glycogen, liberating smaller fragments of linked glucose molecules. (If you chew a piece of bread for a few minutes, it will begin to taste sweet as sugars are released.) Lingual lipase, a fat-digesting enzyme in saliva, also acts in the acidic environment of the stomach. Except for a few drugs that are absorbed through the oral mucosa (for example, nitroglycerine used to alleviate the pain of angina), essentially no absorption occurs in the mouth.

In contrast to the multifunctional mouth, the pharynx and esophagus merely serve as conduits to pass food from the mouth to the stomach. Their single digestive function is food propulsion, accomplished by the role they play in swallowing.

Since we will cover chemical digestion in a special physiology section later in the chapter, only the mechanical processes of chewing and swallowing are discussed here.

Mastication (Chewing)

As food enters the mouth, its mechanical breakdown begins with **mastication**, or chewing. The cheeks and closed lips hold food between the teeth, the tongue mixes food with saliva to soften it, and the teeth cut and grind solid foods into smaller morsels. Mastication is partly voluntary and partly reflexive. We voluntarily put food into our mouths and contract the muscles that close our jaws. The pattern and rhythm of continued jaw movements are controlled mainly by stretch reflexes and in response to pressure inputs from receptors in the cheeks, gums, and tongue, but they can also be voluntary if desired.

Deglutition (Swallowing)

To send food on its way from the mouth, it is first compacted by the tongue into a bolus and then swallowed. **Deglutition** (deg″loo-tish′un), or swallowing, is a complicated process that involves coordinated activity of over 22 separate muscle groups. It has two major phases, the buccal and the pharyngeal-esophageal.

The **buccal phase** occurs in the mouth and is voluntary. In the buccal phase, we place the tip of the tongue against the hard palate, and then contract the tongue to force the bolus into the oropharynx (**Figure 23.13**, ①). As food enters the pharynx and stimulates tactile receptors there, it passes out of our control and into the realm of involuntary reflex activity.

Triggered by that "bit of saliva" or food reaching receptors in the posterior pharynx, the involuntary **pharyngeal-esophageal phase** of swallowing is controlled by the swallowing center located in the brain stem (medulla and lower pons). Motor impulses from that center are transmitted via various cranial nerves, most importantly the vagus nerves, to the muscles of the pharynx and esophagus. Once food enters the pharynx, respiration is momentarily inhibited and as illustrated in Figure 23.13, ②, all routes except the desired one into the digestive tract are blocked off: The tongue blocks off the mouth. The soft palate rises to close off the nasopharynx. The larynx rises so that the epiglottis covers its opening into the respiratory passageways, and the upper esophageal sphincter relaxes.

Food is moved along through the pharynx and into the esophagus by pressure gradients created by wavelike peristaltic contractions (Figure 23.13, ③–⑤). Solid foods pass from the oropharynx to the stomach in about 8 seconds, and fluids, aided by gravity, pass in 1 to 2 seconds. Just before the peristaltic wave (and food) reaches the end of the esophagus, the gastro-esophageal sphincter relaxes reflexively to allow food to enter the stomach. After food entry, that sphincter closes, preventing regurgitation.

If we try to talk or inhale while swallowing, the various protective mechanisms may be short-circuited and food may enter the respiratory passageways instead. This event typically triggers the cough reflex in an attempt to expel the food.

22. What role does the tongue play in swallowing?

23. How are the respiratory passages blocked during swallowing?

For answers, see Appendix G.

The Stomach

▶ Identify structural modifications of the wall of the stomach that enhance the digestive process.

▶ Name the cell types responsible for secreting the various components of gastric juice and indicate the importance of each component in stomach activity.

▶ Describe stomach structure and indicate changes in the basic alimentary canal structure that aid its digestive function.

Below the esophagus, the GI tract expands to form the **stomach** (see Figure 23.1), a temporary "storage tank" where chemical breakdown of proteins begins and food is converted to a creamy paste called **chyme** (kīm; "juice"). The stomach lies in the upper left quadrant of the peritoneal cavity, nearly hidden by the liver

23

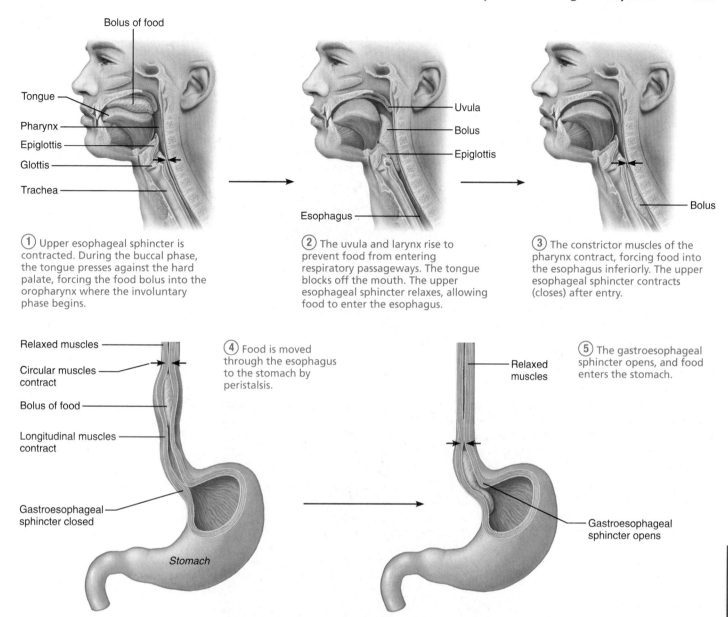

① Upper esophageal sphincter is contracted. During the buccal phase, the tongue presses against the hard palate, forcing the food bolus into the oropharynx where the involuntary phase begins.

② The uvula and larynx rise to prevent food from entering respiratory passageways. The tongue blocks off the mouth. The upper esophageal sphincter relaxes, allowing food to enter the esophagus.

③ The constrictor muscles of the pharynx contract, forcing food into the esophagus inferiorly. The upper esophageal sphincter contracts (closes) after entry.

④ Food is moved through the esophagus to the stomach by peristalsis.

⑤ The gastroesophageal sphincter opens, and food enters the stomach.

Figure 23.13 **Deglutition (swallowing).** The process of swallowing consists of a voluntary (buccal) phase (step ①) and an involuntary (pharyngeal-esophageal) phase (steps ②–⑤).

and diaphragm. Specifically, it lies in the left hypochondriac, epigastric, and umbilical regions of the abdomen. Though relatively fixed at both ends, the stomach is quite movable in between. It tends to lie high and run horizontally in short, stout people (a steer-horn stomach) and is often elongated vertically in tall, thin people (a J-shaped stomach).

Gross Anatomy

The adult stomach varies from 15 to 25 cm (6 to 10 inches) long, but its diameter and volume depend on how much food it contains. An empty stomach has a volume of about 50 ml and a cross-sectional diameter only slightly larger than the large intestine, but when it is really distended it can hold about 4 L (1 gallon) of food and may extend nearly all the way to the pelvis! When empty, the stomach collapses inward, throwing its

mucosa (and submucosa) into large, longitudinal folds called **rugae** (roo′ge; *ruga* = wrinkle, fold).

The major regions of the stomach are shown in **Figure 23.14a**. The small **cardiac region**, or **cardia** ("near the heart"), surrounds the cardiac orifice through which food enters the stomach from the esophagus. The **fundus** is its dome-shaped part, tucked beneath the diaphragm, that bulges superolaterally to the cardia. The **body**, the midportion of the stomach, is continuous inferiorly with the funnel-shaped **pyloric region**. The wider and more superior part of the pyloric region, the **pyloric antrum** (*antrum* = cave) narrows to form the **pyloric canal**, which terminates at the **pylorus**. The pylorus is continuous with the duodenum (the first part of the small intestine) through the **pyloric valve** or **sphincter**, which controls stomach emptying (*pylorus* = gatekeeper).

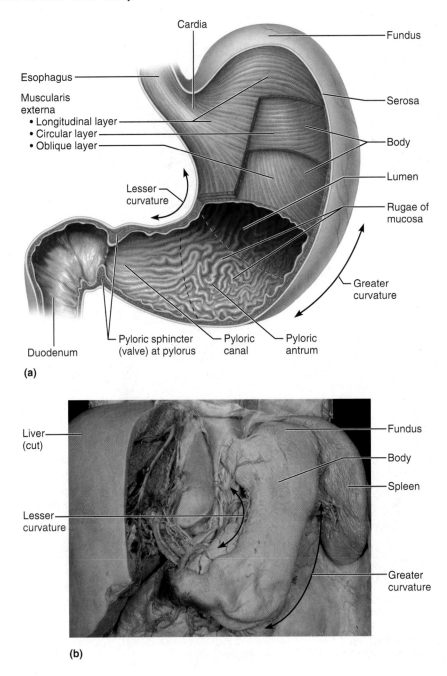

Figure 23.14 Anatomy of the stomach. (a) Gross internal anatomy (frontal section). **(b)** Photograph of external aspect of stomach. (See *A Brief Atlas of the Human Body*, Figure 69a.)

The convex lateral surface of the stomach is its **greater curvature**, and its concave medial surface is the **lesser curvature**. Extending from these curvatures are two mesenteries, called *omenta* (o-men′tah), that help tether the stomach to other digestive organs and the body wall (see Figure 23.30, p. 892). The **lesser omentum** runs from the liver to the lesser curvature of the stomach, where it becomes continuous with the visceral peritoneum covering the stomach. The **greater omentum** drapes inferiorly from the greater curvature of the stomach to cover the coils of the small intestine. It then runs dorsally and superiorly, wrapping the spleen and the transverse portion of

the large intestine before blending with the *mesocolon,* a dorsal mesentery that secures the large intestine to the parietal peritoneum of the posterior abdominal wall. The greater omentum is riddled with fat deposits (*oment* = fatty skin) that give it the appearance of a lacy apron. It also contains large collections of lymph nodes. The immune cells and macrophages in these nodes "police" the peritoneal cavity and intraperitoneal organs.

The stomach is served by the autonomic nervous system. Sympathetic fibers from thoracic splanchnic nerves are relayed through the celiac plexus. Parasympathetic fibers are supplied

Figure 23.15 Microscopic anatomy of the stomach. (l.s. = longitudinal section)

(a) Layers of the stomach wall (l.s.)

Mucosa
Surface epithelium
Lamina propria
Muscularis mucosae
Submucosa (contains submucosal plexus)
Muscularis externa (contains myenteric plexus)
Oblique layer
Circular layer
Longitudinal layer
Serosa
Stomach wall

(b) Enlarged view of gastric pits and gastric glands

Gastric pits
Surface epithelium (mucous cells)
Gastric pit
Mucous neck cells
Parietal cell
Gastric gland
Chief cell
Enteroendocrine cell

(c) Location of the HCl-producing parietal cells and pepsin-secreting chief cells in a gastric gland

Pepsinogen → Pepsin
HCl
Mitochondria
Parietal cell
Chief cell
Enteroendocrine cell

by the vagus nerve. The arterial supply of the stomach is provided by branches (gastric and splenic) of the celiac trunk (see Figure 19.24). The corresponding veins are part of the hepatic portal system and ultimately drain into the hepatic portal vein (see Figure 19.29c).

Microscopic Anatomy

The stomach wall contains the four tunics typical of most of the alimentary canal, but its muscularis and mucosa are modified for the special roles of the stomach. Besides the usual circular and longitudinal layers of smooth muscle, the muscularis externa has an innermost layer of smooth muscle fibers that runs *obliquely* (Figure 23.14a and **Figure 23.15a**). This arrangement allows the stomach not only to mix, churn, and move food along the tract (the job of the circular and longitudinal muscle layers), but also to pummel the food, physically breaking it down into smaller fragments, and to ram the food into the small intestine. (The oblique fibers accomplish the ramming by jackknifing the stomach into a V shape, which provides a propulsive action at the stomach terminus.)

The lining epithelium of the stomach mucosa is a simple columnar epithelium composed entirely of mucous cells. They produce a cloudy, protective two-layer coat of alkaline mucus in which the surface layer consists of viscous, insoluble mucus that traps a layer of bicarbonate-rich fluid beneath it. This otherwise smooth lining is dotted with millions of deep **gastric pits**, which lead into the tubular **gastric glands** that produce the stomach secretion called **gastric juice** (Figure 23.15).

The cells forming the walls of the gastric pits are primarily mucous cells, but those composing the gastric glands vary in different stomach regions. For example, the cells in the glands of the cardia and pylorus are primarily mucus secreting, whereas cells of the pyloric antrum produce mucus and several hormones including most of the stimulatory hormone called gastrin. Glands of the stomach fundus and body, where most chemical digestion occurs, are substantially larger and produce the majority of the stomach secretions. The glands in these regions contain a variety of secretory cells, including these four types:

1. **Mucous neck cells**, found in the upper, or "neck," regions of the glands, produce a thin, soluble mucus quite different from that secreted by the mucous cells of the surface epithelium (Figure 23.15b). It is not yet understood what special function this *acidic* mucus performs.

2. **Parietal cells**, found mainly in the middle region of the glands scattered among the chief cells (described next), simultaneously secrete *hydrochloric acid* (*HCl*) and *intrinsic factor* (Figure 23.15b, c). Although the parietal cells appear spherical when viewed with a light microscope, they actually have three prongs that bear dense microvilli (they look like fuzzy pitchforks!). This structure provides a huge surface area for secreting H^+ and Cl^- into the stomach lumen. HCl makes the stomach contents extremely acidic (pH 1.5–3.5), a condition necessary for activation and optimal activity of pepsin. The acidity also helps in food digestion by denaturing proteins and breaking down cell walls of plant foods, and is harsh enough to kill many of the bacteria ingested with foods. Intrinsic factor is a glycoprotein required for vitamin B_{12} absorption in the small intestine.

3. **Chief cells** occur mainly in the basal regions of the gastric glands. The chief cells produce *pepsinogen* (pep-sin′o-jen), the inactive form of the protein-digesting enzyme **pepsin**. When these cells are stimulated, the first pepsinogen molecules they release are activated by HCl encountered in the apical region of the gland (Figure 23.15c). But once pepsin is present, it also catalyzes the conversion of pepsinogen to pepsin. The activation process involves removal of a small peptide fragment from the pepsinogen molecule, causing it to change shape and expose its active site. This positive feedback process is limited only by the amount of pepsinogen present. Chief cells also secrete insignificant amounts of lipases (fat-digesting enzymes).

4. **Enteroendocrine cells** (en″ter-o-en′do-krin; "gut endocrine"), typically located deep in the gastric glands (Figure 23.15b, c), release a variety of chemical messengers directly into the interstitial fluid of the lamina propria. Some of these, for example **histamine** and **serotonin**, act locally as paracrines. Others, such as **somatostatin**, act both locally and as hormones, diffusing into the blood capillaries to influence several digestive system target organs (**Table 23.1**, p. 875). **Gastrin**, a hormone, plays essential roles in regulating stomach secretion and motility, as we will describe shortly.

The stomach mucosa is exposed to some of the harshest conditions in the entire digestive tract. Gastric juice is corrosively acidic (the H^+ concentration in the stomach can be 100,000 times that found in blood), and its protein-digesting enzymes can digest the stomach itself.

However, the stomach is not a passive victim of its formidable environment. It mounts an aggressive counterattack to protect itself, producing what is called the **mucosal barrier**. Three factors create this barrier:

1. *A thick coating of bicarbonate-rich mucus* is built up on the stomach wall.
2. *The epithelial cells of the mucosa are joined together by tight junctions* that prevent gastric juice from leaking into the underlying tissue layers.
3. *Damaged epithelial mucosal cells are shed and quickly replaced* by division of *undifferentiated stem cells* that reside where the gastric pits join the gastric glands. The stomach surface epithelium of mucous cells is completely renewed every three to six days, because these cells can survive only a few days in the stomach's harsh environment. (However, the more sheltered glandular cells deep within the gastric glands have a much longer life span.)

◣ HOMEOSTATIC IMBALANCE

Anything that breaches the gel-like mucosal barrier causes inflammation of the stomach wall, a condition called *gastritis*. Persistent damage to the underlying tissues can promote **peptic ulcers**, specifically called **gastric ulcers** when they are erosions of the stomach wall (**Figure 23.16a**). The most distressing symptom of gastric ulcers is gnawing epigastric pain that seems to bore through to your back. The pain typically occurs 1–3 hours after eating and is often relieved by eating again. The danger posed by ulcers is perforation of the stomach wall followed by peritonitis and, perhaps, massive hemorrhage.

For years, the blame for causing ulcers was put on factors that favor high HCl production or low mucus secretion such as aspirin and nonsteroidal anti-inflammatory drugs (NSAIDs such as ibuprofen), smoking, spicy food, alcohol, coffee, and stress. Although acid conditions *are* necessary for ulcer formation, acidity in and of itself is not sufficient to cause ulcer formation. Most recurrent ulcers (90%) are the work of a certain strain of acid-resistant, corkscrew-shaped *Helicobacter pylori* bacteria (Figure 23.16b), which burrow much like a drill bit through the mucus and destroy the protective mucosal layer, leaving denuded areas.

These pathological effects occur in 10–20% of infected individuals. The antimicrobial activity of gastric mucin appears to play a major role in protecting the remaining 80–90% from *H. pylori*'s invasive attacks. The bacterial causal theory has been difficult to prove because the bacterium is also found in more than 50% of healthy people. Even more troubling are studies that link this bacterium to some stomach cancers.

These bacteria release several chemicals that help them do their "dirty work," including (1) some that curb HCl production and release ammonia (which then acts as a base to neutralize some of the stomach acid in their locale), (2) a *cytotoxin* that damages the stomach epithelium, (3) proteins that disrupt adhesion molecules and so cause the epithelial cells to detach from each other, and (4) proteins that act as chemotactic agents to attract macrophages and other defensive cells into the area, thus promoting a chronic inflammatory response.

The presence or absence of *H. pylori* is easily detected by a breath test. In ulcers colonized by it, the goal is to kill the embedded bacteria. A simple two-week-long course of antibiotics promotes healing and prevents recurrence. For active ulcers, a blocker for H_2- (histamine) receptors may also help because it inhibits HCl secretion by blocking histamine's effects. The relatively few peptic ulcers not caused by *H. pylori* generally result from the long-term use of NSAIDs. In such noninfectious cases, H_2-receptor blocker drugs such as cimetidine (Tagamet) and ranitidine (Zantac) are the therapy of choice. ■

CHECK YOUR UNDERSTANDING

24. What structural modification of the stomach wall underlies the stomach's ability to mechanically digest food?

25. Two substances secreted by cells of the gastric glands are needed to produce the active protein-digesting enzyme pepsin. What are these substances and what cells secrete them?

26. What protective substances or activities make up the so-called mucosal barrier?

For answers, see Appendix G.

Digestive Processes Occurring in the Stomach

▶ Explain how gastric secretion and stomach motility are regulated.

▶ Define and account for the alkaline tide.

Except for ingestion and defecation, the stomach is involved in the whole "menu" of digestive activities. Besides serving as a holding area for ingested food, the stomach continues the demolition job begun in the oral cavity by further degrading food both physically and chemically. It then delivers chyme, the product of its activity, into the small intestine.

Protein digestion begins in the stomach and is the only significant type of enzymatic digestion that occurs there. Dietary proteins are denatured by HCl produced by stomach glands in preparation for enzymatic digestion. (The unfolded amino acid chain is more accessible to the enzymes.) The most important protein-digesting enzyme produced by the gastric mucosa is

(a) A gastric ulcer lesion

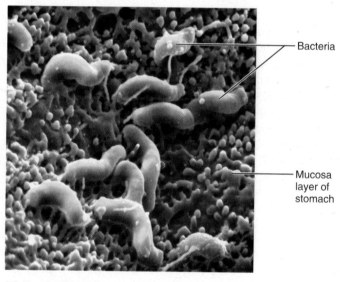

Bacteria

Mucosa layer of stomach

(b) *H. pylori* **bacteria**

Figure 23.16 Photographs of a gastric ulcer lesion and of the bacteria that most commonly cause it.

pepsin. In infants, however, the stomach glands also secrete **rennin**, an enzyme that acts on milk protein (casein), converting it to a curdy substance that looks like soured milk. Additionally, lingual lipase released by the intrinsic salivary glands may digest some triglycerides in the stomach.

Two common lipid-soluble substances—alcohol and aspirin—pass easily through the stomach mucosa into the blood. Alcohol and aspirin may cause gastric bleeding, so these substances should be avoided by people with gastric ulcers.

Despite the obvious benefits of preparing food to enter the intestine, the only stomach function essential to life is secretion of intrinsic factor. **Intrinsic factor** is required for intestinal absorption of vitamin B_{12}, needed to produce mature erythrocytes. In its absence, *pernicious anemia* results. However, if

Stimulatory events   **Inhibitory events**

Cephalic phase

① Sight and thought of food → Cerebral cortex
Conditioned reflex
② Stimulation of taste and smell receptors → Hypothalamus and medulla oblongata → Vagus nerve

Lack of stimulatory impulses to parasympathetic center ← Cerebral cortex ← ① Loss of appetite, depression

Gastric phase

① Stomach distension activates stretch receptors → Vagovagal reflexes → Medulla → Vagus nerve
Local reflexes
② Food chemicals (especially peptides and caffeine) and rising pH activate chemoreceptors → G cells → Gastrin release to blood

Gastrin secretion declines ← G cells ← ① Excessive acidity (pH < 2) in stomach

Overrides parasympathetic controls ← Sympathetic nervous system activation ← ② Emotional upset

Stomach secretory activity

Intestinal phase

① Presence of low pH, partially digested foods, fats, or hypertonic solution in duodenum when stomach begins to empty → Intestinal (enteric) gastrin release to blood → Brief effect

Enterogastric reflex ← Local reflexes
Vagal nuclei in medulla
Pyloric sphincter
← ① Distension of duodenum; presence of fatty, acidic, hypertonic chyme, and/or irritants in the duodenum

Release of intestinal hormones (secretin, cholecystokinin, vasoactive intestinal peptide) ← ② Distension; presence of fatty, acidic, partially digested food in the duodenum

← Stimulate
←-- Inhibit

Figure 23.17 Neural and hormonal mechanisms that regulate release of gastric juice. Stimulatory factors are shown on the left; inhibitory factors are shown on the right.

vitamin B_{12} is administered by injection, individuals can survive with minimal digestive problems even after total gastrectomy (stomach removal). (The stomach's activities are summarized in **Table 23.2**, p. 888).

Since we describe chemical digestion and absorption later, here we will focus on events that (1) control secretory activity of the gastric glands and (2) regulate stomach motility and emptying.

Regulation of Gastric Secretion

Both neural and hormonal mechanisms control gastric secretion. Under normal conditions the gastric mucosa pours out as much as 3 L of gastric juice—an acid brew so potent it can dissolve nails—every day. Nervous control is provided both by long (vagus nerve–mediated) and short (local enteric) nerve reflexes. When the vagus nerves stimulate the stomach, secretory

activity of virtually all of its glands increases. (By contrast, activation of sympathetic nerves depresses secretory activity.) Hormonal control of gastric secretion is largely the province of gastrin, which stimulates secretion of enzymes and HCl, and of hormones produced by the small intestine, which are mostly gastrin antagonists.

Stimuli acting at three distinct sites—the head, stomach, and small intestine—provoke or inhibit gastric secretory activity. Accordingly, the three phases of gastric secretion are called the *cephalic, gastric,* and *intestinal phases* (Figure 23.17). The effector site is the stomach in all cases and, once initiated, one or all three phases may be occurring at the same time.

Phase 1: Cephalic (Reflex) The **cephalic**, or **reflex**, **phase** of gastric secretion occurs *before* food enters the stomach (Figure 23.17). Only a few minutes long, this phase is triggered by the aroma, taste, sight, or thought of food, and it gets the stomach ready for its upcoming digestive chore. Inputs from activated olfactory receptors and taste buds are relayed to the hypothalamus. The hypothalamus, in turn, stimulates the vagal nuclei of the medulla oblongata, causing motor impulses to be transmitted via the vagus nerves to parasympathetic enteric ganglia. Enteric ganglionic neurons then stimulate the stomach glands.

The enhanced secretory activity that results when we see or think of food is a *conditioned reflex* and occurs only when we like or want the food. If we are depressed or have no appetite, this part of the cephalic reflex is suppressed.

Phase 2: Gastric Once food reaches the stomach, local neural and hormonal mechanisms initiate the **gastric phase** (Figure 23.17). This phase lasts three to four hours and provides about two-thirds of the gastric juice released. The most important stimuli are distension, peptides, and low acidity. Stomach distension activates stretch receptors and initiates both local (myenteric) reflexes and the long vagovagal reflexes. In the long type of reflex, impulses travel to the medulla and then back to the stomach via vagal fibers. Both types of reflexes lead to acetylcholine (ACh) release, which in turn stimulates the output of more gastric juice.

Though neural influences initiated by stomach distension are important, the hormone gastrin probably plays a greater role in stimulating stomach gland secretion during the gastric phase. Chemical stimuli provided by partially digested proteins, caffeine, and rising pH directly activate gastrin-secreting enteroendocrine cells called **G cells** in the stomach antrum. Gastrin stimulates the release of enzymes, but its main target is the HCl-secreting parietal cells, which it prods to spew out even more HCl. Highly acidic (pH below 2) gastric contents *inhibit* gastrin secretion.

When protein foods are in the stomach, the pH of the gastric contents generally rises because proteins act as buffers to tie up H^+. The rise in pH stimulates gastrin secretion and subsequently HCl release, which in turn provides the acidic conditions needed for protein digestion. The more protein in the meal, the greater the amount of gastrin and HCl released. As proteins are digested, the gastric contents gradually become more acidic, which again inhibits the gastrin-secreting cells. This negative feedback mechanism helps maintain optimal pH and working conditions for the gastric enzymes.

G cells are also activated by the neural reflexes already described. Emotional upset, fear, anxiety, or anything that triggers the fight-or-flight response inhibits gastric secretion because during such times the sympathetic division overrides parasympathetic controls of digestion (Figure 23.17).

The control of the HCl-secreting parietal cells is multifaceted. HCl secretion is stimulated by three chemicals, all of which work through second-messenger systems. Both *ACh* released by parasympathetic nerve fibers and *gastrin* secreted by G cells bring about their effects by increasing intracellular Ca^{2+} levels. *Histamine*, released by the so-called *enterochromaffin-like* (ECL) cells in response to gastrin (and to a lesser extent in response to ACh) acts through cyclic AMP (cAMP). When only one of the three chemicals binds to the parietal cells, HCl secretion is

scanty, but when all three bind, HCl pours forth as if shot out by a high-pressure hose. [As we noted earlier, antihistamines, such as cimetidine, which bind to and block the H_2 (histamine) receptors of parietal cells, are used to treat gastric ulcers due to hyperacidity.]

The process of HCl formation within the parietal cells is complicated, but it appears to go something like this (Figure 23.18): When parietal cells are appropriately stimulated, H^+ is actively pumped into the stomach lumen against a tremendous concentration gradient by H^+-K^+ ATPases in exchange for K^+ ions that move into the cell. K^+ then cycles back into the lumen via K^+ channels. Chloride ions (Cl^-) follow H^+ into the lumen to maintain an electrical balance in the stomach, completing the process of HCl secretion. The Cl^- is obtained from blood plasma, while H^+ comes from the breakdown of carbonic acid (formed by the combination of carbon dioxide and water) within the parietal cell:

$$CO_2 + H_2O \rightarrow H_2CO_3 \rightarrow H^+ + HCO_3^-$$

As H^+ is pumped from the cell and HCO_3^- (bicarbonate ion) accumulates within the cell, HCO_3^- is ejected through the basal cell membrane into the capillary blood. As a result, blood draining from the stomach is more alkaline than the blood serving it. This phenomenon is called the **alkaline tide**. Notice that HCO_3^- and Cl^- are moved in opposite directions by a HCO_3^--Cl^- antiporter in the basolateral membrane, and this is the means of entry of the Cl^- that moves into the lumen as the chloride part of the HCl product. K^+ and Cl^- move into the stomach lumen by diffusing through membrane channels.

Phase 3: Intestinal The **intestinal phase** of gastric secretion has two components—one excitatory and the other inhibitory (see Figure 23.17). The *excitatory* aspect is set into motion as partially digested food fills the initial part (duodenum) of the small intestine. This stimulates intestinal mucosal cells to release **intestinal (enteric) gastrin**, a hormone that encourages the gastric glands to continue their secretory activity. This stimulatory effect is brief because as the intestine distends with chyme containing large amounts of H^+, fats, partially digested proteins, and various irritating substances, the *inhibitory* component is triggered in the form of the **enterogastric reflex**.

The enterogastric reflex is actually a trio of reflexes that (1) inhibit the vagal nuclei in the medulla, (2) inhibit local reflexes, and (3) activate sympathetic fibers that cause the pyloric sphincter to tighten and prevent further food entry into the small intestine. As a result, gastric secretory activity declines. These "brakes" on gastric activity protect the small intestine from excessive acidity and match the small intestine's processing abilities to the amount of chyme entering it at a given time.

In addition, the factors we just named trigger the release of several intestinal hormones, collectively called **enterogastrones**. They include **secretin** (se-kre′tin), **cholecystokinin (CCK)** (ko″le-sis″to-ki′nin), and **vasoactive intestinal peptide (VIP)**. All of these hormones inhibit gastric secretion when the stomach is very active and also play other roles, which are summarized in Table 23.1.

Figure 23.18 Mechanism of HCl secretion by parietal cells. H^+ and HCO_3^- (bicarbonate ions) are generated from the dissociation of carbonic acid (H_2CO_3) within the parietal cell. As H^+-K^+ ATPase pumps H^+ into the lumen, K^+ enters the cell. Meanwhile, the HCO_3^--Cl^- antiporter transports HCO_3^- into the interstitial space in exchange for chloride ions (Cl^-), establishing the alkaline tide. Cl^- and K^+ then diffuse into the lumen through membrane channels.

Gastric Motility and Emptying

Stomach contractions not only accommodate its filling and cause its emptying, but they also compress, knead, and continually mix the food with gastric juice to produce chyme. The processes of mechanical digestion and propulsion are inseparable in the stomach because the mixing movements are accomplished by a unique type of peristalsis. For example, in the pylorus, peristalsis is bidirectional rather than unidirectional.

Response of the Stomach to Filling The stomach stretches to accommodate incoming food, but internal stomach pressure remains constant until about 1.5 L of food has been ingested. Thereafter, the pressure rises. The relatively unchanging pressure in a filling stomach is due to (1) the reflex-mediated receptive relaxation of the stomach muscle and (2) the plasticity of visceral smooth muscle.

Receptive relaxation of smooth muscle in the stomach fundus and body occurs both in anticipation of and in response to

food movement through the esophagus and into the stomach. This process is coordinated by the swallowing center of the brain stem and mediated by the vagus nerves acting on serotonin and NO-releasing enteric neurons.

Gastric accommodation, an example of smooth muscle *plasticity,* is the intrinsic ability of visceral smooth muscle to exhibit the *stress-relaxation response,* in other words, to be stretched without greatly increasing its tension and contracting expulsively. As we described in Chapter 9, this capability is very important in hollow organs, like the stomach, that must serve as temporary reservoirs.

Gastric Contractile Activity As in the esophagus, the stomach exhibits peristalsis. After a meal, peristalsis begins near the gastroesophageal sphincter, where it produces gentle rippling movements of the thin stomach wall. But as the contractions approach the pylorus, where the stomach musculature is thicker, they become much more powerful. Consequently, the

TABLE 23.1	Hormones and Paracrines That Act in Digestion*			
HORMONE	**SITE OF PRODUCTION**	**STIMULUS FOR PRODUCTION**	**TARGET ORGAN**	**ACTIVITY**
Cholecystokinin (CCK)	Duodenal mucosa	Fatty chyme, in particular, but also partially digested proteins	Liver/pancreas	▪ Potentiates secretin's actions on these organs
			Pancreas	▪ Increases output of enzyme-rich pancreatic juice
			Gallbladder	▪ Stimulates organ to contract and expel stored bile
			Hepatopancreatic sphincter	▪ Relaxes sphincter to allow entry of bile and pancreatic juice into duodenum
Gastric inhibitory peptide (GIP) (or glucose-dependent insulinotropic peptide)	Duodenal mucosa	Glucose, fatty acids, and amino acids in small intestine	Stomach	▪ Inhibits HCl production (minor effect)
			Pancreas (beta cells)	▪ Stimulates insulin release
Gastrin	Stomach mucosa (G cells)	Food (particularly partially digested proteins) in stomach (chemical stimulation); acetylcholine released by nerve fibers	Stomach (parietal cells)	▪ Increases HCl secretion
				▪ Stimulates gastric emptying (minor effect)
			Small intestine	▪ Stimulates contraction of intestinal muscle
			Ileocecal valve	▪ Relaxes ileocecal valve
			Large intestine	▪ Stimulates mass movements
Histamine	Stomach mucosa	Food in stomach	Stomach	▪ Activates parietal cells to release HCl
Intestinal gastrin	Duodenal mucosa	Acidic and partially digested foods in duodenum	Stomach	▪ Stimulates gastric glands and motility
Motilin	Duodenal mucosa	Fasting; periodic release every 1½–2 hours by neural stimuli	Proximal duodenum	▪ Stimulates migrating motility complex
Secretin	Duodenal mucosa	Acidic chyme (also partially digested proteins, fats, hypertonic or hypotonic fluids, or irritants in chyme)	Stomach	▪ Inhibits gastric gland secretion and gastric motility during gastric phase of secretion
			Pancreas	▪ Increases output of pancreatic juice rich in bicarbonate ions; potentiates CCK's action
			Liver	▪ Increases bile output
Serotonin	Stomach mucosa	Food in stomach	Stomach	▪ Causes contraction of stomach muscle
Somatostatin	Stomach mucosa; duodenal mucosa	Food in stomach; stimulation by sympathetic nerve fibers	Stomach	▪ Inhibits gastric secretion of all products
			Pancreas	▪ Inhibits secretion
			Small intestine	▪ Inhibits GI blood flow; thus inhibits intestinal absorption
			Gallbladder and liver	▪ Inhibits contraction and bile release
Vasoactive intestinal peptide (VIP)	Enteric neurons	Chyme containing partially digested foods	Small intestine	▪ Stimulates buffer secretion; dilates intestinal capillaries
				▪ Relaxes intestinal smooth muscle
			Pancreas	▪ Increases secretion
			Stomach	▪ Inhibits acid secretion

* Except for somatostatin, all of these polypeptides also stimulate the growth (particularly of the mucosa) of the organs they affect.

contents of the fundus and body (food storage area) remain relatively undisturbed, while foodstuffs in and around the pyloric antrum receive a truly lively pummeling and mixing.

The pyloric region of the stomach, which holds about 30 ml of chyme, acts as a "dynamic filter" that allows only liquids and small particles to pass through the barely open pyloric valve during the digestive period. Normally, each peristaltic wave reaching the pyloric muscle "spits" or squirts 3 ml or less of chyme into the small intestine. Because the contraction also *closes* the valve, which is normally partially relaxed, the rest (about 27 ml) is

① **Propulsion:** Peristaltic waves move from the fundus toward the pylorus.

② **Grinding:** The most vigorous peristalsis and mixing action occur close to the pylorus.

③ **Retropulsion:** The pyloric end of the stomach acts as a pump that delivers small amounts of chyme into the duodenum, simultaneously forcing most of its contained material backward into the stomach.

Figure 23.19 Peristaltic waves in the stomach.

propelled backward into the stomach, where it is mixed further **(Figure 23.19).** This back-and-forth pumping action (retropulsion) effectively breaks up solids in the gastric contents.

Although the intensity of the stomach's peristaltic waves can be modified, their rate is constant—always around three per minute. This contractile rhythm is set by the spontaneous activity of *pacemaker cells* located in the longitudinal smooth muscle layer. The pacemaker cells, muscle-like noncontractile cells called *interstitial cells of Cajal* (ka-hal′), depolarize and repolarize spontaneously three times each minute, establishing the so-called *cyclic slow waves* of the stomach, or its **basic electrical rhythm (BER).** Since the pacemakers are electrically coupled to the rest of the smooth muscle sheet by gap junctions, their "beat" is transmitted efficiently and quickly to the entire muscularis.

The pacemakers set the maximum rate of contraction, but they do not initiate the contractions or regulate their force. Instead, they generate subthreshold depolarization waves, which are then "ignited" (enhanced by further depolarization and brought to threshold) by neural and hormonal factors.

Factors that increase the strength of stomach contractions are the same factors that enhance gastric secretory activity. Distension of the stomach wall by food activates stretch receptors and gastrin-secreting cells, both of which ultimately stimulate gastric smooth muscle and so increase gastric motility. For this reason, the more food there is in the stomach, the more vigorous the stomach mixing and emptying movements will be—within certain limits—as we describe next.

Regulation of Gastric Emptying The stomach usually empties completely within four hours after a meal. However, the larger the meal (the greater the stomach distension) and the more liquid its contents, the faster the stomach empties. Fluids pass quickly through the stomach. Solids linger, remaining until they are well mixed with gastric juice and converted to the liquid state.

The rate of gastric emptying depends as much—and perhaps more—on the contents of the duodenum as on what is happening in the stomach. The stomach and duodenum act in tandem like a "coupled meter" that functions at less than full capacity. As chyme enters the duodenum, receptors in its wall respond to chemical signals and to stretch, initiating the enterogastric reflex and the hormonal (enterogastrone) mechanisms that inhibit acid and pepsin secretion as we described earlier. These mechanisms inhibit gastric secretory activity and prevent further duodenal filling by reducing the force of pyloric contractions **(Figure 23.20).**

A carbohydrate-rich meal moves through the duodenum rapidly, but fats form an oily layer at the top of the chyme and are digested more slowly by enzymes acting in the small intestine. For this reason, when chyme entering the duodenum is fatty, food may remain in the stomach six hours or more.

HOMEOSTATIC IMBALANCE

Vomiting, or **emesis,** is an unpleasant experience that causes stomach emptying by a different route. Many factors signal the stomach to "launch lunch," but the most common are extreme stretching of the stomach or small intestine or the presence of irritants such as bacterial toxins, excessive alcohol, spicy foods, and certain drugs in those organs. Both bloodborne molecules and sensory impulses streaming from the irritated sites to the **emetic center** (e-met′ik) of the medulla initiate a number of motor responses. The diaphragm and abdominal wall muscles contract, increasing intra-abdominal pressure, the gastroesophageal sphincter relaxes, and the soft palate rises to close off the nasal passages. As a result, the stomach (and perhaps duodenal) contents are forced upward through the esophagus and pharynx and out the mouth.

Before vomiting, an individual typically is pale, feels nauseated, and salivates. Excessive vomiting can cause dehydration and may lead to severe disturbances in the electrolyte and acid-base balance of the body. Since large amounts of HCl are lost in vomitus, the blood becomes alkaline as the stomach attempts to replace its lost acid. ■

Figure 23.20 Neural and hormonal factors inhibiting gastric emptying. These controls ensure that the food will be well liquefied in the stomach and prevent the small intestine from being overwhelmed.

Initial stimulus

Physiological response

Result

→ Stimulate

⇠--- Inhibit

CHECK YOUR UNDERSTANDING

27. Name the three phases of gastric secretion.
28. How does the presence of food in the small intestine inhibit gastric secretion and motility?
29. How does the pH of venous blood leaving the stomach change during a meal?

For answers, see Appendix G.

The Small Intestine and Associated Structures

▶ Identify and describe structural modifications of the wall of the small intestine that enhance the digestive process.

▶ Differentiate between the roles of the various cell types of the intestinal mucosa.

▶ Describe the function of intestinal hormones and paracrines.

In the small intestine, usable food is finally prepared for its journey into the cells of the body. However, this vital function cannot be accomplished without the aid of secretions from the liver (bile) and pancreas (digestive enzymes). We will also consider these accessory organs in this section.

The Small Intestine

The **small intestine** is the body's major digestive organ. Within its twisted passageways, digestion is completed and virtually all absorption occurs.

Gross Anatomy

The small intestine is a convoluted tube extending from the pyloric sphincter in the epigastric region to the **ileocecal valve (sphincter)** (il″e-o-se′kal) in the right iliac region where it joins the large intestine. It is the longest part of the alimentary canal, but is only about half the diameter of the large intestine, ranging from 2.5 to 4 cm (1–1.6 inches). Although it is 6–7 m long (approximately 20 ft, or as tall as a two-story building) in a cadaver, the small intestine is only about 2–4 m (7–13 ft) long during life because of muscle tone.

The small intestine has three subdivisions: the duodenum, which is mostly retroperitoneal, and the jejunum and ileum, both intraperitoneal organs (see Figure 23.1). The relatively immovable **duodenum** (du″o-de′num; "twelve finger widths long"), which curves around the head of the pancreas, is about 25 cm (10 inches) long **(Figure 23.21)**. Although it is the shortest intestinal subdivision, the duodenum has the most features of interest.

The bile duct, delivering bile from the liver, and the main pancreatic duct, carrying pancreatic juice from the pancreas, unite at the wall of the duodenum in a bulblike point called the **hepatopancreatic ampulla** (hep″ah-to-pan″kre-at′ik am-pul′ah; *ampulla* = flask). The ampulla opens into the duodenum via the volcano-shaped **major duodenal papilla**. The entry of bile and pancreatic juice is controlled by a smooth muscle valve called the **hepatopancreatic sphincter**.

The **jejunum** (jĕ-joo′num; "empty"), about 2.5 m (8 ft) long, extends from the duodenum to the ileum. The **ileum** (il′e-um; "twisted"), approximately 3.6 m (12 ft) in length, joins the large intestine at the ileocecal valve. The jejunum and ileum hang in sausagelike coils in the central and lower part of the abdominal cavity, suspended from the posterior abdominal wall by the fan-shaped *mesentery* (see Figure 23.30). These more distal parts of the small intestine are encircled and framed by the large intestine.

Nerve fibers serving the small intestine include parasympathetics from the vagus and sympathetics from the thoracic splanchnic nerves, both relayed through the superior mesenteric (and celiac) plexus.

The arterial supply is primarily from the superior mesenteric artery (pp. 732–733). The veins parallel the arteries and typically drain into the superior mesenteric vein. From there, the

23

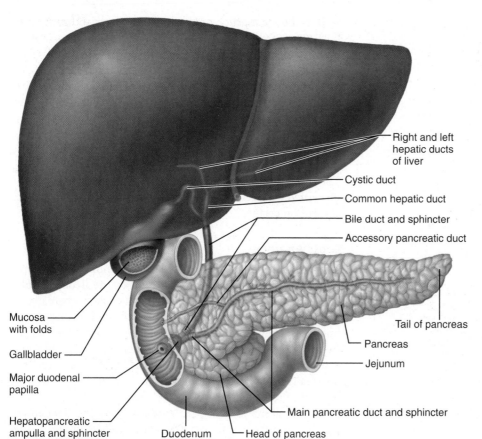

Right and left hepatic ducts of liver

Cystic duct

Common hepatic duct

Bile duct and sphincter

Accessory pancreatic duct

Tail of pancreas

Pancreas

Jejunum

Main pancreatic duct and sphincter

Head of pancreas

Duodenum

Hepatopancreatic ampulla and sphincter

Major duodenal papilla

Gallbladder

Mucosa with folds

nutrient-rich venous blood from the small intestine drains into the hepatic portal vein, which carries it to the liver.

Microscopic Anatomy

Modifications for Absorption The small intestine is highly adapted for nutrient absorption. Its length alone provides a huge surface area, and its wall has three structural modifications—circular folds, villi, and microvilli—that amplify its absorptive surface enormously (by a factor of more than 600 times). One estimate is that the intestinal surface area is about equal to 200 square meters or the surface area of a doubles tennis court. Most absorption occurs in the proximal part of the small intestine, so these specializations decrease in number toward its distal end.

The **circular folds**, or **plicae circulares** (pli′ke ser″ku-lar′ēs), are deep, permanent folds of the mucosa and submucosa (**Figure 23.22a**). Nearly 1 cm tall, these folds force chyme to spiral through the lumen, slowing its movement and allowing time for full nutrient absorption.

Villi (vil′i; "tufts of hair") are fingerlike projections of the mucosa, over 1 mm high, that give it a velvety texture, much like the soft nap of a towel (Figures 23.22 and **Figure 23.23a**). The epithelial cells of the villi (called *enterocytes*) are chiefly absorptive columnar cells. In the core of each villus is a dense capillary bed and a wide lymph capillary called a **lacteal** (lak′te-al). Digested foodstuffs are absorbed through the epithelial cells into both the capillary blood and the lacteal.

The villi are large and leaflike in the duodenum (the intestinal site of most active absorption) and gradually narrow and shorten along the length of the small intestine. A "slip" of smooth muscle in the villus core allows it to alternately shorten and lengthen. These pulsations (1) increase the contact between the villus and the contents of the intestinal lumen, making absorption more efficient, and (2) "milk" lymph along through the lacteals.

The exceptionally long, densely packed **microvilli** of the absorptive cells of the mucosa give the mucosal surface a fuzzy appearance called the **brush border** (Figure 23.22b enlargment and Figure 23.23b). The plasma membranes of the microvilli bear enzymes referred to as **brush border enzymes**, which complete the digestion of carbohydrates and proteins in the small intestine.

Histology of the Wall Externally the subdivisions of the small intestine appear to be nearly identical, but their internal and microscopic anatomies reveal some important differences. The four tunics typical of the GI tract are also seen here, but the mucosa and submucosa are modified to reflect the intestine's functions in the digestive pathway.

The epithelium of the villus mucosa is largely simple columnar *absorptive cells* bound by tight junctions and richly endowed with microvilli. These cells bear the primary responsibility for nutrient and electrolyte absorption. The epithelium also has many mucus-secreting *goblet cells*. Between the villi, the mucosa is studded with *pits* that lead into tubular glands called

23

Vein carrying
blood to
hepatic portal
vessel

Muscle
layers

Lumen

Circular
folds

Villi

(a)

Microvilli
(brush border)

Absorptive
cells

Lacteal

Goblet
cell

Vilus

Blood
capillaries

Mucosa
associated
lymphoid
tissue

Intestinal
crypt

Enteroendocrine
cells

Muscularis
mucosae

Venule

Lymphatic vessel

Duodenal
gland

Submucosa

(b)

Absorptive cells

Goblet
cells

Villi

(c) Intestinal crypt

Figure 23.22 Structural modifications of the small intestine that increase its surface area for digestion and absorption. **(a)** Enlargement of a few circular folds, showing associated fingerlike villi (muscularis and serosa layers not indicated). **(b)** Structure of a villus. Enlargment shows one and part of two other absorptive cells that exhibit microvilli on their free (luminal) surface. **(c)** Photomicrograph of the mucosa, showing villi (250×). (See *A Brief Atlas of the Human Body*, Figure 69b.)

intestinal crypts, or **crypts of Lieberkühn** (le′ber-kun) (see Figure 23.22b, c). Crypt epithelial cells are primarily secretory cells that secrete *intestinal juice,* a watery mixture containing mucus that serves as a carrier fluid for absorbing nutrients from chyme. Scattered through the crypt epithelium are *enteroendocrine cells,* the source of the enterogastrones—secretin and cholecystokinin to name two—and T cells called *intraepithelial lymphocytes (IELs),* which represent an important immunological component. Unlike other T cells, IELs do *not* need "priming." Upon encountering antigens, they immediately release cytokines that cause killing of infected target cells.

Deep in the crypts are specialized secretory cells called *Paneth cells,* which fortify the small intestine's defenses by releasing antimicrobial agents such as defensins and *lysozyme,* an antibacterial enzyme. These secretions destroy certain bacteria and help to determine which bacteria may colonize the intestinal lumen. The crypts decrease in number along the length of the small intestine, but the goblet cells become more abundant.

The various epithelial cells arise from continuously dividing stem cells at the base of the crypts. As the daughter cells gradually migrate up the villi, they differentiate, becoming specialized cell

(a)

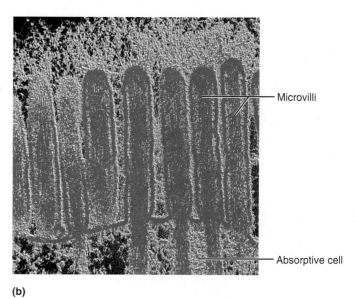

(b)

Figure 23.23 Villi and microvilli of the small intestine. False-color electron micrographs. **(a)** Villi (125×). Dead desquamating cells seen on the ridges of the villi are colored yellow and orange. **(b)** Microvilli (28,000×) of absorptive cells appear as red projections from the surface of the absorptive cell. Yellow granules are mucus granules.

types—absorptive cells, goblet cells, and enteroendocrine cells. The fourth differentiated cell type is the Paneth cells, which remain at the base of the crypts. The other three types undergo apoptosis and are shed from the villus tips, renewing the villus epithelium every two to four days.

The rapid replacement of intestinal (and gastric) epithelial cells has clinical as well as physiological significance. Treatments for cancer, such as radiation therapy and chemotherapy, preferentially target rapidly dividing cells. This kills cancer cells, but it also nearly obliterates the GI tract epithelium, causing nausea, vomiting, and diarrhea after each treatment.

The submucosa is typical areolar connective tissue. It contains both individual and *aggregated lymphoid follicles*, the latter called **Peyer's patches** (pi′erz). Peyer's patches increase in abundance toward the end of the small intestine. Their increasing abundance reflects the fact that this region of the small intestine contains huge numbers of bacteria that must be prevented from entering the bloodstream. The lymphoid tissue of the submucosa also contains proliferating lymphocytes that leave the intestine, enter the blood, and then home in on the intestinal lamina propria. There, in their new home, they release immunoglobin A (IgA), which helps provide protection against intestinal pathogens (see p. 784).

Elaborate mucus-secreting **duodenal glands** (also called *Brunner's glands*) are found in the submucosa of the duodenum only. These glands produce an alkaline (bicarbonate-rich) mucus that helps neutralize the acidic chyme moving in from the stomach. When this protective mucus barrier is inadequate, the intestinal wall erodes and *duodenal ulcers* result.

The muscularis is typical and bilayered. Except for the bulk of the duodenum, which is retroperitoneal and has an adventitia, the external intestinal surface is covered by visceral peritoneum (serosa).

Intestinal Juice: Composition and Control

The intestinal crypts normally secrete 1 to 2 L of **intestinal juice** daily. The major stimulus for its production is distension or irritation of the intestinal mucosa by hypertonic or acidic chyme. Normally, intestinal juice is slightly alkaline (7.4–7.8), and isotonic with blood plasma. Intestinal juice is largely water but it also contains some mucus, which is secreted both by the duodenal glands and by goblet cells of the mucosa. Intestinal juice is enzyme-poor because intestinal enzymes are limited to the bound enzymes of the brush border.

CHECK YOUR UNDERSTANDING

30. What common advantage do circular folds, villi, and microvilli provide to the digestive process? Which of these modifications causes chyme to spiral through the lumen and slows its passage?
31. What are brush border enzymes?
32. What is a lacteal and what is its function?
33. Name three secretory products that help to protect the intestinal mucosa from bacterial damage.

For answers, see Appendix G.

The Liver and Gallbladder

▶ Describe the histologic anatomy of the liver.

▶ State the role of bile in digestion and describe how its entry into the small intestine is regulated.

▶ Describe the role of the gallbladder.

The *liver* and *gallbladder* are accessory organs associated with the small intestine. The liver, one of the body's most important organs, has many metabolic and regulatory roles. However, its *digestive* function is to produce bile for export to the duodenum. Bile is a fat emulsifier. In other words, it breaks up fats into tiny particles so that they are more accessible to digestive enzymes. We will describe bile and the emulsification process when we discuss the digestion and absorption of fats later in the chapter. Although the liver also processes nutrient-laden venous blood delivered to it directly from the digestive organs, this is a metabolic rather than a digestive role. (See Chapter 24.) The gallbladder is chiefly a storage organ for bile.

Gross Anatomy of the Liver

The ruddy, blood-rich **liver** is the largest gland in the body, weighing about 1.4 kg (3 lb) in the average adult. Shaped like a wedge, it occupies most of the right hypochondriac and epigastric regions, extending farther to the right of the body midline than to the left. Located under the diaphragm, the liver lies almost entirely within the rib cage, which provides some protection (see Figure 23.1 and **Figure 23.24**).

Typically, the liver is said to have four primary lobes. The largest of these, the *right lobe*, is visible on all liver surfaces and separated from the smaller *left lobe* by a deep fissure (Figure 23.24a). The posteriormost *caudate lobe* and the *quadrate lobe*, which lies inferior to the left lobe, are visible in an inferior view of the liver (Figure 23.24b).

A mesentery, the **falciform ligament**, separates the right and left lobes anteriorly and suspends the liver from the diaphragm and anterior abdominal wall. Running along the inferior edge of the falciform ligament is the **round ligament**, or **ligamentum teres** (te′rēz; "round"), a fibrous remnant of the fetal umbilical vein. Except for the superiormost liver area (the *bare area*), which touches the diaphragm, the entire liver is enclosed by the visceral peritoneum.

As we mentioned earlier, a ventral mesentery, the lesser omentum, anchors the liver to the lesser curvature of the stomach (see Figure 23.30b). The **hepatic artery** and the **hepatic portal vein**, which enter the liver at the **porta hepatis** ("gateway to the liver"), and the common hepatic duct, which runs inferiorly from the liver, all travel through the lesser omentum to reach their destinations. The gallbladder rests in a recess on the inferior surface of the right liver lobe (Figure 23.24b).

The traditional scheme of defining liver lobes (outlined above) has been criticized because it is based on superficial features of the liver. Some anatomists emphasize that the primary lobes of the liver should be defined as the territories served by the right and left hepatic ducts. These two territories are delineated by a plane drawn from the indentation (sulcus) of the inferior vena cava to the gallbladder recess (Figure 23.24b). The areas to the right of the plane are the *right lobe* and those to its left constitute the *left lobe*. According to this scheme, the small quadrate and caudate lobes are part of the left lobe.

Bile leaves the liver through several bile ducts that ultimately fuse to form the large **common hepatic duct**, which travels downward toward the duodenum. Along its course, that duct fuses with the **cystic duct** draining the gallbladder to form the **bile duct** (see Figure 23.21).

Microscopic Anatomy of the Liver

The liver is composed of sesame seed–sized structural and functional units called **liver lobules**. Each lobule is a roughly hexagonal (six-sided) structure **(Figure 23.25a)** consisting of plates of *liver cells*, or **hepatocytes** (hep′ah-to-sīts), organized like bricks in a garden wall. The hepatocyte plates radiate outward from a **central vein** (Figure 23.25c) running in the longitudinal axis of the lobule. To make a rough "model" of a liver lobule, open a thick paperback book until its two covers meet: The pages represent the plates of hepatocytes and the hollow cylinder formed by the rolled spine represents the central vein.

If you keep in mind that the liver's main function is to filter and process the nutrient-rich blood delivered to it, the description of its anatomy that follows will make a lot of sense. At each of the six corners of a lobule is a **portal triad** (*portal tract* region), so named because three basic structures are always present there: a branch of the *hepatic artery* (supplying oxygen-rich arterial blood to the liver), a branch of the *hepatic portal vein* (carrying venous blood laden with nutrients from the digestive viscera), and a *bile duct* (Figure 23.25c).

Between the hepatocyte plates are enlarged, leaky capillaries, the **liver sinusoids**. Blood from both the hepatic portal vein and the hepatic artery percolates from the triad regions through these sinusoids and empties into the central vein. From the central veins blood eventually enters the hepatic veins, which drain the liver, and empty into the inferior vena cava. Forming part of the sinusoid walls are star-shaped **hepatic macrophages**, also called **Kupffer cells** (koop′fer) (Figure 23.25c). They remove debris such as bacteria and worn-out blood cells from the blood as it flows past.

The versatile hepatocytes have large amounts of both rough and smooth ER, Golgi apparatuses, peroxisomes, and mitochondria. Equipped in this way, the hepatocytes not only can produce some 900 ml of bile daily but also can (1) process the bloodborne nutrients in various ways (e.g., they store glucose as glycogen and use amino acids to make plasma proteins); (2) store fat-soluble vitamins; and (3) play important roles in detoxification, such as ridding the blood of ammonia by converting it to urea (Chapter 24). Thanks to these various jobs, the processed blood leaving the liver contains fewer nutrients and waste materials than the blood that entered it.

In addition to providing the hepatocytes with blood for processing and nutrition, the intimate relationship between the hepatocytes and their blood supply has consequences for liver growth and repair. The regenerative capacity of the liver is exceptional. It can regenerate to its former size even after surgical removal or loss of 70% of its normal mass. During liver injury, hepatocytes secrete *vascular endothelial growth factor* (*VEGF*) which binds to specific receptors on endothelial cells lining the sinusoids. The endothelial cells proliferate and release other growth factors, such as hepatocyte growth factor (HGF) and interleukin 6, which in turn prompt the hepatocytes to multiply and replace dead and dying liver tissue.

Secreted bile flows through tiny canals, called **bile canaliculi** (kan″ah-lik′u-li; "little canals"), that run between adjacent

23

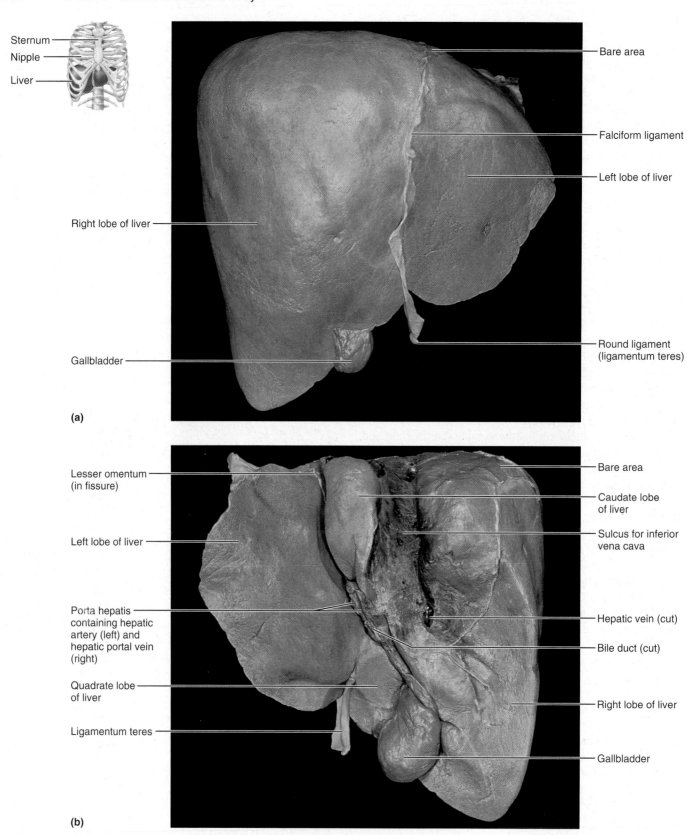

Sternum

Nipple

Liver

Bare area

Falciform ligament

Left lobe of liver

Right lobe of liver

Round ligament
(ligamentum teres)

Gallbladder

(a)

Lesser omentum
(in fissure)

Bare area

Caudate lobe
of liver

Sulcus for inferior
vena cava

Left lobe of liver

Porta hepatis
containing hepatic
artery (left) and
hepatic portal vein
(right)

Hepatic vein (cut)

Bile duct (cut)

Quadrate lobe
of liver

Right lobe of liver

Ligamentum teres

Gallbladder

(b)

Figure 23.24 Gross anatomy of the human liver. (a) Anterior view of the liver. **(b)** Posteroinferior aspect (ventral surface) of the liver. The four liver lobes are separated by a group of fissures
in this view. The porta hepatis is a deep fissure that contains the hepatic portal vein, hepatic
artery, common hepatic duct, and lymphatics. (See *A Brief Atlas of the Human Body*, Figures 64
and 65.)

23

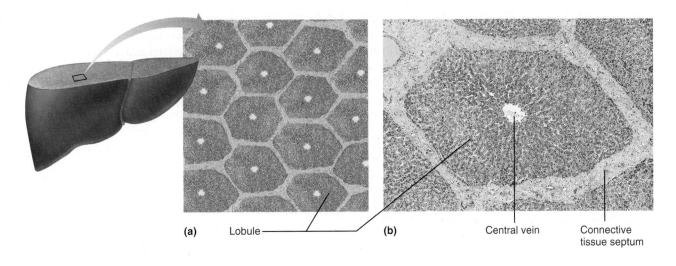

(a) Lobule

(b) Central vein   Connective tissue septum

Interlobular veins (to hepatic vein)

Central vein

Sinusoids

Plates of hepatocytes

Bile canaliculi

Bile duct (receives bile from bile canaliculi)

Fenestrated lining (endothelial cells) of sinusoids

Bile duct
Portal venule — Portal triad
Portal arteriole

Hepatic macrophages in sinusoid walls

Portal vein

(c)

Figure 23.25 Microscopic anatomy of the liver. (a) Normal lobular pattern of the liver. **(b)** Enlarged view of one liver lobule. **(c)** Three-dimensional representation of a small portion of one liver lobule, showing portal triads and the structure of sinusoids. Arrows indicate the direction of blood flow.

hepatocytes toward the bile duct branches in the portal triads (Figure 23.25c). Although most illustrations show the canaliculi as discrete tubular structures (shown here green), their walls are actually formed by the apical membranes of adjoining hepatocytes. Notice that blood and bile flow in opposite directions in the liver lobule. Bile entering the bile ducts eventually leaves the liver via the common hepatic duct to travel toward the duodenum.

HOMEOSTATIC IMBALANCE

More common in men than in women, **hepatitis** (hep″ah-ti′tis), or inflammation of the liver, is most often due to viral infection. So far the catalogue of hepatitis-causing viruses numbers six—from the hepatitis A virus (HVA) to the hepatitis F virus (HVF). Two of these (HVA and HVE) are transmitted enterically and the infections they cause tend to be self-limiting. Those transmitted via blood—most importantly HVB and HVC—are linked to chronic hepatitis and liver cirrhosis (see discussion below). HVD is a mutated virus that needs HVB to be infectious. So far, little is known about HVF. Nonviral causes of acute hepatitis include drug toxicity and wild mushroom poisoning.

In the United States, over 40% of hepatitis cases are due to HVB, which is transmitted via blood transfusions, contaminated needles, or sexual contact. A serious problem in its own right, hepatitis B carries with it a greater menace—an elevated risk of liver cancer. However, childhood immunization using vaccine produced in bacteria is sweeping the feet out from under HVB, and the incidence of acute hepatitis from this strain has fallen dramatically since its peak in 1985.

Hepatitis A, accounting for about 32% of cases, is a more benign form frequently observed in day-care centers. It is transmitted via sewage-contaminated food, raw shellfish, water, and by the feces-mouth route, which explains why it is important for restaurant employees to scrub their hands after using the washroom. The highly successful HepA vaccine is helping to prevent hepatitis infection and shedding of the virus in the stool.

Hepatitis E is transmitted in a way similar to hepatitis A. It causes waterborne epidemics, largely in developing countries, and is a major cause of death (up to 25%) in pregnant women. It is relatively insignificant in the United States, but it is a major problem for one-third of the world's population, mainly in Africa and Asia. However, there is now hope. An experimental vaccine for HepE has proven to be 96% protective in clinical trials among soldiers in Nepal.

Hepatitis C has emerged as the most important liver disease in the United States because it produces persistent or chronic liver infections (as opposed to acute infections). More than 4 million Americans are infected and over 10,000 die annually due to sequels of HVC infection. However, the life-threatening C form of hepatitis is now being successfully treated by combination drug therapy entailing weekly injections of interferon (Pegasys, PEG-Intron) and ribavirin (Rebetol), an oral antiviral drug.

Cirrhosis (sĭr-ro′sis; "orange colored") is a progressive chronic inflammation of the liver that typically results from chronic alcoholism or severe chronic hepatitis. The alcohol-poisoned or damaged hepatocytes regenerate, but the liver's connective (scar) tissue regenerates faster. As a result, the liver becomes fatty and fibrous and its activity is depressed. As the scar tissue shrinks, it obstructs blood flow throughout the hepatic portal system, causing **portal hypertension**.

Fortunately, some veins of the portal system anastomose with veins that drain into the venae cavae (*portal-caval anastomoses*). The main ones are (1) veins in the inferior esophagus, (2) hemorrhoidal veins in the anal canal, and (3) superficial veins around the umbilicus. However, these connecting veins are small and tend to burst when forced to carry large volumes of blood. Signs of their failure include vomiting blood, and a snakelike network of distended veins surrounding the navel. This network is called *caput medusae* (kap′ut mĕ-du′se; "medusa head") after a monster in Greek mythology whose hair was made of writhing snakes. Other complications due to portal hypertension include swollen veins in the esophagus (esophageal varices) and ascites, an accumulation of fluid in the peritoneal cavity.

Liver transplants are the only clinically proven effective treatment for patients with end-stage liver disease. The one- and five-year survival rate of such transplants is approximately 90% and 75% respectively. However, donor organs are scarce and many patients die while waiting for a suitable organ. ■

Composition of Bile

Bile is a yellow-green, alkaline solution containing bile salts, bile pigments, cholesterol, triglycerides, phospholipids (lecithin and others), and a variety of electrolytes. Of these, *only* bile salts and phospholipids aid the digestive process.

Bile salts, primarily cholic and chenodeoxycholic acids, are cholesterol derivatives. Their role is to *emulsify* fats—in other words, to distribute them throughout the watery intestinal contents, just as a dish detergent breaks up a pool of fat drippings in a roasting pan. As a result, large fat globules entering the small intestine are physically separated into millions of small, more accessible fatty droplets that provide large surface areas for the fat-digesting enzymes to work on. Bile salts also facilitate fat and cholesterol absorption (discussed later) and help solubilize cholesterol, both that contained in bile and that entering the small intestine in food.

Many substances secreted in bile leave the body in feces, but bile salts are not among them. Instead, bile salts are conserved by means of a recycling mechanism called the **enterohepatic circulation**. In this process, bile salts are (1) reabsorbed into the blood by the ileum, (2) returned to the liver via the hepatic portal blood, and then (3) resecreted in newly formed bile. This pool of bile salts recirculates five or more times for a single meal.

The chief bile pigment is **bilirubin** (bil″ĭ-roo′bin), a waste product of the heme of hemoglobin formed during the breakdown of worn-out erythrocytes (see Chapter 17). The globin and iron parts of hemoglobin are saved and recycled, but bilirubin is absorbed from the blood by the liver cells, excreted into bile, and metabolized in the small intestine by resident bacteria. One of its breakdown products, *stercobilin* (ster′ko-bi″lin), gives feces a brown color. In the absence of bile, feces are gray-white in color and have fatty streaks (because essentially no fats are digested or absorbed).

The Gallbladder

The **gallbladder** is a thin-walled green muscular sac about 10 cm (4 inches) long. Roughly the size of a kiwi fruit, it snuggles in a shallow fossa on the ventral surface of the liver (see Figures 23.21 and 23.24). Its rounded fundus protrudes from the inferior margin of the liver. The gallbladder stores bile that is not immediately needed for digestion and concentrates it by absorbing some of its water and ions. (In some cases, bile released from the gallbladder is 10 to 20 times as concentrated as that entering it.) When empty, or when storing only small amounts of bile, its mucosa is thrown into honeycomb-like folds (see Figure 23.21) that, like the rugae of the stomach, allow the organ to expand as it fills. When its muscular wall contracts, bile is expelled into its duct, the *cystic duct*, and then flows into the bile duct. The gallbladder, like most of the liver, is covered by visceral peritoneum.

⚖ HOMEOSTATIC IMBALANCE

Bile is the major vehicle for cholesterol excretion from the body, and bile salts keep the cholesterol dissolved within bile. Too much cholesterol or too few bile salts leads to cholesterol crystallization, forming **gallstones**, or *biliary calculi* (bil′e-a″re kal′ku-li), which obstruct the flow of bile from the gallbladder. Then, when the gallbladder or its duct contracts, the sharp crystals cause agonizing pain that radiates to the right thoracic region. Treatments for gallstones include dissolving the crystals with drugs, pulverizing them with ultrasound vibrations (lithotripsy), vaporizing them with lasers, and the classical treatment, surgically removing the gallbladder. When the gallbladder is removed, the bile duct enlarges to assume the bile-storing role. Gallstones are easy to diagnose because they show up well with ultrasound imaging.

Bile duct blockage prevents both bile salts and bile pigments from entering the intestine. As a result, yellow bile pigments accumulate in blood and eventually are deposited in the skin, causing it to become yellow, or *jaundiced*. Jaundice caused by blocked ducts is called *obstructive jaundice*, but jaundice may also reflect liver disease (in which the liver is unable to carry out its normal metabolic duties). ■

CHECK YOUR UNDERSTANDING

34. What is a portal triad?
35. What is the importance of the enterohepatic circulation?
36. What is the role of the Kupffer cells of the liver?

For answers, see Appendix G.

The Pancreas

▶ State the role of pancreatic juice in digestion.

▶ Describe how entry of pancreatic juice into the small intestine is regulated.

The **pancreas** (pan′kre-as; *pan* = all, *creas* = flesh, meat) is a soft, tadpole-shaped gland that extends across the abdomen from its *tail* (abutting the spleen) to its *head*, which is encircled by the C-shaped duodenum (see Figures 23.1 and 23.21). Most

(a)

(b)

Figure 23.26 Structure of the enzyme-producing tissue of the pancreas. (a) Schematic view of one acinus (a secretory unit). The cell apices contain abundant zymogen (enzyme-containing) granules, and the dark-staining rough ER is plentiful (typical of gland cells producing large amounts of protein for export). **(b)** Photomicrograph of pancreatic acinar tissue (250×).

of the pancreas is retroperitoneal and lies deep to the greater curvature of the stomach.

An accessory digestive organ, the pancreas is important to the digestive process because it produces enzymes that break down all categories of foodstuffs, which the pancreas then delivers to the duodenum. This exocrine product, called **pancreatic juice**, drains from the pancreas via the centrally located **main pancreatic duct**. The pancreatic duct generally fuses with the bile duct just as it enters the duodenum (at the hepatopancreatic ampulla). A smaller *accessory pancreatic duct* empties directly into the duodenum just proximal to the main duct.

Within the pancreas are the **acini** (as′i-ni; singular: acinus), clusters of secretory cells surrounding ducts **(Figure 23.26)**. These cells are full of rough endoplasmic reticulum and exhibit deeply staining **zymogen granules** (zi′mo-jen; "fermenting") containing the digestive enzymes they manufacture.

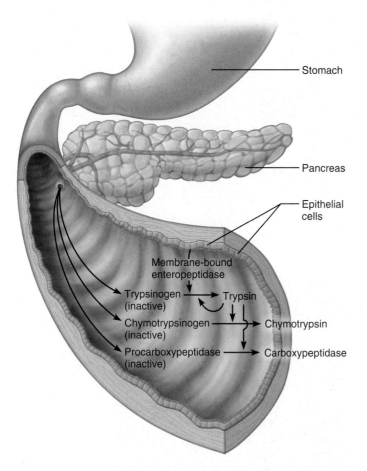

Figure 23.27 Activation of pancreatic proteases in the small intestine. Pancreatic proteases are secreted in an inactive form and are activated in the duodenum.

Scattered amid the acini are the more lightly staining *pancreatic islets* (*islets of Langerhans*). These mini-endocrine glands release insulin and glucagon, hormones that play an important role in carbohydrate metabolism, as well as several other hormones (see Chapter 16).

Composition of Pancreatic Juice

Approximately 1200 to 1500 ml of clear pancreatic juice is produced daily. It consists mainly of water, and contains enzymes and electrolytes (primarily bicarbonate ions). The acinar cells produce the enzyme-rich component of pancreatic juice. The epithelial cells lining the smallest pancreatic ducts release the bicarbonate ions that make it alkaline (about pH 8).

Normally, the amount of HCl produced in the stomach is exactly balanced by the amount of bicarbonate (HCO_3^-) secreted by the pancreas, and as HCO_3^- is secreted into the pancreatic juice, H^+ enters the blood. Consequently, the pH of venous blood returning to the heart remains relatively unchanged because alkaline blood draining from the stomach is neutralized by the acidic blood draining the pancreas.

The high pH of pancreatic fluid helps neutralize acid chyme entering the duodenum and provides the optimal environment for activity of intestinal and pancreatic enzymes. Like pepsin of the stomach, pancreatic *proteases* (protein-digesting enzymes)

are produced and released in inactive forms, which are activated in the duodenum, where they do their work. This protects the pancreas from self-digestion.

For example, within the duodenum, *trypsinogen* is activated to **trypsin** by **enteropeptidase** (formerly called *enterokinase*), an intestinal brush border protease. Trypsin, in turn, activates more trypsinogen and two other pancreatic proteases (*procarboxypeptidase* and *chymotrypsinogen*) to their active forms, **carboxypeptidase** (kar-bok″se-pep′tĭ-dās) and **chymotrypsin** (ky″mo-trip′sin), respectively (**Figure 23.27**).

Other pancreatic enzymes—**amylase, lipases,** and **nucleases**—are secreted in active form, but require that ions or bile be present in the intestinal lumen for optimal activity.

CHECK YOUR UNDERSTANDING

37. What is contained in zymogen granules?

38. Maryanne has pancreatitis and her pancreas is swollen and temporarily unable to produce pancreatic juice. What type of foodstuffs will probably not be digested until she recovers?

For answers, see Appendix G.

Regulation of Bile and Pancreatic Secretion and Entry into the Small Intestine

Secretion of bile and pancreatic juice and the release of these secretions to the small intestine where they "do their business" in food digestion is regulated by the same factors—neural stimuli and, more importantly, hormones (cholecystokinin and secretin).

Bile salts themselves are the major stimulus for enhanced bile secretion (**Figure 23.28**)—when a fatty meal is eaten and the enterohepatic circulation is returning large amounts of bile salts to the liver, its output of bile rises dramatically. *Secretin*, released by intestinal cells exposed to fatty chyme, also stimulates liver cells to secrete bile.

When no digestion is occurring, the hepatopancreatic sphincter (guarding the entry of bile and pancreatic juice into the duodenum) is closed and the released bile backs up the cystic duct into the gallbladder, where it is stored until needed. Although the liver makes bile continuously, bile does not usually enter the small intestine until the gallbladder contracts. Parasympathetic impulses delivered by vagus nerve fibers is a minor stimulus for gallbladder contraction, but the major stimulus is *cholecystokinin* (*CCK*), an intestinal hormone released to the blood when acidic, fatty chyme enters the duodenum (Figure 23.28). Besides causing the gallbladder to contract, CCK (1) stimulates secretion of pancreatic juice and (2) relaxes the hepatopancreatic sphincter so that bile and pancreatic juice can enter the duodenum.

Both secretin and cholecystokinin prompt the pancreas to secrete its juice. Secretin, released in response to the presence of HCl in the intestine, mainly targets the pancreatic duct cells, resulting in a watery *bicarbonate-rich* pancreatic juice. CCK, released in response to proteins and fats in chyme, stimulates the acini to release *enzyme-rich* pancreatic juice, and potentiates

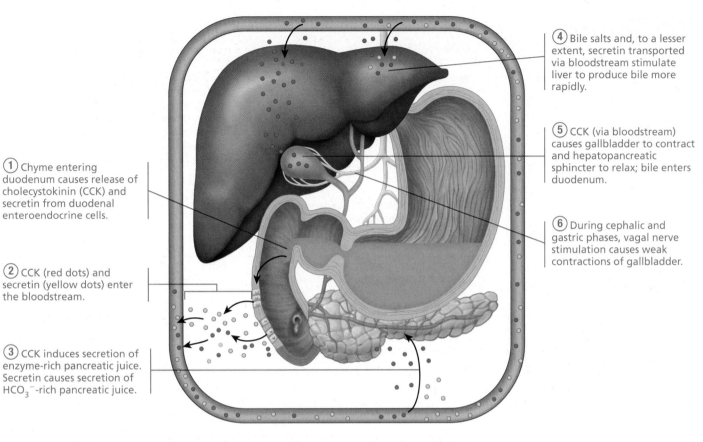

① Chyme entering duodenum causes release of cholecystokinin (CCK) and secretin from duodenal enteroendocrine cells.

② CCK (red dots) and secretin (yellow dots) enter the bloodstream.

③ CCK induces secretion of enzyme-rich pancreatic juice. Secretin causes secretion of HCO_3^--rich pancreatic juice.

④ Bile salts and, to a lesser extent, secretin transported via bloodstream stimulate liver to produce bile more rapidly.

⑤ CCK (via bloodstream) causes gallbladder to contract and hepatopancreatic sphincter to relax; bile enters duodenum.

⑥ During cephalic and gastric phases, vagal nerve stimulation causes weak contractions of gallbladder.

Figure 23.28 Mechanisms promoting secretion and release of bile and pancreatic juice. When digestion is not occurring, bile is stored and concentrated in the gallbladder. When acidic fatty chyme enters the small intestine, several mechanisms are initiated that accelerate the output of pancreatic juice and bile and cause the gallbladder to contract and the hepatopancreatic sphincter to relax. This allows bile and pancreatic juice to enter the small intestine. The single most important stimulus of bile secretion is an increased level of bile salts in the enterohepatic circulation.

the effect of secretin. CCK and the other digestive hormones are summarized in Table 23.1 (p. 875). Vagal stimulation prompts the release of pancreatic juice mainly during the cephalic and gastric phases of gastric secretion.

CHECK YOUR UNDERSTANDING

39. What is the functional difference between pancreatic acini and islets?
40. What is the makeup of the fluid in the pancreatic duct? In the cystic duct? In the bile duct?
41. What stimulates CCK release and what are its effects on the digestive process?

For answers, see Appendix G.

Digestive Processes Occurring in the Small Intestine

Food reaching the small intestine is unrecognizable, but it is far from being digested chemically. Carbohydrates and proteins are partially degraded, but virtually no fat digestion has occurred to

this point. The process of food digestion is accelerated during the chyme's tortuous three- to six-hour journey through the small intestine, and it is here that absorption of most of the water and virtually all nutrients occurs. Like the stomach, the small intestine plays no part in ingestion or defecation.

Requirements for Optimal Intestinal Digestive Activity

Although a primary function of the small intestine is digestion, intestinal juice provides little of what is needed to perform this function. Most substances required for chemical digestion—bile, digestive enzymes (except for the brush border enzymes), and bicarbonate ions (to provide the proper pH for enzymatic catalysis)—are *imported* from the liver and pancreas. Hence, anything that impairs liver or pancreatic function or delivery of their juices to the small intestine severely hinders our ability to digest food and absorb nutrients. The other primary function of the small intestine—absorption—is efficiently accomplished by its absorptive cells with their rich crop of apical microvilli.

Optimal digestive activity in the small intestine also depends on a slow, measured delivery of chyme from the stomach.

23

TABLE 23.2   Overview of the Functions of the Gastrointestinal Organs

ORGAN	MAJOR FUNCTIONS*	COMMENTS/ADDITIONAL FUNCTIONS
Mouth and associated accessory organs	■ Ingestion: food is voluntarily placed into oral cavity ■ Propulsion: voluntary (buccal) phase of deglutition (swallowing) initiated by tongue; propels food into pharynx ■ Mechanical digestion: mastication (chewing) by teeth and mixing movements by tongue ■ Chemical digestion: chemical breakdown of starch is begun by salivary amylase present in saliva produced by salivary glands	Mouth serves as a receptacle; most functions performed by associated accessory organs. Mucus present in saliva helps dissolve foods so they can be tasted and moistens food so that tongue can compact it into a bolus that can be swallowed. Oral cavity and teeth cleansed and lubricated by saliva.
Pharynx and esophagus	■ Propulsion: peristaltic waves move food bolus to stomach, thus accomplishing involuntary (pharyngeal-esophageal) phase of deglutition	Primarily food chutes; mucus produced helps to lubricate food passageways.
Stomach	■ Mechanical digestion and propulsion: peristaltic waves mix food with gastric juice and propel it into the duodenum ■ Chemical digestion: digestion of proteins begun by pepsin ■ Absorption: absorbs a few fat-soluble substances (aspirin, alcohol, some drugs)	Also serves as storage site for food until it can be moved into the duodenum. Hydrochloric acid produced is a bacteriostatic agent and activates protein-digesting enzymes. Mucus produced helps lubricate and protect stomach from self-digestion. Intrinsic factor produced is required for intestinal absorption of vitamin B_{12}.
Small intestine and associated accessory organs (liver, gallbladder, pancreas)	■ Mechanical digestion and propulsion: segmentation by smooth muscle of the small intestine continually mixes contents with digestive juices and moves food along tract and through ileocecal valve at a slow rate, allowing sufficient time for digestion and absorption ■ Chemical digestion: digestive enzymes conveyed in from pancreas and brush border enzymes attached to microvilli membranes complete digestion of all classes of foods ■ Absorption: breakdown products of carbohydrate, protein, fat, and nucleic acid digestion, plus vitamins, electrolytes, and water, are absorbed by active and passive mechanisms	Small intestine is highly modified for digestion and absorption (circular folds, villi, and microvilli). Alkaline mucus produced by intestinal glands and bicarbonate-rich juice ducted in from pancreas help neutralize acidic chyme and provide proper environment for enzymatic activity. Bile produced by liver emulsifies fats and enhances (1) fat digestion and (2) absorption of fatty acids, monoglycerides, cholesterol, phospholipids, and fat-soluble vitamins. Gallbladder stores and concentrates bile, releasing it to small intestine in response to hormonal signals.
Large intestine	■ Chemical digestion: some remaining food residues are digested by enteric bacteria (which also produce vitamin K and some B vitamins) ■ Absorption: absorbs most remaining water, electrolytes (largely NaCl), and vitamins produced by bacteria ■ Propulsion: propels feces toward rectum by peristalsis, haustral churning, and mass movements ■ Defecation: reflex triggered by rectal distension; eliminates feces from body	Temporarily stores and concentrates residues until defecation can occur. Copious mucus produced by goblet cells eases passage of feces through colon.

*The colored boxes beside the functions correspond to the color coding of digestive functions (gastrointestinal tract activities) illustrated in Figure 23.2.

TABLE 23.3	Control of Small Intestinal Motility		
PHASE	**STIMULUS**	**MECHANISM**	**EFFECT ON MOTILITY**
Gastric	↑ Gastric motility and emptying	Long neural reflexes (gastroileal reflex)	↑ Activity in ileum
		Gastrin	↑ Segmenting movements in ileum; relaxes ileocecal sphincter
Intestinal	Distension of small intestine	Long and short neural reflexes	↑ Strength of segmentation
	Reduced intestinal volume; fasting	Long and short neural reflexes; initiated by ↑ blood levels of motilin	Initiates migrating motility complex (peristalsis); repeats until next meal

Why is this so? Entering chyme is usually hypertonic. For this reason, if large amounts of chyme were rushed into the small intestine, the osmotic water loss from the blood into the intestinal lumen would result in dangerously low blood volume. Additionally, the low pH of entering chyme must be adjusted upward and the chyme must be well mixed with bile and pancreatic juice for digestion to continue. These modifications take time, and food movement into the small intestine is carefully controlled by the pumping action of the stomach pylorus (see pp. 874–876 and Figure 23.19) to prevent the duodenum from being overwhelmed.

Since we cover the actual chemistry of digestion and absorption in detail later, next we will examine how the small intestine mixes and propels food along its length, and how its motility is regulated.

Motility of the Small Intestine

Intestinal smooth muscle mixes chyme thoroughly with bile and pancreatic and intestinal juices, and moves food residues through the ileocecal valve into the large intestine. In contrast to the peristaltic waves of the stomach, *segmentation* is the most common motion of the small intestine.

If X-ray fluoroscopy is used to examine the small intestine after it is "loaded" with a meal (the "fed state"), it looks like the intestinal contents are being massaged—the chyme is simply moved backward and forward in the lumen a few centimeters at a time by alternating contraction and relaxation of rings of smooth muscle (see Figure 23.3b). These segmenting movements of the intestine, like the peristalsis of the stomach, are initiated by intrinsic pacemaker cells in the circular smooth muscle layer. However, unlike the stomach pacemakers, which have only one rhythm, the pacemakers in the duodenum depolarize more frequently (12–14 contractions per minute) than those in the ileum (8 or 9 contractions per minute). As a result, segmentation also moves intestinal contents slowly and steadily toward the ileocecal valve at a rate that allows ample time to complete digestion and absorption.

The intensity of segmentation is altered by long and short reflexes, which parasympathetic activity enhances and sympathetic activity decreases, and by hormones (Table 23.3). The more intense the contractions, the greater the mixing effect, but the basic contractile rhythms of the various intestinal regions remain unchanged.

True peristalsis occurs late in the intestinal phase only after most nutrients have been absorbed (the "fasting state"). At this point, segmenting movements wane and the duodenal mucosa begins to release the hormone *motilin*. As motilin blood levels rise, peristaltic waves are initiated in the proximal duodenum every 90 to 120 minutes and begin to sweep slowly along the intestine, moving 50–70 cm (about 2 ft) before dying out. Each successive wave is initiated a bit more distally, and this pattern of peristaltic activity is called the **migrating motility complex (MMC)**. A complete "trip" from duodenum to ileum takes about two hours. The process then repeats itself, sweeping the last remnants of the meal plus bacteria, sloughed-off mucosal cells, and other debris into the large intestine.

This "housekeeping" function is critical for preventing the overgrowth of bacteria that migrate from the large intestine into the small intestine. As food again enters the stomach with the next meal, peristalsis is replaced by segmentation.

The local enteric neurons of the GI tract wall coordinate these intestinal motility patterns and a variety of effects occur depending on which neurons are activated or inhibited. For example, a given ACh-releasing (cholinergic) sensory neuron in the small intestine, once activated, may simultaneously send messages to several different interneurons in the myenteric plexus that regulate peristalsis:

- Impulses sent proximally by effector neurons cause contraction and shortening of the circular muscle layer.
- Impulses sent distally to certain interneurons cause shortening of the longitudinal muscle layer and distension of the intestine.

23

As a result, as the proximal area constricts and forces chyme along the tract, the lumen of the distal part of the intestine enlarges to receive it.

Most of the time, the ileocecal sphincter is constricted and closed. However, two mechanisms—one neural and the other hormonal—cause it to relax and allow food residues to enter the cecum when ileal motility increases.

1. Enhanced activity of the stomach initiates the **gastroileal reflex** (gas″tro-il′e-ul), a long reflex that enhances the force of segmentation in the ileum.
2. Gastrin released by the stomach increases the motility of the ileum and relaxes the ileocecal sphincter. Once the chyme has passed through, it exerts backward pressure that closes the valve's flaps, preventing regurgitation into the ileum. This reflex ensures that the contents of the previous meal are swept completely out of the stomach and small intestine as the next meal is eaten.

HOMEOSTATIC IMBALANCE

Injury to the intestinal wall by severe stretching, some bacterial infections, or mechanical trauma may lead to a total shutdown of small intestine motility, a phenomenon called the intestino-intestinal reflex. ■

CHECK YOUR UNDERSTANDING

42. Distension of the stomach and duodenal walls have different effects on stomach secretory activity. What are these effects?
43. Which is more important in moving food along the small intestine—peristalsis or segmentation?
44. What is the MMC and why is it important?

For answers, see Appendix G.

The Large Intestine

23

▶ List the major functions of the large intestine.
▶ Describe the regulation of defecation.

The **large intestine** frames the small intestine on three sides and extends from the ileocecal valve to the anus (see Figure 23.1). Its diameter, at about 7 cm, is greater than that of the small intestine (hence, *large* intestine), but it is less than half as long (1.5 m versus 6 m). Its major digestive function is to absorb most of the remaining water from indigestible food residues (delivered to it in a fluid state), store the residues temporarily, and then eliminate them from the body as semisolid **feces** (fe′sēz).

Gross Anatomy

The large intestine exhibits three features not seen elsewhere—teniae coli, haustra, and epiploic appendages. Except for its terminal end, the longitudinal muscle layer of its muscularis is mostly reduced to three bands of smooth muscle called **teniae coli** (ten′ne-e ko′li; "ribbons of the colon"). Their tone causes the wall of the large intestine to pucker into pocketlike sacs

called **haustra** (haw′strah; "to draw up"; singular *haustrum*). Another obvious feature of the large intestine is its **epiploic appendages** (ep″ĭ-plo′ik; "membrane covered"), small fat-filled pouches of visceral peritoneum that hang from its surface **(Figure 23.29a)**. Their significance is not known.

Subdivisions

The large intestine has the following subdivisions: cecum, appendix, colon, rectum, and anal canal. The saclike **cecum** (se′kum; "blind pouch"), which lies below the ileocecal valve in the right iliac fossa, is the first part of the large intestine (Figure 23.29a). Attached to its posteromedial surface is the blind, wormlike **vermiform appendix**. The appendix contains masses of lymphoid tissue, and as part of MALT (see p. 761) it plays an important role in body immunity. However, it has an important structural shortcoming—its twisted structure provides an ideal location for enteric bacteria to accumulate and multiply.

HOMEOSTATIC IMBALANCE

Acute inflammation of the appendix, or **appendicitis**, results from a blockage (often by feces) that traps infectious bacteria in its lumen. Unable to empty its contents, the appendix swells, squeezing off venous drainage, which may lead to ischemia and necrosis (death and decay) of the appendix. If the appendix ruptures, feces containing bacteria spray over the abdominal contents, causing *peritonitis*.

The symptoms of appendicitis are variable, but the first is usually pain in the umbilical region. Loss of appetite, nausea and vomiting, and relocalization of pain to the lower right abdominal quadrant follow. Immediate surgical removal of the appendix (appendectomy) is the accepted treatment for suspected appendicitis. Appendicitis is most common during adolescence, when the entrance to the appendix is at its widest. ■

The **colon** has several distinct regions. As the **ascending colon**, it travels up the right side of the abdominal cavity to the level of the right kidney. Here it makes a right-angle turn—the **right colic**, or **hepatic**, **flexure**—and travels across the abdominal cavity as the **transverse colon**. Directly anterior to the spleen, it bends acutely at the **left colic (splenic) flexure** and descends down the left side of the posterior abdominal wall as the **descending colon**. Inferiorly, it enters the pelvis, where it becomes the S-shaped **sigmoid colon**.

The colon is retroperitoneal, except for its transverse and sigmoid parts. These parts are intraperitoneal and anchored to the posterior abdominal wall by mesentery sheets called **mesocolons (Figure 23.30c, d)**.

In the pelvis, at the level of the third sacral vertebra, the sigmoid colon joins the **rectum**, which runs posteroinferiorly just in front of the sacrum. The position of the rectum allows a number of pelvic organs (e.g., the prostate of males) to be examined digitally (with a finger) through the anterior rectal wall. This is called a **rectal exam**.

Despite its name (*rectum* = straight), the rectum has three lateral curves or bends, represented internally as three transverse folds called **rectal valves** (Figure 23.29b). These valves

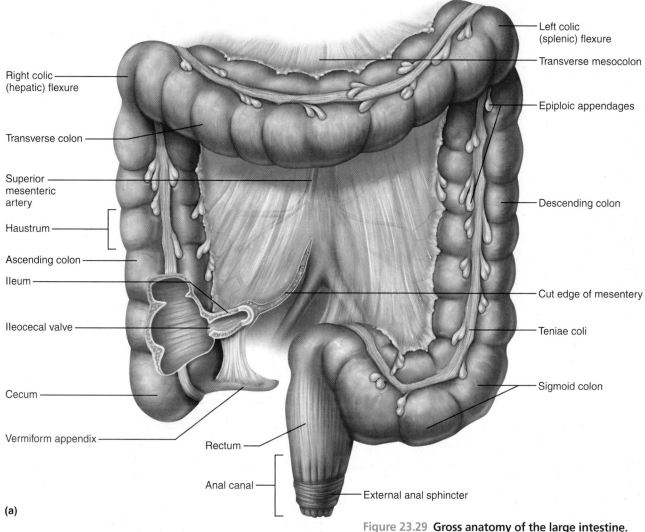

Right colic (hepatic) flexure

Transverse colon

Superior mesenteric artery

Haustrum

Ascending colon

Ileum

Ileocecal valve

Cecum

Vermiform appendix

Left colic (splenic) flexure

Transverse mesocolon

Epiploic appendages

Descending colon

Cut edge of mesentery

Teniae coli

Sigmoid colon

Rectum

Anal canal

External anal sphincter

(a)

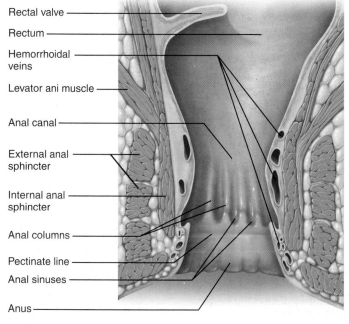

Rectal valve

Rectum

Hemorrhoidal veins

Levator ani muscle

Anal canal

External anal sphincter

Internal anal sphincter

Anal columns

Pectinate line

Anal sinuses

Anus

(b)

Figure 23.29 Gross anatomy of the large intestine.
(a) Diagrammatic view. **(b)** Structure of the anal canal.

separate feces from flatus, in other words, they stop feces from being passed along with gas.

The **anal canal**, the last segment of the large intestine, lies in the perineum, entirely external to the abdominopelvic cavity. About 3 cm long, it begins where the rectum penetrates the levator ani muscle of the pelvic floor and opens to the body exterior at the **anus**. The anal canal has two sphincters, an involuntary **internal anal sphincter** composed of smooth muscle (part of the muscularis), and a voluntary **external anal sphincter** composed of skeletal muscle. The sphincters, which act rather like purse strings to open and close the anus, are ordinarily closed except during defecation.

Microscopic Anatomy

The wall of the large intestine differs in several ways from that of the small intestine. The colon *mucosa* is simple columnar epithelium except in the anal canal. Because most food is absorbed before reaching the large intestine, there are no circular folds, no

23

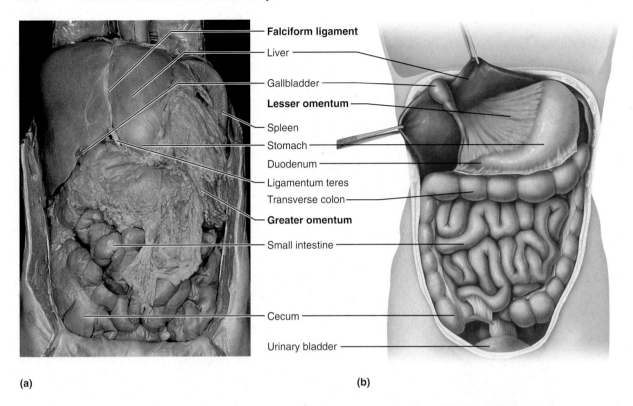

(a)

(b)

Falciform ligament
Liver
Gallbladder
Lesser omentum
Spleen
Stomach
Duodenum
Ligamentum teres
Transverse colon
Greater omentum
Small intestine
Cecum
Urinary bladder

(c)

(d)

Greater omentum
Transverse colon
Transverse mesocolon
Descending colon
Jejunum
Mesentery
Sigmoid mesocolon
Sigmoid colon
Ileum

Liver
Lesser omentum
Pancreas
Stomach
Duodenum
Transverse mesocolon
Transverse colon
Mesentery
Greater omentum
Jejunum
Ileum
Visceral peritoneum
Parietal peritoneum
Urinary bladder
Rectum

23

Figure 23.30 Mesenteries of the abdominal digestive organs. (a) The greater omentum, a dorsal mesentery, is shown in its normal position covering the abdominal viscera. **(b)** The liver and gallbladder have been reflected superiorly to reveal the lesser omentum, a ventral mesentery attaching the liver to the lesser curvature of the stomach. **(c)** The greater omentum has been reflected superiorly to reveal the mesentery attachments of the small and large intestine. **(d)** Sagittal section of the abdominopelvic cavity of a male.

villi, and virtually no cells that secrete digestive enzymes. However, its mucosa is thicker, its abundant crypts are deeper, and there are tremendous numbers of goblet cells in the crypts. Mucus produced by goblet cells eases the passage of feces and protects the intestinal wall from irritating acids and gases released by resident bacteria in the colon.

The mucosa of the anal canal, a stratified squamous epithelium, merges with the true skin surrounding the anus and is quite different from that of the rest of the colon, reflecting the greater abrasion that this region receives. Superiorly, it hangs in long ridges or folds called **anal columns**. **Anal sinuses**, recesses between the anal columns, exude mucus when compressed by feces, which aids in emptying the anal canal (Figure 23.29b).

The horizontal, tooth-shaped line that parallels the inferior margins of the anal sinuses is called the *pectinate line*. Superior to this line, the mucosa is innervated by visceral sensory fibers and is relatively insensitive to pain. The area inferior to the pectinate line is very sensitive to pain, a reflection of the somatic sensory fibers serving it.

Two superficial venous plexuses are associated with the anal canal, one with the anal columns and the other with the anus itself. If these (hemorrhoidal) veins are inflamed, itchy varicosities called *hemorrhoids* result.

Teniae coli and haustra are absent in the rectum and anal canal. However, consistent with its need to generate strong contractions to perform its expulsive role in defecation, the rectum's muscularis muscle layers are complete and well developed.

Bacterial Flora

Although most bacteria entering the cecum from the small intestine are dead (having been killed by the action of lysozyme, defensins, HCl, and protein-digesting enzymes), some are still "alive and kicking." Together with bacteria that enter the GI tract via the anus, these constitute the **bacterial flora** of the large intestine, an astonishing 10 million discrete types of them. These bacteria colonize the colon, metabolize some host-derived molecules (mucin, heparin, and hyaluronic acid) and ferment some of the indigestible carbohydrates (cellulose, xylan, and others), releasing irritating acids and a mixture of gases (including dimethyl sulfide, H_2, N_2, CH_4, and CO_2). Some of these gases (such as dimethyl sulfide) are quite odorous (smelly). About 500 ml of gas (flatus) is produced each day, much more when certain carbohydrate-rich foods (such as beans) are eaten. The bacterial flora also synthesize B complex vitamins and most of the vitamin K the liver requires to synthesize some of the clotting proteins.

Although the huge intestinal population of bacteria would seem to be enough inhabitants, the feces also have others, including viruses and protozoans. Of these, at least 20 are known pathogens.

Most enteric bacteria coexist peacefully with their host as long as they remain in the gut lumen. An elegant system keeps the bacteria from breaching the mucosal barrier. The epithelial cells of the gut mucosa respond to specific bacterial components by releasing chemicals that recruit immune cells, particularly dendritic cells, into the mucosa. The dendritic cells pry

open tight junctions between the epithelial cells and send extensions into the lumen to sample the microbial antigens. They then migrate to the nearby lymphoid follicles (MALT) within the gut mucosa where they present the antigens to T cells. As a result, an IgA antibody–mediated response restricted to the gut lumen is triggered that prevents the bacteria from straying into tissues deep to the mucosa where they might elicit a much more widespread systemic response. Though beneficial in most ways, the coexistence of enteric bacteria with our immune system does sometimes fail. When that happens, the painful and debilitating conditions known as inflammatory bowel disease (see Related Clinical Terms, p. 905) may result.

Digestive Processes Occurring in the Large Intestine

What is finally delivered to the large intestine contains few nutrients, but it still has 12 to 24 hours more to spend there. Except for a small amount of digestion of that residue by the enteric bacteria, no further food breakdown occurs in the large intestine.

Although the large intestine harvests vitamins made by the bacterial flora and reclaims most of the remaining water and some of the electrolytes (particularly sodium and chloride), nutrient absorption is not the *major* function of this organ. As mentioned, the primary concerns of the large intestine are propulsive activities that force the fecal material toward the anus and then eliminate it from the body (defecation).

The large intestine is important for our comfort, but it is not essential for life. If the colon is removed, as may be necessitated by colon cancer, the terminal ileum is brought out to the abdominal wall in a procedure called an *ileostomy* (il″e-os′to-me), and food residues are eliminated from there into a sac attached to the abdominal wall. Another surgical technique, *ileoanal juncture*, links the ileum directly to the anal canal.

Motility of the Large Intestine

The large intestine musculature is inactive much of the time, but pressure in the ileum terminus opens the ileocecal sphincter and then closes it, preventing backward movement of the chyme. When presented with food residue the colon becomes motile, but its contractions are sluggish or short-lived. The movements most seen in the colon are **haustral contractions**, slow segmenting movements lasting about one minute that occur every 30 minutes or so.

These contractions, which occur mainly in the transverse and descending colon, reflect local controls of smooth muscle within the walls of the individual haustra. As a haustrum fills with food residue, the distension stimulates its muscle to contract, which propels the luminal contents into the next haustrum. These movements also mix the residue, which aids in water absorption.

Mass movements (mass peristalsis) are long, slow-moving, but powerful contractile waves that move over large areas of the colon three or four times daily and force the contents toward the rectum. Typically, they occur during or just after eating, which indicates that the presence of food in the stomach activates the

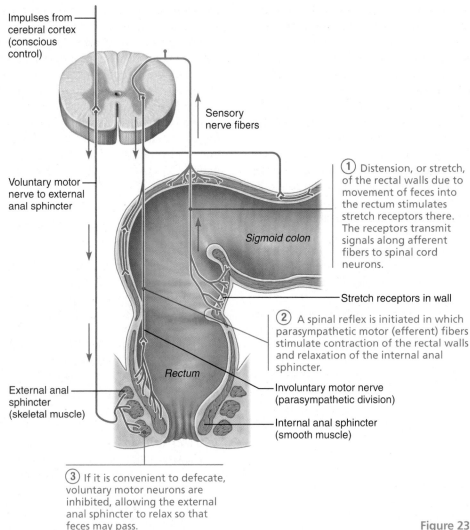

Impulses from cerebral cortex (conscious control)

Sensory nerve fibers

Voluntary motor nerve to external anal sphincter

Sigmoid colon

① Distension, or stretch, of the rectal walls due to movement of feces into the rectum stimulates stretch receptors there. The receptors transmit signals along afferent fibers to spinal cord neurons.

Stretch receptors in wall

② A spinal reflex is initiated in which parasympathetic motor (efferent) fibers stimulate contraction of the rectal walls and relaxation of the internal anal sphincter.

Rectum

External anal sphincter (skeletal muscle)

Involuntary motor nerve (parasympathetic division)

Internal anal sphincter (smooth muscle)

③ If it is convenient to defecate, voluntary motor neurons are inhibited, allowing the external anal sphincter to relax so that feces may pass.

Figure 23.31 Defecation reflex.

gastroileal reflex in the small intestine and the propulsive **gastrocolic reflex** in the colon. Bulk, or fiber, in the diet increases the strength of colon contractions and softens the stool, allowing the colon to act like a well-oiled machine.

HOMEOSTATIC IMBALANCE

When the diet lacks bulk and the volume of residues in the colon is small, the colon narrows and its contractions become more powerful, increasing the pressure on its walls. This promotes formation of **diverticula** (di″ver-tik′u-lah), small herniations of the mucosa through the colon walls. This condition, called **diverticulosis**, most commonly occurs in the sigmoid colon, and affects over half of people over the age of 70. In about 20% of cases, diverticulosis progresses to **diverticulitis**, in which the diverticula become inflamed and may rupture, leaking feces into the peritoneal cavity, which can be life threatening. Foods and products that increase the bulk of the stool help to prevent attacks of diverticulitis.

Irritable bowel syndrome (*IBS*) is a functional GI disorder not explained by anatomical or biochemical abnormalities. Affected individuals have recurring (or persistent) abdominal pain that is relieved by defecation, changes in the consistency (watery to stonelike) and frequency of their stools, and varying complaints of bloating, flatulence, nausea, and depression. Stress is a common precipitating factor, and stress management is an important aspect of treatment. ■

The semisolid product delivered to the rectum, called feces or the stool, contains undigested food residues, mucus, sloughed-off epithelial cells, millions of bacteria, and just enough water to allow its smooth passage. Of the 500 ml or so of food residue entering the cecum daily, approximately 150 ml becomes feces.

Defecation

The rectum is usually empty, but when mass movements force feces into it, stretching of the rectal wall initiates the **defecation reflex**. This spinal cord–mediated parasympathetic reflex causes the sigmoid colon and the rectum to contract, and the internal anal sphincter to relax (**Figure 23.31**, ① and ②). As feces are forced into the anal canal, messages reach the brain allowing us to decide whether the external (voluntary) anal sphincter should be opened or remain constricted to stop feces passage temporarily (Figure 23.31, ③). If defecation is delayed, the reflex contractions end within a few seconds, and the rectal walls relax. With the next mass movement, the defecation reflex is initiated again—and so on, until the person chooses to defecate or the urge to defecate becomes unavoidable.

During defecation, the muscles of the rectum contract to expel the feces. We aid this process voluntarily by closing the glottis and contracting our diaphragm and abdominal wall muscles to increase the intra-abdominal pressure (a procedure called *Valsalva's maneuver*). We also contract the levator ani muscle (pp. 344–345), which lifts the anal canal superiorly. This lifting action leaves the feces below the anus—and outside the body. Involuntary or automatic defecation (incontinence of feces) occurs in infants because they have not yet gained control of their external anal sphincter. It also occurs in those with spinal cord transections.

HOMEOSTATIC IMBALANCE

Watery stools, or **diarrhea**, result from any condition that rushes food residue through the large intestine before that organ has had sufficient time to absorb the remaining water. Causes include irritation of the colon by bacteria or, less commonly, prolonged physical jostling of the digestive viscera (occurs in marathon runners). Prolonged diarrhea may result in dehydration and electrolyte imbalance (acidosis and loss of potassium).

Conversely, when food remains in the colon for extended periods, too much water is absorbed and the stool becomes hard and difficult to pass. This condition, called **constipation**, may result from lack of fiber in the diet, improper bowel habits (failing to heed the "call"), lack of exercise, emotional upset, or laxative abuse. ■

CHECK YOUR UNDERSTANDING

45. What propulsive movements are unique to the large intestine?

46. What is the result of stimulation of stretch receptors in the rectal walls?

47. In what ways are enteric bacteria important to our nutrition?

For answers, see Appendix G.

PART 3

PHYSIOLOGY OF CHEMICAL DIGESTION AND ABSORPTION

▶ List the enzymes involved in chemical digestion; name the foodstuffs on which they act.

▶ List the end products of protein, fat, carbohydrate, and nucleic acid digestion.

▶ Describe the process of absorption of breakdown products of foodstuffs that occurs in the small intestine.

So far in this chapter, we have examined the structure and overall function of the organs that make up the digestive system.

Now let's investigate the entire chemical processing (enzymatic breakdown and absorption) of each class of foodstuffs as it moves through the GI tract. As you read along, you may find it helpful to refer to the summary in **Figure 23.32**.

Chemical Digestion

After foodstuffs have spent even a short time in the stomach, they are unrecognizable. Nonetheless, they are still mostly the starchy, carbohydrate-rich foods, meat proteins, butter and other fats, and so on that we ingested. Only their appearance has been changed by mechanical digestive activities. By contrast, the products of chemical digestion are the chemical building blocks of the ingested foods and are very different molecules chemically.

Mechanism of Chemical Digestion: Enzymatic Hydrolysis

Chemical digestion is a catabolic process in which large food molecules are broken down to *monomers* (chemical building blocks), which are small enough to be absorbed by the GI tract lining. Chemical digestion is accomplished by enzymes secreted by both intrinsic and accessory glands into the lumen of the alimentary canal. The enzymatic breakdown of any type of food molecule is **hydrolysis** (hi-drol′ĭ-sis) because it involves addition of a water molecule to each molecular bond to be broken (lysed).

Chemical Digestion of Carbohydrates

Most of us ingest between 200 and 600 grams of carbohydrate foods each day. **Monosaccharides** (simple sugars), the monomers of carbohydrates, are absorbed immediately without further ado. Only three of these are common in our diet: *glucose*, *fructose*, and *galactose*. The more complex carbohydrates that our digestive system is able to break down to monosaccharides are the disaccharides *sucrose* (table sugar), *lactose* (milk sugar), and *maltose* (grain sugar) and the polysaccharides *glycogen* and *starch*.

In the average diet, most digestible carbohydrates are in the form of starch, with smaller amounts of disaccharides and monosaccharides. Humans lack enzymes capable of breaking down most other polysaccharides, such as cellulose. As a result, indigestible polysaccharides do not nourish us but they do help move the food along the GI tract by providing bulk, or fiber.

Chemical digestion of starch (and perhaps glycogen) begins in the mouth (Figure 23.32). **Salivary amylase**, present in saliva, splits starch into *oligosaccharides*, smaller fragments of two to eight linked glucose molecules. Salivary amylase works best in the slightly acid to neutral environment (pH of 6.75–7.00) maintained in the mouth by the buffering effects of bicarbonate and phosphate ions in saliva. Starch digestion continues until amylase is inactivated by stomach acid and broken apart by the stomach's protein-digesting enzymes. Generally speaking, the larger the meal, the longer amylase continues to work in the stomach because foodstuffs in its relatively immobile fundus are poorly mixed with gastric juices.

Foodstuff	Enzyme(s) and source	Site of action	Path of absorption

Carbohydrate digestion

Starch and disaccharides

→ Salivary amylase — Mouth

↓

→ Pancreatic amylase — Small intestine

Oligosaccharides and disaccharides

↓

Lactose   Maltose   Sucrose

→ Brush border enzymes in small intestine (dextrinase, gluco-amylase, lactase, maltase, and sucrase) — Small intestine

↓

Galactose   Glucose   Fructose

Path of absorption:
- Glucose and galactose are absorbed via cotransport with sodium ions.
- Fructose passes via facilitated diffusion.
- All monosaccharides leave the epithelial cells via facilitated diffusion, enter the capillary blood in the villi, and are transported to the liver via the hepatic portal vein.

Protein digestion

Protein

↓

→ Pepsin (stomach glands) in presence of HCl — Stomach

Large polypeptides

↓

→ Pancreatic enzymes (trypsin, chymotrypsin, carboxypeptidase) — Small intestine

Small polypeptides, small peptides

↓

→ Brush border enzymes (aminopeptidase, carboxypeptidase, and dipeptidase) — Small intestine

Amino acids (some dipeptides and tripeptides)

Path of absorption:
- Amino acids are absorbed by cotransport with sodium ions.
- Some dipeptides and tripeptides are absorbed via cotransport with H^+ and hydrolyzed to amino acids within the cells.
- Amino acids leave the epithelial cells by facilitated diffusion, enter the capillary blood in the villi, and are transported to the liver via the hepatic portal vein.

Fat digestion

Unemulsified fats

↓

→ Emulsification by the detergent action of bile salts ducted in from the liver — Small intestine

↓

→ Pancreatic lipases — Small intestine

↓

Monoglycerides and fatty acids   Glycerol and fatty acids

Path of absorption:
- Fatty acids and monoglycerides enter the intestinal cells via diffusion.
- Fatty acids and monoglycerides are recombined to form triglycerides and then combined with other lipids and proteins within the cells, and the resulting chylomicrons are extruded by exocytosis.
- The chylomicrons enter the lacteals of the villi and are transported to the systemic circulation via the lymph in the thoracic duct.
- Some short-chain fatty acids are absorbed, move into the capillary blood in the villi by diffusion, and are transported to the liver via the hepatic portal vein.

Nucleic acid digestion

Nucleic acids

↓

→ Pancreatic ribonuclease and deoxyribonuclease — Small intestine

↓

→ Brush border enzymes (nucleosidases and phosphatases) — Small intestine

↓

Pentose sugars, N-containing bases, phosphate ions

Path of absorption:
- Units enter intestinal cells by active transport via membrane carriers.
- Units are absorbed into capillary blood in the villi and transported to the liver via the hepatic portal vein.

Figure 23.32 **Flowchart of chemical digestion and absorption of foodstuffs.**

Starchy foods and other digestible carbohydrates that escape being broken down by salivary amylase are acted on by **pancreatic amylase** in the small intestine. Within about 10 minutes of entering the small intestine, starch is entirely converted to various oligosaccharides, mostly maltose.

Intestinal brush border enzymes further digest these products to monosaccharides. The most important of the brush border enzymes are **dextrinase** and **glucoamylase**, which act on oligosaccharides composed of more than three simple sugars, and **maltase**, **sucrase**, and **lactase**, which hydrolyze maltose, sucrose, and lactose respectively into their constituent monosaccharides.

Because the colon does not secrete digestive enzymes, chemical digestion *officially ends* in the small intestine. As noted earlier, however, resident colon bacteria do break down and metabolize the residual complex carbohydrates and some proteins further, adding much to their own nutrition but essentially nothing to ours.

HOMEOSTATIC IMBALANCE

In some people, intestinal lactase is present at birth but then becomes deficient due to genetic factors. In such cases, the person becomes intolerant of milk products (the source of lactose), and undigested lactose creates osmotic gradients that not only prevent water from being absorbed in the small and large intestines but also pull water from the interstitial space into the intestines. The result is diarrhea. Bacterial metabolism of the undigested solutes produces large amounts of gas that result in bouts of bloating, flatulence, and cramping pain. For the most part, the solution to this problem is simple—add lactase enzyme "drops" to your milk or take a lactase tablet before meals containing milk products. ■

Chemical Digestion of Proteins

Proteins digested in the GI tract include not only dietary proteins (typically about 125 g per day), but also 15–25 g of enzyme proteins secreted into the GI tract lumen by its various glands and (probably) an equal amount of protein derived from sloughed and disintegrating mucosal cells. In healthy individuals, much of this protein is digested all the way to its **amino acid** monomers.

Protein digestion begins in the stomach when pepsinogen secreted by the chief cells is activated to **pepsin** (actually a group of protein-digesting enzymes) (Figure 23.32). Pepsin functions optimally in the acidic pH range found in the stomach: 1.5–2.5. It preferentially cleaves bonds involving the amino acids tyrosine and phenylalanine so that proteins are broken into polypeptides and small numbers of free amino acids. Pepsin, which hydrolyzes 10–15% of ingested protein, is inactivated by the high pH in the duodenum, so its proteolytic activity is restricted to the stomach. **Rennin** (the enzyme that coagulates milk protein) is not produced in adults.

Protein fragments entering the small intestine from the stomach are greeted by a host of proteolytic enzymes **(Figure 23.33)**. **Trypsin** and **chymotrypsin** secreted by the pancreas cleave the proteins into smaller peptides, which in turn become the grist for other enzymes. The pancreatic and brush border enzyme **carboxypeptidase** splits off one amino acid at a time from the end of the polypeptide chain that bears the carboxyl group. Other brush border enzymes such as **aminopeptidase** and **dipeptidase** liberate the final amino acid products. Aminopeptidase digests a protein, one amino acid at a time, by working from the amine end. Both carboxypeptidase and aminopeptidase can independently dismantle a protein, but the teamwork between these enzymes and between trypsin and chymotrypsin, which attack the more internal parts of the protein, speeds up the process tremendously.

Chemical Digestion of Lipids

Although the American Heart Association recommends a low-fat diet, the amount of lipids (fats) ingested daily varies tremendously among American adults, ranging from 30 g to 150 g or more. Triglycerides (neutral fats or triacylglycerols) are the most abundant fats in the diet. The small intestine is essentially the sole site of lipid digestion because the pancreas is the only significant source of fat-digesting enzymes, or **lipases** (see Figure 23.32).

Because triglycerides and their breakdown products are insoluble in water, fats need special "pretreatment" with bile salts to be digested and absorbed in the watery environment of the small intestine. In aqueous solutions, triglycerides aggregate to form large fat globules, and only the triglyceride molecules at the surfaces of such fatty masses are accessible to the water-soluble lipase enzymes. However, this problem is quickly resolved because as the fat globules enter the duodenum, they are coated with detergent-like bile salts.

Bile salts have both nonpolar and polar regions. Their nonpolar (hydrophobic) parts cling to the fat molecules, and their polar (ionized hydrophilic) parts allow them to repel each other and to interact with water. As a result, fatty droplets are pulled off the large fat globules, and a stable *emulsion*—an aqueous suspension of fatty droplets, each about 1 mm in diameter—is formed **(Figure 23.34, ①)**.

Emulsification does *not* break chemical bonds. It just reduces the attraction between fat molecules so that they can be more widely dispersed. This process vastly increases the number of triglyceride molecules exposed to the pancreatic lipases. Without bile, lipids would be incompletely digested in the time food is in the small intestine.

The pancreatic lipases catalyze the breakdown of fats by cleaving off two of the fatty acid chains, yielding free **fatty acids** and **monoglycerides**—glycerol with one fatty acid chain attached (Figure 23.34, ②). Fat-soluble vitamins that ride with fats require no digestion.

Chemical Digestion of Nucleic Acids

Both DNA and RNA, present in the nuclei of cells forming the ingested foods, are hydrolyzed to their **nucleotide** monomers by **pancreatic nucleases** present in pancreatic juice. The nucleotides are then broken apart by intestinal brush border enzymes (**nucleosidases** and **phosphatases**), which release their free bases, pentose sugars, and phosphate ions (see Figure 23.32).

23

Lumen of intestine

Amino acids of protein fragments

Pancreatic proteases

Brush border enzymes

Na⁺

Na⁺

Absorptive epithelial cell

Apical membrane (microvilli)

Amino acid carrier

Capillary

(1) Proteins and protein fragments are digested to amino acids by pancreatic proteases (trypsin, chymotrypsin, and carboxypeptidase), and by brush border enzymes (carboxypeptidase, aminopeptidase, and dipeptidase) of mucosal cells.

(2) The amino acids are then absorbed by active transport into the absorptive cells, and move to their opposite side (transcytosis).

(3) The amino acids leave the villus epithelial cell by facilitated diffusion and enter the capillary via intercellular clefts.

← Active transport

← Passive transport

Figure 23.33 Protein digestion and absorption in the small intestine.

Absorption

Up to 10 L of food, drink, and GI secretions enter the alimentary canal daily, but only 1 L or less reaches the large intestine. Virtually all of the foodstuffs, 80% of the electrolytes, and most of the water (remember water follows salt) are absorbed in the small intestine. Although absorption occurs all along the length of the small intestine, most of it is completed by the time chyme reaches the ileum.

The major absorptive role of the ileum is to reclaim bile salts to be recycled back to the liver for resecretion. It is virtually impossible to exceed the absorptive capacity of the human gut, and at the end of the ileum, all that remains is some water, indigestible food materials (largely plant fibers such as cellulose), and millions of bacteria. This debris is passed on to the large intestine.

To understand absorption, remember that the fluid mosaic structure of the plasma membrane dictates that nonpolar substances, which can dissolve in the lipid core of the membrane, can be absorbed passively, and that polar substances must be absorbed by carrier mechanisms. Most nutrients are absorbed through the mucosa of the intestinal villi by *active transport* processes driven directly or indirectly (secondarily) by metabolic energy (ATP). They then enter the capillary blood in the villus to be transported in the hepatic portal vein to the liver. The exception is some lipid digestion products, which are absorbed passively by diffusion and then enter the lacteal in the villus to be carried to the blood via lymphatic fluid.

Because the epithelial cells of the intestinal mucosa are joined at their luminal surfaces by tight junctions, substances cannot move *between* the cells for the most part. Consequently, materials must pass through the epithelial cells and into the

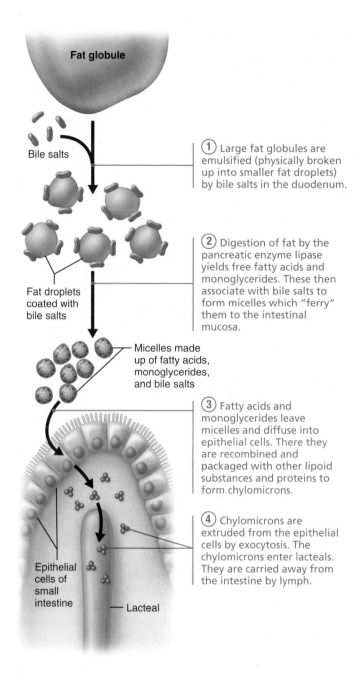

Fat globule

Bile salts

Fat droplets coated with bile salts

① Large fat globules are emulsified (physically broken up into smaller fat droplets) by bile salts in the duodenum.

② Digestion of fat by the pancreatic enzyme lipase yields free fatty acids and monoglycerides. These then associate with bile salts to form micelles which "ferry" them to the intestinal mucosa.

Micelles made up of fatty acids, monoglycerides, and bile salts

③ Fatty acids and monoglycerides leave micelles and diffuse into epithelial cells. There they are recombined and packaged with other lipoid substances and proteins to form chylomicrons.

④ Chylomicrons are extruded from the epithelial cells by exocytosis. The chylomicrons enter lacteals. They are carried away from the intestine by lymph.

Epithelial cells of small intestine

Lacteal

Figure 23.34 Emulsification, digestion, and absorption of fats.

interstitial fluid abutting their basolateral membranes (via transcytosis) if they are to enter the blood capillaries. As we describe the absorption of each nutrient class next, you may want to refer to the absorption summary on the right-hand side of Figure 23.32.

Carbohydrate Absorption

The monosaccharides glucose and galactose, liberated by the breakdown of starch and disaccharides, are shuttled by secondary active transport (cotransport with Na^+) into the epithelial cells by common protein carriers. They then move out of these cells by facilitated diffusion and pass into the capillaries via intercellular clefts. By contrast, fructose moves entirely by facilitated diffusion. The transport proteins, which are located very close to the disaccharidase enzymes on the microvilli, combine with the monosaccharides as soon as the disaccharides are broken down.

Protein Absorption

Several types of carriers transport the different amino acids resulting from protein digestion. Most of these carriers, like those for glucose and galactose, are coupled to the active transport of sodium. Short chains of two or three amino acids (dipeptides and tripeptides, respectively) are actively absorbed by H^+-dependent cotransport and are then digested to their amino acids within the epithelial cells before entering the capillary blood by diffusion (see Figure 23.33).

HOMEOSTATIC IMBALANCE

Whole proteins are not usually absorbed, but in rare cases intact proteins are taken up by endocytosis and released on the opposite side of the epithelial cell by exocytosis. This process is most common in newborn infants, reflecting the immaturity of their intestinal mucosa (gastric acid secretion does not reach normal levels until weeks after birth, and the mucosa is leakier than it is later.) Absorption of whole proteins accounts for many early food allergies. The immune system "sees" the intact proteins as antigenic and mounts an attack. These food allergies usually disappear as the mucosa matures. This mechanism may also provide a route for IgA antibodies present in breast milk to reach an infant's bloodstream. These antibodies confer some passive immunity on the infant, providing temporary protection against antigens to which the mother has been sensitized. ■

Lipid Absorption

Just as bile salts accelerate lipid digestion, they are also essential for the absorption of its end products. As the water-insoluble products of fat digestion—the monoglycerides and free fatty acids—are liberated by lipase activity, they quickly become associated with bile salts and *lecithin* (a phospholipid found in bile) to form micelles (Figure 23.34, ②). **Micelles** (mi-selz′) are collections of fatty elements clustered together with bile salts in such a way that the polar (hydrophilic) ends of the molecules face the water and the nonpolar portions form the core. Also nestled in the hydrophobic core are cholesterol molecules and fat-soluble vitamins. Although micelles are similar to emulsion droplets, they are much smaller "vehicles" and easily diffuse between microvilli to come into close contact with the luminal cell surface.

Upon reaching the epithelial cells, the various lipid substances leave the micelles and move through the lipid phase of the plasma membrane by simple diffusion (Figure 23.34, ③). Without the micelles, the lipids will simply float on the surface of the chyme (like oil on water), inaccessible to the absorptive surfaces of the epithelial cells. Generally, fat absorption is completed in the ileum, but in the absence of bile (as might occur when a gallstone blocks the cystic duct) it happens so slowly that most of the fat passes into the large intestine and is lost in feces.

23

Once inside the epithelial cells, the free fatty acids and monoglycerides are resynthesized into triglycerides by the smooth ER. The triglycerides are then combined with lecithin and other phospholipids and cholesterol, and coated with a "skin" of proteins to form water-soluble lipoprotein droplets called **chylomicrons** (ki"lo-mi'kronz). These are dispatched to the Golgi apparatus where they are processed for extrusion from the cell. This series of events is quite different from the absorption of amino acids and simple sugars, which pass through the epithelial cells unchanged.

The milky-white chylomicrons are too large to pass through either the plasma membranes or the basement membranes of the blood capillaries. Instead, the chylomicron-containing vesicles migrate to the basolateral membrane and are extruded by exocytosis (Figure 23.34, ④). They then enter the more permeable lacteals. Thus, most fat enters the lymphatic stream for distribution in the lymph. Eventually the chylomicrons are emptied into the venous blood in the neck region via the thoracic duct, which drains the digestive viscera.

While in the bloodstream, the triglycerides of the chylomicrons are hydrolyzed to free fatty acids and glycerol by **lipoprotein lipase**, an enzyme associated with the capillary endothelium of liver and adipose tissue. The fatty acids and glycerol can then pass through the capillary walls to be used by tissue cells for energy or stored as fats in adipose tissue. The residual chylomicron material is combined with proteins by the liver cells, and these "new" lipoproteins are used to transport cholesterol in the blood.

Passage of short-chain fatty acids is quite different from what we have just described. These fat breakdown products do not depend on the presence of bile salts or micelles, are not recombined to form triglycerides within the intestinal cells, and simply diffuse into the portal blood for distribution.

Nucleic Acid Absorption

The pentose sugars, nitrogenous bases, and phosphate ions resulting from nucleic acid digestion are transported actively across the epithelium by special carriers in the villus epithelium. They then enter the blood.

Vitamin Absorption

The small intestine absorbs dietary vitamins, and the large intestine absorbs some of the K and B vitamins made by its enteric bacterial "guests." As we already noted, fat-soluble vitamins (A, D, E, and K) dissolve in dietary fats, become incorporated into the micelles, and move across the villus epithelium passively (by diffusion). It follows that gulping pills containing fat-soluble vitamins without simultaneously eating some fat-containing food results in little or no absorption of these vitamins.

Most water-soluble vitamins (B vitamins and vitamin C) are absorbed easily by diffusion or via specific active or passive transporters. The exception is vitamin B_{12}, which is a very large, charged molecule. *Intrinsic factor*, produced by the stomach, binds to vitamin B_{12}. The vitamin B_{12}–intrinsic factor complex then binds to specific mucosal receptor sites in the terminal ileum, which trigger its active uptake by endocytosis.

Electrolyte Absorption

Absorbed electrolytes come from both ingested foods and gastrointestinal secretions. Most ions are actively absorbed along the entire length of the small intestine. However, iron and calcium absorption is largely limited to the duodenum.

As we mentioned earlier, absorption of sodium ions in the small intestine is coupled to active absorption of glucose and amino acids. For the most part, anions passively follow the electrical potential established by sodium transport. In other words, Na^+ is actively pumped out of the epithelial cells by a Na^+-K^+ pump after entering those cells. Chloride ions are also transported actively, and in the terminus of the small intestine HCO_3^- is actively secreted into the lumen in exchange for Cl^-.

Potassium ions move across the intestinal mucosa passively by facilitated diffusion (or via leaky tight junctions) in response to changing osmotic gradients. As water is absorbed from the lumen, the resulting rise in potassium levels in chyme creates a concentration gradient for its absorption. Anything that interferes with water absorption (resulting in diarrhea) not only reduces potassium absorption but also "pulls" K^+ from the interstitial space into the intestinal lumen.

For most nutrients, the amount *reaching* the intestine is the amount absorbed, regardless of the nutritional state of the body. In contrast, absorption of iron and calcium is intimately related to the body's need for them at the time.

Ionic iron, essential for hemoglobin production, is actively transported into the mucosal cells, where it binds to the protein **ferritin** (fer'ĭ-tin). This phenomenon is called the *mucosal iron barrier*. The intracellular iron-ferritin complexes then serve as local storehouses for iron. When body reserves of iron are adequate, little (only 10% to 20%) is allowed to pass into the portal blood, and most of the stored iron is lost as the epithelial cells later slough off. However, when iron reserves are depleted (as during acute or chronic hemorrhage), iron uptake from the intestine and its release to the blood are accelerated. In the blood, iron binds to **transferrin**, a plasma protein that transports it in the circulation.

Menstrual bleeding is a major route of iron loss in females, and premenopausal women require about 50% more iron in their diets. Additionally, the intestinal epithelial cells of women have about four times as many iron transport proteins as do those of men and very little iron is lost from the body other than that lost in menses.

Calcium absorption is closely related to blood levels of ionic calcium. It is locally regulated by the active form of **vitamin D**, which promotes active calcium absorption. Decreased blood levels of ionic calcium prompt *parathyroid hormone* (*PTH*) release from the parathyroid glands. Besides facilitating the release of calcium ions from bone matrix and enhancing the reabsorption of calcium by the kidneys, PTH stimulates activation of vitamin D by the kidneys, which in turn accelerates calcium ion absorption in the small intestine.

Water Absorption

Approximately 9 L of water, mostly derived from GI tract secretions, enter the small intestine daily. Water is the most abundant substance in chyme, and 95% of it is absorbed in the small

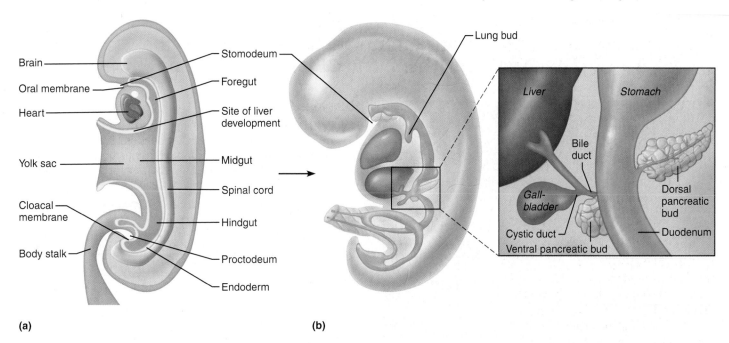

Figure 23.35 Embryonic development of the digestive system. (a) Three-week-old embryo. The endoderm has folded, and the foregut and hindgut have formed. (The midgut is still open and continuous with the yolk sac.) **(b)** By five weeks of development, the accessory organs are budding out from the endodermal layer, as shown in the enlargement.

intestine by osmosis. Most of the rest is absorbed in the large intestine, leaving only about 0.1 L to soften the feces.

The normal rate of water absorption is 300 to 400 ml per hour. Water moves freely in both directions across the intestinal mucosa, but *net osmosis* occurs whenever a concentration gradient is established by the active transport of solutes (particularly Na^+) into the mucosal cells. In this way, water uptake is effectively coupled to solute uptake and, in turn, affects the rate of absorption of substances that normally pass by diffusion. As water moves into the mucosal cells, these substances follow along their concentration gradients.

Malabsorption of Nutrients

Malabsorption, or impaired nutrient absorption, has many and varied causes. It can result from anything that interferes with the delivery of bile or pancreatic juice to the small intestine, as well as factors that damage the intestinal mucosa (severe bacterial infections and antibiotic therapy with neomycin) or reduce its absorptive surface area.

A common malabsorption syndrome is *gluten-sensitive enteropathy* or *celiac disease*, which affects one in 100 people. This chronic genetic condition is caused by an immune reaction to gluten, a protein plentiful in some grains (wheat, rye, barley). Breakdown products of gluten interact with molecules of the immune system in the GI tract, forming complexes that activate T cells, which then mount an attack on the intestinal lining. As a result, the intestinal villi are damaged and the surface area of the brush border is reduced.

The resulting bloating, diarrhea, pain, and malnutrition are usually controlled by eliminating gluten-containing grains (all grains but rice and corn) from the diet. Not many children can

conceive of a world without cookies or pizza, but these are just two of the foods celiac disease victims must avoid.

CHECK YOUR UNDERSTANDING

48. What type of chemical reaction is the basis of all enzymatic food digestion?

49. Fill in the blank: Amylase is to starch as _____ is to fats.

50. What is the role of bile salts in the digestive process? In absorption?

For answers, see Appendix G.

Developmental Aspects of the Digestive System

▶ Describe embryonic development of the digestive system.

▶ Describe abnormalities of the gastrointestinal tract at different stages of life.

As we have described many times before, the very young embryo is flat and consists of three germ layers. From top to bottom, they are ectoderm, mesoderm, and endoderm. This flattened cell mass soon folds to form a cylindrical body, and its internal cavity becomes the cavity of the alimentary canal, which is initially closed at both ends.

The epithelial lining of the developing alimentary canal, or **primitive gut**, forms from endoderm **(Figure 23.35a)**. The rest of the wall arises from mesoderm. The anteriormost endoderm

(Text continues on p. 904.)

System Connections

Homeostatic Interrelationships Between the Digestive System and Other Body Systems

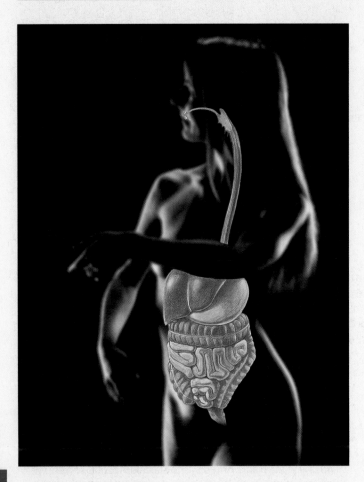

Nervous System

- Digestive system provides nutrients needed for normal neural functioning; nutrient signals influence neural regulation of satiety
- Neural controls of digestive function; in general, parasympathetic fibers accelerate and sympathetic fibers inhibit digestive activity; reflex and voluntary controls of defecation

Endocrine System

- Liver removes hormones from blood, ending their activity; digestive system provides nutrients needed for energy, growth, and repair; pancreas, stomach, and small intestine have hormone-producing cells
- Hormones and paracrines help regulate digestive function

Cardiovascular System

- Digestive system provides nutrients to heart and blood vessels; absorbs iron needed for hemoglobin synthesis; absorbs water necessary for normal plasma volume; liver secretes bilirubin resulting from hemoglobin breakdown in bile and stores iron for reuse
- Cardiovascular system transports nutrients absorbed by alimentary canal to all tissues of body; distributes hormones of the digestive tract

Lymphatic System/Immunity

- Digestive system provides nutrients for normal functioning; lysozyme of saliva and HCl of stomach provide nonspecific protection against bacteria
- Lacteals drain fatty lymph from digestive tract organs and convey it to blood; Peyer's patches and lymphoid tissue in mesentery house macrophages and immune cells that protect digestive tract organs against infection; plasma cells provide IgA in digestive tract secretions

Respiratory System

- Digestive system provides nutrients needed for energy metabolism, growth, and repair
- Respiratory system provides oxygen to and carries away carbon dioxide produced by digestive system organs

Urinary System

- Digestive system provides nutrients for energy fuel, growth, and repair; excretes some bilirubin produced by the liver
- Kidneys transform vitamin D to its active form, which is needed for calcium absorption

Reproductive System

- Digestive system provides nutrients for energy, growth, and repair and extra nutrition needed to support fetal growth

Integumentary System

- Digestive system provides nutrients needed for energy, growth, and repair; supplies fats that provide insulation in the dermis and subcutaneous tissue
- The skin synthesizes vitamin D needed for calcium absorption from the intestine; protects by enclosure

Skeletal System

- Digestive system provides nutrients needed for energy, growth, and repair; absorbs calcium needed for bone salts
- Skeletal system protects some digestive organs by bone; cavities store some nutrients (e.g., calcium, fats)

Muscular System

- Digestive system provides nutrients needed for energy, growth, and repair; liver removes lactic acid, resulting from muscle activity, from the blood
- Skeletal muscle activity increases motility of GI tract

23

The Digestive System and Interrelationships with the Cardiovascular, Lymphatic, and Endocrine Systems

As body systems go, the digestive system is very independent. Although the central nervous system can and does influence its activity, that is not a requirement. Indeed, most digestive system activities can be regulated entirely by local controls. Consider, for example, the following: (1) stomach and intestinal muscle is self-pacing, (2) the enteric neurons of the GI tract's intrinsic nerve plexuses carry out reflex activity that can regulate not only the organ they reside in but also adjacent and more distant GI tract organs, and (3) its enteroendocrine cells are probably even more important than neural influences in controlling digestive activity. Also unique is the fact that the digestive system operates in and regulates an environment that is actually outside the body. This is a difficult chore indeed—consider how quickly that environment can be changed by incoming foods (pizza and beer) or intestinal outflow (diarrhea).

Every cell in the body needs nutrients to stay healthy and grow, so the importance of the digestive system to virtually all body systems is clear-cut. But what systems are essential to the digestive system? If we ignore universal services, like gas exchange and renal regulation of body fluids, then the most crucial interactions are those with the cardiovascular, lymphatic, and endocrine systems. Let's take a look.

Cardiovascular and Lymphatic Systems

The important elements in this interaction are the pickup vessels. Indeed, all digestive activity would be for naught if the digested end products were not absorbed into the blood capillaries and lacteals, where they are accessible to all body cells. The lymphatic organs and tissues also offer protective services via the tonsils, Peyer's patches, and individual lymphoid follicles dispersed all along the length of the alimentary canal. Again, the fact that the alimentary canal is open at both ends makes it easy prey for both pathogenic and opportunistic bacteria and fungi.

Endocrine System

The digestive tract not only has major interactions with the endocrine system, it is itself the largest and most complex endocrine organ in the body. It makes hormones that regulate GI tract motility and secretory activity of the stomach, small intestine, liver, and pancreas (e.g., secretin, CCK), as well as cause local blood vessels to dilate to receive the digested food products being absorbed (VIP). Furthermore, some digestive organ hormones (CCK and glucagon, for example) help mediate hunger or satiety, and pancreatic hormones (insulin and glucagon) are involved in bodywide regulation of carbohydrate, fat, and amino acid metabolism.

Digestive System

Case study: Remember Mr. Gutteman, the gentleman who was dehydrating? It seems that his tremendous output of urine was only one of his current problems. Today, he complains of a headache, gnawing epigastric pain, and "the runs" (diarrhea). To pinpoint the problem, he is asked the following questions.

- Have you had these symptoms previously? (Response: "Yes, but never this bad.")
- Are you allergic to any foods? (Response: "Shellfish doesn't like me and milk gives me the runs.")

As a result of his responses, a lactose-free diet is ordered for Mr. Gutteman instead of the regular diet originally prescribed.

1. Why is the new diet prescribed? (What is believed to be his problem?)

Mr. Gutteman's problem continues despite the diet change. In fact, the frequency of diarrhea increases and by the end of the next day, he is complaining of severe abdominal pain. Again, he is asked some questions to probe his condition. One is whether he has traveled outside the country recently. He has not, reducing the possibility of infection with *Shigella* bacteria, which is associated with poor sanitation. Other questions:

- Do you drink alcohol and how much? (Response: "Little or none.")
- Have you recently eaten raw eggs or a salad containing mayonnaise at a gathering? (Response: "No.")
- Are there certain foods that seem to precipitate these attacks? (Response: "Yes, when I have coffee and a sandwich.")

2. On the basis of these responses, what do you think Mr. Gutteman's diarrhea stems from? How will it be diagnosed and treated?

(Answers in Appendix G)

23

(that of the foregut) touches a depressed area of the surface ectoderm called the **stomodeum** (sto″mo-de′um; "on the way to becoming the mouth"). The two membranes fuse, forming the **oral membrane**, which soon breaks through to form the opening of the mouth. Similarly, the end of the hindgut fuses with an ectodermal depression, called the **proctodeum** (*procto* = anus), to form the **cloacal membrane** (*cloaca* = sewer), which then breaks through to form the anus.

By week 5, the alimentary canal is a continuous "tube" extending from the mouth to the anus and is open to the external environment at each end. Shortly after, the glandular organs (salivary glands, liver with gallbladder, and pancreas) bud out from the mucosa at various points along its length (Figure 23.35b). These glands retain their connections, which become ducts leading into the digestive tract.

HOMEOSTATIC IMBALANCE

The digestive system is susceptible to many congenital defects that interfere with feeding. The most common are **cleft palate**, in which the palatine bones or palatine processes of the maxillae (or both) fail to fuse, and **cleft lip**, which often occur together. Of the two, cleft palate is far more serious because the child is unable to suck properly.

Another common defect is *tracheoesophageal fistula*, in which there is an opening between the esophagus and the trachea, and the esophagus often lacks a connection to the stomach. The baby chokes and becomes cyanotic during feedings because food enters the respiratory passageways. These defects are usually corrected surgically.

Cystic fibrosis (described in more detail in Chapter 22, p. 843) primarily affects the lungs, but it also impairs the activity of the pancreas. In this genetic disease, the mucous glands produce abnormally thick mucus, which blocks the ducts or passageways of involved organs. Blockage of the pancreatic duct prevents pancreatic juice from reaching the small intestine. As a result, digestion of chyme is less than optimal and most fats and fat-soluble vitamins are not digested or absorbed. Consequently the stools are bulky and fat laden. The pancreatic problems can be handled by administering pancreatic enzymes with meals. ■

During fetal life, the developing infant receives all of its nutrients through the placenta. Nonetheless, the fetal GI tract is "trained" in utero for future food digestion as the fetus naturally swallows some of the surrounding amniotic fluid. This fluid contains several chemicals that stimulate GI maturation, including gastrin and epidermal growth factor.

By contrast, feeding is a newborn baby's most important activity, and several reflexes enhance the infant's ability to obtain food: The *rooting reflex* helps the infant find the nipple, and the *sucking reflex* helps the baby hold onto the nipple and swallow.

Newborn babies tend to double their birth weight within six months, and their caloric intake and food processing ability are extraordinary. For example, a 6-week-old infant weighing about 4 kg (less than 9 lb) drinks about 600 ml of milk daily. A 65-kg adult (143 lb) would have to drink 10 L of milk to ingest a corresponding volume of fluid! However, the stomach of a newborn infant is very small, so feeding must be frequent (every 3–4 hours). Peristalsis is inefficient, and vomiting of the feeding is not unusual. As the teeth break through the gums, the infant progresses to solid foods and is usually eating an adult diet by the age of 2 years.

As a rule, the digestive system operates throughout childhood and adulthood with relatively few problems. However, contaminated food or extremely spicy or irritating foods sometimes cause an inflammation of the GI tract, called **gastroenteritis** (gas″tro-en″tĕ-ri′tis). Ulcers and gallbladder problems—inflammation or **cholecystitis** (ko″le-sis-ti′tis), and gallstones—are problems of middle age.

During old age, GI tract activity declines. Fewer digestive juices are produced, absorption is less efficient, and peristalsis slows. The result is less frequent bowel movements and, often, constipation. Taste and smell are less acute, and periodontal disease often develops. Many elderly people live alone or on a reduced income. These factors, along with increasing physical disability, tend to make eating less appealing, and many of our elderly citizens are poorly nourished.

Diverticulosis, fecal incontinence, and cancer of the GI tract are fairly common problems of the aged. Stomach and colon cancers rarely have early signs, and have often metastasized (making it inoperable) before a person seeks medical attention. Should metastasis occur, secondary cancer of the liver is almost guaranteed because of the "detour" the splanchnic venous blood takes through the liver via the hepatic portal circulation. However, when detected early, these cancers are treatable. Perhaps the best advice is to have regular dental and medical checkups. Most oral cancers are detected during routine dental examinations, 50% of all rectal cancers can be felt digitally, and nearly 80% of colon cancers can be seen and removed during a colonoscopy.

Presently, colon cancer is the second leading cancer killer (behind lung cancer) of males in the United States. Until now it was believed that most colorectal cancers derive from initially benign, knobby mucosal tumors called polyps. However, flat pancake-like growths which blend in with the surrounding tissue are more common in Americans than originally thought and are 10 times more likely to be cancerous than polyps. Researchers believe that the flat growths represent a separate pathway to colon cancer, instead of being polyp precursors. This information will likely have a big impact on gastroenterology and scheduling of tests for colon cancer. Currently it is recommended that an occult blood examination be done once a year and that colonoscopies be conducted at 3- to 10-year intervals depending on prior findings.

As we described in *A Closer Look* in Chapter 4, development of colon cancer is a gradual process that involves mutations in several regulatory genes. Recent studies have identified the mutant gene responsible for nearly 50% of all colon cancers. Dubbed *p53*, the gene normally acts as a watchdog to make sure that errors in DNA are not passed on before being corrected. When *p53* is damaged or inhibited, its tumor suppressor effect is lost and damaged DNA accumulates, resulting in carcinogenesis.

CHECK YOUR UNDERSTANDING

51. From what germ layer does the digestive system mucosa develop?

52. How does cystic fibrosis interfere with the digestive process?

53. Why are colon and stomach cancers so dangerous?

For answers, see Appendix G.

As summarized in *Making Connections*, the digestive system keeps the blood well supplied with the nutrients needed by all body tissues to fuel their energy needs and to synthesize new proteins for growth and maintenance of health. Now we are ready to examine how these nutrients are used by body cells, the topic of Chapter 24.

RELATED CLINICAL TERMS

Ascites (ah-si′tēz; *asci* = bag, bladder) Abnormal accumulation of fluid within the peritoneal cavity; if excessive, causes visible bloating of the abdomen. May result from portal hypertension caused by liver cirrhosis or by heart or kidney disease.

Barrett's esophagus A pathological change in the epithelium of the lower esophagus from stratified squamous to a metaplastic columnar epithelium. A possible sequel to untreated chronic gastroesophageal reflux due to hiatal hernia, it predisposes the individual to aggressive esophageal cancer (adenocarcinoma).

Bruxism (bruck′sizm) Grinding or clenching of teeth, usually at night during sleep in response to stress. Can wear down and crack the teeth.

Bulimia (bu-lim′e-ah; *bous* = ox; *limos* = hunger) Binge-purge behavior—episodes of massive overeating are followed by some method of purging (self-induced vomiting, taking laxatives or diuretics, or excessive exercise). Most common in women of high school or college age and in high school males in certain athletic activities (wrestling). Rooted in a pathological fear of being fat, and a need for control; provides a means of handling stress and depression. Consequences include erosion of tooth enamel and stomach trauma or rupture (from vomiting) and severe electrolyte disturbances which impair heart activity. Therapy includes hospitalization to control behavior, and nutritional counseling.

Dysphagia (dis-fa′je-ah; *dys* = difficult, abnormal; *phag* = eat) Difficulty swallowing; usually due to obstruction or physical trauma to the esophagus.

Endoscopy (en-dos′ko-pe; *endo* = within, inside; *scopy* = viewing) Visual examination of a ventral body cavity or the interior of a visceral organ with a flexible tubelike device called an endoscope, which contains a light source and a lens. A general term for a colonoscopy (viewing the colon), sigmoidoscopy (viewing the sigmoid colon), etc.

Enteritis (*enteron* = intestine) Inflammation of the intestine, especially the small intestine.

Hemochromatosis (he″mo-kro″mah-to′sis; *hemo* = blood; *chroma* = color; *osis* = condition of) A disorder in iron metabolism due to excessive/prolonged iron intake or a breakdown of the mucosal iron barrier; excess iron is deposited in the tissues, causing increased skin pigmentation and increased incidence of hepatic cancer and liver cirrhosis; also called *bronze diabetes* and *iron storage disease.*

Ileus (il′e-us) A condition in which all GI tract movement stops and the gut appears to be paralyzed. Can result from electrolyte imbalances and blockade of parasympathetic impulses by drugs (such as those commonly used during abdominal surgery); usu-ally reversed when these interferences end. Restoration of motility is indicated by the reappearance of bowel (intestinal) sounds (gurgling, etc.).

Inflammatory bowel disease (IBD) A noncontagious, periodic inflammation of the intestinal wall now understood to be an abnormal immune and inflammatory response to bacterial antigens that normally occur in the intestine. Linked to a newly discovered T_H cell (T_H17), certain cytokines, and a deficit of antimicrobial substances normally secreted by the gut mucosa (lysozyme, defensins, and others). Afflicts up to two of every 1000 people. Symptoms include cramping, diarrhea, weight loss, and intestinal bleeding. Two subtypes occur: Crohn's disease, a syndrome characterized by relapsing and remitting periods, is more serious, with deep ulcers and fissures developing along the whole intestine, but mostly in the terminal ileum. Ulcerative colitis, by contrast, is characterized by a shallow inflammation of the large-intestinal mucosa, mainly in the rectum. They are treated with a special diet, reducing stress, antibiotics, and anti-inflammatory and immunosuppressant drugs. Extremely severe cases of ulcerative colitis are treated by colectomy (removal of a portion of the colon).

Laparoscopy (lap″ah-ros′ko-pe; *lapar* = the flank; *scopy* = observation) Examination of the peritoneal cavity and its organs with an endoscope inserted through the anterior abdominal wall. Often used to assess the condition of the digestive organs and the pelvic reproductive organs of females.

Orthodontics (or″tho-don′tiks; *ortho* = straight) Branch of dentistry that prevents and corrects misaligned teeth.

Pancreatitis (pan″kre-ah-ti′tis) A rare but extremely serious inflammation of the pancreas. May result from excessively high levels of fat in the blood or excessive alcohol ingestion, but most often results when a gallstone blocks the bile duct and pancreatic enzymes are activated in the pancreatic duct, causing the pancreatic tissue and duct to be digested. This painful condition can lead to nutritional deficiencies because pancreatic enzymes are essential to food digestion in the small intestine.

Peptic ulcers Term referring to gastric and duodenal ulcers.

Proctology (prok-tol′o-je; *procto* = rectum, anus; *logy* = study of) Branch of medicine dealing with treatment of diseases of the colon, rectum, and anus.

Pyloric stenosis (pi-lor′ik stĕ-no′sis; *stenosis* = narrowing, constriction) Congenital abnormality in which the pyloric sphincter is abnormally constricted. There is usually no problem until the baby begins to take solid food, and then projectile vomiting begins. Corrected surgically.

23

Vagotomy (va-got'o-me) Cutting or severing of the vagus nerve to decrease secretion of gastric juice in those with peptic ulcers that do not respond to medication.

Xerostomia (ze"ro-sto'me-ah; *zer* = dry, *stom* = mouth) Extreme dryness of the mouth; can be caused by blockage of salivary glands by cysts or autoimmune invasion of the salivary glands or ducts (Sjögren's syndrome).

CHAPTER SUMMARY

Media study tools that could provide you additional help in reviewing specific key topics of Chapter 23 are referenced below.

iP = *Interactive Physiology*

PART 1: OVERVIEW OF THE DIGESTIVE SYSTEM

1. The digestive system includes organs of the alimentary canal (mouth, pharynx, esophagus, stomach, small and large intestines) and accessory digestive system organs (teeth, tongue, salivary glands, liver, gallbladder, and pancreas).

Digestive Processes   (pp. 853–854)

1. Digestive system activities include six processes: ingestion, or food intake; propulsion, or movement of food through the tract; mechanical digestion, or processes that physically mix or break foods down into smaller fragments; chemical digestion, or food breakdown by enzymatic action; absorption, or transport of products of digestion through the intestinal mucosa into the blood; and defecation, or elimination of the undigested residues (feces) from the body.

Basic Functional Concepts   (p. 854)

1. The digestive system controls the environment within its lumen to ensure optimal conditions for digestion and absorption of foodstuffs.
2. Receptors and hormone-secreting cells in the alimentary canal wall respond to stretch and chemical signals that result in stimulation or inhibition of GI secretory activity or motility. The alimentary canal has an intrinsic nerve supply.

iP Digestive System; Topic: Control of the Digestive System, pp. 1, 3, 4–5, 8.

Digestive System Organs: Relationships   (pp. 854–858)

1. The parietal and visceral layers of the peritoneum are continuous with one another via several extensions (mesenteries, falciform ligament, lesser and greater omenta), and are separated by a potential space containing serous fluid, which decreases friction during organ activity.
2. The digestive viscera are served by the splanchnic circulation, consisting of arterial branches of the celiac trunk and aorta and the hepatic portal circulation.
3. All organs of the GI tract have the same basic pattern of tissue layers in their walls; all have a mucosa, a submucosa, a muscularis, and a serosa (or adventitia). Intrinsic nerve plexuses (enteric nervous system) are found within the wall.

PART 2: FUNCTIONAL ANATOMY OF THE DIGESTIVE SYSTEM

The Mouth and Associated Organs   (pp. 858–864)

1. Food enters the GI tract via the mouth, which is continuous with the oropharynx posteriorly. The boundaries of the mouth are the lips and cheeks, palate, and tongue.
2. The oral mucosa is stratified squamous epithelium, an adaptation seen where abrasion occurs.
3. The tongue is mucosa-covered skeletal muscle. Its intrinsic muscles allow it to change shape; its extrinsic muscles allow it to change position.
4. Saliva is produced by many small buccal glands and three pairs of major salivary glands—parotid, submandibular, and sublingual—that secrete their product into the mouth via ducts. Largely water, saliva also contains ions, proteins, metabolic wastes, lysozyme, defensins, IgA, salivary amylase, a cyanide compound, and mucin.
5. Saliva moistens and cleanses the mouth; moistens foods, aiding their compaction; dissolves food chemicals to allow for taste; and begins chemical digestion of starch (salivary amylase). Saliva output is increased by parasympathetic reflexes initiated by activation of chemical and pressure receptors in the mouth and by conditioned reflexes. The sympathetic nervous system depresses salivation.
6. The 20 deciduous teeth begin to be shed at the age of 6 and are gradually replaced during childhood and adolescence by the 32 permanent teeth.
7. Teeth are classed as incisors, canines, premolars, and molars. Each tooth has an enamel-covered crown and a cementum-covered root. The bulk of the tooth is dentin, which surrounds the central pulp cavity. A periodontal ligament secures the tooth to the bony alveolus.

The Pharynx   (p. 864)

1. Food propelled from the mouth passes through the oropharynx and laryngopharynx. The mucosa of the pharynx is stratified squamous epithelium; skeletal muscles in its wall (constrictor muscles) move food toward the esophagus.

The Esophagus   (pp. 864–866)

1. The esophagus extends from the laryngopharynx and joins the stomach at the cardiac orifice, which is surrounded by the gastroesophageal sphincter.
2. The esophageal mucosa is stratified squamous epithelium. Its muscularis is skeletal muscle superiorly and changes to smooth muscle inferiorly. It has an adventitia rather than a serosa.

Digestive Processes: Mouth to Esophagus   (p. 866)

1. The mouth and associated accessory organs accomplish food ingestion and mechanical digestion (chewing and mixing), initiate the chemical digestion of starch (salivary amylase), and propel food into the pharynx (buccal phase of swallowing).

2. Teeth function to masticate food. Chewing is initiated voluntarily and is then controlled reflexively.

3. The tongue mixes food with saliva, compacts it into a bolus, and initiates swallowing (the voluntary phase). The pharynx and esophagus are primarily food conduits that conduct food to the stomach by peristalsis. The swallowing center in the medulla and pons controls this phase reflexively. When the peristaltic wave approaches the gastroesophageal sphincter, the sphincter relaxes to allow food entry to the stomach.

iP Digestive System; Topic: Motility, pp. 3–5.

The Stomach (pp. 866–877)

1. The J-shaped stomach lies in the upper left quadrant of the abdomen. Its major regions are the cardia, fundus, body, and pyloric region. When empty, its internal surface exhibits rugae.

2. The stomach muscularis contains a third (oblique) layer of smooth muscle that allows it to churn and mix food.

3. The stomach mucosa is simple columnar epithelium dotted with gastric pits that lead into gastric glands. Secretory cells in the gastric glands include pepsinogen-producing chief cells; parietal cells, which secrete hydrochloric acid and intrinsic factor; mucous neck cells, which produce mucus; and enteroendocrine cells, which secrete hormones.

4. The mucosal barrier, which protects the stomach from self-digestion and HCl, reflects the fact that the mucosal cells are connected by tight junctions, secrete a thick mucus, and are quickly replaced when damaged.

5. Protein digestion is initiated in the stomach by activated pepsin and requires acidic conditions (provided by HCl). Few substances are absorbed.

6. Gastric secretory activity is controlled by both nervous and hormonal factors. The three phases of gastric secretion are the cephalic, gastric, and intestinal. Most food-related stimuli acting on the head and stomach (cephalic and gastric respectively) stimulate gastric secretion. Most stimuli acting on the small intestine trigger the enterogastric reflex and release of secretin and CCK, both of which inhibit gastric secretory activity. Sympathetic activity also inhibits gastric secretion.

7. Mechanical digestion in the stomach is triggered by stomach distension and coupled to food propulsion and stomach emptying. Food movement into the duodenum is controlled by the pylorus and feedback signals from the small intestine. Pacemaker cells in the smooth muscle sheet set the maximal rate of peristalsis.

iP Digestive System; Topic: Control of the Digestive System, pp. 3, 5–6, 8.

The Small Intestine and Associated Structures (pp. 877–890)

1. The small intestine is the major digestive and absorptive organ. It extends from the pyloric sphincter to the ileocecal valve. Its three subdivisions are the duodenum, jejunum, and ileum. The bile duct and pancreatic duct join to form the hepatopancreatic ampulla and empty their secretions into the duodenum through the hepatopancreatic sphincter.

2. Circular folds, villi, and microvilli increase the intestinal surface area for digestion and absorption.

3. The duodenal submucosa contains elaborate mucus-secreting duodenal glands (Brunner's glands); that of the ileum contains Peyer's patches (lymphoid follicles). The duodenum is covered not with a serosa but an adventitia.

4. Intestinal juice is largely water and is relatively enzyme-poor. The major stimuli for its release are stretch and chemicals.

5. The liver is a lobed organ overlying the stomach. Its digestive role is to produce bile, which it secretes into the common hepatic duct.

6. The structural and functional units of the liver are the liver lobules. Blood flowing to the liver via the hepatic artery and hepatic portal vein flows into its sinusoids, from which Kupffer cells remove debris and hepatocytes remove nutrients. Hepatocytes store glucose as glycogen, use amino acids to make plasma proteins, and detoxify metabolic wastes and drugs.

7. Bile is made continuously by the hepatocytes. Bile salts and secretin stimulate bile production.

8. The gallbladder, a muscular sac that lies beneath the right liver lobe, stores and concentrates bile.

9. Bile contains electrolytes, a variety of fatty substances, bile salts, and bile pigments in an aqueous medium. Bile salts are emulsifying agents; they disperse fats and form water-soluble micelles, which solubilize the products of fat digestion.

10. Cholecystokinin released by the small intestine stimulates the gallbladder to contract and the hepatopancreatic sphincter to relax, allowing bile (and pancreatic juice) to enter the duodenum.

11. The pancreas is retroperitoneal between the spleen and small intestine. Its exocrine product, pancreatic juice, is carried to the duodenum via the pancreatic duct.

12. Pancreatic juice is an HCO_3^--rich fluid containing enzymes that digest all categories of foods. The secretion of pancreatic juice is controlled by intestinal hormones and the vagus nerves.

iP Digestive System; Topic: Secretion, pp. 11–14.

13. Mechanical digestion and propulsion in the small intestine mix chyme with digestive juices and bile and force the residues, largely by segmentation, through the ileocecal valve. Pacemaker cells set the rate of segmentation. Ileocecal valve opening is controlled by the gastroileal reflex and gastrin.

The Large Intestine (pp. 890–895)

1. The subdivisions of the large intestine are the cecum (and appendix), colon (ascending, transverse, descending, and sigmoid portions), rectum, and anal canal. It opens to the body exterior at the anus.

2. The longitudinal muscle in the muscularis is reduced to three bands (teniae coli), which pucker its wall, producing haustra. The mucosa of most of the large intestine is simple columnar epithelium containing abundant goblet cells.

3. The major functions of the large intestine are absorption of water, some electrolytes, and vitamins made by enteric bacteria, and defecation (evacuation of food residues from the body).

4. The defecation reflex is triggered when feces enter the rectum. It involves parasympathetic reflexes leading to the contraction of the rectal walls and is aided by Valsalva's maneuver.

iP Digestive System; Topic: Anatomy Review, pp. 3–5.

PART 3: PHYSIOLOGY OF CHEMICAL DIGESTION AND ABSORPTION

Chemical Digestion (pp. 895–897)

1. Chemical digestion is accomplished by hydrolysis, catalyzed by enzymes.

2. Most chemical digestion is done in the small intestine by intestinal (brush border) enzymes and, more importantly, by pancreatic enzymes. Alkaline pancreatic juice neutralizes the acidic chyme and provides the proper environment for operation of the enzymes. Both pancreatic juice (the main source of lipases) and bile are necessary for fat breakdown.

Absorption (pp. 898–901)

1. Virtually all of the foodstuffs and most of the water and electrolytes are absorbed in the small intestine. Most nutrients are absorbed by active transport processes, except for fat digestion products, fat-soluble vitamins, and most water-soluble vitamins (which are absorbed by diffusion).

2. Fat breakdown products are solubilized by bile salts (in micelles), resynthesized to triglycerides in the intestinal mucosal cells, and combined with other lipids and protein as chylomicrons that enter the lacteals. Other absorbed substances enter the villus blood capillaries and are transported to the liver via the hepatic portal vein.

Developmental Aspects of the Digestive System (pp. 901, 904–905)

1. The glandular accessory organs (salivary glands, liver, pancreas, and gallbladder) form from outpocketings of the foregut endoderm. The mucosa of the alimentary canal develops from the endoderm, which folds to form a tube. The remaining three tunics of the alimentary canal wall are formed by mesoderm.

2. Important congenital abnormalities of the digestive tract include cleft palate/lip, tracheoesophageal fistula, and cystic fibrosis. All interfere with normal nutrition.

3. Various inflammations plague the digestive system throughout life. Appendicitis is common in adolescents, gastroenteritis and food poisoning can occur at any time (given the proper irritating factors), and ulcers and gallbladder problems increase in middle age.

4. The efficiency of all digestive system processes declines in the elderly, and periodontal disease is common. Diverticulosis, fecal incontinence, and GI tract cancers such as stomach and colon cancer appear with increasing frequency in an aging population.

REVIEW QUESTIONS

Multiple Choice/Matching

(Some questions have more than one correct answer. Select the best answer or answers from the choices given.)

1. The peritoneal cavity (a) is the same thing as the abdominopelvic cavity, (b) is filled with air, (c) like the pleural and pericardial cavities is a potential space containing serous fluid, (d) contains the pancreas and all of the duodenum.

2. Obstruction of the hepatopancreatic sphincter impairs digestion by reducing the availability of (a) bile and HCl, (b) HCl and intestinal juice, (c) pancreatic juice and intestinal juice, (d) pancreatic juice and bile.

3. The action of an enzyme is influenced by (a) its chemical surroundings, (b) its specific substrate, (c) the presence of needed cofactors or coenzymes, (d) all of these.

4. Carbohydrates are acted on by (a) peptidases, trypsin, and chymotrypsin, (b) amylase, maltase, and sucrase, (c) lipases, (d) peptidases, lipases, and galactase.

5. The parasympathetic nervous system influences digestion by (a) relaxing smooth muscle, (b) stimulating peristalsis and secretory activity, (c) constricting sphincters, (d) none of these.

6. The digestive juice product containing enzymes capable of digesting all four major foodstuff categories is (a) pancreatic, (b) gastric, (c) salivary, (d) biliary.

7. The vitamin associated with calcium absorption is (a) A, (b) K, (c) C, (d) D.

8. Someone has eaten a meal of buttered toast, cream, and eggs. Which of the following would you expect to happen? (a) Compared to the period shortly after the meal, gastric motility and secretion of HCl decrease when the food reaches the duodenum; (b) gastric motility increases even as the person is chewing the food (before swallowing); (c) fat will be emulsified in the duodenum by the action of bile; (d) all of these.

9. The site of production of VIP and cholecystokinin is (a) the stomach, (b) the small intestine, (c) the pancreas, (d) the large intestine.

10. Which of the following is not characteristic of the colon? (a) It is divided into ascending, transverse, and descending portions; (b) it contains abundant bacteria, some of which synthesize certain vitamins; (c) it is the main absorptive site; (d) it absorbs much of the water and salts remaining in the wastes.

11. The gallbladder (a) produces bile, (b) is attached to the pancreas, (c) stores and concentrates bile, (d) produces secretin.

12. The sphincter between the stomach and duodenum is (a) the pyloric sphincter, (b) the gastroesophageal sphincter, (c) the hepatopancreatic sphincter, (d) the ileocecal sphincter.

In items 13–17, trace the path of a single protein molecule that has been ingested.

13. The protein molecule will be digested by enzymes secreted by (a) the mouth, stomach, and colon, (b) the stomach, liver, and small intestine, (c) the small intestine, mouth, and liver, (d) the pancreas and stomach.

14. The protein molecule must be digested before it can be transported to and utilized by the cells because (a) protein is only useful directly, (b) protein has a low pH, (c) proteins in the circulating blood produce an adverse osmotic pressure, (d) the protein is too large to be readily absorbed.

15. The products of protein digestion enter the bloodstream largely through cells lining (a) the stomach, (b) the small intestine, (c) the large intestine, (d) the bile duct.

16. Before the blood carrying the products of protein digestion reaches the heart, it first passes through capillary networks in (a) the spleen, (b) the lungs, (c) the liver, (d) the brain.

17. Having passed through the regulatory organ selected above, the products of protein digestion are circulated throughout the body. They will enter individual body cells by (a) active transport, (b) diffusion, (c) osmosis, (d) phagocytosis.

Short Answer Essay Questions

18. Make a simple line drawing of the organs of the alimentary canal and label each organ. Then add three labels to your drawing—salivary glands, liver, and pancreas—and use arrows to show where each of these organs empties its secretion into the alimentary canal.

19. Sara was on a diet but she could not eat less and kept claiming her stomach had a mind of its own. She was joking, but indeed, there is a "gut brain" called the enteric nervous system. Is it part of the parasympathetic and sympathetic nervous system? Explain.

20. Name the layers of the alimentary canal wall. Note the tissue composition and major function of each layer.

23

21. What is a mesentery? Mesocolon? Greater omentum?
22. Name the six functional activities of the digestive system.
23. (a) Describe the boundaries of the oral cavity. (b) Why do you suppose its mucosa is stratified squamous epithelium rather than the more typical simple columnar epithelium?
24. (a) What is the normal number of permanent teeth? Of deciduous teeth? (b) What substance covers the tooth crown? Its root? (c) What substance makes up the bulk of a tooth? (d) What and where is pulp?
25. Describe the two phases of swallowing, noting the organs involved and the activities that occur.
26. Describe the role of these cells found in gastric glands: parietal, chief, mucous neck, and enteroendocrine.
27. Describe the regulation of the cephalic, gastric, and intestinal phases of gastric secretion.
28. (a) What is the relationship between the cystic, common hepatic, bile, and pancreatic ducts? (b) What is the point of fusion of the bile and pancreatic ducts called?
29. Explain why fatty stools result from the absence of bile or pancreatic juice.
30. Indicate the function of the Kupffer cells and the hepatocytes of the liver.
31. What are (a) brush border enzymes? (b) chylomicrons?
32. Activation of pancreatic enzymes in the small intestine is a good example of the wisdom of the body. How so?
33. Name one inflammatory condition of the digestive system particularly common to adolescents, two common in middle age, and one common in old age.
34. What are the effects of aging on digestive system activity?

Critical Thinking and Clinical Application Questions

1. You are a research assistant at a pharmaceutical company. Your group has been asked to develop an effective laxative that (1) provides bulk and (2) is nonirritating to the intestinal mucosa. Explain why these requests are important by describing what would happen if the opposite conditions were present.
2. After a heavy meal rich with fried foods, Debby Collins, an overweight 45-year-old woman, was rushed to the emergency room with severe spasmodic pains in her epigastric region that radiated to the right side of her rib cage. She indicated that the attack came on suddenly, and her abdomen was found to be tender to the touch and somewhat rigid. What do you think is this patient's problem and why is her pain discontinuous (colicky)? What are the treatment options and what might happen if the problem is not resolved?
3. A baby is admitted to the hospital with a history of diarrhea and watery feces occurring over the last three days. The baby has sunken fontanelles, indicating extreme dehydration. Tests indicate that the baby has a bacterium-induced colitis, and antibiotics are prescribed. Because of the baby's loss of intestinal juices, do you think that his blood pH would indicate acidosis or alkalosis? Explain your reasoning.
4. Gary Francis, a middle-aged salesman, complains of a burning pain in the "pit of his stomach," usually beginning about two hours after eating and abating after drinking a glass of milk. When asked to indicate the site, he points to his epigastric region. The GI tract is examined by X-ray fluoroscopy. A gastric ulcer is visualized, and drug therapy using an antibiotic-bismuth approach is recommended. (a) Why is this treatment suggested? (b) What are the possible consequences of nontreatment?
5. Dr. Dolan used an endoscope to view Mr. Habib's colon. He noted the presence of several polyps and removed them during the same procedure. What is an endoscope? Why did Dr. Dolan opt to remove the polyps immediately?
6. Mr. Holden has had severe diarrhea all day and is severely weakened. Explain why his nurse is concerned about his present condition.
7. What is the protective value of having several sets of tonsils at the oral entry to the pharynx?

Access everything you need to practice, review, and self-assess for both your A&P lecture and lab courses at **myA&P** (www.myaandp.com). There, you'll find powerful online resources, including chapter quizzes and tests, games, A&P Flix animations with quizzes, *Interactive Physiology*® with quizzes, MP3 Tutor Sessions, Practice Anatomy Lab™, and more to help you get a better grade in your course.

24

Nutrition, Metabolism, and Body Temperature Regulation

re you a food lover? We are too. In fact, most people can be divided into two camps according to their reactions to food—those who live to eat and those who eat to live. The saying "you are what you eat" is true in that part of the food we eat is converted to our living flesh. In other words, some nutrients are used to build cell structures, replace worn-out parts, and synthesize functional molecules. However, most nutrients we ingest are used as metabolic fuel. That is, they are oxidized and transformed to **ATP**, the chemical energy form used by cells.

The energy value of foods is measured in **kilocalories (kcal)** or "large calories" (C). One kilocalorie is the amount of heat energy needed to raise the temperature of 1 kilogram of water 1°C (1.8°F). This unit is the "calorie" that dieters count so conscientiously.

In Chapter 23, we talked about how foods are digested and absorbed, but what happens to these foods once they enter the blood? Why do we need bread, meat, and fresh vegetables? Why does everything we eat seem to turn to fat? In this chapter we will try to answer these questions as we explain both the nature of nutrients and their metabolic roles.

Diet and Nutrition

▶ Define nutrient, essential nutrient, and calorie.

▶ List the six major nutrient categories. Note important sources and main cellular uses.

A **nutrient** is a substance in food used by the body to promote normal growth, maintenance, and repair. The nutrients needed for health divide neatly into six categories. Three of these—carbohydrates, lipids, and proteins—are collectively called the **major nutrients** and make up the bulk of what we eat. The fourth and fifth categories, vitamins and minerals, though equally crucial for health, are required in minute amounts.

In a strict sense, water, which accounts for about 60% by volume of the food we eat, is also a major nutrient. However, because we described its importance in the body in Chapter 2, here we consider in detail only the five nutrient categories listed above.

Most foods offer a combination of nutrients. For example, cream of mushroom soup contains all the major nutrients plus some vitamins and minerals. A diet consisting of foods from each of the five food groups—grains, fruits, vegetables, meats and fish, and milk products—normally guarantees adequate amounts of all the needed nutrients.

There are several examples of food guide pyramids around, and two are provided in **Figure 24.1**. Fresh out of the oven on April 19, 2005, the U.S. Department of Agriculture's new version of the food guide pyramid—MyPyramid—is a significant departure from traditional food pyramids. MyPyramid separates the food categories vertically (rather than horizontally). Narrowing of each food group from bottom to top of the pyramid suggests moderation in selecting foods from each food group (more "picks" from food choices in the wider bands). Its weakness is that the pyramid itself lacks any notion of a hierarchical ranking of the food in a single group in terms of nutritional

(a) USDA food guide pyramid

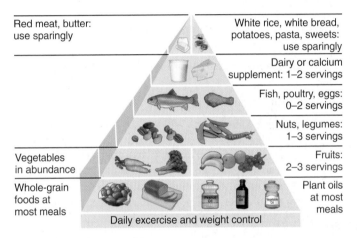

(b) Healthy eating pyramid

Figure 24.1 Food guide pyramids.

desirability. For example, the carbohydrate group would be whole grains, fruits and vegetables at the base of the band (best choices), pasta about halfway up, and Danish pastry at the top (eat less). Also new to this food pyramid version is the emphasis on at least 30 minutes daily of physical activity as represented by the stick person climbing the steps. A person's diet can be personalized by age, sex, and activity level by logging on to the Internet (www.mypyramid.gov), where information is available to help consumers make healthy choices and determine the size and number of servings recommended daily.

The Healthy Eating Pyramid was presented by Walter Willett of Harvard as a healthier alternative to the previous (1992) USDA food guide pyramid. It uses the traditional orientation of food groups, and emphasizes eating whole-grain foods and lots of nonstarchy fruits and vegetables. It also recommends substituting plant oils and nuts for animal fats, and restricting red meat, sweets, and starchy foods.

To be perfectly honest, nutrition advice is constantly in flux and is endlessly argued, and often mired in the self-interest of food companies. Nonetheless, basic dietary principles have not changed in years and are not in dispute—eat less; eat fruits, vegetables, and whole grains, not junk food; and get more exercise.

24

The ability of cells, especially liver cells, to convert one type of molecule to another is truly remarkable. These interconversions allow the body to use the wide range of chemicals found in foods and to adjust to varying food intakes. But there are limits to this ability to conjure up new molecules from old.

At least 45 and possibly 50 molecules, called **essential nutrients**, cannot be made fast enough to meet the body's needs and so must be provided by the diet. As long as all the essential nutrients are ingested, the body can synthesize the hundreds of additional molecules required for life and good health. The use of the word "essential" to describe the chemicals that must be obtained from outside sources is unfortunate and misleading, because both essential and nonessential nutrients are equally vital for normal functioning.

Carbohydrates

▶ Distinguish between simple and complex carbohydrate sources.

▶ Indicate the major uses of carbohydrates in the body.

Dietary Sources

Except for milk sugar (lactose) and negligible amounts of glycogen in meats, all the carbohydrates we ingest are derived from plants. Sugars (monosaccharides and disaccharides) come from fruits, sugar cane, sugar beets, honey, and milk. The polysaccharide starch is found in grains and vegetables.

There are two varieties of polysaccharides that provide fiber. Cellulose, a polysaccharide plentiful in most vegetables, is not digested by humans but provides roughage, or *insoluble fiber*, which increases the bulk of the stool and facilitates defecation. *Soluble fiber*, such as pectin found in apples and citrus fruits, reduces blood cholesterol levels, a desirable goal in those with cardiac disease.

Uses in the Body

The monosaccharide **glucose** is the carbohydrate molecule ultimately used as fuel by body cells to produce ATP. Carbohydrate digestion also yields fructose and galactose, but these monosaccharides are converted to glucose by the liver before they enter the general circulation. Many body cells use fats as energy sources, but neurons and red blood cells rely almost entirely on glucose for their energy needs. Because even a temporary shortage of blood glucose can severely depress brain function and lead to neuron death, the body carefully monitors and regulates blood glucose levels. Any glucose in excess of what is needed for ATP synthesis is converted to glycogen or fat and stored for later use.

Other uses of monosaccharides are meager. Small amounts of pentose sugars are used to synthesize nucleic acids, and a variety of sugars are attached to externally facing plasma membrane proteins and lipids.

Dietary Requirements

The low-carbohydrate diet of the Inuit (Eskimos) and the high-carbohydrate diet of peoples in the Far East indicate that humans can be healthy even with wide variations in carbohydrate intake. The minimum requirement for carbohydrates is not known, but 100 grams per day is presumed to be the smallest amount needed to maintain adequate blood glucose levels. The recommended dietary allowance (130 g/day) is based on the amount needed to fuel the brain, not the total amount need to supply all daily activities. Recommended carbohydrate intake to maintain health is 45–65% of one's total calorie intake, with the emphasis on *complex* carbohydrates (whole grains and vegetables). When less than 50 grams per day is consumed, tissue proteins and fats are used for energy fuel.

American adults typically consume about 46% of dietary food energy in the form of carbohydrates. Because starchy foods (rice, pasta, breads) are less expensive than meat and other high-protein foods, carbohydrates make up an even greater percentage of the diet in low-income groups. Vegetables, fruits, whole grains, and milk have many valuable nutrients, such as vitamins and minerals.

By contrast, highly refined carbohydrate foods such as candy and soft drinks provide concentrated energy sources only—the term "empty calories" is commonly used to describe such foods. Eating refined, sugary foods instead of more complex carbohydrates may cause nutritional deficiencies as well as obesity. Other possible consequences of excessive intake of simple carbohydrates are listed in **Table 24.1.**

Lipids

▶ Indicate uses of fats in the body.

▶ Distinguish between saturated, unsaturated, and trans fatty acid sources.

Dietary Sources

The most abundant dietary lipids are triglycerides, also called neutral fats or triacylglycerols (Chapter 2). We eat saturated fats in animal products such as meat and dairy foods, in a few tropical plant products such as coconut, and in hydrogenated oils (trans fats) such as margarine and solid shortenings used in baking. Unsaturated fats are present in seeds, nuts, olive oil, and most vegetable oils. Fats are digested to monoglycerides or all the way to fatty acids and glycerol, and then reconverted to triglycerides for transport in the lymph.

Major sources of cholesterol are egg yolk, meats and organ meats, shellfish, and milk products. However, it is estimated that the liver produces about 85% of blood cholesterol regardless of dietary intake.

The liver is adept at converting one fatty acid to another, but it cannot synthesize *linoleic acid* (lin″o-le′ik), a fatty acid component of *lecithin* (les′ĭ-thin). For this reason, linoleic acid, an omega-6 fatty acid, is an *essential fatty acid* that must be ingested. Linolenic acid, an omega-3 fatty acid, may also be essential. Fortunately, these two fatty acids are found in most vegetable oils.

Uses in the Body

Fats have fallen into disfavor, particularly among those for whom the "battle of the bulge" is constant. But fats make foods tender, flaky, or creamy, and make us feel full and satisfied. Furthermore,

TABLE 24.1	Summary of Carbohydrate, Lipid, and Protein Nutrients			
FOOD SOURCES	**RECOMMENDED DAILY ALLOWANCE (RDA) FOR ADULTS**	*PROBLEMS*		
		EXCESSES	**DEFICITS**	

Carbohydrates

Total Digestible ▪ **Complex carbohydrates** (starches): bread, cereal, crackers, flour, pasta, nuts, rice, potatoes ▪ **Simple carbohydrates (sugars):** carbonated drinks, candy, fruit, ice cream, pudding, young (immature) vegetables	130 g 45–65% of total caloric intake	Obesity; diabetes mellitus; nutritional deficits; dental caries; gastrointestinal irritation; elevated triglycerides in plasma	Tissue wasting (in extreme deprivation); metabolic acidosis resulting from accelerated fat use for energy
Total Fiber	25–30 g		

Lipids

Total	65 g 20–35% of total caloric intake	Obesity and increased risk of cardiovascular disease (particularly if excesses of saturated and trans fat)	Weight loss; fat stores and tissue proteins catabolized to provide metabolic energy; problems controlling heat loss (due to depletion of subcutaneous fat)
▪ **Animal sources:** lard, meat, poultry, eggs, milk, milk products	20 g		
▪ **Plant sources:** chocolate; corn, soy, cottonseed, olive oils; coconut; corn; peanuts	11–17 g		
▪ **Essential fatty acids:** fish oil; corn, cottonseed, soy oils; wheat germ; vegetable shortenings	1.1–1.6 g	Excess dietary intake of omega-3 fatty acid may increase risk of stroke	Poor growth; skin lesions (eczema-like); depression
▪ **Cholesterol and trans fatty acids:** organ meats (liver, kidneys, brains), egg yolks, fish roe; smaller concentrations in milk products and meat	Not determined	Increased levels of plasma cholesterol and low-density lipoproteins, correlated with increased risk of cardiovascular disease	Increased risk of stroke (CVA) in susceptible individuals

Proteins

▪ **Complete proteins:** eggs, milk, milk products, meat (fish, poultry, pork, beef, lamb) ▪ **Incomplete proteins:** legumes (soybeans, lima beans, kidney beans, lentils); nuts and seeds; grains and cereals; vegetables	0.8 g/kg body weight 12–20% of total caloric intake	Obesity; enhanced calcium excretion and bone loss; high cholesterol levels in blood; kidney stones	Profound weight loss and tissue wasting; growth retardation in children; anemia; edema (due to deficits of plasma proteins) During pregnancy: miscarriage or premature birth

dietary fats *are* essential for several reasons. They help the body absorb fat-soluble vitamins; triglycerides are the major energy fuel of hepatocytes and skeletal muscle; and phospholipids are an integral component of myelin sheaths and cellular membranes. Fatty deposits in adipose tissue provide (1) a protective cushion around body organs, (2) an insulating layer beneath the skin, and (3) an easy-to-store concentrated source of energy fuel. Regulatory molecules called *prostaglandins* (pros″tah-glan′dinz), formed from linoleic acid via arachidonic acid (ah″rah-kĭ-don′ik), play a role in smooth muscle contraction, control of blood pressure, and inflammation.

Unlike triglycerides, cholesterol is not used for energy. It is important as a stabilizing component of plasma membranes and is the precursor from which bile salts, steroid hormones, and other essential molecules are formed.

Dietary Requirements

Fats represent over 40% of the calories in the typical American diet. There are no precise recommendations on amount or type of dietary fats, but the American Heart Association suggests that (1) fats should represent 30% or less of total caloric intake, (2) saturated fats should be limited to 10% or less of total fat intake, and (3) daily cholesterol intake should be no more than 300 mg (the amount in one egg yolk). The goal of these recommendations is to keep total blood cholesterol to less than 200 mg/dl. Because a diet high in saturated fats and cholesterol may contribute to cardiovascular disease, these are wise guidelines. Sources of the various lipid classes and consequences of their deficient or excessive intake are summarized in Table 24.1.

Fat Substitutes

In an attempt to reduce fat intake without losing fat's appetizing aspects, many people have turned to fat substitutes or foods prepared with them. Perhaps the oldest fat substitute is air (beaten into a product to make it fluffy). Other fat substitutes are modified starches and gums, and more recently milk whey protein. Except for those based on dietary fibers (gums), such products are metabolized and provide calories. One of the newest substitutes, Olestra, a fat-based product made from cottonseeds, is not metabolized because it is not digested or absorbed.

Most fat substitutes have two drawbacks: (1) They don't stand up to the intense heat needed to fry foods, and (2) although manufacturers claim otherwise, they don't taste nearly as good as the "real thing." The ones that are not absorbed tend to cause flatus (gas) or diarrhea, and may interfere with absorption of fat-soluble drugs, vitamins, and phytochemicals such as beta-carotene, a precursor of vitamin A.

Proteins

▶ Distinguish between nutritionally complete and incomplete proteins.

▶ Indicate uses of proteins in the body.

▶ Define nitrogen balance and indicate possible causes of positive and negative nitrogen balance.

Dietary Sources

Animal products contain the highest-quality proteins, in other words, those with the greatest amount and best ratios of *essential amino acids* (**Figure 24.2**). Proteins in eggs, milk, fish, and most meats are **complete proteins** that meet all the body's amino acid requirements for tissue maintenance and growth (Table 24.1). Legumes (beans and peas), nuts, and cereals are protein-rich, but their proteins are nutritionally incomplete because they are low in one or more of the essential amino acids.

Strict vegetarians must carefully plan their diets to obtain all the essential amino acids and prevent protein malnutrition. When ingested together, cereal grains and legumes provide all the essential amino acids (Figure 24.2b). Some combination of these foods is found in the diets of all cultures (most obviously in the rice and beans seen on nearly every plate in a Mexican restaurant). For nonvegetarians, grains and legumes are useful as partial substitutes for the more expensive animal proteins.

Uses in the Body

Proteins are important structural materials of the body, including, for example, keratin in skin, collagen and elastin in connective tissues, and muscle proteins. In addition, functional proteins such as enzymes and some hormones regulate an incredible variety of body functions. Whether amino acids are used to synthesize new proteins or are burned for energy depends on a number of factors:

1. **The all-or-none rule.** All amino acids needed to make a particular protein must be present in a cell at the same time and in sufficient amounts. If one is missing, the protein cannot be made. Because essential amino acids cannot be stored, those not used immediately to build proteins are oxidized for energy or converted to carbohydrates or fats.
2. **Adequacy of caloric intake.** For optimal protein synthesis, the diet must supply sufficient carbohydrate or fat calories for ATP production. When it doesn't, dietary and tissue proteins are used for energy.
3. **Nitrogen balance.** In healthy adults the rate of protein synthesis equals the rate of protein breakdown and loss, a homeostatic state called **nitrogen balance**. The body is in nitrogen balance when the amount of nitrogen ingested in proteins equals the amount excreted in urine and feces.

   The body is in *positive nitrogen balance* when the amount of protein incorporated into tissue is greater than the amount being broken down and used for energy—the normal situation in growing children and pregnant women. A positive balance also occurs when tissues are being repaired following illness or injury.

   In *negative nitrogen balance*, protein breakdown for energy exceeds the amount of protein being incorporated into tissues. This occurs during physical and emotional stress (for example, infection, injury, or burns), or when the quality or quantity of dietary protein is poor, or during starvation.
4. **Hormonal controls.** Certain hormones, called *anabolic hormones*, accelerate protein synthesis and growth. The effects of these hormones vary continually throughout life.

(a) **Essential amino acids**

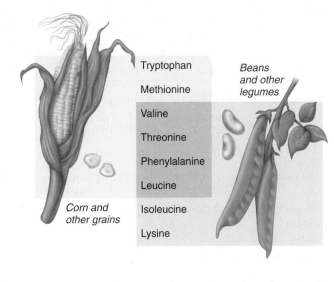

(b) **Vegetarian diets providing the eight essential amino acids for humans**

Figure 24.2 Essential amino acids. In order for protein synthesis to occur, 10 essential amino acids must be available simultaneously and in the correct proportions. **(a)** Relative amounts of the essential amino acids and total proteins needed by adults. Notice that the essential amino acids represent only a small percentage of the total recommended protein intake. Histidine and arginine, graphed with dashed lines, are essential in infants but not in adults. Amino acids shown in parentheses are *not* essential but can substitute in part for methionine and phenylalanine. **(b)** Vegetarian diets must be carefully constructed to provide all essential amino acids. A meal of corn and beans fills the bill: Corn provides the essential amino acids not in beans and vice versa.

For example, pituitary *growth hormone* stimulates tissue growth during childhood and conserves protein in adults, and the *sex hormones* trigger the growth spurt of adolescence. Other hormones, such as the adrenal *glucocorticoids* released during stress, enhance protein breakdown and conversion of amino acids to glucose.

Dietary Requirements

Besides supplying essential amino acids, dietary proteins furnish the raw materials for making nonessential amino acids and various nonprotein nitrogen-containing substances. The amount of protein a person needs reflects his or her age, size, metabolic rate, and current state of nitrogen balance. As a rule of thumb, nutritionists recommend a daily intake of 0.8 g per kilogram of body weight. About 30 g of protein is supplied by a small serving of fish and a glass of milk.

Most Americans eat far more protein than they need. Prolonged high protein consumption may lead to bone loss. This may occur because metabolizing sulfur-containing amino acids makes the blood more acidic and calcium is pulled from the bones to buffer these acids.

CHECK YOUR UNDERSTANDING

1. What are the six major nutrients?
2. Why is it important to include cellulose in a healthy diet even though we do not digest it?
3. How does the body use triglycerides? Cholesterol?

4. John eats nothing but baked bean sandwiches. Is he getting all the essential amino acids he needs in this restricted diet?

For answers, see Appendix G.

Vitamins

▶ Distinguish between fat- and water-soluble vitamins, and list the vitamins in each group.

▶ For each vitamin, list important sources, body functions, and important consequences of its deficit or excess.

Vitamins (*vita* = life) are potent organic compounds needed in minute amounts for growth and good health. Unlike other organic nutrients, vitamins are not used for energy and do not serve as building blocks, but they are crucial in helping the body use those nutrients that do. Without vitamins, all the carbohydrates, proteins, and fats we eat would be useless.

Most vitamins function as **coenzymes** (or parts of coenzymes), which act with an enzyme to accomplish a particular chemical task. For example, the B vitamins act as coenzymes in the oxidation of glucose for energy. We will describe the roles of some vitamins in the metabolism discussion.

Because most vitamins are not made in the body, they must be taken in via foods or vitamin supplements. The exceptions are vitamin D made in the skin, and small amounts of B vitamins and vitamin K synthesized by intestinal bacteria. In addition, the body can convert *beta-carotene* (kar′o-tēn), the orange pigment

TABLE 24.2	Vitamins			
VITAMIN	**RDA* (mg)**	**MAJOR DIETARY SOURCES**	**SOME MAJOR FUNCTIONS IN THE BODY**	**POSSIBLE SYMPTOMS OF DEFICIENCY** OR EXTREME EXCESS
Water-Soluble Vitamins				
Vitamin B_1 (thiamine)	1.2	Lean meats, liver, legumes, peanuts, whole grains	Coenzyme used in removing CO_2 from organic compounds; required for synthesis of acetylcholine and pentose sugars	Beriberi (nerve disorders, emaciation, anemia), profound fatigue None known
Vitamin B_2 (riboflavin)	1.1–1.3	Milk, liver, yeast, meats, enriched grains, vegetables	Component of coenzymes FAD and FMN	Dermatitis, skin lesions such as cracks at corners of mouth, blurred vision None known
Vitamin B_3 (niacin)	14-16	Nuts, poultry, fish, meats, grains	Component of coenzyme NAD^+	Pellagra, skin and gastrointestinal lesions, nervous disorders Liver damage, gout, hyperglycemia
Vitamin B_5 (pantothenic acid)	5.0	Most foods: meats, dairy products, whole grains, etc.	Component of coenzyme A; involved in synthesis of steroids and hemoglobin	Fatigue, numbness, tingling of hands and feet, neuropathy of alcoholism None known
Vitamin B_6 (pyridoxine)	1.3–1.7	Meats, fish, poultry, vegetables, bananas	Coenzyme used in amino acid metabolism; required for glycogenolysis and antibody formation	Irritability, convulsions, muscular twitching, anemia Unstable gait, numb feet, poor coordination, depressed deep tendon reflexes, nerve damage
Vitamin B_9 (folic acid or folacin)	0.2-0.4	Liver, oranges, nuts, legumes, whole grains	Coenzyme in nucleic acid and amino acid metabolism; needed for normal neural tube development in embryos	Anemia, gastrointestinal problems, spina bifida risk in newborns, neural deficits May mask signs of vitamin B_{12} deficiency while allowing its neurological damage
Vitamin B_{12} (cyanocobalamin)	0.0024	Meats, eggs, dairy products except butter (not found in plant foods) (also made by enteric bacteria)	Coenzyme in nucleic acid metabolism; maturation of red blood cells	Pernicious anemia, nervous system disorders (typically due to impaired absorption) None known

in carrots and other foods, to vitamin A. (For this reason, beta-carotene and substances like it are called *provitamins.*) Vitamins are found in all major food groups, but no one food contains all the required vitamins. A balanced diet is the best way to ensure a full vitamin complement.

Initially vitamins were given a convenient letter designation that indicated the order of their discovery. Although more chemically descriptive names have been assigned to the vitamins, this earlier terminology is still commonly used.

Vitamins are either **fat soluble** or **water soluble**. The water-soluble vitamins, which include B-complex vitamins and vitamin C, are absorbed along with water from the gastrointestinal tract. (The exception is vitamin B_{12}: To be absorbed, it must bind to intrinsic factor, a stomach secretion.) Insignificant amounts of water-soluble vitamins are stored in lean tissue of the body, and any ingested amounts not used within an hour or so are excreted in urine. Consequently, few conditions resulting from excessive levels of these vitamins (*hypervitaminoses*) are known.

Fat-soluble vitamins (A, D, E, and K) bind to ingested lipids and are absorbed along with their digestion products. Anything that interferes with fat absorption also interferes with the up-

take of fat-soluble vitamins. Except for vitamin K, fat-soluble vitamins are stored in the body, and pathologies due to fat-soluble vitamin toxicity, particularly vitamin A hypervitaminosis, are well documented clinically.

As we describe in the next section, metabolism uses oxygen, and during these reactions some potentially harmful free radicals are generated. Vitamins C, E, and A (in the form of its dimer beta-carotene) and the mineral selenium are *antioxidants* that neutralize tissue-damaging free radicals. The whole story of how antioxidants interact in the body is still murky, but chemists propose that they act much like a bucket brigade to pass the dangerous free electron from one molecule to the next, until it is finally absorbed by a chemical such as glutathione and flushed from the body in urine. Broccoli, cabbage, cauliflower, and brussels sprouts are all good sources of vitamins A and C.

Controversy abounds concerning the ability of vitamins to work wonders, such as the idea that huge doses of vitamin C will prevent colds. The notion that megadoses of vitamin supplements are the road to eternal youth and glowing health is useless at best and, at worst, may cause serious health problems, particularly in the case of fat-soluble vitamins. **Table 24.2** contains an overview of the roles of vitamins in the body.

TABLE 24.2	(continued)			
VITAMIN	**RDA* (mg)**	**MAJOR DIETARY SOURCES**	**SOME MAJOR FUNCTIONS IN THE BODY**	**POSSIBLE SYMPTOMS OF DEFICIENCY** OR EXTREME EXCESS
Biotin	Unknown	Legumes, other vegetables, meats, liver, egg yolk	Coenzyme in synthesis of fat, glycogen, and amino acids	Scaly skin, pallor, fatigue, neuromuscular disorders, elevated cholesterol levels None known
Vitamin C (ascorbic acid)	75–90	Fruits and vegetables, especially citrus fruits, strawberries, broccoli, cabbage, tomatoes, green peppers	Used in collagen synthesis (such as for bone, cartilage, gums); antioxidant; aids in detoxification; improves iron absorption	Scurvy (degeneration of skin, teeth, blood vessels), weakness, delayed wound healing, impaired immunity Gastrointestinal upset, kidney stone formation, gout
Fat-Soluble Vitamins				
Vitamin A (retinol)	0.7–0.9	Provitamin A (beta-carotene) in deep green and orange vegetables and fruits; retinol in dairy products	Component of visual pigments; maintenance of epithelial tissues; antioxidant; helps prevent damage to cell membranes	Night blindness; dry, scaling skin; increased infection Headache, irritability, vomiting, hair loss, blurred vision, liver and bone damage
Vitamin D (antirachitic factor)	0.01 (twice that amount for African Americans)	Dairy products, egg yolk (also made in human skin in presence of sunlight)	Functionally a hormone; aids in absorption and use of calcium and phosphorus; promotes bone growth	Rickets (bone deformities) in children, bone softening (osteomalacia) in adults, poor muscle tone, joint pain, enhanced vulnerability to infections, increased cancer risk Brain, cardiovascular, and kidney damage, calcification of soft tissues, fatigue, weight loss,
Vitamin E (tocopherol)	15	Wheat germ, vegetable oils, nuts, seeds, dark green leafy vegetables	Antioxidant; helps prevent atherosclerosis and damage to cell membranes	None well documented in humans; possibly anemia Slow wound healing, increased clotting time
Vitamin K (phylloquinone)	0.1	Green vegetables, tea (also made by enteric bacteria)	Important in formation of blood clotting proteins; intermediate in electron transport chain	Defective blood clotting; bruising Liver damage and anemia

* RDA = recommended daily allowance

Notes

1. Because vitamin D is present in natural foods in only very small amounts, infants, pregnant and lactating women, and people who have little exposure to sunlight should use vitamin D supplements (or supplemented foods, e.g., fortified milk).

2. Vitamins A and D are toxic in excessive amounts and should be used in supplementary form only when prescribed by a physician. Because most water-soluble vitamins are excreted in urine when ingested in excess, the effectiveness of taking supplements is questionable.

3. Many vitamin deficiencies are secondary to disease (including anorexia, vomiting, diarrhea, or malabsorption diseases) or reflect increased metabolic requirements due to fever or stress factors. Specific vitamin deficiencies require therapy with the vitamins that are lacking.

Minerals

▶ List minerals essential for health; indicate important dietary sources and describe how each is used.

The body requires moderate amounts of seven **minerals** (calcium, phosphorus, potassium, sulfur, sodium, chlorine, magnesium) and trace amounts of about a dozen others **(Table 24.3)**. Minerals make up about 4% of the body by weight, with calcium and phosphorus (as bone salts) accounting for about three-quarters of this amount.

Minerals, like vitamins, are not used for fuel but work with other nutrients to ensure a smoothly functioning body. Incorporating minerals into structures gives added strength. For example, calcium, phosphorus, and magnesium salts harden the teeth and strengthen the skeleton. Most minerals are ionized in body fluids or bound to organic compounds to form phospholipids, hormones, and various functional proteins. For example, iron is essential to the oxygen-binding heme of hemoglobin, and sodium and chloride ions are the major electrolytes in blood. The amount of a particular mineral in the body gives very few clues to its importance in body function. For example, just a few milligrams of iodine (required for thyroid hormone synthesis) can make a critical difference to health.

A fine balance between uptake and excretion is crucial for retaining needed amounts of minerals while preventing toxic overload. The sodium present in virtually all natural and minimally processed foods poses little or no health risk. However, the large amounts added to processed foods and that sprinkled on prior to eating may contribute to fluid retention and high blood pressure. This is particularly true in American blacks,

TABLE 24.3	Minerals			
MINERAL	**RDA* (mg)**	**DIETARY SOURCES**	**FUNCTIONS IN THE BODY**	**POSSIBLE SYMPTOMS OF DEFICIENCY OR EXTREME EXCESS**
Calcium (Ca)	1300	Dairy products, dark green vegetables, legumes	Bone and tooth formation, blood clotting, nerve and muscle function	Stunted growth, possibly loss of bone mass Depressed neural function, muscle weakness, calcium deposit in soft tissues
Phosphorus (P)	700	Dairy products, meats, whole grains, nuts	Bone and tooth formation, acid-base balance, nucleic acid synthesis	Weakness, loss of minerals from bone, rickets Not known
Sulfur (S)	Unknown	Sulfur-containing proteins from many sources (meats, milk, eggs)	Component of certain amino acids	Symptoms of protein deficiency Not known
Potassium (K)	4700	Meats, dairy products, many fruits and vegetables, grains	Acid-base balance, water balance, nerve function, muscle contraction	Muscular weakness, paralysis Muscular weakness, cardiac problems, alkalosis
Chlorine (Cl)	2300	Table salt, cured meats (ham)	Osmotic pressure, acid-base balance, gastric juice formation	Muscle cramps, reduced appetite Vomiting
Sodium (Na)	1500	Table salt, cured meats	Osmotic pressure, acid-base balance, water-balance, nerve function, important for pumping glucose and other nutrients	Muscle cramps, reduced appetite Hypertension, edema
Magnesium (Mg)	300–400	Whole grains, green leafy vegetables	Component of certain coenzymes in ATP formation	Nervous system disturbances, tremors, muscle weakness, hypertension, sudden cardiac death Diarrhea
Trace Minerals†				
Iron (Fe)	8 ♂ 16–18 ♀	Meats, liver, shellfish, eggs, legumes, whole grains, dried fruit, nuts	Component of hemoglobin and of cytochromes, (electron carriers in oxidative phosphorylation)	Iron-deficiency anemia, weakness, impaired immunity, impaired cognitive performance in children Liver damage, hemochromatosis

whose kidneys have a greater tendency to retain salt than do those of American whites.

Fats and sugars are practically devoid of minerals, and highly refined cereals and grains are poor sources. The most mineral-rich foods are vegetables, legumes, milk, and some meats.

CHECK YOUR UNDERSTANDING

5. Vitamins are not used for energy fuels. What are they used for?
6. Which B vitamin requires the help of a product made in the stomach in order to be absorbed? What is that gastric product?
7. What mineral is essential for thyroxine synthesis? For making bones hard? For hemoglobin synthesis?

For answers, see Appendix G.

Overview of Metabolic Reactions

▶ Define metabolism. Explain how catabolism and anabolism differ.

▶ Define oxidation and reduction and indicate the importance of these reactions in metabolism.

▶ Indicate the role of coenzymes used in cellular oxidation reactions.

▶ Explain the difference between substrate-level phosphorylation and oxidative phosphorylation.

Once inside body cells, nutrients become involved in an incredible variety of biochemical reactions known collectively as **metabolism** (*metabol* = change). During metabolism, substances are constantly being built up and torn down. Cells use energy to extract more energy from foods, and then use some of this extracted energy to drive their activities. Even at rest, the body uses energy on a grand scale.

Anabolism and Catabolism

Metabolic processes are either *anabolic* (synthetic, building up) or *catabolic* (degradative, tearing down). **Anabolism** (ah-nab′o-lizm) is the general term for all reactions in which larger mole-

TABLE 24.3	(continued)			
MINERAL	**RDA* (mg)**	**DIETARY SOURCES**	**FUNCTIONS IN THE BODY**	**POSSIBLE SYMPTOMS OF DEFICIENCY** OR EXTREME EXCESS
Fluorine (F)	3–4	Fluoridated water, tea, seafood	Maintenance of tooth and (probably) bone structure	Higher frequency of tooth decay Mottling of teeth, increased risk of bone fracture, painful stiffening of joints
Zinc (Zn)	11 ♂ 8 ♀	Meats, seafood, grains, legumes	Component of several enzymes and other proteins (needed for wound healing, taste, and smell)	Growth failure, scaly skin, reproductive failure, loss of taste and smell, impaired immunity Slurred speech, tremors, difficulty in walking
Copper (Cu)	0.9–1.5	Liver, seafood, nuts, legumes, whole grains	Hemoglobin synthesis, essential for manufacture of myelin and some components of electron transport chain	Anemia, bone and cardiovascular changes (rare) Abnormal storage of copper in the body
Manganese (Mn)	2.5	Nuts, grains, vegetables, fruits, tea	Component of certain coenzymes; neural function, lactation	Abnormal bone and cartilage Appears to contribute to hallucinations and violent behavior
Iodine (I)	0.15	Cod-liver oil, seafood, dairy products, iodized salt	Component of thyroid hormones	Goiter (enlarged thyroid), cretinism, myxedema Depressed synthesis of thyroid hormones
Cobalt (Co)	Unknown	Meats, poultry, and dairy products	Component of vitamin B_{12}	None, except as B_{12} deficiency Polycythemia, heart disease
Selenium (Se)	0.05–0.07	Seafood, meats, whole grains	Component of enzymes; functions in close association with vitamin E; antioxidant	Muscle pain, maybe heart muscle deterioration Nausea, vomiting, hair loss, weight loss
Chromium (Cr)	0.035	Brewer's yeast, liver, seafood, meats, some vegetables, wine	Involved in glucose and energy metabolism, enhances effectiveness of insulin	Impaired glucose metabolism, diabetes mellitus Not known
Molybdenum (Mo)	0.045	Legumes, grains, some vegetables	Component of certain enzymes	Disorder in excretion of nitrogen-containing compounds

*RDA = recommended daily allowance
†Trace minerals together account for less than 0.005% of body weight.

cules or structures are built from smaller ones, such as the bonding together of amino acids to make proteins. **Catabolism** (kah-tab′o-lizm) refers to all processes that break down complex structures to simpler ones. One example is the hydrolysis of foods in the digestive tract. In the group of catabolic reactions collectively called **cellular respiration**, food fuels, particularly glucose, are broken down in cells and some of the energy released is captured to form ATP, the cells' energy currency. ATP then serves as the "chemical drive shaft" that links energy-releasing catabolic reactions to cellular work.

Recall from Chapter 2 that reactions driven by ATP are coupled. ATP is never hydrolyzed directly. Instead enzymes shift its high-energy phosphate groups to other molecules, which are then said to be **phosphorylated** (fos″for-ĭ-la′ted). Phosphorylation primes the molecule to change in a way that increases its activity, produces motion, or does work. For example, many regulatory enzymes that catalyze key steps in metabolic pathways are activated by phosphorylation.

Three major stages are involved in the processing of energy-containing nutrients in the body, as shown in the overview in **Figure 24.3**. (Note that the blue arrows in the figure represent catabolic reactions and the purple arrows represent anabolic reactions.)

■ *Stage 1* is digestion in the gastrointestinal tract, which is described in Chapter 23. The absorbed nutrients are then transported in blood to the tissue cells.

■ *Stage 2* occurs in the tissue cells. Newly delivered nutrients are either built into lipids, proteins, and glycogen by anabolic pathways or broken down by catabolic pathways to *pyruvic acid* (pi-roo′vik) and *acetyl CoA* (as′ĕ-til ko-a′) in the cell cytoplasm. Notice in Figure 24.3 that a major catabolic pathway of stage 2 is *glycolysis*, which we will discuss later in this chapter.

■ *Stage 3*, which occurs in the mitochondria, is almost entirely catabolic. It requires oxygen, and completes the breakdown of foods, producing carbon dioxide and water and harvesting large amounts of ATP. As Figure 24.3 shows, the *Krebs cycle* is a key pathway in stage 3, as is *oxidative phosphorylation*. We will discuss both later.

Stage 1 Digestion in GI tract lumen to absorbable forms. Transport via blood to tissue cells.

PROTEINS **CARBOHYDRATES** **FATS**

Amino acids | Glucose and other sugars | Glycerol | Fatty acids

Proteins | Glucose | Glycogen | Fats

Glycolysis

Stage 2 Anabolism (incorporation into molecules) and catabolism of nutrients to form intermediates within tissue cells.

NH_3

Pyruvic acid

Acetyl CoA

Stage 3 Oxidative breakdown of products of stage 2 in mitochondria of tissue cells. CO_2 is liberated, and H atoms removed are ultimately delivered to molecular oxygen, forming water. Some energy released is used to form ATP.

Infrequent

Krebs cycle

CO_2

O_2

H

Oxidative phosphorylation (in electron transport chain)

H_2O

ATP ATP ATP

→ Catabolic reactions
→ Anabolic reactions

Figure 24.3 Three stages of metabolism of energy-containing nutrients.

The primary function of *cellular respiration*, which consists of the glycolysis of stage 2 and all events of stage 3, is to generate ATP, which traps some of the chemical energy of the original food molecules in its own high-energy bonds. The body can also store energy in fuels, such as glycogen and fats, and these stores are later mobilized to produce ATP for cellular use.

You do not need to memorize Figure 24.3, but you may want to refer to it as a cohesive summary of nutrient processing and metabolism in the body.

Oxidation-Reduction Reactions and the Role of Coenzymes

Many of the reactions that take place within cells are **oxidation reactions**. *Oxidation* was originally defined as the combination of oxygen with other elements. Examples are the rusting of iron (the slow formation of iron oxide) and the burning of wood and other

fuels. In burning, oxygen combines rapidly with carbon, producing carbon dioxide, water, and an enormous amount of energy, which is liberated as heat and light. Later it was discovered that oxidation *also* occurs when hydrogen atoms are *removed* from compounds and so the definition was expanded to its current form: *Oxidation is the gain of oxygen or the loss of hydrogen.* As explained in Chapter 2, whichever way oxidation occurs, the oxidized substance always *loses* (or nearly loses) electrons as they move to (or toward) a substance that more strongly attracts them.

This loss of electrons can be explained by reviewing the consequences of different electron-attracting abilities of atoms (see p. 31). Consider a molecule made up of a hydrogen atom plus some other kinds of atoms. Hydrogen is very electropositive, so its lone electron usually spends more time orbiting the other atoms of the molecule. But when a hydrogen *atom* is removed, its electron goes with it, and the molecule as a whole loses that electron. Conversely, oxygen is very electron-hungry

(a) Substrate-level phosphorylation

(b) Oxidative phosphorylation

Figure 24.4 Mechanisms of phosphorylation. (a) Substrate-level phosphorylation occurs when a high-energy phosphate group is transferred directly from a substrate to ADP to form ATP. This reaction occurs both in the cytosol and in the mitochondrial matrix. **(b)** Oxidative phosphorylation, which occurs in mitochondria, is carried out by electron transport proteins that act as proton "pumps" to create a proton gradient across the inner mitochondrial membranes. The source of energy for this pumping is energy released during oxidation of food molecules. As the protons flow passively back into the mitochondrial matrix through ATP synthase, some of this gradient energy is captured and used to bind phosphate groups to ADP.

(electronegative), and so when oxygen binds with other atoms the shared electrons spend more time in oxygen's vicinity. Again, the molecule as a whole loses electrons.

As you will soon see, essentially all oxidation of food fuels involves the step-by-step removal of pairs of hydrogen atoms (and also pairs of electrons) from the substrate molecules, eventually leaving only carbon dioxide (CO_2). Molecular oxygen (O_2) is the *final* electron acceptor. It combines with the removed hydrogen atoms at the very end of the process, to form water (H_2O).

Whenever one substance loses electrons (is oxidized), another substance gains them (is reduced). For this reason, oxidation and reduction are coupled reactions and we speak of **oxidation-reduction reactions**, or more commonly, **redox reactions**. The key understanding about redox reactions is that "oxidized" substances *lose* energy and "reduced" substances *gain* energy as energy-rich electrons are transferred from one substance to the next. Consequently, as food fuels are oxidized, their energy is transferred to a "bucket brigade" of other molecules and ultimately to ADP to form energy-rich ATP.

Like all other chemical reactions in the body, redox reactions are catalyzed by enzymes. Those that catalyze redox reactions in which hydrogen atoms are removed are called **dehydrogenases** (de-hi'dro-jen-ās"ez), while those catalyzing the transfer of oxygen are **oxidases**.

Most of these enzymes require the help of a specific coenzyme, typically derived from one of the B vitamins. Although the enzymes catalyze the removal of hydrogen atoms to oxidize a substance, they cannot *accept* the hydrogen (hold on or bond to it). Their *coenzymes*, however, can act as hydrogen (or electron) acceptors, becoming reduced each time a substrate is oxidized.

Two very important coenzymes of the oxidative pathways are **nicotinamide adenine dinucleotide (NAD^+)** (nik"o-tin'ah-mīd), based on *niacin*, and **flavin adenine dinucleotide (FAD)**, derived from *riboflavin*. The oxidation of succinic acid to fumaric acid and the simultaneous reduction of FAD to $FADH_2$, an example of a coupled redox reaction, is

ATP Synthesis

How do our cells capture some of the energy liberated during cellular respiration to make ATP molecules? There appear to be two mechanisms—substrate-level phosphorylation and oxidative phosphorylation.

Substrate-level phosphorylation occurs when high-energy phosphate groups are transferred directly from phosphorylated substrates (metabolic intermediates such as glyceraldehyde phosphate) to ADP **(Figure 24.4a)**. Essentially, this process occurs because the high-energy bonds attaching the phosphate

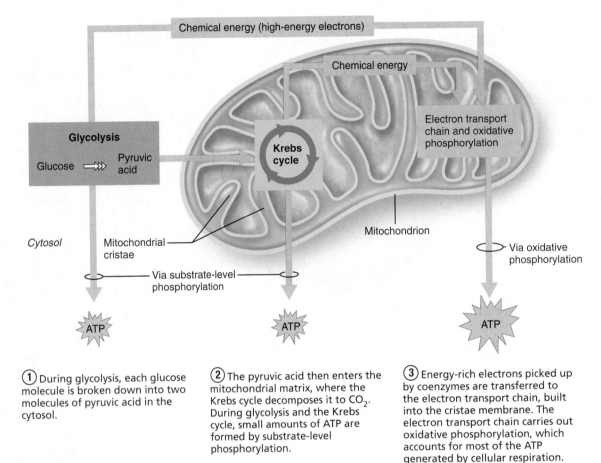

① During glycolysis, each glucose molecule is broken down into two molecules of pyruvic acid in the cytosol.

② The pyruvic acid then enters the mitochondrial matrix, where the Krebs cycle decomposes it to CO_2. During glycolysis and the Krebs cycle, small amounts of ATP are formed by substrate-level phosphorylation.

③ Energy-rich electrons picked up by coenzymes are transferred to the electron transport chain, built into the cristae membrane. The electron transport chain carries out oxidative phosphorylation, which accounts for most of the ATP generated by cellular respiration.

Figure 24.5 During cellular respiration, ATP is formed in the cytosol and in the mitochondria.

groups to the substrates are even more unstable than those in ATP. ATP is synthesized by this route once during glycolysis, and once during each turn of the Krebs cycle. The enzymes catalyzing substrate-level phosphorylations are located in both the cytosol (where glycolysis occurs) and in the watery matrix inside the mitochondria (where the Krebs cycle takes place) **(Figure 24.5)**.

Oxidative phosphorylation is much more complicated, but it also releases most of the energy that is eventually captured in ATP bonds during cellular respiration. This process, which is carried out by electron transport proteins forming part of the inner mitochondrial membranes, is an example of a chemiosmotic process. **Chemiosmotic processes** couple the movement of substances across membranes to chemical reactions.

In this case, some of the energy released during the oxidation of food fuels (the "chemi" part of chemiosmotic) is used to pump (*osmo* = push) protons (H^+) across the inner mitochondrial membrane into the intermembrane space (Figure 24.4b). This creates a steep concentration gradient for protons across the membrane. Then, when H^+ flows back across the membrane (through a membrane channel protein called *ATP synthase*), some of this gradient energy is captured and used to attach phosphate groups to ADP.

CHECK YOUR UNDERSTANDING

8. What is a redox reaction?

9. How are anabolism and catabolism linked by ATP?

10. What is the energy source for the proton pumps of oxidative phosphorylation?

For answers, see Appendix G.

Metabolism of Major Nutrients

Carbohydrate Metabolism

▶ Summarize important events and products of glycolysis, the Krebs cycle, and electron transport.

▶ Define glycogenesis, glycogenolysis, and gluconeogenesis.

The story of carbohydrate metabolism is really a tale of glucose metabolism because all food carbohydrates are eventually transformed to glucose. Glucose enters the tissue cells by facilitated diffusion, a process that is greatly enhanced by insulin. Immediately upon entry into the cell, glucose is phosphorylated to *glucose-6-phosphate* by transfer of a phosphate group to its sixth carbon during a coupled reaction with ATP:

$$\text{Glucose} + \text{ATP} \rightarrow \text{glucose-6-PO}_4 + \text{ADP}$$

Most body cells lack the enzymes needed to reverse this reaction, so it effectively traps glucose inside the cells. Because glucose-6-phosphate is a *different* molecule from simple glucose, the reaction also keeps intracellular glucose levels low, maintaining a concentration gradient for glucose entry. Only intestinal mucosa cells, kidney tubule cells, and liver cells have the enzymes needed to reverse this phosphorylation reaction, which reflects their central roles in glucose uptake *and* release. The catabolic and anabolic pathways for carbohydrates all begin with glucose-6-phosphate.

Oxidation of Glucose

Glucose is the pivotal fuel molecule in the oxidative (ATP-producing) pathways. Glucose is catabolized via the reaction

$$\text{C}_6\text{H}_{12}\text{O}_6 + 6\text{O}_2 \rightarrow 6\text{H}_2\text{O} + 6\text{CO}_2 + 32 \text{ ATP} + \text{heat}$$

$$\quad\text{glucose}\quad\;\;\text{oxygen}\quad\;\;\text{water}\quad\;\;\text{carbon}$$
$$\text{dioxide}$$

This equation gives few hints that glucose breakdown is complex and involves three of the pathways featured in Figures 24.3 and 24.5:

1. Glycolysis (color-coded orange throughout the chapter)
2. The Krebs cycle (color-coded green)
3. The electron transport chain and oxidative phosphorylation (color-coded lavender)

These metabolic pathways occur in a definite order, and we will consider them sequentially.

Glycolysis   Also called the *glycolytic pathway*, **glycolysis** (gli-kol′ĭ-sis; "sugar splitting") occurs in the cytosol of cells. This pathway is a series of ten chemical steps by which glucose is converted to two *pyruvic acid* molecules. All steps are fully *reversible* except the first, during which glucose entering the cell is phosphorylated to glucose-6-phosphate.

Glycolysis is an *anaerobic process* (an-a′er-ōb-ik; *an* = without, *aero* = air). Although this term is sometimes mistakenly interpreted to mean the pathway occurs only in the absence of oxygen, the correct interpretation is that glycolysis *does not use oxygen and occurs whether or not oxygen is present.* **Figure 24.6** shows the three major phases of the glycolytic pathway. The complete glycolytic pathway appears in Appendix D.

Phase 1. Sugar activation. In phase 1, glucose is phosphorylated and converted to fructose-6-phosphate, which is then phosphorylated again. These three steps use two ATP molecules (which are recouped later) and yield fructose-1,6-bisphosphate. The two separate reactions of the sugar with ATP provide the *activation energy* needed to prime the later stages of the pathway, so phase 1 is sometimes called the *energy investment phase.* (Recall the importance of activation energy in preparing substances to react, as described in Chapter 2.)

Figure 24.6 The three major phases of glycolysis. The fate of pyruvic acid depends on whether or not molecular O_2 is available.

Phase 2. Sugar cleavage. During phase 2, fructose-1,6-bisphosphate is split into two 3-carbon fragments that exist (reversibly) as one of two isomers: glyceraldehyde (glis″er-al′dĕ-hīd) 3-phosphate or dihydroxyacetone (dī″hi-drok″se-as′ĕ-tōn) phosphate.

Phase 3. Sugar oxidation and ATP formation. In phase 3, actually consisting of six steps, two major events happen. First, the two 3-carbon fragments are oxidized by the removal of hydrogen, which is picked up by NAD^+. In this way, some of glucose's energy is transferred to NAD^+. Second, inorganic phosphate groups (P_i) are attached to each oxidized fragment by high-energy bonds. Later, when these terminal phosphates are cleaved off, enough energy is captured to form four ATP molecules. As we noted earlier, formation of ATP this way is called *substrate-level phosphorylation.*

The final products of glycolysis are two molecules of **pyruvic acid** and two molecules of reduced NAD^+ (which is NADH + H^+). There is a net gain of two ATP molecules per glucose molecule. Four ATPs are produced, but remember that two are consumed in phase 1 to "prime the pump." Each pyruvic acid molecule has the formula $C_3H_4O_3$, and glucose is $C_6H_{12}O_6$. Between them the two pyruvic acid molecules have lost four hydrogen atoms, which are now bound to two molecules of NAD^+. NAD carries a positive charge (NAD^+), so when it accepts a hydrogen pair, NADH + H^+ is the resulting reduced product. Although a small amount of ATP has been harvested, the other two products of glucose oxidation (H_2O and CO_2) have yet to appear.

The fate of pyruvic acid, which still contains most of glucose's chemical energy, depends on the availability of oxygen at the time the pyruvic acid is produced. Because the supply of NAD^+ is limited, glycolysis can continue only if the reduced coenzymes (NADH + H^+) formed during glycolysis are relieved of their extra hydrogen. Only then can they continue to act as hydrogen acceptors.

When oxygen is readily available, this is no problem. NADH + H^+ delivers its burden of hydrogen atoms to the enzymes of the electron transport chain in the mitochondria, which deliver them to O_2, forming water. However, when oxygen is not present in sufficient amounts, as might occur during strenuous exercise, NADH + H^+ unloads its hydrogen atoms *back onto pyruvic acid*, reducing it. This addition of two hydrogen atoms to pyruvic acid yields **lactic acid** (see bottom right of Figure 24.6). Some of this lactic acid diffuses out of the cells and is transported to the liver for processing.

When oxygen is again available, lactic acid is oxidized back to pyruvic acid and enters the **aerobic pathways** (the oxygen-requiring Krebs cycle and electron transport chain within the mitochondria), and is completely oxidized to water and carbon dioxide. The liver may also convert lactic acid all the way back to glucose-6-phosphate (reverse glycolysis) and then store it as glycogen or free it of its phosphate and release it to the blood if blood sugar levels are low.

Although glycolysis generates ATP rapidly, only 2 ATP molecules are produced per glucose molecule, as compared to the 30 to 32 ATP per glucose harvested when glucose is completely oxidized. Except for red blood cells (which typically carry out *only* glycolysis), prolonged anaerobic metabolism ultimately results in acid-base problems. Consequently, *totally* anaerobic conditions resulting in lactic acid formation provide only a temporary route for rapid ATP production. It can go on without tissue dam-

age for the longest periods in skeletal muscle, for much shorter periods in cardiac muscle, and almost not at all in the brain.

Krebs Cycle Named after its discoverer Hans Krebs, the **Krebs cycle** is the next stage of glucose oxidation. The Krebs cycle, which occurs in the mitochondrial matrix, is fueled largely by pyruvic acid produced during glycolysis and by fatty acids resulting from fat breakdown.

Because pyruvic acid is a charged molecule, it must enter the mitochondrion by active transport with the help of a transport protein. Once in the mitochondrion, the first order of business is a transitional phase that converts it to acetyl CoA. This occurs via a three-step process (**Figure 24.7**, top):

1. **Decarboxylation.** In this step, one of pyruvic acid's carbons is removed and released as carbon dioxide gas. CO_2 diffuses out of the cells into the blood to be expelled by the lungs. This is the first time that CO_2 is released during cellular respiration.
2. **Oxidation.** The remaining 2C fragment (acetic acid) is oxidized by the removal of hydrogen atoms, which are picked up by NAD^+.
3. **Formation of acetyl CoA.** Acetic acid is combined with *coenzyme A* to produce the reactive final product, **acetyl coenzyme A (acetyl CoA)**. Coenzyme A is a sulfur-containing coenzyme derived from vitamin B_5.

Acetyl CoA is now ready to enter the Krebs cycle and be broken down completely by mitochondrial enzymes. Coenzyme A shuttles the 2-carbon acetic acid to an enzyme that condenses it with a 4-carbon acid called **oxaloacetic acid** (ok"sah-lo"ah-sēt'ik) to produce the 6-carbon **citric acid**. Because citric acid is the first substrate of the cycle, biochemists prefer to call the Krebs cycle the **citric acid cycle**.

As the cycle moves through its eight successive steps, the atoms of citric acid are rearranged to produce different intermediate molecules, most called **keto acids** (Figure 24.7). The acetic acid that enters the cycle is broken apart carbon by carbon (decarboxylated) and oxidized, simultaneously generating NADH + H^+ and $FADH_2$. At the end of the cycle, acetic acid has been totally disposed of and oxaloacetic acid, the *pickup molecule*, is regenerated.

What are the products of the Krebs cycle? Because two *decarboxylations* and four *oxidations* occur, the products are two CO_2 molecules and four molecules of reduced coenzymes (3 NADH + H^+ and 1 $FADH_2$). The addition of water at certain steps accounts for some of the released hydrogen. One molecule of ATP is formed (via substrate-level phosphorylation) during each turn of the cycle. The detailed events of each of the eight steps of the Krebs cycle are described in Appendix D.

Now let's back up and account for the pyruvic acid molecules entering the mitochondria. We need to consider the products of both the transitional phase and the Krebs cycle itself. Altogether, each pyruvic acid yields three CO_2 molecules and five molecules of reduced coenzymes—1 $FADH_2$ and 4 NADH + H^+ (equal to the removal of 10 hydrogen atoms). The products of glucose oxidation in the Krebs cycle are twice that (remember 1 glucose = 2 pyruvic acids): six CO_2, ten molecules of reduced coenzymes,

Figure 24.7 Simplified version of the Krebs (citric acid) cycle. During each turn of the cycle, two carbon atoms are removed from the substrates as CO_2 (decarboxylation reactions); four oxidations by removal of hydrogen atoms occur, producing four molecules of reduced coenzymes (3 NADH + H^+ and 1 $FADH_2$); and one ATP is synthesized by substrate-level phosphorylation. An additional decarboxylation and an oxidation reaction occur in the transitional phase that converts pyruvic acid, the product of glycolysis, to acetyl CoA, the molecule that enters the Krebs cycle pathway.

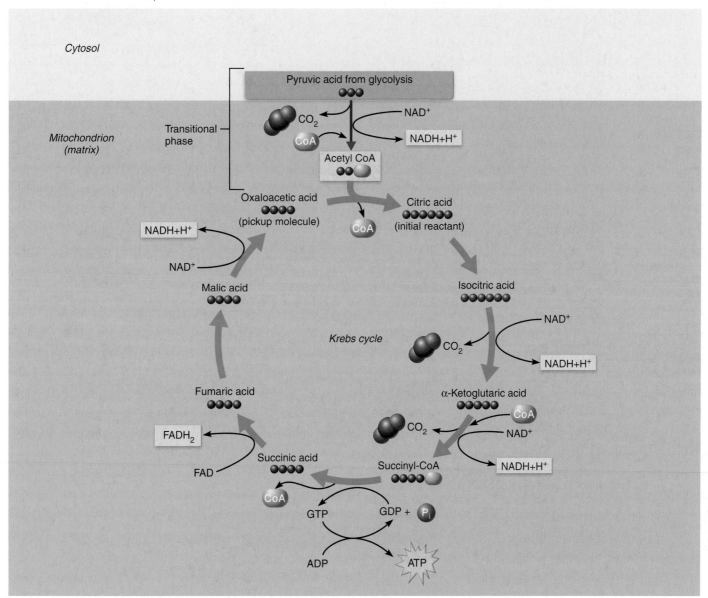

and two ATP molecules. Notice that it is these Krebs cycle reactions that produce the CO_2 evolved during glucose oxidation. The reduced coenzymes, which carry their extra electrons in high-energy linkages, must now be oxidized if the Krebs cycle and glycolysis are to continue.

Although the glycolytic pathway is exclusive to carbohydrate oxidation, breakdown products of carbohydrates, fats, and proteins can feed into the Krebs cycle to be oxidized for energy. On the other hand, some Krebs cycle intermediates can be siphoned off to make fatty acids and nonessential amino acids. Thus, the

Krebs cycle is a source of building materials for anabolic reactions, in addition to serving as the final common pathway for the oxidation of food fuels.

Electron Transport Chain and Oxidative Phosphorylation Like glycolysis, none of the reactions of the Krebs cycle use oxygen directly. This is the exclusive function of the **electron transport chain**, which carries out the final catabolic reactions that occur on the mitochondrial cristae. However, because the reduced coenzymes produced in the Krebs cycle are the substrates for the

Figure 24.8 Mechanism of oxidative phosphorylation. Schematic diagram showing the flow of electrons through the mitochondrial respiratory enzyme complexes of the electron transport chain during the transfer of two electrons from reduced NAD$^+$ to oxygen. Coenzyme Q (ubiquinone) and cytochrome c are mobile and act as carriers between the complexes. Because FADH$_2$ unloads its H atoms to complex II, the small complex just beyond the first major respiratory complex, less energy is captured as a result of its oxidation.

electron transport chain, these two pathways are coupled, and both are considered to be oxygen requiring, or *aerobic.*

In the electron transport chain, the hydrogens removed during the oxidation of food fuels are combined with O$_2$ to form water, and the energy released during those reactions is harnessed to attach P$_i$ groups to ADP, forming ATP. As we noted earlier, this type of phosphorylation process is called *oxidative phosphorylation.* Let's peek under the hood of a cell's power plant and see how this rather complicated process works.

Most components of the electron transport chain are proteins that are bound to metal atoms (known as *cofactors*). These proteins vary in composition and form multiprotein complexes that are firmly embedded in the inner mitochondrial

membrane **(Figure 24.8).** For example, some of the proteins, the **flavins,** contain flavin mononucleotide (FMN) derived from the vitamin riboflavin, and others contain both sulfur (S) and iron (Fe). Most, however, are brightly colored iron-containing pigments called **cytochromes** (si′to-krōmz; *cyto* = cell, *chrom* = color), including complexes III and IV depicted in Figure 24.8. Neighboring carriers are clustered together to form four **respiratory enzyme complexes** that are alternately reduced and oxidized as they pick up electrons and pass them on to the next complex in the sequence.

As Figure 24.8 shows, the first such complex accepts hydrogen atoms from NADH + H$^+$, oxidizing it to NAD$^+$. FADH$_2$ transfers its hydrogen atoms slightly farther along the chain to the small complex II. The hydrogen atoms delivered to the electron transport chain by the reduced coenzymes are quickly split into protons (H^+) plus electrons. The electrons are shuttled along the inner mitochondrial membrane from one complex to the next, losing energy with each transfer. The protons escape into the watery matrix only to be picked up and "pumped" across the inner mitochondrial membrane into the intermembrane space by one of the three major respiratory enzyme complexes (I, III, and IV).

Ultimately the electron pairs are delivered to half a molecule of O_2 (in other words, to an oxygen atom), creating oxygen ions (O^-) that strongly attract H^+ and form water as indicated by the reaction

$$2H^+ + 2e^- + \tfrac{1}{2}O_2 \rightarrow H_2O$$

Virtually all the water resulting from glucose oxidation is formed during oxidative phosphorylation. Because NADH + H^+ and $FADH_2$ are oxidized as they release their burden of picked-up hydrogen atoms, the net reaction for the electron transport chain is

$$\text{Coenzyme -2H} + \tfrac{1}{2}O_2 \rightarrow \text{coenzyme} + H_2O$$
reduced   oxidized
coenzyme   coenzyme

The transfer of electrons from NADH + H^+ to oxygen releases large amounts of energy. If hydrogen combined directly with molecular oxygen, the energy would be released in one big burst and most of it would be lost to the environment as heat. Instead energy is released in many small steps as the electrons stream from one electron acceptor to the next. Each successive carrier has a greater affinity for electrons than those preceding it. For this reason, the electrons cascade "downhill" from NADH + H^+ to progressively lower energy levels until they are finally delivered to oxygen, which has the greatest affinity of all for electrons. You could say that oxygen "pulls" the electrons down the chain (**Figure 24.9**).

The electron transport chain functions as an energy converter by using the stepwise release of electronic energy to pump protons from the matrix into the intermembrane space. Because the inner mitochondrial membrane is nearly impermeable to H^+, this chemiosmotic process creates an **electrochemical proton (H^+) gradient** across that membrane that has potential energy and the capacity to do work. The proton gradient (1) creates a pH gradient, with the H^+ concentration in the matrix much lower than that in the intermembrane space; and (2) generates a voltage across the membrane that is negative on the matrix side and positive between the mitochondrial membranes. Both conditions strongly attract H^+ back into the matrix. But how can they get there?

The only areas of the membrane freely permeable to H^+ are at large enzyme-protein complexes (complex V) called **ATP synthases**. These complexes, which populate the inner mitochondrial membrane (**Figure 24.10**), lay claim to being nature's smallest rotary motors. As the protons take this "route" they create an electrical current, and ATP synthase harnesses this electrical energy to catalyze attachment of a phosphate group to ADP to form ATP (**Figure 24.11**). The enzyme's subunits appear to

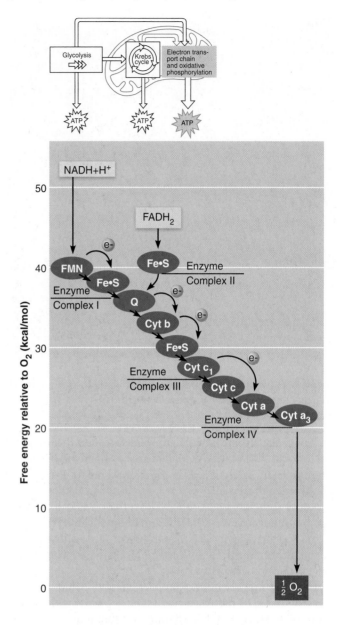

Figure 24.9 Electronic energy gradient in the electron transport chain. Each member of the chain (respiratory enzyme complex) oscillates between a reduced state and an oxidized state. A member becomes reduced by accepting electrons from its "uphill" neighbor and then reverts to its oxidized form as it passes electrons to its "downhill" neighbor. The overall energy drop is 53 kcal/mol, but this fall is broken up into smaller steps by the electron transport chain.

work together like gears. As the ATP synthase core rotates, ADP and inorganic phosphate are pulled in and ATP is churned out, completing the process of oxidative phosphorylation.

How exactly does ATP synthase work? Studies of its molecular structure are providing answers. The enzyme complex consists of two major linked parts, each with several protein subunits: (1) a *rotor* embedded in the inner mitochondrial membrane (Figure 24.11), and (2) a *knob* extending into the mitochondrial matrix, which is stabilized by a *stator* anchored in the membrane. A *rod* connects the rotor and the knob. The

Figure 24.10 Atomic force microscopy reveals the structure of energy-converting ATP synthase rotor rings.

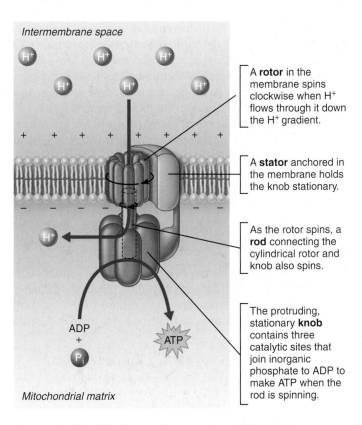

Intermembrane space

A **rotor** in the membrane spins clockwise when H^+ flows through it down the H^+ gradient.

A **stator** anchored in the membrane holds the knob stationary.

As the rotor spins, a **rod** connecting the cylindrical rotor and knob also spins.

The protruding, stationary **knob** contains three catalytic sites that join inorganic phosphate to ADP to make ATP when the rod is spinning.

H^+

ADP + P_i

ATP

Mitochondrial matrix

Figure 24.11 Structure of ATP synthase.

current created by the downhill flow of H^+ causes the rotor and rod to rotate, just as flowing water turns a water wheel. This rotation activates catalytic sites in the knob where ADP and P_i are combined to make ATP.

Notice something here. The ATP synthase works like an ion pump running in reverse. Recall from Chapter 3 that ion pumps use ATP as their energy source to transport ions against an electrochemical gradient. Here we have ATP synthases using the energy of a proton gradient to power ATP synthesis.

The proton gradient also supplies energy to pump needed metabolites (ADP, pyruvic acid, inorganic phosphate) and calcium ions across the relatively impermeable inner mitochondrial membrane. The outer membrane is quite freely permeable to these substances, so no "help" is needed there. The supply of energy from oxidation is not limitless however, so when more of the gradient energy is used to drive these transport processes, less is available to make ATP.

HOMEOSTATIC IMBALANCE

Studies of metabolic poisons support the chemiosmotic model of oxidative phosphorylation. For example, cyanide (the gas used in gas chambers) disrupts the process by binding to cytochrome oxidase and blocking electron flow from complex IV to oxygen (see Figure 24.9). Poisons commonly called "uncouplers" abolish the proton gradient by making the inner mitochondrial membrane permeable to H^+. Consequently, although the electron transport chain continues to deliver electrons to oxygen at a furious pace, and oxygen consumption rises, no ATP is made. ■

The stimulus for ATP production is entry of *ADP* into the mitochondrial matrix. As ADP is transported in, ATP is moved out in a coupled transport process.

Summary of ATP Production   The average person at rest uses energy at the rate of roughly 100 kcal/hour, which is equal to 116 watts or slightly more than that of a standard lightbulb. This seems to be a minuscule amount, but from a biochemical standpoint it places a staggering power demand on our mitochondria. Luckily, they are up to the task.

When O_2 is present, cellular respiration is remarkably efficient. Of the 686 kcal of energy present in 1 mole of glucose, as much as 262 kcal can be captured in ATP bonds. (The rest is liberated as heat.) This corresponds to an energy capture of about 38%, making cells far more efficient than any human-made machines, which use only 10–30% of the energy available to them.

During cellular respiration, most energy flows in this sequence:

Glucose $\rightarrow$ NADH + H^+ $\rightarrow$ electron transport chain $\rightarrow$ proton gradient energy $\rightarrow$ ATP

Let's do a little bookkeeping to summarize the net energy gain from one glucose molecule. First, we tally the results of substrate-level phosphorylation, giving us a net gain of 4 ATP produced directly by substrate-level phosphorylations (2 during glycolysis and 2 during the Krebs cycle). Next we must calculate the much greater number of ATP molecules produced by oxidative phosphorylation **(Figure 24.12)**.

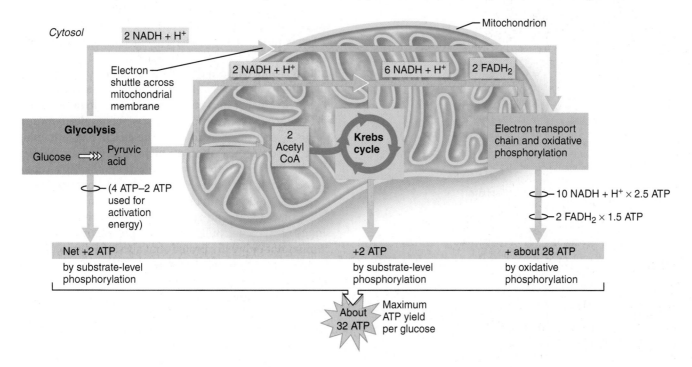

Figure 24.12 Energy yield during cellular respiration.

Each NADH + H⁺ that transfers a pair of high-energy electrons to the electron transport chain contributes enough energy to the proton gradient to generate about 2½ ATP molecules. The oxidation of $FADH_2$ is less efficient because it doesn't donate electrons to the "top" of the electron transport chain as does NADH + H⁺, but to a lower energy level (at complex II). So, for each 2 H delivered by $FADH_2$, just about 1½ ATP molecules are produced. Now we can tally the results of oxidative phosphorylation. The 2 NADH + H⁺ generated during glycolysis yield 5 ATP molecules. The 8 NADH + H⁺ and the 2 $FADH_2$ produced during the Krebs cycle are "worth" 20 and 3 ATP respectively.

Overall, complete oxidation of 1 glucose molecule to CO_2 and H_2O by both substrate-level phosphorylation and oxidative phosphorylation yields a maximum of 32 molecules of ATP (Figure 24.12). Stated another way, this adds up to some 55 kilograms of ATP every day.

However, there is an uncertainty about the energy yield of reduced NAD⁺ generated *outside* the mitochondria by glycolysis. The crista membrane is not permeable to reduced NAD⁺ generated in the cytosol, so NADH + H⁺ formed during glycolysis uses a *shuttle molecule* to deliver its extra electron pair to the electron transport chain. It appears that cells using the malate/aspartate shuttle harvest the whole 2½ ATP from oxidation of reduced NAD⁺, but in cells using a different shuttle (the glycerol phosphate shuttle for example) the shuttle has an energy cost. At present, the consensus is that the net energy yield for reoxidation of reduced NAD⁺ in this case is probably the same as for $FADH_2$, that is, 1½ ATP per electron pair.

So, if we deduct 2 ATP to cover the "fare" for the shuttle, our bookkeeping comes up with a grand total of 30 ATP per glucose as the maximum possible energy yield. (Actually our figures are probably still too high because, as mentioned earlier, the proton gradient energy is also used to do other work and the electron transport chain may not work at maximum capacity all of the time.)

CHECK YOUR UNDERSTANDING

11. Briefly, how do substrate-level and oxidative phosphorylation differ?
12. What happens in the glycolytic pathway if oxygen is absent and NADH + H⁺ cannot transfer its "picked-up" hydrogen to pyruvic acid?
13. What two major kinds of chemical reactions occur in the Krebs cycle, and how are these reactions indicated symbolically?

For answers, see Appendix G.

Glycogenesis, Glycogenolysis, and Gluconeogenesis

Glycogenesis and Glycogenolysis   Although most glucose is used to generate ATP molecules, unlimited amounts of glucose do *not* result in unlimited ATP synthesis, because cells cannot store large amounts of ATP. When more glucose is available than can immediately be oxidized, rising intracellular ATP concentrations eventually inhibit glucose catabolism and initiate processes that store glucose as glycogen or fat. Because the body can store much more fat than glycogen, fats account for 80–85% of stored energy.

When high ATP levels begin to "turn off" glycolysis, glucose molecules are combined in long chains to form glycogen, the animal carbohydrate storage product. This process is called **glycogenesis** (*glyco* = sugar; *genesis* = origin) (Figure 24.13, right side). It begins as glucose entering cells is phosphorylated

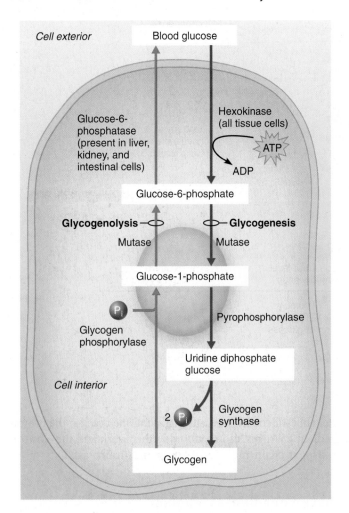

Figure 24.13 Glycogenesis and glycogenolysis. When glucose supplies exceed demands, glycogenesis (conversion of glucose to glycogen) occurs. Glycogenolysis (breakdown of glycogen to release glucose) is stimulated by falling blood glucose levels.

to glucose-6-phosphate and then converted to its isomer, *glucose-1-phosphate*. The terminal phosphate group is cleaved off as the enzyme *glycogen synthase* catalyzes the attachment of glucose to the growing glycogen chain. Liver and skeletal muscle cells are most active in glycogen synthesis and storage.

On the other hand, when blood glucose levels drop, glycogen lysis (splitting) occurs. This process is known as **glycogenolysis** (gli″ko-jĕ-nol′ĭ-sis) (Figure 24.13, left side). The enzyme *glycogen phosphorylase* oversees phosphorylation and cleavage of glycogen to release glucose-1-phosphate, which is then converted to glucose-6-phosphate, a form that can enter the glycolytic pathway to be oxidized for energy.

In muscle cells and most other cells, the glucose-6-phosphate resulting from glycogenolysis is trapped because it cannot cross the cell membrane. However, hepatocytes (and some kidney and intestinal cells) contain *glucose-6-phosphatase*, an enzyme that removes the terminal phosphate, producing free glucose. Because glucose can then readily diffuse from the cell into the blood, the liver can use its glycogen stores to provide blood sugar for the benefit of other organs when blood glucose levels

drop. Liver glycogen is also an important energy source for skeletal muscles that have depleted their own glycogen reserves.

Athletes and Carbohydrates A common misconception is that athletes need to eat large amounts of protein to improve their performance and maintain their muscle mass. Actually, a diet rich in complex carbohydrates, which results in more muscle glycogen storage, is much more effective in sustaining intense muscle activity than are high-protein meals. Notice that the emphasis is on *complex* carbohydrates. Eating a candy bar before an athletic event to provide "quick" energy does more harm than good because it stimulates insulin secretion, which favors glucose use and retards fat use at a time when fat use should be maximal. Building muscle protein or avoiding its loss requires not only extra protein, but also extra (protein-sparing) complex carbohydrate calories to meet the greater energy needs of the increasingly massive muscles.

Endurance athletes, long-distance runners in particular, are well aware of the practice of glycogen loading, popularly called "carbo loading," for endurance events. Carbo loading "tricks" the muscles into storing more glycogen than they normally would. It generally involves eating a carbohydrate-rich diet (75% of energy intake) for three to four days before an endurance event while decreasing activity. This practice has been shown to increase muscle glycogen stores to as much as twice the normal amount. Carbo loading is now standard practice among marathon runners and distance cyclists, because studies have shown that it improves performance and endurance.

Gluconeogenesis When too little glucose is available to stoke the "metabolic furnace," glycerol and amino acids are converted to glucose. **Gluconeogenesis**, the process of forming new (*neo*) glucose from *noncarbohydrate* molecules, occurs in the liver. It takes place when dietary sources and glucose reserves have been depleted and blood glucose levels are beginning to drop. Gluconeogenesis protects the body, the nervous system in particular, from the damaging effects of low blood sugar (*hypoglycemia*) by ensuring that ATP synthesis can continue.

CHECK YOUR UNDERSTANDING

14. What name is given to the chemical reaction in which glycogen is broken down to its glucose subunits?

15. What does carbo loading accomplish?

For answers, see Appendix G.

Lipid Metabolism

▶ Describe the process by which fatty acids are oxidized for energy.

▶ Define ketone bodies, and indicate the stimulus for their formation.

Fats are the body's most concentrated source of energy. They contain very little water, and the energy yield from fat catabolism is approximately twice that from either glucose or protein catabolism—9 kcal per gram of fat versus 4 kcal per gram of carbohydrate or protein. Most products of fat digestion are transported in lymph in the form of fatty-protein droplets called *chylomicrons* (see Chapter 23). Eventually, the lipids in the chylomicrons are hydrolyzed by enzymes on capillary endothelium, and the resulting fatty acids and glycerol are taken up by body cells and processed in various ways.

Oxidation of Glycerol and Fatty Acids

Of the various lipids, only triglycerides are routinely oxidized for energy. Their catabolism involves the separate oxidation of their two different building blocks: glycerol and fatty acid chains (Figure 24.14). Most body cells easily convert glycerol to glyceraldehyde phosphate, a glycolysis intermediate that enters the Krebs cycle. Glyceraldehyde is equal to half a glucose molecule, and ATP energy harvest from its complete oxidation is approximately half that of glucose (16 ATP/glycerol).

Beta oxidation, the initial phase of fatty acid oxidation, occurs in the mitochondria. Although oxidation and other reactions are involved, the net result is that the fatty acid chains are broken apart into two-carbon *acetic acid* fragments, and coenzymes (FAD and NAD^+) are reduced (Figure 24.14, right side). Each acetic acid molecule is fused to coenzyme A, forming acetyl CoA. The term "beta oxidation" reflects the fact that the carbon in the beta (third) position is oxidized during the process and cleavage of the fatty acid in each case occurs between the alpha and beta carbons. Acetyl CoA is then picked up by oxaloacetic acid and enters the aerobic pathways to be oxidized to CO_2 and H_2O.

Notice that unlike glycerol, which enters the glycolytic pathway, acetyl CoA resulting from fatty acid breakdown *cannot* be used for gluconeogenesis because the metabolic pathway is irreversible past pyruvic acid.

Lipogenesis and Lipolysis

There is a continuous turnover of triglycerides in adipose tissue. New fats are "put in the larder" for later use, while stored fats are broken down and released to the blood. That bulge of fatty tissue you see today does *not* contain the same fat molecules it did a month ago.

Glycerol and fatty acids from dietary fats not immediately needed for energy are recombined into triglycerides and stored. About 50% ends up in subcutaneous tissue, and the balance is stockpiled in other fat depots of the body. Triglyceride synthesis, or **lipogenesis**, occurs when cellular ATP and glucose levels are high (Figure 24.15, purple arrows). Excess ATP also leads to an accumulation of acetyl CoA and glyceraldehyde-PO_4, two intermediates of glucose metabolism that would otherwise feed into the Krebs cycle. But when these two metabolites are present in excess, they are channeled into triglyceride synthesis pathways.

Acetyl CoA molecules are condensed together, forming fatty acid chains that grow two carbons at a time. (This accounts for the fact that almost all fatty acids in the body contain an even number of carbon atoms.) Because acetyl CoA, an intermediate in glucose catabolism, is also the *starting point* for fatty acid synthesis, glucose is easily converted to fat. Glyceraldehyde-PO_4 is

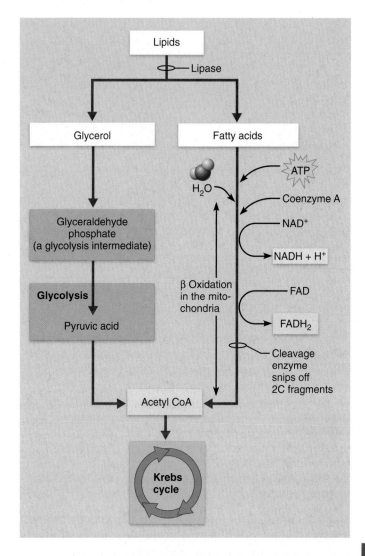

Figure 24.14 Initial phase of lipid oxidation. The glycerol portion is converted to a glycolysis intermediate, and completes the glycolytic pathway through pyruvic acid to acetyl CoA. The fatty acids undergo beta (β) oxidation in which they are first activated by a coupled reaction with ATP, combined with coenzyme A, and then oxidized twice (reducing NAD^+ and FAD). The acetyl CoA created in β oxidation is cleaved off and the process begins again.

converted to glycerol, which is condensed with fatty acids to form triglycerides. Consequently, even if the diet is fat-poor, carbohydrate intake can provide *all the raw materials* needed to form triglycerides. When blood sugar is high, lipogenesis is the major activity in adipose tissues and is also an important liver function.

Lipolysis (lĭ-pol′ĭ-sis; "fat splitting"), the breakdown of stored fats into glycerol and fatty acids, is essentially lipogenesis in reverse (Figure 24.15, blue arrows). The fatty acids and glycerol are released to the blood, helping to ensure that body organs have continuous access to fat fuels for aerobic respiration. (The liver, cardiac muscle, and resting skeletal muscles actually prefer fatty acids as an energy fuel.)

The meaning of the adage "fats burn in the flame of carbohydrates" becomes clear when carbohydrate intake is inadequate. Under such conditions, lipolysis is accelerated as the

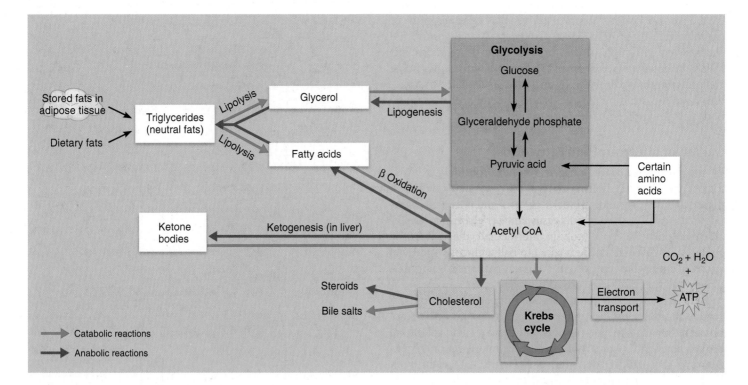

Figure 24.15 Metabolism of triglycerides. When needed for energy, fats enter catabolic pathways. Glycerol enters the glycolytic pathway and the fatty acids are broken down by beta oxidation to acetyl CoA, which enters the Krebs cycle. When fats are to be synthesized (lipogenesis) and stored, the intermediates are drawn from glycolysis and the Krebs cycle in a reversal of the processes noted above. Likewise, excess dietary fats are stored in adipose tissues. When triglycerides are in excess or are the primary energy source, the liver releases their breakdown products in the form of ketone bodies. Excessive amounts of carbohydrates and amino acids are also converted to triglycerides (lipogenesis).

body attempts to fill the fuel gap with fats. However, the ability of acetyl CoA to enter the Krebs cycle depends on the availability of oxaloacetic acid to act as the pickup molecule (see Figure 24.7). When carbohydrates are deficient, oxaloacetic acid is converted to glucose (to fuel the brain). Without oxaloacetic acid, fat oxidation is incomplete, and acetyl CoA accumulates. Via a process called **ketogenesis**, the liver converts acetyl CoA molecules to **ketone bodies**, or **ketones**, which are released into the blood. Ketone bodies include acetoacetic acid, β-hydroxybutyric acid, and acetone. (The *keto acids* cycling through the Krebs cycle and the *ketone bodies* resulting from fat metabolism are quite different and should not be confused.)

HOMEOSTATIC IMBALANCE

When ketone bodies accumulate in the blood, *ketosis* results and large amounts of ketone bodies are excreted in the urine. Ketosis is a common consequence of starvation, unwise dieting (in which inadequate amounts of carbohydrates are eaten), and diabetes mellitus. Because most ketone bodies are organic acids, the outcome of ketosis is *metabolic acidosis*. The body's buffer systems cannot tie up the acids (ketones) fast enough, and blood pH drops to dangerously low levels. The person's breath smells fruity as acetone vaporizes from the lungs, and breathing becomes more rapid as the respiratory system tries to reduce blood carbonic acid by blowing off CO_2 to force the blood pH up. In severe untreated cases, the person may become comatose or even die as the acid pH depresses the nervous system. ■

Synthesis of Structural Materials

All body cells use phospholipids and cholesterol to build their membranes, and phospholipids are important components of myelin sheaths of neurons. In addition, the liver (1) synthesizes lipoproteins for transport of cholesterol, fats, and other substances in the blood; (2) synthesizes cholesterol from acetyl CoA; and (3) uses cholesterol to form bile salts. The ovaries, testes, and adrenal cortex use cholesterol to synthesize their steroid hormones.

CHECK YOUR UNDERSTANDING

16. Which part of triglyceride molecules directly enters the glycolysis pathway?
17. What is the central molecule in fat metabolism?
18. What are the products of beta oxidation?

For answers, see Appendix G.

Protein Metabolism

▶ Describe how amino acids are metabolized for energy.

▶ Describe the need for protein synthesis in body cells.

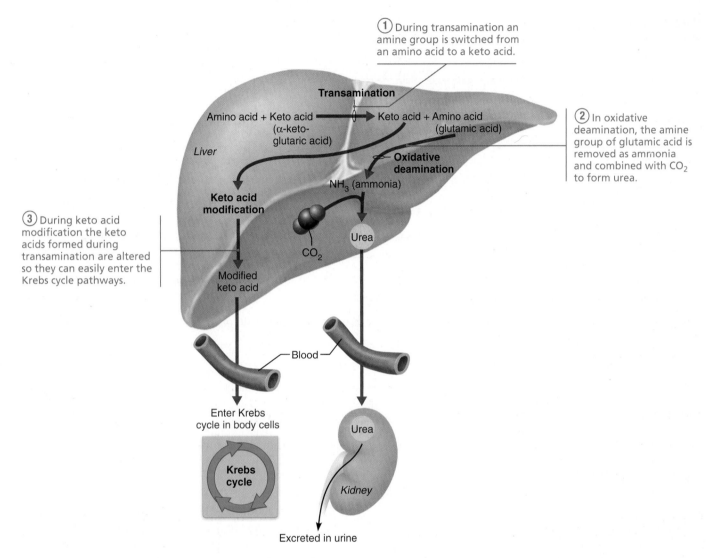

Figure 24.16 Transamination, oxidative deamination, and keto acid modification: processes that occur when amino acids are utilized for energy.

Like all other biological molecules, proteins have a limited life span and must be broken down and replaced before they begin to deteriorate. As proteins are broken down, their amino acids are recycled and used in building new proteins or modified to form a different N-containing compound. Newly ingested amino acids transported in the blood are taken up by cells by active transport processes and used to *replace* tissue proteins at the rate of about 100 grams each day.

Although popular opinion has it that excess protein can be stored by the body, nothing is farther from the truth. When more protein is available than is needed for anabolic purposes, amino acids are oxidized for energy or converted to fat for future energy needs.

Oxidation of Amino Acids

Before amino acids can be oxidized for energy, they must be *deaminated*, that is, their amine group (NH_2) must be removed. (In sulfur-containing amino acids, such as methionine and cysteine, sulfur is released prior to deamination.) The resulting molecule is then converted to pyruvic acid or to one of the keto acid intermediates in the Krebs cycle [acetyl CoA, alpha (α) ketoglutaric acid, succinyl CoA, fumaric acid, or oxaloacetic acid]. The key molecule in these conversions is the nonessential amino acid *glutamic acid* (gloo-tam′ik). As **Figure 24.16** shows, the following events occur:

1. **Transamination** (trans″am-ĭ-na′shun). A number of amino acids can transfer their amine group to α-ketoglutaric acid (a Krebs cycle keto acid), thereby transforming α-ketoglutaric acid to glutamic acid. In the process, the original amino acid becomes a keto acid (that is, it has an oxygen atom where the amine group formerly was). This reaction is fully reversible.

2. **Oxidative deamination.** In the liver, the amine group of glutamic acid is removed as **ammonia (NH_3)**, and α-ketoglutaric acid is regenerated. The liberated NH_3 molecules are combined with CO_2, yielding **urea** and water. The urea is released to the blood and removed from the body in urine. Because ammonia is toxic to body cells, the ease with

TABLE 24.4	Thumbnail Summary of Metabolic Reactions
Carbohydrates	
Cellular respiration	Reactions that together complete the oxidation of glucose, yielding CO_2, H_2O, and ATP
Glycolysis	Conversion of glucose to pyruvic acid
Glycogenesis	Polymerization of glucose to form glycogen
Glycogenolysis	Hydrolysis of glycogen to glucose monomers
Gluconeogenesis	Formation of glucose from noncarbohydrate precursors
Krebs cycle	Complete breakdown of pyruvic acid to CO_2, yielding small amounts of ATP and reduced coenzymes
Electron transport chain	Energy-yielding reactions that split H removed during oxidations to H^+ and e^- and create a proton gradient used to bond ADP to P_i (forming ATP)
Lipids	
Beta oxidation	Conversion of fatty acids to acetyl CoA
Lipolysis	Breakdown of lipids to fatty acids and glycerol
Lipogenesis	Formation of lipids from acetyl CoA and glyceraldehyde phosphate
Proteins	
Transamination	Transfer of an amine group from an amino acid to α-ketoglutaric acid, thereby transforming α-ketoglutaric acid to glutamic acid
Oxidative deamination	Removal of an amine group from glutamic acid as ammonia and regeneration of α-ketoglutaric acid (NH_3 is converted to urea by the liver)

which glutamic acid funnels amine groups into the **urea cycle** is extremely important. This cycle rids the body not only of NH_3 produced during oxidative deamination, but also of bloodborne NH_3 produced by intestinal bacteria.

③ **Keto acid modification.** The goal of amino acid degradation is to produce molecules that can be either oxidized in the Krebs cycle or converted to glucose. Keto acids resulting from transamination are altered as necessary to produce metabolites that can enter the Krebs cycle. The most important of these metabolites are pyruvic acid, acetyl CoA, α-ketoglutaric acid, and oxaloacetic acid (see Figure 24.7). Because the reactions of glycolysis are reversible, deaminated amino acids that are converted to pyruvic acid can be reconverted to glucose and contribute to gluconeogenesis.

Protein Synthesis

Amino acids are the most important anabolic nutrients. Not only do they form all protein structures, but they form the bulk of the body's functional molecules as well. As we described in Chapter 3, protein synthesis occurs on ribosomes, where ribosomal enzymes oversee the formation of peptide bonds linking the amino acids together into protein polymers. The amount and type of protein synthesized are precisely controlled by hormones (growth hormone, thyroxine, sex hormones, insulin-like growth factors, and others), and so protein anabolism reflects the hormonal balance at each stage of life.

During your lifetime, your cells will have synthesized 225–450 kg (about 500–1000 lb) of proteins, depending on your size. However, you do not need to consume anywhere near that amount of protein because nonessential amino acids are easily formed by siphoning keto acids from the Krebs cycle and transferring amine groups to them. Most of these transformations occur in the liver, which provides nearly all the nonessential amino acids needed to produce the relatively small amount of protein that the body synthesizes each day.

However, a complete set of amino acids must be present for protein synthesis to take place, so all essential amino acids must be provided by the diet. If some are not, the rest are oxidized for energy even though they may be needed for anabolism. In such cases, negative nitrogen balance results because body protein is broken down to supply the essential amino acids needed.

To review the various metabolic reactions described so far, consult the brief summary in **Table 24.4**.

CHECK YOUR UNDERSTANDING

19. What does the liver use as its substrates when it synthesizes nonessential amino acids?

20. What happens to the ammonia removed from amino acids when they are used for energy fuel?

For answers, see Appendix G.

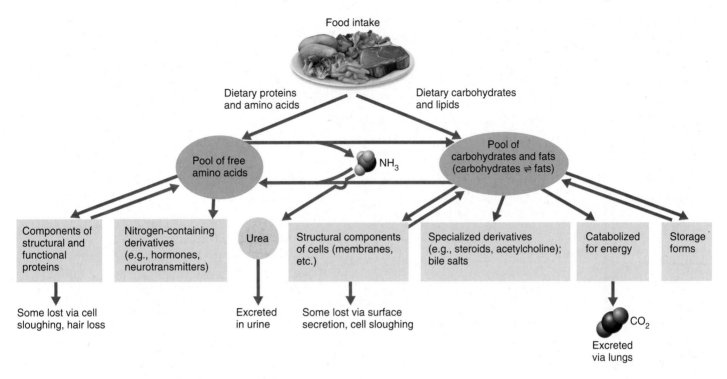

Figure 24.17 Carbohydrate-fat and amino acid pools.

Metabolic States of the Body

▶ Explain the concept of amino acid or carbohydrate-fat pools, and describe pathways by which substances in these pools can be interconverted.

▶ List important events of the absorptive and postabsorptive states, and explain how these events are regulated.

Catabolic-Anabolic Steady State of the Body

The body exists in a *dynamic catabolic-anabolic state* as organic molecules are continuously broken down and rebuilt—frequently at a head-spinning rate.

The blood serves as the transport pool for all body cells, and it contains many kinds of energy sources—glucose, ketone bodies, fatty acids, glycerol, and lactic acid. Some organs routinely use

blood energy sources other than glucose, which saves glucose for tissues with stricter glucose requirements (**Table 24.5**).

The body can draw on its **nutrient pools**—amino acid, carbohydrate, and fat stores—to meet its varying needs (**Figure 24.17**). These pools are interconvertible because their pathways are linked by key intermediates (**Figure 24.18**). The liver, adipose tissue, and skeletal muscles are the primary effector organs or tissues determining the amounts and direction of the conversions shown in the figure.

The **amino acid pool** is the body's total supply of free amino acids. Small amounts of amino acids and proteins are lost daily in urine and in sloughed hairs and skin cells. Typically, these lost molecules are replaced via the diet. Otherwise, amino acids arising from tissue breakdown return to the pool. This pool is the source of amino acids used for protein synthesis and in the formation of amino acid derivatives. In addition,

24

TABLE 24.5	Profiles of the Major Body Organs in Fuel Metabolism		
TISSUE	**FUEL STORES**	**PREFERRED FUEL**	**FUEL SOURCES EXPORTED**
Brain	None	Glucose (ketone bodies during starvation)	None
Skeletal muscle (resting)	Glycogen	Fatty acids	None
Skeletal muscle (during exertion)	None	Glucose, lactate	Lactate
Heart muscle	None	Fatty acids, lactate	None
Adipose tissue	Triglycerides	Fatty acids	Fatty acids, glycerol
Liver	Glycogen, triglycerides	Amino acids, glucose, fatty acids	Fatty acids, glucose, ketone bodies

SOURCE: Adapted from Mathews, van Holde, and Ahern, 2000, *Biochemistry* 3/e, San Francisco: Addison Wesley Longman, p. 832.

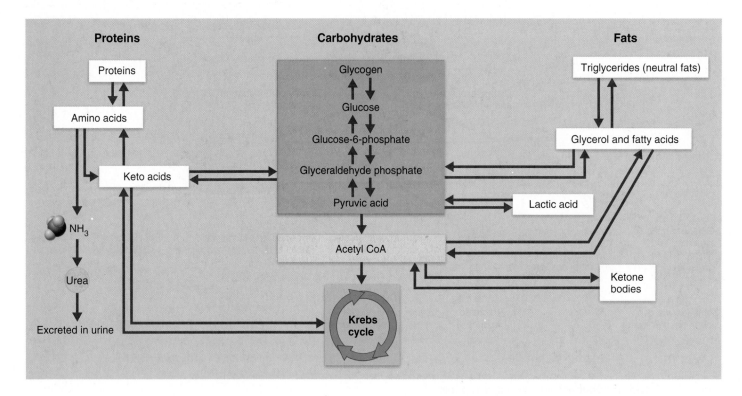

Figure 24.18 Interconversion of carbohydrates, fats, and proteins. The liver, adipose tissue, and skeletal muscles are the primary effectors determining the amounts and direction of the conversions shown.

as we described above, deaminated amino acids can participate in gluconeogenesis.

Not all events of amino acid metabolism occur in all cells. For example, *only* the liver forms urea. Nonetheless, the concept of a common amino acid pool is valid because all cells are connected by the blood.

Because carbohydrates are easily and frequently converted to fats, the **carbohydrate** and **fat pools** are usually considered together (Figures 24.17 and 24.18). There are two major differences between this pool and the amino acid pool: (1) Fats and carbohydrates are oxidized directly to produce cellular energy, whereas amino acids can be used to supply energy *only after being converted to a carbohydrate intermediate* (a keto acid). (2) Excess carbohydrate and fat can be stored as such, whereas excess amino acids are *not* stored as protein. Instead, they are oxidized for energy or converted to fat or glycogen for storage.

Metabolic controls act to equalize blood concentrations of energy sources between two nutritional states. Sometimes referred to as the *fed state*, the **absorptive state** is the time during and shortly after eating, when nutrients are flushing into the blood from the gastrointestinal tract. The **postabsorptive state**, or *fasting state*, is the period when the GI tract is empty and energy sources are supplied by the breakdown of body reserves.

People who eat "three squares" a day are in the absorptive state for the four hours during and after each meal and in the postabsorptive state in the late morning, late afternoon, and all night. However, postabsorptive mechanisms can sustain the body for much longer intervals if necessary—even to accommodate weeks of fasting—as long as water is taken in.

Absorptive State

During the absorptive state anabolism exceeds catabolism (Figure 24.19). Glucose is the major energy fuel. Dietary amino acids and fats are used to remake degraded body protein or fat, and small amounts are oxidized to provide ATP. Excess metabolites, regardless of source, are transformed to fat if not used for anabolism. We will consider the fate and hormonal control of each nutrient group during this phase.

Carbohydrates

Absorbed monosaccharides are delivered directly to the liver, where fructose and galactose are converted to glucose. Glucose, in turn, is released to the blood or converted to glycogen and fat. Glycogen formed in the liver is stored there, but most fat synthesized there is packaged with proteins as *very low density lipoproteins (VLDLs)* and released to the blood to be picked up for storage by adipose tissues. Bloodborne glucose not sequestered by the liver enters body cells to be metabolized for energy, and any excess is stored in skeletal muscle cells as glycogen or in adipose cells as fat.

Triglycerides

Nearly all products of fat digestion enter the lymph in the form of chylomicrons, which are hydrolyzed to fatty acids and glycerol before they can pass through the capillary walls. *Lipoprotein lipase*, the enzyme that catalyzes fat hydrolysis, is particularly active in the capillaries of muscle and fat tissues. Adipose cells, skeletal and cardiac muscle cells, and liver cells use triglycerides

(a) Major events of the absorptive state

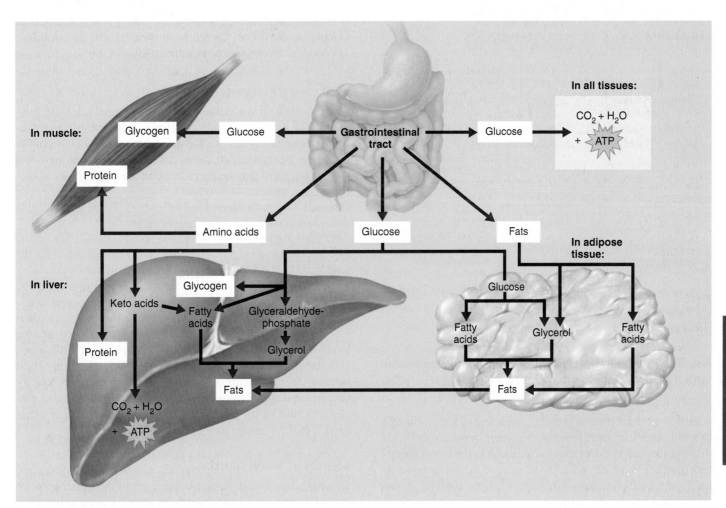

(b) Principal pathways of the absorptive state

Figure 24.19 Major events and principal metabolic pathways of the absorptive state. Although not indicated in **(b)**, amino acids are also taken up by tissue cells and used for protein synthesis, and fats (triglycerides) are the primary energy fuel of muscle, liver cells, and adipose tissue.

as their primary energy source, and when dietary carbohydrates are limited, other cells begin to oxidize more fat for energy. Although some fatty acids and glycerol are used for anabolic purposes by tissue cells, most enter adipose tissue to be reconverted to triglycerides and stored.

Amino Acids

Absorbed amino acids are delivered to the liver, which deaminates some of them to keto acids. The keto acids may flow into the Krebs cycle to be used for ATP synthesis, or they may be converted to liver fat stores. The liver also uses some of the amino

Initial stimulus

Physiological response

Result

Figure 24.20 Insulin directs nearly all events of the absorptive state. (Note: Not all effects shown occur in all cells.)

acids to synthesize plasma proteins, including albumin, clotting proteins, and transport proteins. However, most amino acids flushing through the liver sinusoids remain in the blood for uptake by other body cells, where they are used for protein synthesis. Figure 24.19 has been simplified to show nonliver amino acid uptake only by muscle.

Hormonal Control

Insulin directs essentially all events of the absorptive state (Figure 24.20). Rising blood glucose levels after a carbohydrate-containing meal act as a humoral stimulus that prods the beta cells of the pancreatic islets to secrete more insulin. [This glucose-induced stimulation of insulin release is enhanced by the GI tract hormone glucose-dependent insulinotropic peptide (GIP) and parasympathetic stimulation.] A second important stimulus for insulin release is elevated amino acid levels in the blood.

Insulin binding to membrane receptors of its target cells stimulates the translocation of the glucose transporter (GLUT-4 in

muscle and adipose tissue) to the plasma membrane, which enhances the carrier-mediated facilitated diffusion of glucose into those cells. Within minutes, the rate of glucose entry into tissue cells (particularly muscle and adipose cells) increases about 20-fold. (The exception is brain and liver cells, which take up glucose whether or not insulin is present.)

Once glucose enters tissue cells, insulin enhances glucose oxidation for energy and stimulates its conversion to glycogen and, in adipose tissue, to triglycerides. Insulin also "revs up" the active transport of amino acids into cells, promotes protein synthesis, and inhibits liver export of glucose and virtually all liver enzymes that promote gluconeogenesis.

As you can see, insulin is a **hypoglycemic hormone** (hi″po-gli-se′mik). It sweeps glucose out of the blood into the tissue cells, lowering blood glucose levels. Additionally, it enhances glucose oxidation or storage while simultaneously inhibiting any process that might increase blood glucose levels.

HOMEOSTATIC IMBALANCE

Diabetes mellitus is a consequence of inadequate insulin production or abnormal insulin receptors. Without insulin or receptors that "recognize" it, glucose becomes unavailable to most body cells. For this reason, blood glucose levels remain high, and large amounts of glucose are excreted in urine. Metabolic acidosis, protein wasting, and weight loss occur as large amounts of fats and tissue proteins are used for energy. (Diabetes mellitus is described in more detail in Chapter 16.) ■

Postabsorptive State

In the postabsorptive state, net synthesis of fat, glycogen, and proteins ends, and catabolism of these substances begins to occur. The primary goal during this state, between meals when blood glucose levels are dropping, is to maintain blood glucose levels within the homeostatic range (70–110 mg of glucose per 100 ml). Remember that constant blood glucose is important because the brain almost always uses glucose as its energy source. Most events of the postabsorptive state either make glucose available to the blood or save glucose for the organs that need it most by using fats for energy (Figure 24.21).

Sources of Blood Glucose

So where does blood glucose come from in the postabsorptive state? Glucose can be obtained from stored glycogen, from tissue proteins, and in limited amounts from fats. Let's look at the sources, illustrated in Figure 24.21b, more closely.

① **Glycogenolysis in the liver.** The liver's glycogen stores (about 100 g) are the first line of glucose reserves. They are mobilized quickly and efficiently and can maintain blood sugar levels for about four hours during the postabsorptive state.

② **Glycogenolysis in skeletal muscle.** Glycogen stores in skeletal muscle are approximately equal to those of the liver. Before liver glycogen is exhausted, glycogenolysis begins in skeletal muscle (and to a lesser extent in other tissues). However, the glucose produced is not released to

(a) Major events of the postabsorptive state

(b) Principal pathways of the postabsorptive state

Figure 24.21 **Major events and principal metabolic pathways of the postabsorptive state.**

the blood because, unlike the liver, skeletal muscle does not have the enzymes needed to dephosphorylate glucose. Instead, glucose is partly oxidized to pyruvic acid (or, during anaerobic conditions, lactic acid), which enters the blood, is reconverted to glucose by the liver, and is released to the blood again. Thus, skeletal muscle con-

tributes to blood glucose homeostasis indirectly, via liver mechanisms.

③ **Lipolysis in adipose tissues and the liver.** Adipose and liver cells produce glycerol by lipolysis, and the liver converts the glycerol to glucose (gluconeogenesis) and releases it to the blood. Because acetyl CoA, a product of the beta oxidation

Figure 24.22 Glucagon is a hyperglycemic hormone that stimulates a rise in blood glucose levels. Negative feedback control exerted by rising plasma glucose levels on glucagon secretion is indicated by the dashed arrow.

of fatty acids, is produced beyond the *reversible* steps of glycolysis, fatty acids *cannot* be used to bolster blood glucose levels.

④ **Catabolism of cellular protein.** Tissue proteins become the major source of blood glucose when fasting is prolonged and glycogen and fat stores are nearly exhausted. Cellular amino acids (mostly from muscle) are deaminated and converted to glucose in the liver. During fasts lasting several weeks, the kidneys also carry out gluconeogenesis and contribute as much glucose to the blood as the liver.

Even during prolonged fasting or starvation, the body sets priorities. Muscle proteins are the first to go (to be catabolized). Movement is not nearly as important as maintaining wound healing and the immune response. But as long as life continues, so does the body's ability to produce the ATP needed to drive life processes.

Of course there are limits to the amount of tissue protein that can be catabolized before the body stops functioning.

The heart is almost entirely muscle protein, and when it is severely catabolized, the result is death. In general, the amount of fat the body contains determines the time a person can survive without food.

Glucose Sparing

Even collectively, all of the manipulations aimed at increasing blood glucose are not enough to provide energy supplies for prolonged fasting. Luckily, the body can adapt to burn more fats and proteins, which enter the Krebs cycle along with glucose breakdown products. The increased use of noncarbohydrate fuel molecules (especially triglycerides) to conserve glucose is called **glucose sparing**.

As the body progresses from the absorptive to the postabsorptive state, the brain continues to take its share of blood glucose, but virtually every other organ switches to fatty acids as its major energy source, sparing glucose for the brain. During this transition phase, lipolysis begins in adipose tissues and released fatty acids are picked up by tissue cells and oxidized for energy. In addition, the liver oxidizes fats to ketone bodies and releases them to the blood for use by tissue cells.

If fasting continues for longer than four or five days, the brain too begins to use large quantities of ketone bodies as well as glucose as its energy fuel (Table 24.5). The brain's ability to use an alternative fuel source has survival value—much less tissue protein has to be ravaged to form glucose.

Hormonal and Neural Controls

The sympathetic nervous system and several hormones interact to control events of the postabsorptive state. Consequently, regulation of this state is much more complex than that of the absorptive state when a single hormone, insulin, holds sway.

An important trigger for initiating postabsorptive events is dampening of insulin release, which occurs as blood glucose levels drop. As insulin levels decline, all insulin-induced cellular responses are inhibited as well. Interestingly, drinking moderate amounts of beer, wine, or gin before or during a meal improves the body's use of insulin. That is, it lowers blood glucose without increasing insulin release. The advantage of this is obvious because although blood glucose naturally spikes after a meal, prolonged elevation can increase the risk of developing diabetes mellitus and heart disease.

Declining glucose levels also stimulate the alpha cells of the pancreatic islets to release the insulin antagonist **glucagon**. Like other hormones acting during the postabsorptive state, glucagon is a **hyperglycemic hormone**, in other words, it promotes a rise in blood glucose levels. Glucagon targets the liver and adipose tissue (**Figure 24.22**). The hepatocytes respond by accelerating glycogenolysis and gluconeogenesis. Adipose cells mobilize their fatty stores (lipolysis) and release fatty acids and glycerol to the blood. In this way, glucagon "refurbishes" blood energy sources by enhancing both glucose and fatty acid levels. Under certain hormonal conditions and persistent low glucose levels or prolonged fasting, most of the fat mobilized is converted to ketone bodies. Glucagon release is inhibited after the next meal or whenever blood glucose levels rise and insulin secretion begins again.

TABLE 24.6	Summary of Normal Hormonal Influences on Metabolism						
HORMONE'S EFFECTS	INSULIN	GLUCAGON	EPINEPHRINE	GROWTH HORMONE	THYROXINE	CORTISOL	TESTOSTERONE
Stimulates glucose uptake by cells	✓				✓		
Stimulates amino acid uptake by cells	✓			✓			
Stimulates glucose catabolism for energy	✓				✓		
Stimulates glycogenesis	✓						
Stimulates lipogenesis and fat storage	✓						
Inhibits gluconeogenesis	✓						
Stimulates protein synthesis (anabolic)	✓			✓	✓		✓
Stimulates glycogenolysis		✓	✓				
Stimulates lipolysis and fat mobilization		✓	✓	✓	✓	✓	
Stimulates gluconeogenesis		✓	✓	✓		✓	
Stimulates protein breakdown (catabolic)						✓	

So far, the picture is pretty straightforward. Increasing blood glucose levels trigger insulin release, which "pushes" glucose out of the blood and into the cells. This drop in blood glucose stimulates secretion of glucagon, which "pulls" glucose from the cells into the blood. However, there is more than a push-pull mechanism here because *both* insulin and glucagon release are strongly stimulated by rising amino acid levels in the blood.

This effect is insignificant when we eat a balanced meal, but it has an important adaptive role when we eat a high-protein, low-carbohydrate meal. In this instance, the stimulus for insulin release is strong, and if it were not counterbalanced, the brain might be damaged by the abrupt onset of hypoglycemia as glucose is rushed out of the blood. Simultaneous release of glucagon modulates the effects of insulin and helps stabilize blood glucose levels.

The sympathetic nervous system also plays a crucial role in supplying fuel quickly when blood glucose levels drop suddenly. Adipose tissue is well supplied with sympathetic fibers, and epinephrine released by the adrenal medulla in response to sympathetic activation acts on the liver, skeletal muscle, and adipose tissues. Together, these stimuli mobilize fat and promote glycogenolysis—essentially the same effects prompted by glucagon.

Injury, anxiety, or any other stressor that mobilizes the fight-or-flight response will trigger this control pathway, as does exercise. During exercise, large amounts of fuels must be made available for muscle use, and the metabolic profile is essentially the same as that of a fasting person when glucagon and the sympathetic nervous system are in control except that the facilitated diffusion of glucose into muscle is enhanced. (The mechanism of this enhancement is not yet understood.)

In addition to glucagon and epinephrine, a number of other hormones—including growth hormone (GH), thyroxine, sex hormones, and corticosteroids—influence metabolism and nutrient flow. Growth hormone secretion is enhanced by prolonged fasting or rapid declines in blood glucose levels, and GH exerts important anti-insulin effects. For example, it reduces the ability of insulin to promote glucose uptake in fat and muscle. However, the release and activity of most of these hormones are not specifically related to absorptive or postabsorptive metabolic events. Typical metabolic effects of various hormones are summarized in **Table 24.6**.

CHECK YOUR UNDERSTANDING

21. What three organs or tissues are the primary effector organs determining the amounts and directions of interconversions in the nutrient pools?
22. Generally speaking, what kinds of reactions and events characterize the absorptive state? The postabsorptive state?
23. What hormone is glucagon's main antagonist?
24. What event increases both glucagon and insulin release?

For answers, see Appendix G.

The Metabolic Role of the Liver

▶ Describe several metabolic functions of the liver.

▶ Differentiate between LDLs and HDLs relative to their structures and major roles in the body.

TABLE 24.7	Summary of Metabolic Functions of the Liver
METABOLIC PROCESSES TARGETED	**FUNCTIONS**
Carbohydrate Metabolism	
Particularly important in maintaining blood glucose homeostasis	▪ Converts galactose and fructose to glucose ▪ Glucose buffer function: stores glucose as glycogen when blood glucose levels are high; in response to hormonal controls, performs glycogenolysis and releases glucose to blood ▪ Gluconeogenesis: converts amino acids and glycerol to glucose when glycogen stores are exhausted and blood glucose levels are falling ▪ Converts glucose to fats for storage
Fat Metabolism	
Although most cells are capable of some fat metabolism, liver bears the major responsibility	▪ Primary body site of beta oxidation (breakdown of fatty acids to acetyl CoA) ▪ Converts excess acetyl CoA to ketone bodies for release to tissue cells ▪ Stores fats ▪ Forms lipoproteins for transport of fatty acids, fats, and cholesterol to and from tissues ▪ Synthesizes cholesterol from acetyl CoA; catabolizes cholesterol to bile salts, which are secreted in bile
Protein Metabolism	
Other metabolic functions of the liver could be dispensed with and body could still survive; however, without liver metabolism of proteins, severe survival problems ensue: many essential clotting proteins would not be made, and ammonia would not be disposed of, for example	▪ Deaminates amino acids (required for their conversion to glucose or use for ATP synthesis); amount of deamination that occurs outside the liver is unimportant ▪ Forms urea for removal of ammonia from body; inability to perform this function (e.g., in cirrhosis or hepatitis) results in accumulation of ammonia in blood ▪ Forms most plasma proteins (exceptions are gamma globulins and some hormones and enzymes); plasma protein depletion causes rapid mitosis of the hepatocytes and actual growth of liver, which is coupled with increase in synthesis of plasma proteins until blood values are again normal ▪ Transamination: intraconversion of nonessential amino acids; amount that occurs outside liver is inconsequential
Vitamin/Mineral Storage	
	▪ Stores vitamin A (1–2 years' supply) ▪ Stores sizable amounts of vitamins D and B_{12} (1–4 months' supply) ▪ Stores iron; other than iron bound to hemoglobin, most of body's supply is stored in liver as ferritin until needed; releases iron to blood as blood levels drop
Biotransformation Functions	
	▪ Metabolizes alcohol and drugs by performing synthetic reactions yielding inactive products for excretion by the kidneys and nonsynthetic reactions that may result in products which are more active, changed in activity, or less active ▪ Processes bilirubin resulting from RBC breakdown and excretes bile pigments in bile ▪ Metabolizes bloodborne hormones to forms that can be excreted in urine

The liver is one of the most biochemically complex organs in the body. It processes nearly every class of nutrients and plays a major role in regulating plasma cholesterol levels. While mechanical contraptions can, in a pinch, stand in for a failed heart, lungs, or kidney, the only thing that can do the versatile liver's work is a hepatocyte.

The hepatocytes carry out some 500 or more intricate metabolic functions. A description of all of these functions is well beyond the scope of this text, but we provide a brief summary in **Table 24.7**.

Cholesterol Metabolism and Regulation of Blood Cholesterol Levels

Cholesterol, though an important dietary lipid, has received little attention in this discussion so far, primarily because it is not used as an energy source. It serves instead as the structural basis of bile salts, steroid hormones, and vitamin D and as a major component of plasma membranes. Additionally, cholesterol is part of a key signaling molecule (the *hedgehog protein*) that helps direct embryonic development.

About 15% of blood cholesterol comes from the diet. The other 85% is made from acetyl CoA by the liver, and to a lesser extent other body cells, particularly intestinal cells. Cholesterol is lost from the body when it is catabolized and secreted in bile salts, which are eventually excreted in feces.

Cholesterol Transport

Because triglycerides and cholesterol are insoluble in water, they do not circulate free in the blood. Instead, they are transported to and from tissue cells bound to small lipid-protein complexes called **lipoproteins**. These complexes solubilize the hydrophobic lipids, and the protein part of the complexes contains signals that regulate lipid entry and exit at specific target cells.

Lipoproteins vary considerably in their relative fat-protein composition, but they all contain triglycerides, phospholipids, and cholesterol in addition to protein **(Figure 24.23)**. In general, the higher the percentage of lipid in the lipoprotein, the lower its density; and the greater the proportion of protein, the higher its density. On this basis, there are **very low density lipoproteins (VLDLs)**, **low-density lipoproteins (LDLs)**, and **high-density lipoproteins (HDLs)**. *Chylomicrons*, which transport absorbed lipids from the GI tract, are a separate class and have the lowest density of all.

The liver is the primary source of VLDLs, which transport triglycerides from the liver to the peripheral tissues, mostly to *adipose tissues*. Once the triglycerides are unloaded, the VLDL residues are converted to LDLs, which are cholesterol-rich. The role of the LDLs is to transport cholesterol to *peripheral* (non-liver) *tissues*, making it available to the tissue cells for membrane or hormone synthesis and for storage for later use. The LDLs also regulate cholesterol synthesis in the tissue cells. Docking of LDL to the LDL receptor triggers receptor-mediated endocytosis of the entire particle.

The major function of HDLs, which are particularly rich in phospholipids and cholesterol, is to scoop up and transport excess cholesterol *from peripheral tissues to the liver*, where it is broken down and becomes part of bile. The liver makes the protein envelopes of the HDL particles and then ejects them into the bloodstream in collapsed form, rather like deflated beach balls. Once in the blood, these still-incomplete HDL particles fill with cholesterol picked up from the tissue cells and "pulled" from the artery walls.

HDL also provides the steroid-producing organs, like the ovaries and adrenal glands, with their raw material (cholesterol). These organs have the ability to selectively remove cholesterol from the HDL particles without engulfing them.

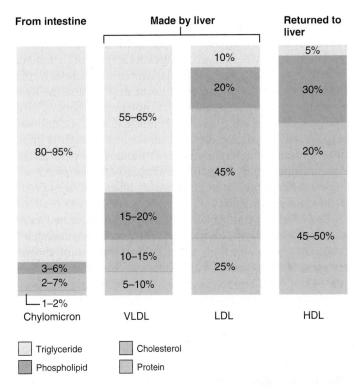

Figure 24.23 Approximate composition of lipoproteins that transport lipids in body fluids. VLDL = very low density lipoprotein, LDL = low-density lipoprotein, HDL = high-density lipoprotein.

Recommended Total Cholesterol, HDL, and LDL Levels

For adults, a total cholesterol level of 200 mg/dl of blood (or lower) is recommended. Blood cholesterol levels above 200 mg/dl have been linked to risk of atherosclerosis, which clogs the arteries and causes strokes and heart attacks. However, it is not enough to simply measure total cholesterol. The form in which cholesterol is transported in the blood is more important clinically.

As a rule, high levels of HDLs are considered *good* because the transported cholesterol is destined for degradation. In the United States, the average HDL level in males is 40–50 and in women is 50–60. Levels below 40 are considered undesirable. HDL levels above 60 are thought to protect against heart disease.

High LDL levels (130 or above) are considered *bad* because when LDLs are excessive, potentially lethal cholesterol deposits are laid down in the artery walls. The goal for LDL levels is 100 or less, but new guidelines for those at risk for cardiac disease recommend 70 mg/dl or less. A good rule of thumb is that HDL levels can't be too high and LDL levels can't be too low.

If LDLs are "bad" cholesterol, then one variety of LDL—lipoprotein (a)—is "really nasty." This lipid appears to promote plaque formation that thickens and stiffens the blood vessel walls. Additionally, lipoprotein (a) inhibits fibrinolysis, which increases the incidence of thrombus formation and can double a man's risk of a heart attack before the age of 55. It is estimated that one in five males has elevated levels of this lipoprotein in the blood.

24

Factors Regulating Plasma Cholesterol Levels

A negative feedback loop partially adjusts the amount of cholesterol produced by the liver according to the amount of cholesterol in the diet. A high cholesterol intake inhibits its synthesis by the liver, but it is not a one-to-one relationship because the liver produces a certain basal amount of cholesterol (about 85% of desirable values) even when dietary intake is high. For this reason, severely restricting dietary cholesterol, although helpful, does not result in a steep reduction in plasma cholesterol levels. Additionally, severely restricting dietary cholesterol may remove important nutrients found in meats, shellfish, and dairy products from a person's diet.

The relative amounts of saturated and unsaturated fatty acids in the diet have an important effect on blood cholesterol levels. Saturated fatty acids *stimulate liver synthesis* of cholesterol and *inhibit its excretion* from the body. In contrast, unsaturated (mono- and polyunsaturated) fatty acids (found in olive oil and in most vegetable oils respectively) *enhance excretion* of cholesterol and its catabolism to bile salts, thereby reducing total cholesterol levels.

The unhappy exception to this good news about unsaturated fats concerns **trans fats**, "healthy" oils that have been hardened by hydrogenation to make them more solid. Trans fats cause serum changes worse than those caused by saturated fats. The trans fatty acids spark a greater increase in LDLs and a greater reduction in HDLs, producing the unhealthiest ratio of total cholesterol to HDL.

The unsaturated omega-3 fatty acids found in especially large amounts in some cold-water fish lower the proportions of both saturated fats and cholesterol. The omega-3 fatty acids have a powerful antiarrhythmic effect on the heart and also make blood platelets less sticky, thus helping prevent spontaneous clotting that can block blood vessels. They also appear to lower blood pressure (even in nonhypertensive people). In those with moderate to high cholesterol levels, replacing half of the lipid- and cholesterol-rich animal proteins in the diet with soy protein lowers cholesterol significantly.

Factors other than diet also influence blood cholesterol levels. For example, cigarette smoking, coffee drinking, and stress appear to lower HDL levels, whereas regular aerobic exercise and estrogen lower LDL levels and increase HDL levels. Interestingly, body shape, that is, the distribution of body fat, provides clues to risky blood levels of cholesterol and fats. "Apples" (people with upper body and abdominal fat distribution, seen more often in men) tend to have higher levels of cholesterol in general and higher LDLs in particular than "pears" where fat is localized in the hips and thighs, a pattern more common in women.

Most cells other than liver and intestinal cells obtain the bulk of the cholesterol they need for membrane synthesis from the blood. When a cell needs cholesterol, it makes receptor proteins for LDL and inserts them in its plasma membrane. LDL binds to the receptors and is engulfed in coated pits by endocytosis. Within 15 minutes the endocytotic vesicles fuse with lysosomes, where the cholesterol is freed for use. When excessive cholesterol accumulates in a cell, it inhibits both the cell's own cholesterol synthesis and its synthesis of LDL receptors.

HOMEOSTATIC IMBALANCE

Previously, high cholesterol and LDL:HDL ratios were considered the most valid predictors of risk for atherosclerosis, cardiovascular disease, and heart attack. However, almost half of those who get heart disease have normal cholesterol levels, while others with poor lipid profiles remain free of heart disease. Presently, LDL levels and assessments of risk factors are believed to be more accurate indicators of whether treatment is needed or not, and many physicians recommend dietary changes regardless of total cholesterol or HDL levels.

Cholesterol-lowering drugs such as the *statins* (e.g., lovastatin and pravastatin) are routinely prescribed for cardiac patients with LDL levels over 130. It is estimated that more than 10 million Americans are now taking statins, and tests of a vaccine that lowers LDL while raising HDL are under way. ■

CHECK YOUR UNDERSTANDING

25. If you had your choice, would you prefer to have high blood levels of HDLs or LDLs? Explain your answer.

26. What is the maximum recommended cholesterol level for adults?

27. What are trans fats and what is their effect on LDL and HDL levels?

For answers, see Appendix G.

Energy Balance

▶ Explain what is meant by body energy balance.

▶ Describe some theories of food intake regulation.

When any fuel is burned, it consumes oxygen and liberates heat. The "burning" of food fuels by our cells is no exception. As we described in Chapter 2, energy can be neither created nor destroyed—only converted from one form to another. If we apply this principle (actually the *first law of thermodynamics*) to cell metabolism, it means that bond energy released as foods are catabolized must be precisely balanced by the total energy output of the body. For this reason, a dynamic balance exists between the body's energy intake and its energy output:

Energy intake = energy output
(heat + work + energy storage)

Energy intake is the energy liberated during food oxidation. (Undigested foods are not part of the equation because they contribute no energy.) **Energy output** includes energy (1) immediately lost as heat (about 60% of the total), (2) used to do work (driven by ATP), and (3) stored as fat or glycogen. Because losses of organic molecules in urine, feces, and perspiration are very small in healthy people, they are usually ignored in calculating energy output.

A close look at this situation reveals that *nearly all the energy derived from foodstuffs is eventually converted to heat.* Heat is lost during every cellular activity—when ATP bonds are formed and when they are cleaved to do work, as muscles contract, and through friction as blood flows through blood vessels. Though cells cannot use this energy to do work, the heat warms the tissues and blood and helps maintain the homeostatic body temperature that allows metabolic reactions to occur efficiently. Energy storage is an important part of the equation only during periods of growth and net fat deposit.

When energy intake and energy output are balanced, body weight remains stable. When they are not, weight is either gained or lost. Body weight in most people is surprisingly stable. This fact indicates the existence of physiological mechanisms that control food intake (and as a result, the amount of food oxidized) or heat production or both. Unhappily for many people, the body's weight-controlling systems appear to be designed more to protect us against weight loss than weight gain.

Obesity

How fat is too fat? What distinguishes a person who is obese from one that is merely overweight? Let's take a look. The bathroom scale, though helpful to determine degrees of overweight, is an inaccurate guide because body weight tells little of body composition. Dense bones and well-developed muscles can make a fit, healthy person technically overweight. Arnold Schwarzenegger, for example, has tipped the scales at a hefty 257 lb.

The official medical measure of obesity and body fatness is the **body mass index (BMI)**, an index of a person's weight relative to height. To estimate BMI, multiply weight in pounds by 705 and then divide by your height in inches squared:

$$BMI = wt(lb) \times 705/ht(inches)^2$$

Overweight is defined by a BMI between 25 and 30 and carries some health risk. Obesity is a BMI greater than 30 and has a markedly increased health risk. The most common view of obesity is that it is a condition of excessive triglyceride storage. We bewail our inability to rid ourselves of fat, but the real problem is that we keep refilling the storehoses by consuming too many calories. A body fat content of 18–20% of body weight (males and females respectively) is deemed normal for adults.

However it's defined, obesity is perplexing and poorly understood, and the economic toll of obesity-related disease is staggering. People who are obese have a higher incidence of atherosclerosis, diabetes mellitus, hypertension, heart disease, and osteoarthritis. Nonetheless, the U.S. is big and getting bigger, at least around its middle. Two out of three adults are overweight. Of that number, one out of three is obese and one in twelve has diabetes, a common sequel of weight problems. U.S. kids are getting fatter too: 20 years ago, 5% were overweight; today over 15% are and more are headed that way. Furthermore, because kids are opting for video games and nachos instead of tag or touch football and an apple, their general cardiovascular fitness is declining as well and health risks associated with excess weight start frighteningly early. For example, obesity-related heart problems, such as an enlarged heart—a risk factor for heart attack and congestive heart failure—may start developing in the early teens or even younger. Some weight-loss or

weight-control methods used by people who are obese are discussed in *A Closer Look* on pp. 948–949.

Regulation of Food Intake

Control of food intake poses difficult questions to researchers. For example, what type of receptor could sense the body's total calorie content and alert one to start eating or to put down that fork? Despite heroic research efforts, no such single receptor type has been found.

It has been known for some time that the hypothalamus, particularly its *arcuate nucleus (ARC)* and two other areas—the *lateral hypothalamic area (LHA)* and the *ventromedial nucleus (VMN)*—release several peptides that influence feeding behavior. Most importantly, this influence ultimately reflects the activity of two distinct sets of neurons—one set that promotes hunger and the other that causes satiety. The NPY/AgRP group of ARC release neuropeptide Y (NPY) and agouti-related peptides, which collectively enhance appetite and food-seeking behavior by stimulating the second-order neurons of the LHA (**Figure 24.24**, right side). The other neuron group in ARC consists of the POMC/CART neurons, which release pro-opiomelanocortin (POMC) and cocaine- and amphetamine-regulated transcript (CART), appetite-suppressing peptides. These peptides act on the VMN, causing its neurons to release CRH (corticotropin-releasing hormone), an important appetite-suppressing peptide.

Current theories of how feeding behavior and hunger are regulated focus on several factors, most importantly neural signals from the digestive tract, bloodborne signals related to body energy stores, and hormones. To a smaller degree, body temperature and psychological factors also seem to play a role. All these factors appear to operate through feedback signals to the feeding centers of the brain. Brain receptors include thermoreceptors, chemoreceptors (for glucose, insulin, and others), and receptors that respond to a number of peptides (leptin, neuropeptide Y, and others). The hypothalamic nuclei play an essential role in regulating hunger and satiety, but brain stem areas are also involved. Sensors in peripheral locations have also been suggested, with the liver and gut itself (alimentary canal) the prime candidates. Controls of food intake come in two varieties—short term and long term.

Short-Term Regulation of Food Intake

Short-term regulation of appetite and feeding behavior involves neural signals from the GI tract, blood levels of nutrients, and GI tract hormones. For the most part, the short-term signals target hypothalamic centers via the solitary tract (and nucleus) of the brain stem (Figure 24.24).

Neural Signals from the Digestive Tract   One way the brain evaluates the contents of the gut depends on vagal nerve fibers that carry on a two-way conversation between gut and brain. For example, clinical tests show that 2 kcal worth of protein produces a 30–40% larger and longer response in vagal afferents than does 2 kcal worth of glucose. Furthermore, activation of

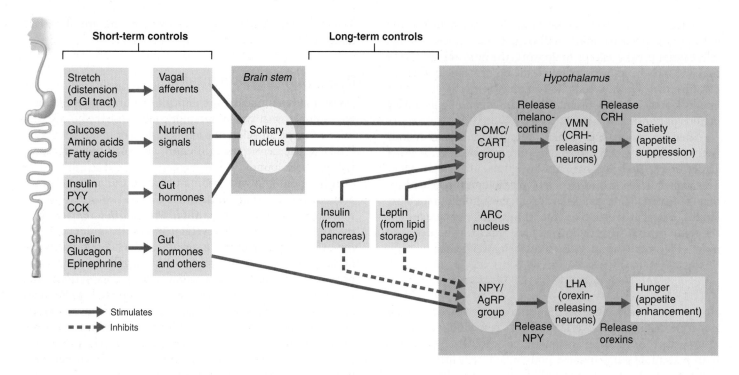

Figure 24.24 Model for hypothalamic command of appetite and food intake. The arcuate nucleus (ARC) of the brain contains two sets of neurons with opposing effects. Activation of the NPY and orexin neurons enhances appetite, whereas activation of POMC/CART neurons has the opposite effect. These centers connect with interneurons in other brain centers, and signals are transmitted through the brain stem to the body. Many appetite-regulating hormones act through the ARC, though they may also exert direct effects on other brain centers. (AgRP = agouti-related peptide, ARC = arcuate, CART = cocaine- and amphetamine-regulated transcript, CCK = cholecystokinin, CRH = corticotropin-releasing hormone, LHA = lateral hypothalamic area, NPY = neuropeptide Y, POMC = pro-opiomelanocortin, PYY = peptide YY, VMN = ventromedial nucleus)

stretch receptors ultimately inhibits appetite, because GI tract distension sends signals along vagus nerve afferents that suppress the appetite-enhancing or hunger center. Using these signals, together with others it receives, the brain can decode what is eaten and how much.

Nutrient Signals Related to Energy Stores At any time, blood levels of glucose, amino acids, and fatty acids provide information to the brain that may help adjust energy intake to energy output. For example, nutrient signals that indicate fullness or satiety include the following:

1. *Rising blood glucose levels.* When we eat, blood glucose levels rise and subsequent activation of glucose receptors in the brain ultimately depresses eating. During fasting and hypoglycemia, this signal is absent, resulting in hunger and a "turning on" of food-seeking behavior by ultimately activating orexin-containing neurons in the LHA. Although these hypothalamic responses to the presence or absence of glucose are well known, these are not the only responses of the brain to glucose or high-caloric food. It seems that the brain's reward (pleasure) system "gives off fireworks" in the form of rising dopamine levels to a greater or lesser degree with sugar ingestion. Perhaps this response is the genesis of overeating (hedonistic) behavior.

2. *Elevated blood levels of amino acids* depress eating, but the precise mechanism mediating this effect is unknown.

3. *Blood concentrations of fatty acids* provide a mechanism for controlling hunger. The larger the amount of fatty acids in the blood, the greater the inhibition of eating behavior.

Hormones Gut hormones, including insulin and cholecystokinin (CCK) released during food absorption, act as satiety signals to depress hunger. Most important is the effect of cholecystokinin, which thwarts the appetite-inducing effect of NPY.

In contrast, glucagon and epinephrine levels rise during fasting and stimulate hunger. Ghrelin (Ghr), produced by the stomach, is a powerful appetite stimulant. In fact, ghrelin appears to be the "dinner bell" or trigger for meal initiation. Its levels peak just before mealtime, letting the brain know that it is time to eat, and then it troughs out after the meal.

Long-Term Regulation of Food Intake

A key component of the long-term controls of feeding behavior is the hormone **leptin** ("thin"). Leptin is secreted exclusively by adipose cells in response to an increase in body fat mass and it serves as an indicator of the body's total energy stores in fat tissue. (Thus adipose tissue acts as a "Fat-o-Stat" that sends chemical messages to the brain in the form of leptin.)

When leptin levels rise in the blood, it binds to receptors in ARC that specifically (1) suppress the release of NPY and

(2) stimulate the expression of CART. Neuropeptide Y is the most potent appetite stimulant known. By blocking its release, leptin prevents the release of the appetite-enhancing orexins from the LHA. This decreases appetite and subsequently food intake, eventually promoting weight loss.

When fat stores shrink, leptin blood levels drop, an event that exerts opposite effects on the two sets of ARC neurons. It activates the NPY neurons and blocks the activity of the POMC/CART neurons. Consequently, appetite and food intake increase, and (eventually) weight gain occurs.

Initially it seemed that leptin was the magic bullet that obesity researchers were looking for, but their hopes were soon dashed. Rising leptin levels do promote weight loss, but only to a certain point. Furthermore, individuals who are obese have higher-than-normal leptin blood levels, but for some unknown reason, they are resistant to its action. Now the consensus is that leptin's main role is to protect against weight loss in times of nutritional deprivation.

Although leptin has received the most attention as a long-term appetite and metabolism regulator, there are several other players. Insulin, like leptin, inhibits NPY release in non-insulin-resistant individuals, but its effect is less potent.

Additional Regulatory Factors

In actuality, there is no pat or easy answer to explain how body weight is regulated, but theories abound. Rising ambient temperature discourages food seeking, whereas cold temperature activates the hunger center. Depending on the individual, stress may increase or decrease food-seeking behavior, but chronic stress in combination with a junk food (high-fat and -sugar) diet promotes sharply increased release of NPY. Psychological factors are thought to be very important in people who are obese, but even when psychological factors contribute to obesity, individuals do not continue to gain weight endlessly. Controls still operate but at a higher weight set-point level. Certain adenovirus infections, sleep deprivation, and even the composition of gut bacteria are additional factors that may affect a person's fat mass and weight regulation, according to some clinical studies.

Whew! How does all this information fit together? So far we only have bits and pieces of the story, but the best current model based on animal studies is shown in Figure 24.24.

CHECK YOUR UNDERSTANDING

28. What three groups of stimuli influence short-term regulation of feeding behavior?

29. What is the most important long-term regulator of feeding behavior and appetite?

For answers, see Appendix G.

Metabolic Rate and Heat Production

▶ Define basal metabolic rate and total metabolic rate. Name factors that influence each.

The body's rate of energy output is called the **metabolic rate**. It is the total heat produced by all the chemical reactions and mechanical work of the body. It can be measured directly or indirectly. In the *direct method*, a person enters a chamber called a **calorimeter** and heat liberated by the body is absorbed by water circulating around the chamber. The rise in water temperature is directly related to the heat produced by the person's body. The *indirect method* uses a **respirometer** to measure oxygen consumption, which is directly proportional to heat production. For each liter of oxygen used, the body produces about 4.8 kcal of heat.

Because many factors influence metabolic rate, it is usually measured under standardized conditions. The person is in a postabsorptive state (has not eaten for at least 12 hours), is reclining, and is mentally and physically relaxed. The temperature of the room is a comfortable 20–25°C. The measurement obtained under these circumstances is called the **basal metabolic rate (BMR)** and reflects the energy the body needs to perform only its most essential activities, such as breathing and maintaining resting levels of organ function. Although named the *basal* metabolic rate, this measurement is *not* the lowest metabolic state of the body. That situation occurs during sleep, when the skeletal muscles are completely relaxed.

The BMR, often referred to as the "energy cost of living," is reported in kilocalories per square meter of body surface per hour ($kcal/m^2/h$). A 70-kg adult has a BMR of approximately 66 kcal/h. You can approximate your BMR by multiplying weight in kilograms (2.2 lb = 1 kg) by 1 if you are male and by 0.9 if you are female.

What factors influence BMR? There are several, including body surface area, age, gender, stress, and hormones. BMR is related to overall weight and size, but the critical factor is body surface area. As the ratio of body surface area to body volume increases, heat loss to the environment increases and the metabolic rate must be higher to replace the lost heat. For this reason, if two people weigh the same, the taller or thinner person will have the higher BMR.

In general, the younger a person, the higher the BMR. Children and adolescents require large amounts of energy for growth. In old age, BMR declines dramatically as skeletal muscles begin to atrophy. (This helps explain why those elderly who fail to reduce their caloric intake gain weight.) Gender also plays a role. Metabolic rate is disproportionately higher in males than in females, because males typically have more muscle, which is very active metabolically even during rest. Fatty tissue, present in greater relative amounts in females, is metabolically more sluggish than muscle.

Surprisingly, physical training has little effect on BMR. Although it would appear that athletes, especially those with greatly enhanced muscle mass, should have much higher BMRs than nonathletes, there is little difference between those of the same sex and surface area.

Body temperature and BMR tend to rise and fall together. Fever (hyperthermia) results in a marked increase in metabolic rate. Stress, whether physical or emotional, increases BMR by mobilizing the sympathetic nervous system. As norepinephrine

A CLOSER LOOK
Obesity: Magical Solution Wanted

Fat—unwanted, unloved, and yet often overabundant. Besides the physical toll, the social stigma and economic disadvantages of obesity are legendary. A fat person pays higher insurance premiums, is discriminated against in the job market, has fewer clothing choices, and endures frequent humiliation throughout life.

Theories of Obesity Causes

It's a fair bet that few people choose to become obese. So what causes it?

1. **Overeating during childhood promotes adult obesity.** Some believe that the "clean your plate" order sets the stage for adult obesity by increasing the number of adipose cells formed during childhood. The more adipose cells there are, the more fat can be stored.

2. **People who are obese are more fuel efficient and more effective "fat storers."** Although it is often assumed that people who are obese eat more, this is not necessarily true—many actually eat less than people of normal weight. When yo-yo dieters lose weight, their metabolic rate falls sharply. But, when they subsequently gain weight, their metabolic rate increases like a furnace being stoked. Each successive weight loss occurs more slowly, but regaining weight occurs three times as fast.

   Furthermore, fats pack more wallop per calorie (are more fattening) than proteins or carbohydrates because of the way the body processes them. If 100 excess carbohydrate calories are ingested, 23 are used in metabolic processing and 77 are stored. However, if the 100 excess calories come from fat, only 3 calories are "burned" and the rest (97) are stored.

These facts apply to everyone, but when you are obese the picture is even bleaker. "Fat" fat cells of overweight people

- Sprout more alpha receptors, which favor fat accumulation.

- Send different molecular messages than "thin" fat cells. They spew out inflammatory cytokines (tumor necrosis factor and others) that can act as triggers for insulin resistance and they release less *adiponectin*, a hormone that improves the action of insulin in glucose uptake and storage.

- Have exceptionally efficient lipoprotein lipases, which unload fat from the blood (usually to fat cells).

Although it would appear that the so-called satiety chemicals (hormones and others) should prevent massive fat deposit, this seems not to be the case in people who are obese. It may be that excess weight promotes not only insulin resistance but leptin resistance as well.

3. **Genetic predisposition.** Morbid obesity is the destiny of those inheriting two obesity genes. These people, given extra calories, will always lay them down as fat, as opposed to those that lay down more muscle with some of the excess. However, a true genetic predisposition for "fatness" appears to account for only about 5% of Americans who are obese.

Treatments—The Bad and the Good

Some so-called treatments for obesity are almost more dangerous than the disease itself. Unfortunate strategies include

1. **"Water pills."** Diuretics prompt the kidneys to excrete more water and may cause a few pounds of weight loss for a few hours. They can also cause serious dehydration and electrolyte imbalance.

2. **Diets.** Diet products and books sell well, but do any of the currently popular diets work and are they safe? At the present time there is a duel between those promoting low-carbohydrate (high-protein and -fat) diets such as the Atkins and South Beach diets, and those espousing the traditional low-fat (high–complex carbohydrates) diet. Clinical studies show that people on the low-carbohydrate diets lose weight more quickly at first, but tend to plateau at 6 months. They seem to preferentially lose fat from the body trunk, a weight

and epinephrine (released by adrenal medullary cells) flood into the blood, they provoke a rise in BMR primarily by stimulating fat catabolism.

The amount of **thyroxine** produced by the thyroid gland is probably the most important hormonal factor in determining BMR. For this reason, thyroxine has been dubbed the "metabolic hormone." Its direct effect on most body cells (except brain cells) is to increase O_2 consumption and heat production, presumably by accelerating the use of ATP to operate the sodium-potassium pump. As ATP reserves decline, cellular respiration accelerates. Thus, the more thyroxine produced, the higher the BMR.

HOMEOSTATIC IMBALANCE

Hyperthyroidism causes a host of problems resulting from the excessive BMR it produces. The body catabolizes stored fats and tissue proteins, and, despite increased hunger and food intake, the person often loses weight. Bones weaken and muscles, including the heart, begin to atrophy. In contrast, *hypothyroidism* results in slowed metabolism, obesity, and diminished thought processes. ■

distribution pattern (the "apple") associated with heart disease and diabetes mellitus. (This propensity to these diseases, called "metabolic syndrome," appears to be due to the large amounts of inflammatory cytokines released by visceral fat cells.) When dieting was continued for a year, those on the low-fat diets lost just as much weight as did those on the low-carbohydrate diets. Although there was concern that the low-carbohydrate diets would promote undesirable plasma cholesterol and lipid values, for the most part this has not been the case.

Diets that have users counting the glycemic indexes of the food they eat, such as the New Glucose Revolution diet, distinguish between good carbs (whole grains, nonstarchy vegetables and fruits) and bad carbs (starches, sugary foods, refined grains) and have the approval of many physicians. The oldie-but-goodie Weight Watcher's diet, which has dieters counting points, still works and allows virtually any food choice as long as the allowed point count isn't exceeded.

Some over-the-counter liquid high-protein diets contain such poor-quality (incomplete) protein that they are actually dangerous. The worst are those that contain collagen protein instead of milk or soybean sources.

3. **Surgery.** Sometimes sheer desperation prompts surgical solutions: reducing stomach volume by banding; gastric bypass surgery, which may involve stomach stapling and intestinal bypass surgery, or the more radical biliopancreatic diversion (BPD); and liposuction (removal of fat by suctioning).

BPD rearranges the digestive tract. Up to two-thirds of the stomach is removed and the small intestine is cut in half and one portion is sutured to the stomach opening. Pancreatic juice and bile are diverted away from the "new intestine," so far fewer nutrients and no fats are absorbed. Patients can eat anything they want without gaining weight, but exceeding the stomach capacity leads to the dumping syndrome, in which nausea and vomiting occur. Many of these procedures have been remarkably effective at promoting weight loss and restoring health. Blood pressure returns to normal in many that were originally hypertensive, and sleep apnea is reduced. Additionally, many patients with long-standing diabetes mellitus find they are suddenly *diabetes free* within weeks after the procedure. This result may prove to be the single greatest benefit of BPD.

Liposuction reshapes the body by suctioning off fat deposits, but it is not a good choice for losing weight. It carries all the risks of surgery, and unless eating habits change, fat depots elsewhere in the body overfill.

4. **Diet drugs and weight-loss supplements.** Currently popular weight-loss drugs include phentermine, sibutramine, and orlistat. Phentermine is one-half of the former fen-phen (Redux) combination that caused heart problems, deaths, and litigation for its producer in the 1990s. It acts via increased sympathetic nervous system activity, which increases blood pressure and heart rate. Sibutramine (Meridia) has amphetamine-like effects and has come under fire because of suspected cardiovascular side effects. Orlistat (Xenical) interferes with pancreatic lipase so that part of the fat eaten is not digested or absorbed, which also interferes with the absorption of fat-soluble vitamins. It is effective as a weight-loss agent, but its side effects (diarrhea and anal leakage) are unpleasant to say the least. Currently a number of drugs are being developed that act at several different CNS sites, including neuropeptide Y inhibitors.

Some over-the-counter weight-loss supplements that are claimed to increase metabolism and burn calories at an accelerated rate have proved to be very dangerous. For example:

- Capsules containing usnic acid, a chemical found in some lichens, damages hepatocytes and has led to liver failure in a few cases.

- Ephedra-containing supplements are notorious—over 100 deaths and 16,000 cases of problems including strokes, seizures, and headaches have been reported.

When it comes to such supplements, the burden of proof is on the U.S. FDA to show that the product is unsafe. For this reason, the true extent of ills caused by weight-loss supplements is not known—while the worst cases attract attention, less serious ones go unreported or undiagnosed.

So are there any good treatments for obesity? The only realistic way to lose weight is to take in fewer calories and increase physical activity. Fidgeting helps and so does resistance exercise, which increases muscle mass. Physical exercise depresses appetite and increases metabolic rate not only during activity but also for some time after. The only way to keep the weight off is to make dietary and exercise changes lifelong habits.

24

The **total metabolic rate (TMR)** is the rate of kilocalorie consumption needed to fuel *all* ongoing activities—involuntary and voluntary. BMR accounts for a surprisingly large part of TMR. For example, a woman whose total energy needs per day are about 2000 kcal may spend 1400 kcal or so supporting vital body activities. Because skeletal muscles make up nearly half of body mass, skeletal muscle activity causes the most dramatic short-term changes in TMR. Even slight increases in muscular work can cause remarkable leaps in TMR and heat production. When a well-trained athlete exercises vigorously for several minutes, TMR may increase 20-fold, and it remains elevated for several hours after exercise stops.

Food ingestion also induces a rapid increase in TMR. This effect, called **food-induced thermogenesis**, is greatest when proteins are eaten. The heightened metabolic activity of the liver during such periods probably accounts for the bulk of additional energy use. In contrast, fasting or very low caloric intake depresses TMR and results in a slower breakdown of body reserves.

Figure 24.25 Body temperature remains constant as long as heat production and heat loss are balanced.

CHECK YOUR UNDERSTANDING

30. Which of the following contributes to a person's BMR? Kidney function, breathing, jogging, eating, fever.

31. Samantha is tall and slim, but athletic and well toned. Her friend, Ginger, is short and stocky, bordering on obese. Which would be expected to have a greater BMR, relatively speaking?

For answers, see Appendix G.

Regulation of Body Temperature

▶ Distinguish between core and shell body temperature.

▶ Describe how body temperature is regulated, and indicate the common mechanisms regulating heat production/retention and heat loss from the body.

As shown in **Figure 24.25**, body temperature represents the balance between heat production and heat loss. All body tissues produce heat, but those most active metabolically produce the greatest amounts. When the body is at rest, most heat is generated by the liver, heart, brain, kidneys, and endocrine organs, with the inactive skeletal muscles accounting for only 20–30%.

This situation changes dramatically with even slight alterations in muscle tone. When we are cold, shivering soon warms us up, and during vigorous exercise, heat production by the skeletal muscles can be 30 to 40 times that of the rest of the body. A change in muscle activity is one of the most important means of modifying body temperature.

Body temperature averages 37°C ± 0.5°C (98.6°F) and is usually maintained within the range 35.8–38.2°C (96–101°F), de-

spite considerable change in external (air) temperature. A healthy individual's body temperature fluctuates approximately 1°C (1.8°F) in 24 hours, with the low occurring in early morning and the high in late afternoon or early evening.

The adaptive value of this precise temperature homeostasis becomes apparent when we consider the effect of temperature on the rate of enzymatic activity. At normal body temperature, conditions are optimal for enzymatic activity. As body temperature rises, enzymatic catalysis is accelerated: With each rise of 1°C, the rate of chemical reactions increases about 10%. As the temperature spikes above the homeostatic range, neurons are depressed and proteins begin to denature. Children below the age of 5 go into convulsions when body temperature reaches 41°C (106°F), and 43°C (about 109°F) appears to be the absolute limit for life.

In contrast, most body tissues can withstand marked reductions in temperature if other conditions are carefully controlled. This fact underlies the use of body cooling during open heart surgery when the heart must be stopped. Low body temperature reduces metabolic rate (and consequently nutrient requirements of body tissues and the heart), allowing more time for surgery without incurring tissue damage.

Core and Shell Temperatures

Different body regions have different resting temperatures. The body's **core** (organs within the skull and the thoracic and abdominal cavities) has the highest temperature and its **shell** (essentially the skin) has the lowest temperature in most circumstances. Of the two body sites used routinely to obtain body temperature clinically, the rectum typically has a temperature about 0.4°C (0.7°F) higher than the mouth and is a better indicator of core temperature.

It is core temperature that is precisely regulated. Blood serves as the major *agent of heat exchange* between the core and shell. Whenever the shell is warmer than the external environment, heat is lost from the body as warm blood is allowed to flush into the skin capillaries. On the other hand, when heat must be conserved, blood largely bypasses the skin. This reduces heat loss and allows the shell temperature to fall toward that of the environment. For this reason, the core temperature stays relatively constant, but the temperature of the shell may fluctuate substantially, for example, between 20°C (68°F) and 40°C (104°F), as it adapts to changes in body activity and external temperature. (You really *can* have cold hands and a warm heart.)

Mechanisms of Heat Exchange

Heat exchange between our skin and the external environment works in the same way as heat exchange between inanimate objects (**Figure 24.26**). It helps to think of an object's temperature—whether that object is the skin or a radiator—as a guide to its heat content (think "heat concentration"). Then just remember that heat always flows down its concentration gradient from a warmer region to a cooler region. The body uses four mechanisms of heat transfer—radiation, conduction, convection, and evaporation.

Radiation is the loss of heat in the form of infrared waves (thermal energy). Any object that is warmer than objects in its environment—for example, a radiator and (usually) the body—will transfer heat to those objects. Under normal conditions, close to half of your body heat loss occurs by radiation.

Because radiant energy flows from warmer to cooler, radiation explains why a cold room warms up shortly after it is filled with people (the "body heat furnace," so to speak). Your body also gains heat by radiation, as demonstrated by the warming of the skin during sunbathing.

Conduction is the transfer of heat from a warmer object to a cooler one when the two are in direct contact with each other. For example, when you step into a hot tub, some of the heat of the water is transferred to your skin, and warm buttocks transfer heat to the seat of a chair by conduction.

Convection is the process that occurs because warm air expands and rises and cool air, being denser, falls. Consequently, the warmed air enveloping the body is continually replaced by cooler air molecules. Convection substantially enhances heat transfer from the body surface to the air because the cooler air absorbs heat by conduction more rapidly than the already-warmed air. Together, conduction and convection account for 15–20% of heat loss to the environment. These processes are enhanced by anything that moves air more rapidly across the body surface, such as wind or a fan, in other words, by *forced convection*.

Evaporation is the fourth mechanism by which the body loses heat. Water evaporates because its molecules absorb heat from the environment and become energetic enough—in other words, vibrate fast enough—to escape as a gas, which we know as water vapor. The heat absorbed by water during evaporation is called **heat of vaporization**. Water absorbs a great deal of heat before vaporizing, so its evaporation from body surfaces removes large amounts of body heat. For every gram of water evaporated, about 0.58 kcal of heat is removed from the body.

There is a basal level of body heat loss due to the continuous evaporation of water from the lungs, from the oral mucosa, and through the skin. The unnoticeable water loss occurring via these routes is called **insensible water loss**, and the heat loss that accompanies it is called **insensible heat loss**. Insensible heat loss dissipates about 10% of the basal heat production of the body and is a constant not subject to body temperature controls. When necessary, however, the body's control mechanisms do initiate heat-promoting activities to counterbalance this insensible heat loss.

Evaporative heat loss becomes an active or *sensible* process when body temperature rises and sweating produces increased amounts of water for vaporization. Extreme emotional states activate the sympathetic nervous system, causing body temperature to rise one degree or so, and vigorous exercise can thrust body temperature upward as much as 2–3°C (3.6–5.4°F). During vigorous muscular activity, 1–2 L/h of perspiration can be produced and evaporated, removing 600–1200 kcal of heat from the body each hour. This is more than 30 times the amount of heat lost via insensible heat loss!

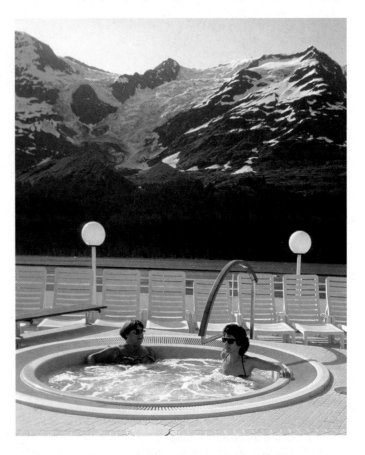

Figure 24.26 Mechanisms of heat exchange. Passengers enjoying a hot tub on a cruise to Alaska illustrate several mechanisms of heat exchange between the body and its environment. (1) Conduction: Heat transfers from the hot water to the skin. (2) Radiation: Heat transfers from the exposed part of the body to the cooler air. (3) Convection: Warmed air moves away from the body via breezes. There may also be (4) evaporation of perspiration: Excess body heat is carried away.

HOMEOSTATIC IMBALANCE

When sweating is heavy and prolonged, especially in untrained individuals, losses of water and NaCl may cause painful muscle spasms called *heat cramps*. This situation is easily rectified by ingesting fluids. ■

Role of the Hypothalamus

Although other brain regions contribute, the hypothalamus, particularly its *preoptic* region, is the main integrating center for thermoregulation. Together the **heat-loss center** (located more anteriorly) and the **heat-promoting center** make up the brain's **thermoregulatory centers**.

The hypothalamus receives afferent input from (1) **peripheral thermoreceptors** located in the shell (the skin), and (2) **central thermoreceptors** sensitive to blood temperature and located in the body core including the anterior portion of the hypothalamus. Much like a thermostat, the hypothalamus responds to this input by reflexively initiating appropriate heat-promoting or heat-loss activities. The central thermoreceptors

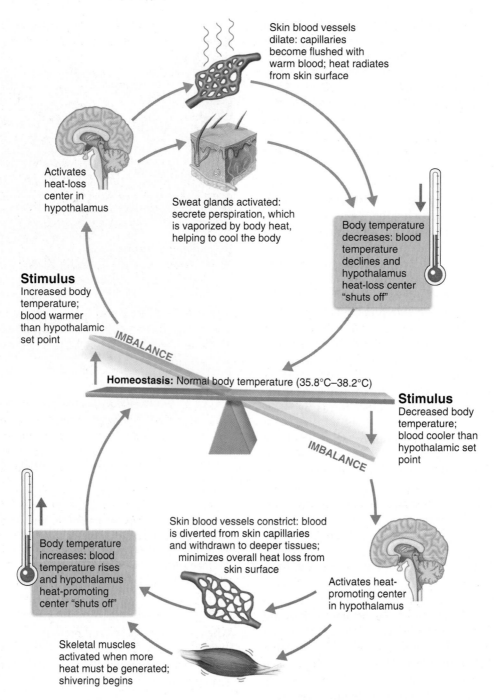

Skin blood vessels dilate: capillaries become flushed with warm blood; heat radiates from skin surface

Activates heat-loss center in hypothalamus

Sweat glands activated: secrete perspiration, which is vaporized by body heat, helping to cool the body

Body temperature decreases: blood temperature declines and hypothalamus heat-loss center "shuts off"

Stimulus Increased body temperature; blood warmer than hypothalamic set point

IMBALANCE

Homeostasis: Normal body temperature (35.8°C–38.2°C)

Stimulus Decreased body temperature; blood cooler than hypothalamic set point

IMBALANCE

Skin blood vessels constrict: blood is diverted from skin capillaries and withdrawn to deeper tissues; minimizes overall heat loss from skin surface

Activates heat-promoting center in hypothalamus

Body temperature increases: blood temperature rises and hypothalamus heat-promoting center "shuts off"

Skeletal muscles activated when more heat must be generated; shivering begins

Figure 24.27 Mechanisms of body temperature regulation.

are more critically located than the peripheral ones, but varying inputs from the shell probably alert the hypothalamus of the need to act to prevent temperature changes in the core. In other words, they allow the hypothalamus to anticipate possible changes to be made.

Heat-Promoting Mechanisms

When the external temperature is low or blood temperature falls for any reason, the heat-promoting center is activated. It triggers one or more of the following four mechanisms to maintain or increase core body temperature (Figure 24.27, bottom).

1. **Constriction of cutaneous blood vessels.** Activation of the sympathetic vasoconstrictor fibers serving the blood vessels of the skin causes strong vasoconstriction. As a result, blood is restricted to deep body areas and largely bypasses the skin. Because the skin is separated from deeper organs by a layer of insulating subcutaneous (fatty) tissue, heat loss from the shell is dramatically reduced and shell temperature drops toward that of the external environment.

24

HOMEOSTATIC IMBALANCE

Restricting blood flow to the skin is not a problem for a brief period, but if it is extended (as during prolonged exposure to very cold weather), skin cells deprived of oxygen and nutrients begin to die. This extremely serious condition is called *frostbite*. ■

2. **Shivering.** Shivering, involuntary shuddering contractions, is triggered when brain centers controlling muscle tone are activated and muscle tone reaches sufficient levels to alternately stimulate stretch receptors in antagonistic muscles. Shivering is very effective in increasing body temperature because muscle activity produces large amounts of heat.

3. **Increase in metabolic rate.** Cold stimulates the release of epinephrine and norepinephrine by the adrenal medulla in reponse to sympathetic nerve stimuli, which elevates the metabolic rate and enhances heat production. This mechanism, called **chemical**, or **nonshivering**, **thermogenesis**, is known to occur in infants but is still controversial in adults.

4. **Enhanced thyroxine release.** When environmental temperature decreases gradually, as in the transition from summer to winter, the hypothalamus of infants releases *thyrotropin-releasing hormone*. This hormone activates the anterior pituitary to release *thyroid-stimulating hormone*, which induces the thyroid to liberate larger amounts of thyroid hormone to the blood. Because thyroid hormone increases metabolic rate, body heat production increases. A similar TSH response to cold exposure does not appear to occur in adults.

Besides these involuntary adjustments, we humans make a number of *behavioral modifications* to prevent overcooling of our body core:

■ Putting on more or warmer clothing to restrict heat loss (a hat, gloves, and "insulated" outer garments)
■ Drinking hot fluids
■ Changing posture to reduce exposed body surface area (hunching over or clasping the arms across the chest)
■ Increasing physical activity to generate more heat (jumping up and down, clapping the hands)

Heat-Loss Mechanisms

Heat-loss mechanisms protect the body from excessively high temperatures. Most heat loss occurs through the skin via radiation, conduction, convection, and evaporation. How do the heat-exchange mechanisms fit into the heat-loss temperature regulation scheme? The answer is quite simple. Whenever core body temperature rises above normal, the hypothalamic heat-promoting center is inhibited. At the same time, the heat-loss center is activated and triggers one or both of the following (Figure 24.27, top):

1. **Dilation of cutaneous blood vessels.** Inhibiting the vasomotor fibers serving blood vessels of the skin allows the vessels to dilate. As the blood vessels swell with warm blood, heat is lost from the shell by radiation, conduction, and convection.

2. **Enhanced sweating.** If the body is extremely overheated or if the environment is so hot—over 33°C (about 92°F)—that heat cannot be lost by other means, evaporation becomes necessary. The sweat glands are strongly activated by sympathetic fibers and spew out large amounts of perspiration. Evaporation of perspiration is an efficient means of ridding the body of surplus heat as long as the air is dry.

However, when the relative humidity is high, evaporation occurs much more slowly. In such cases, the heat-liberating mechanisms cannot work well, and we feel miserable and irritable. Behavioral or voluntary measures commonly taken to reduce body heat in such circumstances include

■ Reducing activity ("laying low")
■ Seeking a cooler environment (a shady spot) or using a device to increase convection (a fan) or cooling (an air conditioner)
■ Wearing light-colored, loose clothing that reflects radiant energy. (This is actually cooler than being nude because bare skin absorbs most of the radiant energy striking it.)

HOMEOSTATIC IMBALANCE

Under conditions of overexposure to a hot and humid environment, normal heat-loss processes become ineffective. The **hyperthermia** (elevated body temperature) that ensues depresses the hypothalamus. At a core temperature of around 41°C (105°F), heat-control mechanisms are suspended, creating a vicious *positive feedback cycle*. Increasing temperatures increase the metabolic rate, which increases heat production. The skin becomes hot and dry and, as the temperature continues to spiral upward, multiple organ damage becomes a distinct possibility, including brain damage. This condition, called **heat stroke**, can be fatal unless corrective measures are initiated immediately (immersing the body in cool water and administering fluids).

The terms *heat exhaustion* and *exertion-induced heat exhaustion* are often used to describe the heat-associated extreme sweating and collapse of an individual during or following vigorous physical activity. This condition, evidenced by elevated body temperature and mental confusion and/or fainting, is due to dehydration and consequent low blood pressure. In contrast to heat stroke, heat-loss mechanisms are still functional in heat exhaustion, as indicated by its symptoms. However, heat exhaustion can rapidly progress to heat stroke if the body is not cooled and rehydrated promptly.

Hypothermia (hi″po-ther′me-ah) is low body temperature resulting from prolonged uncontrolled exposure to cold. Vital signs (respiratory rate, blood pressure, and heart rate) decrease as cellular enzymes become sluggish. Drowsiness sets in and, oddly, the person becomes comfortable even though previously he or she felt extremely cold. Shivering stops at a core temperature of 30–32°C (87–90°F) when the body has exhausted its heat-generating capabilities. Uncorrected, the situation progresses to coma and finally death (by cardiac arrest), when body temperatures approach 21°C (70°F). ■

24

Fever

Fever is *controlled hyperthermia*. Most often, it results from infection somewhere in the body, but it may be caused by cancer, allergic reactions, or CNS injuries. Whatever the cause, macrophages and other cells release cytokines, originally called *pyrogens* (literally, "fire starters"), at least two of which are now known to be interleukins. These chemicals act on the hypothalamus, causing release of prostaglandins which reset the hypothalamic thermostat to a higher-than-normal temperature, so that heat-promoting mechanisms kick in. As a result of vasoconstriction, heat loss from the body surface declines, the skin cools, and shivering begins to generate heat. These "chills" are a sure sign body temperature is rising.

The temperature rises until it reaches the new setting, and then is maintained at that setting until natural body defenses or antibiotics reverse the disease process, and chemical messengers called *cryogens* (vasopressin and others) act to prevent fever from becoming excessive and reset the thermostat to a lower (or normal) level. Then, heat-loss mechanisms swing into action. Sweating begins and the skin becomes flushed and warm. Physicians have long recognized these signs as signals that body temperature is falling (aah, she has passed the crisis).

As we explained in Chapter 21, fever helps speed healing by increasing the metabolic rate, and it also appears to inhibit bacterial growth. The danger of fever is that if the body thermostat is set too high, proteins may be denatured and permanent brain damage may occur.

CHECK YOUR UNDERSTANDING

32. What is the body's core?
33. Cindy is flushed and her teeth are chattering even though her bedroom temperature is 72°F. Why do you think this is happening?
34. How does convection differ from conduction in causing heat loss?

For answers, see Appendix G.

Developmental Aspects of Nutrition and Metabolism

▶ Describe the effects of inadequate protein intake on the fetal nervous system.

▶ Describe the cause and consequences of the low metabolic rate typical of the elderly.

▶ List ways that medications commonly used by aged people may influence their nutrition and health.

Good nutrition is essential in utero, as well as throughout life. If the mother is ill nourished, the development of her infant is affected. Most serious is the lack of adequate calories, proteins, and vitamins needed for fetal tissue growth, especially brain growth. Additionally, inadequate nutrients during the first three years after birth will lead to mental deficits or learning disorders because brain growth continues during this time. Proteins are needed for muscle and bone growth, and calcium is required for strong bones. Although anabolic processes are less critical after growth is completed, sufficient nutrients are still essential to maintain normal tissue replacement and metabolism.

HOMEOSTATIC IMBALANCE

There are many inborn errors of metabolism (or genetic disorders), but perhaps the two most common are *cystic fibrosis* and *phenylketonuria* (*PKU*) (fen″il-ke″to-nu′re-ah). Cystic fibrosis is described in Chapter 22. In PKU, the tissue cells are unable to use the amino acid phenylalanine (fen″il-al′ah-nīn), which is present in all protein foods. The defect involves a deficiency of the enzyme that converts phenylalanine to tyrosine. Phenylalanine cannot be metabolized, so it and its deaminated products accumulate in the blood and act as neurotoxins that cause brain damage and retardation within a few months. These consequences are uncommon today because most states require a urine or blood test to identify affected newborns, and these children are put on a low-phenylalanine diet. When this special diet should be terminated is controversial. Some believe it should be continued through adolescence, but others order it discontinued when the child is 6 years old. Expectant women are sometimes encouraged to follow a controlled phenylalanine diet during their pregnancy.

There are a number of other enzyme defects, classified according to the impaired process as carbohydrate, lipid, or mineral metabolic disorders. The carbohydrate deficit *galactosemia* results from an abnormality in or lack of the liver enzymes needed to transform galactose to glucose. Galactose accumulates in the blood and leads to mental deficits.

In the carbohydrate disorder *glycogen storage disease*, glycogen synthesis is normal, but one of the enzymes needed to convert it back to glucose is missing. As excessive amounts of glycogen are stored, its storage organs (liver and skeletal muscles) become glutted with glycogen and enlarge tremendously. ▪

With the exception of *insulin-dependent diabetes mellitus*, children free of genetic disorders rarely exhibit metabolic problems. However, by middle age and particularly old age, *non-insulin-dependent diabetes mellitus* becomes a major problem, particularly in people who are obese.

Metabolic rate declines throughout the life span. In old age, muscle and bone wasting and declining efficiency of the endocrine system take their toll. Because many elderly are also less active, the metabolic rate is sometimes so low that it becomes nearly impossible to obtain adequate nutrition without gaining weight. The elderly also use more medications than any other group, at a time of life when the liver has become less efficient in its detoxifying duties. Consequently, many of the agents prescribed for age-related medical problems influence nutrition. For example:

▪ Some diuretics prescribed for congestive heart failure or hypertension (to flush fluids out of the body) can cause severe hypokalemia by promoting excessive loss of potassium.

- Some antibiotics, for example, sulfa drugs, tetracycline, and penicillin, interfere with food digestion and absorption. They may also cause diarrhea, further decreasing nutrient absorption.
- Although its use is discouraged by physicians because it interferes with absorption of fat-soluble vitamins, mineral oil is still a popular laxative with the elderly.
- Alcohol is used by about half the elderly population in the U.S. When it is substituted for food, nutrient stores can be depleted. Excessive alcohol intake leads to absorption problems, certain vitamin and mineral deficiencies, deranged metabolism, and damage to the liver and pancreas.

In short, the elderly are at risk not only from the declining efficiency of their metabolic processes, but also from a huge variety of lifestyle and medication factors that affect their nutrition.

Although malnutrition and a waning metabolic rate present problems to some elderly, certain nutrients—notably glucose—appear to contribute to the aging process in people of all ages. Nonenzymatic reactions (the so-called *browning reactions*) between glucose and proteins, long known to discolor and toughen foods, may have the same effects on body proteins. When enzymes attach sugars to proteins, they do so at specific sites and the glycoproteins produced play well-defined roles in the body. By contrast, nonenzymatic binding of glucose to proteins (a process that increases with age) is haphazard and eventually causes cross-links between proteins. The increase in this type of binding probably contributes to lens clouding, and the general tissue stiffening and loss of elasticity so common in the aged.

CHECK YOUR UNDERSTANDING

35. List at least two reasons that the metabolic rate declines in old age.

36. List two types of drugs or over-the-counter products that can interfere with the nutrition of elderly people.

For answers, see Appendix G.

Nutrition is one of the most overlooked areas in clinical medicine. Yet, what we eat and drink influences nearly every phase of metabolism and plays a major role in our overall health. Now that we have examined the fates of nutrients in body cells, we are ready to study the urinary system, the organ system that works tirelessly to rid the body of nitrogen wastes resulting from metabolism and to maintain the purity of our internal fluids.

RELATED CLINICAL TERMS

Appetite A desire for food. A psychological phenomenon dependent on memory and associations, as opposed to hunger, which is a physiological need to eat.

Familial hypercholesterolemia (hi″per-ko-les″ter-ol-e′me-ah). An inherited condition in which the LDL receptors are absent or abnormal, the uptake of cholesterol by tissue cells is blocked, and the total concentration of cholesterol (and LDLs) in the blood is enormously elevated (e.g., 680 mg of cholesterol per 100 ml of blood). Affected individuals develop atherosclerosis at an early age, heart attacks begin in the third or fourth decade, and most die by age 60 from coronary artery disease. Treatment entails dietary modifications, exercise, and various cholesterol-reducing drugs.

Kwashiorkor (kwash″e-or′kor) Severe protein and calorie deficiency which is particularly devastating in children, resulting in mental retardation and failure to grow. A consequence of malnutrition or starvation, it is characterized by a bloated abdomen because the level of plasma proteins is inadequate to keep fluid in the bloodstream. Skin lesions and infections are likely.

Marasmus (mah-raz′mus) Protein-calorie malnutrition, accompanied by progressive wasting. Often due to ingestion of food of very poor quality. Growth for age is severely stunted.

Pica (pi′kah) Craving and eating substances not normally considered nutrients, such as clay, cornstarch, or dirt.

Skin-fold test Clinical test of body fatness. A skin fold in the back of the arm or below the scapula is measured with a caliper. A fold over 1 inch in thickness indicates excess fat. Also called the fat-fold test.

CHAPTER SUMMARY

Media study tools that could provide you additional help in reviewing specific key topics of Chapter 24 are referenced below.

iP = *Interactive Physiology*

Diet and Nutrition (pp. 911–918)

1. Nutrients include water, carbohydrates, lipids, proteins, vitamins, and minerals. The bulk of the organic nutrients is used as fuel to produce cellular energy (ATP). The energy value of foods is measured in kilocalories (kcal).
2. Essential nutrients are those that are inadequately synthesized by body cells and must be ingested in the diet.

Carbohydrates (p. 912)

3. Carbohydrates are obtained primarily from plant products. Absorbed monosaccharides other than glucose are converted to glucose by the liver.
4. Monosaccharides are used primarily for cellular fuel. Small amounts are used for nucleic acid synthesis and to add sugar residues to plasma membranes.
5. Recommended carbohydrate intake for adults is 45–65% of daily caloric intake.

24

Lipids   (pp. 912–914)

6. Most dietary lipids are triglycerides. The primary sources of saturated fats are animal products, tropical oils, and hydrogenated oils; unsaturated fats are present in plant products, nuts, and cold-water fish. The major sources of cholesterol are egg yolk, meats, and milk products.
7. Linoleic and linolenic acids are essential fatty acids.
8. Triglycerides provide reserve energy, cushion body organs, and insulate the body. Phospholipids are used to synthesize plasma membranes and myelin. Cholesterol is used in plasma membranes and is the structural basis of vitamin D, steroid hormones, and bile salts.
9. Fat intake should represent 35% or less of caloric intake, and saturated and trans fats should be replaced by mono- and polyunsaturated fats if possible.

Proteins   (pp. 914–915)

10. Animal products provide high-quality complete protein containing all (10) essential amino acids. Most plant products lack one or more of the essential amino acids.
11. Amino acids are the structural building blocks of the body and of important regulatory molecules.
12. Protein synthesis can and will occur if all essential amino acids are present and sufficient carbohydrate (or fat) calories are available to produce ATP. Otherwise, amino acids will be burned for energy.
13. Nitrogen balance occurs when protein synthesis equals protein loss.
14. A dietary intake of 0.8 g of protein per kg of body weight is recommended for most healthy adults.

Vitamins   (pp. 915–917)

15. Vitamins are organic compounds needed in minute amounts. Most act as coenzymes. The richest sources are whole grains, vegetables, legumes, and fruit.
16. Except for vitamin D and the K and B vitamins made by enteric bacteria, vitamins are not made in the body.
17. Water-soluble vitamins (B and C) are not stored to excess in the body. Fat-soluble vitamins include vitamins A, D, E, and K; all but vitamin K are stored and can accumulate to toxic amounts.

Minerals   (pp. 917–918)

18. Besides calcium, phosphorus, potassium, sulfur, sodium, chloride, and magnesium, the body requires trace amounts of at least a dozen other minerals.
19. Minerals are not used for energy. Some are used to mineralize bone; others are bound to organic compounds or exist as ions in body fluids, where they play various roles in cell processes and metabolism.
20. Mineral uptake and excretion are carefully regulated to prevent mineral toxicity. The richest sources of minerals are some meats, vegetables, nuts, and legumes.

Overview of Metabolic Reactions   (pp. 918–922)

1. Metabolism encompasses all chemical reactions necessary to maintain life. Metabolic processes are either anabolic or catabolic.
2. Cellular respiration refers to catabolic processes during which energy is released and some is captured in ATP bonds.
3. Energy is released when organic compounds are oxidized. Cellular oxidation is accomplished primarily by the removal of hydrogen (electrons). When molecules are oxidized, others are simultaneously reduced by accepting hydrogen (or electrons).

4. Most enzymes catalyzing oxidation-reduction reactions require coenzymes as hydrogen acceptors. Two important coenzymes in these reactions are NAD^+ and FAD.
5. In animal cells, the two mechanisms of ATP synthesis are substrate-level phosphorylation and oxidative phosphorylation.

iP   Muscular System; Topic: Muscle Metabolism, pp. 3–8.

Metabolism of Major Nutrients   (pp. 922–934)

Carbohydrate Metabolism   (pp. 922–930)

1. Carbohydrate metabolism is essentially glucose metabolism.
2. Phosphorylation of glucose on entry into cells effectively traps it in most tissue cells.
3. Glucose is oxidized to carbon dioxide and water via three successive pathways: glycolysis, Krebs cycle, and electron transport chain. Some ATP is harvested in each pathway, but the bulk is captured in the electron transport chain.
4. Glycolysis is a reversible pathway in which glucose is converted to two pyruvic acid molecules; two molecules of reduced NAD^+ are formed, and there is a net gain of 2 ATP. Under aerobic conditions, pyruvic acid enters the Krebs cycle; under anaerobic conditions, it is reduced to lactic acid.
5. The Krebs cycle is fueled by pyruvic acid (and fatty acids). To enter the cycle, pyruvic acid is converted to acetyl CoA. The acetyl CoA is then oxidized and decarboxylated. Complete oxidation of two pyruvic acid molecules yields $6 CO_2$, $8 NADH + H^+$, $2 FADH_2$, and a net gain of 2 ATP. Much of the energy originally present in the bonds of pyruvic acid is now present in the reduced coenzymes.
6. In the electron transport chain, (a) reduced coenzymes are oxidized by delivering hydrogen to a series of oxidation-reduction acceptors; (b) hydrogen is split into hydrogen ions and electrons (as electrons run downhill from acceptor to acceptor, the energy released is used to pump H^+ into the mitochondrial intermembrane space, which creates an electrochemical proton gradient); (c) the energy stored in the electrochemical proton gradient drives H^+ back through ATP synthase, which uses the energy to form ATP; (d) H^+ and electrons are combined with oxygen to form water.
7. For each glucose molecule oxidized to carbon dioxide and water, there is a net gain of 32 ATP: 4 ATP from substrate-level phosphorylation and 28 ATP from oxidative phosphorylation. The shuttle for reduced NAD^+ produced in the cytosol may use 2 ATP of that amount.
8. When cellular ATP reserves are high, glucose catabolism is inhibited and glucose is converted to glycogen (glycogenesis) or to fat (lipogenesis). Much more fat than glycogen is stored.
9. When blood glucose levels begin to fall, glycogenolysis occurs, in which glycogen stores are converted to glucose. The liver can also perform gluconeogenesis, the formation of glucose from noncarbohydrate (fat or protein) molecules.

iP   Muscular System; Topic: Muscle Metabolism, pp. 10–22.

Lipid Metabolism   (pp. 930–932)

10. End products of lipid digestion (and cholesterol) are transported in blood in the form of chylomicrons.
11. Glycerol is converted to glyceraldehyde-PO_4 and enters the Krebs cycle or is converted to glucose.
12. Fatty acids are oxidized by beta oxidation into acetic acid fragments. These are bound to coenzyme A and enter the Krebs cycle as acetyl CoA. Dietary fats not needed for energy or structural materials are stored in adipose tissue.
13. There is a continual turnover of fats in fat depots. Breakdown of fats to fatty acids and glycerol is called lipolysis.

14. When excessive amounts of fats are used, the liver converts acetyl CoA to ketone bodies and releases them to the blood. Excessive levels of ketone bodies (ketosis) lead to metabolic acidosis.

15. All cells use phospholipids and cholesterol to build their plasma membranes. The liver forms many functional molecules (lipoproteins, bile salts, etc.) from lipids.

Protein Metabolism   (pp. 932–934)

16. To be oxidized for energy, amino acids are converted to keto acids that can enter the Krebs cycle. This involves transamination, oxidative deamination, and keto acid modification.

17. Amine groups removed during deamination (as ammonia) are combined with carbon dioxide by the liver to form urea. Urea is excreted in urine.

18. Deaminated amino acids may also be converted to fatty acids and glucose.

19. Amino acids are the body's most important building blocks. Non-essential amino acids are made in the liver by transamination.

20. In adults, most protein synthesis serves to replace tissue proteins and to maintain nitrogen balance.

21. Protein synthesis requires the presence of all 10 essential amino acids. If any are lacking, amino acids are used as energy fuels.

Metabolic States of the Body   (pp. 935–941)

Catabolic-Anabolic Steady State of the Body   (pp. 935–936)

1. The amino acid pool provides amino acids for synthesis of proteins and amino acid derivatives, ATP synthesis, and energy storage. To be stored, amino acids are first deaminated and then converted to fats or glycogen.

2. The carbohydrate-fat pool primarily provides fuels for ATP synthesis and other molecules that can be stored as energy reserves.

3. The nutrient pools are connected by the bloodstream; fats, carbohydrates, and proteins may be interconverted via common intermediates.

Absorptive State   (pp. 936–938)

4. During the absorptive state (during and shortly after a meal), glucose is the major energy source; needed structural and functional molecules are made; excesses of carbohydrates, fats, and amino acids are stored as glycogen and fat.

5. Events of the absorptive state are controlled by insulin, which enhances the entry of glucose (and amino acids) into cells and accelerates its use for ATP synthesis or storage as glycogen or fat.

Postabsorptive State   (pp. 938–941)

6. The postabsorptive state is the period when bloodborne fuels are provided by breakdown of energy reserves. Glucose is made available to the blood by glycogenolysis, lipolysis, and gluconeogenesis. Glucose sparing begins and, if fasting is prolonged (4–5 days), the brain also begins to metabolize ketone bodies.

7. Events of the postabsorptive state are controlled largely by glucagon and the sympathetic nervous system, which mobilize glycogen and fat reserves and trigger gluconeogenesis.

The Metabolic Role of the Liver   (pp. 941–944)

1. The liver is the body's main metabolic organ and it plays a crucial role in processing (or storing) virtually every nutrient group. It helps maintain blood energy sources, metabolizes hormones, and detoxifies drugs and other substances.

Cholesterol Metabolism and Regulation of Blood Cholesterol Levels   (pp. 943–944)

2. The liver synthesizes cholesterol, catabolizes cholesterol and secretes it in the form of bile salts, and makes lipoproteins. The liver makes a basal amount of cholesterol (85%) even when dietary cholesterol intake is excessive.

3. LDLs transport triglycerides and cholesterol from the liver to the tissues, whereas HDLs transport cholesterol from the tissues to the liver (for catabolism and elimination).

4. Excessively high LDL levels are implicated in atherosclerosis, cardiovascular disease, and strokes.

Energy Balance   (pp. 944–954)

1. Body energy intake (derived from food oxidation) is precisely balanced by energy output (heat, work, and energy storage). Eventually, all of the energy intake is converted to heat.

Obesity   (p. 945)

2. When energy balance is maintained, weight remains stable. When excess amounts of energy are stored, the result is obesity (condition of excessive fat storage resulting in a BMI above 30).

Regulation of Food Intake   (pp. 945–947)

3. The hypothalamus (particularly its arcuate nucleus) and other brain centers are involved in the regulation of eating behavior.

4. Factors thought to be involved in regulating food intake include (a) neural signals from the gut to the brain, (b) nutrient signals related to total energy storage (e.g., large fatty reserves and increased plasma levels of glucose and amino acids depress hunger and eating); (c) plasma concentrations of hormones that control events of the absorptive and postabsorptive states, and hormones that provide feedback signals to brain feeding centers (leptin appears to exert the main long-term controls of appetite and energy metabolism); (d) body temperature; psychological factors; and others.

Metabolic Rate and Heat Production   (pp. 947–950)

5. Energy used by the body per hour is the metabolic rate.

6. Basal metabolic rate (BMR), reported in $kcal/m^2/h$, is the measurement obtained under basal conditions: The person is at comfortable room temperature, supine, relaxed, and in the postabsorptive state. BMR indicates energy needed to drive only the resting body processes.

7. Factors influencing metabolic rate include age, sex, size, body surface area, thyroxine levels, specific dynamic action of foods, and muscular activity.

Regulation of Body Temperature   (pp. 950–954)

8. Body temperature reflects the balance between heat production and heat loss and is normally 37°C (± 0.5°C), which is optimal for physiological activities.

9. At rest, most body heat is produced by the liver, heart, brain, kidneys, and endocrine organs. Activation of skeletal muscles causes dramatic increases in body heat production.

10. The body core (organs within the skull and the ventral body cavity) generally has the highest temperature. The shell (the skin) is the heat-exchange surface, and is usually coolest.

11. Blood serves as the major heat-exchange agent between the core and the shell. When skin capillaries are flushed with blood and the skin is warmer than the environment, heat is lost from the body. When blood is withdrawn to deep organs, heat loss from the shell is inhibited.

24

12. Heat-exchange mechanisms include radiation, conduction, convection, and evaporation. Evaporation, the conversion of water to water vapor, requires the absorption of heat. For each gram of water vaporized, about 0.6 kcal of heat is absorbed.

13. The hypothalamus acts as the body's thermostat. Its heat-promotion and heat-loss centers receive inputs from peripheral and central thermoreceptors, integrate these inputs, and initiate responses leading to heat loss or heat promotion.

14. Heat-promoting mechanisms include constriction of skin vasculature, increase in metabolic rate in infants (via release of norepinephrine), and shivering. If environmental cold is prolonged, the thyroid gland may be stimulated to release more thyroxine.

15. When heat must be removed from the body, dermal blood vessels are dilated, allowing heat loss through radiation, conduction, and convection. When greater heat loss is mandated (or the environmental temperature is so high that radiation and conduction are ineffective), sweating is initiated. Evaporation of perspiration is an efficient means of heat loss as long as the humidity is low.

16. Profuse sweating can lead to heat exhaustion, indicated by a rise in temperature, a drop in blood pressure, and collapse. When the body cannot rid itself of surplus heat, body temperature rises to the point where all thermoregulatory mechanisms become ineffective—a potentially lethal condition called heat stroke.

17. Fever is controlled hyperthermia, which follows thermostat resetting to higher levels by prostaglandins and initiation of heat-promotion mechanisms, evidenced by the chills. When the disease process is reversed, heat-loss mechanisms are initiated.

Developmental Aspects of Nutrition and Metabolism (pp. 954–955)

1. Good nutrition is essential for normal fetal development and normal growth during childhood.

2. Inborn errors of metabolism include cystic fibrosis, PKU, glycogen storage disease, galactosemia, and many others. Hormonal disorders, such as lack of insulin or thyroid hormone, may also lead to metabolic abnormalities. Diabetes mellitus is the most significant metabolic disorder in middle-aged and older adults.

3. In old age, metabolic rate declines as enzyme and endocrine systems become less efficient and skeletal muscles atrophy. Reduced caloric needs make it difficult to obtain adequate nutrition without becoming overweight.

4. Elderly individuals ingest more medications than any other age group, and many of these drugs negatively affect their nutrition.

REVIEW QUESTIONS

Multiple Choice/Matching

(Some questions have more than one correct answer. Select the best answer or answers from the choices given.)

1. Which of the following reactions would liberate the most energy? (a) complete oxidation of a molecule of sucrose to CO_2 and water, (b) conversion of a molecule of ADP to ATP, (c) respiration of a molecule of glucose to lactic acid, (d) conversion of a molecule of glucose to carbon dioxide and water.

2. The formation of glucose from glycogen is (a) gluconeogenesis, (b) glycogenesis, (c) glycogenolysis, (d) glycolysis.

3. The net gain of ATP from the complete metabolism (aerobic) of glucose is closest to (a) 2, (b) 32, (c) 3, (d) 4.

4. Which of the following best defines cellular respiration? (a) intake of carbon dioxide and output of oxygen by cells, (b) excretion of waste products, (c) inhalation of oxygen and exhalation of carbon dioxide, (d) oxidation of substances by which energy is released in usable form to the cells.

5. What is formed during aerobic respiration when electrons are passed down the electron transport chain? (a) oxygen, (b) water, (c) glucose, (d) $NADH + H^+$.

6. Metabolic rate is relatively low in (a) youth, (b) physical exercise, (c) old age, (d) fever.

7. In a temperate climate under ordinary conditions, the greatest loss of body heat occurs through (a) radiation, (b) conduction, (c) evaporation, (d) none of the above.

8. Which of the following is not a function of the liver? (a) glycogenolysis and gluconeogenesis, (b) synthesis of cholesterol, (c) detoxification of alcohol and drugs, (d) synthesis of glucagon, (e) deamination of amino acids.

9. Amino acids are essential (and important) to the body for all the following except (a) production of some hormones, (b) production of antibodies, (c) formation of most structural materials, (d) as a source of quick energy.

10. A person has been on a hunger strike for seven days. Compared to normal, he has (a) increased release of fatty acids from adipose tissue, and ketosis, (b) elevated glucose concentration in the blood, (c) increased plasma insulin concentration, (d) increased glycogen synthase (enzyme) activity in the liver.

11. Transamination is a chemical process by which (a) protein is synthesized, (b) an amine group is transferred from an amino acid to a keto acid, (c) an amine group is cleaved from the amino acid, (d) amino acids are broken down for energy.

12. Three days after removal of the pancreas from an animal, the researcher finds a persistent increase in (a) acetoacetic acid concentration in the blood, (b) urine volume, (c) blood glucose, (d) all of the above.

13. Hunger, appetite, obesity, and physical activity are interrelated. Thus, (a) hunger sensations arise primarily from the stimulation of receptors in the stomach and intestinal tract in response to the absence of food in these organs; (b) obesity, in most cases, is a result of the abnormally high enzymatic activity of the fat-synthesizing enzymes in adipose tissue; (c) in all cases of obesity, the energy content of the ingested food has exceeded the energy expenditure of the body; (d) in a normal individual, increasing blood glucose concentration increases hunger sensations.

14. Body temperature regulation is (a) influenced by temperature receptors in the skin, (b) influenced by the temperature of the blood perfusing the heat regulation centers of the brain, (c) subject to both neural and hormonal control, (d) all of the above.

15. Which of the following yields the greatest caloric value per gram? (a) fats, (b) proteins, (c) carbohydrates, (d) all are equal in caloric value.

Short Answer Essay Questions

16. What is cellular respiration? What is the common role of FAD and NAD^+ in cellular respiration?

17. Describe the site, major events, and outcomes of glycolysis.

18. Pyruvic acid is a product of glycolysis, but it is not the substance that joins with the pickup molecule to enter the Krebs cycle. What is that substance?

19. Define glycogenesis, glycogenolysis, gluconeogenesis, and lipogenesis. Which is (are) likely to be occurring (**a**) shortly after a carbohydrate-rich meal, (**b**) just before waking up in the morning?

20. What is the harmful result when excessive amounts of fats are burned for energy? Name two conditions that might lead to this result.

21. Make a flowchart that indicates the pivotal intermediates through which glucose can be converted to fat.

22. Distinguish between the role of HDLs and that of LDLs.

23. List some factors that influence plasma cholesterol levels. Also list the sources and fates of cholesterol in the body.

24. What is meant by "body energy balance," and what happens if the balance is not precise?

25. Explain the effect of the following on metabolic rate: thyroxine levels, eating, body surface area, muscular exercise, emotional stress, starvation.

26. Explain the terms "core" and "shell" relative to body temperature balance. What serves as the heat-transfer agent from one to the other?

27. Compare and contrast mechanisms of heat loss with mechanisms of heat promotion, and explain how these mechanisms determine body temperature.

Critical Thinking and Clinical Application Questions

1. Calculate the number of ATP molecules that can be harvested during the complete oxidation of an 18-carbon fatty acid. (Take a deep breath and think about it—you *can* do it.)

2. Every year dozens of elderly people are found dead in their unheated apartments and listed as victims of hypothermia. What is hypothermia, and how does it kill? Why are the elderly more susceptible to hypothermia than the young?

3. Frank Moro has been diagnosed as having severe atherosclerosis and high blood cholesterol levels. He is told that he is at risk for a stroke or a heart attack. First, what foods would you suggest that he avoid like the plague? What foods would you suggest he add or substitute? What activities would you recommend?

4. In the 1940s, some physicians prescribed low doses of a chemical called dinitrophenol (DNP) to help patients lose weight. This drug therapy was abandoned after a few patients died. DNP uncouples the chemiosmotic machinery. Explain how this causes weight loss.

5. While attempting to sail solo from Los Angeles to Tahiti, Simon encountered a storm that marooned him on an uninhabited island. He was able, using his ingenuity and a pocket knife, to obtain plenty of fish to eat, and roots were plentiful. However, the island was barren of fruits and soon his gums began to bleed and he started to develop several infections. Analyze his problem.

6. Gregor, a large beefy man, came home from the doctor's office and complained to his wife that his blood tests "were bad." He told her that the doctor said he would have to give up some of his steaks and butter. He went on to mourn the fact that he would have to start eating more cottage cheese and olive oil instead. What kind of problem was revealed by his "bad" blood tests? How should his wife respond to his choice of food substitutes and why? What foods should she suggest?

24

25

The Urinary System

Every day the kidneys filter nearly 200 liters of fluid from the bloodstream, allowing toxins, metabolic wastes, and excess ions to leave the body in urine while returning needed substances to the blood. Much like a water purification plant that keeps a city's water drinkable and disposes of its wastes, the kidneys are usually unappreciated until they malfunction and body fluids become contaminated. Although the lungs and skin also participate in excretion, the kidneys are the major excretory organs.

As the kidneys perform these excretory functions, they also act as essential regulators of the volume and chemical makeup of the blood, maintaining the proper balance between water and salts and

Hepatic veins (cut)
Esophagus (cut)
Inferior vena cava
Adrenal gland
Aorta
Iliac crest
Rectum (cut)
Uterus (part of female reproductive system)

Renal artery
Renal hilum
Renal vein
Kidney
Ureter
Urinary bladder
Urethra

Figure 25.1 The urinary system. Anterior view of the female urinary organs. (Most unrelated abdominal organs have been omitted.)

between acids and bases. Frankly, this would be tricky work for a chemical engineer, but the kidneys do it efficiently most of the time.

Other renal functions include

- Gluconeogenesis during prolonged fasting (see p. 930).
- Producing the hormones renin and erythropoietin (see Chapter 16). *Renin* (re′nin; *ren* = kidney) acts as an enzyme to help regulate blood pressure and kidney function. *Erythropoietin* (ĕ-rith″ro-poi′ĕ-tin) stimulates red blood cell production.
- Metabolizing vitamin D to its active form (see Chapter 16).

Besides the urine-forming kidneys, the **urinary system** includes the *urinary bladder*, a temporary storage reservoir for urine, plus three tubelike organs—the paired *ureters* (u-re′terz) and the *urethra* (u-re′thrah), all three of which furnish transportation channels for urine **(Figure 25.1)**.

Kidney Anatomy

▶ Describe the gross anatomy of the kidney and its coverings.

Location and External Anatomy

The bean-shaped kidneys lie in a retroperitoneal position (between the dorsal body wall and the parietal peritoneum) in the *superior* lumbar region **(Figure 25.2)**. Extending approximately from T_{12} to L_3, the kidneys receive some protection from the lower part of the rib cage (Figure 25.2b). The right kidney is crowded by the liver and lies slightly lower than the left. An

adult's kidney has a mass of about 150 g (5 ounces) and its average dimensions are 12 cm long, 6 cm wide, and 3 cm thick—about the size of a large bar of soap. The lateral surface is convex. The medial surface is concave and has a vertical cleft called the **renal hilum** that leads into an internal space within the kidney called the *renal sinus*. The ureter, renal blood vessels, lymphatics, and nerves all join each kidney at the hilum and occupy the sinus. Atop each kidney is an *adrenal* (or *suprarenal*) *gland*, an endocrine gland that is functionally unrelated to the kidney.

Three layers of supportive tissue surround each kidney (Figure 25.2a):

1. The **renal fascia**, an outer layer of dense fibrous connective tissue that anchors the kidney and the adrenal gland to surrounding structures
2. The **perirenal fat capsule**, a fatty mass that surrounds the kidney and cushions it against blows
3. The **fibrous capsule**, a transparent capsule that prevents infections in surrounding regions from spreading to the kidney

HOMEOSTATIC IMBALANCE

The fatty encasement of the kidneys is important in holding the kidneys in their normal body position. If the amount of fatty tissue dwindles (as with extreme emaciation or rapid weight loss), one or both kidneys may drop to a lower position, an event called *renal ptosis* (to′sis; "a fall"). Renal ptosis may cause a ureter to become kinked, which creates problems because the urine, unable to drain, backs up into the kidney and exerts

25

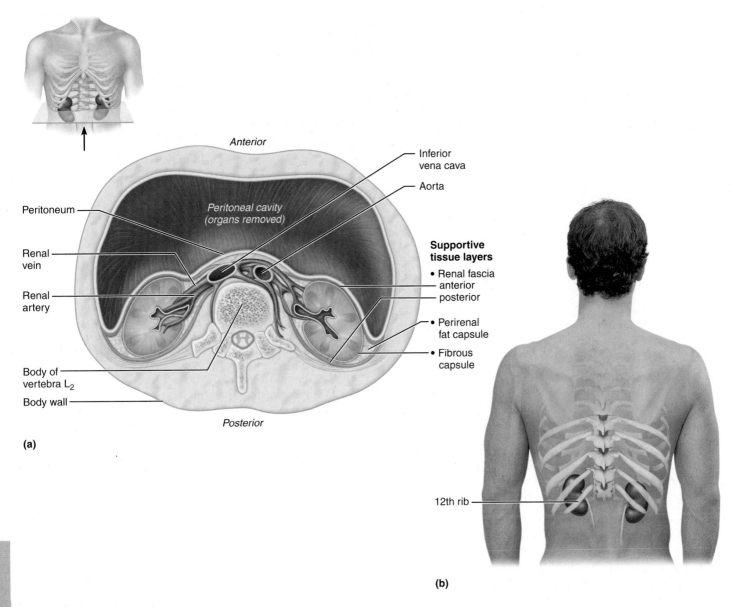

Figure 25.2 Position of the kidneys against the posterior body wall. (a) Cross-section viewed from inferior direction. Note the retroperitoneal position and the supportive tissue layers of the kidney. **(b)** Posterior in situ view showing relationship of the kidneys to the 12th rib pair.

pressure on its tissue. Backup of urine from ureteral obstruction or other causes is called *hydronephrosis* (hi″dro-nĕ-fro′sis; "water in the kidney"). Hydronephrosis can severely damage the kidney, leading to necrosis (tissue death) and renal failure. ■

Internal Anatomy

A frontal section through a kidney reveals three distinct regions: *cortex, medulla,* and *pelvis* **(Figure 25.3)**. The most superficial region, the **renal cortex**, is light in color and has a granular appearance. Deep to the cortex is the darker, reddish-brown **renal medulla**, which exhibits cone-shaped tissue masses called **medullary** or **renal pyramids**. The broad *base* of each pyramid faces toward the cortex, and its apex, or *papilla* ("nipple"), points internally. The pyramids appear striped because they are formed almost entirely of parallel bundles of microscopic

urine-collecting tubules and capillaries. The **renal columns**, inward extensions of cortical tissue, separate the pyramids. Each pyramid and its surrounding cortical tissue constitutes one of approximately eight **lobes** of a kidney.

The **renal pelvis**, a funnel-shaped tube, is continuous with the ureter leaving the hilum. Branching extensions of the pelvis form two or three **major calyces** (ka′lih-sēz; singular: calyx). Each one subdivides to form several **minor calyces**, cup-shaped areas that enclose the papillae.

The calyces collect urine, which drains continuously from the papillae, and empty it into the renal pelvis. The urine then flows through the renal pelvis and into the ureter, which moves it to the bladder to be stored. The walls of the calyces, pelvis, and ureter contain smooth muscle that contracts rhythmically to propel urine along its course by peristalsis.

Renal hilum

Renal cortex

Renal medulla

Major calyx

Papilla of pyramid

Renal pelvis

Minor calyx

Ureter

Renal pyramid in renal medulla

Renal column

Fibrous capsule

(a) Photograph of right kidney, frontal section

(b) Diagrammatic view

Figure 25.3 Internal anatomy of the kidney. Frontal sections. (See *A Brief Atlas of the Human Body*, Figure 71.)

HOMEOSTATIC IMBALANCE

Infection of the renal pelvis and calyces produces the condition called *pyelitis* (pi″ĕ-li′tis). Infections or inflammations that affect the entire kidney are *pyelonephritis* (pi″ĕ-lo-nĕ-fri′tis). Kidney infections in females are usually caused by fecal bacteria that spread from the anal region to the urinary tract. Less often they result from bloodborne bacteria (traveling from other infected sites) that lodge and multiply in the kidneys. In severe cases of pyelonephritis, the kidney swells, abscesses form, and the pelvis fills with pus. Untreated, the kidneys may be severely damaged, but antibiotic therapy can usually treat the infection successfully. ■

Blood and Nerve Supply

▶ Trace the blood supply through the kidney.

The kidneys continuously cleanse the blood and adjust its composition, and so it is not surprising that they have a rich blood supply. Under normal resting conditions, the large **renal arter-**ies deliver one-fourth of the total cardiac output (about 1200 ml) to the kidneys each minute.

The renal arteries issue at right angles from the abdominal aorta, and the right renal artery is longer than the left because the aorta lies to the left of the midline. As each renal artery approaches a kidney, it divides into five **segmental arteries** (Figure 25.4). Within the renal sinus, each segmental artery branches further to form several **interlobar arteries**.

At the medulla-cortex junction, the interlobar arteries branch into the **arcuate arteries** (ar′ku-āt) that arch over the bases of the medullary pyramids. Small **cortical radiate arteries** radiate outward from the arcuate arteries to supply the cortical tissue. More than 90% of the blood entering the kidney perfuses the renal cortex.

Afferent arterioles branching from the cortical radiate arteries begin a complex arrangement of microscopic blood vessels. These vessels are key elements of kidney function, and we will examine them in detail later when we describe the nephron.

Veins pretty much trace the pathway of the arterial supply in reverse (Figure 25.4). Blood leaving the renal cortex drains

25

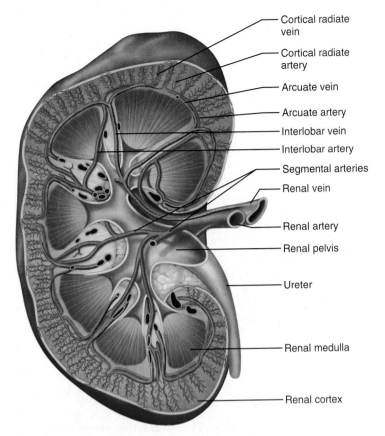

(a) Frontal section illustrating major blood vessels

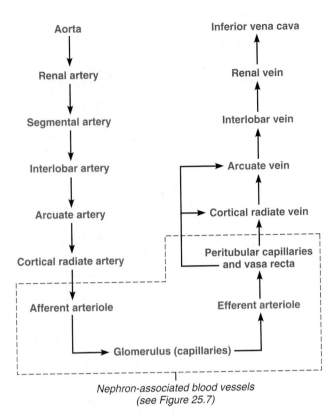

Nephron-associated blood vessels
(see Figure 25.7)

(b) Path of blood flow through renal blood vessels

Figure 25.4 **Blood vessels of the kidney.**

sequentially into the **cortical radiate**, **arcuate**, **interlobar**, and finally **renal veins**. (There are no segmental veins.) The renal veins issue from the kidneys and empty into the inferior vena cava. Because the inferior vena cava lies to the right of the vertebral column, the left renal vein is about twice as long as the right.

The **renal plexus**, a variable network of autonomic nerve fibers and ganglia, provides the nerve supply of the kidney and its ureter. An offshoot of the celiac plexus, the renal plexus is largely supplied by sympathetic fibers from the most inferior thoracic and first lumbar splanchnic nerves, which course along with the renal artery to reach the kidney. These sympathetic vasomotor fibers regulate renal blood flow by adjusting the diameter of renal arterioles and also influence the urine-forming role of the nephrons.

CHECK YOUR UNDERSTANDING

1. Roger is hit in the lower back by an errant baseball. What protects his kidneys from this mechanical trauma?
2. From inside to outside, list the three layers of supportive tissue that surround each kidney. Where is the parietal peritoneum in relation to these layers?
3. The lumen of the ureter is continuous with a space inside the kidney. This space has branching extensions. What are the names of this space and its extensions?

For answers, see Appendix G.

Nephrons

▶ Describe the anatomy of a nephron.

Nephrons (nef′ronz) are the structural and functional units of the kidneys. Each kidney contains over 1 million of these tiny blood-processing units, which carry out the processes that form urine **(Figure 25.5)**. In addition, there are thousands of *collecting ducts*, each of which collects fluid from several nephrons and conveys it to the renal pelvis.

Each nephron consists of a **glomerulus** (glo-mer′u-lus; *glom* = ball of yarn), which is a tuft of capillaries, and a **renal tubule**. The renal tubule has a cup-shaped end, the **glomerular capsule** (or **Bowman's capsule**), which is blind and completely surrounds the glomerulus, much as a well-worn baseball glove encloses a ball. Collectively, the glomerular capsule and the enclosed glomerulus are called the **renal corpuscle**.

The endothelium of the glomerular capillaries is *fenestrated* (penetrated by many pores), which makes them exceptionally porous. This allows large amounts of solute-rich, virtually protein-free fluid to pass from the blood into the glomerular capsule. This plasma-derived fluid or **filtrate** is the raw material that the renal tubules process to form urine.

The external *parietal layer* of the glomerular capsule is simple squamous epithelium (Figures 25.5, 25.8, and 25.9). This layer simply contributes to the capsule structure and plays no part in forming filtrate.

Figure 25.5 Location and structure of nephrons. Schematic view of a nephron depicting the structural characteristics of epithelial cells forming its various regions.

Renal corpuscle
• Glomerular capsular space
• Squamous epithelium of parietal layer of glomerular capsule
• Glomerulus

Artery

Distal convoluted tubules (clear lumens)

Proximal convoluted tubules (fuzzy lumens due to long microvilli)

(a) Photomicrograph of renal cortical tissue (200×)

(b) Scanning electron micrograph of cut renal tubules (430×)

Figure 25.6 Renal cortical tissue and renal tubules.

The *visceral layer*, which clings to the glomerular capillaries, consists of highly modified, branching epithelial cells called **podocytes** (pod'o-sīts; "foot cells") (see Figure 25.9). The octopus-like podocytes terminate in **foot processes**, which intertwine as they cling to the basement membrane of the glomerulus. The clefts or openings between the foot processes are called **filtration slits**. Through these slits, filtrate enters the **capsular space** inside the glomerular capsule.

The remainder of the renal tubule is about 3 cm (1.2 inches) long and has three major parts. It leaves the glomerular capsule as the elaborately coiled **proximal convoluted tubule (PCT)**, makes a hairpin loop called the **loop of Henle** (also called the **nephron loop** or **Henle's loop**), and then winds and twists again as the **distal convoluted tubule (DCT)** before emptying into a collecting duct. The terms *proximal* and *distal* indicate relationship of the convoluted tubules to the renal corpuscle— filtrate from the renal corpuscle passes through the PCT first and then the DCT, which is thus "further away" from the renal corpuscle. The meandering nature of the renal tubule increases its length and enhances its filtrate processing capabilities.

The **collecting ducts**, each of which receives filtrate from many nephrons, run through the medullary pyramids and give them their striped appearance. As the collecting ducts approach the renal pelvis, they fuse together and deliver urine into the minor calyces via papillae of the pyramids.

Throughout its length, the renal tubule consists of a single layer of polar epithelial cells on a basement membrane, but each of its regions has a unique cellular anatomy that reflects its role in processing filtrate. The walls of the PCT are formed by cuboidal epithelial cells with large mitochondria, and their luminal (exposed) surfaces bear dense microvilli (Figure 25.5 and Figure 25.6). Just as in the intestine, this *brush border* dramatically increases the surface area and capacity for reabsorbing water and solutes from the filtrate and secreting substances into it.

The U-shaped *loop of Henle* has *descending* and *ascending limbs*. The proximal part of the descending limb is continuous with the proximal tubule and its cells are similar. The rest of the

descending limb, called the **thin segment**, is a simple squamous epithelium freely permeable to water. The epithelium becomes cuboidal or even low columnar in the ascending part of the loop of Henle, which therefore becomes the **thick segment**. In some nephrons, the thin segment is found only in the descending limb. In others, it extends into the ascending limb as well.

The epithelial cells of the DCT, like those of the PCT, are cuboidal and confined to the cortex, but they are thinner and almost entirely lack microvilli (Figure 25.5). The transition between the DCT and the collecting duct is marked by the appearance of a heterogeneous collection of cells. The two cell types seen in the collecting ducts are *intercalated* cells, cuboidal cells with abundant microvilli, and the more numerous *principal cells*, which have sparse, short microvilli. The two varieties (type A and B) of intercalated cells play a major role in maintaining the acid-base balance of the blood. The principal cells help maintain the body's water and Na$^+$ balance.

Nephrons are generally divided into two major groups. **Cortical nephrons** represent 85% of the nephrons in the kidneys. Except for small parts of their loops of Henle that dip into the outer medulla, they are located entirely in the cortex. The remaining **juxtamedullary nephrons** (juks"tah-mĕ'dul-ah-re) originate close to (*juxta* = near to) the cortex-medulla junction, and they play an important role in the kidneys' ability to produce concentrated urine. Their loops of Henle deeply invade the medulla, and their thin segments are much more extensive than those of cortical nephrons. Figure 25.7a compares the anatomy of these two types of nephrons.

Nephron Capillary Beds

The renal tubule of every nephron is closely associated with two capillary beds: the *glomerulus* and the *peritubular capillaries* (Figure 25.7). The glomerulus, in which the capillaries run in parallel, is specialized for filtration. It differs from all other capillary beds in the body in that it is both fed and drained by arterioles—the **afferent arteriole** and the **efferent arteriole**, respectively.

Cortical nephron
- Has short loop of Henle and glomerulus further from the corticomedullary junction
- Efferent arteriole supplies peritubular capillaries

Juxtamedullary nephron
- Has long loop of Henle and glomerulus closer to the corticomedullary junction
- Efferent arteriole supplies vasa recta

Renal corpuscle
Glomerular capillaries (glomerulus)
Glomerular (Bowman's) capsule
Proximal convoluted tubule
Efferent arteriole

Cortical radiate vein
Cortical radiate artery
Afferent arteriole
Collecting duct
Distal convoluted tubule
Afferent arteriole
Efferent arteriole

Cortex
Medulla
Renal pelvis
Ureter
Kidney

Peritubular capillaries
Ascending or thick limb of the loop of Henle
Arcuate vein
Arcuate artery
Loop of Henle
Descending or thin limb of loop of Henle

(a)

Cortico-medullary junction
Vasa recta

Afferent arteriole
Glomerulus
Efferent arteriole
Peritubular capillary bed

(b)

Figure 25.7 Blood vessels of cortical and juxtamedullary nephrons. (a) Arrows indicate direction of blood flow. Capillary beds from adjacent nephrons (not shown) overlap. **(b)** Scanning electron micrograph of a cast of blood vessels associated with nephrons (60×). View looking down onto the cortex.

SOURCE: (b) Kessel and Kardon/Visuals Unlimited.

25

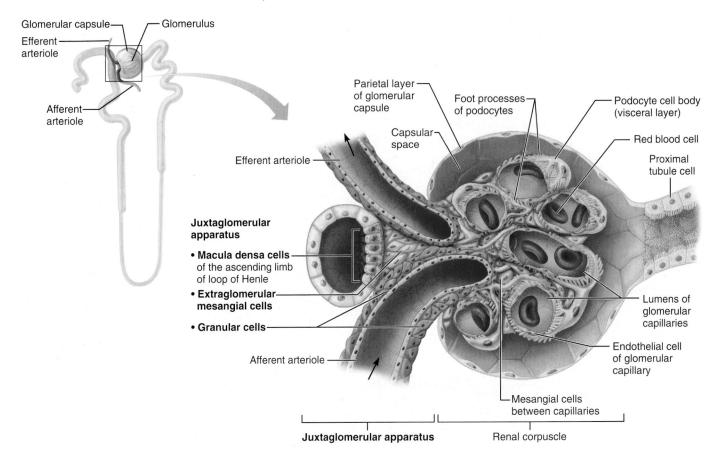

Figure 25.8 Juxtaglomerular apparatus (JGA) of a nephron. Mesangial cells that surround the glomerular capillaries (glomerular mesangial cells) are not part of the JGA.

The afferent arterioles arise from the *cortical radiate arteries* that run through the renal cortex. The blood pressure in the glomerulus is extraordinarily high for a capillary bed because (1) arterioles are high-resistance vessels and (2) the afferent arteriole has a larger diameter than the efferent. This high blood pressure easily forces fluid and solutes out of the blood into the glomerular capsule. Most of the resulting filtrate (99%) is reabsorbed by the renal tubule cells and returned to the blood in the peritubular capillary beds.

The **peritubular capillaries** arise from the efferent arterioles draining the glomeruli. These capillaries cling closely to adjacent renal tubules and empty into nearby venules. They are low-pressure, porous capillaries that readily absorb solutes and water from the tubule cells as these substances are reclaimed from the filtrate.

Notice in Figure 25.7a that the efferent arterioles serving the juxtamedullary nephrons tend *not* to break up into meandering peritubular capillaries. Instead they form bundles of long straight vessels called **vasa recta** (va'sah rek'tah; "straight vessels") that extend deep into the medulla paralleling the longest loops of Henle. The thin-walled vasa recta play an important role in forming concentrated urine, as we will describe shortly.

In summary, the microvasculature of the nephrons consists of two capillary beds separated by intervening efferent arterioles. The first capillary bed (glomerulus) produces the filtrate. The second (peritubular capillaries) reclaims most of that filtrate.

Vascular Resistance in the Microcirculation Blood flowing through the renal circulation encounters high resistance, first in the afferent and then in the efferent arterioles. As a result, renal blood pressure declines from approximately 95 mm Hg in the renal arteries to 8 mm Hg or less in the renal veins. The resistance of the afferent arterioles protects the glomeruli from large fluctuations in systemic blood pressure. Resistance in the efferent arterioles reinforces the high glomerular pressure and reduces the hydrostatic pressure in the peritubular capillaries.

Juxtaglomerular Apparatus

Each nephron has a region called a **juxtaglomerular apparatus (JGA)** (juks"tah-glo-mer'u-lar), where the most distal portion of the ascending limb of the loop of Henle lies against the afferent arteriole feeding the glomerulus (and sometimes the efferent arteriole) **(Figure 25.8)**. Both the ascending limb and the afferent arteriole are modified at the point of contact.

The JGA includes two cell populations that play important roles in regulating the rate of filtrate formation and systemic blood pressure, as we will describe shortly. In the arteriole walls are the **granular cells**, also called **juxtaglomerular (JG) cells**, which are enlarged, smooth muscle cells with prominent secretory granules containing *renin*. Granular cells act as mechanoreceptors that sense the blood pressure in the afferent arteriole. The **macula densa** (mak'u-lah den'sah; "dense spot")

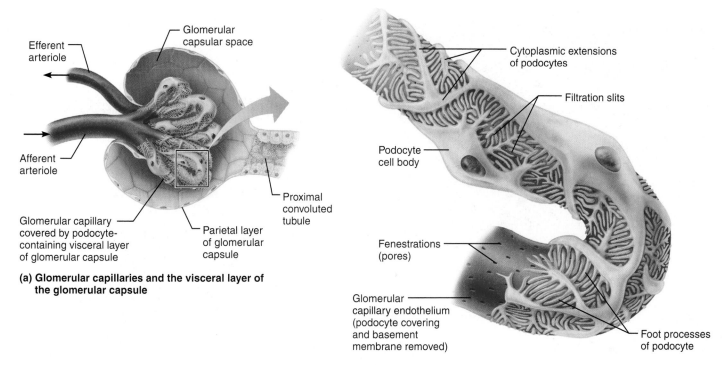

Figure 25.9 The filtration membrane. The filtration membrane is composed of three layers: the fenestrated endothelium of the glomerular capillaries, the podocyte-containing visceral layer of the glomerular capsule, and the intervening basement membrane. **(a)** Diagrammatic view of the relationship of the visceral layer of the glomerular capsule to the glomerular capillaries. The visceral epithelium is drawn incompletely to show the fenestrations in the underlying capillary wall.

is a group of tall, closely packed cells of the ascending limb of the loop of Henle that lies adjacent to the granular cells (Figure 25.8). The macula densa cells are chemoreceptors that respond to changes in the NaCl content of the filtrate. A third population of cells, the *extraglomerular mesangial cells*, is also part of the JGA. These cells are interconnected by gap junctions and may pass signals between macula densa and granular cells.

The Filtration Membrane

The **filtration membrane** lies between the blood and the interior of the glomerular capsule. It is a porous membrane that allows free passage of water and solutes smaller than plasma proteins. As **Figure 25.9c** shows, its three layers are: (1) the fenestrated endothelium of the glomerular capillaries; (2) the visceral membrane of the glomerular capsule, made of podocytes which have filtration slits between their foot processes; and between these two layers, (3) the basement membrane composed of the fused basal laminae of the two other layers.

The fenestrations (capillary pores) allow passage of all plasma components but not blood cells. The basement membrane restricts all but the smallest proteins while permitting most other solutes to pass. The structural makeup of the gel-like basement membrane also confers electrical selectivity on the filtration process. Most of the proteins in the membrane are negatively charged glycoproteins that repel other macromolecular anions and hinder their passage into the tubule. Because most plasma proteins also bear a net negative charge, this electrical repulsion reinforces the plasma protein blockage imposed by molecular size.

Almost all macromolecules that do manage to make it through the basement membrane are prevented from traveling further by thin membranes (*slit diaphragms*) that extend across the filtration slits. Macromolecules that get "hung up" in the filtration membrane are engulfed and degraded by mesangial cells within the glomerulus. These *glomerular mesangial cells* can also contract, changing the total surface area of the capillaries available for filtration.

CHECK YOUR UNDERSTANDING

4. Name the tubular components of a nephron in the order that filtrate passes through them.
5. What are the structural differences between juxtamedullary and cortical nephrons?
6. What type of capillaries are the glomerular capillaries? What is their function?

For answers, see Appendix G.

Kidney Physiology: Mechanisms of Urine Formation

Urine formation and the adjustment of blood composition involve three major processes: *glomerular filtration* by the glomeruli, and *tubular reabsorption* and *tubular secretion* in the renal tubules **(Figure 25.10)**. In addition, the collecting ducts work in concert with the nephrons to make concentrated or dilute urine.

25

(b) Filtration slits between the podocyte foot processes

(c) Three parts of the filtration membrane

Figure 25.9 (*continued*) **The filtration membrane. (b)** Scanning electron micrograph of the visceral layer. Filtration slits between the podocyte foot processes are evident (6000×). **(c)** Diagrammatic view of a section through the filtration membrane showing all three structural elements.

Let's first look at the big picture to see how the kidneys use these three processes to maintain the volume and chemical makeup of the blood—in other words, how do they "clean" the blood? Conceptually, it's really very simple. The kidneys "dump" (by glomerular filtration, Figure 25.10, ❶) cell- and protein-free blood into a separate "container" (the renal tubules and collecting ducts). From this container, the kidneys reclaim (by tubular reabsorption, Figure 25.10, ❷) everything the body needs to keep. This is almost everything—all of the glucose and amino acids, and some 99% of the water, salt, and other components. Anything that is *not* reabsorbed becomes urine. In addition, some things are selectively added to the container (by tubular secretion, Figure 25.10, ❸), fine-tuning the body's chemical balance.

The volume of blood processed by the kidneys each day is enormous. Of the approximately 1200 ml of blood that passes through the glomeruli each minute, some 650 ml is plasma, and about one-fifth of this (120–125 ml) is forced into the renal tubules. This is equivalent to filtering out your entire plasma volume more than 60 times each day! Considering the magnitude of their task, it is not surprising that the kidneys (which account for only 1% of body weight) consume 20–25% of all oxygen used by the body at rest.

Filtrate and urine are quite different. Filtrate contains everything found in blood plasma except proteins. **Urine** contains mostly metabolic wastes and unneeded substances. The kidneys process about 180 L (47 gallons!) of blood-derived fluid daily.

Of this amount, less than 1% (1.5 L) typically leaves the body as urine; the rest returns to the circulation.

Step 1: Glomerular Filtration

▶ Describe the forces (pressures) that promote or counteract glomerular filtration.

▶ Compare the intrinsic and extrinsic controls of the glomerular filtration rate.

Glomerular filtration is a passive process in which hydrostatic pressure forces fluids and solutes through a membrane (see Chapter 19). The glomeruli can be viewed as simple mechanical filters because filtrate formation does not consume metabolic energy.

The glomerulus is a much more efficient filter than are other capillary beds. One reason is that its *filtration membrane* has a large surface area and is thousands of times more permeable to water and solutes (Figure 25.9). Furthermore, glomerular blood pressure is much higher than that in other capillary beds (approximately 55 mm Hg as opposed to 18 mm Hg or less), resulting in a much higher *net filtration pressure*, which we will discuss shortly. As a result of these differences, the kidneys produce about 180 L of filtrate daily, in contrast to the 2 to 4 L formed daily by all other capillary beds of the body combined.

Molecules smaller than 3 nm in diameter—such as water, glucose, amino acids, and nitrogenous wastes—pass freely from the blood into the glomerular capsule. As a result, these substances

(1) **colloid osmotic (oncotic) pressure of glomerular blood** (OP_g) and (2) **capsular hydrostatic pressure** (HP_c) exerted by fluids in the glomerular capsule. Using the values shown in the key to Figure 25.11, we calculate the NFP responsible for forming renal filtrate from plasma as 10 mm Hg:

$$NFP = HP_g - (OP_g + HP_c)$$
$$= 55 \text{ mm Hg} - (30 \text{ mm Hg} + 15 \text{ mm Hg})$$
$$= 10 \text{ mm Hg}$$

Glomerular Filtration Rate

The **glomerular filtration rate** or **GFR** is the volume of filtrate formed each minute by the combined activity of all 2 million glomeruli of the kidneys. Factors governing filtration rate at the capillary beds are (1) total surface area available for filtration,

Three major renal processes:

1 ➡ Glomerular filtration

2 ➡ Tubular reabsorption

3 ➡ Tubular secretion

Figure 25.10 **A schematic, uncoiled nephron showing the three major renal processes that adjust plasma composition.** A kidney actually has more than a million nephrons acting in parallel.

usually show similar concentrations in the blood and the glomerular filtrate. Larger molecules pass with greater difficulty, and those larger than 5 nm are generally barred from entering the tubule. Keeping the plasma proteins *in* the capillaries maintains the colloid osmotic (oncotic) pressure of the glomerular blood, preventing the loss of all its water to the renal tubules. The presence of proteins or blood cells in the urine usually indicates a problem with the filtration membrane.

Net Filtration Pressure

The **net filtration pressure (NFP)**, responsible for filtrate formation, involves forces acting at the glomerular bed **(Figure 25.11)**. **Glomerular hydrostatic pressure (HPg)**, which is essentially glomerular blood pressure, is the chief force pushing water and solutes out of the blood and across the filtration membrane. Although theoretically the colloid osmotic pressure in the capsular space of the glomerular capsule "pulls" the filtrate into the tubule, this pressure is essentially zero because virtually no proteins enter the capsule.

The HPg is opposed by two forces that inhibit fluid loss from glomerular capillaries. These filtration-opposing forces are

10 mm Hg

Net filtration pressure

➡ Glomerular (blood) hydrostatic pressure (HP_g = 55 mm Hg)

➡ Blood colloid osmotic pressure (OP_g = 30 mm Hg)

➡ Capsular hydrostatic pressure (HP_c = 15 mm Hg)

Figure 25.11 **Forces determining glomerular filtration and filtration pressure.** The glomerular hydrostatic (blood) pressure is the major factor forcing fluids and solutes out of the blood. This pressure is opposed by the colloid osmotic pressure of the blood and the hydrostatic pressure in the glomerular capsule. The pressure values cited in the diagram are approximate.

25

(2) filtration membrane permeability, and (3) NFP. In adults the normal GFR in both kidneys is 120–125 ml/min. Because glomerular capillaries are exceptionally permeable and have a huge surface area (collectively equal to the surface area of the skin), huge amounts of filtrate can be produced even with the usual modest NFP of 10 mm Hg. The opposite side of this "coin" is that a drop in glomerular pressure of only 18% stops filtration altogether.

The GFR is *directly proportional* to the NFP, so any change in any of the pressures acting at the filtration membrane changes both the NFP and the GFR. In the absence of regulation, an increase in arterial (and glomerular) blood pressure in the kidneys increases the GFR. As we shall see in the next section however, GFR is tightly regulated.

Regulation of Glomerular Filtration

GFR is regulated by both intrinsic and extrinsic controls. These two types of controls serve two different (and sometimes opposing) needs. The kidneys need a relatively constant GFR in order to do their job and maintain extracellular homeostasis. On the other hand, the body as a whole needs a constant blood pressure, and therefore a constant blood volume.

Intrinsic controls (*renal autoregulation*) act locally within the kidney to maintain GFR, while extrinsic controls by the nervous and endocrine systems maintain blood pressure. In extreme changes of blood pressure (mean arterial pressure less than 80 or greater than 180 mm Hg), extrinsic controls take precedence over intrinsic controls. Next we examine both types of control.

Intrinsic Controls: Renal Autoregulation By adjusting its own resistance to blood flow, a process called **renal autoregulation**, the kidney can maintain a nearly constant GFR despite fluctuations in systemic arterial blood pressure. Renal autoregulation entails two types of controls: (1) a *myogenic mechanism* and (2) a *tubuloglomerular feedback mechanism* (**Figure 25.12**, left side).

1. **Myogenic mechanism.** The **myogenic mechanism** (mi″o-jen′ik) reflects the tendency of vascular smooth muscle to contract when stretched. Increasing systemic blood pressure causes the afferent arterioles to constrict, which restricts blood flow into the glomerulus and prevents glomerular blood pressure from rising to damaging levels. Declining systemic blood pressure causes dilation of afferent arterioles and raises glomerular hydrostatic pressure. Both responses help maintain a normal GFR.
2. **Tubuloglomerular feedback mechanism.** Autoregulation by the flow-dependent **tubuloglomerular feedback mechanism** is "directed" by the *macula densa cells* of the *juxtaglomerular apparatus* (see Figure 25.8). These cells, located in the walls of the ascending limb of Henle's loop, respond to filtrate NaCl concentration (which varies directly with filtrate flow rate). When GFR increases, there is insufficient time for reabsorption and the concentration of NaCl in the filtrate remains high. This causes the macula densa cells to release a vasoconstrictor chemical (probably ATP) that causes intense constriction of the afferent arteriole. This constriction hinders blood flow into the

glomerulus, which decreases the NFP and GFR, allowing more time for filtrate processing (NaCl reabsorption).

On the other hand, when the macula densa cells are exposed to slowly flowing filtrate with its low NaCl concentration, ATP release is inhibited, causing vasodilation of the afferent arterioles, as shown in Figure 25.12. This allows more blood to flow into the glomerulus, thus increasing the NFP and GFR.

Autoregulatory mechanisms maintain a relatively constant GFR over an arterial pressure range from about 80 to 180 mm Hg. Consequently, our normal day-to-day activities (such as exercise, sleep, or changes in posture) do not cause large changes in water and solute excretion. However, the intrinsic controls cannot handle extremely low systemic blood pressure, such as might result from serious hemorrhage (*hypovolemic shock*). Once the mean arterial pressure drops below 80 mm Hg, autoregulation ceases.

Extrinsic Controls: Neural and Hormonal Mechanisms The purpose of the extrinsic controls regulating the GFR is to maintain systemic blood pressure—sometimes to the detriment of the kidneys (Figure 25.12, right side).

1. **Sympathetic nervous system controls.** Neural renal controls serve the needs of the body as a whole. When the volume of the extracellular fluid is normal and the sympathetic nervous system is at rest, the renal blood vessels are dilated and renal autoregulation mechanisms prevail. However, during extreme stress or emergency when it is necessary to shunt blood to vital organs, neural controls may overcome renal autoregulatory mechanisms.

   Norepinephrine released by sympathetic nerve fibers (and epinephrine released by the adrenal medulla) acts on alpha-adrenergic receptors on vascular smooth muscle, strongly constricting afferent arterioles, thereby inhibiting filtrate formation. This, in turn, indirectly trips the renin-angiotensin mechanism by stimulating the macula densa cells. The sympathetic nervous system also directly stimulates the granular cells to release renin, as we discuss next.
2. **Renin-angiotensin mechanism.** The **renin-angiotensin mechanism** is triggered when various stimuli cause the granular cells to release the hormone **renin**. Renin acts enzymatically on **angiotensinogen**, a plasma globulin made by the liver, converting it to **angiotensin I**. This, in turn, is converted to **angiotensin II** by **angiotensin converting enzyme (ACE)** associated with the capillary endothelium in various body tissues, particularly the lungs.

   Angiotensin II acts in five ways to stabilize systemic blood pressure and extracellular fluid volume. (1) As a potent vasoconstrictor, angiotensin II activates smooth muscle of arterioles throughout the body, raising mean arterial blood pressure. (2) Angiotensin II stimulates reabsorption of sodium, both directly by acting on renal tubules and indirectly by triggering the release of aldosterone from the adrenal cortex. Because water follows sodium osmotically, blood volume and blood pressure rise (Figure 25.12). (3) Angiotensin II stimulates the hypothalamus to release

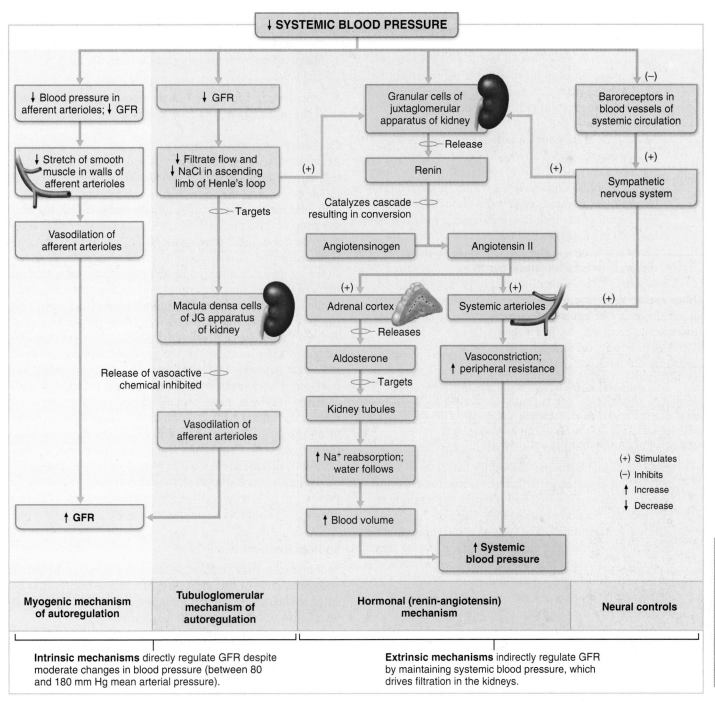

Figure 25.12 Physiological mechanisms regulating glomerular filtration rate (GFR) in the kidneys. (Note that while the extrinsic controls are aimed at maintaining blood pressure, they also maintain GFR since blood pressure drives filtration in the kidneys.)

antidiuretic hormone and activates the hypothalamic thirst center, both of which increase blood volume (see Chapter 26). (4) Angiotensin II also increases fluid reabsorption by decreasing peritubular capillary hydrostatic pressure. This pressure drop occurs because the efferent arterioles constrict, and the downstream drop in hydrostatic pressure allows more fluid to move back into the peritubular capillary bed. (5) Finally, angiotensin II targets

the glomerular mesangial cells, causing them to contract and reduce the GFR by decreasing the total surface area of glomerular capillaries available for filtration.

While this seems like a daunting list at first, it will help if you remember that all of the effects of angiotensin II are aimed at restoring blood volume and blood pressure. Of angiotensin II's many effects, the first two are the most important.

Several factors acting independently or collectively can trigger renin release.

- *Reduced stretch of the granular cells.* A drop in mean systemic blood pressure below 80 mm Hg (as might be due to hemorrhage, dehydration, etc.) reduces the stretch of the granular cells and stimulates them to release more renin.
- *Stimulation of the granular cells by input from activated macula densa cells.* When macula densa cells sense low NaCl concentration (slowly moving filtrate), they signal the granular cells to release renin. This signal may be *decreased* release of ATP (also thought to be the tubuloglomerular feedback messenger), *increased* release of the prostaglandin PGE$_2$, or both.
- *Direct stimulation of granular cells* via β$_1$-adrenergic receptors by renal sympathetic nerves.

Other Factors Affecting GFR   Renal cells produce a battery of chemicals, many of which act as paracrines (local signaling molecules).

1. *Prostaglandin E$_2$ (PGE$_2$):* The vasodilatory paracrine PGE$_2$, in addition to its role discussed above, counteracts vasoconstriction by norepinephrine and angiotensin II within the kidney. The adaptive value of these opposing actions is to prevent renal damage while responding to body demands to increase peripheral resistance.
2. *Intrarenal angiotensin II:* Although we usually think of angiotensin II as a hormone, the kidney makes its own, locally acting angiotensin II that reinforces the effects of hormonal angiotensin II. It also dampens the resulting renal vasoconstriction by causing PGE$_2$ release.
3. *Adenosine:* Adenosine can be released as such or produced extracellularly from ATP released by macula densa cells. Although it functions as a vasodilator systemically, adenosine constricts the renal vasculature.

HOMEOSTATIC IMBALANCE

Abnormally low urinary output (less than 50 ml/day), called *anuria* (ah-nu′re-ah), may indicate that glomerular blood pressure is too low to cause filtration. However, renal failure and anuria can result from situations in which the nephrons cease to function for a variety of other reasons, including acute nephritis, transfusion reactions, and crush injuries. ■

CHECK YOUR UNDERSTANDING

7. Extrinsic and intrinsic controls of GFR serve two different purposes. What are they?
8. Calculate net filtration pressure given the following values: glomerular hydrostatic pressure = 50 mm Hg, blood colloid osmotic pressure = 25 mm Hg, capsular hydrostatic pressure = 20 Hg.
9. Describe two main ways in which angiotensin II increases blood pressure and blood volume.

For answers, see Appendix G.

Step 2: Tubular Reabsorption

▶ Describe the mechanisms underlying water and solute reabsorption from the renal tubules into the peritubular capillaries.

▶ Describe how sodium and water reabsorption is regulated in the distal tubule and collecting duct.

Our total plasma volume filters into the renal tubules about every 22 minutes, so all our plasma would be drained away as urine in less than 30 minutes were it not for the fact that most of the tubule contents are quickly reclaimed and returned to the blood. This reclamation process, called **tubular reabsorption**, is a selective *transepithelial process* that begins as soon as the filtrate enters the proximal tubules. To reach the blood, reabsorbed substances follow either the *transcellular* or *paracellular route* **(Figure 25.13)**. In the transcellular route, transported substances move through the *luminal membrane*, the cytosol, and the *basolateral membrane* of the tubule cell and then the endothelium of the peritubular capillaries. Movement of substances in the paracellular route *between* the tubule cells is limited because these cells are connected by tight junctions. In the proximal nephron, however, these tight junctions are "leaky" and allow some important ions (Ca^{2+}, Mg^{2+}, K^+, and some Na^+) through the paracellular route.

Given healthy kidneys, virtually all organic nutrients such as glucose and amino acids are completely reabsorbed to maintain or restore normal plasma concentrations. On the other hand, the reabsorption of water and many ions is continuously regulated and adjusted in response to hormonal signals. Depending on the substances transported, the reabsorption process may be *passive* (no ATP required) or *active* (at least one of its steps is driven by ATP directly or indirectly).

Sodium Reabsorption

Sodium ions are the single most abundant cation in the filtrate, and about 80% of the energy used for active transport is devoted to their reabsorption. Sodium reabsorption is almost always active and via the transcellular route.

In general, two basic processes that promote active Na^+ reabsorption occur in each tubule segment. First, Na^+ is actively transported out of the tubule cell by *primary active transport*—a Na^+-K^+ ATPase pump present in the basolateral membrane **(Figure 25.14, ①)**. From there, Na^+ is swept along by the bulk flow of water into adjacent peritubular capillaries. This bulk flow of water and solutes into the peritubular capillaries is rapid because the blood there has low hydrostatic pressure and high osmotic pressure (remember, most proteins remain in the blood instead of being filtered out into the tubule).

Second, active pumping of Na^+ from the tubule cells results in a strong electrochemical gradient that favors its passive entry at the luminal face via *secondary active transport* (symport or antiport) carriers (Figure 25.14, ②, ③) or via facilitated diffusion through channels. This occurs because (1) the pump maintains the intracellular Na^+ concentration at low levels, and (2) the K^+ pumped into the tubule cells almost immediately diffuses out into the interstitial fluid via leakage channels, leaving the interior of the tubule cell with a net negative charge.

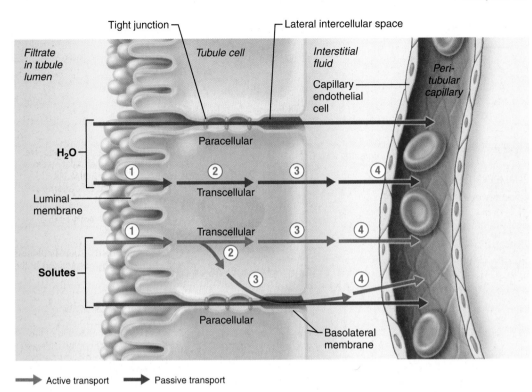

Movement via the transcellular route involves:

① Transport across the luminal membrane.

② Diffusion through the cytosol.

③ Transport across the basolateral membrane. (Often involves the lateral intercellular spaces because membrane transporters transport ions into these spaces.)

④ Movement through the interstitial fluid and into the capillary.

The paracellular route involves:
- Movement through leaky tight junctions, particularly in the PCT.

Figure 25.13 Transcellular and paracellular routes of tubular reabsorption. Generally, fluids and solutes move into the peritubular capillaries through intercellular clefts. For simplicity, transporters, ion channels, intercellular clefts, and aquaporins are not depicted.

Because each tubule segment plays a slightly different role in reabsorption, the precise mechanism by which Na^+ is reabsorbed at the luminal membrane varies.

Reabsorption of Nutrients, Water, and Ions

The reabsorption of Na^+ by primary active transport provides the energy and the means for reabsorbing almost every other substance, including water. Substances reabsorbed by **secondary active transport** (the "push" comes from the gradient created by Na^+-K^+ pumping at the basolateral membrane) include glucose, amino acids, lactate, and vitamins. In nearly all these cases, a luminal carrier moves Na^+ down its concentration gradient as it cotransports (symports) another solute (Figure 25.14, ③). Cotransported solutes diffuse (via different transport proteins) across the basolateral membrane before moving into the peritubular capillaries. Although there is some overlap of carriers, the transport systems for the various solutes are quite specific *and limited*.

There is a **transport maximum (T_m)** for nearly every substance that is reabsorbed using a transport protein in the membrane. The T_m (reported in mg/min) reflects the number of transport proteins in the renal tubules available to ferry each particular substance. In general, there are plenty of transporters and therefore high T_m values for substances such as glucose that need to be retained, and few or no transporters for substances of no use to the body.

When the transporters are saturated—that is, all bound to the substance they transport—the excess is excreted in urine.

This is what happens in individuals who become hyperglycemic because of uncontrolled diabetes mellitus. As plasma levels of glucose approach and exceed 180 mg/dl, the glucose T_m is exceeded and large amounts of glucose may be lost in the urine even though the renal tubules are still functioning normally.

In **passive tubular reabsorption**, which encompasses osmosis, diffusion, and facilitated diffusion, substances move down their electrochemical gradients without the use of ATP. The movement of Na^+ and other solutes establishes a strong osmotic gradient, and water moves by osmosis into the peritubular capillaries, a process aided by transmembrane proteins called **aquaporins** that form water channels across cell membranes (Figure 25.14, ④). In continuously water-permeable regions of the renal tubules, such as the PCT, aquaporins are constant components of the tubule cell membranes. Because these channels are always present, the body is "obliged" to absorb water in the proximal nephron regardless of its state of over- or underhydration. This water flow is referred to as **obligatory water reabsorption**. Aquaporins are virtually absent in the luminal membranes of the collecting duct unless antidiuretic hormone (ADH) is present.

As water leaves the tubules, the concentration of solutes in the filtrate increases and, if able, they too begin to follow their concentration gradients into the peritubular capillaries. This phenomenon of solutes following solvent explains the passive reabsorption of a number of solutes present in the filtrate, such as lipid-soluble substances, certain ions, and some urea (Figure 25.14, ⑤, ⑥). It also explains in part why lipid-soluble drugs and environmental toxins are difficult to excrete: Since lipid-soluble compounds can generally pass through membranes,

① At the basolateral membrane, Na$^+$ is pumped into the interstitial space by the Na$^+$-K$^+$ ATPase. Active Na$^+$ transport creates concentration gradients that drive:

② "Downhill" Na$^+$ entry at the luminal membrane.

③ Reabsorption of organic nutrients and certain ions by cotransport at the luminal membrane.

④ Reabsorption of water by osmosis. Water reabsorption increases the concentration of the solutes that are left behind. These solutes can then be reabsorbed as they move down their concentration gradients:

⑤ Lipid-soluble substances diffuse by the transcellular route.

⑥ Cl$^-$ (and other anions), K$^+$, and urea diffuse by the paracellular route.

Figure 25.14 Reabsorption by PCT cells. Though not illustrated here, most organic nutrients reabsorbed in the PCT move through the basolateral membrane by facilitated diffusion. Microvilli have been omitted for simplicity.

they will follow their concentration gradients and be reabsorbed, even if this is "not desirable."

As they move through the tubule cells into the peritubular capillary blood, Na$^+$ ions also establish an electrical gradient that favors passive reabsorption of anions (primarily Cl$^-$) to restore electrical neutrality in the filtrate and plasma (Figure 25.14, ⑥).

Any plasma proteins that squeeze through the filtration membrane are removed from the filtrate in the proximal tubule by endocytosis and digested to their amino acids, which are moved into the peritubular blood.

Reabsorptive Capabilities of the Renal Tubules and Collecting Ducts

Table 25.1 compares the reabsorptive abilities of various regions of the renal tubules and collecting ducts.

Proximal Convoluted Tubule The entire renal tubule is involved in reabsorption to some degree, but the PCT cells are by far the most active "reabsorbers" and the events just described occur mainly in this tubular segment. Normally, the PCT reab-

sorbs *all* of the glucose, lactate, and amino acids in the filtrate and 65% of the Na$^+$ and water. Additionally, 80% of the filtered bicarbonate (HCO$_3$$^-$), 60% of the Cl$^-$, and about 55% of the K$^+$ are reclaimed in the PCT. The bulk of the reabsorption of electrolytes is accomplished by the time the filtrate reaches the loop of Henle. Nearly all of the uric acid and about half of the urea are reabsorbed in the proximal tubule, but both are later secreted back into the filtrate.

Loop of Henle Beyond the PCT, the permeability of the tubule epithelium changes dramatically. Here, for the first time, water reabsorption is not coupled to solute reabsorption. Water can leave the descending limb of the loop of Henle but *not* the ascending limb, where aquaporins are scarce or absent in the tubule membrane. For reasons that we will explain shortly, these permeability differences play a vital role in the kidneys' ability to form dilute and concentrated urine.

The rule for water is that it leaves the descending (but not the ascending) limb of Henle's loop, and the opposite is true for solutes. Virtually no solute reabsorption occurs in the descending

TABLE 25.1	Reabsorption Capabilities of Different Segments of the Renal Tubules and Collecting Ducts	
TUBULE SEGMENT	**SUBSTANCE REABSORBED**	**MECHANISM**

Proximal Convoluted Tubule

	Sodium ions (Na^+)	Primary active transport via basolateral Na^+-K^+ pump; sets up electrochemical gradient for passive solute diffusion, osmosis, and secondary active transport (cotransport) with Na^+
	Virtually all nutrients (glucose, amino acids, vitamins)	Secondary active transport with Na^+
	Cations (K^+, Mg^{2+}, Ca^{2+}, and others)	Passive paracellular diffusion driven by electrochemical gradient
	Cl^-	Passive paracellular diffusion driven by electrochemical gradient
	HCO_3^-	Secondary active transport linked to H^+ secretion and Na^+ reabsorption (see Chapter 26)
	Water	Osmosis; driven by solute reabsorption (obligatory)
	Lipid-soluble solutes	Passive diffusion driven by the concentration gradient created by reabsorption of water
	Urea	Passive paracellular diffusion driven by chemical gradient; some transcellular facilitated diffusion may also occur
	Small proteins	Endocytosed by tubule cells and digested to amino acids within tubule cells

Loop of Henle

Descending limb	Water	Osmosis
Ascending limb	Na^+, Cl^+, K^+	Secondary active transport of Cl^-, Na^+, and K^+ via Na^+-K^+-$2Cl^-$ cotransporter in thick portion; paracellular diffusion; Na^+-H^+ antiport
	Ca^{2+}, Mg^{2+}	Passive paracellular diffusion driven by electrochemical gradient

Distal Convoluted Tubule

| | Na^+, Cl^- | Primary active Na^+ transport at basolateral membrane; secondary active transport at luminal membrane via Na^+-Cl^- symporter and channels; aldosterone-regulated at distal portion |
| | Ca^{2+} | Passive uptake via PTH-modulated channels in luminal membrane; primary and secondary active transport (antiport with Na^+) in basolateral membrane |

Collecting Duct

	Na^+, H^+, K^+, HCO_3^-, Cl^-	Primary active transport of Na^+ (requires aldosterone); passive paracellular diffusion of some Cl^-; cotransport of H^+, Cl^-, and HCO_3^-; K^+ is both reabsorbed and secreted (aldosterone dependent), usually resulting in net K^+ secretion
	Water	Osmosis; controlled (facultative) water reabsorption; ADH required to insert aquaporins
	Urea	Facilitated diffusion in response to concentration gradient in the deep medulla region; recycles and contributes to medullary osmotic gradient

limb, but both active and passive reabsorption of solute occurs in the ascending limb. In the thin portion of the ascending limb, Na^+ moves passively down the concentration gradient created by water reabsorption. A Na^+-K^+-$2Cl^-$ symporter is the main means of Na^+ entry at the luminal surface in the thick portion of the ascending limb. A Na^+-K^+ ATPase operates at the basolateral membrane to create the ionic gradient that drives the symporter. The thick ascending limb also has Na^+-H^+ antiporters. In addition, some 50% of Na^+ passes via the paracellular route in this region.

Distal Convoluted Tubule and Collecting Duct By the time the DCT is reached, only about 10% of the originally filtered NaCl and 25% of the water remain in the tubule. Most reabsorption from this point on depends on the body's needs at the time and is regulated by hormones (mainly aldosterone for Na^+, ADH for water, and PTH for Ca^{2+} as we will describe in Chapter 26). If necessary, nearly all of the water and Na^+ reaching these regions can be reclaimed.

In the absence of antidiuretic hormone (ADH), the collecting ducts are relatively impermeable to water. Reabsorption of more water depends on the presence of ADH, which makes the collecting ducts more permeable to water by inserting aquaporins into the collecting duct luminal membranes.

Aldosterone "fine-tunes" reabsorption of the remaining Na^+. Decreased blood volume or blood pressure, low extracellular Na^+ concentration (hyponatremia), or high extracellular K^+ concentration (hyperkalemia) can cause the adrenal cortex to release aldosterone to the blood. Except for hyperkalemia (which *directly* stimulates the adrenal cortex to secrete aldosterone), these conditions promote the renin-angiotensin mechanism, which in turn prompts the release of aldosterone (see Figure 25.12). Aldosterone targets the principal cells of the collecting ducts and cells of the distal portion of the DCT (prodding them to synthesize and retain more luminal Na^+ and K^+ channels, and more basolateral Na^+-K^+ ATPases). As a result, little or no Na^+ leaves the body in urine. In the absence of aldosterone, much less Na^+ is reabsorbed by these segments, resulting in Na^+ losses of about 2% of Na^+ filtered daily, an amount incompatible with life.

Physiologically, aldosterone's role is to increase blood volume, and therefore blood pressure, by enhancing Na^+ reabsorption. In general, water follows Na^+ if it can. Aldosterone also reduces blood K^+ concentrations because aldosterone-induced reabsorption of Na^+ is coupled to K^+ secretion in the principal cells. That is, as Na^+ enters, K^+ moves into the lumen.

In contrast to aldosterone, which acts to conserve Na^+, atrial natriuretic peptide (ANP) reduces blood Na^+, thereby decreasing blood volume and blood pressure. Released by cardiac atrial cells when blood volume or blood pressure is elevated, ANP exerts several effects that lower blood Na^+ content, including direct inhibition of Na^+ reabsorption at the collecting ducts. These actions are described more fully in Chapter 26 (see Figure 26.9).

Step 3: Tubular Secretion

▶ Describe the importance of tubular secretion and list several substances that are secreted.

The failure of tubule cells to reabsorb some solutes is an important way of clearing plasma of unwanted substances. Another way is **tubular secretion**—essentially, reabsorption in reverse. Substances such as H^+, K^+, NH_4^+, creatinine, and certain organic acids either move into the filtrate from the peritubular capillaries through the tubule cells or are synthesized in the tubule cells and secreted. As a result, the urine eventually excreted contains *both filtered* and *secreted substances*. With one major exception (K^+), the PCT is the main site of secretion, but the cortical parts of the collecting ducts are also active (see Figure 25.18, p. 983).

Tubular secretion is important for

1. *Disposing of substances, such as certain drugs and metabolites, that are tightly bound to plasma proteins.* Because plasma proteins are generally not filtered, the substances they bind are not filtered and so must be secreted.
2. *Eliminating undesirable substances or end products that have been reabsorbed by passive processes.* Urea and uric acid, two nitrogenous wastes, are both handled in this way. Urea handling in the nephron is complicated and will be discussed on p. 981, but the net effect is that 40–50% of the urea in the filtrate is excreted.
3. *Ridding the body of excess K^+.* Because virtually all K^+ present in the filtrate is reabsorbed in the PCT and ascending loop of Henle, nearly all K^+ in urine is from aldosterone-driven active tubular secretion into the late DCT and collecting ducts.
4. *Controlling blood pH.* When blood pH drops toward the acidic end of its homeostatic range, the renal tubule cells actively secrete more H^+ into the filtrate and retain and generate more HCO_3^- (a base). As a result, the blood pH rises and the urine drains off the excess H^+. Conversely, when blood pH approaches the alkaline end of its range, Cl^- is reabsorbed instead of HCO_3^-, which is allowed to leave the body in urine. We will discuss the kidneys' role in pH homeostasis in more detail in Chapter 26.

CHECK YOUR UNDERSTANDING

10. In what part of the nephron does the majority of reabsorption occur?
11. How are primary and secondary active transport processes (both shown in Figure 25.14) different?
12. How does the movement of Na^+ drive the reabsorption of water and solutes?
13. List several substances that are secreted into the kidney tubules.

For answers, see Appendix G.

Regulation of Urine Concentration and Volume

▶ Describe the mechanisms responsible for the medullary osmotic gradient.

▶ Explain formation of dilute versus concentrated urine.

One crucial renal function is to keep the solute concentration of body fluids constant. We use *osmolality* to measure the amount of solutes in body fluids. A solution's **osmolality** (oz″mo-lal′ĭ-te) is the number of solute particles dissolved in 1 kg of water and reflects the solution's ability to cause osmosis. For any solution interfacing with a selectively permeable membrane, this ability, called *osmotic activity*, is determined only by the number of solute particles unable to pass through the membrane (called nonpenetrating solute particles) and is independent of their type. For example, 10 sodium ions have the same osmotic activity as 10 glucose molecules or 10 amino acids in the same volume of water.

Because 1 *osmol* (equivalent to 1 mole of particles) is a fairly large unit, the **milliosmol (mOsm)** (mil″e-oz′mōl), equal to 0.001 osmol, is generally used. In the discussion that follows, we use mOsm to mean mOsm/kg.

The kidneys keep the solute load of body fluids constant at about 300 mOsm, the osmotic concentration of blood plasma, by regulating urine concentration and volume. The kidneys accomplish this feat using **countercurrent mechanisms**. In the kidneys, the term *countercurrent* means that fluid flows in opposite directions through adjacent segments of the same tube connected by a hairpin turn (see Figure 25.16). These countercurrent mechanisms are (1) the interaction between the flow of filtrate through the ascending and descending limbs of the long loops of Henle of juxtamedullary nephrons (the *countercurrent multiplier*), and (2) the flow of blood through the ascending and descending portions of the vasa recta blood vessels (the *countercurrent exchanger*).* These countercurrent mechanisms establish and maintain an osmotic gradient extending from the cortex through the depths of the medulla (**Figure 25.15**). This gradient allows the kidneys to vary urine concentration dramatically.

The osmolality of the filtrate entering the PCT is identical to that of plasma, about 300 mOsm. As we described earlier, because of PCT reabsorption of water *and* solutes, the filtrate is still isosmotic with plasma by the time it reaches the descending limb of the loop of Henle. However, its osmolality increases from 300 to about 1200 mOsm in the deepest part of the medulla (**Figure 25.16a**).

How does this increase in concentration occur? The answer lies in the unique workings of the long loops of Henle of the juxtamedullary nephrons, and the vasa recta. Notice in Figure 25.16 that in each case the fluids involved—filtrate in the loops of Henle and blood in the vasa recta—first descend and then ascend through parallel limbs.

The Countercurrent Multiplier

First, we will follow filtrate processing through the loop of Henle, as portrayed in Figure 25.16a, to see how the loop functions as a **countercurrent multiplier** to establish the osmotic

*The term "countercurrent" is commonly misunderstood to mean that the direction of fluid flow in the loops of Henle is opposite that of the blood in the vasa recta. In fact, there is no one-to-one relationship between individual loops of Henle and capillaries of the vasa recta as might be suggested by two-dimensional diagrams such as Figure 25.16. Instead, there are many tubules and capillaries packed together. Each tubule is surrounded by many blood vessels, whose flow is not necessarily counter to flow in that tubule (see Figure 25.7).

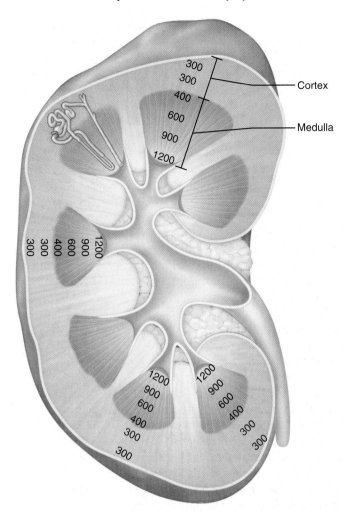

Figure 25.15 Osmotic gradient in the renal medulla. The osmolality of the interstitial fluid in the renal cortex is isotonic at 300 mOsm, but the osmolality of the interstitial fluid in the renal medulla increases progressively from 300 mOsm at the cortico-medullary junction to 1200 mOsm at the medullary-pelvis junction. One greatly enlarged nephron and its collecting duct are depicted to show their positions relative to the medullary gradient.

gradient. The countercurrent multiplier functions because of two factors:

1. **The descending limb of the loop of Henle is relatively impermeable to solutes and freely permeable to water.** Water passes osmotically out of the filtrate all along this limb because the osmolality of the medullary interstitial fluid increases all along the descending limb. (We will explain the mechanism of this increase shortly). The filtrate osmolality reaches its highest point (1200 mOsm) at the bend of the loop.

2. **The ascending limb is permeable to solutes, but not to water.** As the filtrate rounds the bend into the ascending limb, the tubule permeability changes, becoming impermeable to water and selectively permeable to salt. The Na^+ and Cl^- concentration in the filtrate entering the ascending limb is very high (and interstitial fluid concentrations of these two ions are lower). Na^+ and Cl^- reabsorption in

Filtrate entering the loop of Henle is isosmotic to both blood plasma and cortical interstitial fluid.

The **descending limb:**
• Permeable to H_2O
• Impermeable to NaCl
As filtrate flows, it becomes increasingly concentrated as H_2O leaves the tubule by osmosis. The filtrate osmolality increases from 300 to 1200 mOsm.

Loop of Henle

Osmolality of interstitial fluid (mOsm)

300 — Cortex

400

600 — Outer medulla

900

Inner medulla

1200

Blood from efferent arteriole

To vein

Vasa recta

→ Active transport

→ Passive transport

▬ Water impermeable

The **ascending limb:**
• Impermeable to H_2O
• Permeable to NaCl
Filtrate becomes increasingly dilute as NaCl leaves, eventually becoming hypo-osmotic to blood at 100 mOsm in the cortex. NaCl leaving the ascending limb increases the osmolality of the medullary interstitial fluid.

The **vasa recta:**
• Highly permeable to H_2O and solute
• Nearly isosmotic to interstitial fluid due to sluggish blood flow
Blood becomes more concentrated as it descends deeper into the medulla and less concentrated as it approaches the cortex.

(a) Countercurrent multiplier. The long loops of Henle of the juxtamedullary nephrons create the medullary osmotic gradient.

(b) Countercurrent exchanger. The vasa recta preserve the medullary gradient while removing reabsorbed water and solutes.

Figure 25.16 Countercurrent mechanism for establishing and maintaining the medullary osmotic gradient. Notice in **(a)** that the descending limb of the loop of Henle produces increasingly salty filtrate, while the ascending limb uses this high salt concentration to establish the high osmolality of the interstitial fluid in the medulla and the medullary osmotic gradient.

the ascending limb is both passive (mostly in the thin segment) and active (via the Na^+-K^+-$2Cl^-$ cotransporter in the thick segment). As Na^+ and Cl^- are extruded from the filtrate into the medullary interstitial fluid, they contribute to the high osmolality there. Because it loses salt but not water, the filtrate in the ascending limb becomes increasingly dilute. Finally, at 100 mOsm at the DCT, it is hypo-osmotic, or hypotonic, to blood plasma and cortical interstitial fluids.

Notice in Figure 25.16 that there is a constant difference in filtrate concentration (200 mOsm) between the two limbs of the loop of Henle, and between the ascending limb and the interstitial fluid. This difference reflects the power of the ascending limb's NaCl pumps, which are just powerful enough to create a 200 mOsm difference between the inside and outside of the ascending limb. A 200 mOsm gradient by itself would not be enough to allow excretion of very concentrated urine. The beauty of this system lies in the fact that, because of countercurrent flow, the loop of

Henle is able to "multiply" these small changes in solute concentration into a gradient change along the vertical length of the loop (both inside and outside) that is closer to 900 mOsm (1200 mOsm – 300 mOsm).

Although the two limbs of the loop of Henle are not in direct contact with each other, they are close enough to influence each other's exchanges with the interstitial fluid they share. Water diffusing out of the descending limb leaves behind an increasingly "salty" filtrate that the ascending limb then uses to raise the osmolality of the medullary interstitial fluid. Furthermore, the more NaCl the ascending limb extrudes, the more water diffuses out of the descending limb and the saltier the filtrate in the descending limb becomes. This establishes a positive feedback cycle that produces the high osmolality of the fluids in the descending limb and the interstitial fluid.

Urea Recycling and the Medullary Osmotic Gradient

In addition to Na^+, urea forms an important part of the medullary osmotic gradient. As shown in **Figure 25.17**, urea enters the filtrate by facilitated diffusion in the ascending thin limb of the loop of Henle. As the filtrate moves on, water is usually reabsorbed in the cortical collecting duct, leaving urea behind. When filtrate reaches the collecting duct in the deep medullary region, urea, now highly concentrated, is transported by facilitated diffusion out of the tubule into the interstitial fluid of the medulla, forming a pool of urea that recycles back into the thin limb of the loop of Henle. This pool of urea contributes substantially to the high osmolality in the medulla.

Antidiuretic hormone (ADH), which stimulates excretion of highly concentrated urine (as we will see shortly), enhances urea transport in the medullary collecting duct. When ADH is present, urea recycling is enhanced, the medullary osmotic gradient is enhanced, and more concentrated urine can be formed.

The Countercurrent Exchanger

As shown in Figure 25.16b, the vasa recta function as **countercurrent exchangers**, maintaining the osmotic gradient established by the cycling of salt while delivering blood to cells in the area and removing reabsorbed water and solutes. These vessels receive only about 10% of the renal blood supply, making blood flow through the vasa recta sluggish. Moreover, they are freely permeable to water and NaCl, allowing blood to make passive exchanges with the surrounding interstitial fluid. Consequently, as the blood flows into the medullary depths, it loses water and gains salt (becomes hypertonic). Then, as it emerges from the medulla into the cortex, the process is reversed: It picks up water and loses salt. The water picked up by the ascending vasa recta includes not only water lost from the descending vasa recta, but also water reabsorbed from the loop of Henle and collecting duct. As a result, the volume of blood at the end of the vasa recta is greater than at the beginning.

Because blood leaving and reentering the cortex via the vasa recta has nearly the same solute concentration, the vessels of the vasa recta act as countercurrent exchangers. This system does not create the medullary gradient, but it protects it by preventing rapid removal of salt from the medullary interstitial space, and by removing reabsorbed water.

Formation of Dilute or Concentrated Urine

As we have just seen, the kidneys go to a great deal of trouble to create the medullary osmotic gradient. What is its purpose? Without this gradient, you would not be able to raise the concentration of urine above 300 mOsm—the osmolality of interstitial fluid. As a result, you would not be able to excrete excess solutes to lower your body's osmolality.

Controlling the reabsorption of water from filtrate in the collecting ducts in order to adjust the body's osmolality is the job of **antidiuretic hormone (ADH)**. As its name reveals, ADH inhibits *diuresis* (di″u-re′sis), or urine output. It accomplishes this via a second-messenger system using cyclic AMP that causes insertion of aquaporins into the luminal membrane of the principal cells of the collecting ducts. The amount of ADH determines the number of aquaporins in the collecting ducts and so the amount of water that is reabsorbed there.

Dilute Urine Tubular filtrate is diluted as it travels through the ascending limb of the loop of Henle, so all the kidney needs to do to secrete dilute (hypo-osmotic) urine is allow the filtrate to continue on its way into the renal pelvis (Figure 25.17a). When ADH is not being released by the posterior pituitary, that is exactly what happens. The collecting ducts remain essentially impermeable to water due to the absence of aquaporins in their luminal cell membranes, and no further water reabsorption occurs. Moreover, as noted, Na^+ and selected other ions can be removed from the filtrate by DCT and collecting duct cells so that urine becomes even more dilute before entering the renal pelvis. The osmolality of urine can plunge as low as 50 mOsm, about one-sixth the concentration of glomerular filtrate or blood plasma.

Concentrated Urine The formation of concentrated urine depends on the medullary osmotic gradient and the presence of ADH. In the distal tubules, the filtrate osmolality is approximately 100 mOsm, but as the filtrate flows through the collecting ducts and is subjected to the hyperosmolar conditions in the medulla, water rapidly leaves the filtrate, followed by urea (Figure 25.17b and **Figure 25.18e**). Depending on the amount of ADH released (which is keyed to the level of body hydration), urine concentration may rise as high as 1200 mOsm, the concentration of interstitial fluid in the deepest part of the medulla. With maximal ADH secretion, up to 99% of the water in the filtrate is reabsorbed and returned to the blood, and half a liter per day of highly concentrated urine is excreted. The ability of our kidneys to produce such concentrated urine is critically tied to our ability to survive without water. Water reabsorption that depends on the presence of ADH is called **facultative water reabsorption**.

ADH is released more or less continuously unless the blood solute concentration drops too low. Release of ADH is enhanced by any event that raises plasma osmolality above 300 mOsm, such as sweating or diarrhea, or by greatly reduced blood volume or blood pressure (see Chapter 26). Although release of ADH is the "signal" to produce concentrated urine that opens

Active transport

Passive transport

Figure 25.17 Mechanisms for forming dilute and concentrated urine. (a) In the absence of ADH, dilute filtrate produced by the countercurrent mechanism remains dilute as it passes through the collecting duct. **(b)** In the presence of maximal ADH, concentrated urine is excreted. ADH causes insertion of aquaporins in luminal membranes of principal cells of the collecting duct. Consequently water rapidly leaves the filtrate in the collecting duct. ADH also enhances urea recycling by increasing the number of urea transporters. More urea diffuses out of the collecting duct, contributing to the medullary osmotic gradient.

the door for water reabsorption (through aquaporins), the kidneys' ability to respond to this signal depends on the high medullary osmotic gradient.

Diuretics

There are several types of **diuretics**, chemicals that enhance urinary output. An *osmotic diuretic* is a substance that is not reabsorbed and that carries water out with it (for example, the high blood glucose levels of a diabetes mellitus patient). Alcohol, essentially a sedative, encourages diuresis by inhibiting release of

ADH. Other diuretics increase urine flow by inhibiting Na^+ reabsorption and the obligatory water reabsorption that normally follows. Examples include caffeine (found in coffee, tea, and colas) and many drugs prescribed for hypertension or the edema of congestive heart failure. Common diuretics inhibit Na^+-associated symporters. "Loop diuretics" [like furosemide (Lasix)] are powerful because they inhibit formation of the medullary gradient by acting at the ascending limb of Henle's loop. Thiazides are less potent and act at the DCT.

25

Milliosmols

→ Active transport (primary or secondary)
⇒ Passive transport

Figure 25.18 Summary of tubular reabsorption and secretion. The glomerulus provides the filtrate processed by the renal tubule. The various regions of the renal tubule carry out reabsorption and secretion and maintain a gradient of osmolality within the medullary interstitial fluid. Varying osmolality at different points in the interstitial fluid is symbolized by gradients of color in the overview figure at left. **(a–d)** The main transport functions of the four regions of the nephron tubule. **(e)** Summary of transport activities occurring in both the cortical and medullary regions of the collecting duct.

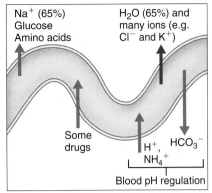

(a) Proximal convoluted tubule:
- 65% of filtrate volume reabsorbed
- Na^+, glucose, amino acids, and other nutrients actively transported; H_2O and many ions follow passively
- H^+ and NH_4^+ secretion and HCO_3^- reabsorption to maintain blood pH (see Chapter 26)
- Some drugs are secreted

(b) Descending limb of loop of Henle
- Freely permeable to H_2O
- Not permeable to NaCl
- Filtrate becomes increasingly concentrated as H_2O leaves by osmosis

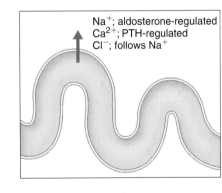

(c) Ascending limb of loop of Henle
- Impermeable to H_2O
- Permeable to NaCl
- Filtrate becomes increasingly dilute as salt is reabsorbed

(d) Distal convoluted tubule
- Na^+ reabsorption regulated by aldosterone
- Ca^{2+} reabsortion regulated by parathyroid hormone (PTH)
- Cl^- cotransported with Na^+

(e) Collecting duct
- H_2O reabsorption through aquaporins regulated by ADH
- Na^+ reabsorption and K^+ secretion regulated by aldosterone
- H^+ and HCO_3^- reabsorption or secretion to maintain blood pH (see Chapter 26)
- Urea reabsorption increased by ADH

Renal Clearance

▶ Define renal clearance and explain how this value summarizes the way a substance is handled by the kidney.

Renal clearance refers to the volume of plasma that is cleared of a particular substance in a given time, usually 1 minute. Renal clearance tests are done to determine the GFR, which allows us to detect glomerular damage and follow the progress of renal disease.

The renal clearance rate (RC) of any substance, in ml/min, is calculated from the equation

$$RC = UV/P$$

where

U = concentration of the substance in urine (mg/ml)

V = flow rate of urine formation (ml/min)

P = concentration of the substance in plasma (mg/ml)

Because it is freely filtered and neither reabsorbed nor secreted by the kidneys, *inulin* (in′u-lin) is the standard used to determine the GFR. A polysaccharide with a molecular weight of approximately 5000, inulin has a renal clearance value equal to the GFR. When inulin is infused such that its plasma concentration is 1 mg/ml ($P = 1$ mg/ml), then generally $U = 125$ mg/ml, and $V = 1$ ml/min. Therefore, its renal clearance is RC = $(125 \times 1)/1 = 125$ ml/min, meaning that in 1 minute the kidneys have removed (cleared) all the inulin present in 125 ml of plasma.

The clearance value tells us about the net handling of a substance by the kidneys. There are three possible cases:

- A clearance value less than that of inulin means that a substance is reabsorbed. An example is urea with an RC of 70 ml/min, meaning that of the 125 ml of glomerular filtrate formed each minute, approximately 70 ml is completely cleared of urea, while the urea in the remaining 55 ml is recovered and returned to the plasma. If the RC is zero (such as for glucose in healthy individuals), reabsorption is complete or the substance is not filtered.
- If the RC is equal to that of inulin, there is no net reabsorption or secretion.
- If the RC is greater than that of inulin, the tubule cells are secreting the substance into the filtrate. This is the case with most drug metabolites. Knowing a drug's renal clearance value is essential because if it is high, the drug dosage must also be high and administered frequently to maintain a therapeutic level.

Creatinine, which has an RC of 140 ml/min, is freely filtered but also secreted in small amounts. It is often used nevertheless to give a "quick and dirty" estimate of GFR.

HOMEOSTATIC IMBALANCE

Chronic renal disease, defined as a GFR of less than 60 ml/min for at least three months, often develops silently and insidiously over many years. Filtrate formation decreases gradually, nitrogenous wastes accumulate in the blood, and the blood pH drifts toward the acidic range. The leading cause of chronic renal disease is diabetes mellitus (44% of new cases), with hypertension a close second (28% of new cases). Other causes include repeated kidney infections, physical trauma, and chemical poisoning by heavy metals.

In **renal failure** (GFR < 15 ml/min), filtrate formation decreases or stops completely. Ionic and pH imbalances build up and wastes accumulate quickly in the blood. At this point, the treatment options are hemodialysis or a kidney transplant. **Hemodialysis** uses an "artificial kidney" apparatus, passing the patient's blood through a membrane tubing that is permeable only to selected substances. The tubing is immersed in a bathing solution that differs slightly from normal cleansed plasma. As blood circulates through the tubing, substances such as nitrogenous wastes and K^+ present in the blood (but not in the bath) diffuse out of the blood into the surrounding solution, and substances to be added to the blood, mainly buffers for H^+ (and glucose for malnourished patients), move from the bathing solution into the blood. In this way, needed substances are retained in the blood or added to it, while wastes and ion excesses are removed. ■

CHECK YOUR UNDERSTANDING

14. Describe the special characteristics of the descending and ascending limbs of the loop of Henle that cause the formation of the medullary osmotic gradient.

15. Under what conditions is ADH released from the posterior pituitary? What effect does ADH have on the collecting ducts?

16. What would you expect the normal clearance value for amino acids to be? Explain.

For answers, see Appendix G.

Urine

▶ Describe the normal physical and chemical properties of urine.

▶ List several abnormal urine components, and name the condition characterized by the presence of detectable amounts of each.

Physical Characteristics

Color and Transparency

Freshly voided urine is clear and pale to deep yellow. Its yellow color is due to **urochrome** (u′ro-krōm), a pigment that results from the body's destruction of hemoglobin. The more concentrated the urine, the deeper the yellow color.

An abnormal color such as pink or brown, or a smoky tinge, may result from eating certain foods (beets, rhubarb) or may be due to the presence in the urine of bile pigments or blood. Additionally, some commonly prescribed drugs and vitamin supplements alter the color of urine. Cloudy urine may indicate a urinary tract infection.

TABLE 25.2	Abnormal Urinary Constituents	
SUBSTANCE	**NAME OF CONDITION**	**POSSIBLE CAUSES**
Glucose	Glycosuria	Diabetes mellitus
Proteins	Proteinuria, or albuminuria	Nonpathological: excessive physical exertion, pregnancy, high-protein diet Pathological (over 250 mg/day): heart failure, severe hypertension, glomerulonephritis, often initial sign of asymptomatic renal disease
Ketone bodies	Ketonuria	Excessive formation and accumulation of ketone bodies, as in starvation and untreated diabetes mellitus
Hemoglobin	Hemoglobinuria	Various: transfusion reaction, hemolytic anemia, severe burns, etc.
Bile pigments	Bilirubinuria	Liver disease (hepatitis, cirrhosis) or obstruction of bile ducts from liver or galbladder
Erythrocytes	Hematuria	Bleeding urinary tract (due to trauma, kidney stones, infection, or neoplasm)
Leukocytes (pus)	Pyuria	Urinary tract infection

Odor

Fresh urine is slightly aromatic, but if allowed to stand, it develops an ammonia odor as bacteria metabolize its urea solutes. Some drugs and vegetables alter the usual odor of urine, as do some diseases. For example, in uncontrolled diabetes mellitus the urine smells fruity because of its acetone content.

pH

Urine is usually slightly acidic (around pH 6), but changes in body metabolism or diet may cause the pH to vary from about 4.5 to 8.0. A predominantly *acidic* diet that contains large amounts of protein and whole wheat products produces acidic urine. A vegetarian (*alkaline*) diet, prolonged vomiting, and bacterial infection of the urinary tract all cause the urine to become alkaline.

Specific Gravity

Because urine is water plus solutes, a given volume has a greater mass than the same volume of distilled water. The ratio of the mass of a substance to the mass of an equal volume of distilled water is its **specific gravity**. The specific gravity of distilled water is 1.0 and that of urine ranges from 1.001 to 1.035, depending on its solute concentration.

Chemical Composition

Water accounts for about 95% of urine volume; the remaining 5% consists of solutes. The largest component of urine by weight, apart from water, is *urea*, which is derived from the normal breakdown of amino acids. Other **nitrogenous wastes** in urine include *uric acid* (an end product of nucleic acid metabolism) and *creatinine* (a metabolite of creatine phosphate, which stores energy for the regeneration of ATP and is found in large amounts in skeletal muscle tissue).

Normal solute constituents of urine, in order of decreasing concentration, are urea, Na^+, K^+, PO_4^{3-}, SO_4^{2-}, creatinine, and uric acid. Much smaller but highly variable amounts of Ca^{2+}, Mg^{2+}, and HCO_3^- are also present in urine.

Unusually high concentrations of any solute, or the presence of abnormal substances such as blood proteins, WBCs (pus), or bile pigments, may indicate pathology (**Table 25.2**). (Normal urine values are listed in Appendix F.)

Ureters

▶ Describe the general location, structure, and function of the ureters.

The **ureters** are slender tubes that convey urine from the kidneys to the bladder (Figure 25.1 and **Figure 25.19**). Each ureter begins at the level of L_2 as a continuation of the renal pelvis.

Kidney

Renal pelvis

Ureter

Urinary bladder

Figure 25.19 Pyelogram. This X-ray image was obtained using a contrast medium to show the ureters, kidneys, and bladder.

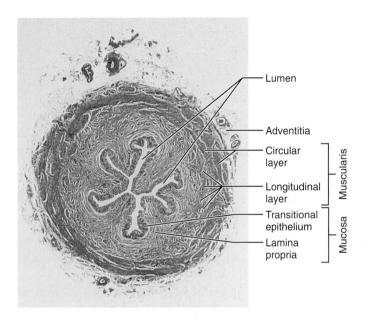

Figure 25.20 Cross-sectional view of the ureter wall (10×). The prominent mucosal folds seen in an empty ureter stretch and flatten to accommodate large pulses of urine.

From there, it descends behind the peritoneum and runs obliquely through the posterior bladder wall. This arrangement prevents backflow of urine during bladder filling because any increase in bladder pressure compresses and closes the distal ends of the ureters.

Histologically, the ureter wall has three layers. The transitional epithelium of its lining *mucosa* is continuous with that of the kidney pelvis superiorly and the bladder medially. Its middle *muscularis* is composed chiefly of two smooth muscle sheets: the internal longitudinal layer and the external circular layer. An additional smooth muscle layer, the external longitudinal layer, appears in the lower third of the ureter. The *adventitia* covering the ureter's external surface is typical fibrous connective tissue (Figure 25.20).

The ureter plays an active role in transporting urine. Incoming urine distends the ureter and stimulates its muscularis to contract, propelling urine into the bladder. (Urine does *not* reach the bladder through gravity alone.) The strength and frequency of the peristaltic waves are adjusted to the rate of urine formation. Each ureter is innervated by both sympathetic and parasympathetic fibers, but neural control of peristalsis appears to be insignificant compared to the way ureteral smooth muscle responds to stretch.

⚖ HOMEOSTATIC IMBALANCE

On occasion, calcium, magnesium, or uric acid salts in urine may crystallize and precipitate in the renal pelvis, forming **renal calculi** (kal′ku-li; *calculus* = little stone), or kidney stones. Most calculi are under 5 mm in diameter and pass through the urinary tract without causing problems. However, larger calculi can obstruct a ureter and block urine drainage. Increasing pressure in the kidney causes excruciating pain, which radiates from the flank to the anterior abdominal wall on the same side. Pain also

occurs when the contracting ureter wall closes in on the sharp calculi as they are being eased through a ureter by peristalsis.

Predisposing conditions are frequent bacterial infections of the urinary tract, urine retention, high blood levels of calcium, and alkaline urine. Surgical removal of calculi has been almost entirely replaced by *shock wave lithotripsy*, a noninvasive procedure that uses ultrasonic shock waves to shatter the calculi. The pulverized, sandlike remnants of the calculi are then painlessly eliminated in the urine. People with a history of kidney stones are encouraged to acidify their urine by drinking cranberry juice and to ingest enough water to keep the urine dilute. ∎

CHECK YOUR UNDERSTANDING

17. What are the three major nitrogenous wastes excreted in the urine?

18. A kidney stone blocking a ureter would interfere with urine flow to which organ? Why would the pain occur in waves?

For answers, see Appendix G.

Urinary Bladder

▶ Describe the general location, structure, and function of the urinary bladder.

The **urinary bladder** is a smooth, collapsible, muscular sac that stores urine temporarily. It is located retroperitoneally on the pelvic floor just posterior to the pubic symphysis. The prostate (part of the male reproductive system) lies inferior to the bladder neck, which empties into the urethra. In females, the bladder is anterior to the vagina and uterus.

The interior of the bladder has openings for both ureters and the urethra (Figure 25.21). The smooth, triangular region of the bladder base outlined by these three openings is the **trigone** (tri′gōn; *trigon* = triangle), important clinically because infections tend to persist in this region.

The bladder wall has three layers: a mucosa containing transitional epithelium, a thick muscular layer, and a fibrous adventitia (except on its superior surface, where it is covered by the peritoneum). The muscular layer, called the **detrusor muscle** (de-tru′sor; "to thrust out"), consists of intermingled smooth muscle fibers arranged in inner and outer longitudinal layers and a middle circular layer.

The bladder is very distensible and uniquely suited for its function of urine storage. When empty, the bladder collapses into its basic pyramidal shape and its walls are thick and thrown into folds (*rugae*). As urine accumulates, the bladder expands, becomes pear shaped, and rises superiorly in the abdominal cavity. The muscular wall stretches and thins, and rugae disappear. These changes allow the bladder to store more urine without a significant rise in internal pressure.

A moderately full bladder is about 12 cm (5 inches) long and holds approximately 500 ml (1 pint) of urine, but it can hold nearly double that if necessary. When tense with urine, it can be palpated well above the pubic symphysis. The maximum capacity of the bladder is 800–1000 ml and when it is

Peritoneum

Ureter

Rugae

Detrusor muscle

Adventitia

Ureteric orifices

Trigone of bladder

Bladder neck

Internal urethral sphincter

Prostate

Prostatic urethra

Membranous urethra

External urethral sphincter

Urogenital diaphragm

Trigone

Urethra

External urethral orifice

(b) Female.

Spongy urethra

Erectile tissue of penis

External urethral orifice

(a) Male. The long male urethra has three regions: prostatic, membranous and spongy.

Figure 25.21 Structure of the urinary bladder and urethra. The anterior wall of the bladder has been reflected or omitted to reveal the position of the trigone.

overdistended, it may burst. Although urine is formed continuously by the kidneys, it is usually stored in the bladder until its release is convenient.

Urethra

▶ Describe the general location, structure, and function of the urethra.

▶ Compare the course, length, and functions of the male urethra with those of the female.

The **urethra** is a thin-walled muscular tube that drains urine from the bladder and conveys it out of the body. The epithelium of its mucosal lining is mostly pseudostratified columnar epithelium. However, near the bladder it becomes transitional epithelium, and near the external opening it changes to a protective stratified squamous epithelium.

At the bladder-urethra junction a thickening of the detrusor smooth muscle forms the **internal urethral sphincter** (Figure 25.21). This involuntary sphincter keeps the urethra closed when urine is not being passed and prevents leaking between voiding. This sphincter is unusual in that contraction opens it and relaxation closes it.

The **external urethral sphincter** surrounds the urethra as it passes through the *urogenital diaphragm*. This sphincter is formed of skeletal muscle and is voluntarily controlled. The *levator ani* muscle of the pelvic floor also serves as a voluntary constrictor of the urethra (see Table 10.7, pp. 344–345).

The length and functions of the urethra differ in the two sexes. In females the urethra is only 3–4 cm (1.5 inches) long and tightly bound to the anterior vaginal wall by fibrous connective tissue. Its external opening, the **external urethral orifice**, lies anterior to the vaginal opening and posterior to the clitoris.

In males the urethra is approximately 20 cm (8 inches) long and has three regions. The **prostatic urethra**, about 2.5 cm (1 inch) long, runs within the prostate. The **membranous urethra**, which runs through the urogenital diaphragm, extends about 2 cm from the prostate to the beginning of the penis. The **spongy urethra**, about 15 cm long, passes through the penis and opens at its tip via the **external urethral orifice**. The male urethra has a double function: It carries semen as well as urine out of the body. We discuss the reproductive function of the male urethra in Chapter 27.

25

HOMEOSTATIC IMBALANCE

Because the female's urethra is very short and its external orifice is close to the anal opening, improper toilet habits (wiping back to front after defecation) can easily carry fecal bacteria into the urethra. Actually, most urinary tract infections occur in sexually active women, because intercourse drives bacteria from the vagina and external genital region toward the bladder. The use of spermicides magnifies this problem, because the spermicide kills helpful bacteria, allowing infectious fecal bacteria to colonize the vagina. Overall, 40% of all women get urinary tract infections.

The urethral mucosa is continuous with that of the rest of the urinary tract, and an inflammation of the urethra (*urethritis*) can ascend the tract to cause bladder inflammation (*cystitis*) or even renal inflammations (*pyelitis* or *pyelonephritis*). Symptoms of urinary tract infection include *dysuria* (painful urination), urinary *urgency* and *frequency*, fever, and sometimes cloudy or blood-tinged urine. When the kidneys are involved, back pain and a severe headache often occur. Most urinary tract infections are easily cured by antibiotics. ∎

Micturition

▶ Define micturition and describe its neural control.

Micturition (mik″tu-rish′un; *mictur* = urinate), also called **urination** or *voiding*, is the act of emptying the urinary bladder. In order for micturition to occur, three things must happen simultaneously: (1) the detrusor muscle must contract, (2) the internal urethral sphincter must open, and (3) the external urethral sphincter must open. The detrusor muscle and its internal urethral sphincter are composed of smooth muscle and are innervated by both the parasympathetic and sympathetic nervous systems, which have opposing actions. The external urethral sphincter, in contrast, is skeletal muscle, and therefore is innervated by the somatic nervous system.

How are the three events required for micturition coordinated? Micturition is most easily understood in infants where a spinal reflex coordinates the process. As urine accumulates, distension of the bladder activates stretch receptors in its walls. Impulses from the activated receptors travel via visceral afferent fibers to the sacral region of the spinal cord. Visceral afferent impulses, relayed by sets of interneurons, excite parasympathetic neurons and inhibit sympathetic neurons (**Figure 25.22**). As a result, the detrusor muscle contracts and the internal sphincter opens. Visceral afferent impulses also inhibit tonically active somatic efferents that keep the external urethral sphincter closed, allowing it to relax and urine to flow.

Between ages two and three, descending circuits from the brain have matured enough to begin to override reflexive urination. The pons has two centers that participate in control of micturition. The *pontine storage center* inhibits micturition, whereas the *pontine micturition center* promotes this reflex. Afferent impulses from bladder stretch receptors are relayed to the pons, as well as to higher brain centers that provide the conscious awareness of bladder fullness.

Lower bladder volumes primarily activate the pontine storage center, which acts to inhibit urination by suppressing parasympathetic and enhancing sympathetic output to the bladder. When a person chooses not to void, reflex bladder contractions subside within a minute or so and urine continues to accumulate. Because the external sphincter is voluntarily controlled, we can choose to keep it closed and postpone bladder emptying temporarily. After additional urine has collected, the micturition reflex occurs again and, if urination is delayed again, is damped once more. The urge to void gradually becomes greater and greater, and micturition usually occurs before urine volume exceeds 400 ml. After normal micturition, only about 10 ml of urine remains in the bladder.

HOMEOSTATIC IMBALANCE

After the toddler years, **incontinence** is usually a result of emotional problems, physical pressure during pregnancy, or nervous system problems. In *stress incontinence*, a sudden increase in intra-abdominal pressure (during laughing and coughing) forces urine through the external sphincter. This condition is common during pregnancy when the heavy uterus stretches the muscles of the pelvic floor and the urogenital diaphragm that support the external sphincter. In *overflow incontinence*, urine dribbles from the urethra whenever the bladder overfills.

In **urinary retention**, the bladder is unable to expel its contained urine. Urinary retention is normal after general anesthesia (it seems that it takes a little time for the detrusor muscle to regain its activity). Urinary retention in men often reflects hypertrophy of the prostate, which narrows the urethra, making it difficult to void. When urinary retention is prolonged, a slender rubber drainage tube called a **catheter** (kath′ĕ-ter) must be inserted through the urethra to drain the urine and prevent bladder trauma from excessive stretching. ∎

CHECK YOUR UNDERSTANDING

19. What is the trigone of the bladder, and which landmarks define its borders?

20. Name the three regions of the male urethra.

21. How does the detrusor muscle respond to increased firing of the parasympathetic fibers that innervate it? How does this affect the internal urethral sphincter?

For answers, see Appendix G.

Developmental Aspects of the Urinary System

▶ Trace the embryonic development of the urinary organs.

▶ List several changes in urinary system anatomy and physiology that occur with age.

As the kidneys develop in a young embryo, it almost seems as if they are unable to "make up their mind" how to go about it. As illustrated in **Figure 25.23**, three different sets of kidneys develop from the *urogenital ridges*, paired elevations of the intermediate

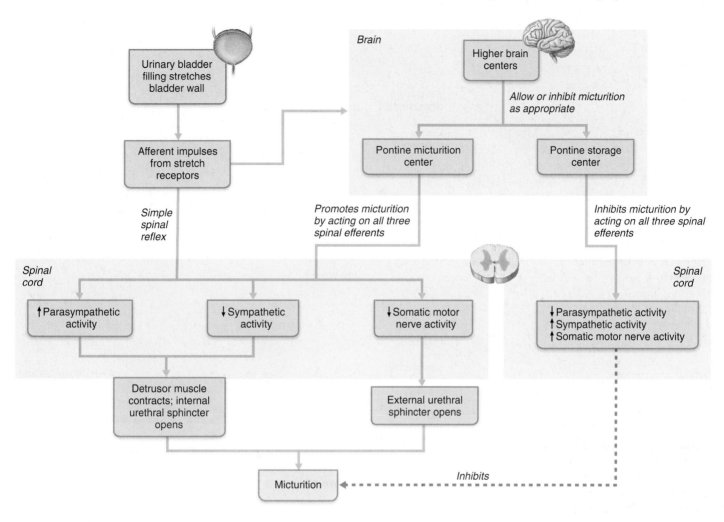

Figure 25.22 Control of micturition.

mesoderm that give rise to both the urinary organs and the reproductive organs. Only the last set persists to become adult kidneys.

During the fourth week of development, the first tubule system, the **pronephros** (pro-nef′ros; "prekidney"), forms and then quickly degenerates as a second, lower set appears. Although the pronephros never functions and is gone by the sixth week, the **pronephric duct** that connects it to the cloaca persists and is used by the later-developing kidneys. (The cloaca is the terminal part of the gut that opens to the body exterior.)

As the second renal system, the **mesonephros** (mez″o-nef′ros; "middle kidney"), claims the pronephric duct, it comes to be called the **mesonephric duct** (Figure 25.23a, b). The mesonephric kidneys degenerate (with remnants incorporated into the male reproductive system) once the third set, the **metanephros** (met″ah-nef′ros; "after kidney"), makes its appearance (Figure 25.23b, c).

The metanephros starts to develop at about five weeks as hollow **ureteric buds** that push superiorly from the mesonephric duct into the urogenital ridge, inducing the mesoderm there to form nephrons. The distal ends of the ureteric buds form the renal pelves, calyces, and collecting ducts, and their unexpanded proximal parts, now called the **ureteric ducts**, become the ureters (Figure 25.23d).

Because the kidneys develop in the pelvis and then ascend to their final position, they receive their blood supply from successively higher sources. Although the lower blood vessels usually degenerate, they sometimes persist so that multiple renal arteries are common. The metanephric kidneys are excreting urine by the third month of fetal life, and most of the amniotic fluid that surrounds a developing fetus is fetal urine. Nonetheless, the fetal kidneys do not work nearly as hard as they will after birth because exchange through the placenta allows the mother's urinary system to clear most of the undesirable substances from the fetal blood.

As the metanephros is developing, the cloaca subdivides to form the future rectum and anal canal and the **urogenital sinus**, into which the urinary and genital ducts empty. The urinary bladder and the urethra then develop from the urogenital sinus (Figure 25.23b–d).

⚖ HOMEOSTATIC IMBALANCE

Three of the most common congenital abnormalities of the urinary system are horseshoe kidney, hypospadias, and polycystic kidney.

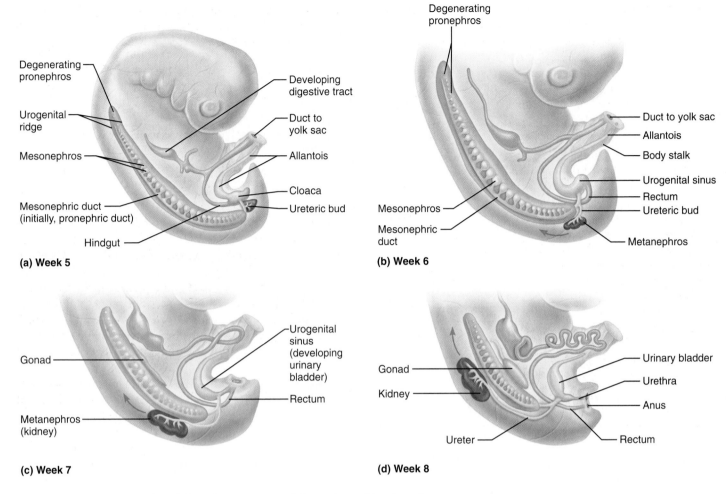

(a) Week 5

Degenerating pronephros

Urogenital ridge

Mesonephros

Mesonephric duct (initially, pronephric duct)

Hindgut

Developing digestive tract

Duct to yolk sac

Allantois

Cloaca

Ureteric bud

(b) Week 6

Degenerating pronephros

Mesonephros

Mesonephric duct

Duct to yolk sac

Allantois

Body stalk

Urogenital sinus

Rectum

Ureteric bud

Metanephros

(c) Week 7

Gonad

Metanephros (kidney)

Urogenital sinus (developing urinary bladder)

Rectum

(d) Week 8

Gonad

Kidney

Ureter

Urinary bladder

Urethra

Anus

Rectum

Figure 25.23 Development of the urinary system of the embryo. Direction of metanephros migration as it develops is indicated by red arrows.

When ascending from the pelvis the kidneys are very close together, and in 1 out of 600 people they fuse across the midline, forming a single, U-shaped *horseshoe kidney*. This condition is usually asymptomatic, but it may be associated with other kidney abnormalities, such as obstructed drainage, that place a person at risk for frequent kidney infections.

Hypospadias (hi"po-spa′de-as), found in male infants only, is the most common congenital abnormality of the urethra. It occurs when the urethral orifice is located on the ventral surface of the penis. This problem is corrected surgically when the child is around 12 months old.

Polycystic kidney disease (*PKD*) is a group of disorders characterized by the presence of many fluid-filled cysts in the kidneys, which interfere with renal function, ultimately leading to renal failure. These disorders can be grouped into two general forms. The less severe form is inherited in an autosomal dominant manner and is much more common, affecting 1 in 500 people. The cysts develop so gradually that they produce no symptoms until about 40 years of age. Then both kidneys begin to enlarge as blisterlike cysts containing fluid accumulate. The damage caused by these cysts progresses slowly, and many victims live without problems until their 60s. Ultimately, however, the

kidneys become "knobby" and grossly enlarged, reaching a mass of up to 14 kg (30 lb) each.

The much less common and more severe form follows an autosomal recessive pattern of inheritance. Almost half of newborns with recessive PKD die just after birth, and survivors generally develop renal failure in early childhood. Recessive PKD results from a mutation in a single huge gene, but the dominant form of PKD (described above) is usually caused by a mutation in one of two different genes, which code for proteins involved in cell signaling. It is not yet clear how defects in these proteins lead to cyst formation. As yet, the only treatments are the usual treatments for kidney failure—renal dialysis or a kidney transplant. ■

Because its bladder is very small and its kidneys are less able to concentrate urine for the first two months, a newborn baby voids 5 to 40 times daily, depending on fluid intake. By 2 months of age, the infant is voiding approximately 400 ml/day, and the amount steadily increases until adolescence, when adult urine output (about 1500 ml/day) is achieved.

Incontinence, the inability to control micturition, is normal in infants because they have not yet learned to control the external urethral sphincter. Reflex voiding occurs each time a baby's bladder fills enough to activate the stretch receptors. Control of the voluntary urethral sphincter goes hand in hand with nervous system development. By 15 months, most toddlers know when they have voided. By 18 months, they can usually hold urine for about two hours. By 24 months, some children are ready to begin toilet training. Daytime control usually is achieved first. It is unrealistic to expect complete nighttime control before age 4.

From childhood through late middle age, most urinary system problems are infectious conditions. *Escherichia coli* (esh″ĕ-rik′e-ah ko′li) bacteria are normal residents of the digestive tract and cause no problems there, but these bacteria account for 80% of all urinary tract infections. *Sexually transmitted diseases* can also inflame the urinary tract and clog some of its ducts. Childhood streptococcal infections such as strep throat and scarlet fever, if not treated promptly, may cause long-term inflammatory renal damage.

Only about 3% of elderly people have histologically normal kidneys, and kidney function declines with advancing age. The kidneys shrink as the nephrons decrease in size and number, and the tubule cells become less efficient. By age 80, the GFR is only half that of young adults, possibly due to atherosclerotic narrowing of the renal arteries. Diabetics are particularly at risk for renal disease, and nearly 50% of those who have had diabetes mellitus for 20 years are in renal failure.

The bladder of an aged person is shrunken, with less than half the capacity of a young adult (250 ml versus 600 ml). Loss of bladder tone causes an annoying increase in frequency of micturition. *Nocturia* (nok-tu′re-ah), the need to get up during the night to urinate, plagues almost two-thirds of this population. Many people eventually experience incontinence, which can usually be treated with exercise, medications, or surgery.

CHECK YOUR UNDERSTANDING

22. Name the three sets of embryonic kidneys in the order that they develop.

23. List two factors that might contribute to urinary retention in elderly men.

For answers, see Appendix G.

The ureters, urinary bladder, and urethra play important roles in transporting, storing, and eliminating urine from the body, but when the term "urinary system" is used, it is the kidneys that capture center stage. As summarized in *Making Connections* in Chapter 26, other organ systems of the body contribute to the well-being of the urinary system in many ways. In turn, without continuous kidney function, the electrolyte and fluid balance of the blood is dangerously disturbed, and internal body fluids quickly become contaminated with nitrogenous wastes. No body cell can escape the harmful effects of such imbalances.

Now that we have described renal mechanisms, we are ready to integrate kidney function into the larger topic of fluid and electrolyte balance in the body—the focus of Chapter 26.

RELATED CLINICAL TERMS

Acute glomerulonephritis (GN) (glo-mer″u-lo-nef-ri′tis) Inflammation of the glomeruli, leading to increased permeability of the filtration membrane. In some cases, circulating immune complexes (antibodies bound to foreign substances, such as streptococcal bacteria) become trapped in the glomerular basement membranes. In other cases, immune responses are mounted against one's own kidney tissues, leading to glomerular damage. In either case, the inflammatory response that follows damages the filtration membrane, allowing blood proteins and even blood cells to pass into the renal tubules and into the urine. As the osmotic pressure of blood drops, fluid seeps from the bloodstream into the tissue spaces, causing bodywide edema. Renal shutdown requiring dialysis may occur temporarily, but normal renal function usually returns within a few months. If permanent glomerular damage occurs, chronic GN and ultimately renal failure result.

Bladder cancer Bladder cancer, three times more common in men than in women, accounts for about 2% of all cancer deaths. It usually involves neoplasms of the bladder's lining epithelium and may be induced by carcinogens from the environment or the workplace that end up in urine. Smoking, exposure to industrial chemicals, and arsenic in drinking water also have been linked to bladder cancer. Blood in the urine is a common warning sign.

Cystocele (sis′to-sēl; *cyst* = a sac, the bladder; *cele* = hernia, rupture) Herniation of the urinary bladder into the vagina; a common result of tearing of the pelvic floor muscles during childbirth.

Cystoscopy (sis-tos′ko-pe; *cyst* = bladder; *scopy* = observation) Procedure in which a thin viewing tube is threaded into the bladder through the urethra to examine the bladder's mucosal surface.

Diabetes insipidus (in-si′pĭ-dus; *insipid* = tasteless, bland) Condition in which large amounts (up to 40 L/day) of dilute urine flush from the body; results from malfunction or deficiency of aquaporins or ADH receptors in the collecting duct (nephrogenic diabetes insipidus), or little or no ADH release due to injury to, or a tumor in, the hypothalamus or posterior pituitary. Can lead to severe dehydration and electrolyte imbalances unless the individual drinks large volumes of liquids. See Chapter 16, p. 608.

Intravenous pyelogram (IVP) (pi′ĕ-lo-gram; *pyelo* = kidney pelvis; *gram* = written) An X ray of the kidneys and ureters obtained after intravenous injection of a contrast medium (as in Figure 25.19). Allows assessment for obstructions, viewing of renal anatomy (pelvis and calyces), and determination of rate of excretion of the contrast medium.

Nephrotoxin A substance (heavy metal, organic solvent, or bacterial toxin) that is toxic to the kidney.

Nocturnal enuresis (NE) (en″u-re′sis) An inability to control urination at night during sleep; bed-wetting. In children over 6, called primary NE if control has never been achieved and secondary NE if control was achieved and then lost. Secondary NE often has psychological causes. Primary NE is more common and results from a combination of inadequate nocturnal ADH production, unusually sound sleep, or a small bladder capacity. Synthetic ADH often corrects the problem.

25

Renal infarct Area of dead, or necrotic, renal tissue due to blockage of the vascular supply to the kidney or hemorrhage. A common cause of localized renal infarct is obstruction of an interlobar artery. Because interlobar arteries are end arteries (do not anastomose), their obstruction leads to ischemic necrosis of the portions of the kidney they supply.

Urinalysis Analysis of urine as an aid to diagnosing health or disease. The most significant indicators of disease in urine are proteins, glucose, acetone, blood, and pus.

Urologist (u-rol′o-jist) Physician who specializes in diseases of urinary structures in both sexes and in diseases of the reproductive tract of males.

CHAPTER SUMMARY

Media study tools that could provide you additional help in reviewing specific key topics of Chapter 25 are referenced below.

iP = *Interactive Physiology*

Kidney Anatomy   (pp. 961–969)

Location and External Anatomy   (pp. 961–962)

1. The paired kidneys are retroperitoneal in the superior lumbar region.
2. A fibrous capsule, a perirenal fat capsule, and renal fascia surround each kidney. The perirenal fat capsule helps hold the kidneys in position.

Internal Anatomy   (pp. 962–963)

3. A kidney has a superficial cortex, a deeper medulla consisting mainly of medullary pyramids, and a medial pelvis. Extensions of the pelvis (calyces) surround and collect urine draining from the apices of the medullary pyramids.

Blood and Nerve Supply   (pp. 963–964)

4. The kidneys receive 25% of the total cardiac output per minute.
5. The vascular pathway through a kidney is as follows: renal artery → segmental arteries → interlobar arteries → arcuate arteries → cortical radiate arteries → afferent arterioles → glomeruli → efferent arterioles → peritubular capillary beds → cortical radiate veins → arcuate veins → interlobar veins → renal vein.
6. The nerve supply of the kidneys is derived from the renal plexus.

Nephrons   (pp. 964–969)

7. Nephrons are the structural and functional units of the kidneys.
8. Each nephron consists of a glomerulus (a high-pressure capillary bed) and a renal tubule. Subdivisions of the renal tubule (from the glomerulus) are the glomerular capsule, proximal convoluted tubule, loop of Henle, and distal convoluted tubule. A second capillary bed, the low-pressure peritubular capillary bed, is closely associated with the renal tubule of each nephron.
9. The more numerous cortical nephrons are located almost entirely in the cortex; only a small part of their loop of Henle penetrates into the medulla. Glomeruli of juxtamedullary nephrons are located at the cortex-medulla junction, and their loop of Henle dips deeply into the medulla. Instead of directly forming peritubular capillaries, the efferent arterioles of many of the juxtamedullary nephrons form unique bundles of straight vessels, called vasa recta, that serve tubule segments in the medulla. Juxtamedullary nephrons and the vasa recta play an important role in establishing the medullary osmotic gradient.
10. Collecting ducts receive urine from many nephrons and help concentrate urine. They form the medullary pyramids.
11. The juxtaglomerular apparatus is at the point of contact between the afferent arteriole and the most distal part of the ascending limb of the loop of Henle. It consists of the granular cells, the macula densa, and extraglomerular mesangial cells.

iP **Urinary System; Topic: Anatomy Review, pp. 1–20.**

12. The filtration membrane consists of the fenestrated glomerular endothelium, the intervening basement membrane, and the podocyte-containing visceral layer of the glomerular capsule. It permits free passage of substances smaller than (most) plasma proteins.

Kidney Physiology: Mechanisms of Urine Formation (pp. 969–984)

1. Functions of the nephrons include glomerular filtration, tubular reabsorption, and tubular secretion. Via these functional processes, the kidneys regulate the volume, composition, and pH of the blood, and eliminate nitrogenous metabolic wastes.

Step 1: Glomerular Filtration   (pp. 970–974)

2. The glomeruli function as filters. High glomerular blood pressure (55 mm Hg) occurs because the glomeruli are fed and drained by arterioles, and the afferent arterioles are larger in diameter than the efferent arterioles.
3. About one-fifth of the plasma flowing through the kidneys is filtered from the glomeruli into the renal tubules.
4. Usually about 10 mm Hg, the net filtration pressure (NFP) is determined by the relationship between forces favoring filtration (glomerular hydrostatic pressure) and forces that oppose it (capsular hydrostatic pressure and blood colloid osmotic pressure).
5. The glomerular filtration rate (GFR) is directly proportional to the net filtration pressure and is about 125 ml/min (180 L/day).
6. Renal autoregulation, which enables the kidneys to maintain a relatively constant renal blood flow and glomerular filtration rate, involves a myogenic mechanism and a tubuloglomerular feedback mechanism mediated by the macula densa.
7. Extrinsic control of GFR, via nerves and hormones, maintains blood pressure. Strong sympathetic nervous system activation causes constriction of the afferent arterioles, which decreases filtrate formation and stimulates renin release by the granular cells.

iP **Urinary System; Topic: Glomerular Filtration, pp. 1–15.**

8. The renin-angiotensin mechanism mediated by the granular cells raises systemic blood pressure via generation of angiotensin II, which promotes aldosterone secretion.

Step 2: Tubular Reabsorption   (pp. 974–978)

9. During tubular reabsorption, needed substances are removed from the filtrate by the tubule cells and returned to the peritubular capillary blood. The primary active transport of Na^+ by a Na^+-K^+ ATPase pump at the basolateral membrane accounts for Na^+ reabsorption and establishes the electrochemical gradient that drives the reabsorption of most other solutes and H_2O. Na^+ enters at the luminal surface of the tubule cell via facilitated diffusion through channels or as part of a cotransport mechanism.

10. Passive tubular reabsorption is driven by electrochemical gradients established by active reabsorption of sodium ions. Water, many ions, and various other substances (for example, urea) are reabsorbed passively by diffusion via transcellular or paracellular pathways.

11. Secondary active tubular reabsorption occurs by cotransport with Na^+ via transport proteins. Transport of such substances is limited by the number of carriers available. Actively reabsorbed substances include glucose, amino acids, and some ions.

12. The proximal tubule cells are most active in reabsorption. Most of the nutrients, 65% of the water and sodium ions, and the bulk of actively transported ions are reabsorbed in the proximal convoluted tubules.

13. Reabsorption of additional sodium ions and water occurs in the distal tubules and collecting ducts and is hormonally controlled. Aldosterone increases the reabsorption of sodium; antidiuretic hormone enhances water reabsorption by the collecting ducts.

Step 3: Tubular Secretion　(p. 978)

14. Tubular secretion is a means of adding substances to the filtrate (from the blood or tubule cells). It is an active process that is important in eliminating drugs, certain wastes, and excess ions and in maintaining the acid-base balance of the blood.

Regulation of Urine Concentration and Volume　(pp. 978–983)

15. The graduated hyperosmolality of the medullary fluids (largely due to the cycling of NaCl and urea) ensures that the filtrate reaching the distal convoluted tubule is dilute (hypo-osmolar). This allows urine with osmolalities ranging from 50 to 1200 mOsm to be formed.
    - The descending limb of the loop of Henle is permeable to water, which leaves the filtrate and enters the medullary interstitium. The filtrate and medullary fluid at the bend of the loop of Henle are hyperosmolar.
    - The ascending limb is impermeable to water. Na^+ and Cl^- move out of the filtrate into the interstitial space, passively in the thin segment and actively in the thick segment. The filtrate becomes more dilute.
    - As filtrate flows through the collecting ducts in the inner medulla, urea diffuses into the interstitial space. From here, urea reenters the ascending thin limb and is recycled.
    - The blood flow in the vasa recta is sluggish, and the contained blood equilibrates with the medullary interstitial fluid. Hence, blood exiting the medulla in the vasa recta is nearly isotonic to blood plasma and the high solute concentration of the medulla is maintained.

16. In the absence of antidiuretic hormone, dilute urine is formed because the dilute filtrate reaching the collecting duct is simply allowed to pass from the kidneys.

17. As blood levels of antidiuretic hormone rise, the collecting ducts become more permeable to water, and water moves out of the filtrate as it flows through the hyperosmotic medullary areas. Consequently, more concentrated urine is produced, and in smaller amounts.

iP Urinary System; Topics: Early Filtrate Processing, pp. 1–22; Late Filtrate Processing, pp. 1–13.

Renal Clearance　(p. 984)

18. Renal clearance is the volume of plasma that is completely cleared of a particular substance per minute. Studies of renal clearance provide information about renal function or the course of renal disease.

19. Renal failure has serious consequences: The kidneys are unable to concentrate urine, acid-base and electrolyte imbalances occur, and nitrogenous wastes accumulate in the blood.

Urine　(pp. 984–985)

1. Urine is typically clear, yellow, aromatic, and slightly acidic. Its specific gravity ranges from 1.001 to 1.035.

2. Urine is 95% water; solutes include nitrogenous wastes (urea, uric acid, and creatinine) and various ions (always sodium, potassium, sulfate, and phosphate).

3. Substances not normally found in urine include glucose, proteins, erythrocytes, leukocytes, hemoglobin, and bile pigments.

4. Daily urinary volume is typically 1.5–1.8 L, but this depends on the state of hydration of the body.

Ureters　(pp. 985–986)

1. The ureters are slender tubes running retroperitoneally from each kidney to the bladder. They conduct urine by peristalsis from the renal pelvis to the urinary bladder.

Urinary Bladder　(pp. 986–987)

1. The urinary bladder, which functions to store urine, is a distensible muscular sac that lies posterior to the pubic symphysis. It has two inlets (ureters) and one outlet (urethra) that outline the trigone. In males, the prostate surrounds the bladder outlet.

2. The bladder wall consists of a transitional epithelium–containing mucosa, a three-layered detrusor muscle, and an adventitia.

Urethra　(pp. 987-988)

1. The urethra is a muscular tube that conveys urine from the bladder to the body exterior.

2. Where the urethra leaves the bladder, it is surrounded by an internal urethral sphincter, an involuntary smooth muscle sphincter. Where it passes through the urogenital diaphragm, the voluntary external urethral sphincter is formed by skeletal muscle.

3. In females the urethra is 3–4 cm long and conducts only urine. In males it is 20 cm long and conducts both urine and semen.

Micturition　(p. 988)

1. Micturition is emptying of the bladder.

2. Stretching of the bladder wall by accumulating urine initiates the micturition reflex. In infants, this is a simple spinal reflex: Parasympathetic fibers are excited (and sympathetic fibers inhibited), causing the detrusor muscle to contract and the internal urethral sphincter to open. In adults, pontine storage and micturition centers can override this simple reflex.

3. Because the external sphincter is voluntarily controlled, micturition can usually be delayed temporarily.

Developmental Aspects of the Urinary System (pp. 988–991)

1. Three sets of kidneys (pronephric, mesonephric, and metanephric) develop from the intermediate mesoderm. The metanephros is excreting urine by the third month of development.

2. Common congenital abnormalities are horseshoe kidney, polycystic kidney, and hypospadias.

3. The kidneys of newborns are less able to concentrate urine; their bladder is small and voiding is frequent. Neuromuscular maturation generally allows toilet training for micturition to begin by 24 months of age.

4. The most common urinary system problems in children and young to middle-aged adults are bacterial infections.

5. With age, nephrons are lost, the filtration rate decreases, and tubule cells become less efficient at concentrating urine.

6. Bladder capacity and tone decrease with age, leading to frequent micturition and (often) incontinence. Urinary retention is a common problem of elderly men.

25

Multiple Choice/Matching

(Some questions have more than one correct answer. Select the best answer or answers from the choices given.)

1. The lowest blood concentration of nitrogenous waste occurs in the **(a)** hepatic vein, **(b)** inferior vena cava, **(c)** renal artery, **(d)** renal vein.

2. The glomerular capillaries differ from other capillary networks in the body because they **(a)** have a larger area of anastomosis, **(b)** are derived from and drain into arterioles, **(c)** are not made of endothelium, **(d)** are sites of filtrate formation.

3. Damage to the renal medulla would interfere *first* with the functioning of the **(a)** glomerular capsules, **(b)** distal convoluted tubules, **(c)** collecting ducts, **(d)** proximal convoluted tubules.

4. Which is reabsorbed by the proximal convoluted tubule cells? **(a)** Na^+, **(b)** K^+, **(c)** amino acids, **(d)** all of the above.

5. Glucose is not normally found in the urine because it **(a)** does not pass through the walls of the glomerulus, **(b)** is kept in the blood by colloid osmotic pressure, **(c)** is reabsorbed by the tubule cells, **(d)** is removed by the body cells before the blood reaches the kidney.

6. Filtration at the glomerulus is inversely related to **(a)** water reabsorption, **(b)** capsular hydrostatic pressure, **(c)** arterial blood pressure, **(d)** acidity of the urine.

7. Tubular reabsorption **(a)** of glucose and many other substances is a T_m-limited active transport process, **(b)** of chloride is always linked to the passive transport of Na^+, **(c)** is the movement of substances from the blood into the nephron, **(d)** of sodium occurs only in the proximal tubule.

8. If a freshly voided urine sample contains excessive amounts of urochrome, it has **(a)** an ammonia-like odor, **(b)** a pH below normal, **(c)** a dark yellow color, **(d)** a pH above normal.

9. Conditions such as diabetes mellitus and starvation are closely linked to **(a)** ketonuria, **(b)** pyuria, **(c)** albuminuria, **(d)** hematuria.

10. Which of the following is/are true about ADH? **(a)** It promotes obligatory water reabsorption, **(b)** it is secreted in response to an increase in extracellular fluid osmolality, **(c)** it causes insertion of aquaporins in the PCT, **(d)** it promotes Na^+ reabsorption.

Short Answer Essay Questions

11. What is the importance of the perirenal fat capsule that surrounds the kidney?

12. Trace the pathway a creatinine molecule takes from a glomerulus to the urethra. Name every microscopic or gross structure it passes through on its journey.

13. Explain the important differences between blood plasma and glomerular filtrate, and relate the differences to the structure of the filtration membrane.

14. Describe the mechanisms that contribute to renal autoregulation.

15. Describe the mechanisms of extrinsic regulation of GFR, and their physiological role.

16. Describe what is involved in active and passive tubular reabsorption.

17. Explain how the peritubular capillaries are adapted for receiving reabsorbed substances.

18. Explain the process and purpose of tubular secretion.

19. How does aldosterone modify the chemical composition of urine?

20. Explain why the filtrate becomes hypotonic as it flows through the ascending limb of the loop of Henle. Also explain why the filtrate at the bend of the loop of Henle (and the interstitial fluid of the deep portions of the medulla) is hypertonic.

21. How does urinary bladder anatomy support its storage function?

22. Define micturition and describe the micturition reflex.

23. Describe the changes that occur in kidney and bladder anatomy and physiology in old age.

Critical Thinking and Clinical Application Questions

1. Mrs. Bigda, a 60-year-old woman, was brought to the hospital by the police after falling to the pavement. She is found to have alcoholic hepatitis. She is put on a salt- and protein-restricted diet and diuretics are prescribed to manage her ascites (accumulated fluid in the peritoneal cavity). How will diuretics reduce this excess fluid? Name and describe the mechanisms of action of three types of diuretics. Why is her diet salt-restricted?

2. While repairing a frayed utility wire, Herbert, an experienced lineman, slips and falls to the ground. Medical examination reveals a fracture of his lower spine and transection of the lumbar region of the spinal cord. How will Herbert's micturition be controlled from this point on? Will he ever again feel the need to void? Will there be dribbling of urine between voidings? Explain the reasoning behind all your responses.

3. What is cystitis? Why are women more frequent cystitis sufferers than men?

4. Hattie, aged 55, is awakened by excruciating pain that radiates from her right abdomen to the loin and groin regions on the same side. The pain is not continuous but recurs at intervals of 3 to 4 minutes. Diagnose her problem, and cite factors that might favor its occurrence. Also, explain why Hattie's pain comes in "waves."

5. Why does use of a spermicide increase a woman's risk for urinary tract infection?

6. Why are renal failure patients undergoing dialysis at risk for anemia and osteoporosis? What medications or supplements could you give them to prevent these problems?

26

Fluid, Electrolyte, and Acid-Base Balance

Have you ever wondered why on certain days you don't urinate for hours at a time, while on others it seems like you void every few minutes? Or why on occasion you cannot seem to quench your thirst? These situations and many others reflect one of the body's most important functions: maintaining fluid, electrolyte, and acid-base balance.

Cell function depends not only on a continuous supply of nutrients and removal of metabolic wastes, but also on the physical and chemical homeostasis of the surrounding fluids. The French physiologist

Figure 26.1 The major fluid compartments of the body. [Values are for a 70-kg (154-lb) male.]

Claude Bernard recognized this truth with style in 1857 when he said, "It is the fixity of the internal environment which is the condition of free and independent life."

In this chapter, we first examine the composition and distribution of fluids in the internal environment and then consider the roles of various body organs and functions in establishing, regulating, and altering this balance.

Body Fluids

▶ List the factors that determine body water content and describe the effect of each factor.

▶ Indicate the relative fluid volume and solute composition of the fluid compartments of the body.

▶ Contrast the overall osmotic effects of electrolytes and nonelectrolytes.

▶ Describe factors that determine fluid shifts in the body.

Body Water Content

If you are a healthy young adult, water probably accounts for about half your body mass. However, not all bodies contain the same amount of water. Total body water is a function not only of age and body mass, but also of sex and the relative amount of body fat. Infants, with their low body fat and low bone mass, are 73% or more water. (This high level of hydration accounts for their "dewy" skin, like that of a freshly picked peach.) After infancy total body water declines throughout life, accounting for only about 45% of body mass in old age.

A healthy young man is about 60% water, and a healthy young woman about 50%. This difference between the sexes reflects the fact that females have relatively more body fat and relatively less skeletal muscle than males. Of all body tissues, adipose tissue is *least* hydrated (containing up to 20% water), and even bone contains more water than does fat. By contrast, skeletal muscle is about 75% water, so people with greater muscle mass have proportionately more body water.

Fluid Compartments

Water occupies two main **fluid compartments** within the body (**Figure 26.1**). A little less than two-thirds by volume is in the **intracellular fluid (ICF) compartment**, which actually consists of trillions of tiny individual "compartments": the cells. In an adult male of average size (70 kg, or 154 lb), ICF accounts for about 25 L of the 40 L of body water.

The remaining one-third or so of body water is outside cells, in the **extracellular fluid (ECF) compartment**. The ECF constitutes the body's "internal environment" referred to by Claude Bernard and is the external environment of each cell. As Figure 26.1 shows, the ECF compartment is divisible into two *subcompartments*: (1) **plasma**, the fluid portion of blood, and (2) **interstitial fluid (IF)**, the fluid in the microscopic spaces between tissue cells. There are numerous other examples of ECF that are distinct from both plasma and interstitial fluid—lymph, cerebrospinal fluid, humors of the eye, synovial fluid, serous fluid, secretions of the gastrointestinal tract—but most of these are similar to IF and are usually considered part of it.

Composition of Body Fluids

Water serves as the *universal solvent* in which a variety of solutes are dissolved. Solutes may be classified broadly as *electrolytes* and *nonelectrolytes*.

Electrolytes and Nonelectrolytes

Nonelectrolytes have bonds (usually covalent bonds) that prevent them from dissociating in solution, and for this reason, no electrically charged species are created when nonelectrolytes dissolve in water. Most nonelectrolytes are organic molecules—glucose, lipids, creatinine, and urea, for example.

In contrast, **electrolytes** are chemical compounds that *do* dissociate into ions in water. (See Chapter 2 if necessary to review these concepts of chemistry.) Because ions are charged particles, they can conduct an electrical current—and so have the name *electrolyte*. Typically, electrolytes include inorganic salts, both inorganic and organic acids and bases, and some proteins.

Although all dissolved solutes contribute to the osmotic activity of a fluid, electrolytes have much greater osmotic power than nonelectrolytes because each electrolyte molecule dissociates into at least two ions. For example, a molecule of sodium chloride (NaCl) contributes twice as many solute particles as glucose (which remains undissociated), and a molecule of magnesium chloride ($MgCl_2$) contributes three times as many:

$NaCl \rightarrow Na^+ + Cl^-$ (electrolyte; two particles)

$MgCl_2 \rightarrow Mg^{2+} + 2Cl^-$ (electrolyte; three particles)

glucose → glucose   (nonelectrolyte; one particle)

Regardless of the type of solute particle, water moves according to osmotic gradients—from an area of lesser osmolality to an area of greater osmolality. For this reason, electrolytes have the greatest ability to cause fluid shifts.

Electrolyte concentrations of body fluids are usually expressed in **milliequivalents per liter (mEq/L)**, a measure of the number

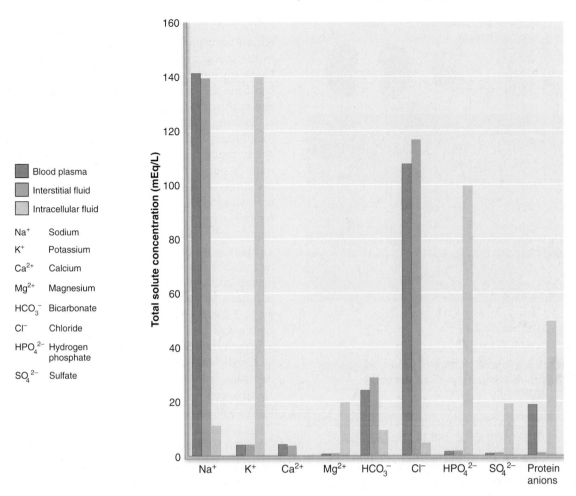

Figure 26.2 Electrolyte composition of blood plasma, interstitial fluid, and intracellular fluid. The very low intracellular Ca^{2+} concentration (10^{-7} M) does not include Ca^{2+} stores sequestered inside organelles. The high concentration of intracellular HPO_4^{2-} includes large amounts bound to intermediate metabolites, proteins, and lipids.

of electrical charges in 1 liter of solution. The concentration of any ion in solution can be computed using the equation

$$mEq/L = \frac{\text{ion concentration (mg/L)}}{\text{atomic weight of ion (mg/mmol)}} \times \begin{array}{l}\text{no. of}\\\text{electrical}\\\text{charges}\\\text{on}\\\text{one ion}\end{array}$$

To compute the mEq/L of sodium or calcium ions in solution in plasma, we would determine the normal concentration of these ions in plasma, look up their atomic weights in the periodic table (see Appendix E), and plug these values into the equation:

$$Na^+: \frac{3300 \text{ mg/L}}{23 \text{ mg/mmol}} \times 1 = 143 \text{ mEq/L}$$

$$Ca^{2+}: \frac{100 \text{ mg/L}}{40 \text{ mg/mmol}} \times 2 = 5 \text{ mEq/L}$$

Notice that for ions with a single charge, 1 mEq is equal to 1 mmol, which, when dissolved in 1 kg of water, produces 1 mOsm (see p. 979). On the other hand, 1 mEq of ions with a double charge (like calcium) is equal to 1/2 mOsm. In either case, 1 mEq provides the same amount of charge.

Comparison of Extracellular and Intracellular Fluids

A quick glance at the bar graphs in **Figure 26.2** reveals that each fluid compartment has a distinctive pattern of electrolytes. Except for the relatively high protein content in plasma, however, the extracellular fluids are very similar. Their chief cation is sodium, and their major anion is chloride. However, plasma contains somewhat fewer chloride ions than interstitial fluid, because the nonpenetrating plasma proteins are normally anions and plasma is electrically neutral.

In contrast to extracellular fluids, the ICF contains only small amounts of Na^+ and Cl^-. Its most abundant cation is potassium, and its major anion is HPO_4^{2-}. Cells also contain substantial quantities of soluble proteins (about three times the amount found in plasma).

Notice that sodium and potassium ion concentrations in ECF and ICF are nearly opposite (Figure 26.2). The characteristic distribution of these ions on the two sides of cellular membranes reflects the activity of cellular ATP-dependent sodium-potassium pumps, which keep intracellular Na^+ concentrations low and K^+ concentrations high. Renal mechanisms can reinforce these ion distributions by secreting K^+ into the filtrate as Na^+ is reabsorbed from the filtrate.

26

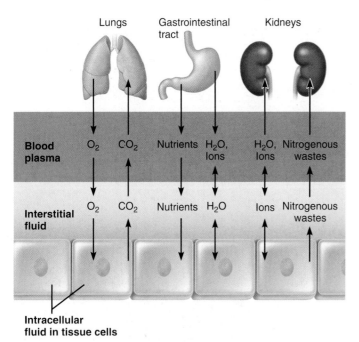

Figure 26.3 Exchange of gases, nutrients, water, and wastes between the three fluid compartments of the body.

Electrolytes are the most abundant solutes in body fluids and determine most of their chemical and physical reactions, but they do not constitute the *bulk* of dissolved solutes in these fluids. Proteins and some of the nonelectrolytes (phospholipids, cholesterol, and triglycerides) found in the ECF are large molecules. They account for about 90% of the mass of dissolved solutes in plasma, 60% in the IF, and 97% in the ICF.

Fluid Movement Among Compartments

The continuous exchange and mixing of body fluids are regulated by osmotic and hydrostatic pressures. Although water moves freely between the compartments along osmotic gradients, solutes are unequally distributed because of their size, electrical charge, or dependence on transport proteins. Anything that changes the solute concentration in any compartment leads to net water flows.

Figure 26.3 summarizes the exchanges of gases, solutes, and water across the body's borders and between the three fluid compartments within the body. In general, substances must pass through both the plasma and IF in order to reach the ICF. In the lungs, gastrointestinal tract, and kidneys, exchanges between the "outside world" and the plasma occur almost continuously. These exchanges alter plasma composition and volume, with the plasma serving as the "highway" for delivering substances throughout the body (see Chapter 17). Compensating adjustments between the plasma and the other two fluid compartments follow quickly so that balance is restored.

Exchanges between plasma and IF occur across capillary membranes. We described in detail the pressures driving these fluid movements in Chapter 19 on pp. 718–719. Here we will simply review the outcome of these mechanisms. Nearly protein-free plasma is forced out of the blood into the interstitial space by the hydrostatic pressure of blood. This filtered fluid is then almost completely reabsorbed into the bloodstream in response to the colloid osmotic (oncotic) pressure of plasma proteins. Under normal circumstances, the small net leakage that remains behind in the interstitial space is picked up by lymphatic vessels and returned to the blood.

Exchanges between the IF and ICF occur across plasma membranes and depend on the membranes' complex permeability properties. As a general rule, two-way osmotic flow of water is substantial. But ion fluxes are restricted and, in most cases, ions move selectively by active transport or through channels. Movements of nutrients, respiratory gases, and wastes are typically unidirectional. For example, glucose and oxygen move into the cells and metabolic wastes move out.

Many factors can change ECF and ICF volumes. Because water moves freely between compartments, however, the osmolalities of all body fluids are equal (except during the first few minutes after a change in one of the fluids occurs). Increasing the ECF solute content (mainly the NaCl concentration) can be expected to cause osmotic and volume changes in the ICF— namely, a shift of water out of the cells. Conversely, decreasing ECF osmolality causes water to move into the cells. Thus, the ICF volume is determined by the ECF solute concentration. These concepts underlie all events that control fluid balance in the body and should be understood thoroughly.

CHECK YOUR UNDERSTANDING

1. Which do you have more of, extracellular or intracellular fluid? Plasma or interstitial fluid?
2. What is the major cation in the ECF? In ICF? What are the intracellular anion counterparts of ECF's chloride ions?
3. If you eat salty pretzels without drinking, what happens to the volume of your extracellular fluid? Explain.

For answers, see Appendix G.

Water Balance and ECF Osmolality

▶ List the routes by which water enters and leaves the body.

▶ Describe feedback mechanisms that regulate water intake and hormonal controls of water output in urine.

▶ Explain the importance of obligatory water losses.

▶ Describe possible causes and consequences of dehydration, hypotonic hydration, and edema.

For the body to remain properly hydrated, water intake must equal water output. *Water intake* varies widely from person to person and is strongly influenced by habit, but it is typically about 2500 ml a day in adults **(Figure 26.4)**. Most water enters the body through ingested liquids and solid foods. Body water produced by cellular metabolism is called **metabolic water** or **water of oxidation**.

Water output occurs by several routes. Water that vaporizes out of the lungs in expired air or diffuses directly through the skin is called **insensible water loss**. Some is lost in obvious

Figure 26.4 Major sources of water intake and output. When intake and output are in balance, the body is adequately hydrated.

perspiration and in feces. The balance (about 60%) is excreted by the kidneys in urine.

Healthy people have a remarkable ability to maintain the tonicity of their body fluids within very narrow limits (280–300 mOsm/kg). A rise in plasma osmolality triggers (1) thirst, which prompts us to drink water, and (2) release of antidiuretic hormone (ADH), which causes the kidneys to conserve water and excrete concentrated urine. On the other hand, a decline in osmolality inhibits both thirst and ADH release, the latter followed by output of large volumes of dilute urine.

Regulation of Water Intake

The **thirst mechanism** is the driving force for water intake. An increase in plasma osmolality of only 2–3% excites the hypothalamic *thirst center*. A dry mouth also occurs because the rise in plasma colloid osmotic pressure causes less fluid to leave the bloodstream. Because the salivary glands obtain the water they require from the blood, they produce less saliva, reinforcing the drive to drink. A decrease in blood volume (or pressure) also triggers the thirst mechanism. However, because a substantial decrease (10–15%) is required, this is the less potent stimulus.

The hypothalamic thirst center neurons are stimulated when their *osmoreceptors* lose water by osmosis to the hypertonic ECF, or are activated by angiotensin II, by baroreceptor inputs, or other stimuli. Collectively, these events cause a subjective sensation of thirst, which motivates us to get a drink (Figure 26.5). This mechanism helps explain why it is that some cocktail lounges and bars provide free *salty* snacks to their patrons.

Curiously, thirst is quenched almost as soon as we begin drinking water, even though the water has yet to be absorbed into the blood. The damping of thirst begins as the mucosa of the mouth and throat is moistened and continues as stretch receptors in the stomach and intestine are activated, providing

Figure 26.5 The thirst mechanism for regulating water intake. The major stimulus is increased osmolality of blood plasma. (Not all effects of angiotensin II are depicted.)

feedback signals that inhibit the thirst center. This premature quenching of thirst prevents us from drinking more than we need and overdiluting our body fluids, and allows time for the osmotic changes to come into play as regulatory factors.

As effective as thirst is, it is not always a reliable indicator of need. This is particularly true during athletic events, when thirst can be satisfied long before sufficient liquids have been drunk to

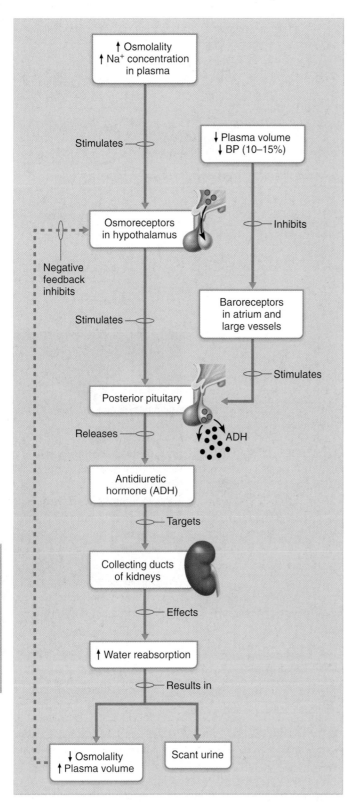

Figure 26.6 Mechanisms and consequences of ADH release. (Vasoconstrictor effects of ADH are not shown.)

maintain the body in top form. Additionally, elderly or confused people may not recognize or heed thirst signals. In contrast, fluid-overloaded renal or cardiac patients may feel thirsty despite their condition.

Regulation of Water Output

Output of certain amounts of water is unavoidable. Such **obligatory water losses** help to explain why we cannot survive for long without drinking. Even the most heroic conservation efforts by the kidneys cannot compensate for zero water intake. Obligatory water loss includes the *insensible water losses* described above, water that accompanies undigested food residues in feces, and a minimum daily **sensible water loss** of 500 ml in urine.

Obligatory water loss in urine reflects the fact that human kidneys must normally flush 600 mmol per day of urine solutes (end products of metabolism and so forth) out of the body in water. The maximum concentration of urine is about 1200 mOsm, so a minimum of 500 ml of water must be excreted.

Beyond obligatory water loss, the solute concentration and volume of urine excreted depend on fluid intake, diet, and water loss via other avenues. For example, if you perspire profusely on a hot day, much less urine than usual has to be excreted to maintain water balance. Normally, the kidneys begin to eliminate excess water about 30 minutes after it is ingested. This delay reflects the time required to inhibit ADH release. Diuresis reaches a peak in 1 hour after drinking and then declines to its lowest level after 3 hours.

The body's water volume is closely tied to a powerful water "magnet," ionic sodium. Moreover, our ability to maintain water balance through urinary output is really a problem of sodium *and* water balance because the two are always regulated in tandem by mechanisms that serve cardiovascular function and blood pressure. Before dealing with Na^+ issues, we will recap ADH's effect on water output.

Influence of ADH

The amount of water reabsorbed in the renal collecting ducts is proportional to ADH release. When ADH levels are low, most of the water reaching the collecting ducts is not reabsorbed but simply allowed to pass through because the lack of aquaporins in the luminal membranes of the principal cells prevents the movement of water. The result is dilute urine and a reduced volume of body fluids. When ADH levels are high, aquaporins are inserted in the principal cell luminal membranes, nearly all of the filtered water is reabsorbed, and a small volume of concentrated urine is excreted.

Osmoreceptors of the hypothalamus sense the ECF solute concentration and trigger or inhibit ADH release from the posterior pituitary accordingly **(Figure 26.6)**. A decrease in ECF osmolality inhibits ADH release and allows more water to be excreted in urine, restoring normal blood osmolality. In contrast, an increase in ECF osmolality stimulates ADH release by stimulating the hypothalamic osmoreceptors.

26

ADH secretion is also influenced by *large* changes in blood volume or blood pressure. A decrease in BP triggers an increase in ADH secretion from the posterior pituitary both directly via baroreceptors in the atria and various blood vessels, and indirectly via the renin-angiotensin mechanism.

The key word here is "large" because changes in ECF osmolality are much more important as stimulatory or inhibitory factors. Factors that trigger ADH release by reducing blood volume include prolonged fever; excessive sweating, vomiting, or diarrhea; severe blood loss; and traumatic burns. Under these conditions, ADH also acts to constrict arterioles, directly increasing blood pressure—hence its other name: *vasopressin*. For a summary of how renal mechanisms involving ADH, aldosterone, and angiotensin II tie into overall controls of blood volume and blood pressure, see Figure 26.10 (p. 1007).

Disorders of Water Balance

Few people really appreciate the importance of water in keeping the body's "machinery" working at peak efficiency. The principal abnormalities of water balance are dehydration, hypotonic hydration, and edema, and each of these conditions presents a special set of problems for its victims.

Dehydration

When water output exceeds intake over a period of time and the body is in negative fluid balance, the result is **dehydration**. Dehydration is a common sequel to hemorrhage, severe burns, prolonged vomiting or diarrhea, profuse sweating, water deprivation, and diuretic abuse. Dehydration may also be caused by endocrine disturbances, such as diabetes mellitus or diabetes insipidus (see Chapter 16).

Early signs and symptoms of dehydration include a "cottony" or sticky oral mucosa, thirst, dry flushed skin, and decreased urine output (*oliguria*). If prolonged, dehydration may lead to weight loss, fever, and mental confusion. Another serious consequence of water loss from plasma is inadequate blood volume to maintain normal circulation and ensuing *hypovolemic shock*.

In all these situations, water is lost from the ECF **(Figure 26.7a)**. This loss is followed by the osmotic movement of water from the cells into the ECF, which equalizes the osmolality of the extracellular and intracellular fluids even though the total fluid volume has been reduced. The overall effect is called dehydration, but it rarely involves only a water deficit, because most often electrolytes are lost as well.

Hypotonic Hydration

When the ECF osmolality starts to drop, several compensatory mechanisms are set into motion. ADH release is inhibited, and as a result, less water is reabsorbed and excess water is quickly flushed from the body in urine. But, when there is renal insufficiency or when an extraordinary amount of water is drunk very quickly, a type of cellular *overhydration* called **hypotonic hydration** may occur. In either case, the ECF is diluted—its sodium content is normal, but excess water is present. For this reason, the hallmark of this condition is **hyponatremia** (low

(a) Mechanism of dehydration

(b) Mechanism of hypotonic hydration

Figure 26.7 Disturbances in water balance.

ECF Na^+ concentration), which promotes net osmosis into the tissue cells, causing them to swell as they become abnormally hydrated (Figure 26.7b).

Hypotonic hydration leads to severe metabolic disturbances evidenced by nausea, vomiting, muscular cramping, and cerebral edema. It is particularly damaging to neurons. Uncorrected cerebral edema quickly leads to disorientation, convulsions, coma, and death. Indeed, several marathon runners have recently died because of overhydration. Sudden and severe hyponatremia is treated by intravenous administration of hypertonic saline to reverse the osmotic gradient and "pull" water out of the cells.

Edema

Edema (ĕ-de′mah; "a swelling") is an atypical accumulation of fluid in the interstitial space, leading to tissue (but not cell) swelling. Unlike hypotonic hydration, which increases the amount of fluid in all compartments due to an imbalance between water intake and output, edema is an increase in volume of *only* the IF. It may be caused by any event that steps up the flow of fluid out of the blood or hinders its return.

Factors that accelerate fluid loss from the blood include increases in capillary hydrostatic pressure and permeability. Increased capillary hydrostatic pressure can result from incompetent venous valves, localized blood vessel blockage, congestive heart failure, or high blood volume. Whatever the cause, the abnormally high capillary hydrostatic pressure intensifies filtration at the capillary beds.

Increased capillary permeability is usually due to an ongoing inflammatory response. Recall from p. 769 that inflammatory chemicals cause local capillaries to become very porous, allowing large amounts of exudate (containing not only clotting proteins but also other plasma proteins, nutrients, and immune elements) to form.

Edema caused by hindered fluid return to the blood usually reflects an imbalance in the colloid osmotic pressures on the two sides of the capillary membranes. For example, **hypoproteinemia** (hi″po-pro″te-ĭ-ne′me-ah), a condition of unusually low levels of plasma proteins, results in tissue edema because protein-deficient plasma has an abnormally low colloid osmotic pressure. Fluids are forced out of the capillary beds at the arterial ends by blood pressure as usual, but fail to return to the blood at the venous ends. As a result, the interstitial spaces become congested with fluid. Hypoproteinemia may result from protein malnutrition, liver disease, or *glomerulonephritis* (in which plasma proteins pass through "leaky" renal filtration membranes and are lost in urine).

Although the cause differs, the result is the same when lymphatic vessels are blocked or have been surgically removed. The small amounts of plasma proteins that seep out of the bloodstream are not returned to the blood as usual. As the leaked proteins accumulate in the IF, they exert an ever-increasing colloid osmotic pressure, which draws fluid from the blood and holds it in the interstitial space.

Edema can impair tissue function because excess fluid in the interstitial space increases the distance nutrients and oxygen must diffuse between the blood and the cells. However, the most serious problems resulting from edema affect the cardiovascular system. When fluid leaves the bloodstream and accumulates in the interstitial space, both blood volume and blood pressure decline and the efficiency of the circulation can be severely impaired.

CHECK YOUR UNDERSTANDING

4. What change in plasma is most important for triggering thirst? Where is that change sensed?

5. ADH, by itself, cannot reduce an increase in osmolality in body fluids. Why not? What other mechanism is required?

6. For each of the following, state whether it might result in dehydration, hypotonic hydration, or edema: (a) loss of plasma proteins due to liver failure; (b) copious sweating; (c) using ecstasy (MDMA), which promotes ADH secretion.

For answers, see Appendix G.

Electrolyte Balance

▶ Indicate routes of electrolyte entry and loss from the body.

▶ Describe the importance of ionic sodium in fluid and electrolyte balance of the body, and indicate its relationship to normal cardiovascular system functioning.

▶ Describe mechanisms involved in regulating sodium balance, blood volume, and blood pressure.

▶ Explain how potassium, calcium, and anion balances in plasma are regulated.

Electrolytes include salts, acids, and bases, but the term **electrolyte balance** usually refers to the salt balance in the body. Salts are important in controlling fluid movements and provide minerals essential for excitability, secretory activity, and membrane permeability. Although many electrolytes are crucial for cellular activity, here we will specifically examine the regulation of sodium, potassium, and calcium. In the next section we will consider acids and bases, which are intimately involved in determining the pH of body fluids.

Salts enter the body in foods and fluids, and small amounts are generated during metabolic activity. For example, phosphates are liberated during catabolism of nucleic acids and bone matrix. Obtaining enough electrolytes is usually not a problem. Indeed, most of us have a far greater taste than need for salt. We shake table salt (NaCl) on our food even though natural foods contain ample amounts and processed foods contain exorbitant quantities. The taste for very salty foods is learned, but some liking for salt may be innate to ensure adequate intake of these two vital ions.

Salts are lost from the body in perspiration, feces, and urine. Even though sweat is normally hypotonic, large amounts of salt can be lost on a hot day simply because more sweat is produced. Gastrointestinal disorders can also lead to large salt losses in feces or vomitus. Consequently, the flexibility of renal mechanisms that regulate the electrolyte balance of the blood is a critical asset. Some causes and consequences of electrolyte imbalances are summarized in **Table 26.1**.

HOMEOSTATIC IMBALANCE

Severe electrolyte deficiencies may prompt a craving for salty or sour foods, such as smoked meats or pickled eggs. This is common in those with *Addison's disease*, a disorder entailing deficient mineralocorticoid hormone production by the adrenal cortex. When minerals such as iron are deficient, a person may even eat substances not usually considered foods, like chalk, clay, starch, and burnt match tips. This appetite for abnormal substances is called *pica*. ■

The Central Role of Sodium in Fluid and Electrolyte Balance

Sodium holds a central position in fluid and electrolyte balance and overall body homeostasis. Indeed, regulating the balance between sodium input and output is one of the most important renal functions. The salts $NaHCO_3$ and NaCl account for 90–95% of all solutes in the ECF, and they contribute about 280 mOsm of the total ECF solute concentration (300 mOsm).

At its normal plasma concentration of about 142 mEq/L, Na^+ is the single most abundant cation in the ECF and the only one exerting *significant* osmotic pressure. Additionally, cellular plasma membranes are relatively impermeable to Na^+, but some does manage to diffuse in and must be pumped out against its electrochemical gradient. These two qualities give sodium the primary role in controlling ECF volume and water distribution in the body.

It is important to understand that while the sodium content of the body may change, *its ECF concentration normally remains*

TABLE 26.1	Causes and Consequences of Electrolyte Imbalances		
ION	**ABNORMALITY (SERUM VALUE)**	**POSSIBLE CAUSES**	**CONSEQUENCES**
Sodium	Hypernatremia (Na$^+$ excess: >145 mEq/L)	Dehydration; uncommon in healthy individuals; may occur in infants or the confused aged (individuals unable to indicate thirst) or may be a result of excessive intravenous NaCl administration	Thirst. CNS dehydration leads to confusion and lethargy progressing to coma; increased neuromuscular irritability evidenced by twitching and convulsions.
	Hyponatremia (Na$^+$ deficit: <135 mEq/L)	Solute loss, water retention, or both (e.g., excessive Na$^+$ loss through vomiting, diarrhea, burned skin, tubal drainage of stomach, and as a result of excessive use of diuretics); deficiency of aldosterone (Addison's disease); renal disease; excess ADH release; excess H$_2$O ingestion	Most common signs are those of neurologic dysfunction due to brain swelling. If sodium amounts are actually normal but water is excessive, the symptoms are the same as those of water excess: mental confusion; giddiness; coma if development occurs slowly; muscular twitching, irritability, and convulsions if the condition develops rapidly. In hyponatremia accompanied by water loss, the main signs are decreased blood volume and blood pressure (circulatory shock)·
Potassium	Hyperkalemia (K$^+$ excess: >5.5 mEq/L)	Renal failure; deficit of aldosterone; rapid intravenous infusion of KCl; burns or severe tissue injuries which cause K$^+$ to leave cells	Nausea, vomiting, diarrhea; bradycardia; cardiac arrhythmias, depression, and arrest; skeletal muscle weakness; flaccid paralysis.
	Hypokalemia (K$^+$ deficit: <3.5 mEq/L)	Gastrointestinal tract disturbances (vomiting, diarrhea), gastrointestinal suction; Cushing's syndrome; inadequate dietary intake (starvation); hyperaldosteronism; diuretic therapy	Cardiac arrhythmias, flattened T wave; muscular weakness; metabolic alkalosis; mental confusion; nausea; vomiting.
Phosphate	Hyperphosphatemia (HPO$_4^{2-}$ excess: >2.9 mEq/L)	Decreased urinary loss due to renal failure; hypoparathyroidism; major tissue trauma; increased intestinal absorption	Clinical symptoms arise because of reciprocal changes in Ca^{2+} levels rather than directly from changes in plasma phosphate concentrations.
	Hypophosphatemia (HPO$_4^{2-}$ deficit: <1.6 mEq/L)	Decreased intestinal absorption; increased urinary output; hyperparathyroidism	
Chloride	Hyperchloremia (Cl$^-$ excess: >105 mEq/L)	Dehydration; increased retention or intake; metabolic acidosis; hyperparathyroidism	No direct clinical symptoms; symptoms generally associated with the underlying cause, which is often related to pH abnormalities.
	Hypochloremia (Cl$^-$ deficit: <95 mEq/L)	Metabolic alkalosis (e.g., due to vomiting or excessive ingestion of alkaline substances); aldosterone deficiency	
Calcium	Hypercalcemia (Ca^{2+} excess: >5.2 mEq/L or 10.5 mg%)*	Hyperparathyroidism; excessive vitamin D; prolonged immobilization; renal disease (decreased excretion); malignancy	Decreased neuromuscular excitability leading to cardiac arrhythmias and arrest, skeletal muscle weakness, confusion, stupor, and coma; kidney stones; nausea and vomiting.
	Hypocalcemia (Ca^{2+} deficit: <4.5 mEq/L or 9 mg%)*	Burns (calcium trapped in damaged tissues); hypoparathyroidism; vitamin D deficiency; renal tubular disease; renal failure; hyperphosphatemia; diarrhea; alkalosis	Increased neuromuscular excitability leading to tingling of fingers, tremors, skeletal muscle cramps, tetany, convulsions; depressed excitability of the heart; osteomalacia; fractures.
Magnesium	Hypermagnesemia (Mg^{2+} excess: >2.2 mEq/L)	Rare; occurs in renal failure when Mg^{2+} is not excreted normally; excessive ingestion of Mg^{2+}-containing antacids	Lethargy; impaired CNS functioning, coma, respiratory depression; cardiac arrest.
	Hypomagnesemia (Mg^{2+} deficit: <1.4 mEq/L)	Alcoholism; loss of intestinal contents, severe malnutrition; diuretic therapy	Tremors, increased neuromuscular excitability, tetany, convulsions.

*1 mg% = 1 mg/100 ml

stable because of immediate movement of water into or out of the ICF and longer-term adjustments due to the ADH and thirst mechanisms. Remember, *water follows salt*. Because all body fluids are in osmotic equilibrium, a change in plasma Na$^+$ levels affects not only plasma volume and blood pressure, but also the ICF and IF volumes. In addition, sodium ions continuously move back and forth between the ECF and body secretions. For example, about 8 L of Na$^+$-containing secretions (gastric, intestinal, and pancreatic juice, saliva, bile) are spewed into the digestive tract daily, only to be almost completely reabsorbed. Finally,

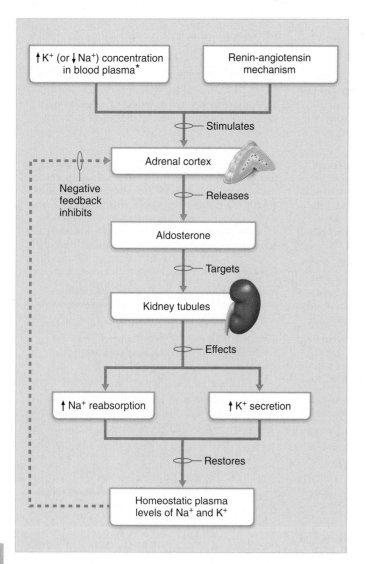

Figure 26.8 Mechanisms and consequences of aldosterone release.

*The adrenal cortex is much less sensitive to decreased plasma Na^+ than to increased plasma K^+.

26

renal acid-base control mechanisms (which we will discuss shortly) are coupled to Na^+ transport.

Regulation of Sodium Balance

Despite the crucial importance of sodium, receptors that specifically monitor Na^+ levels in body fluids have yet to be found. Regulation of the Na^+-water balance is inseparably linked to blood pressure and volume, and involves a variety of neural and hormonal controls. Reabsorption of Na^+ does *not* exhibit a transport maximum, and in healthy individuals nearly all Na^+ in the urinary filtrate can be reabsorbed. We will begin our coverage of sodium balance by reviewing the regulatory effect of aldosterone and angiotensin II. Then we will examine various feedback loops that interact to regulate sodium and water balance and blood pressure.

Influence of Aldosterone and Angiotensin II

The hormone **aldosterone** "has the most to say" about renal regulation of sodium ion concentrations in the ECF. But whether aldosterone is present or not, some 65% of the Na^+ in the renal filtrate is reabsorbed in the proximal tubules of the kidneys and another 25% is reclaimed in the loops of Henle (see Chapter 25).

When aldosterone concentrations are high, essentially all the remaining filtered Na^+ is actively reabsorbed in the distal convoluted tubules and collecting ducts. Consistent with aldosterone's central role in maintaining blood volume and blood pressure, water always follows Na^+. This water comes from either the intracellular fluid or, if ADH is present, from the filtrate in the collecting ducts. One way or another, aldosterone increases ECF volume.

When aldosterone release is inhibited, virtually no Na^+ reabsorption occurs beyond the distal tubule. Urinary excretion of large amounts of Na^+ *always* results in the excretion of large amounts of water as well, but the reverse is *not* true. Substantial amounts of nearly sodium-free urine can be eliminated as needed to achieve water balance.

The most important trigger for aldosterone release from the adrenal cortex is the renin-angiotensin mechanism mediated by the juxtaglomerular apparatus of the renal tubules (see Figures 26.8 and 26.10). When the juxtaglomerular (JG) apparatus responds to (1) sympathetic stimulation, (2) decreased filtrate NaCl concentration, or (3) decreased stretch (due to decreased blood pressure), its granular cells release renin. Renin catalyzes the initial step in the reactions that produce angiotensin II, which prompts aldosterone release. Conversely, high renal blood pressure and high filtrate NaCl concentrations depress release of renin, angiotensin II, and aldosterone. The adrenal cortical cells are also directly stimulated to release aldosterone by elevated K^+ levels in the ECF **(Figure 26.8)**.

Angiotensin II is an important intermediate in the pathway linking renin to aldosterone release. Angiotensin II prods the adrenal cortex to release aldosterone, and also directly increases Na^+ reabsorption by kidney tubules. In addition, it has a number of other actions, all aimed at raising blood volume and blood pressure. We described these actions in Chapter 25 (p. 972).

Aldosterone brings about its effects slowly, over a period of hours to days. The principal effects of aldosterone are to diminish urinary output and increase blood volume. However, before these factors can change by more than a few percent, feedback mechanisms for blood volume control come into play.

HOMEOSTATIC IMBALANCE

People with Addison's disease (hypoaldosteronism) lose tremendous amounts of NaCl and water to urine. They are perpetually teetering on the brink of hypovolemia, but as long as they ingest adequate amounts of salt and fluids, they can avoid problems with Na^+ balance. ■

Influence of Atrial Natriuretic Peptide

The influence of **atrial natriuretic peptide (ANP)** can be summarized in one sentence: It reduces blood pressure and blood

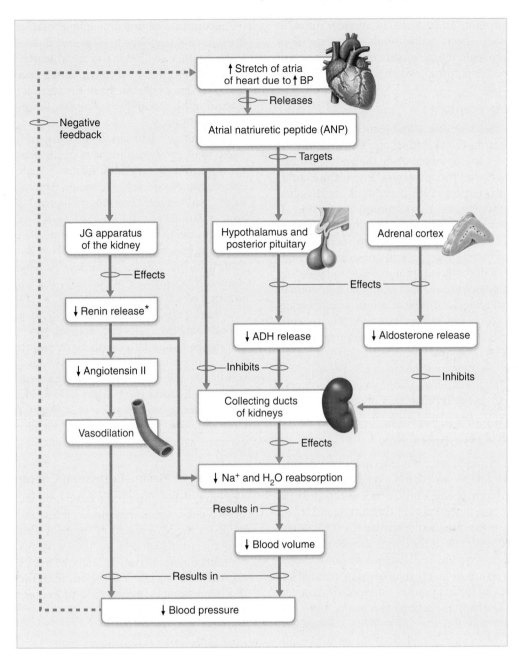

Figure 26.9 Mechanisms and consequences of ANP release.

*↓ Renin release also inhibits ADH and aldosterone release and hence the effects of those hormones.

volume by inhibiting nearly all events that promote vasoconstriction and Na$^+$ and water retention **(Figure 26.9)**. A hormone that is released by certain cells of the heart atria when they are stretched by the effects of elevated blood pressure, ANP has diuretic and natriuretic (salt-excreting) effects. It promotes excretion of Na$^+$ and water by the kidneys by inhibiting the ability of the collecting ducts to reabsorb Na$^+$ and by suppressing the release of ADH, renin, and aldosterone. Additionally, ANP acts both directly and indirectly (by inhibiting renin-induced generation of angiotensin II) to relax vascular smooth muscle, and in this way it causes vasodilation. Collectively, these effects reduce blood pressure.

Influence of Other Hormones

Female Sex Hormones The **estrogens** are chemically similar to aldosterone and, like aldosterone, enhance NaCl reabsorption by the renal tubules. Because water follows, many women retain fluid as their estrogen levels rise during the menstrual cycle. The edema experienced by many pregnant women is also largely due to the effect of estrogens. **Progesterone** appears to decrease Na$^+$ reabsorption by blocking the effect aldosterone has on the renal tubules. Thus, progesterone has a diuretic-like effect and promotes Na$^+$ and water loss.

Glucocorticoids The usual effect of **glucocorticoids**, such as cortisol and hydrocortisol, is to enhance tubular reabsorption of

Na^+, but they also promote an increased glomerular filtration rate that may mask their effects on the tubules. However, when their plasma levels are high, the glucocorticoids exhibit potent aldosterone-like effects and promote edema.

Cardiovascular Baroreceptors

Blood volume is carefully monitored and regulated to maintain blood pressure and cardiovascular function. As blood volume (and with it, pressure) rises, baroreceptors in the heart and in the large vessels of the neck and thorax (carotid arteries and aorta) alert the cardiovascular centers in the brain stem. Shortly after, sympathetic nervous system impulses to the kidneys decline, allowing the afferent arterioles to dilate. As the glomerular filtration rate rises, Na^+ output and water output increase. This phenomenon, part of the baroreceptor reflex described in Chapter 19 (pp. 707–708), reduces blood volume and blood pressure.

Drops in systemic blood pressure lead to reflex constriction of systemic arterioles including the afferent arterioles, which reduces filtrate formation and urinary output and increases systemic blood pressure (Figure 26.10). The baroreceptors provide information on the "fullness" or volume of the circulation that is critical for maintaining cardiovascular homeostasis. Because Na^+ content determines fluid volume and fluid volume determines blood pressure, the baroreceptors indirectly monitor Na^+ content.

Regulation of Potassium Balance

Potassium, the chief intracellular cation, is required for normal neuromuscular functioning as well as for several essential metabolic activities. Even slight changes in K^+ concentration in the ECF have profound and potentially life-threatening effects on neurons and muscle fibers because the relative ICF-ECF potassium concentration directly affects the resting membrane potential of these cells. K^+ excess in the ECF decreases their membrane potential, causing depolarization, often followed by reduced excitability. Too little K^+ in the ECF causes hyperpolarization and nonresponsiveness. The heart is particularly sensitive to K^+ levels. Both too much and too little K^+ (hyperkalemia and hypokalemia, respectively) can disrupt electrical conduction in the heart, leading to sudden death (Table 26.1).

Potassium is also part of the body's buffer system, which resists changes in the pH of body fluids. Shifts of hydrogen ions (H^+) into and out of cells induce corresponding shifts of K^+ in the opposite direction to maintain cation balance. Consequently, ECF potassium levels rise with acidosis, as K^+ leaves and H^+ enters the cells, and fall with alkalosis, as K^+ moves into the cells and H^+ leaves them to enter the ECF. Although these pH-driven shifts do not change the total amount of K^+ in the body, they can seriously interfere with the activity of excitable cells.

Regulatory Site: The Cortical Collecting Duct

Like Na^+ balance, K^+ balance is maintained chiefly by renal mechanisms. However, there are important differences in the way this balance is achieved. The amount of Na^+ reabsorbed in the tubules is precisely tailored to need, and Na^+ is *never* secreted into the filtrate.

In contrast, the proximal tubules reabsorb about 60–80% of the filtered K^+, and the thick ascending limb of Henle's loop absorbs another 10–20% or so regardless of need, leaving about 10% at the beginning of the collecting ducts. The responsibility for K^+ balance falls chiefly on the cortical collecting ducts, and is accomplished mainly by changing the amount of K^+ *secreted* into the filtrate.

As a rule, K^+ levels in the ECF are sufficiently high that K^+ needs to be excreted, and the rate at which the principal cells of the cortical collecting ducts secrete K^+ into the filtrate is accelerated over basal levels. (At times, the amount of K^+ excreted may actually exceed the amount filtered.) When ECF potassium concentrations are abnormally low, K^+ moves from the tissue cells into the ECF and the renal principal cells conserve K^+ by reducing its secretion and excretion to a minimum. Note that these principal cells are the same cells that mediate aldosterone-induced reabsorption of Na^+ and the ADH-stimulated reabsorption of water.

Additionally, *type A intercalated cells*, a unique population of collecting duct cells, can reabsorb some of the K^+ left in the filtrate (in conjunction with active secretion of H^+), thereby helping to reestablish K^+ (and pH) balance. However, keep in mind that the main thrust of renal regulation of K^+ is to *excrete* it. Because the kidneys have a limited ability to retain K^+, it may be lost in urine even in the face of a deficiency. Consequently, failure to ingest potassium-rich substances eventually results in a severe deficiency.

Influence of Plasma Potassium Concentration

The single most important factor influencing K^+ secretion is the K^+ concentration in blood plasma. A high-potassium diet increases the K^+ content of the ECF. This favors entry of K^+ into the principal cells of the cortical collecting duct and prompts them to secrete K^+ into the filtrate so that more of it is excreted. Conversely, a low-potassium diet or accelerated K^+ loss depresses its secretion (and promotes its limited reabsorption) by the collecting ducts.

Influence of Aldosterone

The second factor influencing K^+ secretion into the filtrate is aldosterone. As it stimulates the principal cells to reabsorb Na^+, aldosterone simultaneously enhances K^+ secretion (see Figure 26.8). Adrenal cortical cells are *directly* sensitive to the K^+ content of the ECF bathing them. When it increases even slightly, the adrenal cortex is strongly stimulated to release aldosterone, which increases K^+ secretion by the exchange process we just described. The result is that K^+ controls its own concentrations in the ECF via feedback regulation of aldosterone release.

Aldosterone is also secreted in response to the renin-angiotensin mechanism previously described. Given the opposing effects of aldosterone on plasma Na^+ and K^+, you might expect that Na^+- and volume-driven changes in aldosterone would cause K^+ imbalances. This generally does not occur because other compensatory mechanisms in the kidneys maintain plasma K^+.

Figure 26.10 Mechanisms regulating sodium and water balance help maintain blood pressure homeostasis.

 HOMEOSTATIC IMBALANCE

In an attempt to reduce NaCl intake, many people have turned to salt substitutes, which are high in potassium. However, heavy consumption of these substitutes is safe only when aldosterone release in the body is normal. In the absence of aldosterone, hy-perkalemia is swift and lethal regardless of K+ intake (Table 26.1). Conversely, when a person has an adrenocortical tumor that pumps out tremendous amounts of aldosterone, ECF potassium levels fall so low that neurons all over the body hyperpolarize and paralysis occurs. ■

26

Regulation of Calcium and Phosphate Balance

About 99% of the body's calcium is found in bones in the form of calcium phosphate salts, which provide strength and rigidity to the skeleton. The bony skeleton provides a dynamic reservoir from which calcium and phosphate can be withdrawn or deposited to maintain the balance of these electrolytes in the ECF.

Ionic calcium in the ECF is important for normal blood clotting, cell membrane permeability, and secretory behavior, but its most important effect by far is on neuromuscular excitability. Hypocalcemia increases excitability and causes muscle tetany. Hypercalcemia is equally dangerous because it inhibits neurons and muscle cells and may cause life-threatening cardiac arrhythmias (Table 26.1).

ECF calcium ion levels are closely regulated by **parathyroid hormone (PTH)**, and rarely deviate from normal limits. (The hormone calcitonin, produced by the thyroid, is often thought of as a calcium-lowering hormone, but, as we discussed in Chapter 16, its effects on blood calcium levels in adults are negligible.) Parathyroid hormone is released by the tiny parathyroid glands located on the posterior aspect of the thyroid gland in the neck. Declining plasma levels of Ca^{2+} directly stimulate the parathyroid glands to release PTH, which promotes an increase in calcium levels by targeting the following organs (see also Figure 16.12 on p. 614):

1. **Bones.** PTH activates bone-digesting osteoclasts, which break down the bone matrix, resulting in the release of Ca^{2+} and HPO_4^{2-} to the blood.
2. **Small intestine.** PTH enhances intestinal absorption of Ca^{2+} indirectly by stimulating the kidneys to transform vitamin D to its active form, which is necessary for Ca^{2+} absorption by the small intestine.
3. **Kidneys.** PTH increases Ca^{2+} reabsorption by the renal tubules while decreasing phosphate ion reabsorption. In this way, calcium conservation and phosphate excretion go hand in hand. The *product* of Ca^{2+} and HPO_4^{2-} concentrations in the ECF remains constant, preventing calcium-salt deposits in bones or soft body tissues.

Most Ca^{2+} is reabsorbed passively in the PCT via diffusion through the paracellular route (a process driven by its electro-chemical gradient). However, as with other ions, "fine-tuning" of Ca^{2+} reabsorption occurs in the distal nephron. PTH-regulated Ca^{2+} channels control Ca^{2+} entry into DCT cells at the luminal membrane, while Ca^{2+} pumps and antiporters export it at the basolateral membrane. Under normal circumstances about 98% of the filtered Ca^{2+} is reabsorbed owing to the action of PTH.

As a rule, 75% of the filtered phosphate ions (including $H_2PO_4^-$, HPO_4^{2-}, and PO_4^{3-}) are reabsorbed in the PCT by active transport. Phosphate reabsorption is set by its transport maximum. Amounts present in excess of that maximum simply flow out in urine. PTH inhibits active transport of phosphate by decreasing its T_m.

When ECF calcium levels are within normal limits (9–11 mg/100 ml of blood) or higher, PTH secretion is inhibited. Consequently, release of Ca^{2+} from bone is inhibited, larger amounts

of Ca^{2+} are lost in feces and urine, and more phosphate is retained. Hormones other than PTH alter phosphate reabsorption. For example, insulin increases it while glucagon decreases it.

Regulation of Anions

Chloride is the major anion accompanying Na^+ in the ECF and, like sodium, Cl^- helps maintain the osmotic pressure of the blood. When blood pH is within normal limits or slightly alkaline, about 99% of filtered Cl^- is reabsorbed. In the PCT, it moves passively and simply follows sodium ions out of the filtrate and into the peritubular capillary blood. In most other tubule segments, Na^+ and Cl^- transport are coupled.

When acidosis occurs, less Cl^- accompanies Na^+ because HCO_3^- reabsorption is stepped up to restore blood pH to its normal range. Thus, the choice between Cl^- and HCO_3^- serves acid-base regulation. Most other anions, such as sulfates and nitrates, have transport maximums, and when their concentrations in the filtrate exceed the amount that can be reabsorbed, excesses spill into urine.

CHECK YOUR UNDERSTANDING

7. Jacob has Addison's disease (insufficient aldosterone release). How does this affect his plasma Na^+ and K^+ levels? How does this affect his blood pressure? Explain?
8. Renal handling of Na^+ can be summed up as "The kidneys reabsorb almost all of the Na^+ as filtrate passes through its tubules." Make a similar summary for K^+.
9. What hormone is the major regulator of Ca^{2+} in the blood? What are the effects of hypercalcemia? Hypocalcemia?

For answers, see Appendix G.

Acid-Base Balance

▶ List important sources of acids in the body.

Because of their abundant hydrogen bonds, all functional proteins (enzymes, hemoglobin, cytochromes, and others) are influenced by H^+ concentration. It follows then that nearly all biochemical reactions are influenced by the pH of their fluid environment, and the acid-base balance of body fluids is closely regulated. (For a review of the basic principles of acid-base reactions and pH, see Chapter 2.)

Optimal pH varies from one body fluid to another, but not by much. The normal pH of arterial blood is 7.4, that of venous blood and IF is 7.35, and that of ICF averages 7.0. The lower pH in cells and venous blood reflects their greater amounts of acidic metabolites and carbon dioxide, which combines with water to form carbonic acid, H_2CO_3.

Whenever the pH of arterial blood rises above 7.45, a person is said to have **alkalosis** (al″kah-lo′sis) or **alkalemia**. A drop in arterial pH to below 7.35 results in **acidosis** (as″ĭ-do′sis) or **acidemia**. Because pH 7.0 is neutral, chemically speaking 7.35 is not acidic. However, it is a higher-than-optimal H^+ concentration for most cells, so any arterial pH between 7.35 and 7.0 is called *physiological acidosis*.

Although small amounts of acidic substances enter the body via ingested foods, most hydrogen ions originate as metabolic by-products or end products. For example, (1) breakdown of phosphorus-containing proteins releases *phosphoric acid* into the ECF, (2) anaerobic respiration of glucose produces *lactic acid*, (3) fat metabolism yields other organic acids, such as fatty acids and *ketone bodies*, and (4) the loading and transport of carbon dioxide in the blood as HCO_3^- liberates hydrogen ions.

The H^+ concentration in blood is regulated sequentially by (1) chemical buffers, (2) the brain stem respiratory centers, and (3) renal mechanisms. Chemical buffers act within a fraction of a second to resist pH changes and are the first line of defense. Within 1–3 minutes, changes in respiratory rate and depth are occurring to compensate for acidosis or alkalosis. The kidneys, the body's most potent acid-base regulatory system, ordinarily require hours to a day or more to effect changes in blood pH.

Chemical Buffer Systems

▶ List the three major chemical buffer systems of the body and describe how they resist pH changes.

Recall that acids are *proton donors*, and that the acidity of a solution reflects only the *free* hydrogen ions, not those bound to anions. *Strong acids* dissociate completely and liberate all their H^+ in water (Figure 26.11a). They can dramatically change a solution's pH. By contrast, *weak acids* dissociate only partially (Figure 26.11b). Accordingly, they have a much smaller effect on pH. However, weak acids are efficient at preventing pH changes, and this feature allows them to play important roles in chemical buffer systems.

Bases are *proton acceptors*. Strong bases are those that dissociate easily in water and quickly tie up H^+. Conversely, weak bases are slower to accept protons.

A **chemical buffer** is a system of one or more compounds that acts to resist changes in pH when a strong acid or base is added. They do this by binding to H^+ whenever the pH drops and releasing them when pH rises.

The three major chemical buffer systems in the body are the *bicarbonate, phosphate,* and *protein buffer systems*. Anything that causes a shift in H^+ concentration in one fluid compartment simultaneously causes a change in the others. As a result, the buffer systems actually buffer one another, so that any drifts in pH are resisted by the *entire* buffer system.

Bicarbonate Buffer System

The **bicarbonate buffer system** is a mixture of carbonic acid (H_2CO_3) and its salt, sodium bicarbonate ($NaHCO_3$, a weak base), in the same solution. Although it also buffers the ICF, it is the *only* important *ECF* buffer.

Carbonic acid, a weak acid, does not dissociate to any great extent in neutral or acidic solutions. When a strong acid such as HCl is added to this buffer system, the existing carbonic acid remains intact. However, the bicarbonate ions of the salt act as weak bases to tie up the H^+ released by the stronger acid (HCl), forming *more* carbonic acid:

(a) **A strong acid such as HCl dissociates completely into its ions.**

(b) **A weak acid such as H_2CO_3 does *not* dissociate completely.**

Figure 26.11 Dissociation of strong and weak acids in water. HCl: hydrochloric acid; H_2CO_3: carbonic acid. Undissociated molecules are shown in colored ovals.

$$HCl \ + \ NaHCO_3 \rightarrow H_2CO_3 \ + \ NaCl$$
strong acid   weak base   weak acid   salt

Because it is converted to the weak acid H_2CO_3, HCl lowers the pH of the solution only slightly.

When a strong base such as sodium hydroxide (NaOH) is added to the same buffer solution, a weak base such as sodium bicarbonate ($NaHCO_3$) does not dissociate further under the alkaline conditions. However, the added base forces the carbonic acid to dissociate further, donating more H^+ to tie up the OH^- released by the strong base:

$$NaOH \ + \ H_2CO_3 \rightarrow NaHCO_3 \ + \ H_2O$$
strong base   weak acid   weak base   water

The net result is replacement of a strong base (NaOH) by a weak one ($NaHCO_3$), so that the pH of the solution rises very little.

Although the bicarbonate salt in the example is sodium bicarbonate, other bicarbonate salts function in the same way because HCO_3^- is the important ion, not the cation it is paired with. In cells, where little Na^+ is present, potassium and magnesium bicarbonates are part of the bicarbonate buffer system.

The buffering power of this type of system is directly related to the concentrations of the buffering substances. If acids enter the blood at such a rate that all the available HCO_3^- ions, often referred to as the **alkaline reserve**, are tied up, the buffer system becomes ineffective and blood pH changes. The bicarbonate ion concentration in the ECF is normally around 25 mEq/L and is closely regulated by the kidneys. The concentration of H_2CO_3 is just over 1 mEq/L but the supply of H_2CO_3 (which comes from the CO_2 released during cellular respiration) is almost limitless,

26

so obtaining that member of the buffer pair is usually not a problem. The H_2CO_3 content of the blood is subject to respiratory controls.

Phosphate Buffer System

The operation of the **phosphate buffer system** is nearly identical to that of the bicarbonate buffer. The components of the phosphate system are the sodium salts of dihydrogen phosphate ($H_2PO_4^-$) and monohydrogen phosphate (HPO_4^{2-}). NaH_2PO_4 acts as a weak acid. Na_2HPO_4, with one less hydrogen atom, acts as a weak base.

Again, H^+ released by strong acids is tied up in weak acids:

$$HCl + Na_2HPO_4 \rightarrow NaH_2PO_4 + NaCl$$
strong acid   weak base   weak acid   salt

and strong bases are converted to weak bases:

$$NaOH + NaH_2PO_4 \rightarrow Na_2HPO_4 + H_2O$$
strong base   weak acid   weak base   water

Because the phosphate buffer system is present in low concentrations in the ECF (approximately one-sixth that of the bicarbonate buffer system), it is relatively unimportant for buffering blood plasma. However, it is a very effective buffer in urine and in ICF, where phosphate concentrations are usually higher.

Protein Buffer System

Proteins in plasma and in cells are the body's most plentiful and powerful source of buffers, and constitute the **protein buffer system**. In fact, at least three-quarters of all the buffering power of body fluids resides in cells, and most of this reflects the buffering activity of intracellular proteins.

As described in Chapter 2, proteins are polymers of amino acids. Some of the linked amino acids have exposed groups of atoms called *organic acid (carboxyl) groups* (—COOH), which dissociate to release H^+ when the pH begins to rise:

$$R\text{—}COOH \rightarrow R\text{—}COO^- + H^+$$

(Note that R indicates the rest of the organic molecule, which contains many atoms.)

Other amino acids have exposed groups that can act as bases and accept H^+. For example, an exposed —NH_2 group can bind with a hydrogen ion, becoming —NH_3^+:

$$R\text{—}NH_2 + H^+ \rightarrow R\text{—}NH_3^+$$

Because this binding removes free hydrogen ions from the solution, it prevents the solution from becoming too acidic. Consequently, a single protein molecule can function reversibly as either an acid or a base depending on the pH of its environment. Molecules with this ability are called **amphoteric molecules** (am″fo-ter′ik).

Hemoglobin of red blood cells is an excellent example of a protein that functions as an intracellular buffer. As we explained earlier, CO_2 released from the tissues forms H_2CO_3, which dissociates to liberate H^+ and HCO_3^- in the blood. Meanwhile, hemoglobin is unloading oxygen, becoming reduced hemoglobin, which carries a negative charge. Because H^+ rapidly binds

to the hemoglobin anions, pH changes are minimized. In this case, carbonic acid, a weak acid, is buffered by an even weaker acid, hemoglobin.

Respiratory Regulation of H^+

▶ Describe the influence of the respiratory system on acid-base balance.

The respiratory and renal systems together form the *physiological buffering systems* that control pH by controlling the amount of acid or base in the body. Although such buffer systems act more slowly than the chemical buffer systems, they have many times the buffering power of all the body's chemical buffers combined.

As we described in Chapter 22, the respiratory system eliminates CO_2, an acid, from the blood while replenishing its supply of O_2. Carbon dioxide generated by cellular respiration enters erythrocytes in the circulation and is converted to bicarbonate ions for transport in the plasma:

$$\underset{\substack{\text{carbonic} \\ \text{acid}}}{CO_2 + H_2O \overset{\substack{\text{carbonic} \\ \text{anhydrase}}}{\rightleftharpoons} H_2CO_3} \rightleftharpoons \underset{\substack{\text{bicarbonate} \\ \text{ion}}}{H^+ + HCO_3^-}$$

The first set of double arrows indicates a reversible equilibrium between dissolved carbon dioxide and water on the left and carbonic acid on the right. The second set indicates a reversible equilibrium between carbonic acid on the left and hydrogen and bicarbonate ions on the right. Because of these equilibria, an increase in any of these chemical species pushes the reaction in the opposite direction. Notice also that the right side of the equation is equivalent to the bicarbonate buffer system.

In healthy individuals, CO_2 is expelled from the lungs at the same rate it is formed in the tissues. During carbon dioxide unloading, the reaction shifts to the left, and H^+ generated from carbonic acid is reincorporated into water. Because of the protein buffer system, H^+ produced by CO_2 transport is not allowed to accumulate and has little or no effect on blood pH. However, when hypercapnia occurs, it activates medullary chemoreceptors (via cerebral acidosis promoted by excessive accumulation of CO_2) that respond by increasing respiratory rate and depth (see Figure 22.25, p. 837). Additionally, a rising plasma H^+ concentration resulting from any metabolic process excites the respiratory center indirectly (via peripheral chemoreceptors) to stimulate deeper, more rapid respiration. As ventilation increases, more CO_2 is removed from the blood, pushing the reaction to the left and reducing the H^+ concentration.

When blood pH rises, the respiratory center is depressed. As respiratory rate drops and respiration becomes shallower, CO_2 accumulates, and the equilibrium is pushed to the right, causing the H^+ concentration to increase. Again blood pH is restored to the normal range. These respiratory system–mediated corrections of blood pH are accomplished within a minute or so.

Changes in alveolar ventilation can produce dramatic changes in blood pH—far more than is needed. For example, a doubling or halving of alveolar ventilation can raise or lower blood pH by about 0.2 pH unit. Because normal arterial pH is 7.4, a change of 0.2 pH unit yields a blood pH of 7.6 or 7.2—both well beyond the normal limits of blood pH. Respiratory controls of blood pH have a tremendous reserve capacity because alveolar ventilation can be increased about 15-fold or reduced to zero.

Anything that impairs respiratory system functioning causes acid-base imbalances. For example, net carbon dioxide retention (hypoventilation) leads to acidosis. On the other hand, hyperventilation, which causes net elimination of CO_2, causes alkalosis. When the cause of the pH imbalance is respiratory system problems, the resulting condition is either *respiratory acidosis* or *respiratory alkalosis* (see Table 26.2 on p. 1016).

CHECK YOUR UNDERSTANDING

10. Define acidemia and alkalemia.

11. To minimize a shift in pH brought about by adding a strong acid to a solution, would it be better if the solution contained a weak base or a strong base?

12. What are the body's three major chemical buffer systems? What is the most important buffer inside cells?

13. Joanne, a diabetic patient, is at the emergency department with acidosis due to the production of ketone bodies. Would you expect her ventilation to be increased or decreased? Why?

For answers, see Appendix G.

Renal Mechanisms of Acid-Base Balance

▶ Describe how the kidneys regulate hydrogen and bicarbonate ion concentrations in the blood.

The ultimate acid-base regulatory organs are the kidneys, which act slowly but surely to compensate for acid-base imbalances resulting from variations in diet or metabolism, or from disease. Chemical buffers can tie up excess acids or bases temporarily, but they cannot eliminate them from the body. And while the lungs can dispose of the **volatile acid** carbonic acid by eliminating CO_2, only the kidneys can rid the body of other acids generated by cellular metabolism: phosphoric, uric, and lactic acids, and ketone bodies. These acids are sometimes referred to as **metabolic (fixed) acids**, but this terminology is both unfortunate and incorrect because CO_2 and carbonic acid are also products of metabolism. Additionally, only the kidneys can regulate blood levels of alkaline substances and renew chemical buffers that are used up in regulating H^+ levels in the ECF.

The most important renal mechanisms for regulating acid-base balance of the blood involve (1) conserving (reabsorbing) or generating new HCO_3^-, and (2) excreting HCO_3^-. If we look back at the equation for the operation of the carbonic acid–bicarbonate buffer system of the blood, we can see that losing a HCO_3^- from the body produces the same net effect as gaining a H^+, because it pushes the equation to the right, increasing the H^+ level. By the same token, generating or reabsorbing HCO_3^- is the same as losing H^+ because it pushes the equation to the left, decreasing the H^+ level. For this reason, to

reabsorb bicarbonate, the kidney has to secrete H^+, and when it excretes excess HCO_3^-, H^+ is retained (not secreted).

Because the mechanisms for regulating acid-base balance depend on H^+ being secreted into the filtrate, we consider that process first. Secretion of H^+ occurs mainly in the PCT and in type A intercalated cells of the collecting duct. The H^+ secreted comes from the dissociation of carbonic acid, created from the combination of CO_2 and water within the tubule cells, a reaction catalyzed by *carbonic anhydrase* (**Figure 26.12**, ①, ②). For each H^+ secreted into the lumen of the PCT, one Na^+ is reabsorbed from the filtrate, maintaining the electrical balance (Figure 26.12, ③a).

The rate of H^+ secretion rises and falls with CO_2 levels in the ECF. The more CO_2 in the peritubular capillary blood, the faster the rate of H^+ secretion. Because blood CO_2 levels directly relate to blood pH, this system can respond to both rising and falling H^+ concentrations. Notice that secreted H^+ can combine with HCO_3^- in the filtrate, generating CO_2 and water (Figure 26.12, ④, ⑤). In this case, H^+ is bound in water. The rising concentration of CO_2 in the filtrate creates a steep diffusion gradient for its entry into the tubule cell, where it promotes still more H^+ secretion (Figure 26.12, ⑥).

Conserving Filtered Bicarbonate Ions: Bicarbonate Reabsorption

Bicarbonate ions (HCO_3^-) are an important part of the bicarbonate buffer system, the most important inorganic blood buffer. If this reservoir of base, or *alkaline reserve*, is to be maintained, the kidneys must do more than just eliminate enough hydrogen ions to counter rising blood H^+ levels. Depleted stores of HCO_3^- have to be replenished. This task is more complex than it seems because the tubule cells are almost completely impermeable to the HCO_3^- in the filtrate—they cannot reabsorb them.

However, the kidneys can conserve filtered HCO_3^- in a rather roundabout way, also illustrated in Figure 26.12. As you can see, dissociation of carbonic acid liberates HCO_3^- as well as H^+ (Figure 26.12, ②). Although the tubule cells cannot reclaim HCO_3^- directly from the filtrate, they can and do shunt HCO_3^- generated within them (as a result of splitting H_2CO_3) into the peritubular capillary blood (Figure 26.12, ③b). HCO_3^- leaves the tubule cell either accompanied by Na^+ or in exchange for Cl^-. For this reason, reabsorption of HCO_3^- depends on the active secretion of H^+, mostly by a Na^+-H^+ antiporter, but also by a H^+ ATPase (Figure 26.12, ③a). In the filtrate, H^+ combines with filtered HCO_3^-, as we saw earlier (Figure 26.12, ④, ⑤).

In short, for each filtered HCO_3^- that "disappears," a HCO_3^- generated within the tubule cells enters the blood—a one-for-one exchange. When large amounts of H^+ are secreted, correspondingly large amounts of HCO_3^- enter the peritubular blood. The net effect is that HCO_3^- is almost completely removed from the filtrate.

Generating New Bicarbonate Ions

Two renal mechanisms commonly carried out by cells of the PCT and collecting ducts generate *new* HCO_3^- that can be

Filtrate in tubule lumen

Nucleus

PCT cell

Peri-tubular capillary

① CO_2 combines with water within the tubule cell, forming H_2CO_3.

② H_2CO_3 is quickly split, forming H^+ and bicarbonate ion (HCO_3^-).

③a H^+ is secreted into the filtrate.

③b For each H^+ secreted, a HCO_3^- enters the peritubular capillary blood either via symport with Na^+ or via antiport with Cl^-.

④ Secreted H^+ combines with HCO_3^- in the filtrate, forming carbonic acid (H_2CO_3). HCO_3^- disappears from the filtrate at the same rate that HCO_3^- (formed within the tubule cell) enters the peritubular capillary blood.

⑤ The H_2CO_3 formed in the filtrate dissociates to release CO_2 and H_2O.

⑥ CO_2 diffuses into the tubule cell, where it triggers further H^+ secretion.

→ Primary active transport
┅► Secondary active transport
➡ Simple diffusion
● Transport protein
(CA) Carbonic anhydrase

Figure 26.12 Reabsorption of filtered HCO_3^- is coupled to H^+ secretion.
*The breakdown of H_2CO_3 to CO_2 and H_2O in the tubule lumen is catalyzed by carbonic anhydrase only in the PCT.

added to plasma. Both mechanisms involve renal excretion of acid, *via secretion and excretion* of either H^+ or ammonium ions in urine. Let's examine how these mechanisms differ.

Via Excretion of Buffered H^+   As long as *filtered bicarbonate* is reclaimed, as we saw in Figure 26.12, the secreted H^+ is *not excreted or lost* from the body in urine. Instead, the H^+ is buffered by HCO_3^- in the filtrate and ultimately becomes part of water molecules (most of which are reabsorbed).

However, once the filtered HCO_3^- is "used up" (usually by the time the filtrate reaches the collecting ducts), any additional H^+ secreted is excreted in urine. More often than not, this is the case.

Reclaiming filtered HCO_3^- simply restores the bicarbonate concentration of plasma that exists at the time. However, a normal diet introduces new H^+ into the body, and this additional H^+ must be balanced by the generation of *new* HCO_3^- (as opposed to filtered HCO_3^-) that moves into the blood to counteract acidosis. This process of alkalinizing the blood is the way the kidneys compensate for acidosis.

The excreted H^+ also must bind with buffers in the filtrate. Otherwise, a urine pH incompatible with life would result. (H^+ secretion ceases when urine pH falls to 4.5.) The most important urine buffer is the *phosphate buffer system*, specifically its weak base *monohydrogen phosphate* (HPO_4^{2-}).

The components of the phosphate buffer system filter freely into the tubules, and about 75% of the filtered phosphate is reabsorbed. However, their reabsorption is inhibited during acidosis.

As a result, the buffer pair becomes more and more concentrated as the filtrate moves through the renal tubules. As shown in **Figure 26.13**, ③a, the type A intercalated cells secrete H^+ actively via a H^+ ATPase pump and via a K^+-H^+ antiporter (not illustrated). The secreted H^+ combines with HPO_4^{2-}, forming $H_2PO_4^-$ which then flows out in urine (Figure 26.13, ④ and ⑤).

Bicarbonate ions generated in the cells during the same reaction move into the interstitial space via a $HCO_3^- - Cl^-$ antiport process and then move passively into the peritubular capillary blood (Figure 26.13, ③b). Notice again that when H^+ is being excreted, "brand new" bicarbonate ions are added to the blood—over and above those reclaimed from the filtrate. As you can see, in response to acidosis, the kidneys generate new HCO_3^- and add it to the blood (alkalinizing the blood) while adding an equal amount of H^+ to the filtrate (acidifying the urine).

Via NH_4^+ Excretion   The second and more important mechanism for excreting acid uses the ammonium ion (NH_4^+) produced by glutamine metabolism in the PCT cells. Ammonium ions are weak acids that donate few H^+ at physiological pH. As **Figure 26.14** step ① shows, for each glutamine metabolized (deaminated, oxidized, and acidified by combination with H^+), two NH_4^+ and two HCO_3^- result. The HCO_3^- moves through the basolateral membrane into the blood (Figure 26.14, ②b). The NH_4^+, in turn, is excreted and lost in urine (Figure 26.14, ②a, ③). As with the phosphate buffer system, this buffering mechanism replenishes the alkaline reserve of the blood, because the newly made HCO_3^- enters the blood as NH_4^+ is secreted.

26

① CO_2 combines with water within the type A intercalated cell, forming H_2CO_3.

② H_2CO_3 is quickly split, forming H^+ and bicarbonate ion (HCO_3^-).

③a H^+ is secreted into the filtrate by a H^+ ATPase pump.

③b For each H^+ secreted, a HCO_3^- enters the peritubular capillary blood via an antiport carrier in a HCO_3^--Cl^- exchange process.

④ Secreted H^+ combines with HPO_4^{2-} in the tubular filtrate, forming $H_2PO_4^-$.

⑤ The $H_2PO_4^-$ is excreted in the urine.

Figure 26.13 New HCO_3^- is generated via buffering of secreted H^+ by HPO_4^{2-} (mono-hydrogen phosphate).

① PCT cells metabolize glutamine to NH_4^+ and HCO_3^-.

②a The weak acid NH_4^+ (ammonium) is secreted into the filtrate, taking the place of H^+ on a Na^+-H^+ antiport carrier.

②b For each NH_4^+ secreted, a bicarbonate ion (HCO_3^-) enters the peritubular capillary blood via a symport carrier.

③ The NH_4^+ is excreted in the urine.

26

Figure 26.14 New HCO_3^- is generated via glutamine metabolism and NH_4^+ secretion.

Bicarbonate Ion Secretion

When the body is in alkalosis, another population of intercalated cells (type B) in the collecting ducts exhibit net HCO_3^- secretion (rather than net HCO_3^- reabsorption) while reclaiming H^+ to acidify the blood. Overall we can think of the type B cells as "flipped" type A cells, and we can visualize the HCO_3^- secretion process as the exact opposite of the HCO_3^- reabsorption process illustrated in Figure 26.12. However, the predominant process in the nephrons and collecting ducts is HCO_3^- reabsorption, and even during alkalosis, the amount of HCO_3^- excreted is much less than the amount conserved.

CHECK YOUR UNDERSTANDING

14. Reabsorption of HCO_3^- is always tied to the secretion of which ion?

15. What is the most important urinary buffer of H^+?

16. List the two mechanisms by which tubule and collecting duct cells generate new HCO_3^-.

For answers, see Appendix G.

Abnormalities of Acid-Base Balance

▶ Distinguish between acidosis and alkalosis resulting from respiratory and metabolic factors. Describe the importance of respiratory and renal compensations to acid-base balance.

All cases of acidosis and alkalosis can be classed according to cause as *respiratory* or *metabolic* (**Table 26.2**). The methods for determining the cause of an acid-base disturbance and whether it is being compensated (whether the lungs or kidneys are taking steps to correct the imbalance) are described in *A Closer Look* on p. 1017.

Respiratory Acidosis and Alkalosis

Respiratory pH imbalances result from some failure of the respiratory system to perform its normal pH-balancing role. The partial pressure of carbon dioxide (P_{CO_2}) is the single most important indicator of the adequacy of respiratory function. When respiratory function is normal, the P_{CO_2} fluctuates between 35 and 45 mm Hg. Generally speaking, higher values indicate respiratory acidosis, and lower values indicate respiratory alkalosis.

Respiratory acidosis is the most common cause of acid-base imbalance. It most often occurs when a person breathes shallowly or when gas exchange is hampered by diseases such as pneumonia, cystic fibrosis, or emphysema. Under such conditions, CO_2 accumulates in the blood. Thus, respiratory acidosis is characterized by falling blood pH and rising P_{CO_2}.

Respiratory alkalosis results when carbon dioxide is eliminated from the body faster than it is produced. This is called *hyperventilation* (see p. 837), and results in the blood becoming more alkaline. While respiratory acidosis is frequently associated with respiratory system pathology, respiratory alkalosis is often due to stress or pain.

Metabolic Acidosis and Alkalosis

Metabolic pH imbalances include all abnormalities of acid-base imbalance *except* those caused by too much or too little carbon dioxide in the blood. Bicarbonate ion levels below or above the normal range of 22–26 mEq/L indicate a metabolic acid-base imbalance.

The second most common cause of acid-base imbalance, **metabolic acidosis**, is recognized by low blood pH and HCO_3^- levels. Typical causes of metabolic acidosis are ingestion of too much alcohol (which is metabolized to acetic acid) and excessive loss of HCO_3^-, as might result from persistent diarrhea. Other causes are accumulation of lactic acid during exercise or shock, the ketosis that occurs in diabetic crisis or starvation, and, infrequently, kidney failure.

Metabolic alkalosis, indicated by rising blood pH and HCO_3^- levels, is much less common than metabolic acidosis. Typical causes are vomiting of the acidic contents of the stomach (or loss of those secretions through gastrointestinal suctioning) and intake of excess base (antacids, for example).

Effects of Acidosis and Alkalosis

The absolute blood pH limits for life are a low of 7.0 and a high of 7.8. When blood pH falls below 7.0, the central nervous system is so depressed that the person goes into coma and death soon follows. When blood pH rises above 7.8, the nervous system is overexcited, leading to such characteristic signs as muscle tetany, extreme nervousness, and convulsions. Death often results from respiratory arrest.

Respiratory and Renal Compensations

When an acid-base imbalance is due to inadequate functioning of one of the physiological buffer systems (the lungs or kidneys), the other system tries to compensate. The respiratory system attempts to compensate for metabolic acid-base imbalances, and the kidneys (although much slower) work to correct imbalances caused by respiratory disease. These **respiratory** and **renal compensations** can be recognized by changes in plasma P_{CO_2} and bicarbonate ion concentrations (see *A Closer Look*). Because the compensations act to restore normal blood pH, the pH may actually be in the normal range when the patient has a significant medical problem.

Respiratory Compensations As a rule, changes in respiratory rate and depth are evident when the respiratory system is attempting to compensate for metabolic acid-base imbalances. In metabolic acidosis, the respiratory rate and depth are usually elevated—an indication that the respiratory centers are stimulated by the high H^+ levels. The blood pH is low (below 7.35) and the HCO_3^- level is below 22 mEq/L. As the respiratory system "blows off" CO_2 to rid the blood of excess acid, the P_{CO_2} falls below 35 mm Hg. By contrast, in respiratory acidosis, the respiratory rate is often depressed and *is the immediate cause of the acidosis* (with some exceptions such as pneumonia or emphysema where gas exchange is impaired).

Respiratory compensation for metabolic alkalosis involves slow, shallow breathing, which allows CO_2 to accumulate in the blood. A metabolic alkalosis being compensated by respiratory mechanisms is revealed by a pH over 7.45 (at least initially), elevated bicarbonate levels (over 26 mEq/L), and a P_{CO_2} above 45 mm Hg.

Renal Compensations When an acid-base imbalance is of respiratory origin, renal mechanisms are stepped up to compensate for the imbalance. For example, a hypoventilating individual will exhibit acidosis. When renal compensation is occurring, both the P_{CO_2} and the HCO_3^- levels are high. The high P_{CO_2} is the cause of the acidosis, and the rising HCO_3^- level indicates that the kidneys are retaining bicarbonate to offset the acidosis.

Conversely, a person with renal-compensated respiratory alkalosis will have a high blood pH and a low P_{CO_2}. Bicarbonate ion levels begin to fall as the kidneys eliminate more HCO_3^- from the body by failing to reclaim it or by actively secreting it. Note that the kidneys cannot compensate for alkalosis or acidosis if that condition reflects a *renal* problem.

CHECK YOUR UNDERSTANDING

17. What two abnormalities in plasma are key features of an uncompensated metabolic alkalosis? An uncompensated respiratory acidosis?

18. How do the kidneys compensate for respiratory acidosis?

For answers, see Appendix G.

Developmental Aspects of Fluid, Electrolyte, and Acid-Base Balance

▶ Explain why infants and the aged are at greater risk for fluid and electrolyte imbalances than are young adults.

An embryo and a very young fetus are more than 90% water, but solids accumulate as fetal development continues, and at birth an infant is "only" 70–80% water. (The average value for adults is 58%.) Infants have proportionately more ECF than adults and, consequently, a much higher NaCl content in relation to K^+, Mg^{2+}, and PO_4^{3-} salts. Distribution of body water begins to change about two months after birth and achieves the adult pattern by the time the child is 2 years old. Plasma electrolyte concentrations are similar in infants and adults, but K^+ and Ca^{2+} values are higher and Mg^{2+}, HCO_3^-, and total protein levels are lower in the first few days of life than at any other time. At puberty, sex differences in body water content become obvious as males develop relatively greater amounts of skeletal muscle.

Problems with fluid, electrolyte, and particularly acid-base balance are most common in infancy, reflecting the following conditions:

1. *The very low residual volume of infant lungs* (approximately half that of adults relative to body weight). When respiration is altered, rapid and dramatic changes in P_{CO_2} can result.

2. *The high rate of fluid intake and output in infants* (about seven times higher than in adults). Infants may exchange fully half their ECF daily. Though infants have proportionately much more body water than adults, this does not protect them from excessive fluid shifts. Even slight alterations in fluid balance can cause serious problems. Further, although adults can live without water for about ten days, infants can survive for only three to four days.

3. *The relatively high infant metabolic rate* (about twice that of adults). The higher metabolic rate yields much larger amounts of metabolic wastes and acids that need to be excreted by the kidneys. This, along with buffer systems that are not yet fully effective, results in a tendency toward acidosis.

4. *The high rate of insensible water loss in infants* because of their larger surface area relative to body volume (about three times that of adults). Infants lose substantial amounts of water through their skin.

5. *The inefficiency of infant kidneys.* At birth, the kidneys are immature, only about half as proficient as adult kidneys at concentrating urine, and notably inefficient at ridding the body of acids.

All these factors put newborns at risk for dehydration and acidosis, at least until the end of the first month when the kidneys achieve reasonable efficiency. Bouts of vomiting or diarrhea greatly amplify the risk.

In old age, total body water often decreases (the loss is largely from the intracellular compartment) because muscle mass progressively declines and body fat rises. Few changes occur in the solute concentrations of body fluids, but the speed with which homeostasis is restored after being disrupted declines with age. Elders may be unresponsive to thirst cues and thus are at risk for dehydration. Additionally, they are the most frequent prey of diseases that lead to severe fluid, electrolyte, or acid-base problems, such as congestive heart failure (and its attendant edema) and diabetes mellitus. Because most fluid, electrolyte, and acid-base imbalances occur when body water content is highest or lowest, the very young and the very old are the most frequent victims.

CHECK YOUR UNDERSTANDING

19. Infants have a higher urine output than adults relative to their body weight. In addition to their relatively higher fluid intake, what are the reasons for this?

For answers, see Appendix G.

TABLE 26.2	Causes and Consequences of Acid-Base Imbalances
CONDITION AND HALLMARK	**POSSIBLE CAUSES; COMMENTS**
Metabolic Acidosis	
If uncompensated (uncorrected): HCO_3^- <22 mEq/L; pH <7.35	**Severe diarrhea:** bicarbonate-rich intestinal (and pancreatic) secretions rushed through digestive tract before their solutes can be reabsorbed; bicarbonate ions are replaced by renal mechanisms that generate new bicarbonate ions
	Renal disease: failure of kidneys to rid body of acids formed by normal metabolic processes
	Untreated diabetes mellitus: lack of insulin or inability of tissue cells to respond to insulin, resulting in inability to use glucose; fats are used as primary energy fuel, and ketoacidosis occurs
	Starvation: lack of dietary nutrients for cellular fuels; body proteins and fat reserves are used for energy—both yield acidic metabolites as they are broken down for energy
	Excess alcohol ingestion: results in excess acids in blood
	High ECF potassium concentrations: potassium ions compete with H^+ for secretion in renal tubules; when ECF levels of K^+ are high, H^+ secretion is inhibited
Metabolic Alkalosis	
If uncompensated: HCO_3^- >26 mEq/L; pH >7.45	**Vomiting or gastric suctioning:** loss of stomach HCl requires that H^+ be withdrawn from blood to replace stomach acid; thus H^+ decreases and HCO_3^- increases proportionately
	Selected diuretics: cause K^+ depletion and H_2O loss. Low K^+ directly stimulates the tubule cells to secrete H^+. Reduced blood volume elicits the renin-angiotensin mechanism, which stimulates Na^+ reabsorption and H^+ secretion.
	Ingestion of excessive sodium bicarbonate (antacid): bicarbonate moves easily into ECF, where it enhances natural alkaline reserve
	Excess aldosterone (e.g., adrenal tumors): promotes excessive reabsorption of Na^+, which pulls increased amount of H^+ into urine. Hypovolemia promotes the same relative effect because aldosterone secretion is increased to enhance Na^+ (and H_2O) reabsorption.
Respiratory Acidosis (Hypoventilation)	
If uncompensated: P_{CO_2} >45 mm Hg; pH <7.35	**Impaired lung function** (e.g., in chronic bronchitis, cystic fibrosis, emphysema): impaired gas exchange or alveolar P_{CO_2} ventilation
	Impaired ventilatory movement: paralysis of respiratory muscles, chest injury, extreme obesity
	Narcotic or barbiturate overdose or injury to brain stem: depression of respiratory centers, resulting in hypoventilation and respiratory arrest
Respiratory Alkalosis (Hyperventilation)	
If uncompensated: P_{CO_2} <35 mm Hg; pH >7.45	**Strong emotions:** pain, anxiety, fear, panic attack
	Hypoxia: asthma, pneumonia, high altitude; represents effort to raise P_{O_2} at the expense of excessive CO_2 excretion
	Brain tumor or injury: abnormality of respiratory controls

26

In this chapter we have examined the chemical and physiological mechanisms that provide the optimal internal environment for survival. The kidneys are the superstars among homeostatic organs in regulating water, electrolyte, and acid-base balance, but they do not and cannot act alone. Rather, their activity is made possible by a host of hormones and enhanced both by bloodborne buffers, which give the kidneys time to react, and by the respiratory system, which shoulders a substantial responsibility for acid-base balance of the blood.

Now that we have discussed the topics relevant to renal functioning, and once you read in *Making Connections* how the urinary system interacts with other body systems, the topics in Chapters 25 and 26 should draw together in an understandable way.

A CLOSER LOOK

Sleuthing: Using Blood Values to Determine the Cause of Acidosis or Alkalosis

Students, particularly nursing students, are often given blood values and asked to determine (1) whether the patient is in acidosis or alkalosis, (2) the cause of the condition (respiratory or metabolic), and (3) whether the condition is being compensated. If such determinations are approached systematically, they are not nearly as difficult as they may appear. To analyze a person's acid-base balance, scrutinize the blood values in the following order:

1. *Note the pH.* This tells you whether the person is in acidosis (pH below 7.35) or alkalosis (pH above 7.45), but it does not tell you the cause.

2. *Check the P_{CO_2} to see if this is the cause of the acid-base imbalance.* Because the respiratory system is a fast-acting system, an excessively high or low P_{CO_2} may indicate either that the condition is respiratory system caused or that the respiratory system is compensating. For example, if the pH indicates acidosis and

   a. The P_{CO_2} is over 45 mm Hg, then the respiratory system is the cause of the problem and the condition is a respiratory acidosis

   b. The P_{CO_2} is below normal limits (below 35 mm Hg), then the respiratory system is *not the cause but is compensating*

   c. The P_{CO_2} is within normal limits, then the condition is *neither caused nor compensated* by the respiratory system

3. *Check the bicarbonate level.* If step 2 proves that the respiratory system is not responsible for the imbalance, then the condition is metabolic and should be reflected in increased or decreased bicarbonate levels. Metabolic acidosis is indicated by HCO_3^- values below 22 mEq/L, and metabolic alkalosis by values over 26 mEq/L. Notice that whereas P_{CO_2} levels vary inversely with blood pH (P_{CO_2} rises as blood pH falls), HCO_3^- levels vary directly with blood pH (increased HCO_3^- results in increased pH).

Beyond this bare-bones approach there is something else to consider when you are assessing acid-base problems. If an imbalance is fully compensated, the pH may be normal even while the patient is in trouble. Hence, when the pH is normal, carefully scrutinize the P_{CO_2} or HCO_3^- values for clues to what imbalance may be occurring.

Consider the following two examples of the three-step approach.

Problem 1

Blood values: pH 7.6; P_{CO_2} 24 mm Hg; HCO_3^- 23 mEq/L

Analysis:

1. The pH is elevated: alkalosis.

2. The P_{CO_2} is very low: the cause of the alkalosis.

3. The HCO_3^- value is within normal limits.

Conclusion: This is a respiratory alkalosis not compensated by renal mechanisms, as might occur during short-term hyperventilation.

Problem 2

Blood values: pH 7.48; P_{CO_2} 46 mm Hg; HCO_3^- 33 mEq/L

Analysis:

1. The pH is elevated: alkalosis.

2. The P_{CO_2} is elevated: the cause of acidosis, not alkalosis; thus, the respiratory system is compensating and is not the cause.

3. The HCO_3^- is elevated: the cause of the alkalosis.

Conclusion: This is a metabolic alkalosis being compensated by respiratory acidosis (retention of CO_2 to restore blood pH to the normal range).

See the accompanying simple chart to help you in your future determinations.

Acid-Base Disturbance	Normal Range in Plasma		
	pH 7.35–7.45	P_{CO_2} 35–45 mm Hg	HCO_3^- 22–26 mEq/L
Respiratory acidosis	↓	↑	↑ if compensating
Respiratory alkalosis	↑	↓	↓ if compensating
Metabolic acidosis	↓	↓ if compensating	↓
Metabolic alkalosis	↑	↑ if compensating	↑

System Connections

Homeostatic Interrelationships Between the Urinary System and Other Body Systems

Nervous System

- Kidneys dispose of nitrogenous wastes; maintain fluid, electrolyte, and acid-base balance of blood; renal control of K^+, Ca^{2+}, and Na^+ in ECF essential for normal neural function
- Neural controls involved in micturition; sympathetic nervous system activity triggers the renin-angiotensin mechanism

Endocrine System

- Kidneys dispose of nitrogenous wastes; maintain fluid, electrolyte, and acid-base balance of blood; produce erythropoietin; renal regulation of Na^+ and water balance essential for blood pressure homeostasis and hormone transport in blood
- ADH, aldosterone, ANP, and other hormones help regulate renal reabsorption of water and electrolytes

Cardiovascular System

- Kidneys dispose of nitrogenous wastes; maintain fluid, electrolyte, and acid-base balance of blood; renal regulation of Na^+-water balance essential for blood pressure homeostasis. K^+, Ca^{2+}, and Na^+ regulation maintains cardiac excitability
- Systemic arterial blood pressure is the driving force for glomerular filtration; heart secretes atrial natriuretic peptide; blood transports nutrients, oxygen, etc. to urinary organs

Lymphatic System/Immunity

- Kidneys dispose of nitrogenous wastes; maintain fluid, electrolyte, and acid-base balance of blood
- By returning leaked plasma fluid to cardiovascular system, lymphatic vessels help ensure normal systemic arterial pressure required for kidney function; immune cells protect urinary organs from infection and cancer

Respiratory System

- Kidneys dispose of nitrogenous wastes; maintain fluid, electrolyte, and long-term acid-base balance of blood
- Respiratory system provides oxygen required by kidney cells for their high metabolic activity; disposes of carbon dioxide; rapid acid-base balance of blood; lung capillary endothelial cells convert angiotensin I to angiotensin II

Digestive System

- Kidneys dispose of nitrogenous wastes; maintain fluid, electrolyte, and acid-base balance of blood; metabolize vitamin D to the active form needed for calcium absorption
- Digestive organs provide nutrients needed for kidney cell health; liver synthesizes urea and glutamine to transport waste nitrogen to the kidneys for excretion

Reproductive System

- Kidneys dispose of nitrogenous wastes; maintain fluid, electrolyte, and acid-base balance of blood

Integumentary System

- Kidneys dispose of nitrogenous wastes; maintain fluid, electrolyte, and acid-base balance of blood
- Skin provides external protective barrier; site of water loss (via perspiration); vitamin D synthesis site

Skeletal System

- Kidneys dispose of nitrogenous wastes; maintain fluid, electrolyte, and acid-base balance of blood
- Bones of rib cage provide some protection to kidneys; form major store of calcium and phosphate ions

Muscular System

- Kidneys dispose of nitrogenous wastes; maintain fluid, electrolyte, and acid-base balance of blood; renal regulation of K^+, Ca^{2+}, and Na^+ content in ECF crucial for muscle excitability and contractility
- Muscles of pelvic diaphragm and external urethral sphincter function in voluntary control of micturition; creatinine is a nitrogenous waste product of muscle metabolism that must be excreted by the kidneys

26

The Urinary System and Interrelationships with the Cardiovascular, Endocrine, and Nervous Systems

A drink of water—such a simple thing. It quenches a powerful thirst, but that's not all. Inadequate hydration can cause poor functioning, both mental and physical, and fatigue, illness, and even death. The body also needs water to regulate its temperature via perspiration, to wash wastes and toxins out of the body in urine, to maintain proper blood volume and pressure, and to keep the skeletal muscles well hydrated (otherwise they feel weak and tire quickly, and even stop working altogether).

A drink provides that needed water, but it takes the kidneys to keep it balanced so that all of these vital activities can continue to occur. Seemingly wise, the exceedingly tiny nephrons "know" which blood solutes are valuable and which disposable, and that alcohol and caffeine are diuretics and as such drain water from the body. Make no mistake about it, the kidneys are crucially important to the body—all systems, all cells. The body systems that most influence the kidneys' ability to do their life-sustaining work are the cardiovascular, endocrine, and nervous systems.

Cardiovascular System

As important as they are, and as intricate as their functioning is, the kidneys cannot work without blood to process and blood pressure to drive filtrate through the glomerular filters. When we hemorrhage severely, the GFR drops and the kidneys stop functioning altogether. When blood pressure is normal, it provides the driving force that allows the nephrons to perform their job. On the other hand, by excreting or retaining water, the kidneys maintain the blood volume that furnishes that filtration pressure.

Endocrine System and Nervous System

The kidneys have a whole "toolbox" of ways to ensure that their own blood pressure is normal. However, autoregulation can be overridden by hormonal mechanisms (the renin-angiotensin mechanism which calls aldosterone and ADH into service, and release of ANP by the heart) in order to maintain systemic blood pressure. Sympathetic activity also ensures that bodywide blood pressure is maintained within homeostatic limits so as to maintain adequate GFR. Alternatively, the kidneys' needs are overcome as necessary by the same sympathetic fibers to make sure that the heart and brain receive adequate blood perfusion in periods of dramatically falling blood pressure. Now that's flexibility!

Urinary System

Case study: Mr. Heyden, a somewhat stocky 72-year-old man, is brought in to the emergency room (ER). The paramedics report that his left arm and the left side of his body trunk were pinned beneath some wreckage, and that when he was freed, his left hypogastric and lumbar areas appeared to be compressed and his left arm was blanched and without sensation. On admission, Mr. Heyden is alert, slightly cyanotic, and complaining of pain in his left side; he loses consciousness shortly thereafter. His vital signs are taken, blood is drawn for laboratory tests, and Mr. Heyden is catheterized and immediately scheduled for a CT scan of his left abdominal region.

Analyze the information that was subsequently recorded on Mr. Heyden's chart:

- Vital signs: Temperature 39°C (102°F); BP 90/50 mm Hg and falling; heart rate 116 beats/min and thready; 30 respirations/min

1. Given the values above and his attendant cyanosis, what would you guess is Mr. Heyden's immediate problem? Explain your reasoning.

- CT scan reveals a ruptured spleen and a large hematoma in the upper left abdominal quadrant. Splenic repair surgery is scheduled but unsuccessful; the spleen is removed.

2. Rupture of the spleen results in massive hemorrhage. Explain this observation. What organs (if any) will compensate for the removal of Mr. Heyden's spleen?

- Hematology: Most blood tests yield normal results. However, renin, aldosterone, and ADH levels are elevated.

3. Explain the cause and consequence of each of the hematology findings.

- Urinalysis: Some granular casts (particulate cell debris) are noted, and the urine is brownish-red in color; other values are normal, but urine output is very low. An order is given to force fluids.

4. (a) What might account for the low volume of urine output? (Name at least two possibilities.) (b) What might explain the casts and abnormal color of his urine? Can you see any possible relationship between his crush injury and these findings?

The next day, Mr. Heyden is awake and alert. He says that he now has feeling in his arm, but he is still complaining of pain. However, the pain site appears to have moved from the left upper quadrant to his lumbar region. His urine output is still low. He is scheduled once again for a CT scan, this time of his lumbar region. The order to force fluids is renewed and some additional and more specific blood tests are ordered. We will visit Mr. Heyden again shortly, but in the meantime think about what these new findings may indicate.

(Answers in Appendix G)

26

RELATED CLINICAL TERMS

Antacid An agent that counteracts acidity, such as sodium bicarbonate, aluminum hydroxide gel, and magnesium trisilicate. Commonly used in the management of heartburn.

Hyperaldosteronism (Conn's disease) A condition of hypersecretion of aldosterone by adrenal cortical cells accompanied by excessive loss of potassium and generalized muscular weakness, hypernatremia, and hypertension. Usual cause is adrenal tumor; usual treatment is adrenal-suppressing drugs prior to tumor removal.

Renal tubular acidosis A metabolic acidosis resulting from impaired renal reabsorption of bicarbonate; the urine is alkaline.

Syndrome of inappropriate ADH secretion (SIADH) A group of disorders associated with excessive ADH secretion in the absence of appropriate (osmotic or nonosmotic) stimuli. Characterized by hypotonic hydration (hyponatremia, fluid retention, and weight gain) and concentrated urine. Usual causes are ectopic secretion of ADH by cancer cells (e.g., bronchogenic cancer cells) and brain disorders or trauma affecting the ADH-secreting hypothalamic neurons. Temporary management involves water restriction.

CHAPTER SUMMARY

Media study tools that could provide you additional help in reviewing specific key topics of Chapter 26 are referenced below.

iP = *Interactive Physiology*

Body Fluids   (pp. 996–998)

Body Water Content   (p. 996)

1. Water accounts for 45–75% of body weight, depending on age, sex, and amount of body fat.

Fluid Compartments   (p. 996)

2. About two-thirds (25 L) of body water is found within cells in the intracellular fluid (ICF) compartment; the balance (15 L) is in the extracellular fluid (ECF) compartment. The ECF includes plasma and interstitial fluid.

Composition of Body Fluids   (pp. 996–998)

3. Solutes dissolved in body fluids include electrolytes and nonelectrolytes. Electrolyte concentration is expressed in mEq/L.
4. Plasma contains more proteins than does interstitial fluid; otherwise, extracellular fluids are similar. The most abundant ECF electrolytes are sodium, chloride, and bicarbonate ions.
5. Intracellular fluids contain large amounts of protein anions and potassium, phosphate, and magnesium ions.

iP Fluid, Electrolyte, and Acid/Base Balance; Topic: Introduction to Body Fluids, pp. 1–8.

Fluid Movement Among Compartments   (p. 998)

6. Substances usually pass through the plasma and interstitial fluid to reach the intracellular fluid.
7. Fluid exchanges between compartments are regulated by osmotic and hydrostatic pressures: (a) Filtrate is forced out of the capillaries by hydrostatic pressure and pulled back in by colloid osmotic pressure. (b) Water moves freely between the ECF and the ICF by osmosis, but solute movements are restricted by size, charge, and dependence on transport proteins. (c) Water flows always follow changes in ECF osmolality.

iP Fluid, Electrolyte, and Acid/Base Balance; Topic: Introduction to Body Fluids, pp. 19–23.

Water Balance and ECF Osmolality   (pp. 998–1002)

1. Sources of body water are ingested foods and fluids and metabolic water.

2. Water leaves the body primarily via the lungs, skin, gastrointestinal tract, and kidneys.

Regulation of Water Intake   (pp. 999–1000)

3. Increased plasma osmolality triggers the thirst mechanism, mediated by hypothalamic osmoreceptors. Thirst, inhibited by distension of the gastrointestinal tract by ingested water and then by reduced osmolality, may be damped before body needs for water are met.

Regulation of Water Output   (p. 1000)

4. Obligatory water loss is unavoidable and includes insensible water losses from the lungs, the skin, and in feces, and about 500 ml of urine output daily.
5. Beyond obligatory water loss, the volume of urinary output depends on water intake and loss via other routes and reflects the influence of antidiuretic hormone on the renal collecting ducts.

Influence of ADH   (pp. 1000–1001)

6. Antidiuretic hormone causes aquaporins (water channels) to be inserted in the cell membranes of the collecting ducts, so that most filtered water is reabsorbed. ADH release is triggered if ECF osmolality is high, or if a large drop in blood volume or pressure occurs.

Disorders of Water Balance   (pp. 1001–1002)

7. Dehydration occurs when water loss exceeds water intake over time. It is evidenced by thirst, dry skin, and decreased urine output. A serious consequence is hypovolemic shock.
8. Hypotonic hydration occurs when body fluids are excessively diluted and cells become swollen by water entry. The most serious consequence is cerebral edema.
9. Edema is an abnormal accumulation of fluid in the interstitial space (increased IF), which may impair blood circulation.

iP Fluid, Electrolyte, and Acid/Base Balance; Topic: Water Homeostasis, pp. 1–27.

Electrolyte Balance   (pp. 1002–1008)

1. Most electrolytes (salts) are obtained from ingested foods and fluids. Salts, particularly NaCl, are often ingested in excess of need.
2. Electrolytes are lost in perspiration, feces, and urine. The kidneys are most important in regulating electrolyte balance.

26

The Central Role of Sodium in Fluid and Electrolyte Balance   (pp. 1002–1004)

3. Sodium salts are the most abundant solutes in ECF. They exert the bulk of ECF osmotic pressure and control water volume and distribution in the body.

Regulation of Sodium Balance   (pp. 1004–1006)

4. Sodium ion balance is linked to ECF volume and blood pressure regulation and involves both neural and hormonal controls.

5. Aldosterone promotes Na^+ reabsorption to maintain blood volume and blood pressure.

6. Declining blood pressure and falling filtrate NaCl concentration stimulate the granular cells to release renin. Renin, via angiotensin II, enhances systemic blood pressure, Na^+ reabsorption, and aldosterone release.

7. Cardiovascular system baroreceptors sense changing arterial blood pressure, prompting changes in sympathetic vasomotor activity. Rising arterial pressure leads to vasodilation and enhanced Na^+ and water loss in urine. Falling arterial pressure promotes vasoconstriction and conserves Na^+ and water.

8. Atrial natriuretic peptide, released by certain atrial cells in response to rising blood pressure (or blood volume), causes systemic vasodilation and inhibits renin, aldosterone, and ADH release. Hence, it enhances Na^+ and water excretion, reducing blood volume and blood pressure.

9. Estrogens and glucocorticoids increase renal retention of sodium. Progesterone promotes enhanced sodium and water excretion in urine.

Regulation of Potassium Balance   (pp. 1006–1007)

10. About 90% of filtered potassium is reabsorbed by the more proximal regions of the nephrons.

11. The main thrust of renal regulation of K^+ is to excrete it. Potassium ion secretion by the principal cells of the cortical collecting ducts is enhanced by increased plasma K^+ content and aldosterone. Type A intercalated cells of the collecting duct reabsorb small amounts of K^+ during K^+ deficit.

Regulation of Calcium and Phosphate Balance (p. 1008)

12. Calcium balance is regulated primarily by parathyroid hormone (PTH), which enhances blood Ca^{2+} levels by targeting the bones, intestine, and kidneys. PTH-regulated reabsorption occurs primarily in the DCT.

13. PTH decreases renal reabsorption of phosphate ions.

Regulation of Anions   (p. 1008)

14. When blood pH is normal or slightly high, chloride is the major anion accompanying sodium reabsorption. In acidosis, chloride is replaced by bicarbonate.

15. Reabsorption of most other anions is regulated by their transport maximums (T_m).

iP Fluid, Electrolyte, and Acid/Base Balance; Topic: Electrolyte Homeostasis, pp. 1–38.

Acid-Base Balance   (pp. 1008–1015)

1. The homeostatic pH range of arterial blood is 7.35 to 7.45. A higher pH represents alkalosis; a lower pH reflects acidosis.

2. Some acids enter the body in foods, but most are generated by breakdown of phosphorus-containing proteins, incomplete oxidation of fats or glucose, and the loading and transport of carbon dioxide in the blood.

3. Acid-base balance is achieved by chemical buffers, respiratory regulation, and in the long term by renal regulation of bicarbonate ion (hence, hydrogen ion) concentration of body fluids.

iP Fluid, Electrolyte, and Acid/Base Balance; Topic: Acid/Base Homeostasis, pp. 1–15.

Chemical Buffer Systems   (pp. 1009–1010)

4. Acids are proton (H^+) donors; bases are proton acceptors. Acids that dissociate completely in solution are strong acids; those that dissociate incompletely are weak acids. Strong bases are more effective proton acceptors than are weak bases.

5. Chemical buffers are single or paired sets (a weak acid and its salt) of molecules that act rapidly to resist excessive shifts in pH by releasing or binding H^+.

6. Chemical buffers of the body include the bicarbonate, phosphate, and protein buffer systems.

iP IP Fluid, Electrolyte, and Acid/Base Balance; Topic: Acid/Base Homeostasis, pp. 16–26.

Respiratory Regulation of H^+ (pp. 1010–1011)

7. Respiratory regulation of acid-base balance of the blood utilizes the bicarbonate buffer system and the fact that CO_2 and H_2O are in reversible equilibrium with H_2CO_3.

8. Acidosis activates the respiratory center to increase respiratory rate and depth, which eliminates more CO_2 and causes blood pH to rise. Alkalosis depresses the respiratory center, resulting in CO_2 retention and a fall in blood pH.

iP Fluid, Electrolyte, and Acid/Base Balance; Topic: Acid/Base Homeostasis, pp. 27–28.

Renal Mechanisms of Acid-Base Balance   (pp. 1011–1014)

9. The kidneys provide the major long-term mechanism for controlling acid-base balance by maintaining stable HCO_3^- levels in the ECF. Metabolic acids (organic acids other than carbonic acid) can be eliminated from the body only by the kidneys.

10. Secreted hydrogen ions come from the dissociation of carbonic acid generated within the tubule cells.

11. Tubule cells are impermeable to bicarbonate in the filtrate, but they can conserve filtered bicarbonate ions indirectly by absorbing HCO_3^- generated within them (by dissociation of carbonic acid to HCO_3^- and H^+). For each HCO_3^- (and Na^+) reabsorbed, one H^+ is secreted into the filtrate, where it combines with HCO_3^-.

12. To generate and add new HCO_3^- to plasma to counteract acidosis, either of two mechanisms may be used:
    - Secreted H^+, buffered by bases other than HCO_3^-, is excreted from the body in urine (the major urine buffer is the phosphate buffer system).
    - NH_4^+ (derived from glutamine catabolism) is excreted in urine.

13. To counteract alkalosis, bicarbonate ion is secreted into the filtrate and H^+ is reabsorbed.

iP Fluid, Electrolyte, and Acid/Base Balance; Topic: Acid/Base Homeostasis, pp. 29–37.

Abnormalities of Acid-Base Balance   (pp. 1014–1015)

14. Classification of acid-base imbalances as metabolic or respiratory indicates the cause of the acidosis or alkalosis.

15. Respiratory acidosis results from carbon dioxide retention; respiratory alkalosis occurs when carbon dioxide is eliminated faster than it is produced.

16. Metabolic acidosis occurs when fixed acids (lactic acid, ketone bodies, and others) accumulate in the blood or when bicarbonate

is lost from the body; metabolic alkalosis occurs when bicarbonate levels are excessive.

17. Extremes of pH for life are 7.0 and 7.8.

18. Compensations occur when the respiratory system or kidneys act to counteract acid-base imbalances resulting from abnormal or inadequate functioning of the alternate system. Respiratory compensations involve changes in respiratory rate and depth. Renal compensations modify blood levels of HCO_3^-.

iP Fluid, Electrolyte, and Acid/Base Balance; Topic: Acid/Base Homeostasis, pp. 38–59.

Developmental Aspects of Fluid, Electrolyte, and Acid-Base Balance (pp. 1015–1016)

1. Infants have a higher risk of dehydration and acidosis because of their low lung residual volume, high rate of fluid intake and output, high metabolic rate, relatively large body surface area, and functionally immature kidneys at birth.

2. The elderly are at risk for dehydration because of their low percentage of body water and insensitivity to thirst cues. Diseases that promote fluid and acid-base imbalances (cardiovascular disease, diabetes mellitus, and others) are most common in the aged.

REVIEW QUESTIONS

Multiple Choice/Matching

(Some questions have more than one correct answer. Select the best answer or answers from the choices given.)

1. Body water content is greatest in (a) infants, (b) young adults, (c) elderly adults.

2. Potassium, magnesium, and phosphate ions are the predominant electrolytes in (a) plasma, (b) interstitial fluid, (c) intracellular fluid.

3. Sodium balance is regulated primarily by control of amount(s) (a) ingested, (b) excreted in urine, (c) lost in perspiration, (d) lost in feces.

4. Water balance is regulated by control of amount(s) (use choices in question 3).

Answer questions 5 through 10 by choosing responses from the following:

(a) ammonium ions	(f) magnesium
(b) bicarbonate	(g) phosphate
(c) calcium	(h) potassium
(d) chloride	(i) sodium
(e) hydrogen ions	(j) water

5. Three substances regulated (at least in part) by the influence of aldosterone on the kidney tubules.

6. Two substances regulated by parathyroid hormone.

7. Two substances secreted into the proximal convoluted tubules in exchange for sodium ions.

8. Part of an important chemical buffer system in plasma.

9. Two ions produced during catabolism of glutamine.

10. Substance regulated by ADH's effects on the renal tubules.

11. Which of the following factors will enhance ADH release? (a) increase in ECF volume, (b) decrease in ECF volume, (c) decrease in ECF osmolality, (d) increase in ECF osmolality.

12. The pH of blood varies *directly* with (a) HCO_3^-, (b) P_{CO_2} (c) H^+, (d) none of the above.

13. In an individual with metabolic acidosis, a clue that the respiratory system is compensating is provided by (a) high blood bicarbonate levels, (b) low blood bicarbonate levels, (c) rapid, deep breathing, (d) slow, shallow breathing.

Short Answer Essay Questions

14. Name the body fluid compartments, noting their locations and the approximate fluid volume in each.

15. Describe the thirst mechanism, indicating how it is triggered and terminated.

16. Explain why and how ECF osmolality is maintained.

17. Explain why and how sodium balance, ECF volume, and blood pressure are jointly regulated.

18. Describe the role of the respiratory system in controlling acid-base balance.

19. Explain how the chemical buffer systems resist changes in pH.

20. Explain the relationship of the following to renal secretion and excretion of hydrogen ions: (a) plasma carbon dioxide levels, (b) phosphate, and (c) sodium bicarbonate reabsorption.

21. List several factors that place newborn babies at risk for acid-base imbalances.

Critical Thinking and Clinical Application Questions

1. Mr. Jessup, a 55-year-old man, is operated on for a cerebral tumor. About a month later, he appears at his physician's office complaining of excessive thirst. He claims to have been drinking about 20 liters of water daily for the past week and says he has been voiding nearly continuously. A urine sample is collected and its specific gravity is reported as 1.001. What is your diagnosis of Mr. Jessup's problem? What connection might exist between his previous surgery and his present problem?

2. For each of the following sets of blood values, name the acid-base imbalance (acidosis or alkalosis), determine its cause (metabolic or respiratory), decide whether the condition is being compensated, and cite at least one possible cause of the imbalance.
   Problem 1: pH 7.63; P_{CO_2} 19 mm Hg; HCO_3^- 19.5 mEq/L
   Problem 2: pH 7.22; P_{CO_2} 30 mm Hg; HCO_3^- 12.0 mEq/L

3. Explain how emphysema and congestive heart failure can lead to acid-base imbalance.

4. Mrs. Bush, a 70-year-old woman, is admitted to the hospital. Her history states that she has been suffering from diarrhea for three weeks. On admission, she complains of severe fatigue and muscle weakness. A blood chemistry study yields the following information: Na^+ 142 mEq/L; K^+ 1.5 mEq/L; Cl^- 92 mEq/L; P_{CO_2} 32 mm Hg. Which electrolytes are within normal limits? Which are so abnormal that the patient has a medical emergency? Which of the following represents the greatest danger to Mrs. Bush? (a) a fall due to her muscular weakness, (b) edema, (c) cardiac arrhythmia and cardiac arrest.

5. During a routine medical checkup, Candace, a 26-year-old physiotherapy student, is surprised to hear that her blood pressure is 180/110. She also has a rumbling systolic and diastolic abdominal bruit (murmur) that is loudest at the mid-epigastric area. Her physician suspects renal artery stenosis (narrowing). She orders

26

an abdominal ultrasound and renal artery arteriography, which confirms that Candace has a small right kidney, and that the distal part of her right renal artery is narrowed by more than 70%. Her physician prescribes diuretics and calcium channel blockers as temporary measures, and refers Candace to a cardiovascular surgeon. Explain the connection between Candace's renal artery stenosis and her hypertension. Why is her right kidney smaller than her left? What would you expect Candace's blood levels of K^+, Na^+, aldosterone, angiotensin II, and renin to be?

Access everything you need to practice, review, and self-assess for both your A&P lecture and lab courses at **myA&P** (www.myaandp.com). There, you'll find powerful online resources, including chapter quizzes and tests, games, A&P Flix animations with quizzes, *Interactive Physiology*® with quizzes, MP3 Tutor Sessions, Practice Anatomy Lab™, and more to help you get a better grade in your course.

27

The Reproductive System

Most organ systems of the body function almost continuously to maintain the well-being of the individual. The **reproductive system**, however, appears to "slumber" until puberty. The **primary sex organs**, or **gonads** (go′nadz; "seeds"), are the *testes* in males and the *ovaries* in females. The gonads produce sex cells, or **gametes** (gam′ēts; "spouses"), and secrete a variety of steroid hormones commonly called **sex hormones**. The remaining reproductive structures—ducts, glands, and external genitalia (jen-ĭ-ta′le-ah)—are referred to as **accessory reproductive organs**. Although male and female reproductive organs are quite different, their common purpose is to produce offspring.

The male's reproductive role is to manufacture male gametes called *sperm* and deliver them to the female reproductive tract, where fertilization can occur. The complementary role of the female is to produce female gametes, called *ova* or *eggs*. As a result of appropriately timed intercourse, a sperm and egg may fuse to form a fertilized egg, the first cell of the new individual, from which all body cells will arise. The male and female reproductive systems are equal partners in events leading up to fertilization, but once fertilization has occurred, the female partner's uterus provides the protective environment in which the embryo develops until birth. Sex hormones—androgens in males and estrogens and progesterone in females—play vital roles both in the development and function of the reproductive organs and in sexual behavior and drives. These hormones also influence the growth and development of many other organs and tissues of the body.

Anatomy of the Male Reproductive System

▶ Describe the structure and function of the testes, and explain the importance of their location in the scrotum.

The sperm-producing **testes** (tes′tez; "witnesses"), or **male gonads**, lie within the *scrotum*. From the testes, the sperm are delivered to the body exterior through a system of ducts including (in order) the *epididymis*, the *ductus deferens*, the *ejaculatory duct*, and finally the *urethra*, which opens to the outside at the tip of the *penis*. The accessory sex glands, which empty their secretions into the ducts during ejaculation, are the *seminal vesicles, prostate*, and *bulbourethral glands*. Take a moment to trace the duct system in **Figure 27.1**, and identify the testis and accessory glands before continuing.

The Scrotum

The **scrotum** (skro′tum; "pouch") is a sac of skin and superficial fascia that hangs outside the abdominopelvic cavity at the root of the penis **(Figures** 27.1 and **27.2)**. It is covered with sparse hairs, and contains paired oval testes. A midline septum divides the scrotum, providing a compartment for each testis.

This seems a rather vulnerable location for a man's testes, which contain his entire ability to father offspring. However, because viable sperm cannot be produced in abundance at core body temperature (37°C), the superficial location of the scrotum, which provides a temperature about 3°C lower, is an essential adaptation.

Furthermore, the scrotum is affected by temperature changes. When it is cold, the testes are pulled closer to the pelvic floor and the warmth of the body wall, and the scrotum becomes shorter and heavily wrinkled, reducing its surface area

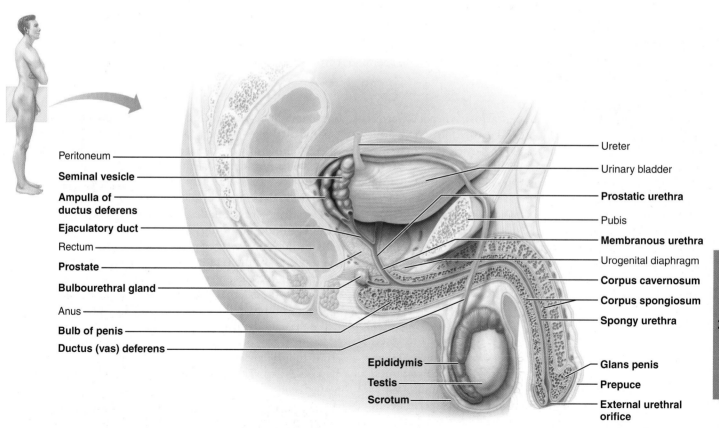

Peritoneum

Seminal vesicle

Ampulla of ductus deferens

Ejaculatory duct

Rectum

Prostate

Bulbourethral gland

Anus

Bulb of penis

Ductus (vas) deferens

Epididymis

Testis

Scrotum

Ureter

Urinary bladder

Prostatic urethra

Pubis

Membranous urethra

Urogenital diaphragm

Corpus cavernosum

Corpus spongiosum

Spongy urethra

Glans penis

Prepuce

External urethral orifice

Figure 27.1 Reproductive organs of the male, sagittal view. A portion of the pubis of the coxal bone has been left to show the relationship of the ductus deferens to the bony pelvis. (See *A Brief Atlas of the Human Body*, Figures 72 and 73.)

27

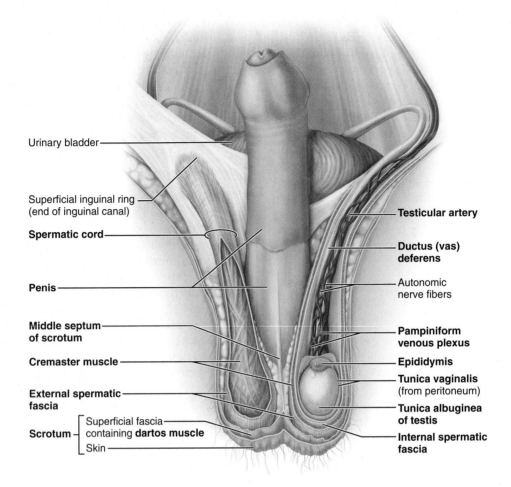

Figure 27.2 Relationships of the testis to the scrotum and spermatic cord. The scrotum has been opened and its anterior portion removed.

and increasing its thickness to reduce heat loss. When it is warm, the scrotal skin is flaccid and loose to increase the surface area for cooling (sweating) and the testes hang lower, away from the body trunk.

These changes in scrotal surface area help maintain a fairly constant intrascrotal temperature and reflect the activity of two sets of muscles which respond to changes in ambient temperature. The **dartos muscle** (dar′tos; "skinned"), a layer of smooth muscle in the superficial fascia, wrinkles the scrotal skin. The **cremaster muscles** (kre-mas′ter; "a suspender"), bands of skeletal muscle that arise from the internal oblique muscles of the trunk, elevate the testes.

The Testes

Each plum-sized testis is approximately 4 cm (1.5 inches) long and 2.5 cm (1 inch) in width and is surrounded by two tunics. The outer tunic is the two-layered **tunica vaginalis** (vaj″ĭ-nal′is), derived from an outpocketing of the peritoneum (Figure 27.2 and **Figure 27.3**). Deep to this serous layer is the **tunica albuginea** (al″bu-jin′e-ah; "white coat"), the fibrous capsule of the testis.

Septa extending from the tunica albuginea divide the testis into about 250 wedge-shaped *lobules* (Figure 27.3). Each contains one to four tightly coiled **seminiferous tubules** (sem″ĭ-nif′er-us; "sperm-carrying"), the actual "sperm factories." Surrounding each seminiferous tubule are three to five layers of smooth muscle–like **myoid cells** (Figure 27.3c). By contracting rhythmically, these cells may help to squeeze sperm and testicular fluids through the tubules and out of the testes.

The seminiferous tubules of each lobule converge to form a **straight tubule**, or **tubulus rectus**, that conveys sperm into the **rete testis** (re′te), a tubular network on the posterior side of the testis. From the rete testis, sperm leave the testis through the *efferent ductules* and enter the *epididymis* (ep″ĭ-did′ĭ-mis), which hugs the external testis surface posteriorly. The immature sperm pass through the head, the body, and then move into the tail of the epididymis, where they are stored until ejaculation.

Lying in the soft connective tissue surrounding the seminiferous tubules are the **interstitial cells**, also called *Leydig cells* (Figure 27.3c). These cells produce androgens (most importantly *testosterone*), which they secrete into the surrounding interstitial fluid. Thus, the sperm-producing and hormone-producing functions of the testis are carried out by completely different cell populations.

The long **testicular arteries**, which branch from the abdominal aorta superior to the pelvis (see *gonadal arteries* in Figure 19.24c, p. 733), supply the testes. The **testicular veins** draining

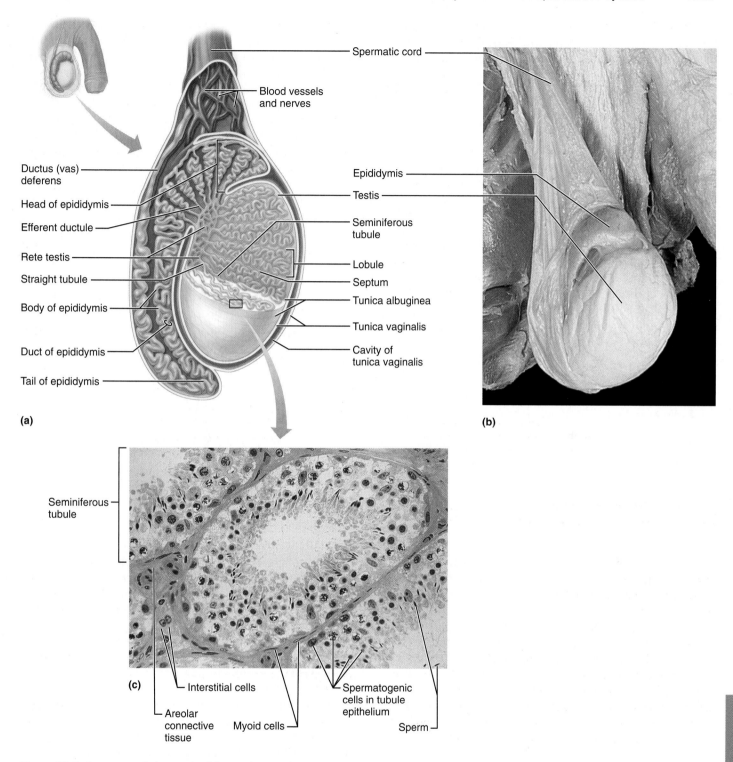

Spermatic cord

Blood vessels and nerves

Ductus (vas) deferens

Head of epididymis

Efferent ductule

Rete testis

Straight tubule

Body of epididymis

Duct of epididymis

Tail of epididymis

Epididymis

Testis

Seminiferous tubule

Lobule

Septum

Tunica albuginea

Tunica vaginalis

Cavity of tunica vaginalis

(a)

(b)

Epididymis

Testis

Seminiferous tubule

Interstitial cells

Areolar connective tissue

Myoid cells

Spermatogenic cells in tubule epithelium

Sperm

(c)

Figure 27.3 Structure of the testis. (a) Partial sagittal section through the testis and epididymis. The anterior aspect is to the right. (See *A Brief Atlas of the Human Body*, Figure 73). **(b)** External view of a testis from a cadaver; same orientation as in (a). **(c)** Seminiferous tubule in cross section (270×). Note the spermatogenic (sperm-forming) cells in the tubule epithelium and the interstitial cells in the connective tissue between the tubules.

27

the testes arise from a network called the **pampiniform venous plexus** (pam-pin′ĭ-form; "tendril-shaped") that surrounds the portion of each testicular artery within the scrotum like a climbing vine (see Figure 27.2). The cooler venous blood in each pampiniform plexus absorbs heat from the arterial blood, cool-

ing it before it enters the testes. In this way, these plexuses help to keep the testes at their cool homeostatic temperature.

The testes are served by both divisions of the autonomic nervous system. Associated sensory nerves transmit impulses that result in agonizing pain and nausea when the testes are hit forcefully. The nerve fibers are enclosed, along with the blood vessels and lymphatics, in a connective tissue sheath. Collectively these structures make up the **spermatic cord**, which passes through the inguinal canal (see Figure 27.2).

⚔ HOMEOSTATIC IMBALANCE

Although *testicular cancer* is relatively rare (affecting one of every 50,000 males), it is the most common cancer in young men (ages 15 to 35 years). A history of mumps or orchitis (inflammation of the testis) and substantial maternal exposure to environmental toxins before birth increases the risk, but the most important risk factor for this cancer is *cryptorchidism* (nondescent of the testes, see p. 1062).

Because the most common sign of testicular cancer is a painless solid mass in the testis, self-examination of the testes should be practiced by every male. If detected early, it has an impressive cure rate. Over 90% of testicular cancers are cured by surgical removal of the cancerous testis (*orchiectomy*) either alone or in combination with radiation therapy or chemotherapy. ■

CHECK YOUR UNDERSTANDING

1. What are the two major functions of the testes?
2. Which of the tubular structures shown in Figure 27.3a are the sperm "factories"?
3. Muscle activity and the pampiniform venous plexus help to keep testicular temperature at homeostatic levels. How do they do that?

For answers, see Appendix G.

The Penis

▶ Describe the location, structure, and function of the accessory reproductive organs of the male.

The **penis** ("tail") is a copulatory organ, designed to deliver sperm into the female reproductive tract (Figure 27.1 and Figure 27.4). The penis and scrotum, which hang suspended from the perineum, make up the external reproductive structures, or **external genitalia**, of the male. The male **perineum** (per″ĭ-ne′um; "around the anus") is the diamond-shaped region located between the pubic symphysis anteriorly, the coccyx posteriorly, and the ischial tuberosities laterally. The floor of the perineum is formed by muscles described in Chapter 10 (pp. 344–345).

The penis consists of an attached *root* and a free *shaft* or *body* that ends in an enlarged tip, the **glans penis**. The skin covering the penis is loose, and it slides distally to form a cuff called the **prepuce** (pre′pūs), or **foreskin**, around the glans. Frequently, the foreskin is surgically removed shortly after birth, a procedure called *circumcision* ("cutting around"). Interestingly, about 60% of newborn boys in the United States are circumcised, whereas the rate in other parts of the world is around 15%.

To understand penile anatomy, it is important to know that its dorsal and ventral surfaces are named in reference to the erect penis. Internally, the penis contains the spongy urethra and three long cylindrical bodies (*corpora*) of erectile tissue, each covered by a sheath of dense fibrous connective tissue. This *erectile tissue* is a spongy network of connective tissue and smooth muscle riddled with vascular spaces. During sexual excitement, the vascular spaces fill with blood, causing the penis to enlarge and become rigid. This event, called *erection*, enables the penis to serve as a penetrating organ.

The midventral erectile body, the **corpus spongiosum** (spon″je-o′sum; "spongy body") surrounds the urethra. It expands distally to form the glans and proximally to form the part of the root called the **bulb of the penis**. The bulb is covered externally by the sheetlike bulbospongiosus muscle and is secured to the urogenital diaphragm.

The paired dorsal erectile bodies, called the **corpora cavernosa** (kor′por-ah kă-ver-no′sah; "cavernous bodies"), make up most of the penis and are bound by the fibrous tunica albuginea. Their proximal ends form the **crura of the penis** (kroo′rah; "legs"; singular: crus). Each crus is surrounded by an ischiocavernosus muscle and anchors to the pubic arch of the bony pelvis.

The Male Duct System

As we mentioned earlier, sperm travel from the testes to the body exterior through a system of ducts. In order (proximal to distal), the **accessory ducts** are the epididymis, the ductus deferens, the ejaculatory duct, and the urethra.

The Epididymis

The cup-shaped **epididymis** (*epi* = beside; *didym* = the testes) is about 3.8 cm (1.5 inches) long (Figures 27.1 and Figures 27.3a, b). Its *head*, which contains the efferent ductules, caps the superior aspect of the testis. Its *body* and *tail* are on the posterolateral area of the testis. Most of the epididymis consists of the highly coiled *duct of the epididymis* with an uncoiled length of about 6 m (20 feet). Some pseudostratified epithelial cells of the duct mucosa exhibit long, nonmotile microvilli (*stereocilia*). The huge surface area of these stereocilia allows them to absorb excess testicular fluid and to pass nutrients to the many sperm stored temporarily in the lumen.

The immature, nearly nonmotile sperm that leave the testis are moved slowly along the duct of the epididymis through fluid that contains a number of antimicrobial proteins, including several β-defensins. As they move along its tortuous course (a trip that takes about 20 days), the sperm gain the ability to swim.

Sperm are ejaculated from the epididymis, not the testes as many believe. When a male is sexually stimulated and ejaculates, the smooth muscle in the ducts of the epididymis contracts, expelling sperm into the next segment of the duct system, the *ductus deferens*. Sperm can be stored in the epididymis for several months, but if held longer, they are eventually phagocytized by epithelial cells of the epididymis. This is not a problem for the man, as sperm are generated continuously.

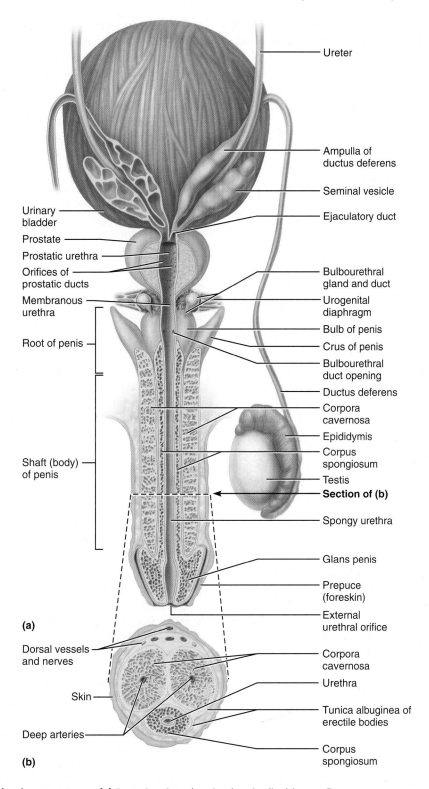

Ureter

Ampulla of ductus deferens

Seminal vesicle

Ejaculatory duct

Urinary bladder

Prostate

Prostatic urethra

Orifices of prostatic ducts

Membranous urethra

Root of penis

Shaft (body) of penis

Bulbourethral gland and duct

Urogenital diaphragm

Bulb of penis

Crus of penis

Bulbourethral duct opening

Ductus deferens

Corpora cavernosa

Epididymis

Corpus spongiosum

Testis

Section of (b)

Spongy urethra

Glans penis

Prepuce (foreskin)

External urethral orifice

(a)

Dorsal vessels and nerves

Skin

Deep arteries

Corpora cavernosa

Urethra

Tunica albuginea of erectile bodies

Corpus spongiosum

(b)

Figure 27.4   Male reproductive structures. (a) Posterior view showing longitudinal (coronal) section of the penis. **(b)** Transverse section of the penis.

The Ductus Deferens and Ejaculatory Duct

The **ductus deferens** (duk′tus def′er-ens; "carrying away"), or *vas deferens*, is about 45 cm (18 inches) long. It runs upward as part of the spermatic cord from the epididymis through the inguinal canal into the pelvic cavity (Figure 27.1). Easily palpated as it passes anterior to the pubic bone, it then loops medially over the ureter and descends along the posterior bladder wall. Its terminus expands to form the **ampulla** of the ductus deferens and then joins with the duct of the seminal vesicle (a gland) to form the short **ejaculatory duct**. Each ejaculatory duct enters the prostate, and there it empties into the urethra.

27

Like that of the epididymis, the mucosa of the ductus deferens is pseudostratified epithelium. However, its muscular layer is extremely thick and the duct feels like a hard wire when squeezed between the fingertips. At the moment of ejaculation, the thick layers of smooth muscle in its walls create strong peristaltic waves that rapidly squeeze the sperm forward along the tract and into the urethra.

As Figure 27.3 illustrates, part of the ductus deferens lies in the scrotal sac. Some men opt to take full responsibility for birth control by having a **vasectomy** (vah-sek′to-me; "cutting the vas"). In this relatively minor operation, the physician makes a small incision into the scrotum and then cuts through and ligates (ties off) each ductus deferens. Sperm are still produced, but they can no longer reach the body exterior. Eventually, they deteriorate and are phagocytized. Vasectomy is simple and provides highly effective birth control (close to 100%). For those wishing to reverse that procedure, the success rate is about 50%.

The Urethra

The **urethra** is the terminal portion of the male duct system (Figures 27.1 and 27.4). It conveys both urine and semen (at different times), so it serves both the urinary and reproductive systems. Its three regions are (1) the *prostatic urethra*, the portion surrounded by the prostate; (2) the *membranous* (or *intermediate part of the*) *urethra* in the urogenital diaphragm; and (3) the *spongy* (*penile*) *urethra*, which runs through the penis and opens to the outside at the *external urethral orifice*. The spongy urethra is about 15 cm (6 inches) long and accounts for 75% of urethral length. Its mucosa contains scattered *urethral glands* that secrete mucus into the lumen just before ejaculation.

CHECK YOUR UNDERSTANDING

4. What is the function of the erectile tissue of the penis?
5. Name the organs of the male duct system in order, from the epididymis to the body exterior.
6. What are two functions of the stereocilia on the epididymal epithelium?
7. Which accessory organ of the male duct system runs from the scrotum into the abdominal cavity?

For answers, see Appendix G.

Accessory Glands

▶ Discuss the sources and functions of semen.

The **accessory glands** include the paired seminal vesicles and bulbourethral glands and the single prostate (Figures 27.1 and 27.4). Together these glands produce the bulk of *semen* (sperm plus accessory gland secretions).

The Seminal Vesicles

The **seminal vesicles** (sem′ĭ-nul), or **seminal glands**, lie on the posterior bladder surface. Each of these fairly large, hollow glands is about the shape and length (5–7 cm) of a little finger.

However, because a seminal vesicle is pouched, coiled, and folded back on itself, its uncoiled length is actually about 15 cm. Its fibrous capsule encloses a thick layer of smooth muscle which contracts during ejaculation to empty the gland.

Stored within the mucosa's honeycomb of crypts and blind alleys is a yellowish viscous alkaline fluid containing fructose sugar, ascorbic acid, a coagulating enzyme (*vesiculase*), and prostaglandins, as well as other substances that enhance sperm motility or fertilizing ability. As noted, the duct of each seminal vesicle joins that of the ductus deferens on the same side to form the ejaculatory duct. Sperm and seminal fluid mix in the ejaculatory duct and enter the prostatic urethra together during ejaculation. Seminal gland secretion accounts for some 70% of the volume of semen.

The Prostate

The **prostate** (pros′tāt) is a single doughnut-shaped gland about the size of a peach pit (Figures 27.1 and 27.4). It encircles the urethra just inferior to the bladder. Enclosed by a thick connective tissue capsule, it is made up of 20 to 30 compound tubuloalveolar glands embedded in a mass (stroma) of smooth muscle and dense connective tissue.

The prostatic gland secretion enters the prostatic urethra via several ducts when prostatic smooth muscle contracts during ejaculation. It plays a role in activating sperm and accounts for up to one-third of the semen volume. It is a milky, slightly acid fluid that contains citrate (a nutrient source), several enzymes (fibrinolysin, hyaluronidase, acid phosphatase), and prostate-specific antigen (PSA).

⬥ HOMEOSTATIC IMBALANCE

The prostate has a reputation as a health destroyer (perhaps reflected in the common mispronunciation "prostrate"). Hypertrophy of the prostate, called *benign prostatic hyperplasia* (*BPH*) which affects nearly every elderly male, distorts the urethra. Its precise cause is unknown, but it may be associated with changes in hormone levels as a result of aging. The more the man strains to urinate, the more the valvelike prostatic mass blocks the opening, enhancing the risk of bladder infections (cystitis) and kidney damage.

Traditional treatment has been surgical. Some newer options include using microwaves or drugs to shrink the prostate; inserting and inflating a small balloon to compress the prostate tissue away from the prostatic urethra; and inserting a catheter containing a tiny needle in order to incinerate excess prostate tissue with burstlike releases of radio-frequency radiation.

Finasteride, which ratchets down production of dihydrotestosterone, the hormone linked to male pattern balding and prostate enlargement, is helpful in some cases. Additionally, several drugs are available that relax the smooth muscles at the bladder outlet, facilitating bladder emptying and providing relief.

Prostatitis (pros″tah-ti′tis), inflammation of the prostate, is the most common reason for a man to consult a urologist.

Prostate cancer is the second most common cause of cancer death in men (after lung cancer) and is twice as common in blacks as in whites. Risk factors include fatty diet and genetic predisposition. Screening for prostate cancer typically involves digital examination (palpating the prostate through the anterior rectal wall) and assessment of PSA levels in the blood. Although a normal component of blood at levels below 2.5 ng/ml, PSA is a tumor marker and its rising serum level follows BPH as well as the clinical disease course of prostate cancer. Screening procedures are followed by biopsies of suspicious prostate areas, if deemed necessary, and metastases (most commonly to the pelvic lymph nodes and the skeleton) are detected by bone or MRI scans.

When possible, prostate cancer is treated surgically, alone or in conjunction with radiotherapy. Because prostate cancer is typically androgen dependent, alternative therapies for metastasized cancers involve castration or therapy with drugs that block androgen receptors (flutamide), or that inhibit gonadotropin release, such as LHRH (luteinizing hormone–releasing hormone) analogues. LHRH is another term for GnRH (gonadotropin-releasing hormone, see p. 605). Deprived of the stimulatory effects of androgens, the prostatic tissue regresses and urinary symptoms typically decline.

However, many prostate cancers are very slow growing and may never represent a threat to the patient, particularly if the patient is elderly. In such cases, frequent tests to monitor the tumor may be all that is necessary. ■

The Bulbourethral Glands

The **bulbourethral glands** (bul″bo-u-re′thral) are pea-sized glands inferior to the prostate (Figures 27.1 and 27.4). They produce a thick, clear mucus, some of which drains into the spongy urethra and lubricates the glans penis when a man becomes sexually excited. Additionally, the mucus neutralizes traces of acidic urine in the urethra just prior to ejaculation.

Semen

Semen (se′men) is a milky white, somewhat sticky mixture of sperm, testicular fluid, and accessory gland secretions. The liquid provides a transport medium and nutrients and contains chemicals that protect and activate the sperm and facilitate their movement. Mature sperm cells are streamlined cellular "missiles" containing little cytoplasm or stored nutrients. Catabolism of the fructose in seminal vesicle secretions provides nearly all the fuel needed for sperm ATP synthesis.

Prostaglandins in semen decrease the viscosity of mucus guarding the entry (cervix) of the uterus and stimulate reverse peristalsis in the uterus, facilitating sperm movement through the female reproductive tract. The presence of the hormone *relaxin* and certain enzymes in semen enhance sperm motility. The relative alkalinity of semen as a whole (pH 7.3–7.7) helps neutralize the acid environment of the male's urethra and the female's vagina, thereby protecting the delicate sperm and enhancing their motility. Sperm are very sluggish under acidic conditions particularly (below pH 6).

Semen also contains substances that suppress the immune response in the female's reproductive tract, and has antibiotic chemicals that destroy certain bacteria. Clotting factors found in semen coagulate it just after it is ejaculated. Coagulation causes the sperm to stick to the walls of the vagina and prevents their draining out of the vagina while initially immobile. Soon after, its contained fibrinolysin liquefies the sticky mass, enabling the sperm to swim out and begin their journey through the female duct system.

The amount of semen propelled out of the male duct system during ejaculation is relatively small, only 2–5 ml and only 10% sperm, but there are between 20 and 150 million sperm per milliliter.

CHECK YOUR UNDERSTANDING

8. Adolph, a 68-year-old gentleman, has trouble urinating and is scheduled for a rectal exam. What is his most probable condition and what is the purpose of the rectal exam?

9. Which glandular accessory organ produces the largest proportion of semen?

10. What is semen?

For answers, see Appendix G.

Physiology of the Male Reproductive System

Male Sexual Response

▶ Describe the phases of the male sexual response.

Although there is more to it, the chief phases of the male sexual response are (1) *erection* of the penis, which allows it to penetrate the female vagina, and (2) *ejaculation*, which expels semen into the vagina.

Erection

Erection, enlargement and stiffening of the penis, results from engorgement of the erectile bodies with blood. When a man is not sexually aroused, arterioles supplying the erectile tissue are constricted and the penis is flaccid. However, during sexual excitement a parasympathetic reflex is triggered that promotes release of nitric oxide (NO) locally. NO relaxes smooth muscle in the penile blood vessel walls, causing these arterioles to dilate, which allows the erectile bodies to fill with blood. Expansion of the corpora cavernosa of the penis compresses their drainage veins, retarding blood outflow and maintaining engorgement. The corpus spongiosum expands but not nearly as much as the cavernosa. Its main job is to keep the urethra open during ejaculation. It is important that the erect penis not kink or buckle during intercourse. This problem is prevented by the longitudinal and circular arrangement of collagen fibers surrounding the penis.

Erection of the penis is one of the rare examples of parasympathetic control of arterioles. Another parasympathetic effect is stimulation of the bulbourethral glands, the secretion of which lubricates the glans penis.

27

Erection is initiated by a variety of sexual stimuli, such as touching the genital skin, mechanical stimulation of the pressure receptors in the penis, and erotic sights, sounds, and smells. The CNS responds to such stimuli by activating parasympathetic neurons that innervate the internal pudendal arteries serving the penis. Sometimes erection is induced solely by emotional or higher mental activity (the thought of a sexual encounter). Emotions and thoughts can also inhibit erection, causing vasoconstriction and resumption of the flaccid penile state.

Ejaculation

Ejaculation (*ejac* = to shoot forth) is the propulsion of semen from the male duct system. Although erection is under parasympathetic control, ejaculation is under sympathetic control. When impulses provoking erection reach a certain critical level, a spinal reflex is initiated, and a massive discharge of nerve impulses occurs over the sympathetic nerves serving the genital organs (largely at the level of L_1 and L_2). As a result,

1. The bladder sphincter muscle constricts, preventing expulsion of urine or reflux of semen into the bladder.
2. The reproductive ducts and accessory glands contract, emptying their contents into the urethra.
3. Semen in the urethra triggers a spinal reflex through somatic motor neurons that cause the bulbospongiosus muscles of the penis to undergo a rapid series of contractions, propelling semen at a speed of up to 500 cm/s (200 inches/s or close to 11 mi/h) from the urethra. These rhythmic contractions are accompanied by intense pleasure and many systemic changes, such as generalized muscle contraction, rapid heartbeat, and elevated blood pressure.

The entire ejaculatory event is referred to as **climax** or **orgasm**. Orgasm is quickly followed by *resolution,* a period of muscular and psychological relaxation. Activity of sympathetic nerve fibers constricts the *internal pudendal arteries* (and penile arterioles), reducing blood flow into the penis, and activates small muscles that squeeze the cavernous bodies, forcing blood from the penis into the general circulation. Although the erection may persist a little longer, the penis soon becomes flaccid once again. After ejaculation, there is a *latent,* or *refractory, period,* ranging in time from minutes to hours, during which a man is unable to achieve another orgasm. The latent period lengthens with age.

CHECK YOUR UNDERSTANDING

11. What is erection and what division of the ANS regulates it?
12. What occurs during resolution and what is the result?

For answers, see Appendix G.

⚖ **HOMEOSTATIC IMBALANCE**

Erectile dysfunction (ED), the inability to attain an erection when desired, is due to deficient release of NO by the parasympathetic nerves serving the penis. Approximately 50% of American men over the age of 40 (some 32 million men) have some degree of erectile dysfunction. Psychological factors, alcohol, or certain drugs (antihypertensives, antidepressants, and others) can cause temporary ED. When chronic, the condition is largely the result of hormonal (diabetes mellitus), vascular (arteriosclerosis, varicose veins), or nervous system problems (stroke, penile nerve damage, MS).

Until recently, most remedies entailed using a vacuum pump to suck blood into the penis, injecting drugs into the penis that dilate penile blood vessels, or implanting a device into the penis to make it rigid. Viagra, approved in 1998, and two similar drugs (Cialis and Levitra) released in late 2003 potentiate the effect of the existing NO, a remedy that most men can live with. These drugs work within minutes to an hour to produce a sustained blood flow to the penis, are taken orally, and have essentially no significant side effects in healthy males. However, to avoid a fatal result, those with preexisting heart disease or diabetes mellitus must heed the warning that these drugs reduce systemic blood pressure. ■

Spermatogenesis

▶ Define meiosis. Compare and contrast it to mitosis.

▶ Outline events of spermatogenesis.

Spermatogenesis (sper″mah-to-jen′ĕ-sis; "sperm formation") is the sequence of events in the seminiferous tubules of the testes that produces male gametes—*sperm* or *spermatozoa.* The process begins around the age of 14 years (and often earlier) in males, and continues throughout life. Every day, a healthy adult male makes about 400 million sperm. It seems that nature has made sure that the human species will not be endangered for lack of sperm.

Before we describe the process of spermatogenesis, let's define some terms. First, having two sets of chromosomes, one from each parent, is a key factor in the human life cycle. The normal chromosome number in most body cells is referred to as the **diploid chromosomal number** (dip′loid) of the organism, symbolized as **2*n*.** In humans, this number is 46, and such diploid cells contain 23 pairs of similar chromosomes called **homologous chromosomes** (ho-mol′ŏ-gus) or **homologues.** One member of each pair is from the male parent (the *paternal chromosome*), and the other is from the female parent (the *maternal chromosome*).

Generally speaking, the two homologues of each chromosome pair look alike and carry genes that code for the same traits, though not necessarily for identical expression of those traits. (Consider, for example, the homologous genes controlling the expression of freckles. The paternal gene might code for an ample sprinkling of freckles and the maternal gene for no freckles.) In Chapter 29, we will consider how our mom's and dad's genes interact to produce our visible traits.

The number of chromosomes in human gametes is 23, referred to as the **haploid chromosomal number** (hap′loid), or ***n.*** Gametes contain only one member of each homologous pair. When sperm and egg fuse, they form a fertilized egg that reestablishes the typical diploid chromosomal number of human cells (2*n*).

Gamete formation in both sexes involves **meiosis** (mi-o′sis; "a lessening"), a unique kind of nuclear division that, for the most part, occurs only in the gonads. Recall that *mitosis* (the process by which most body cells divide) distributes replicated chromosomes equally between the two daughter cells. Consequently, each daughter cell receives a full set of chromosomes identical to that of the mother cell. Meiosis, on the other hand, consists of two consecutive nuclear divisions that follow one round of DNA replication. Its product is four daughter cells instead of two, each with *half* as many chromosomes as typical body cells. In other words, meiosis reduces the chromosomal number by half (from *2n* to *n*) in gametes. Additionally, it introduces genetic variation because each of the haploid daughter cells have only some of the genes of each parent, as explained shortly.

Meiosis Compared to Mitosis

The two nuclear divisions of meiosis, called *meiosis I* and *meiosis II*, are divided into phases for convenience. These phases have the same names as those of mitosis (prophase, metaphase, anaphase, and telophase), but some events of meiosis I are quite different from those of mitosis. As we detail those events, you may find it helpful to refer to the comparison of mitosis and meiosis in Figure 27.5.

Recall that prior to mitosis all the chromosomes are replicated. Then the identical copies remain together as *sister chromatids* connected by a centromere throughout prophase and during metaphase. At anaphase, the centromeres split and the sister chromatids separate from each other so that each daughter cell inherits a copy of *every* chromosome possessed by the mother cell (Figure 27.5, left side). Let's look at how meiosis differs (Figure 27.5, right side).

Meiosis I Meiosis I is sometimes called the **reduction division of meiosis** because it reduces the chromosome number from *2n* to *n*. As in mitosis, chromosomes replicate before meiosis begins and in prophase the chromosomes coil and condense, the nuclear envelope and nucleolus break down and disappear, and a spindle forms. But in prophase of meiosis I, an event never seen in mitosis (nor in meiosis II for that matter) occurs. The replicated chromosomes seek out their homologous partners and pair up with them along their entire length. This alignment takes place at discrete spots along the length of the homologues—more like buttoning together than zipping. As a result of this process, called **synapsis**, little groups of four chromatids called **tetrads** are formed (Figure 27.5 and Figure 27.6).

During synapsis, a second unique event, called crossover, occurs. **Crossovers**, also called **chiasmata** (singular: chiasma), are formed within each tetrad as the free ends of one maternal and one paternal chromatid wrap around each other at one or more points. Crossover allows an exchange of genetic material between the paired maternal and paternal chromosomes. Prophase I accounts for about 90% of the total period of meiosis. By its end, the tetrads are attached to the spindle and are moving toward the spindle equator.

During metaphase I, the tetrads line up *randomly* at the spindle equator, so that either the paternal or maternal chromosome can be on a given side of the equator (Figure 27.6). During anaphase I, the sister chromatids representing each homologue

behave as a unit—almost as if replication had not occurred—and the *homologous chromosomes* (each still composed of two joined sister chromatids) are distributed to opposite ends of the cell.

As a result, when meiosis I is completed, the following conditions exist: Each daughter cell has (1) *two* copies of one member of each homologous pair (either the paternal or maternal) and none of the other, and (2) a *haploid* chromosomal number (because the still-united sister chromatids are considered to be a single chromosome) but twice the amount of DNA in each chromosome.

Meiosis II The second meiotic division, meiosis II, mirrors mitosis in every way, except that the chromosomes are *not* replicated before it begins. Instead, the sister chromatids in the two daughter cells of meiosis I are simply parceled out among four cells. Meiosis II is sometimes referred to as the **equational division of meiosis** because the chromatids are distributed equally to the daughter cells (as in mitosis) (Figure 27.6).

In short, meiosis accomplishes two important tasks: (1) It reduces the chromosomal number by half and (2) it introduces genetic variability. The random alignment of the homologous pairs during meiosis I provides tremendous variability in the resulting gametes by scrambling genetic characteristics of the two parents in different combinations. Variability is also increased by crossover—when, during late prophase I, the homologues break at crossover points and exchange chromosomal segments (Figure 27.6). (We will describe this process in Chapter 29.) As a result, it is likely that no two gametes are exactly alike, and all are different from the original mother cells.

Spermatogenesis: Summary of Events in the Seminiferous Tubules

A histological section of an adult testis shows that most cells making up the epithelial walls of the seminiferous tubules are in various stages of cell division (Figure 27.7a). These cells, collectively called **spermatogenic cells** (*spermatogenic* = sperm forming), give rise to sperm in the following series of divisions and cellular transformations (Figure 27.7b, c).

Mitosis of Spermatogonia: Forming Spermatocytes The outermost tubule cells, which are in direct contact with the epithelial basal lamina, are stem cells called **spermatogonia** (sper″mah-to-go′ne-ah; "sperm seed"). The spermatogonia divide more or less continuously by *mitosis* and, until puberty, all their daughter cells become spermatogonia.

Spermatogenesis begins during puberty, and from then on, each mitotic division of a spermatogonium results in two distinctive daughter cells—types A and B. The **type A daughter cell** remains at the basal lamina to maintain the germ cell line. The **type B cell** gets pushed toward the lumen, where it becomes a **primary spermatocyte** destined to produce four sperm. (To keep these cell types straight, remember that just as the letter A is always at the beginning of our alphabet, a type A cell is always at the tubule basal lamina ready to begin a new generation of gametes.)

(*Text continues on p. 1037.*)

	MITOSIS	MEIOSIS
Number of divisions	One, consisting of prophase, metaphase, anaphase, and telophase.	Two, each consisting of prophase, metaphase, anaphase, and telophase. DNA replication does not occur between the two nuclear divisions.
Synapsis of homologous chromosomes	Does not occur.	Occurs during mitosis I; tetrads formed, allowing crossovers.
Daughter cell number and genetic composition	Two. Each diploid (2n) cell is identical to the mother cell.	Four. Each haploid (n) cell contains half as many chromosomes as the mother cell and is genetically different from the mother cell.
Roles in the body	For development of multicellular adult from zygote. Produces cells for growth and tissue repair. Ensures constancy of genetic makeup of all body cells.	Produces cells for reproduction (gametes). Introduces genetic variability in the gametes and reduces chromosomal number by half so that when fertilization occurs, the normal diploid chromosomal number is restored (in humans, 2n = 46).

Figure 27.5 Comparison of mitosis and meiosis in a mother cell with a diploid number (2n) of 4. (Not all the phases of mitosis and meiosis are shown.)

Interphase cell

Interphase events
As in mitosis, meiosis is preceded by DNA replication and other preparations for cell division.

MEIOSIS I

Prophase I
Prophase events occur, as in mitosis. Additionally, synapsis occurs: Homologous chromosomes come together along their length to form tetrads. During synapsis, the "arms" of homologous chromatids wrap around each other, forming several crossovers. The nonsister chromatids trade segments at points of crossover. Crossover is followed through the diagrams below.

Metaphase I
The tetrads align randomly on the spindle equator in preparation for anaphase.

Anaphase I
Unlike anaphase of mitosis, the centromeres do not separate during anaphase I of meiosis, so the sister chromatids (dyads) remain firmly attached. However, the homologous chromosomes do separate from each other and the dyads move toward opposite poles of the cell.

Telophase I
The nuclear envelopes re-form around the chromosomal masses, the spindle breaks down, and the chromatin reappears as telophase and cytokinesis are completed. The 2 daughter cells (now haploid) enter a second interphase-like period, called interkinesis, before meiosis II occurs. There is no second replication of DNA before meiosis II.

MEIOSIS II

Prophase II

Meiosis II begins with the products of meiosis I (2 haploid daughter cells) and undergoes a mitosis-like nuclear division process referred to as the equational division of meiosis.

Metaphase II

Anaphase II

After progressing through the phases of meiosis and cytokinesis, the product is 4 haploid cells, each genetically different from the original mother cell. (During human spermatogenesis, the daughter cells remain interconnected by cytoplasmic extensions during the meiotic phases.)

Telophase II and cytokinesis

Products of meiosis: haploid daughter cells

Figure 27.6 Meiosis. The series of events in meiotic cell division for an animal cell with a diploid number (2n) of 4. The behavior of the chromosomes is emphasized.

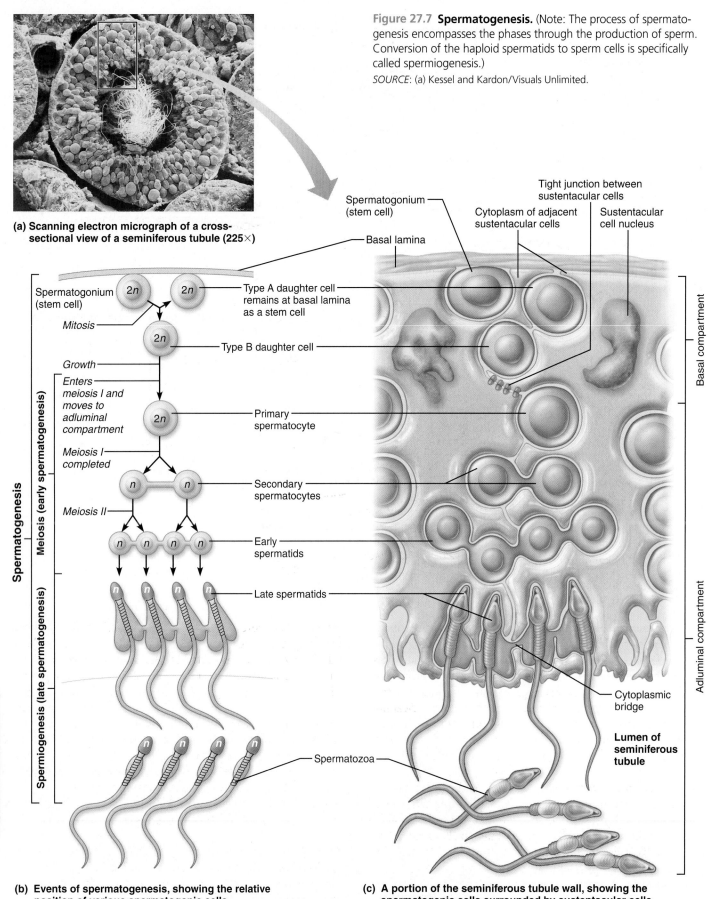

(a) Scanning electron micrograph of a cross-sectional view of a seminiferous tubule (225×)

Figure 27.7 **Spermatogenesis.** (Note: The process of spermatogenesis encompasses the phases through the production of sperm. Conversion of the haploid spermatids to sperm cells is specifically called spermiogenesis.)

SOURCE: (a) Kessel and Kardon/Visuals Unlimited.

(b) Events of spermatogenesis, showing the relative position of various spermatogenic cells

(c) A portion of the seminiferous tubule wall, showing the spermatogenic cells surrounded by sustentacular cells (colored gold)

Approximately 24 days

Figure 27.8 Spermiogenesis: transformation of a spermatid into a functional sperm.
(a) The stepwise process of spermiogenesis consists of ① packaging of the acrosomal enzymes by
the Golgi apparatus, ② forming the acrosome at the anterior end of the nucleus and positioning the centrioles at the opposite end of the nucleus, ③ elaboration of microtubules to form
the flagellum, ④ mitochondrial multiplication and their positioning around the proximal portion
of the flagellum, and ⑤ sloughing off excess cytoplasm. ⑥ Structure of an immature sperm
that has just been released from a sustentacular cell. ⑦ Structure of a fully mature sperm.
(b) Scanning electron micrograph of mature sperm (900×).

Meiosis: Spermatocytes to Spermatids   Each primary spermatocyte generated during the first phase undergoes meiosis I, forming two smaller haploid cells called **secondary spermatocytes**
(Figure 27.7b, c). The secondary spermatocytes continue on
rapidly into meiosis II. Their daughter cells, called **spermatids**
(sper′mah-tidz), are small round cells, with large spherical nuclei, seen closer to the lumen of the tubule. Midway through
spermatogenesis, the developing sperm "turn off" nearly all
their genes and compact their DNA into dense pellets.

Spermiogenesis: Spermatids to Sperm   Each spermatid has
the correct chromosomal number for fertilization (*n*), but is
nonmotile. It still must undergo a streamlining process called
spermiogenesis, during which it elongates, sheds its excess cytoplasmic baggage, and forms a tail. Follow the details of this
process in **Figure 27.8a**, steps ①–⑦.

   The resulting sperm, or **spermatozoon** (sper″mah-to-zo′on;
"animal seed"), has a head, a midpiece, and a tail, which correspond roughly to *genetic*, *metabolic*, and *locomotor regions*,

respectively (Figure 27.8a, ⑦). Sperm "pack" lightly. The **head**
of a sperm consists almost entirely of its flattened nucleus,
which contains the compacted DNA. Adhering to the top of the
nucleus is a helmetlike **acrosome** (ak′ro-sōm; "tip piece")
(Figure 27.8a, ⑤ and ⑥). The lysosome-like acrosome is produced by the Golgi apparatus and contains hydrolytic enzymes
that enable the sperm to penetrate and enter an egg. The sperm
midpiece contains mitochondria spiraled tightly around the
microtubules of the tail. The long **tail** is a typical flagellum produced by one centriole (actually a basal body) near the nucleus.
The mitochondria provide the metabolic energy (ATP) needed
for the whiplike movements of the tail that will propel the
sperm along its way in the female reproductive tract.

Role of the Sustentacular Cells   Throughout spermatogenesis, descendants of the same spermatogonium remain closely attached to one another by cytoplasmic bridges (see Figure 27.7c).
They are also surrounded by and connected to nonreplicating
supporting cells of a special type, called **sustentacular cells** or

27

Sertoli cells, which extend from the basal lamina to the lumen of the tubule. The sustentacular cells, bound to each other laterally by tight junctions, divide the seminiferous tubule into two compartments. The **basal compartment** extends from the basal lamina to their tight junctions and it contains spermatogonia and the earliest primary spermatocytes. The **adluminal compartment** lies internal to the tight junctions and includes the meiotically active cells and the tubule lumen (see Figure 27.7c).

The tight junctions between the sustentacular cells form the **blood-testis barrier**. This barrier prevents the membrane antigens of differentiating sperm from escaping through the basal lamina into the bloodstream where they would activate the immune system. Because sperm are not formed until puberty, they are absent when the immune system is being programmed to recognize a person's own tissues early in life. The spermatogonia, which are recognized as "self," are outside the barrier and for this reason can be influenced by bloodborne chemical messengers that prompt spermatogenesis. Following mitosis of the spermatogonia, the tight junctions of the sustentacular cells open to allow primary spermatocytes to pass into the adluminal compartment—much as locks in a canal open to allow a boat to pass.

In the adluminal compartment, spermatocytes and spermatids are nearly enclosed in recesses in the sustentacular cells (see Figure 27.7). They are anchored there by a particular glycoprotein on the spermatogenic cell's surface. The sustentacular cells provide nutrients and essential signals to the dividing cells, even telling them to live or die. They also move the cells along to the lumen, secrete **testicular fluid** (rich in androgens and metabolic acids) that provides the transport medium for sperm in the lumen, and phagocytize faulty germ cells and the excess cytoplasm sloughed off as the spermatids transform into sperm. The sustentacular cells also produce chemical mediators (inhibin and androgen-binding protein) that help regulate spermatogenesis, as we describe below.

Given hospitable temperature conditions, spermatogenesis—from formation of a primary spermatocyte to release of immature sperm into the lumen—takes 64 to 72 days. Sperm in the lumen are unable to "swim" and are incapable of fertilizing an egg. They are pushed by the pressure of the testicular fluid through the tubular system of the testes into the epididymis, where they gain increased motility and fertilizing power.

HOMEOSTATIC IMBALANCE

Roughly one in seven American couples seek treatment for infertility, mostly because of problems with sperm quality or quantity. According to some studies, a gradual decline in male fertility has been occurring in the past 50 years.

Some believe the main cause is *xenobiotics*, alien molecules that have invaded our lives in a variety of forms including environmental toxins, PVCs, phthalates (oily solvents that make plastics flexible), certain components in pesticides and herbicides, and especially compounds with estrogenic effects, some of which are injected into beef cattle to encourage growth. These estrogen-like compounds block the action of male sex hormones as they program sexual development, and are now found in our meat supply as well as in the air. Common

antibiotics such as tetracycline may suppress sperm formation, and radiation, lead, marijuana, lack of selenium, and excessive alcohol can cause abnormal (two-headed, multiple-tailed, etc.) sperm to be produced. Male infertility may also be caused by the lack of a specific type of Ca^{2+} channel (Ca^{2+} is needed for normal sperm motility), anatomical obstructions, hormonal imbalances, and oxidative stress (which contributes to DNA fragmentation in sperm).

A low sperm count accompanied by a high percentage of immature sperm may hint that a man has a *varicocele* (var′ĭ-ko-sēl″). This condition hinders drainage of the testicular vein, resulting in an elevated temperature in the scrotum that interferes with normal sperm development. Other thermal-related events that inhibit sperm maturation are fever and overuse of hot tubs. ■

CHECK YOUR UNDERSTANDING

13. How is the final product of meiosis different from that of mitosis?
14. Describe the major structural and functional regions of a sperm.
15. What is the role of sustentacular cells? Of interstitial cells?

For answers, see Appendix G.

Hormonal Regulation of Male Reproductive Function

▶ Discuss hormonal regulation of testicular function and the physiological effects of testosterone on male reproductive anatomy.

Hormonal regulation of gamete and gonadal hormone production involves interactions between the hypothalamus, anterior pituitary gland, and gonads, a relationship called the **hypothalamic-pituitary-gonadal (HPG) axis**.

The Hypothalamic-Pituitary-Gonadal Axis

The sequence of regulatory events involving the HPG axis, shown schematically in **Figure 27.9**, is as follows:

1. The hypothalamus releases **gonadotropin-releasing hormone (GnRH)**, which reaches the anterior pituitary cells via the blood of the hypophyseal portal system. GnRH controls the release of the two anterior pituitary gonadotropins: **follicle-stimulating hormone (FSH)** and **luteinizing hormone (LH)**, both named for their effects on the female gonad.
2. Binding of GnRH to pituitary cells (gonadotrophs) prompts them to secrete FSH and LH into the blood.
3. FSH stimulates spermatogenesis indirectly by stimulating the sustentacular cells to release **androgen-binding protein (ABP)**. ABP keeps the concentration of **testosterone** in the vicinity of the spermatogenic cells high, which in turn stimulates spermatogenesis. In this way, FSH makes these cells receptive to testosterone's stimulatory effects.

④ LH binds to the interstitial cells in the soft connective tissue surrounding the seminiferous tubules, prodding them to secrete testosterone (and a small amount of estrogen).

⑤ Locally, rising testosterone levels serve as the final trigger for spermatogenesis.

⑥ Testosterone entering the bloodstream exerts a number of effects at other body sites. It stimulates maturation of sex organs, development and maintenance of secondary sex characteristics, and libido.

⑦ Rising levels of testosterone feed back to inhibit hypothalamic release of GnRH and act directly on the anterior pituitary to inhibit gonadotropin release.

⑧ **Inhibin** (in-hib′in), a protein hormone produced by the sustentacular cells, serves as a "barometer" of the normalcy of spermatogenesis. When the sperm count is high, inhibin release increases, and it inhibits anterior pituitary release of FSH and hypothalamic release of GnRH. (The inhibitory effect of testosterone and inhibin on the hypothalamus is not illustrated in Figure 27.9.) When sperm count falls below 20 million/ml, inhibin secretion declines steeply.

As you can see, the amount of testosterone and sperm produced by the adult testes reflects a balance among the three interacting sets of hormones that make up the HPG axis: (1) GnRH, which indirectly stimulates the testes via its effect on FSH and LH release; (2) gonadotropins (FSH and LH), which directly stimulate the testes; and (3) gonadal hormones (testosterone and inhibin), which can exert negative feedback controls on the hypothalamus and anterior pituitary. Once this balance is established during puberty (a process which takes about three years), the amount of testosterone and sperm produced remains fairly stable throughout life.

Because the hypothalamus is also influenced by input from other brain areas, the whole axis is under CNS control. In the absence of GnRH and gonadotropins, the testes atrophy, and sperm and testosterone production cease.

Development of male reproductive structures (discussed later in the chapter) depends on prenatal secretion of male hormones, and for a few months after birth, a male infant has plasma gonadotropin and testosterone levels nearly equal to those of a midpubertal boy. Soon afterwards, blood levels of these hormones recede and they remain low throughout childhood. As puberty nears, much higher levels of testosterone are required to suppress hypothalamic release of GnRH. So, as more GnRH is released, more testosterone is secreted by the testes, but the threshold for hypothalamic inhibition keeps rising until the adult pattern of hormone interaction is achieved, as evidenced by the presence of mature sperm in the semen.

Mechanism and Effects of Testosterone Activity

Like all steroid hormones, testosterone is synthesized from cholesterol and exerts its effects by activating specific genes, which results in enhanced synthesis of certain proteins in the target cells. (See Chapter 16 for mechanisms of steroid hormone action.) In some target cells, testosterone must be transformed into another steroid to exert its effects. In the prostate, testosterone is converted to *dihydrotestosterone* (*DHT*) before it can bind in the

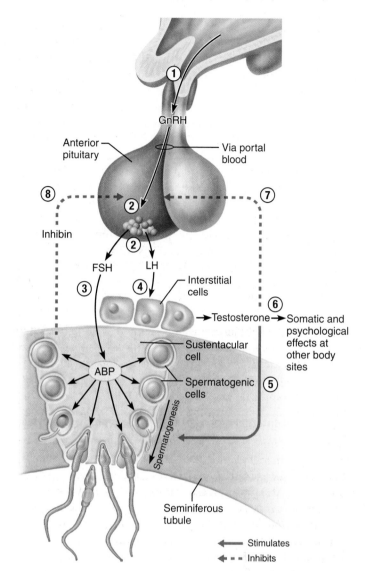

Figure 27.9 Hormonal regulation of testicular function, the hypothalamic-pituitary-gonadal axis. (Only one sustentacular cell is depicted so that its structural relationship to the spermatogenic cells it encloses is clearly seen. However, it would be flanked by sustentacular cells on each side.)

nucleus, and in certain neurons of the brain, testosterone is converted to *estradiol* (es′trah-di-ol), a female sex hormone, to bring about its stimulatory effects. These transformations often occur in a single enzymatic step because testosterone and the other gonadal hormones are structurally very similar.

As puberty ensues, testosterone not only prompts spermatogenesis but also has multiple anabolic effects throughout the body (see Table 27.1, p. 1057). It targets accessory reproductive organs—ducts, glands, and the penis—causing them to grow and assume adult size and function. In adult males, normal plasma levels of testosterone maintain these organs. When the hormone is deficient or absent, all accessory organs atrophy, semen volume declines markedly, and erection and ejaculation are impaired. Thus, a man becomes both sterile and unable to carry out sexual intercourse. This situation is easily remedied by testosterone replacement therapy.

27

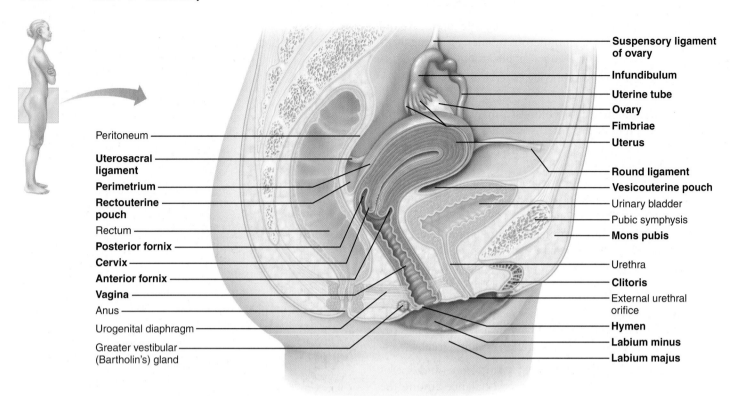

Peritoneum

Uterosacral ligament

Perimetrium

Rectouterine pouch

Rectum

Posterior fornix

Cervix

Anterior fornix

Vagina

Anus

Urogenital diaphragm

Greater vestibular (Bartholin's) gland

Suspensory ligament of ovary

Infundibulum

Uterine tube

Ovary

Fimbriae

Uterus

Round ligament

Vesicouterine pouch

Urinary bladder

Pubic symphysis

Mons pubis

Urethra

Clitoris

External urethral orifice

Hymen

Labium minus

Labium majus

Figure 27.10 **Internal organs of the female reproductive system, midsagittal section.** (See *A Brief Atlas of the Human Body*, Figure 74.)

Male secondary sex characteristics—that is, features induced in the *nonreproductive* organs by the male sex hormones (mainly testosterone)—make their appearance at puberty. These include the appearance of pubic, axillary, and facial hair, enhanced hair growth on the chest or other body areas in some men, and a deepening of the voice as the larynx enlarges. The skin thickens and becomes oilier (which predisposes young men to acne), bones grow and increase in density, and skeletal muscles increase in size and mass. The last two effects are often referred to as the *somatic effects* of testosterone (*soma* = body). Epiphyseal plate closure and termination of skeletal growth in height occurs in response to rising estrogen levels late in puberty in both boys and girls. Testosterone also boosts basal metabolic rate and influences behavior. It is the basis of the sex drive (libido) in males, be they heterosexual or homosexual. As noted later (p. 1058), the adrenal androgen DHEA appears to be more important than testosterone in creating or driving the *female* libido.

In embryos, the presence of testosterone masculinizes the brain. Testosterone also appears to continue to shape certain regions of the male brain well into adult life, as indicated by the differences in males' and females' brain areas involved in sexual arousal (for example, the amygdala).

The testes are not the only source of androgens. The adrenal glands of both sexes also release androgens. However, the relatively small amounts of adrenal androgens are unable to support normal testosterone-mediated functions when the testes fail to produce androgens, so we can assume that it is the testosterone production by the testes that supports male reproductive function.

CHECK YOUR UNDERSTANDING

16. What is the HPG axis?

17. How does FSH indirectly stimulate spermatogenesis?

18. What are three secondary sex characteristics promoted by testosterone?

For answers, see Appendix G.

Anatomy of the Female Reproductive System

The reproductive role of the female is far more complex than that of a male. Not only must she produce gametes, but her body must prepare to nurture a developing fetus for a period of approximately nine months. **Ovaries**, the **female gonads**, are the primary reproductive organs of a female, and like the male testes, ovaries serve a dual purpose: They produce the female gametes (ova) and sex hormones, **estrogen** and **progesterone** (pro-ges'tĕ-rōn). Estrogen includes *estradiol, estrone,* and *estriol,* but estradiol is the most abundant and is most responsible for estrogenic effects.

As illustrated in **Figure 27.10**, the ovaries and duct system, collectively known as the **internal genitalia**, are mostly located in the pelvic cavity. The female's accessory ducts, from the vicinity of the ovary to the body exterior, are the *uterine tubes,* the *uterus,* and the *vagina.* They transport or otherwise serve the

27

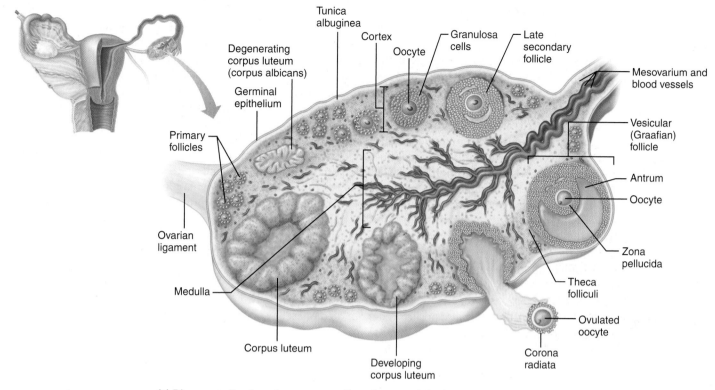

(a) Diagrammatic view of an ovary sectioned to reveal the follicles in its interior

(b) Photomicrograph of a mammalian ovary showing follicles of different developmental phases

Figure 27.11 Structure of an ovary. (a) Diagrammatic view. Note that not all of these structures would appear in the ovary at the same time. **(b)** Photomicrograph (4×).

needs of the reproductive cells and a developing fetus. The external sex organs of females are referred to as the **external genitalia**.

The Ovaries

▶ Describe the location, structure, and function of the ovaries.

The paired ovaries flank the uterus on each side (Figure 27.10). Shaped like an almond and about twice as large, each ovary is held in place by several ligaments in the fork of the iliac blood vessels within the peritoneal cavity. The **ovarian ligament** anchors the ovary medially to the uterus; the **suspensory ligament** anchors it laterally to the pelvic wall; and the **mesovarium** (mez″o-va′re-um) suspends it in between (see

Figures 27.10 and 27.12a). The suspensory ligament and the mesovarium are part of the **broad ligament**, a peritoneal fold that "tents" over the uterus and supports the uterine tubes, uterus, and vagina. The ovarian ligaments are enclosed by the broad ligament.

The ovaries are served by the **ovarian arteries**, branches of the abdominal aorta (see Figure 19.24c), and by the *ovarian branch of the uterine arteries*. The ovarian blood vessels reach the ovaries by traveling through the suspensory ligaments and mesovaria (see Figure 27.12a).

Like each testis, each ovary is surrounded externally by a fibrous **tunica albuginea (Figure 27.11a)**, which is in turn covered externally by a layer of cuboidal epithelial cells called the *germinal epithelium*, actually a continuation of the peritoneum. The ovary

27

has an outer *cortex*, which houses the forming gametes, and an inner *medulla* containing the largest blood vessels and nerves, but the relative extent of each region is poorly defined.

Embedded in the highly vascular connective tissue of the ovary cortex are many tiny saclike structures called **ovarian follicles**. Each follicle consists of an immature egg, called an **oocyte** (o'o-sīt; *oo* = egg), encased by one or more layers of very different cells. The surrounding cells are called **follicle cells** if a single layer is present, and **granulosa cells** when more than one layer is present. Follicles at different stages of maturation are distinguished by their structure (Figure 27.11a). In a **primordial follicle**, one layer of squamouslike follicle cells surrounds the oocyte.

A **primary follicle** has a single layer of cuboidal or columnar-type follicle cells enclosing the oocyte.

A **secondary follicle** is formed when two or more layers of granulosa cells surround the oocyte.

A **late secondary follicle** results when small fluid-filled spaces appear between the granulosa cells.

The mature **vesicular follicle**, also called a **Graafian** (graf' e-an) or **tertiary follicle**, forms when the fluid-filled pockets coalesce to form a central fluid-filled cavity called an *antrum*. At this stage, the follicle extends from the deepest part of the ovarian cortex and bulges from the surface of the ovary (Figure 27.11) and its oocyte "sits" on a stalk of granulosa cells at one side of the antrum.

Each month in women of childbearing age, one of the ripening follicles ejects its oocyte from the ovary, an event called *ovulation* (see Figure 27.18). After ovulation, the ruptured follicle is transformed into a very different looking glandular structure called the **corpus luteum** (lu'te-um; "yellow body"; plural: corpora lutea), which eventually degenerates (Figure 27.11a). As a rule, most of these structures can be seen within the same ovary. In older women, the surfaces of the ovaries are scarred and pitted, revealing that many oocytes have been released.

CHECK YOUR UNDERSTANDING

19. Briefly, what are the internal genitalia of a woman?
20. What two roles do the ovaries assume?
21. How does a primary follicle differ from a secondary follicle? From a vesicular follicle?

For answers, see Appendix G.

The Female Duct System

▶ Describe the location, structure, and function of each of the organs of the female reproductive duct system.

Unlike the male duct system, which is continuous with the tubules of the testes, the female duct system has little or no actual contact with the ovaries. An ovulated oocyte is cast into the peritoneal cavity, and some oocytes are lost there.

The Uterine Tubes

The **uterine tubes** (u'ter-in), also called **fallopian tubes** or **oviducts**, form the initial part of the female duct system

(Figure 27.10 and Figure 27.12a). They receive the ovulated oocyte and are the site where fertilization generally occurs. Each uterine tube is about 10 cm (4 inches) long and extends medially from the region of an ovary to empty into the superolateral region of the uterus via a constricted region called the **isthmus** (is'mus). The distal end of each uterine tube expands as it curves around the ovary, forming the **ampulla**, and fertilization usually occurs in this region. The ampulla ends in the **infundibulum** (in"fun-dib'u-lum), an open, funnel-shaped structure bearing ciliated, fingerlike projections called **fimbriae** (fim'bre-e; "fringe") that drape over the ovary.

Around the time of ovulation, the uterine tube performs complex movements to capture oocytes. It bends to drape over the ovary while the fimbriae stiffen and sweep the ovarian surface. The beating cilia on the fimbriae then create currents in the peritoneal fluid that tend to carry an oocyte into the uterine tube, where it begins its journey toward the uterus.

The uterine tube contains sheets of smooth muscle, and its thick, highly folded mucosa contains both ciliated and nonciliated cells. The oocyte is carried toward the uterus by a combination of muscular peristalsis and the beating of the cilia. Nonciliated cells of the mucosa have dense microvilli and produce a secretion that keeps the oocyte (and sperm, if present) moist and nourished.

Externally, the uterine tubes are covered by visceral peritoneum and supported along their length by a short mesentery (part of the broad ligament) called the **mesosalpinx** (mez"o-sal'pinks; "mesentery of the trumpet"; *salpin* = trumpet), a reference to the trumpet-shaped uterine tube it supports (Figure 27.12a).

HOMEOSTATIC IMBALANCE

The fact that the uterine tubes are not continuous with the ovaries places women at risk for *ectopic pregnancy*, in which an oocyte fertilized in the peritoneal cavity or distal portion of the uterine tube begins developing there. Because the tube lacks adequate mass and vascularization to support the full term of pregnancy, such pregnancies tend to naturally abort, often with substantial bleeding.

Another potential problem is infection spreading into the peritoneal cavity from other parts of the reproductive tract. Gonorrhea bacteria and other sexually transmitted microorganisms sometimes infect the peritoneal cavity in this way, causing an extremely severe inflammation called **pelvic inflammatory disease (PID)**. Unless treated promptly with broad-spectrum antibiotics, PID can cause scarring of the narrow uterine tubes and of the ovaries, resulting in sterility. Indeed, scarring and closure of the uterine tubes, which have an internal diameter as small as the width of a human hair in some regions, is one of the major causes of female infertility. ■

The Uterus

The **uterus** (Latin for "womb") is located in the pelvis, anterior to the rectum and posterosuperior to the bladder (Figures 27.10 and 27.12). It is a hollow, thick-walled, muscular organ that functions to receive, retain, and nourish a fertilized ovum. In a

(a)

(b)

Figure 27.12 Internal reproductive organs of a female. (a) Posterior view of the female reproductive organs. The posterior walls of the vagina, uterus, and uterine tubes, and the broad ligament (a peritoneal fold) have been removed on the right side to reveal the shape of the lumen of these organs. **(b)** Anterior view of the reproductive organs of a female cadaver. (See *A Brief Atlas of the Human Body*, Figure 75.)

27

fertile woman who has never been pregnant, the uterus is about the size and shape of an inverted pear, but it is usually somewhat larger in women who have borne children. Normally, the uterus flexes anteriorly where it joins the vagina (see Figure 27.10), causing the uterus as a whole to be inclined forward, or *anteverted*. However, the organ is frequently turned backward, or *retroverted*, in older women.

The major portion of the uterus is referred to as the **body** (Figures 27.10 and 27.12). The rounded region superior to the entrance of the uterine tubes is the **fundus**, and the slightly narrowed region between the body and the cervix is the *isthmus*. The **cervix** of the uterus is its narrow neck, or outlet, which projects into the vagina inferiorly.

The cavity of the cervix, called the **cervical canal**, communicates with the vagina via the *external os* (*os* = mouth) and with the cavity of the uterine body via the *internal os.* The mucosa of the cervical canal contains *cervical glands* that secrete a mucus that fills the cervical canal and covers the external os, presumably to block the spread of bacteria from the vagina into the uterus. Cervical mucus also blocks the entry of sperm, except at midcycle, when it becomes less viscous and allows sperm to pass through.

HOMEOSTATIC IMBALANCE

Cancer of the cervix strikes about 450,000 women worldwide each year, killing about half. It is most common among women between the ages of 30 and 50. Risk factors include frequent cervical inflammations, sexually transmitted infections, including genital warts, and multiple pregnancies. The cancer cells arise from the epithelium covering the cervical tip.

In a *Papanicolaou (Pap) smear,* or cervical smear test, some of these cells are scraped away and then examined for abnormalities. A Pap smear is the most effective way to detect this slow-growing cancer, and American Cancer Society guidelines advise women to have one yearly until the age of 70, when this monitoring can be stopped if there have been no abnormal results in the past 10 years. When results are inconclusive, a test for the sexually transmitted human papillomavirus (HPV), the cause of most cervical cancer, can be done from the same Pap sample or from a blood sample. *Gardasil,* a three-dose vaccine that provides protection from HPV-induced cervical cancer, is the latest addition to the official childhood immunization schedule. It is recommended for all 11- and 12-year-old girls, although it may be administered to girls as young as 9 years old. In unexposed girls, the vaccine specifically blocks two cancer-causing kinds of HPV as well as two additional types which are not associated with cervical cancer. All four types of the virus are associated with genital warts and mild Pap test abnormalities. Whether or not this vaccine will become a requirement for school is presently decided on a state-to-state basis. ■

Supports of the Uterus   The uterus is supported laterally by the **mesometrium** ("mesentery of the uterus") portion of the broad ligament (Figure 27.12a). More inferiorly, the **lateral cervical (cardinal) ligaments** extend from the cervix and superior vagina to the lateral walls of the pelvis, and the paired **uterosacral ligaments** secure the uterus to the sacrum posteriorly. The uterus is bound to the anterior body wall by the fibrous **round ligaments**, which run through the inguinal canals to anchor in the subcutaneous tissue of the labia majora. These ligaments allow the uterus a good deal of mobility, and its position changes as the rectum and bladder fill and empty.

HOMEOSTATIC IMBALANCE

Despite the many anchoring ligaments, the principal support of the uterus is provided by the muscles of the pelvic floor, namely the muscles of the urogenital and pelvic diaphragms (Table 10.7). These muscles are stretched and sometimes torn during childbirth. Subsequently, the unsupported uterus may sink inferiorly, until the tip of the cervix protrudes through the external vaginal opening. This condition is called **prolapse of the uterus.** ■

The undulating course of the peritoneum produces several cul-de-sacs, or blind-ended peritoneal pouches. The most important of these are the *vesicouterine pouch* (ves″i-ko-u′ter-in) between the bladder and uterus, and the *rectouterine pouch* between the rectum and uterus (see Figure 27.10).

The Uterine Wall   The wall of the uterus is composed of three layers (Figure 27.12a). The **perimetrium**, the incomplete outermost serous layer, is the peritoneum. The **myometrium** (mi″o-me′tre-um; "muscle of the uterus") is the bulky middle layer, composed of interlacing bundles of smooth muscle. It contracts rhythmically during childbirth to expel the baby from the mother's body. The **endometrium** is the mucosal lining of the uterine cavity **(Figure 27.13)**. It is a simple columnar epithelium underlain by a thick lamina propria. If fertilization occurs, the young embryo burrows into the endometrium (implants) and resides there for the rest of its development.

The endometrium has two chief *strata* (layers). The **stratum functionalis** (fungk-shun-a′lis), or **functional layer**, undergoes cyclic changes in response to blood levels of ovarian hormones and is shed during menstruation (approximately every 28 days). The thinner, deeper **stratum basalis** (ba-să′lis), or **basal layer**, forms a new functionalis after menstruation ends. It is unresponsive to ovarian hormones. The endometrium has numerous *uterine glands* that change in length as endometrial thickness changes.

The vascular supply of the uterus is key to understanding the cyclic changes of the uterine endometrium, which we will discuss later in the chapter. The **uterine arteries** arise from the *internal iliacs* in the pelvis, ascend along the sides of the uterus, and send branches into the uterine wall (Figures 27.12a and 27.13b). These branches break up into several **arcuate arteries** (ar′ku-āt) within the myometrium. The arcuate arteries send **radial branches** into the endometrium, where they in turn give off **straight arteries** to the stratum basalis and **spiral (coiled) arteries** to the stratum functionalis. The spiral arteries repeatedly degenerate and regenerate, and it is their spasms that actually cause the functionalis layer to be shed during menstruation. Veins in the endometrium are thin-walled and form an extensive network with occasional sinusoidal enlargements.

The Vagina

The **vagina** ("sheath") is a thin-walled tube, 8–10 cm (3–4 inches) long. It lies between the bladder and the rectum and extends from the cervix to the body exterior (see Figure 27.10). The urethra parallels its course anteriorly. Often called the *birth canal*, the vagina provides a passageway for delivery of an infant and for menstrual flow. Because it receives the penis (and semen) during sexual intercourse, it is the *female organ of copulation.*

The distensible wall of the vagina consists of three coats: an outer fibroelastic *adventitia*, a smooth muscle *muscularis*, and an inner *mucosa* marked by transverse ridges or *rugae*, which stimulate the penis during intercourse. The mucosa is a stratified

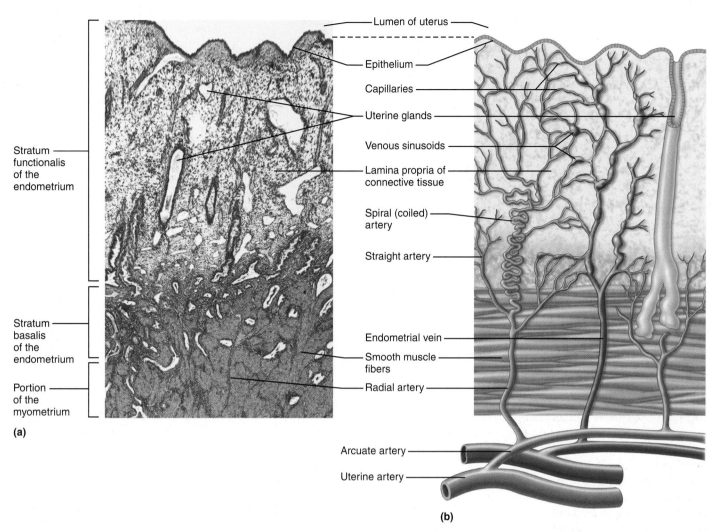

Lumen of uterus

Epithelium

Capillaries

Uterine glands

Venous sinusoids

Lamina propria of connective tissue

Spiral (coiled) artery

Straight artery

Stratum functionalis of the endometrium

Stratum basalis of the endometrium

Portion of the myometrium

Endometrial vein

Smooth muscle fibers

Radial artery

(a)

(b)

Arcuate artery

Uterine artery

Figure 27.13 The endometrium and its blood supply. (a) Photomicrograph of the endometrium, longitudinal section, showing its functionalis and basalis regions (40×). **(b)** Diagrammatic view of the endometrium, showing the straight arteries that serve the stratum basalis and the spiral arteries that serve the stratum functionalis. The thin-walled veins and venous sinusoids are also illustrated.

squamous epithelium adapted to stand up to friction. Certain cells in the mucosa (*dendritic cells*) act as antigen-presenting cells and are thought to provide the route of HIV transmission from an infected male to the female during sexual intercourse. (AIDS, the immune deficiency disease caused by HIV, is described in Chapter 21.)

The vaginal mucosa has no glands. Instead, it is lubricated by the cervical mucous glands and the mucosal transudate that "weeps" from the vaginal walls. Its epithelial cells release large amounts of glycogen, which is anaerobically metabolized to lactic acid by resident bacteria. Consequently, the pH of a woman's vagina is normally quite acidic. This acidity helps keep the vagina healthy and free of infection, but it is also hostile to sperm. Although vaginal fluid of adult females is *acidic*, it tends to be alkaline in adolescents, predisposing sexually active teenagers to sexually transmitted infections.

In virgins (those who have never participated in sexual intercourse), the mucosa near the distal **vaginal orifice** forms an incomplete partition called the **hymen** (hi′men) (Figure 27.14a). The hymen is very vascular and may bleed when it is stretched or ruptured during the first coitus (sexual intercourse). However, its durability varies. In some females, it is ruptured during a sports activity, tampon insertion, or pelvic examination. Occasionally, it is so tough that it must be breached surgically if intercourse is to occur.

The upper end of the vaginal canal loosely surrounds the cervix of the uterus, producing a vaginal recess called the **vaginal fornix**. The posterior part of this recess, the *posterior fornix*, is much deeper than the *lateral* and *anterior fornices* (see Figures 27.10 and Figures 27.12a). Generally, the lumen of the vagina is quite small and, except where it is held open by the cervix, its posterior and anterior walls are in contact with one another. The vagina stretches considerably during copulation and childbirth, but its lateral distension is limited by the ischial spines and the sacrospinous ligaments.

27

(a)

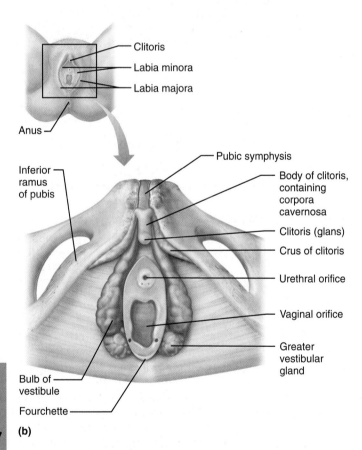

(b)

Figure 27.14 **The external genitalia (vulva) of the female.**
(a) Superficial structures. The region enclosed by the dashed lines is the perineum. **(b)** Deep structures. The labia majora and associated skin have been removed to show the underlying erectile bodies. For the associated superficial muscles, see Figure 10.12 on p. 345.

▲ HOMEOSTATIC IMBALANCE

The uterus tilts away from the vagina. For this reason, attempts by untrained persons to induce an abortion by entering the uterus with a surgical instrument may result in puncturing of the posterior wall of the vagina, followed by hemorrhage and—if the instrument is unsterile—peritonitis. ■

CHECK YOUR UNDERSTANDING

22. Why are women more at risk for PID than men?

23. Oocytes are ovulated into the peritoneal cavity and yet women do get pregnant. What action of the uterine tubes helps to direct the oocytes into the woman's duct system?

24. What portion of the female duct system is the usual site of fertilization? Which is the "incubator" for fetal development?

For answers, see Appendix G.

The External Genitalia and Female Perineum

▶ Describe the anatomy of the female external genitalia.

The female reproductive structures that lie external to the vagina are called the *external genitalia* (Figure 27.14). Also called the **vulva** (vul′vah; "covering") or **pudendum** ("shameful"), these structures include the mons pubis, labia, clitoris, and structures associated with the vestibule.

The **mons pubis** (mons pu′bis; "mountain on the pubis") is a fatty, rounded area overlying the pubic symphysis. After puberty, this area is covered with pubic hair. Running posteriorly from the mons pubis are two elongated, hair-covered fatty skin folds, the **labia majora** (la′be-ah mah-jor′ah; "larger lips"). These are the counterpart, or *homologue*, of the male scrotum (that is, they derive from the same embryonic tissue). The labia majora enclose the **labia minora** (mi-nor′ah; "smaller"), two thin, hair-free skin folds, homologous to the ventral penis.

The labia minora enclose a recess called the **vestibule** ("entrance hall"), which contains the external openings of the urethra and the vagina. Flanking the vaginal opening are the pea-size **greater vestibular glands**, homologous to the bulbourethral glands of males (Figure 27.14b). These glands release mucus into the vestibule and help to keep it moist and lubricated, facilitating intercourse. At the extreme posterior end of the vestibule the labia minora come together to form a ridge called the **fourchette.**

Just anterior to the vestibule is the **clitoris** (klit′o-ris; "hill"), a small, protruding structure composed largely of erectile tissue, which is homologous to the penis of the male. Its exposed portion is called the **glans clitoris** or **glans of the clitoris**. It is hooded by a skin fold called the **prepuce of the clitoris**, formed by the junction of the labia minora folds.

The clitoris is richly innervated with sensory nerve endings sensitive to touch. It becomes swollen with blood and erect during tactile stimulation, contributing to a female's sexual arousal. Like the penis, the **body of the clitoris** has dorsal erectile columns

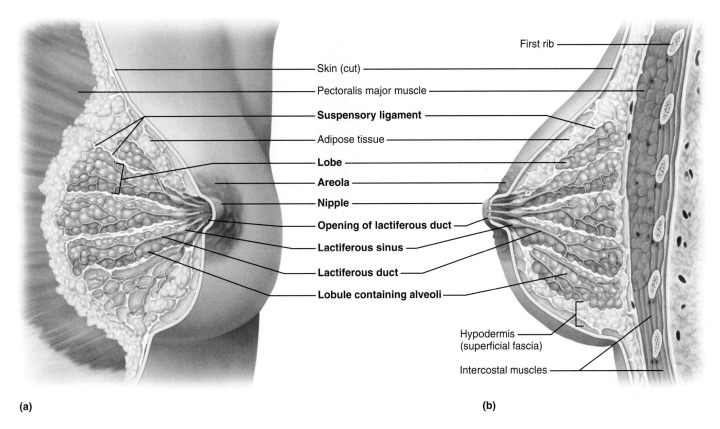

First rib

Skin (cut)

Pectoralis major muscle

Suspensory ligament

Adipose tissue

Lobe

Areola

Nipple

Opening of lactiferous duct

Lactiferous sinus

Lactiferous duct

Lobule containing alveoli

Hypodermis
(superficial fascia)

Intercostal muscles

(a)

(b)

Figure 27.15 **Structure of lactating mammary glands. (a)** Anterior view of a partially dissected breast. **(b)** Sagittal section of a breast.

(corpora cavernosa) attached proximally by crura, but it lacks a corpus spongiosum that conveys a urethra.

In males the urethra carries both urine and semen and runs through the penis, but the female urinary and reproductive tracts are completely separate. Instead, the **bulbs of the vestibule** (Figure 27.14b), which lie along each side of the vaginal orifice and deep to the bulbospongiosus muscles, are the homologues of the single penile bulb and corpus spongiosum of the male. During sexual stimulation the bulbs of the vestibule engorge with blood. This may help grip the penis within the vagina and also squeezes the urethral orifice shut, which prevents semen (and bacteria) from traveling superiorly into the bladder during intercourse.

The female **perineum** is a diamond-shaped region located between the pubic arch anteriorly, the coccyx posteriorly, and the ischial tuberosities laterally (Figure 27.14a). The soft tissues of the perineum overlie the muscles of the pelvic outlet, and the posterior ends of the labia majora overlie the *central tendon*, into which most muscles supporting the pelvic floor insert (see Table 10.7).

CHECK YOUR UNDERSTANDING

25. What is the female homologue of the bulbourethral glands of males?
26. Cite similarities and differences between the penis and clitoris.

For answers, see Appendix G.

The Mammary Glands

▶ Discuss the structure and function of the mammary glands.

The **mammary glands** are present in both sexes, but they normally function only in females **(Figure 27.15)**. The biological role of the mammary glands is to produce milk to nourish a newborn baby, so they are important only when reproduction has already been accomplished.

Developmentally, mammary glands are modified sweat glands that are really part of the *skin*, or *integumentary system*. Each mammary gland is contained within a rounded skin-covered breast within the hypodermis (superficial fascia), anterior to the pectoral muscles of the thorax. Slightly below the center of each breast is a ring of pigmented skin, the **areola** (ah-re′o-lah), which surrounds a central protruding **nipple**. Large sebaceous glands in the areola make it slightly bumpy and produce sebum that reduces chapping and cracking of the skin of the nipple. Autonomic nervous system controls of smooth muscle fibers in the areola and nipple cause the nipple to become erect when stimulated by tactile or sexual stimuli and when exposed to cold.

Internally, each mammary gland consists of 15 to 25 **lobes** that radiate around and open at the nipple. The lobes are padded and separated from each other by fibrous connective tissue and fat. The interlobar connective tissue forms **suspensory ligaments** that attach the breast to the underlying muscle fascia and to the overlying dermis. As suggested by their name, the suspensory ligaments provide natural support for the breasts, like a built-in brassiere.

27

(a) Mammogram procedure

(b) Film of normal breast

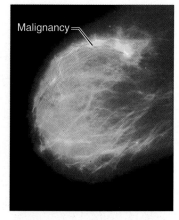

(c) Film of breast with tumor

Figure 27.16   **Mammograms.**

Within the lobes are smaller units called **lobules**, which contain glandular **alveoli** that produce milk when a woman is lactating. These compound alveolar glands pass the milk into the **lactiferous ducts** (lak-tif′er-us), which open to the outside at the nipple. Just deep to the areola, each duct has a dilated region called a **lactiferous sinus** where milk accumulates during nursing. We describe the process and regulation of lactation in Chapter 28.

The description of mammary glands that we have just given applies only to nursing women or women in the last trimester of pregnancy. In nonpregnant women, the glandular structure of the breast is largely undeveloped and the duct system is rudimentary. For this reason, breast size is largely due to the amount of fat deposits.

Breast Cancer

Invasive breast cancer is the most common malignancy and the second most common cause of cancer death of U.S. women. Thirteen percent of women in the general population (132 out of 1000 individuals) will develop this condition. Breast cancer usually arises from the epithelial cells of the smallest ducts, not from the alveoli. A small cluster of cancer cells grows into a lump in the breast from which cells eventually metastasize.

Known risk factors for developing breast cancer include (1) early onset menstruation and late menopause; (2) no pregnancies or first pregnancy later in life and no or short periods of breast feeding; and (3) family history of breast cancer (especially in a sister or mother). Some 10% of breast cancers stem from hereditary defects and half of these can be traced to dangerous mutations in a pair of genes, dubbed *BRCA1* (breast cancer 1) and *BRCA2*, which cause 80% of those who carry the altered gene to develop breast cancer. Notice that, with the possible exception of family history, these factors reflect increased lifelong exposure to estrogen. However, more than 70% of women who develop breast cancer have no known risk factors for the disease.

Breast cancer is often signaled by a change in skin texture, puckering, or leakage from the nipple. Since most breast lumps are discovered by women themselves in routine monthly breast exams, this simple examination should be a health maintenance priority in every woman's life. The American Cancer Society had recommended scheduling **mammography**—X-ray examination that detects breast cancers too small to feel (less than 1 cm)—every two years for women between 40 and 49 years old and yearly after that (Figure 27.16). However, some authorities suggest that yearly is too frequent. A new study suggests that diagnostic MRI scans are preferable for at-risk women who carry a mutated *BRCA* gene.

Once diagnosed, breast cancer is treated in various ways depending on specific characteristics of the lesion. Current therapies include (1) radiation therapy, (2) chemotherapy, and (3) surgery, often followed by irradiation or chemotherapy to destroy stray cancer cells. Drug therapies for estrogen-responsive cancers include trastuzumab (Herceptin), a drug containing bioengineered antibodies that jam estrogen receptors that control aggressive growth in breast cancer cells; tamoxifen, an antiestrogen compound that blocks estrogen's effects and significantly improves the outcome for premenopausal women with early- or late-stage breast cancer; and letrozole (Femara), which disables the enzyme needed to make estrogen and reduces breast cancer recurrences in women (particularly postmenopausal women) who have exhausted the usefulness of tamoxifen.

Until the 1970s, the standard treatment was **radical mastectomy** (mas-tek′to-me; "breast cutting"), removal of the entire affected breast, plus all underlying muscles, fascia, and associated lymph nodes. Most physicians now recommend **lumpectomy**, less extensive surgery in which only the cancerous part (lump) is excised, or **simple mastectomy**, removal of the breast tissue only (and perhaps some of the axillary lymph nodes). Many mastectomy patients opt for breast reconstruction to replace the excised tissue. Currently tissue "flaps," containing muscle, fat, and skin taken from the patient's abdomen or back, are used for "sculpting" a natural-looking breast.

27

27. Developmentally, mammary glands are modifications of certain skin glands. Which type?

28. From what cell types does breast cancer usually arise?

For answers, see Appendix G.

Physiology of the Female Reproductive System

Gamete production in males begins at puberty and continues throughout life, but the situation is quite different in females. It has been assumed that a female's total supply of eggs is already determined by the time she is born, and the time span during which she releases them extends only from puberty to menopause (about the age of 50). However, studies done in adult mice in 2004 and 2005 indicated that egg stem cells are alive and generating little "egglets" throughout life and there have been hopes that egg stem cells also exist in adult women. These findings might seem to overturn the assumption that the number of oocytes (the potential eggs) is limited—an idea that has been part of the bedrock of biology. As of 2008, however, these findings have not been confirmed and it has not been shown that newly formed "oocytes" restore fertility to otherwise sterile mice. Furthermore, the reproductive cycles of mice and humans are noticeably different when life span is considered. So, it is still too early to retire the "no new eggs" doctrine.

Oogenesis

▶ Describe the process of oogenesis and compare it to spermatogenesis.

Meiosis, the specialized nuclear division that occurs in the testes to produce sperm, also occurs in the ovaries. In this case, female sex cells are produced, and the process is called **oogenesis** (o″o-gen′e-sis; "the beginning of an egg"). The process of oogenesis takes years to complete, as indicated in **Figure 27.17**.

First, in the fetal period the **oogonia**, the diploid stem cells of the ovaries, multiply rapidly by mitosis and then enter a growth phase and lay in nutrient reserves. Gradually, *primordial follicles* begin to appear as the oogonia are transformed into **primary oocytes** and become surrounded by a single layer of flattened follicle cells. The primary oocytes begin the first meiotic division, but become "stalled" late in prophase I and do not complete it.

By birth, a female is presumed to have her lifetime supply of primary oocytes. Of the original 7 million oocytes, approximately 2 million of them escape programmed death and are already in place in the cortical region of the immature ovary. Since they remain in their state of suspended animation all through childhood, the wait is a long one—10 to 14 years at the very least!

At puberty, perhaps 250,000 oocytes remain. Beginning at this time a small number of primary oocytes are recruited (activated) each month in response to an LH surge midcycle (see Figure 27.20a). However, only one is "selected" each time to continue meiosis I, ultimately producing two haploid cells (each with 23 replicated chromosomes) that are quite dissimilar in size. The smaller cell is called the **first polar body**. The larger cell, which contains nearly all the cytoplasm of the primary oocyte, is the **secondary oocyte**.

The events of this first maturation division ensure that the polar body receives almost no cytoplasm or organelles. Notice in Figure 27.17 (left) that a spindle forms at the very edge of the oocyte. A little "nipple" also appears at that edge, and the polar body chromosomes are cast into it.

The first polar body may continue its development and undergo meiosis II, producing two even smaller polar bodies. However, in humans, the secondary oocyte arrests in metaphase II, and it is this cell (not a functional ovum) that is ovulated. If an ovulated secondary oocyte is not penetrated by a sperm, it simply deteriorates. But, if sperm penetration *does* occur, the oocyte quickly completes meiosis II, yielding one large **ovum** and a tiny **second polar body** (Figure 27.17). The union of the egg and sperm nuclei, described in Chapter 28, constitutes fertilization.

What you should realize now is that the potential end products of oogenesis are three tiny polar bodies, nearly devoid of cytoplasm, and one large ovum. All of these cells are haploid, but only the ovum is a *functional gamete*. This is quite different from spermatogenesis, where the product is four viable gametes—spermatozoa.

The unequal cytoplasmic divisions that occur during oogenesis ensure that a fertilized egg has ample nutrients for its six- to seven-day journey to the uterus. Lacking nutrient-containing cytoplasm, the polar bodies degenerate and die. Since the reproductive life of a female is at most about 40 years (from the age of 11 to approximately 51) and typically only one ovulation occurs each month, fewer than 500 oocytes out of her estimated pubertal potential of 250,000 are released during a woman's lifetime.

Perhaps the most striking difference between male and female meiosis is the error rate. As many as 20% of oocytes but only 3–4% of sperm have the wrong number of chromosomes, a situation that often results from failure of the homologues to separate during meiosis I. It appears that faced with meiotic disruption, meiosis in males grinds to a halt but in females it marches on.

29. How do the haploid cells arising from oogenesis differ structurally and functionally from those arising from spermatogenesis?

For answers, see Appendix G.

The Ovarian Cycle

▶ Describe ovarian cycle phases, and relate them to events of oogenesis.

The monthly series of events associated with the maturation of an egg is called the **ovarian cycle**. The ovarian cycle is best

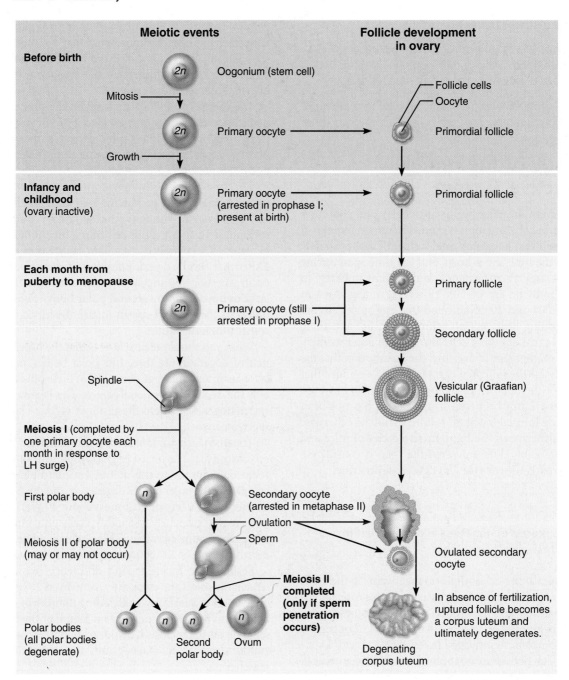

Figure 27.17 Events of oogenesis. Left, flowchart of meiotic events. Right, correlation with follicle development and ovulation in the ovary.

described in terms of two consecutive phases. The **follicular phase** is the period of follicle growth, typically indicated as lasting from the first to the fourteenth day of the cycle. The **luteal phase** is the period of corpus luteum activity, days 14–28. The so-called typical ovarian cycle repeats at intervals of 28 days, with *ovulation* occurring midcycle.

However, only 10–15% of women naturally have 28-day cycles, and cycles as long as 40 days or as short as 21 days are fairly common. In such cases, the length of the follicular phase and timing of ovulation vary, but the luteal phase remains constant: It is 14 days between the time of ovulation and the end of the cycle.

The Follicular Phase

Maturation of a primordial follicle occupies the first half of the cycle and involves several events as shown in **Figure 27.18**, stages ①–⑥.

A Primordial Follicle Becomes a Primary Follicle   When a primordial follicle ① is activated (by a process directed by the oocyte), the squamouslike cells surrounding the primary oocyte grow, becoming cuboidal cells, and the oocyte enlarges. The follicle is now called a primary (1°) follicle ②.

27

① **Primordial follicles**

② **Primary follicle**

③ **Secondary follicle**

④ **Late secondary follicle**

Theca folliculi
Primary oocyte
Zona pellucida

Antrum
Secondary oocyte

Secondary oocyte
Corona radiata

⑤ **Mature vesicular follicle carries out meiosis I; ready to be ovulated**

⑥ **Follicle ruptures; secondary oocyte ovulated**

⑦ **Corpus luteum (forms from ruptured follicle)**

Figure 27.18 Schematic and microscopic views of the ovarian cycle: development and fate of ovarian follicles. The numbers on the diagram indicate the sequence of stages in follicle development, not the movement of a developing follicle within the ovary. No photomicrograph is provided for ⑧ which identifies the corpus albicans.

27

A Primary Follicle Becomes a Secondary Follicle Next, follicular cells proliferate, forming a stratified epithelium around the oocyte. As mentioned earlier, as soon as more than one cell layer is present, the follicle is called a secondary (2°) follicle ③ and the follicle cells take on the name *granulosa cells*. The granulosa cells are connected to the developing oocyte by gap junctions, through which ions, metabolites, and signaling molecules can pass. From this point on, bidirectional "conversations" occur between the oocyte and granulosa cells, so they guide one another's development. One of the signals passing from the granulosa cells to the oocyte "tells" the oocyte to grow. Others dictate asymmetry (polarity) in the future egg.

A Secondary Follicle Becomes a Late Secondary Follicle In stage ④, a layer of connective tissue condenses around the follicle, forming the **theca folliculi** (the′kah fah-lik′u-li; "box around the follicle"). As the follicle grows, the thecal and granulosa cells cooperate to produce estrogens. (The inner thecal cells produce androgens, which the granulosa cells convert to estrogens.) At the same time, the oocyte secretes a glycoprotein-rich substance that forms a thick transparent extracellular layer or membrane, called the **zona pellucida** (pĕ-lu′sid-ah), that encapsulates it (see Figure 27.11).

At the end of this stage, clear liquid begins to accumulate between the granulosa cells, producing the late secondary follicle.

A Late Secondary Follicle Becomes a Vesicular Follicle In stage ⑤, the fluid between the granulosa cells coalesces to form a large fluid-filled cavity called the **antrum** ("cave"), an event that distinguishes the vesicular follicle from the late secondary follicle. The antrum continues to expand with fluid until it isolates the oocyte, along with its surrounding capsule of granulosa cells called a **corona radiata** ("radiating crown"), on a stalk on one side of the follicle. When a follicle is full size (about 2.5 cm, or 1 inch, in diameter), it becomes a vesicular follicle and bulges from the external ovarian surface like an "angry boil." This usually occurs by day 14.

As one of the final events of follicle maturation, the primary oocyte completes meiosis I to form the secondary oocyte and first polar body (see Figure 27.17). Once this has occurred, the stage is set for ovulation. At this point, the granulosa cells send another important signal to the oocyte that says, in effect, "Wait, do not complete meiosis yet!"

Ovulation

Ovulation (stage ⑥) occurs when the ballooning ovary wall ruptures and expels the secondary oocyte, still surrounded by its corona radiata, into the peritoneal cavity. Some women experience a twinge of pain in the lower abdomen when ovulation occurs. The precise cause of this episode, called *mittelschmerz* (mit′el-shmārts; German for "middle pain"), is not known, but possible reasons for the pain include intense stretching of the ovarian wall during ovulation and irritation of the peritoneum by blood or fluid released from the ruptured follicle.

In the ovaries of adult females, there are always several follicles at different stages of maturation. As a rule, one follicle outstrips the others to become the *dominant follicle* and is at the

peak stage of maturation when the hormonal (LH) stimulus is given for ovulation. How this follicle is selected, or selects itself, is still uncertain, but it is probably the one that attains the greatest FSH sensitivity the quickest. The others degenerate (undergo programmed cell death, or apoptosis) and are reabsorbed.

In 1–2% of all ovulations, more than one oocyte is ovulated. This phenomenon, which increases with age, can result in multiple births. Since, in such cases, different oocytes are fertilized by different sperm, the siblings are *fraternal*, or nonidentical, twins. *Identical twins* result from the fertilization of a single oocyte by a single sperm, followed by separation of the fertilized egg's daughter cells in early development. Additionally, it now appears that in some women, oocytes may be released at times unrelated to the woman's hormone levels. This timing may help to explain why a rhythm method of contraception sometimes fails and why some fraternal twins have different conception dates.

The Luteal Phase

After ovulation, the ruptured follicle collapses, and the antrum fills with clotted blood. This *corpus hemorrhagicum* is eventually absorbed. The remaining granulosa cells increase in size and along with the internal thecal cells they form a new, quite different endocrine structure, the *corpus luteum* ("yellow body") (Figure 27.18, stage ⑦). It begins to secrete progesterone and some estrogen.

If pregnancy does not occur, the corpus luteum starts degenerating in about 10 days and its hormonal output ends. In this case, all that ultimately remains is a scar called the *corpus albicans* (al′bĭ-kans; "white body") (Figure 27.18, stage ⑧). The last two or three days of the luteal phase, when the endometrium is just beginning to erode, is sometimes called the *luteolytic* or *ischemic phase*.

On the other hand, if the oocyte is fertilized and pregnancy ensues, the corpus luteum persists until the placenta is ready to take over its hormone-producing duties in about three months.

CHECK YOUR UNDERSTANDING

30. How do identical twins differ developmentally from fraternal twins?

31. What occurs in the luteal phase of the ovarian cycle?

For answers, see Appendix G.

Hormonal Regulation of the Ovarian Cycle

▶ Describe the regulation of the ovarian and uterine cycles.

Ovarian events are much more complicated than those occurring in the testes, but the hormonal controls set into motion at puberty are similar in the two sexes. Gonadotropin-releasing hormone (GnRH), the pituitary gonadotropins, and, in this case, ovarian estrogen and progesterone interact to produce the cyclic events occurring in the ovaries.

However, in females another hormone plays an important role in stimulating the hypothalamus to release GnRH. The onset of puberty in females is linked to adiposity, and the

Figure 27.19 Feedback interactions in the regulation of ovarian function. Numbers refer to events listed in the text. Note that all feedback signals exerted by ovarian hormones are negative except one—that exerted by estrogens immediately before ovulation. Events that follow step ⑧ (negative feedback inhibition of the hypothalamus and anterior pituitary by progesterone and estrogens) are not depicted, but involve a gradual deterioration of the corpus luteum and, therefore, a decline in ovarian hormone production. Ovarian hormones reach their lowest blood levels around day 28.

——— Stimulates

- - - - Inhibits

messenger from fatty tissue to the hypothalamus is *leptin*. If blood levels of lipids and leptin (better known for its role in energy production and appetite) are low, puberty is delayed.

Establishing the Ovarian Cycle

During childhood, the ovaries grow and continuously secrete small amounts of estrogens, which inhibit hypothalamic release of GnRH. Provided that leptin levels are adequate, the hypothalamus becomes less sensitive to estrogen as puberty nears and begins to release GnRH in a rhythmic pulselike manner. GnRH, in turn, stimulates the anterior pituitary to release FSH and LH, which prompt the ovaries to secrete hormones (primarily estrogens).

Gonadotropin levels continue to increase for about four years and, during this time, pubertal girls are still not ovulating and for this reason are incapable of getting pregnant. Eventually, the adult cyclic pattern is achieved, and hormonal interactions stabilize. These events are heralded by the young woman's first menstrual period, referred to as **menarche** (mĕ-nar′ke; *men* = month, *arche* = first). Usually, it is not until the third year postmenarche that the cycles become regular and all are ovulatory.

Hormonal Interactions During the Ovarian Cycle

Next we describe the waxing and waning of anterior pituitary gonadotropins (FSH and LH) and ovarian hormones and the negative and positive feedback interactions that regulate ovarian function. Events ①–⑧ in the following discussion directly correspond to the same-numbered steps in **Figure 27.19**. We assume a 28-day cycle.

27

① *GnRH stimulates FSH and LH secretion.* On day 1 of the cycle, GnRH secreted by the hypothalamus stimulates production and release of follicle-stimulating hormone (FSH) and luteinizing hormone (LH) by the anterior pituitary.

② *FSH and LH stimulate follicle growth and maturation and estrogen secretion.* FSH exerts its main effects on the granulosa cells of the late secondary or vesicular follicles, whereas LH (at least initially) targets the thecal cells. (Why only *some* follicles respond to these hormonal stimuli is still a mystery. However, there is little doubt that enhanced responsiveness is due to formation of more gonadotropin receptors.) As the follicles enlarge, LH prods the thecal cells to produce androgens. These hormones diffuse through the basement membrane, where they are converted to estrogens by the granulosa cells. Only tiny amounts of ovarian androgens enter the blood, because they are almost completely converted to estrogens within the ovaries.

③ *Negative feedback.* The rising estrogen levels in the plasma exert *negative feedback* on the hypothalamus and anterior pituitary, inhibiting release of FSH and LH, while simultaneously prodding the pituitary to synthesize and accumulate these gonadotropins. Within the ovary, estrogen enhances estrogen output by intensifying the effect of FSH on follicle maturation. *Inhibin,* released by the granulosa cells, also exerts negative feedback controls on FSH release during this period. Only the dominant follicle survives this dip in FSH—the remaining developing follicles fail to develop further, and they deteriorate.

④ *Positive feedback.* Although the initial small rise in blood-borne estrogen inhibits the hypothalamic-pituitary axis, high estrogen levels, produced by the dominant follicle and other maturing follicles, have the opposite effect. Once estrogen reaches a critical blood concentration, it briefly exerts *positive feedback* on the brain and anterior pituitary.

⑤ *LH surge.* High estrogen levels set a cascade of events into motion. There is a sudden burstlike release of accumulated LH (and, to a lesser extent, FSH) by the anterior pituitary about midcycle (also see Figure 27.20a).

⑥ *Ovulation.* The LH surge stimulates the primary oocyte of the dominant follicle to complete the first meiotic division, forming a secondary oocyte that continues on to metaphase II. At or around day 14, LH stimulates many events that lead to ovulation: It increases local vascular permeability, stimulates release of prostaglandins, and triggers an inflammatory response that promotes the release of metalloproteinase enzymes that help to weaken the ovary wall. As a result, blood stops flowing through the protruding part of the follicle wall. Within minutes, that region of the follicle wall thins, bulges out, and then ruptures, accomplishing ovulation. The role (if any) of FSH in this process is unknown. Shortly after ovulation, estrogen levels decline. This probably reflects the damage to the dominant estrogen-secreting follicle during ovulation.

⑦ *Corpus luteum forms.* The LH surge also transforms the ruptured follicle into a corpus luteum (which gives LH the name "luteinizing" hormone). LH stimulates this newly formed endocrine structure to produce progesterone and some estrogen almost immediately after it is formed. Progesterone helps maintain the stratum functionalis and thus is essential for maintaining a pregnancy should conception occur.

⑧ *Negative feedback inhibits LH and FSH release.* Rising progesterone and estrogen blood levels exert a powerful negative feedback effect on the hypothalamus and the anterior pituitary release of LH and FSH. Release of inhibin by the corpus luteum enhances this inhibitory effect. Declining gonadotropin levels inhibit the development of new follicles and prevent additional LH surges that might cause additional oocytes to be ovulated.

In nonfertile cycles, as LH blood levels fall, the stimulus for luteal activity ends, and the corpus luteum degenerates. As goes the corpus luteum, so go the levels of ovarian hormones, and blood estrogen and progesterone levels drop sharply. The marked decline in ovarian hormones at the end of the cycle (days 26–28) ends their blockade of FSH and LH secretion, and the cycle starts anew.

We have just described the ovarian events as if we are following one follicle through the 28-day cycle, but this is not really the case. What is happening is that the increase of FSH at the beginning of each cycle activates several follicles to mature. Then, with the midcycle LH surge, one (or more) vesicular follicles undergo ovulation. However, the ovulated oocyte would actually have been activated about 110 days (some three months) before, not 14 days before.

The Uterine (Menstrual) Cycle

Although the uterus is where the young embryo implants and develops, it is receptive to implantation for only a short period each month. Not surprisingly, this brief interval is exactly the time when a developing embryo would normally begin implanting, six to seven days after ovulation. The **uterine**, or **menstrual** (men′stroo-al), **cycle** is a series of cyclic changes that the uterine endometrium goes through each month as it responds to the waxing and waning of ovarian hormones in the blood. These endometrial changes are coordinated with the phases of the ovarian cycle, which are dictated by gonadotropins released by the anterior pituitary.

The events of the uterine cycle, depicted in **Figure 27.20d**, are driven by changes in ovarian steroid hormone levels as follows:

1. **Days 1–5: Menstrual phase.** In this phase, **menstruation** (men″stroo-a′shun) or **menses**, the uterus sheds all but the deepest part of its endometrium. (Note in Figure 27.20a and c that at the beginning of this stage, ovarian hormones are at their lowest normal levels and gonadotropins are beginning to rise.) The thick, hormone-dependent functional layer of the endometrium detaches from the

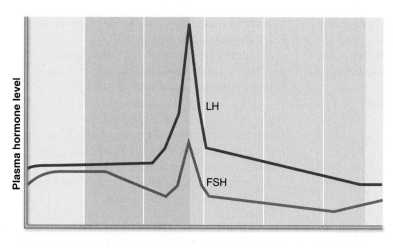

(a) Fluctuation of gonadotropin levels: Fluctuating levels of pituitary gonadotropins (follicle-stimulating hormone and luteinizing hormone) in the blood regulate the events of the ovarian cycle.

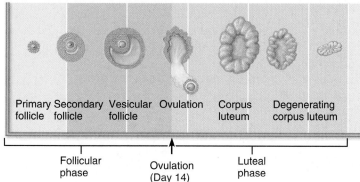

(b) Ovarian cycle: Structural changes in the ovarian follicles during the ovarian cycle are correlated with **(d)** changes in the endometrium of the uterus during the uterine cycle.

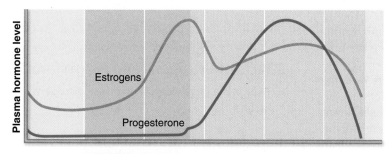

(c) Fluctuation of ovarian hormone levels: Fluctuating levels of ovarian hormones (estrogens and progesterone) cause the endometrial changes of the uterine cycle. The high estrogen levels are also responsible for the LH/FSH surge in (a).

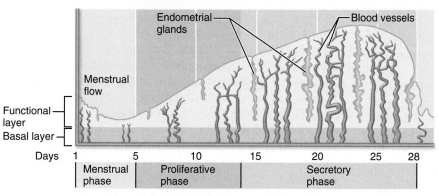

(d) The three phases of the uterine cycle:
- Menstrual: Shedding of the functional layer of the endometrium.
- Proliferative: Rebuilding of the functional layer of the endometrium.
- Secretory: Begins immediately after ovulation. Enrichment of the blood supply and glandular secretion of nutrients prepare the endometrium to receive an embryo.

Both the menstrual and proliferative phases occur before ovulation, and together they correspond to the follicular phase of the ovarian cycle. The secretory phase corresponds in time to the luteal phase of the ovarian cycle.

27

Figure 27.20 Correlation of anterior pituitary and ovarian hormones with structural changes of the ovary and uterus. The time bar at the bottom of the figure, reading Days 1 to 28, applies to all four parts of this figure. (See *A Brief Atlas of the Human Body*, Plate 53.)

uterine wall, a process that is accompanied by bleeding for 3–5 days. The detached tissue and blood pass out through the vagina as the menstrual flow. By day 5, the growing ovarian follicles start to produce more estrogen (Figure 27.20c).

2. **Days 6–14: Proliferative (preovulatory) phase.** In this phase, the endometrium rebuilds itself: Under the influence of rising blood levels of estrogens, the basal layer of the endometrium generates a new functional layer. As this new layer thickens, its glands enlarge and its spiral arteries increase in number (also see Figure 27.13). Consequently, the endometrium once again becomes velvety, thick, and well vascularized. During this phase, estrogens also induce synthesis of progesterone receptors in the endometrial cells, readying them for interaction with progesterone.

   Normally, cervical mucus is thick and sticky, but rising estrogen levels cause it to thin and form channels that facilitate the passage of sperm into the uterus. *Ovulation*, which takes less than five minutes, occurs in the ovary at the end of the proliferative stage (day 14) in response to the sudden release of LH from the anterior pituitary. As we saw earlier, LH also converts the ruptured follicle to a corpus luteum.

3. **Days 15–28: Secretory (postovulatory) phase.** This 14-day phase is the most constant timewise. During the secretory phase the endometrium prepares for implantation of an embryo. Rising levels of progesterone from the corpus luteum act on the estrogen-primed endometrium, causing the spiral arteries to elaborate and converting the functional layer to a secretory mucosa. The endometrial glands enlarge, coil, and begin secreting nutritious glycogen into the uterine cavity. These nutrients sustain the embryo until it has implanted in the blood-rich endometrial lining. Increasing progesterone levels also cause the cervical mucus to become viscous again, forming the *cervical plug*, which helps to block entry of sperm and pathogens or other foreign materials, and plays an important role in keeping the uterus "private" in the event an embryo has begun to implant. Rising progesterone (and estrogen) levels inhibit LH release by the anterior pituitary.

   If fertilization has not occurred, the corpus luteum degenerates toward the end of the secretory phase as LH blood levels decline. Progesterone levels fall, depriving the endometrium of hormonal support, and the spiral arteries kink and go into spasms. Denied oxygen and nutrients, the ischemic endometrial cells die, setting the stage for menstruation to begin on day 28. The spiral arteries constrict one final time and then suddenly relax and open wide. As blood gushes into the weakened capillary beds, they fragment, causing the functional layer to slough off. The menstrual cycle starts over again on this first day of menstrual flow.

Figure 27.20b and d also illustrate how the ovarian and uterine cycles fit together. Notice that the menstrual and proliferative phases overlap the follicular phase and ovulation in the ovarian cycle, and that the uterine secretory phase corresponds to the ovarian luteal phase.

Extremely strenuous physical activity can delay menarche in girls and can disrupt the normal menstrual cycle in adult women, even causing *amenorrhea* (a-men″o-re′ah), cessation of menstruation. Female athletes have little body fat, and fat deposits help convert adrenal androgens to estrogens and are the source of leptin which, as noted above, plays a critical permissive role in the onset of puberty in females. Leptin keeps the hypothalamus informed about whether energy stores are sufficient to support the high energy demands of reproduction. If not, the reproductive cycles are shut down.

These effects are usually totally reversible when the athletic training is discontinued, but a worrisome consequence of amenorrhea in young, healthy adult women is that they suffer dramatic losses in bone mass normally seen only in osteoporosis of old age. Once estrogen levels drop and the menstrual cycle stops (regardless of cause), bone loss begins.

CHECK YOUR UNDERSTANDING

32. What hormone plays an important role in "letting the brain know" that puberty may occur in girls?

33. What hormone(s) prompt follicle growth? What hormone prompts ovulation?

34. What gonadal hormone exerts positive feedback on the anterior pituitary that results in a burstlike release of LH?

For answers, see Appendix G.

Effects of Estrogens and Progesterone

▶ Discuss the physiological effects of estrogens and progesterone.

With a name meaning "generators of sexual activity," estrogens are analogous to testosterone, the male steroid. As estrogen levels rise during puberty, they (1) promote oogenesis and follicle growth in the ovary and (2) exert anabolic effects on the female reproductive tract (Table 27.1). Consequently, the uterine tubes, uterus, and vagina enlarge and become functional—more ready to support a pregnancy. The uterine tubes and uterus exhibit enhanced motility; the vaginal mucosa thickens; and the external genitalia mature.

Estrogens also support the growth spurt at puberty that makes girls grow much more quickly than boys during the ages of 11 and 12. But this growth is short-lived because rising estrogen levels also cause the epiphyses of long bones to close sooner, and females reach their full height between the ages of 13 and 15 years. In contrast, the aggressive growth of males continues until the age of 15 to 19 years, at which point rising estrogen levels cause epiphyseal closure.

The estrogen-induced secondary sex characteristics of females include (1) growth of the breasts; (2) increased deposit of subcutaneous fat, especially in the hips and breasts; and (3) widening and lightening of the pelvis (adaptations for childbirth).

27

TABLE 27.1	Summary of Hormonal Effects of Gonadal Estrogens, Progesterone, and Testosterone		
SOURCE, STIMULUS, EFFECTS	**ESTROGENS**	**PROGESTERONE**	**TESTOSTERONE**
Major source	Ovary: developing follicles and corpus luteum.	Ovary: mainly the corpus luteum.	Testes: interstitial cells.
Stimulus for release	FSH (and LH).	LH.	LH and declining levels of inhibin produced by the sustentacular cells.
Feedback effects exerted	Both negative and positive feedback exerted on anterior pituitary release of gonadotropins.	Negative feedback exerted on anterior pituitary release of gonadotropins.	Negative feedback suppresses release of LH by the anterior pituitary and release of GnRH by the hypothalamus.
Effects on reproductive organs	Stimulate growth and maturation of reproductive organs and breasts at puberty and maintain their adult size and function. Promote the proliferative phase of the uterine cycle. Stimulate production of watery cervical mucus and activity of fimbriae and uterine tube cilia.	Cooperates with estrogen in stimulating growth of breasts. Promotes the secretory phase of the uterine cycle. Stimulates production of viscous cervical mucus.	Stimulates formation of male reproductive ducts, glands, and external genitalia. Promotes descent of the testes. Stimulates growth and maturation of the internal and external genitalia at puberty; maintains their adult size and function.
	Promote oogenesis and ovulation by stimulating formation of FSH and LH receptors on follicle cells. Stimulate capacitation of sperm in the female reproductive tract.	During pregnancy, quiets the myometrium and acts with estrogen to cause mammary glands to achieve their mature milk-producing state.	Required for normal spermatogenesis via effects promoted by ABP, which keeps its concentration high near spermatogenic cells. Suppresses mammary gland development.
	During pregnancy stimulate growth of the uterus and enlargement of the external genitalia and mammary glands.		
Promotion of secondary sex characteristics and somatic effects	Promote long bone growth and feminization of the skeleton (particularly the pelvis); inhibit bone reabsorption and then stimulate epiphyseal closure. Promote hydration of the skin and female pattern of fat deposit.		Stimulates the growth spurt at puberty; promotes increased skeletal and muscle mass during adolescence. Promotes growth of the larynx and vocal cords and deepening of the voice. Enhances sebum secretion and hair growth, especially on the face, axillae, genital region, and chest.
	During pregnancy act with relaxin (placental hormone) to induce softening and relaxation of the pelvic ligaments and pubic symphysis.		
Metabolic effects	Generally anabolic. Stimulate Na^+ reabsorption by the renal tubules, hence inhibit diuresis. Enhance HDL (and reduce LDL) blood levels (cardiovascular sparing effect).	Promotes diuresis (antiestrogenic effect). Increases body temperature.	Generally anabolic. Stimulates hematopoiesis. Enhances the basal metabolic rate.
Neural effects	Along with DHEA (an androgen produced by the adrenal cortex) are partially responsible for female libido (sex drive).		Responsible for libido in males; promotes aggressiveness.

Estrogens have several metabolic effects, including maintaining low total blood cholesterol levels (and high HDL levels) and facilitating calcium uptake, which helps sustain the density of the skeleton. These metabolic effects are initiated under estrogen's influence during puberty, but they are not true secondary sex characteristics.

Progesterone works with estrogen to establish and then help regulate the uterine cycle and promotes changes in cervical mucus (see Table 27.1). Its other effects are exhibited largely during pregnancy, when it inhibits uterine motility and takes up where estrogen leaves off in preparing the breasts for lactation. Indeed, progesterone is named for these important roles (*pro* = for, *gestation* = pregnancy). However, the source of progesterone and estrogen during most of pregnancy is the placenta, not the ovaries.

Female Sexual Response

▶ Describe the phases of the female sexual response.

The **female sexual response** is similar to that of males in most respects. During sexual excitement, the clitoris, vaginal mucosa, bulbs of the vestibule, and breasts engorge with blood; the nipples erect; and increased activity of the vestibular glands and "sweating" of the vaginal walls lubricates the vestibule and facilitates entry of the penis. These events, though more widespread, are analogous to the *erection* phase in men. Touch and psychological stimuli promote sexual excitement, which is mediated along the same autonomic nerve pathways as in males.

The final phase of the female sexual response, *orgasm*, is not accompanied by ejaculation, but muscle tension increases throughout the body, pulse rate and blood pressure rise, and the uterus begins to contract rhythmically. As in males, orgasm is accompanied by a sensation of intense pleasure and followed by relaxation. Orgasm in females is not followed by a refractory period, so females may experience multiple orgasms during a single sexual experience. A man must achieve orgasm and ejaculate if fertilization is to occur, but female orgasm is not required for conception. Indeed, some women never experience orgasm, yet are perfectly able to conceive.

Although the female libido was formerly believed to be prompted by testosterone, new studies indicate that dehydroepiandrosterone (DHEA), an androgen produced by the adrenal cortex, is in fact the male sex hormone associated with desire or lack of it in females.

CHECK YOUR UNDERSTANDING

35. Which gonadal hormone causes the secondary sex characteristics to appear in a young woman?
36. What gonadal hormone promotes epiphyseal closure in both males and females?

For answers, see Appendix G.

Sexually Transmitted Infections

▶ Indicate the infectious agents and modes of transmission of gonorrhea, syphilis, chlamydia, trichomoniasis, genital warts, and genital herpes.

Sexually transmitted infections (STIs) also called *sexually transmitted diseases* (*STDs*) or *venereal diseases* (*VDs*), are infectious diseases spread through sexual contact. The United States has the highest rates of infection among developed countries. Over 12 million people in the United States, a quarter of them adolescents, get STIs each year.

As a group, STIs are the single most important cause of reproductive disorders. Until recently, the bacterial infections gonorrhea and syphilis were the most common STIs, but now viral diseases have taken center stage. AIDS, the most notorious STI, is caused by HIV, the virus that cripples the immune system. We describe AIDS in Chapter 21 and focus on the other important bacterial and viral STIs here. Condoms are effective in helping to prevent the spread of STIs, and their use is strongly urged, particularly since the advent of AIDS.

Gonorrhea

The causative agent of **gonorrhea** (gon″o-re′ah) is *Neisseria gonorrhoeae*, which invades the mucosae of the reproductive and urinary tracts. These bacteria are spread by contact with genital, anal, and pharyngeal mucosal surfaces. Commonly called "the clap," gonorrhea occurs most frequently in adolescents and young adults.

The most common symptom of gonorrhea in males is *urethritis*, accompanied by painful urination and discharge of pus from the penis (penile "drip"). Symptoms vary in women, ranging from none (about 20% of cases) to abdominal discomfort, vaginal discharge, abnormal uterine bleeding, and occasionally, urethral symptoms similar to those seen in males.

Untreated gonorrhea can cause urethral constriction and inflammation of the entire male duct system. In women, it causes pelvic inflammatory disease and sterility. These consequences declined with the advent in the 1950s of penicillin, tetracycline, and certain other antibiotics. However, strains resistant to those antibiotics are becoming increasingly prevalent. Currently, ceftriaxone is the antibiotic used most often to treat gonorrhea.

Syphilis

Syphilis (sif′ĭ-lis), caused by *Treponema pallidum*, a corkscrew-shaped bacterium, is usually transmitted sexually, but it can be contracted congenitally from an infected mother. Fetuses infected with syphilis are usually stillborn or die shortly after birth.

The bacterium easily penetrates intact mucosae and abraded skin. Within a few hours of exposure, an asymptomatic bodywide infection is in progress. After an incubation period of two to three weeks, a red, painless primary lesion called a *chancre* (shang′ker) appears at the site of bacterial invasion. In males, this is typically the penis, but in females the lesion often goes undetected within the vagina or on the cervix. The chancre ulcerates and becomes crusty, and then it heals spontaneously and disappears within a few weeks.

If syphilis is untreated, its secondary signs appear several weeks later. A pink skin rash all over the body is one of the first symptoms. Fever and joint pain are common. These signs and symptoms disappear spontaneously in three to twelve weeks. Then the disease enters the *latent period* and is detectable only by a blood test. The latent stage may last a person's lifetime (or the bacteria may be killed by the immune system), or it may be followed by the signs of *tertiary syphilis*. Tertiary syphilis is characterized by *gummas* (gum′ahs), destructive lesions of the CNS, blood vessels, bones, and skin. Penicillin is still the treatment of choice for all stages of syphilis.

Chlamydia

Chlamydia (klah-mid′e-ah; *chlamys* = cloak) is a largely undiagnosed, silent epidemic that is currently on the rise in college-age people. It infects perhaps 4–5 million people yearly, making it the most common bacterial sexually transmitted infection in the United States. Chlamydia is responsible for 25–50% of all diagnosed cases of pelvic inflammatory disease (and, consequently, at least a one-in-four chance of ectopic pregnancy). Each year more than 150,000 infants are born to infected mothers. About 20% of men and 30% of women infected with gonorrhea are also infected by *Chlamydia trachomatis*, the causative agent of chlamydia.

Chlamydia is a bacterium with a viruslike dependence on host cells. Its incubation period within the body cells is about one week. Symptoms include urethritis (involving painful, frequent urination and a thick penile discharge); vaginal discharge; abdominal, rectal, or testicular pain; painful intercourse; and irregular menses. In men, it can cause arthritis as well as widespread urogenital tract infection. In women, 80% of whom suffer *no* symptoms from the infection, it is a major cause of sterility. Newborns infected in the birth canal tend to develop conjunctivitis (specifically, *trachoma*, a painful eye infection that leads to corneal scarring if untreated, often the case in third-world countries) and respiratory tract inflammations including pneumonia. The disease can be diagnosed by cell culture techniques and is easily treated with tetracycline.

Trichomoniasis

Trichomoniasis is the most common *curable* STI in sexually active young women in the United States. Accounting for about 7.4 million new cases of STI per year, this parasitic infection is easily and inexpensively treated once diagnosed. Trichomoniasis is indicated by a yellow-green vaginal discharge with a strong odor. However, many of its victims exhibit no symptoms.

Genital Warts

Genital warts due to the *human papillomavirus* (*HPV*)—actually a group of about 60 viruses—is the second most common STI in the United States. About 6.2 million new cases of genital warts develop in Americans each year, and it appears that HPV infection increases the risk for cancers in infected body regions. Indeed, the virus is linked to 80% of all cases of invasive cervical cancer. Importantly, most of the strains that cause genital warts do not cause cervical cancer.

Treatment is difficult and controversial, and the warts tend to disappear. Some clinicians prefer to leave the warts untreated unless they become widespread, whereas others recommend their removal by cryosurgery or laser therapy, and/or treatment with alpha interferon.

Genital Herpes

The cause of **genital herpes** is the *human herpes virus type 2*, and these viruses are among the most difficult human pathogens to control. They remain silent for weeks or years and then suddenly flare up, causing a burst of blisterlike lesions.

Transmission of the virus is via infectious secretions or via direct skin-to-skin contact when the virus is shedding. The painful lesions that appear on the reproductive organs of infected adults are usually more of a nuisance than a threat. However, congenital herpes infections can cause severe malformations of a fetus.

Most people who have genital herpes do not know it, and it has been estimated that one-quarter to one-half of all adult Americans harbor the type 2 herpes simplex virus. Only about 15% of that population displays signs of infection. The antiviral *acyclovir*, which speeds healing of the lesions and reduces the frequency of flare-ups, is the drug of choice for treatment. Once contracted, genital herpes never leaves. It just goes into periodic remissions.

CHECK YOUR UNDERSTANDING

37. Which pathogen is most associated with cervical cancer?

38. What is the most common bacterial STI in the United States?

For answers, see Appendix G.

Developmental Aspects of the Reproductive System

So far, we have described the reproductive organs as they exist and operate in adults. Now we are ready to look at events that cause us to become reproductive individuals. These events begin long before birth and end, at least in women, in late middle age.

Embryological and Fetal Events

▶ Discuss the determination of genetic sex and prenatal development of male and female structures.

Determination of Genetic Sex

Aristotle believed that the "heat" of lovemaking determined maleness. Not so! Genetic sex is determined at the instant the genes of a sperm combine with those of an ovum, and the determining factor is the **sex chromosomes** each gamete contains. Of the 46 chromosomes in the fertilized egg, two (one pair) are sex chromosomes. The other 44 are called **autosomes.**

Two types of sex chromosomes, quite different in size, exist in humans: the large **X chromosome** and the much smaller **Y chromosome.** The body cells of females have two X chromosomes and are designated XX, and the ovum resulting from normal meiosis in a female always contains an X chromosome. Males have one X chromosome and one Y in each body cell (XY). Approximately half of the sperm produced by normal meiosis in males contain an X and the other half a Y.

If the fertilizing sperm delivers an X chromosome, the fertilized egg and its daughter cells will contain the female (XX) composition, and the embryo will develop ovaries. If the sperm bears the Y, the offspring will be male (XY) and will

27

develop testes. A single gene on the Y chromosome—the *SRY* (for **s**ex-determining **r**egion of the **Y** chromosome) gene—is the master switch that initiates testes development and hence maleness. Thus, the father's gamete determines the genetic sex of the offspring. All subsequent events of sexual differentiation depend on which gonads are formed during embryonic life. However, genes present in autosomes are necessary for a male to become a functional male. Mutation of the *SRY* gene can result in XY females with the male chromosome but female sex characteristics.

⚖ HOMEOSTATIC IMBALANCE

When meiosis distributes the sex chromosomes to the gametes improperly, an event called **nondisjunction**, abnormal combinations of sex chromosomes occur in the zygote and cause striking abnormalities in sexual and reproductive system development. For example, females with a single X chromosome (XO), a condition called *Turner's syndrome*, never develop ovaries. Males with no X chromosome (YO) die during embryonic development. Most XXX females have learning disabilities and lower-than-average IQs. Females carrying four or more X chromosomes as a rule are mentally retarded and have underdeveloped ovaries and limited fertility.

Klinefelter's syndrome, which affects one out of 500 live male births, is the most common sex chromosome abnormality. Affected individuals usually have a single Y chromosome, two or more X chromosomes, and are sterile males. Although XXY males are normal (or only slightly below normal) intellectually, the incidence of mental retardation increases as the number of X chromosomes rises. ■

Sexual Differentiation of the Reproductive System

The gonads of both males and females begin their development during week 5 of gestation as masses of mesoderm called the **gonadal ridges** (Figure 27.21). The gonadal ridges bulge from the dorsal abdominal wall just medial to the mesonephros (a transient kidney system, see p. 989). The **paramesonephric**, or **Müllerian**, **ducts** (future female ducts) develop lateral to the **mesonephric (Wolffian) ducts** (future male ducts), and both sets of ducts empty into a common chamber called the *cloaca*. At this stage of development, the embryo is said to be in the **sexually indifferent stage**, because the gonadal ridge tissue can develop into either male or female gonads and both duct systems are present.

Shortly after the gonadal ridges appear, **primordial germ cells** migrate to them from a different region of the embryo, presumably guided by a gradient of chemical signals (chemokines), and seed the developing gonads with stem cells destined to become spermatogonia or oogonia. Once these cells are in residence, the gonadal ridges form testes or ovaries, depending on the genetic makeup of the embryo.

The process begins in week 7 in male embryos. Seminiferous tubules form in the internal part of the gonadal ridges and join the mesonephric duct via the efferent ductules. Further development of the mesonephric duct produces the duct system of the male. The paramesonephric ducts play no part in male development and degenerate unless the tiny testes fail to secrete a hormone variously called *Müllerian inhibitory factor* (*MIF*) or *Müllerian inhibitory substance* (*MIS*). This hormone causes the breakdown of the paramesonephric (Müllerian) ducts, which give rise to the female duct system (oviducts and uterus).

In female embryos the process begins about a week later. The outer, or cortical, part of each immature ovary forms follicles, and the paramesonephric ducts differentiate into the structures of the female duct system. The mesonephric ducts degenerate.

Like the gonads, the external genitalia arise from the same structures in both sexes (Figure 27.22). During the indifferent stage, all embryos exhibit a small projection called the **genital tubercle** on their external body surface. The urogenital sinus, which develops from subdivision of the cloaca (future urethra and bladder), lies deep to the tubercle. The **urethral groove**, the external opening of the urogenital sinus, is on the tubercle's inferior surface. The urethral groove is flanked laterally by the **urethral folds** and then the **labioscrotal swellings**.

During week 8, the external genitalia begin to develop rapidly. In males, the genital tubercle enlarges, forming the penis. The urethral folds fuse in the midline, forming the spongy urethra in the penis. Only the tips of the folds remain unfused to form the *urethral orifice* at the tip of the penis. The labioscrotal swellings also fuse in the body midline to form the scrotum.

In females, the genital tubercle gives rise to the clitoris and the urethral groove persists as the vestibule. The unfused urethral folds become the labia minora, and the unfused labioscrotal folds become the labia majora.

Differentiation of accessory structures and the external genitalia as male or female structures depends on the presence or absence of testosterone. When testes are formed, they quickly begin to release testosterone, which continues until four to five days after birth and which causes the development of male accessory ducts and external genitalia. In the absence of testosterone, the female ducts and external genitalia develop.

⚖ HOMEOSTATIC IMBALANCE

Any interference with the normal pattern of sex hormone production in the embryo results in abnormalities. For example, if the embryonic testes do not produce testosterone, a genetic male develops the female accessory structures and external genitalia. If the testes fail to produce MIF, both the female and male duct systems form, but the external genitalia are those of the male. On the other hand, if a genetic female is exposed to testosterone (as might happen if the mother has an androgen-producing tumor of her adrenal gland), the embryo has ovaries but develops the male ducts and glands, as well as a penis and an empty scrotum. It appears that the female pattern of reproductive structures has an intrinsic ability to develop (is the default condition), and in the absence of testosterone it proceeds to do so, regardless of the embryo's genetic makeup.

Individuals with external genitalia that do not "match" their gonads are called *pseudohermaphrodites* (soo-do-her-maf′ro-dīts).

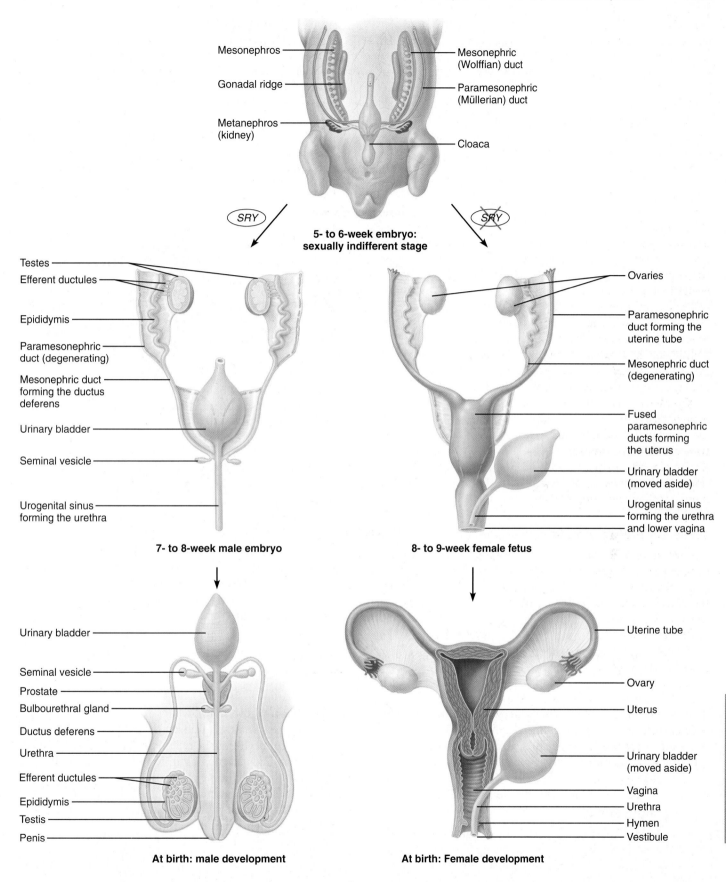

Figure 27.21 Development of the internal reproductive organs.

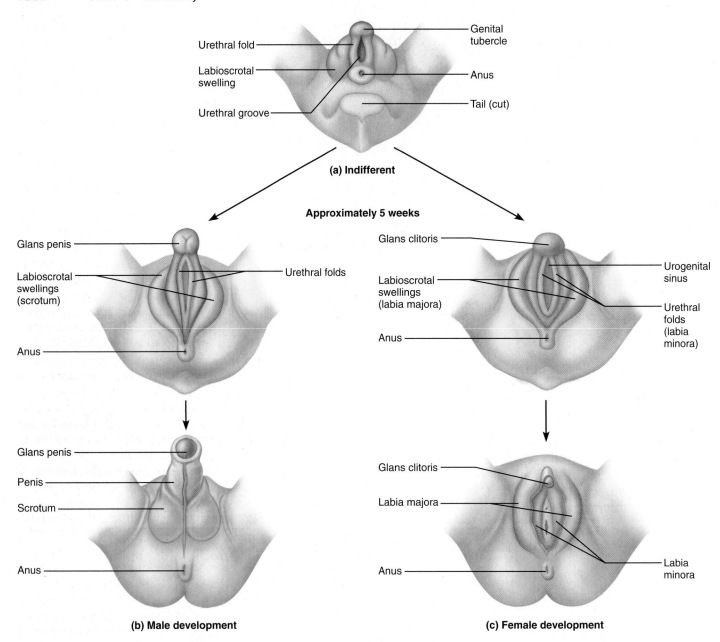

Figure 27.22 Development of homologous structures of the external genitalia in both sexes. The two pictures at the bottom of the figure show the fully developed perineal region.

(True *hermaphrodites* are rare and possess both ovarian and testicular tissue.) Many pseudohermaphrodites have sought sex-change operations to match their outer selves (external genitalia) with their inner selves (gonads). ■

Descent of the Gonads

About two months before birth, the testes begin their descent toward the scrotum, dragging their supplying blood vessels and nerves along behind them. They finally exit from the pelvic cavity via the inguinal canals and enter the scrotum. This migration is stimulated by testosterone made by the male fetus's testes, and is guided mechanically by a strong fibrous cord called the

gubernaculum ("governor"), which extends from the testis to the floor of the scrotal sac. Initially the gubernaculum is a column of soft connective tissue rich in hyaluronic acid, but it becomes increasingly fibrous as it continues to grow. By the seventh month of fetal development, its growth ceases and its inferior part fills the inguinal canal. The gubernaculum's cessation of growth, coupled with the rapid growth of the fetal body, helps to pull the testes into the scrotum.

The *tunica vaginalis* covering of the testis is derived from a fingerlike outpocketing of the parietal peritoneum, the *vaginal process*. The accompanying blood vessels, nerves, and fascial layers form part of the *spermatic cord*, which helps suspend the testis within the scrotum.

27

Like the testes, the ovaries descend during fetal development, but in this case only to the pelvic brim, where their progress is stopped by the tentlike broad ligament. Each ovary is guided in its descent by a gubernaculum (anchored in the labium majus) that later divides, becoming the ovarian and round ligaments that help support the internal genitalia in the pelvis.

HOMEOSTATIC IMBALANCE

Failure of the testes to make their normal descent leads to *cryptorchidism* (*crypt* = hidden, concealed; *orchi* = testicle). Because this condition causes sterility and increases the risk of testicular cancer, surgery is usually performed during early childhood to rectify this problem. ■

CHECK YOUR UNDERSTANDING

39. If the fertilized egg contains X and Y sex chromosomes, a baby girl will develop, right?

40. What is the sexually indifferent stage of development?

41. What structure guides the descent of the testis into the scrotum?

For answers, see Appendix G.

Puberty

▶ Describe the significant events of puberty and menopause.

FSH and LH levels, elevated at birth, fall to low levels within a few months and remain low throughout the prepubertal years. Between the ages of 10 and 15 years, a host of interacting hormones bring on the changes of puberty. **Puberty** is the period of life when the reproductive organs grow to adult size and become functional. As puberty nears, these changes occur in response to rising levels of gonadal hormones (testosterone in males and estrogen in females). Secondary sex characteristics and regulatory events of puberty were described earlier. But it is important to remember that puberty represents the earliest time that reproduction is possible.

The events of puberty occur in the same sequence in all individuals, but the age at which they occur varies widely. In males, secretion of adrenal androgens, particularly dehydroepiandrosterone (DHEA), begins to rise several years before the testosterone surge of puberty and initiates facial, pubic, and axillary hair growth and other pubertal events. The major event that signals puberty's onset in males is enlargement of the testes and scrotum between the ages of 8 and 14. Growth of the penis goes on over the next two years, and sexual maturation is evidenced by the presence of mature sperm in the semen. In the meantime, the young man has unexpected erections and occasional nocturnal emissions ("wet dreams") as his hormones surge and the hormonal control axis struggles to achieve a normal balance.

The first sign of puberty in females is budding breasts, apparent between the ages of 8 and 13 years, followed by the appearance of axillary and pubic hair. Menarche usually occurs about two years later. Dependable ovulation and fertility await the

maturation of the hormonal controls, which takes nearly two more years.

Menopause

Most women reach the peak of their reproductive abilities in their late 20s. After that, ovarian function declines gradually, presumably because the ovaries become less and less responsive to gonadotropin signals. At the age of 30, there are still some 100,000 oocytes in the ovaries but the quality (hence fertility) has begun to decline. By the age of 50, there are probably 3 eggs left (the pantry is nearly bare).

As estrogen production declines, many ovarian cycles become anovulatory, while in others 2 to 4 oocytes per month are ovulated, a sign of declining control. These increasingly frequent multiple ovulations explain why twins and triplets are more common in women who have deferred childbearing until their late 30s. In the perimenopausal period, menstrual periods become erratic and increasingly shorter. Eventually, ovulation and menstruation cease entirely. This normally occurs between the ages of 46 and 54 years, an event called *menopause*. **Menopause** is considered to have occurred when a whole year has passed without menstruation.

Although ovarian estrogen production continues for a while after menopause, the ovaries finally stop functioning as endocrine organs. Without sufficient estrogen the reproductive organs and breasts begin to atrophy, the vagina becomes dry, and vaginal infections become increasingly common. Other sequels due to lack of estrogen include irritability and depression (in some); intense vasodilation of the skin's blood vessels, which causes uncomfortable, sweat-drenching "hot flashes"; gradual thinning of the skin; and loss of bone mass.

Slowly rising total blood cholesterol levels and falling HDL levels place postmenopausal women at risk for cardiovascular disorders. At one time physicians prescribed low-dose estrogen-progesterone preparations to help women through this often difficult period and to prevent the skeletal and cardiovascular complications. These seemed like great bonuses and until July 2002, some 14 million American women were taking some form of estrogen-containing hormone replacement therapy (HRT). Then, on July 9, the Women's Health Initiative (WHI) abruptly ended a clinical trial of 16,000 postmenopausal women, reporting that in those taking a popular progesterone-estrogen hormone combination there was an increase of 51% in heart disease, 24% in invasive breast cancer, 31% in stroke, and a doubling of the risk of dementia compared to those taking placebos. The backlash of this information (aired in the popular press) is still spreading through physicians' offices and research labs and is restricting funding and the ability to find new volunteers for future studies, and has dampened enthusiasm for HRT in both the medical community and postmenopausal women. However, newer data suggest that the smallest dose of HRT for the shortest time is OK to reduce symptoms in women that do not have existing breast cancer or mutated *BRCA* gene(s).

There is no equivalent of menopause in males, and healthy men are able to father offspring well into their eighth decade

(*Text continues on p. 1066.*)

27

Homeostatic Interrelationships Between the Reproductive System and Other Body Systems

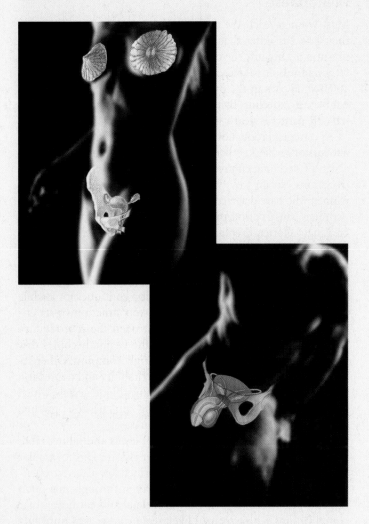

Nervous System

- Sex hormones masculinize or feminize the brain and influence sex drive
- Hypothalamus regulates timing of puberty; neural reflexes regulate events of sexual response

Endocrine System

- Gonadal hormones exert feedback effects on hypothalamic-pituitary axis; placental hormones promote maternal hypermetabolism
- Gonadotropins (and GnRH) help regulate function of gonads; leptin signals the hypothalamus about the body's state of energy availability (in fat stores)

Cardiovascular System

- Estrogens lower blood cholesterol levels and promote cardiovascular health in premenopausal women; pregnancy increases workload of the cardiovascular system
- Cardiovascular system transports needed substances to organs of reproductive system; local vasodilation involved in erection; blood transports sex hormones

Lymphatic System/Immunity

- Developing embryo/fetus escapes immune surveillance (not rejected)
- Lymphatic vessels drain leaked tissue fluids; transport sex hormones; immune cells protect reproductive organs from disease; IgA is present in breast milk

Respiratory System

- Pregnancy impairs descent of the diaphragm, promotes dyspnea
- Respiratory system provides oxygen; disposes of carbon dioxide; tidal volume rate increases, during pregnancy while residual volume declines

Digestive System

- Digestive organs crowded by developing fetus; heartburn, constipation common during pregnancy
- Digestive system provides nutrients needed for health

Urinary System

- Hypertrophy of the prostate inhibits urination; compression of bladder during pregnancy leads to urinary frequency and urgency
- Kidneys dispose of nitrogenous wastes and maintain acid-base balance of blood of mother and fetus; semen discharged through the urethra of the male

Integumentary System

- Androgens activate oil glands that lubricate skin and hair; gonadal hormones stimulate characteristic fat distribution and appearance of pubic and axillary hair; estrogen increases skin hydration, and during pregnancy it enhances facial skin pigmentation
- Skin protects all body organs by external enclosure; mammary gland secretions (milk) nourish the infant

Skeletal System

- Androgens masculinize the skeleton and increase bone density; estrogen feminizes the skeleton and maintains bone mass in females
- The bony pelvis encloses some reproductive organs; if narrow, the bony pelvis may hinder vaginal delivery of an infant

Muscular System

- Androgens promote increase in muscle mass
- Abdominal muscles active during childbirth; muscles of the pelvic floor support reproductive organs and aid erection of penis/clitoris

27

Closer Connections

The Reproductive System and Interrelationships with the Endocrine, Skeletal, and Muscular Systems

The reproductive system seems to be a particularly "selfish" system—interested only in its own well-being. But when we reflect on the importance of reproduction and continuity in the scheme of things, that selfishness is a benefit, not a drawback. Indeed, the reproductive system ensures (or tries to) that a person's gene pool passes on and, rather than directing its main energy to other body systems, it builds a whole new organism. Quite an incredible feat, don't you think?

Though reproductive system interactions with other body systems are relatively meager, one—that with the endocrine system—stands out and will receive the bulk of our attention. Indeed, these two systems are difficult to divorce from one another, particularly since the gonads themselves function as endocrine organs. Most other reproductive system interactions, such as those with the nervous and cardiovascular systems, are mediated through its hormones. For example, testosterone and estrogen imprint the brain as male or female, respectively, and estrogens help stave off atherosclerosis and help keep a woman's cardiovascular system (particularly her blood vessels) youthful. The gonadal hormones also play major roles in somatic development, particularly at puberty, and these are explored below.

Endocrine System

First of all, specific endocrine organs of the body—the hypothalamus via its gonadotropin-releasing hormones and the anterior pituitary gland via FSH and LH—help orchestrate virtually all reproductive functions. Without them, the gonads would never mature to adult functional status during adolescence, gametes would not be produced, and subsequent effects mediated by gonadal hormones would fail to occur. We would forever remain sexually infantile with a childlike reproductive system.

On the other hand, if testosterone were not secreted by the tiny male fetal testes, the male reproductive tract would not be formed to begin with. Furthermore, gonadal hormones produced in response to gonadotropins also help to regulate gonadotropin release (via negative and positive feedback mechanisms), as well as that of GnRH. So what we have here is an interlocking cycle in which one part cannot function without the other.

Let's not forget leptin—that hormonal messenger from adipose tissue—which alerts the hypothalamus when the young woman's body has the energy stores needed to undertake reproduction.

Skeletal and Muscular Systems

Once the reproductive system gonads are "up and running," they in turn start producing hormones that not only cause maturation of their own system's accessory organs and help maintain gametogenesis, but also are crucial for the incredible growth spurt that occurs during puberty and converts the child's body to an adult's. The most important effects are the anabolic effects exerted on bone and skeletal muscle. The skeleton becomes taller, heavier, and denser, and in females its pelvis is shaped to accommodate birth. All through a woman's reproductive years, estrogen helps maintain a healthy bone mass. (Its lack is quickly obvious after menopause.) The skeletal muscles, too, increase in size and mass, and become capable of great strength. Testosterone in particular is the muscle builder. Although the gonadal hormones do not act alone, and their effects are superimposed on those of growth hormone and thyroid hormone, they certainly promote adult stature and are responsible for the musculoskeletal changes that distinguish the sexes anatomically.

Clinical Connections

Reproductive System

Case study: We are back to look in on Mr. Heyden today. Since we last saw him (Chapter 26), he has had an X ray to try to determine the cause of his back pain, and his blood test results have come in. According to the note recorded at radiology:

- X irradiation of skeleton displays numerous carcinomatous metastases in his skull and lumbar vertebrae.

The hematology note of interest here reads:

- Serum acid phosphatase levels abnormally high.

1. What is carcinoma? What do you suppose is the primary source of the secondary carcinoma lesions in his skull and spine?
2. On what basis did you come to this conclusion?
3. What other tests might be of some diagnostic help here?
4. What type of therapy do you predict Mr. Heyden will be given to treat his carcinoma? Why?

(Answers in Appendix G).

27

of life thanks to their small but enduring population of stem cells (spermatogonia). However, aging men do exhibit a steady decline in testosterone secretion and a longer latent period after orgasm, a condition sometimes called *andropause*, and testosterone replacement therapy is currently being prescribed for more older men. Additionally, there is a noticeable difference in sperm motility with aging. Sperm of a young man can make it up the uterine tubes in 20–50 minutes, whereas those of a 75-year-old take 2½ days for the same trip.

CHECK YOUR UNDERSTANDING

42. What are the early signs of puberty's onset in boys?
43. What is the definition of menopause?

For answers, see Appendix G.

The reproductive system is unique among organ systems in at least two ways: (1) It is nonfunctional during the first 10–15 years of life, and (2) it is capable of interacting with the complementary system of another person—indeed, it *must* do so to carry out its biological function of pregnancy and birth. To be sure, having a baby is not always what the interacting partners have in mind, and we humans have devised a variety of techniques for preventing this outcome (see *A Closer Look* on pp. 1095–1096).

The major goal of the reproductive system is ensuring the healthy function of its own organs so that conditions are optimal for producing offspring. However, as illustrated in *Making Connections*, gonadal hormones do influence other body organs, and the reproductive system depends on other body systems for oxygen and nutrients and to carry away and dispose of its wastes.

Now that we know how the reproductive system functions to prepare itself for childbearing, we are ready to consider the events of pregnancy and prenatal development of a new living being, the topics of Chapter 28.

RELATED CLINICAL TERMS

Dysmenorrhea (dis″men-ŏ-re′ah; *dys* = bad, *meno* = menses, a month) Painful menstruation; may reflect abnormally high prostaglandin activity during menses.

Endometrial cancer (en″do-me′tre-al; *endo* = within, *metrio* = the uterus, womb) Cancer which arises from the uterine endometrium (usually from uterine glands); the fourth most common cancer of women. Most important sign is vaginal bleeding, which allows early detection. Risk factors include obesity and HRT.

Endometriosis (en″do-me″tre-o′sis) An inflammatory condition in which endometrial tissue occurs and grows atypically in the pelvic cavity. Characterized by abnormal uterine or rectal bleeding, dysmenorrhea, and pelvic pain. May cause sterility.

Gynecology (gi″nĕ-kol′o-je; *gyneco* = woman, *ology* = study of) Specialized branch of medicine that deals with the diagnosis and treatment of female reproductive system disorders.

Gynecomastia (gi″nĕ-ko-mas′te-ah) Development of breast tissue in the male; a consequence of adrenal cortex hypersecretion of estrogens, certain drugs (cimetidine, spironolactone, and some chemotherapeutic agents), and marijuana use.

Hysterectomy (his″tĕ-rek′to-me; *hyster* = uterus, *ectomy* = cut out) Surgical removal of the uterus.

Inguinal hernia Protrusion of part of the intestine into the scrotum or through a separation in the abdominal muscles in the groin region. Since the inguinal canals represent weak points in the abdominal wall, inguinal hernia may be caused by heavy lifting or other activities that increase intra-abdominal pressure.

Laparoscopy (lap″ah-ros′ko-pe; *lapar* = the flank, *scopy* = observation) Examination of the abdominopelvic cavity with a laparoscope, a viewing device at the end of a thin tube inserted through the anterior abdominal wall. Laparoscopy is often used to assess the condition of the pelvic reproductive organs of females.

Oophorectomy (o″of-o-rek′to-me; *oophor* = ovary) Surgical removal of the ovary.

Orchitis (or-ki′tis; *orcho* = testis) Inflammation of the testes, sometimes caused by the mumps virus.

Ovarian cancer Malignancy that typically arises from the cells in the germinal epithelial covering of the ovary. The fifth most common reproductive system cancer, its incidence increases with age. Called the "disease that whispers" because early symptoms are nondescript and easily mistaken for other disorders (back pain, abdominal discomfort, nausea, bloating, and flatulence). Diagnosis may involve palpating a mass during a physical exam, visualizing it with an ultrasound probe, or conducting blood tests for a protein marker for ovarian cancer (CA-125). However, medical assessment is often delayed until after metastasis has occurred; five-year survival rate is 90% if the condition is diagnosed before metastasis.

Ovarian cysts The most common disorders of the ovary; some are tumors. Types include (1) *simple follicle retention cysts* in which single or clustered follicles become enlarged with a clear fluid; (2) *dermoid cysts*, which are filled with a thick yellow fluid and contain partially developed hair, teeth, bone, etc.; and (3) *chocolate cysts* filled with dark gelatinous material, which are the result of endometriosis of the ovary. None of these is malignant, but the latter two may become so.

Polycystic ovary syndrome (PCOS) The most common endocrinopathy in women and the most common cause of anovulatory infertility. Affects 5–10% of women; characterized by signs of androgen excess, increased cardiovascular risk (evidenced by high blood pressure, decreased HDL cholesterol levels, and high triglycerides); and linked to extreme obesity and some degree of insulin resistance. Treated with insulin-sensitizing drugs.

Salpingitis (sal″pin-ji′tis; *salpingo* = uterine tube) Inflammation of the uterine tubes.

CHAPTER SUMMARY

1. The function of the reproductive system is to produce offspring. The gonads produce gametes (sperm or ova) and sex hormones. All other reproductive organs are accessory organs.

Anatomy of the Male Reproductive System (pp. 1025–1031)

The Scrotum (pp. 1025–1026)

1. The scrotum contains the testes. It provides a temperature slightly lower than that of the body, as required for viable sperm production.

The Testes (pp. 1026–1028)

2. Each testis is covered externally by a tunica albuginea that extends internally to divide the testis into many lobules. Each lobule contains sperm-producing seminiferous tubules and interstitial cells that produce androgens.

The Penis (p. 1028)

3. The penis, the male copulatory organ, is largely erectile tissue (corpus spongiosum and corpora cavernosa). Engorgement of the erectile tissue with blood causes the penis to become rigid, an event called erection.

4. The male perineum is the region encompassed by the pubic symphysis, ischial tuberosities, and coccyx.

The Male Duct System (pp. 1028–1030)

5. The epididymis hugs the external surface of the testis and serves as a site for sperm maturation and storage.

6. The ductus (vas) deferens, extending from the epididymis to the ejaculatory duct, propels sperm into the urethra by peristalsis during ejaculation. Its terminus fuses with the duct of the seminal vesicle, forming the ejaculatory duct, which empties into the urethra within the prostate.

7. The urethra extends from the urinary bladder to the tip of the penis. It conducts semen and urine to the body exterior.

Accessory Glands (pp. 1030–1031)

8. The accessory glands produce the bulk of the semen, which contains fructose from the seminal vesicles, an activating fluid from the prostate, and mucus from the bulbourethral glands.

Semen (p. 1031)

9. Semen is an alkaline fluid that dilutes and transports sperm. Important chemicals in semen are nutrients, prostaglandins, and antibiotic chemicals. An ejaculation contains 2–5 ml of semen, with 20–150 million sperm/ml in normal adult males.

Physiology of the Male Reproductive System (pp. 1031–1040)

Male Sexual Response (pp. 1031–1032)

1. Erection is controlled by parasympathetic reflexes.

2. Ejaculation is expulsion of semen from the male duct system, promoted by the sympathetic nervous system. Ejaculation is part of male orgasm, which also includes pleasurable sensations and increased pulse and blood pressure.

Spermatogenesis (pp. 1032–1038)

3. Spermatogenesis, the production of male gametes in the seminiferous tubules, begins at puberty.

4. Meiosis, the basis of gamete production, consists of two consecutive nuclear divisions without DNA replication in between. Meiosis reduces the chromosomal number by half and introduces genetic variability. Events unique to meiosis include synapsis and crossover of homologous chromosomes.

5. Spermatogonia divide by mitosis to maintain the germ cell line. Some of their progeny become primary spermatocytes, which undergo meiosis I to produce secondary spermatocytes. Secondary spermatocytes undergo meiosis II, each producing a total of four haploid (n) spermatids.

6. Spermatids are converted to functional sperm by spermiogenesis, during which superfluous cytoplasm is stripped away and an acrosome and a flagellum (tail) are produced.

7. Sustentacular cells form the blood-testis barrier, nourish spermatogenic cells, move them toward the lumen of the tubules, and secrete fluid for sperm transport.

Hormonal Regulation of Male Reproductive Function (pp. 1038–1040)

8. GnRH, produced by the hypothalamus, stimulates the anterior pituitary gland to release FSH and LH. FSH causes sustentacular cells to produce androgen-binding protein (ABP). LH stimulates interstitial cells to release testosterone, which binds to ABP, stimulating spermatogenesis. Testosterone and inhibin (produced by sustentacular cells) feed back to inhibit the hypothalamus and anterior pituitary.

9. Maturation of hormonal controls occurs during puberty and takes about three years.

10. Testosterone stimulates maturation of the male reproductive organs and triggers the development of the secondary sex characteristics of the male. It exerts anabolic effects on the skeleton and skeletal muscles, stimulates spermatogenesis, and is responsible for sex drive.

Anatomy of the Female Reproductive System (pp. 1040–1049)

1. The female reproductive system produces gametes and sex hormones and houses a developing infant until birth.

The Ovaries (pp. 1041–1042)

2. The ovaries flank the uterus laterally and are held in position by the ovarian and suspensory ligaments and mesovaria.

3. Within each ovary are oocyte-containing follicles at different stages of development and corpora lutea.

The Female Duct System (pp. 1042–1046)

4. The uterine tube, supported by the mesosalpinx, extends from near the ovary to the uterus. Its fimbriae and ciliated distal end creates currents that help move an ovulated oocyte into the uterine tube. Cilia of the uterine tube mucosa and peristalsis help propel the oocyte toward the uterus.

5. The uterus has fundus, body, and cervical regions. It is supported by the broad, lateral cervical, uterosacral, and round ligaments.

6. The uterine wall is composed of the outer perimetrium, the myometrium, and the inner endometrium. The endometrium consists of a functional layer (stratum functionalis), which sloughs off periodically unless an embryo has implanted, and an underlying basal layer (stratum basalis), which rebuilds the functional layer.

7. The vagina extends from the uterus to the exterior. It is the copulatory organ and allows passage of the menstrual flow and a baby.

The External Genitalia and Female Perineum   (pp. 1046–1047)

8. The female external genitalia (vulva) include the mons pubis, labia majora and minora, clitoris, and the urethral and vaginal orifices. The labia majora house the mucus-secreting greater vestibular glands.

The Mammary Glands   (pp. 1047–1049)

9. The mammary glands lie over the pectoral muscles of the chest and are surrounded by adipose and fibrous connective tissue. Each mammary gland consists of many lobules, which contain milk-producing alveoli.

Physiology of the Female Reproductive System (pp. 1049–1058)

Oogenesis   (p. 1049)

1. Oogenesis, the production of eggs, begins in the fetus. Oogonia, the diploid stem cells of female gametes, are converted to primary oocytes before birth. The infant female's ovaries contain about 2 million primary oocytes arrested in prophase of meiosis I.

2. At puberty, meiosis resumes. Each month, one primary oocyte completes meiosis I, producing a large secondary oocyte and a tiny first polar body. Meiosis II of the secondary oocyte produces a functional ovum and a second polar body, but does not occur in humans unless the secondary oocyte is penetrated by a sperm.

3. The ovum contains most of the primary oocyte's cytoplasm. The polar bodies are nonfunctional and degenerate.

The Ovarian Cycle   (pp. 1049–1052)

4. During the follicular phase (days 1–14), several primary follicles begin to mature. The follicle cells proliferate and a connective tissue capsule (theca) is formed around the maturing follicle. The theca produces androgens that the follicle cells convert to estrogens. Generally, only one follicle per month completes the maturation process and protrudes from the ovarian surface. Late in this phase, the oocyte in the dominant follicle completes meiosis I. Ovulation occurs about day 14, releasing the secondary oocyte into the peritoneal cavity. Other developing follicles deteriorate.

5. In the luteal phase (days 15–28), the ruptured follicle is converted to a corpus luteum, which produces progesterone and estrogen for the remainder of the cycle. If fertilization does not occur, the corpus luteum degenerates after about 10 days.

Hormonal Regulation of the Ovarian Cycle   (pp. 1052–1054)

6. Beginning at puberty, the hormones of the hypothalamus, anterior pituitary, and ovaries interact to establish and regulate the ovarian cycle. Establishment of the mature cyclic pattern, indicated by menarche, takes about four years. Leptin serves a permissive role in puberty's onset, stimulating the hypothalamus when adipose tissue is sufficient for the energy requirements of reproduction.

7. The hormonal events of each ovarian cycle are as follows: (1) GnRH stimulates the anterior pituitary to release FSH and LH, which stimulate follicle maturation and estrogen production. (2) When blood estrogen reaches a certain level, positive feedback exerted on the hypothalamic-pituitary axis causes a sudden release of LH that stimulates the primary oocyte to continue meiosis and triggers ovulation. LH then causes conversion of the ruptured follicle to a corpus luteum and stimulates its secretory

activity. (3) Rising levels of progesterone and estrogen inhibit the hypothalamic-pituitary-gonadal axis, the corpus luteum deteriorates, ovarian hormones drop to their lowest levels, and the cycle begins anew.

The Uterine (Menstrual) Cycle   (pp. 1054–1056)

8. Varying levels of ovarian hormones in the blood trigger events of the uterine cycle.

9. During the menstrual phase of the uterine cycle (days 1–5), the functional layer sloughs off in menses. During the proliferative phase (days 6–14), rising estrogen levels stimulate its regeneration, making the uterus receptive to implantation about one week after ovulation. During the secretory phase (days 15–28), the uterine glands secrete glycogen, and endometrial vascularity increases further.

10. Falling levels of ovarian hormones during the last few days of the ovarian cycle cause the spiral arteries to become spastic and cut off the blood supply of the functional layer, and the uterine cycle begins again with menstruation.

Effects of Estrogens and Progesterone   (pp. 1056–1057)

11. Estrogen promotes oogenesis. At puberty, it stimulates the growth of the reproductive organs and the growth spurt and promotes the appearance of the secondary sex characteristics.

12. Progesterone cooperates with estrogen in breast maturation and regulation of the uterine cycle.

Female Sexual Response   (p. 1058)

13. The female sexual response is similar to that of males. Orgasm in females is not accompanied by ejaculation and is not necessary for conception.

Sexually Transmitted Infections   (pp. 1058–1059)

1. Sexually transmitted infections (STIs) are infectious diseases spread via sexual contact. Gonorrhea, syphilis, and chlamydia, are bacterial diseases; if untreated, they can cause sterility. Syphilis has broader consequences than most other sexually transmitted bacterial diseases since it can infect organs throughout the body. Trichomoniasis is a parasitic infection. Genital herpes and genital warts are viral infections; genital warts are implicated in cervical cancer. AIDS, a condition of immune suppression, can also be transmitted sexually.

Developmental Aspects of the Reproductive System (pp. 1059–1063, 1066)

Embryological and Fetal Events   (pp. 1059–1063)

1. Genetic sex is determined by the sex chromosomes: an X from the mother, an X or a Y from the father. If the fertilized egg contains XX, it is a female and develops ovaries; if it contains XY, it is a male and develops testes.

2. Gonads of both sexes arise from the mesodermal gonadal ridges. The mesonephric ducts produce the male accessory ducts and glands. The paramesonephric ducts produce the female duct system.

3. The external genitalia arise from the genital tubercle and associated structures. The development of male accessory structures and external genitalia depends on the presence of testosterone produced by the embryonic testes. In its absence, female structures develop.

4. The testes form in the abdominal cavity and descend into the scrotum.

Puberty (p. 1063)

5. Puberty is the interval when reproductive organs mature and become functional. It begins in males with penile and scrotal growth and in females with breast development.

Menopause (pp. 1063, 1066)

6. During menopause, ovarian function declines, and ovulation and menstruation cease. Hot flashes and mood changes may oc-

cur. Postmenopausal events include atrophy of the reproductive organs, bone mass loss, and increasing risk for cardiovascular disease. The milder signs and symptoms of gonadal steroid hormone deficit in men are called andropause.

REVIEW QUESTIONS

Multiple Choice/Matching

(Some questions have more than one correct answer. Select the best answer or answers from the choices given.)

1. The structures that draw an ovulated oocyte into the female duct system are (a) cilia, (b) fimbriae, (c) microvilli, (d) stereocilia.
2. The usual site of embryo implantation is (a) the uterine tube, (b) the peritoneal cavity, (c) the vagina, (d) the uterus.
3. The male homologue of the female clitoris is (a) the penis, (b) the scrotum, (c) the penile urethra, (d) the testis.
4. Which of the following is correct relative to female anatomy? (a) The vaginal orifice is the most dorsal of the three openings in the perineum, (b) the urethra is between the vaginal orifice and the anus, (c) the anus is between the vaginal orifice and the urethra, (d) the urethra is the more ventral of the two orifices in the vulva.
5. Secondary sex characteristics are (a) present in the embryo, (b) a result of male or female sex hormones increasing in amount at puberty, (c) the testis in the male and the ovary in the female, (d) not subject to withdrawal once established.
6. Which of the following produces the male sex hormones? (a) seminal vesicles, (b) corpus luteum, (c) developing follicles of the testes, (d) interstitial cells.
7. Which will occur as a result of nondescent of the testes? (a) Male sex hormones will not be circulated in the body, (b) sperm will have no means of exit from the body, (c) inadequate blood supply will retard the development of the testes, (d) viable sperm will not be produced.
8. The normal diploid number of human chromosomes is (a) 48, (b) 47, (c) 46, (d) 23, (e) 24.
9. Relative to differences between mitosis and meiosis, choose the statements that apply *only* to events of meiosis. (a) tetrads present, (b) produces two daughter cells, (c) produces four daughter cells, (d) occurs throughout life, (e) reduces the chromosomal number by half, (f) synapsis and crossover of homologues occur.
10. Match the key choices with the descriptive phrases below.
    Key: (a) androgen-binding protein   (b) estrogens
           (c) FSH   (d) GnRH
           (e) inhibin   (f) LH
           (g) progesterone   (h) testosterone

    _____ (1) Hormones that directly regulate the ovarian cycle
    _____ (2) Chemicals in males that inhibit the pituitary-testicular axis
    _____ (3) Hormone that makes the cervical mucus viscous
    _____ (4) Potentiates the activity of testosterone on spermatogenic cells
    _____ (5) In females, exerts feedback inhibition on the hypothalamus and anterior pituitary
    _____ (6) Stimulates the secretion of testosterone

11. The menstrual cycle can be divided into three continuous phases. Starting from the first day of the cycle, their consecutive order is (a) menstrual, proliferative, secretory, (b) menstrual, secretory, proliferative, (c) secretory, menstrual, proliferative, (d) proliferative, menstrual, secretory, (e) secretory, proliferative, menstrual.
12. Spermatozoa are to seminiferous tubules as oocytes are to (a) fimbriae, (b) corpus albicans, (c) ovarian follicles, (d) corpora lutea.
13. Which of the following does not add a secretion that makes a major contribution to semen? (a) prostate, (b) bulbourethral glands, (c) testes, (d) vas deferens.
14. The corpus luteum is formed at the site of (a) fertilization, (b) ovulation, (c) menstruation, (d) implantation.
15. The sex of a child is determined by (a) the sex chromosome contained in the sperm, (b) the sex chromosome contained in the oocyte, (c) the number of sperm fertilizing the oocyte, (d) the position of the fetus in the uterus.
16. FSH is to estrogen as estrogen is to (a) progesterone, (b) LH, (c) FSH, (d) testosterone.
17. A drug that "reminds the pituitary" to produce gonadotropins might be useful as (a) a contraceptive, (b) a diuretic, (c) a fertility drug, (d) an abortion stimulant.

Short Answer Essay Questions

18. Why is the term *urogenital system* more applicable to males than to females?
19. Describe the major structural (and functional) regions of a sperm.
20. Oogenesis in the female results in one functional gamete—the egg, or ovum. What other cells are produced? What is the significance of this rather wasteful type of gamete production—that is, production of a single functional gamete instead of four, as seen in males?
21. Describe the events and possible consequences of menopause.
22. Define menarche. What does it indicate?
23. Trace the pathway of a sperm from the male testes to the uterine tube of a female.
24. In menstruation, the stratum functionalis is shed from the endometrium. Explain the hormonal and physical factors responsible for this shedding. (Hint: See Figure 27.20.)
25. Both the epithelium of the vagina and the cervical glands of the uterus help prevent the invasion and spread of vaginal pathogens. Explain how each of these mechanisms works.
26. Some anatomy students were saying that the bulbourethral glands of males act like city workers who come around and clear parked cars from the street before a parade. What did they mean by this analogy?
27. A man swam in a cold lake for an hour and then noticed that his scrotum was shrunken and wrinkled. His first thought was that he had lost his testicles. What had really happened?

27

Critical Thinking and Clinical Application Questions

1. Gina Marciano, a 44-year-old mother of eight children, visited her physician complaining of a "bearing down" sensation in her pelvis, low backache, and urinary incontinence. A vaginal examination showed that the external os of her cervix was just inside the vaginal orifice and her perineum exhibited large keloids (masses of scar tissue). Her history revealed that she was a member of a commune located in the nearby mountains that shunned hospital births (if at all possible). What do you think Gina's problem is and what caused it? (Be anatomically specific.)

2. Harry, a sexually active adolescent, appeared in the emergency room complaining of a penile "drip" and pain during urination. An account of his recent sexual behavior was requested and recorded. (a) What do you think Harry's problem is? (b) What is the causative agent of this disorder? (c) How is the condition treated, and what may happen if it isn't treated?

3. A 36-year-old mother of four is considering tubal ligation as a means of ensuring that her family gets no larger. She asks the physician if she will become "menopausal" after the surgery. (a) How would you answer her question and explain away her concerns? (b) Explain what a tubal ligation is.

4. Mr. Scanlon, a 76-year-old gentleman, is interested in a much younger woman. Concerned because of his age, he asks his urologist if he will be able to father a child. What questions would a physician ask of this man, and what diagnostic tests would be ordered?

5. Lucy had both her left ovary and her right uterine tube removed surgically at age 17 because of a cyst and a tumor in these organs. Now, at age 32, she remains healthy and is expecting her second child. How could Lucy conceive a child with just one ovary and one uterine tube, widely separated on opposite sides of the pelvis like this?

28

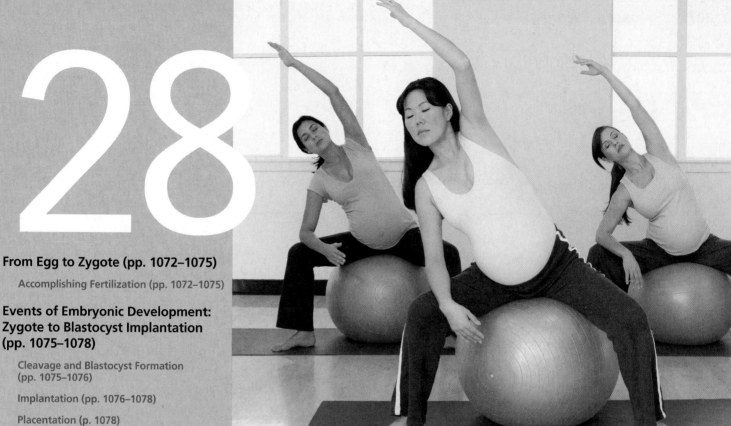

Pregnancy and Human Development

The birth of a baby is such a familiar event that we tend to lose sight of the wonder of this accomplishment: How does a single cell, the fertilized egg, grow to become a complex human being consisting of trillions of cells? The details of this process can fill a good-sized book. Our intention here is simply to outline the important events of gestation and to consider briefly the events occurring immediately after birth.

Figure 28.1 **Diagrams showing the approximate size of a human conceptus from fertilization to the early fetal stage.** The embryonic stage is from fertilization through week 8; the fetal stage begins in week 9. (Measurements are crown to rump length.)

Let's get started by defining some terms. The term **pregnancy** refers to events that occur from the time of fertilization (conception) until the infant is born. The pregnant woman's developing offspring is called the **conceptus** (konsep′tus; "that which is conceived"). Development occurs during the **gestation period** (*gestare* = to carry), which extends by convention from the last menstrual period (a date the woman is likely to remember) until birth, approximately 280 days. So, at the moment of fertilization, the mother is officially (but illogically) two weeks pregnant!

From fertilization through week 8, the *embryonic period*, the conceptus is called an **embryo**, and from week 9 through birth, the *fetal period*, the conceptus is called a **fetus** ("the young in the womb"). At birth, it is an infant. **Figure 28.1** shows the changing size and shape of the conceptus as it progresses from fertilization to the early fetal stage.

From Egg to Zygote

▶ Describe the importance of sperm capacitation.

▶ Explain the mechanism of the slow block to polyspermy.

▶ Define fertilization.

Before fertilization can occur, sperm must reach the ovulated secondary oocyte. The oocyte is viable for 12 to 24 hours after it is cast out of the ovary. The chance of pregnancy drops to almost zero the next day. Most sperm retain their fertilizing power for 24 to 48 hours after ejaculation. Consequently, for successful fertilization to occur, coitus must occur no more than two days before ovulation and no later than 24 hours after. At this point the oocyte is approximately one-third of the way down the length of the uterine tube.

Accomplishing Fertilization

Fertilization occurs when a sperm's chromosomes combine with those of an egg (actually a secondary oocyte) to form a fertilized egg, or **zygote** (zi′gōt; "yoked together"), the first cell of the new individual. Let's look at the events leading to fertilization.

Sperm Transport and Capacitation

During copulation, a man expels millions of sperm with considerable force into his partner's vaginal canal. Despite this "head start," most sperm don't reach the oocyte, even though it is only about 12 cm (5 inches) away. Millions of sperm leak from the vagina almost immediately after being deposited there. Of those remaining, millions more are destroyed by the vagina's acidic environment. Millions more fail to make it through the cervix, unless the thick "curtain" of cervical mucus has been made fluid by estrogens.

Sperm that do reach the uterus, propelled by their whiplike tail movements, are then subjected to forceful uterine contractions that act in a washing machine–like manner to disperse them throughout the uterine cavity, where thousands more are destroyed by resident phagocytes. Only a few thousand (and sometimes fewer than 100) sperm, out of the millions in the male ejaculate, are conducted by reverse peristalsis into the uterine tube, where the oocyte may be moving leisurely toward the uterus.

These difficulties aside, there is still another hurdle to overcome. Sperm freshly deposited in the vagina are incapable of penetrating an oocyte. They must first be **capacitated** over the

28

next 8 to 10 hours. Specifically, their motility must be enhanced and their membranes must become fragile so that the hydrolytic enzymes in their acrosomes can be released. As sperm swim through the cervical mucus, uterus, and uterine tubes, secretions of the female tract cause some of their membrane proteins to be removed, and the cholesterol that keeps their acrosomal membranes "tough" and stable is depleted. Even though the sperm may reach the oocyte within a few minutes, they must "wait around" (so to speak) for capacitation to occur.

This elaborate mechanism prevents the spilling of acrosomal enzymes. But consider the alternative. Fragile acrosomal membranes could rupture prematurely in the male reproductive tract, causing some degree of autolysis (self-digestion) of the male reproductive organs.

How do sperm navigate to find a released oocyte in the uterine tube? This question is an area of active research. It now appears that they "sniff" their way to the oocyte. Sperm bear proteins called *olfactory receptors* that respond to chemical stimuli. It is presumed that the oocyte or its surrounding cells release signaling molecules that direct the sperm.

Acrosomal Reaction and Sperm Penetration

The ovulated oocyte is encapsulated by the corona radiata and by the deeper zona pellucida, a transparent layer of glycoprotein-rich extracellular matrix secreted by the oocyte. Both must be breached before the oocyte can be penetrated. Once a sperm gets to the immediate vicinity of the oocyte, it weaves its way through the cells of the corona radiata. This journey is assisted by a cell-surface hyaluronidase on the sperm that digests the intercellular cement between the granulosa cells in the immediate area, causing them to fall away from the oocyte (**Figure 28.2**, ①).

After breaching the corona, the sperm head binds to the ZP3 glycoprotein of the zona pellucida, which functions as a sperm receptor. This binding leads to a rise in Ca^{2+} inside the sperm that triggers the acrosomal (ak′ro-sōm-al) reaction (**Figure 28.2**, ②). The **acrosomal reaction** involves the breakdown of the plasma membrane and the acrosomal membrane, and release of acrosomal enzymes (hyaluronidase, acrosin, proteases, and others) that digest holes through the zona pellucida (**Figure 28.2**, ③). Hundreds of acrosomes must undergo exocytosis to digest holes in the zona pellucida. This is one case that does not bear out the adage, "The early bird catches the worm." A sperm that comes along later, after hundreds of sperm have undergone acrosomal reactions to expose the oocyte membrane, is in the best position to be *the* fertilizing sperm.

Once a path is cleared, the sperm's whiplike tail gyrates, forcing the sperm head toward the oocyte membrane. At the same time, actin filaments in the sperm head form an *acrosomal process* that quickly finds and binds to the oocyte's sperm-binding membrane receptors (**Figure 28.2**, ④). This binding event has two consequences. (1) It causes the oocyte and sperm membranes to fuse, and then (2) the contents of the sperm enter the oocyte cytoplasm (**Figure 28.2**, ⑤). The gametes fuse together with such perfect contact that the contents of both cells are combined within a single membrane—all without spilling a drop.

Blocks to Polyspermy

Polyspermy (entry of several sperm into an egg) occurs in some animals, but in humans only one sperm is allowed to penetrate the oocyte, ensuring **monospermy**, the one-sperm-per-oocyte condition. Once the sperm head has entered the oocyte, waves of Ca^{2+} are released by the oocyte's endoplasmic reticulum into its cytoplasm, which activates the oocyte to prepare for cell division. These calcium surges also cause the **cortical reaction** (Figure 28.2, ⑥), in which granules located just inside the plasma membrane spill their enzymes into the extracellular space beneath the zona pellucida. These enzymes, called *zonal inhibiting proteins (ZIPs)*, destroy the sperm receptors, preventing further sperm entry.

Additionally, the spilled material binds water, and as it swells and hardens, it detaches all sperm still bound to receptors on the oocyte membrane, accomplishing the so-called *slow block to polyspermy*. In the rare cases of polyspermy that do occur, the embryos contain too much genetic material and die.

Completion of Meiosis II and Fertilization

As the sperm's cytoplasmic contents enter the oocyte, it loses its plasma membrane. The centrosome from its midpiece elaborates microtubules which the sperm uses to locomote its DNA-rich nucleus toward the oocyte nucleus. On the way, its nucleus swells to about five times its normal size to form the **male pronucleus** (pro-nu′kle-us; *pro* = before). Meanwhile the secondary oocyte, stimulated into activity by the calcium surges, completes meiosis II, forming the ovum nucleus and the second polar body (**Figure 28.3a**, ① and ②).

This accomplished, the ovum nucleus swells, becoming the **female pronucleus**, and the two pronuclei approach each other. As a mitotic spindle develops between them (Figure 28.3a, ③), the pronuclei membranes rupture, releasing their chromosomes together into the immediate vicinity of the newly formed spindle.

The true moment of fertilization occurs as the maternal and paternal chromosomes combine and produce the diploid *zygote*, or fertilized egg (Figure 28.3a, ④). Some sources define the term fertilization simply as the act of oocyte penetration by the sperm. However, unless the chromosomes in the male and female pronuclei are actually joined, the zygote is never formed in humans. Almost as soon as the male and female pronuclei come together, their chromosomes replicate. The zygote, the first cell of a new individual, is now ready to undergo the first mitotic division of the conceptus.

CHECK YOUR UNDERSTANDING

1. What has to happen before ejaculated sperm can penetrate an oocyte?
2. What is the cortical reaction and what does it accomplish?

For answers, see Appendix G.

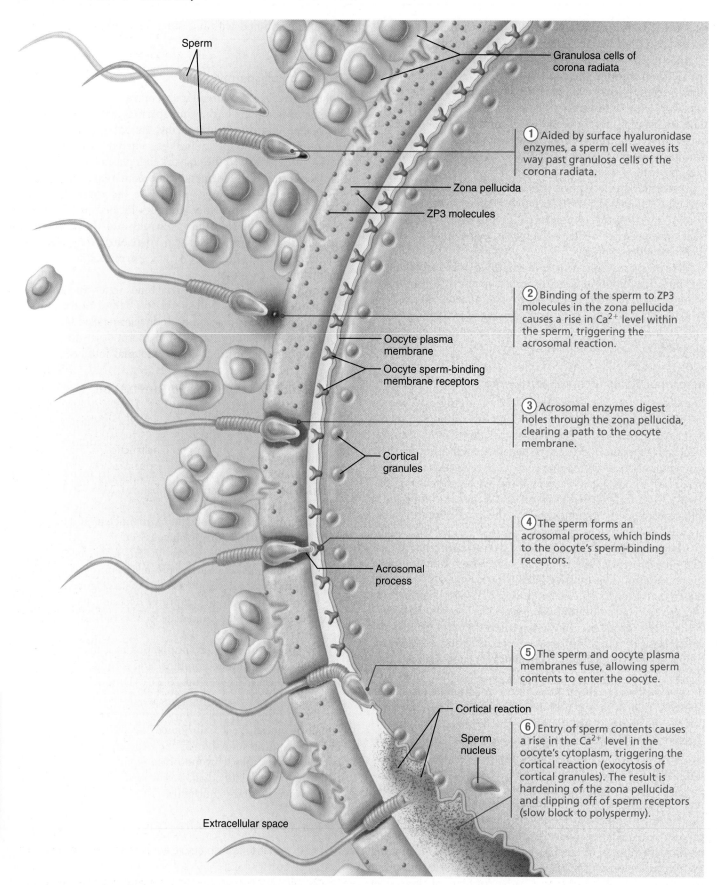

Figure 28.2 Sperm penetration and the cortical reaction (slow block to polyspermy).
The sequential steps of oocyte penetration by a sperm are depicted from top to bottom.

Sperm

Granulosa cells of corona radiata

① Aided by surface hyaluronidase enzymes, a sperm cell weaves its way past granulosa cells of the corona radiata.

Zona pellucida

ZP3 molecules

② Binding of the sperm to ZP3 molecules in the zona pellucida causes a rise in Ca^{2+} level within the sperm, triggering the acrosomal reaction.

Oocyte plasma membrane

Oocyte sperm-binding membrane receptors

③ Acrosomal enzymes digest holes through the zona pellucida, clearing a path to the oocyte membrane.

Cortical granules

④ The sperm forms an acrosomal process, which binds to the oocyte's sperm-binding receptors.

Acrosomal process

⑤ The sperm and oocyte plasma membranes fuse, allowing sperm contents to enter the oocyte.

Cortical reaction

Sperm nucleus

⑥ Entry of sperm contents causes a rise in the Ca^{2+} level in the oocyte's cytoplasm, triggering the cortical reaction (exocytosis of cortical granules). The result is hardening of the zona pellucida and clipping off of sperm receptors (slow block to polyspermy).

Extracellular space

28

① After the sperm penetrates the secondary oocyte, the oocyte completes meiosis II, forming the ovum and second polar body.

Sperm nucleus

Extracellular space

Corona radiata

Zona pellucida

Second meiotic division of oocyte

Second meiotic division of first polar body

② Sperm and ovum nuclei swell, forming pronuclei.

Male pronucleus

Female pronucleus (swollen ovum nucleus)

Polar bodies

③ Pronuclei approach each other and mitotic spindle forms between them.

Male pronucleus

Mitotic spindle

Centriole

Female pronucleus

④ Chromosomes of the pronuclei intermix. Fertilization is accomplished. Then, the DNA replicates in preparation for the first cleavage division.

Zygote

(a)

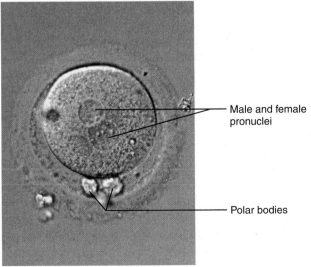

Male and female pronuclei

Polar bodies

(b)

Figure 28.3 Events of fertilization. (a) Events from sperm penetration to zygote formation. **(b)** Micrograph of an oocyte in which the male and female pronuclei are beginning to fuse to accomplish fertilization and form the zygote. Occurs in time between steps ③ and ④ of **(a)**.

Events of Embryonic Development: Zygote to Blastocyst Implantation

Early embryonic development begins with fertilization and continues as the embryo travels through the uterine tube, floats free in the cavity of the uterus, and finally implants in the uterine wall. Significant events of this early embryonic period are *cleavage*, which produces a structure called a blastocyst, and *implantation* of the blastocyst.

Cleavage and Blastocyst Formation

▶ Explain the process and product of cleavage.

Cleavage is a period of fairly rapid mitotic divisions of the zygote without intervening growth **(Figure 28.4)**. Cleavage produces small cells with a high surface-to-volume ratio, which enhances their uptake of nutrients and oxygen and the disposal of wastes. It also provides a large number of cells to serve as building blocks for constructing the embryo. Consider, for a moment, the difficulty of trying to construct a building from one huge block of granite. If you now consider how much easier it would be if instead you could use hundreds of bricks, you will quickly grasp the importance of cleavage.

Some 36 hours after fertilization, the first cleavage division has produced two identical cells called *blastomeres*. These divide to produce four cells (Figure 28.4b), then eight, and so on. By 72 hours after fertilization, a loose collection of cells that form a berry-shaped cluster of 16 or more cells called the **morula** (mor′u-lah; "little mulberry") has been formed (Figure 28.4c). All the while, transport of the embryo toward the uterus continues.

By day 3 or 4 after fertilization, the embryo consists of about 100 cells and floats free in the uterus (Figure 28.4d). By this time, it has tightened its connections between neighboring cells and begins accumulating fluid within an internal cavity. The zona pellucida now starts to break down and the inner structure, now called a blastocyst, "hatches" from it. The **blastocyst** (blas′to-sist) is a fluid-filled hollow sphere composed of a single layer of large, flattened cells called **trophoblast cells** (tro′fo-blast) and a small cluster of 20 to 30 rounded cells, called the **inner cell mass**, located at one side (Figure 28.4e).

Soon after the blastocyst forms, trophoblast cells begin to display L-selectin adhesion molecules on their surface. They take part in placenta formation, as suggested by the literal translation of "trophoblast" (nourishment generator). They also secrete and display several factors with immunosuppressive effects that protect the trophoblast (and the developing embryo) from attack by the mother's cells.

28

(a) Zygote (fertilized egg)

Zona pellucida

(b) 4-cell stage 2 days

(c) Morula (a solid ball of blastomeres). 3 days

(d) Early blastocyst (Morula hollows out, fills with fluid, and "hatches" from the zona pellucida). 4 days

Degenerating zona pellucida

Blastocyst cavity

(e) Implanting blastocyst (Consists of a sphere of trophoblast cells and an eccentric cell cluster called the inner cell mass). 7 days

Sperm

Uterine tube

Fertilization (sperm meets and enters egg)

Oocyte (egg)

Ovary

Ovulation

Uterus

Endometrium

Cavity of uterus

Trophoblast

Blastocyst cavity

Inner cell mass

Figure 28.4 Cleavage from zygote to blastocyst. The zygote begins to divide about 24 hours after fertilization, and continues the rapid mitotic divisions of cleavage as it travels down the uterine tube. Three to four days after ovulation, the embryo reaches the uterus and floats freely for two to three days, nourished by secretions of the endometrial glands. Because there is very little time for growth between successive cleavage divisions, the resulting blastocyst is only slightly larger than the zygote. At the late blastocyst stage, the embryo implants into the endometrium; this begins at about day 7 after ovulation.

The inner cell mass becomes the *embryonic disc*, which forms the embryo proper, and three of the four extraembryonic membranes. (The fourth membrane, the chorion, is a trophoblast derivative.)

CHECK YOUR UNDERSTANDING

3. Why is the multicellular blastocyst only slightly larger than the single-cell zygote?

4. What is the function of the trophoblast cells?

For answers, see Appendix G.

Implantation

▶ Describe implantation.

While the blastocyst floats in the uterine cavity for two to three days, it is nourished by the glycogen-rich uterine secretions. Then, some six to seven days after ovulation, given a properly prepared endometrium, **implantation** begins. The receptivity of the endometrium to implantation—the so-

called *window of implantation*—is opened by the surging levels of ovarian hormones (estrogens and progesterone) in the blood. If the mucosa is properly prepared, integrin and selectin proteins on the trophoblast cells bind respectively to the extracellular matrix components (collagen, fibronectin, laminin, and others) of the endometrial cells and to selectin-binding carbohydrates on the inner uterine wall, and the blastocyst implants high in the uterus. If the endometrium is not yet optimally mature, the blastocyst detaches and floats to a lower level, implanting when it finds a site with the proper receptors and chemical signals.

The trophoblast cells overlying the inner cell mass adhere to the endometrium **(Figure 28.5a, b)** and secrete digestive enzymes and growth factors against the endometrial surface. The endometrium quickly thickens at the point of contact and takes on characteristics of an acute inflammatory response—the uterine blood vessels become more permeable and leaky, and inflammatory cells including lymphocytes, natural killer cells, and macrophages invade the area.

The trophoblast then proliferates and forms two distinct layers (Figure 28.5c). The cells in the inner layer, collectively

(a)

(b)

(c)

(d)

Figure 28.5 Implantation of the blastocyst. (a) Diagrammatic view of a blastocyst that has just adhered to the uterine endometrium and **(b)** microscopic view. **(c)** Slightly later stage of an implanting embryo (approximately seven days after ovulation), depicting the cytotrophoblast and syncytiotrophoblast of the eroding trophoblast. **(d)** Light micrograph of an implanted blastocyst (approximately 12 days after ovulation).
SOURCE: (b) R. O'Rahilly and R. Muller, *Human Embryology and Teratology*, Wiley–Liss, 3rd Edition, 2001. This material is reproduced with permission of Wiley–Liss, Inc., a subsidiary of John Wiley & Sons, Inc.

called the **cytotrophoblast** (si″to-tro′fo-blast) or **cellular trophoblast**, retain their cell boundaries. The cells in the outer layer lose their plasma membranes and form a multinuclear cytoplasmic mass called the **syncytiotrophoblast** (sin-sit″e-o-tro′fo-blast; *syn* = together, *cyt* = cell) or **syncytial trophoblast**, which invades the endometrium and rapidly digests the uterine cells it contacts. As the endometrium is eroded, the blastocyst burrows into this thick, velvety lining and is surrounded by a pool of blood leaked from degraded endometrial blood vessels. Shortly, the implanted blastocyst is covered over and sealed off from the uterine cavity by proliferation of the endometrial cells (Figure 28.5d).

In cases where implantation fails to occur, a receptive uterus becomes nonreceptive once again. It is estimated that a minimum of two-thirds of all zygotes formed fail to implant by the end of the first week or spontaneously abort. Moreover, an estimated 30% of implanted embryos later miscarry due to genetic defects of the embryo, uterine malformation, or other, often unknown, problems.

When successful, implantation takes about five days and is usually completed by the 12th day after ovulation—just before the endometrium normally begins to slough off. Menstruation would flush away the embryo as well and must be prevented if the pregnancy is to continue. Viability of the corpus luteum is maintained by an LH-like hormone called **human chorionic gonadotropin (hCG)** (ko″re-on′ik go-nad″o-trōp′in) secreted by the trophoblast cells. hCG bypasses hypothalamic-pituitary-ovarian controls at this critical time and prompts the corpus luteum to continue secreting progesterone and estrogen. The *chorion*, the extraembryonic membrane that develops from the trophoblast after implantation, continues this hormonal stimulus. In this way, the developing conceptus takes over the hormonal control of the uterus during this early phase of development.

Usually detectable in the mother's blood one week after fertilization, blood levels of hCG continue to rise until the end of the second month. Then blood levels decline sharply to reach a low value by 4 months, a situation that persists for the remainder

28

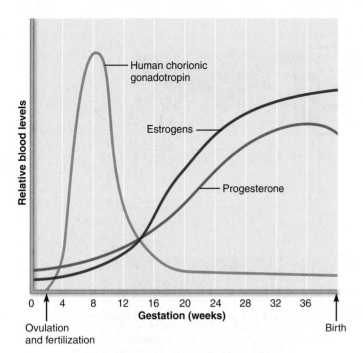

Figure 28.6 Hormonal changes during pregnancy. The relative changes in maternal blood levels of three hormones that maintain pregnancy are depicted, rather than actual blood concentrations.

of gestation **(Figure 28.6)**. Between the second and third month, the placenta (which we describe next) assumes the role of progesterone and estrogen production for the remainder of the pregnancy. The corpus luteum then degenerates and the ovaries remain inactive until after birth. All pregnancy tests used today are antibody tests that detect hCG in a woman's blood or urine.

Initially, the implanted embryo obtains its nutrition by digesting the endometrial cells, but by the second month, the placenta is providing nutrients and oxygen to the embryo and carrying away embryonic metabolic wastes. Since placenta formation is a continuation of the events of implantation, we will consider it next, although we will be getting a little ahead of ourselves as far as embryonic development is concerned.

CHECK YOUR UNDERSTANDING

5. Which portion of the trophoblast accomplishes implantation?
6. Marie, wondering if she is pregnant, buys an over-the-counter pregnancy test to assess this possibility. How will the blastocyst, if present, "make itself known?"

For answers, see Appendix G.

Placentation

▶ Describe placenta formation, and list placental functions.

Placentation (plas″en-ta′shun) refers to the formation of a **placenta** ("flat cake"), a temporary organ that originates from both embryonic and maternal (endometrial) tissues. Cells from the original inner cell mass give rise to a layer of extraem-

bryonic mesoderm that lines the inner surface of the trophoblast **(Figure 28.7b)**. Together these become the **chorion**. The chorion develops fingerlike **chorionic villi**, which become especially elaborate where they are in contact with maternal blood (Figure 28.7c).

Soon the mesodermal cores of the chorionic villi become richly vascularized by newly forming blood vessels, which extend to the embryo as the umbilical arteries and vein. The continuing erosion produces large, blood-filled **lacunae**, or **intervillous spaces**, in the stratum functionalis of the endometrium (see Figure 27.13, p. 1045), and the villi come to lie in these spaces totally immersed in maternal blood (Figure 28.7d). The part of the endometrium that lies between the chorionic villi and the stratum basalis becomes the **decidua basalis** (de-sid′u-ah), and that surrounding the uterine cavity face of the implanted embryo forms the **decidua capsularis** (Figure 28.7d and e). Together, the chorionic villi and the decidua basalis form the disc-shaped placenta.

The placenta detaches and sloughs off after the infant is born, so the name of the maternal portion—*decidua* ("that which falls off")—is appropriate. During development, the decidua capsularis expands to accommodate the fetus, which eventually fills and stretches the uterine cavity. As the developing fetus grows, the villi in the decidua capsularis are compressed and degenerate, and the villi in the decidua basalis increase in number and branch even more profusely.

The placenta is usually fully functional as a nutritive, respiratory, excretory, and endocrine organ by the end of the third month of pregnancy. However, well before this time, oxygen and nutrients are diffusing from maternal to embryonic blood, and embryonic metabolic wastes are passing in the opposite direction. The barriers to free passage of substances between the two blood supplies are embryonic barriers—the membranes of the chorionic villi and the endothelium of embryonic capillaries. Although the maternal and embryonic blood supplies are very close, they normally do not intermix **(Figure 28.8)**.

The placenta secretes hCG from the beginning, but the ability of its syncytiotrophoblast cells (the "hormone manufacturers") to produce the estrogens and progesterone of pregnancy matures much more slowly. If, for some reason, placental hormones are inadequate when hCG levels wane, the endometrium degenerates and the pregnancy is aborted. Throughout pregnancy, blood levels of estrogens and progesterone continue to increase (see Figure 28.6). They encourage growth and further differentiation of the mammary glands and ready them for lactation. The placenta also produces other hormones, such as *human placental lactogen, human chorionic thyrotropin,* and *relaxin*. Shortly we will describe the effects of these hormones on the mother.

CHECK YOUR UNDERSTANDING

7. What is the composition of the chorion?
8. What endometrial decidua cooperates with the chorionic villi to form the placenta?
9. Generally speaking, when does the placenta become fully functional?

For answers, see Appendix G.

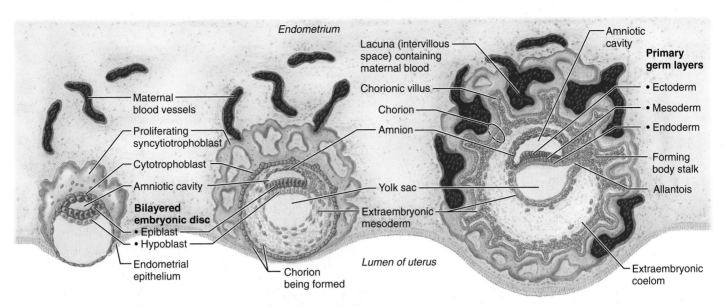

a) Implanting 7½-day blastocyst. The syncytiotrophoblast is eroding the endometrium. Cells of the embryonic disc are now separated from the amnion by a fluid-filled space.

(b) 12-day blastocyst. Implantation is complete. Extraembryonic mesoderm is forming a discrete layer beneath the cytotrophoblast.

(c) 16-day embryo. Cytotrophoblast and associated mesoderm have become the chorion, and chorionic villi are elaborating. The embryo exhibits all three germ layers, a yolk sac and an allantois, which forms the basis of the umbilical cord.

d) 4½-week embryo. The decidua capsularis, decidua basalis, amnion, and yolk sac are well formed. The chorionic villi lie in blood-filled intervillous spaces within the endometrium. The embryo is now receiving its nutrition via the umbilical vessels that connect it (through the umbilical cord) to the placenta.

(e) 13-week fetus.

Figure 28.7 Events of placentation, early embryonic development, and extraembryonic membrane formation.

Events of Embryonic Development: Gastrula to Fetus

Having followed placental development into the fetal stage, we will now backtrack and consider development of the embryo during and after implantation, referring again to Figure 28.7. Even while implantation is occurring, the blastocyst is being converted to a **gastrula** (gas′troo-lah), in which the three primary germ layers form, and the extraembryonic membranes develop. Before becoming three-layered, the inner cell mass first subdivides into two layers—the upper *epiblast* and the lower *hypoblast* (Figure 28.7a, b). The subdivided inner cell mass is now called the **embryonic disc.**

Figure 28.8 Detailed anatomy of the vascular relationships in the mature decidua basalis. This state of development has been accomplished by the end of the third month of development.

Formation and Roles of the Extraembryonic Membranes

▶ Name and describe the formation, location, and function of the extraembryonic membranes.

The **extraembryonic membranes** that form during the first two to three weeks of development include the amnion, yolk sac, allantois, and chorion (Figure 28.7c). The **amnion** (am′ne-on) develops when cells of the epiblast fashion themselves into a transparent membranous sac. This sac, the amnion, becomes filled with **amniotic fluid**. Later, as the embryonic disc curves to form the tubular body, the amnion curves with it. Eventually, the sac extends all the way around the embryo, broken only by the umbilical cord (Figure 28.7d).

Sometimes called the "bag of waters," the amnion provides a buoyant environment that protects the developing embryo against physical trauma, and helps maintain a constant homeostatic temperature. The fluid also prevents the rapidly growing embryonic parts from adhering and fusing together and allows the embryo considerable freedom of movement. Initially, the fluid is derived from the maternal blood, but as the fetal kidneys become functional later in development, fetal urine contributes to amniotic fluid volume.

The **yolk sac** forms from cells of the primitive gut (see below), which arrange themselves into a sac that hangs from the ventral surface of the embryo (Figure 28.7b–d). The amnion and yolk

sac resemble two balloons touching one another with the embryonic disc at the point of contact. In many species, the yolk sac is the main source of nutrition for the embryo, but human eggs contain very little yolk and nutritive functions have been taken over by the placenta. Nevertheless, the yolk sac is important in humans because it (1) forms part of the gut (digestive tube), and (2) is the source of the earliest blood cells and blood vessels.

The **allantois** (ah-lan′to-is) forms as a small outpocketing of embryonic tissue at the caudal end of the yolk sac (Figure 28.7c). In animals that develop in shelled eggs, the allantois is a disposal site for solid metabolic wastes (excreta). In humans, the allantois is the structural base for the **umbilical cord** that links the embryo to the placenta, and ultimately it becomes part of the urinary bladder. The fully formed umbilical cord contains a core of embryonic connective tissue (Wharton's jelly), the umbilical arteries and vein, and is covered externally by amniotic membrane.

We have already described the *chorion*, which helps to form the placenta (Figure 28.7c). As the outermost membrane, the chorion encloses the embryonic body and all other membranes.

CHECK YOUR UNDERSTANDING

10. What is the function of the amnion?

11. Which extraembryonic membrane provides a path for the embryonic blood vessels to reach the placenta?

For answers, see Appendix G.

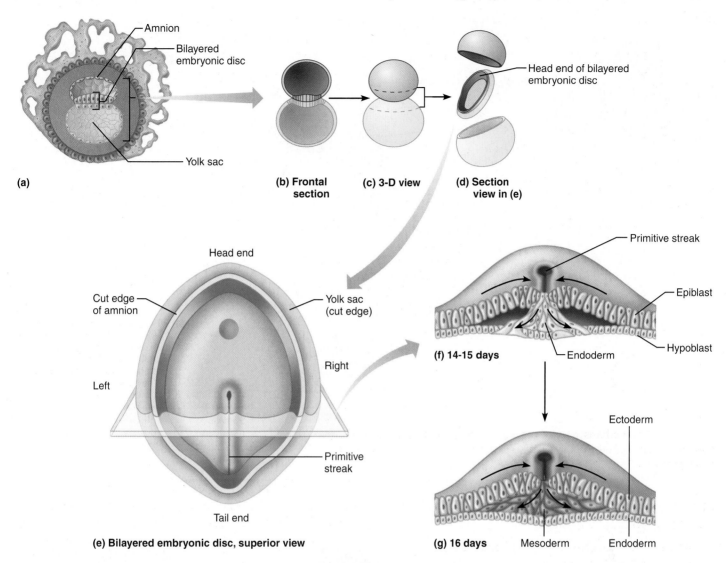

Figure 28.9 Formation of the three primary germ layers. (a–d) Orienting diagrams. **(e)** Surface view of an embryonic disc, amnion and yolk sac removed. **(f, g)** Cross sections of the embryonic disc, showing the germ layers resulting from cell migration. The first epiblast cells that migrate medially into the primitive streak **(f)** become endoderm. Those that follow **(g)** become mesoderm. The epiblast surface is now called ectoderm.

Gastrulation: Germ Layer Formation

▶ Describe gastrulation and its consequence.

During week 3, the two-layered embryonic disc transforms into a three-layered *embryo* in which the **primary germ layers**—*ectoderm, mesoderm,* and *endoderm*—are present (Figure 28.7c). This process, called **gastrulation** (gas″troo-la′shun), involves cellular rearrangements and migrations.

Figure 28.9 focuses on the changes that take place in the days between Figure 28.7b (12-day embryo) and Figure 28.7c (16-day embryo). Gastrulation begins when a groove with raised edges called the **primitive streak** appears on the dorsal surface of the embryonic disc and establishes the longitudinal axis of the embryo (Figure 28.9e). Surface (epiblast) cells of the embryonic disc then migrate medially across other cells and enter the primitive streak. The first cells to enter the groove displace the

hypoblast cells of the yolk sac and form the most inferior germ layer, the **endoderm** (Figure 28.9f). Those that follow push laterally between the cells at the upper and lower surfaces, forming the **mesoderm** (Figure 28.9g). As soon as the mesoderm is formed, the mesodermal cells immediately beneath the early primitive streak aggregate, forming a rod of mesodermal cells called the **notochord** (no′to-kord), the first axial support of the embryo **(Figure 28.10a)**. The cells that remain on the embryo's dorsal surface are the **ectoderm**. At this point, the embryo is about 2 mm long.

The three primary germ layers serve as the *primitive tissues* from which all body organs derive. Ectoderm ("outer skin") fashions structures of the nervous system and the skin epidermis. Endoderm ("inner skin") forms the epithelial linings of the digestive, respiratory, and urogenital systems, and associated glands. Mesoderm ("middle skin") forms virtually everything else.

28

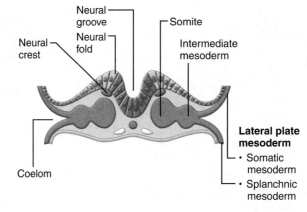

(a) 17 days. The flat three-layered embryo has completed gastrulation. Notochord and neural plate are present.

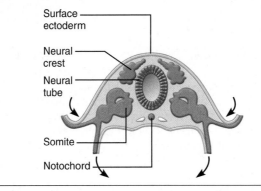

(b) 20 days. The neural folds form by folding of the neural plate, which then deepens, producing the neural groove. Three mesodermal aggregates form on each side of the notochord (somite, intermediate mesoderm, and lateral plate mesoderm).

(c) 22 days. The neural folds have closed, forming the neural tube which has detached from the surface ectoderm and lies between the surface ectoderm and the notochord. Embryonic body is beginning to undercut.

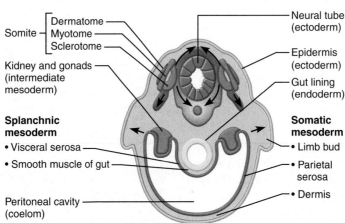

(d) End of week 4. Embryo undercutting is complete. Somites have subdivided into sclerotome, myotome, and dermatome, which form the vertebrae, skeletal muscles, and dermis respectively. Body coelom present.

28

Figure 28.10 Neurulation and early mesodermal differentiation.

Both ectoderm and endoderm consist mostly of cells that are securely joined to each other and are *epithelia*. Mesoderm, by contrast, is a *mesenchyme* [literally, "poured into the middle (of the embryo)"], an embryonic tissue with star-shaped cells that are free to migrate widely within the embryo. Figure 28.13 (p. 1085) lists the germ layer derivatives. Some of the details of the differentiation processes are described next.

Organogenesis: Differentiation of the Germ Layers

▶ Define organogenesis and indicate the important roles of the three primary germ layers in this process.

▶ Describe unique features of the fetal circulation.

Gastrulation lays down the basic structural framework of the embryo and sets the stage for the rearrangements that occur during **organogenesis** (or"gah-no-jen′ĕ-sis), formation of body organs and organ systems. By the end of the embryonic period at 8 weeks, when the embryo is about 22 mm (slightly less than 1 inch) long from head to buttocks (referred to as the *crown-rump measurement*), all the adult organ systems are recognizable. It is truly amazing how much organogenesis occurs in such a short time in such a small amount of living matter.

Specialization of the Ectoderm

The first major event in organogenesis is **neurulation**, the differentiation of ectoderm that produces the brain and spinal cord (Figure 28.10). This process is *induced* (stimulated to happen) by chemical signals from the *notochord*, the rod of mesoderm that defines the body axis, mentioned earlier. The ectoderm overlying the notochord thickens, forming the **neural plate** (Figure 28.10a). Then the ectoderm starts to fold inward as a **neural groove**. As the neural groove deepens it forms prominent **neural folds** (Figure 28.10b). By day 22, the superior margins of the neural folds fuse, forming a **neural tube**, which soon pinches off from the ectodermal layer and becomes covered by surface ectoderm (Figure 28.10c).

As we described in Chapter 12, the anterior end of the neural tube becomes the brain and the rest becomes the spinal cord. The associated **neural crest cells** (Figure 28.10c) migrate widely and give rise to the cranial, spinal, and sympathetic ganglia (and associated nerves), to the medulla of the adrenal gland, and to pigment cells, and contribute to some connective tissues.

By the end of the first month of development, the three primary brain vesicles (fore-, mid-, and hindbrain) are apparent. By the end of the second month, all brain flexures are evident, the cerebral hemispheres cover the top of the brain stem (see Figure 12.3), and brain waves can be recorded. Most of the remaining ectoderm forming the surface layer of the embryonic body differentiates into the epidermis of the skin. Other ectodermal derivatives are indicated in Figure 28.13.

Specialization of the Endoderm

As Figure 28.11 shows, the embryo starts off as a flat plate, but as it grows, it folds to achieve a cylindrical body shape which lifts

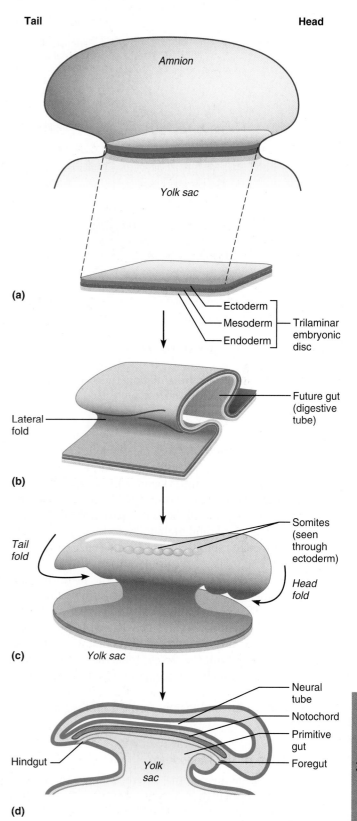

Figure 28.11 Folding of the embryonic body, lateral views.
(a) Model of the flat three-layered embryo as three sheets of paper. **(b, c)** Folding begins with lateral folds, then head and tail folds appear. **(d)** A 24-day embryo in sagittal section. Notice the primitive gut, which derives from the yolk sac, and the notochord and neural tube dorsally.

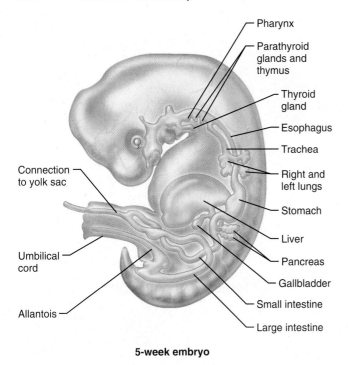

Pharynx
Parathyroid glands and thymus
Thyroid gland
Esophagus
Trachea
Right and left lungs
Stomach
Liver
Pancreas
Gallbladder
Small intestine
Large intestine

Connection to yolk sac
Umbilical cord
Allantois

5-week embryo

Figure 28.12 Endodermal differentiation. Endoderm forms the epithelial linings of the digestive and respiratory tracts and associated glands.

off the yolk sac and protrudes into the amniotic cavity. In the simplest sense, this process resembles three stacked sheets of paper folding laterally into a tube (Figure 28.11a, b). At the same time, the folding occurs from both ends (the head and tail regions) and progresses toward the central part of the embryonic body, where the yolk sac and umbilical vessels protrude. As the endoderm undercuts and its edges come together and fuse, it encloses part of the yolk sac (Figure 28.11d).

The tube of endoderm formed, called the **primitive gut**, forms the epithelial lining (mucosa) of the gastrointestinal tract (Figure 28.12). The organs of the GI tract (pharynx, esophagus, etc.) quickly become apparent, and then the oral and anal openings perforate. The mucosal lining of the respiratory tract forms as an outpocketing from the *foregut* (pharyngeal endoderm), and glands arise as endodermal outpocketings at various points further along the tract. For example, the epithelium of the thyroid, parathyroids, and thymus forms from the pharyngeal endoderm.

Specialization of the Mesoderm

The first evidence of mesodermal differentiation is the appearance of the notochord in the embryonic disc (see Figure 28.10a). The notochord is eventually replaced by the vertebral column, but its remnants persist in the springy *nucleus pulposus* of the intervertebral discs. Shortly thereafter, three mesodermal aggregates appear on either side of the notochord (Figure 28.10b, c). The largest of these, the *somites* (so′mīts), are paired mesodermal blocks that hug the notochord on either side. All 40 pairs of somites are present by the end of week 4. Flanking the somites laterally are small clusters of segmented mesoderm called

intermediate mesoderm and then double sheets of *lateral plate mesoderm.*

Each **somite** has three functional parts—*sclerotome, dermatome,* and *myotome* (Figure 28.10d). Cells of the **sclerotome** (skle′ro-tōm; "hard piece") migrate medially, gather around the notochord and neural tube, and produce the vertebra and rib at the associated level. **Dermatome** ("skin piece") cells help form the dermis of the skin in the dorsal part of the body. The **myotome** (mi′o-tōm; "muscle piece") cells develop in conjunction with the vertebrae. They form the skeletal muscles of the neck, body trunk, and, via their **limb buds,** the muscles of the limbs.

Cells of the **intermediate mesoderm** form the gonads and kidneys. The **lateral plate mesoderm** consists of paired mesodermal plates: the *somatic mesoderm* and the *splanchnic mesoderm* (Figure 28.10d). Cells of the **somatic mesoderm** (1) help to form the dermis of the skin in the ventral body region; (2) form the parietal serosa that lines the ventral body cavity; and (3) migrate into the forming limbs and produce the bones, ligaments, and dermis of the limbs (see Figure 28.10d). **Splanchnic mesoderm** provides the mesenchymal cells that form the heart and blood vessels and most connective tissues of the body. Splanchnic mesodermal cells also form the smooth muscle, connective tissues, and serosal coverings (in other words, nearly the entire wall) of the digestive and respiratory organs. Thus, the lateral mesodermal layers cooperate to form the serosae of the **coelom** (se′lom), or ventral body cavity. The mesodermal derivatives are summarized in **Figure 28.13**.

By the end of the embryonic period, the bones have begun to ossify and the skeletal muscles are well formed and contracting spontaneously. Metanephric kidneys are developing, gonads are formed, and the lungs and digestive organs are attaining their final shape and body position. Blood delivery to and from the placenta via the umbilical vessels is constant and efficient. The heart and the liver are competing for space and form a conspicuous bulge on the ventral surface of the embryo's body. All this by the end of eight weeks in an embryo about 2.5 cm (1 inch) long from crown to rump!

Development of the Fetal Circulation Embryonic development of the cardiovascular system lays the groundwork for the fetal circulatory pattern, which is converted to the adult pattern at birth. The first blood cells arise in the yolk sac. Before week 3 of development, tiny spaces appear in the splanchnic mesoderm. These are quickly lined by endothelial cells, covered with mesenchyme, and linked together into rapidly spreading vascular networks, destined to form the heart, blood vessels, and lymphatics. By the end of week 3, the embryo has a system of paired blood vessels, and the two vessels forming the heart have fused and bent into an S shape. By 3½ weeks, the miniature heart is pumping blood for an embryo less than a quarter inch long.

Unique cardiovascular modifications seen only during prenatal development include the **umbilical arteries** and **vein** and three *vascular shunts* **(Figure 28.14)**. All of these structures are occluded at birth. As you read about these vessels, keep in mind that the blood is flowing from and to the fetal heart. The large umbilical vein carries freshly oxygenated blood returning from the placenta into the embryonic body, where it is conveyed to

28

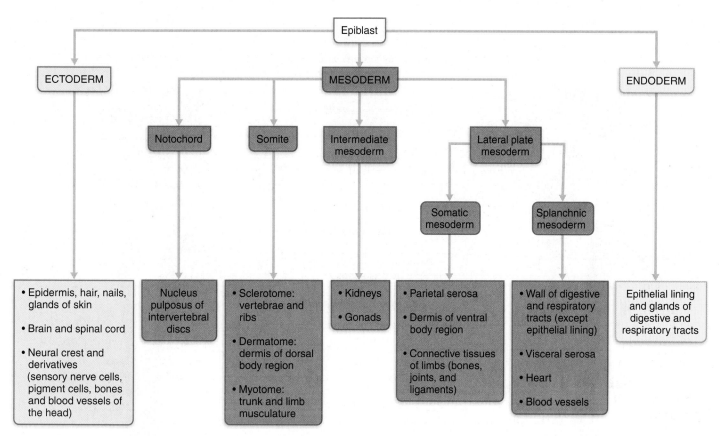

Figure 28.13 **Flowchart showing major derivatives of the embryonic germ layers.**

the liver. There, some of the returning blood percolates through the liver sinusoids and out the hepatic veins. Most of the blood coursing through the umbilical vein, however, enters the **ductus venosus** (duk′tus ve-no′sus), a venous shunt that bypasses the liver sinusoids. Both the hepatic veins and the ductus venosus empty into the inferior vena cava where the placental blood mixes with deoxygenated blood returning from the lower parts of the fetus's body. The vena cava in turn conveys this "mixed load" of blood directly to the right atrium of the heart.

After birth, the liver plays an important role in nutrient processing, but during embryonic life the mother's liver performs these functions. Consequently, blood flow through the fetal liver during development is important only to ensure that the liver cells remain healthy.

Blood entering and leaving the heart encounters two more shunt systems, each serving to bypass the nonfunctional lungs. Some of the blood entering the right atrium flows directly into the left atrium via the **foramen ovale** ("oval hole"), an opening in the interatrial septum loosely closed by a flap of tissue. Blood that enters the right ventricle is pumped out into the pulmonary trunk. However, the second shunt, the **ductus arteriosus**, transfers most of that blood directly into the aorta, again bypassing the pulmonary circuit. (The lungs *do* receive adequate blood to maintain their growth.) Blood enters the two pulmonary bypass shunts because the heart chamber or vessel on the other side of each shunt is a lower-pressure area, owing to the low volume of venous return from the lungs. Blood flow-

ing distally through the aorta eventually reaches the umbilical arteries, which are branches of the internal iliac arteries serving the pelvis. From here the largely deoxygenated blood, laden with metabolic wastes, is delivered back to the capillaries in the chorionic villi of the placenta. The changes in the circulatory plan that occur at birth are illustrated in Figure 28.14b.

HOMEOSTATIC IMBALANCE

Because many potentially harmful substances can cross placental barriers and enter the fetal blood, a pregnant woman should be aware of what she is taking into her body, particularly during the embryonic period when the body's foundations are laid down. **Teratogens** (ter′ah-to-jenz; *terato* = monster), factors that may cause severe congenital abnormalities or even fetal death, include alcohol, nicotine, many drugs (anticoagulants, sedatives, antihypertensives, and some antibiotics), and maternal infections, particularly German measles. For example, when a woman drinks alcohol, her fetus becomes inebriated as well. However, the fetal consequences may be much more lasting and result in the *fetal alcohol syndrome (FAS)* typified by microcephaly (small head), mental retardation, and abnormal growth. Nicotine hinders oxygen delivery to the fetus, impairing normal growth and development. The sedative **thalidomide** (thah-lid′o-mīd) was used by thousands of pregnant women in the 1960s to alleviate morning sickness. When taken during the period of limb bud differentiation (days 26–56), it sometimes resulted in tragically deformed infants with short flipperlike legs and arms. ∎

28

Fetus   **Newborn**

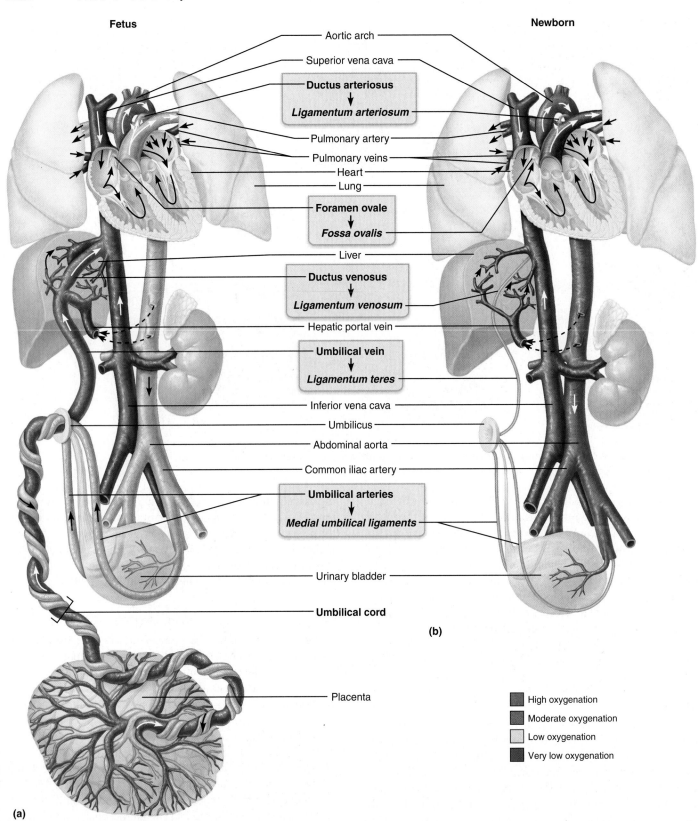

Aortic arch

Superior vena cava

Ductus arteriosus
↓
Ligamentum arteriosum

Pulmonary artery

Pulmonary veins

Heart

Lung

Foramen ovale
↓
Fossa ovalis

Liver

Ductus venosus
↓
Ligamentum venosum

Hepatic portal vein

Umbilical vein
↓
Ligamentum teres

Inferior vena cava

Umbilicus

Abdominal aorta

Common iliac artery

Umbilical arteries
↓
Medial umbilical ligaments

Urinary bladder

Umbilical cord

(b)

Placenta

High oxygenation
Moderate oxygenation
Low oxygenation
Very low oxygenation

(a)

28

Figure 28.14 Circulation in fetus and new-born. Arrows on blood vessels indicate direction of blood flow. Arrows in color screens go from the fetal structure to what it becomes after birth. **(a)** Special adaptations for embryonic and fetal life. The umbilical vein carries oxygen- and nutrient-rich blood from the placenta to the fetus. The umbilical arteries carry waste-laden blood from the fetus to the placenta. The ductus arteriosus and foramen ovale bypass the nonfunctional lungs. The ductus venosus allows blood to partially bypass the liver. **(b)** Changes in the cardiovascular system at birth. The umbilical vessels as well as the liver and lung bypasses are occluded.

Amniotic sac   Umbilical cord   Umbilical vein

Chorionic villi

Cut edge of chorion

Yolk sac

(a) Embryo at week 7, about 17 mm long.

Figure 28.15 **Photographs of a developing fetus.** By birth, the fetus is typically 36 cm long from crown to rump.

(b) Fetus in month 3, about 6 cm long.

(c) Fetus late in month 5, about 19 cm long.

CHECK YOUR UNDERSTANDING

12. The early embryo is flat like a three-layered pancake. What event must occur before organogenesis can get going in earnest?
13. What germ layer gives rise to essentially all body tissues except nervous tissue, the epidermis, and mucosae?

For answers, see Appendix G.

Events of Fetal Development

▶ Indicate the duration of the fetal period, and note the major events of fetal development.

The main events of the fetal period—weeks 9 through 38—are listed chronologically in **Table 28.1.** The fetal period is a time of rapid growth of the body structures that were established in the embryo. During the first half of this period, cells are still differentiating into specific cell types to form the body's distinctive tissues and are completing the fine details of body structure. During the fetal period, the developing fetus grows from a crown-to-rump length of about 22 mm (slightly less than 1 inch) and a weight of approximately 2 g (0.06 ounce) to about 360 mm (14 inches) and 3.2 kg (7 lb) or more. (Total body length at birth is about 550 mm, or 22 inches.) As you might expect with such tremendous growth, the changes in fetal appearance are quite dramatic **(Figure 28.15).** Nevertheless, the greatest

28

TABLE 28.1	Developmental Events of the Fetal Period
TIME	**CHANGES AND ACCOMPLISHMENTS**

8 weeks (end of embryonic period) 8 weeks	Head nearly as large as body; all major brain regions present; first brain waves in brain stem Liver disproportionately large and begins to form blood cells Limbs present; digits are initially webbed, but fingers and toes are free by the end of this interval Ossification just begun; weak, spontaneous muscle contractions occur Cardiovascular system fully functional (heart has been pumping blood since the fourth week) All body systems present in at least rudimentary form Approximate crown-to-rump length: 22 mm (0.9 inch); weight: 2 grams (0.06 ounce)
9–12 weeks (month 3) 12 weeks	Head still dominant, but body elongating; brain continues to enlarge, shows its general structural features; cervical and lumbar enlargements apparent in spinal cord; retina of eye is present Skin epidermis and dermis obvious; facial features present in crude form Liver prominent and bile being secreted; palate is fusing; most glands of endodermal origin are developed; walls of hollow visceral organs gaining smooth muscle Blood cell formation begins in bone marrow Notochord degenerating and ossification accelerating; limbs well molded Sex readily detected from the genitals Approximate crown-to-rump length at end of interval: 90 mm
13–16 weeks (month 4) 16 weeks	Cerebellum becoming prominent; general sensory organs differentiated; eyes and ears assume characteristic position and shape; blinking of eyes and sucking motions of lips occur Face looks human and growth of the body beginning to outpace that of the head Glands developed in GI tract; meconium is collecting Kidneys attain typical structure Most bones are now distinct and joint cavities are apparent Approximate crown-to-rump length at end of interval: 140 mm
17–20 weeks (month 5)	Vernix caseosa (fatty secretions of sebaceous glands) covers body; lanugo (silklike hair) covers skin Fetal position (body flexed anteriorly) assumed because of space restrictions Limbs reach near-final proportions Quickening occurs (mother feels spontaneous muscular activity of fetus) Approximate crown-to-rump length at end of interval: 190 mm
21–30 weeks (months 6 and 7) 	Period of substantial increase in weight (may survive if born prematurely at 27–28 weeks, but hypothalamic temperature regulation and lung production of surfactant are still inadequate) Myelination of spinal cord begins; eyes are open Distal limb bones are beginning to ossify Skin is wrinkled and red; fingernails and toenails are present; tooth enamel is forming on deciduous teeth Body is lean and well proportioned Bone marrow becomes sole site of blood cell formation Testes reach scrotum in seventh month (in males) Approximate crown-to-rump length at end of interval: 280 mm
30–40 weeks (term) (months 8 and 9) At birth	Skin whitish pink; fat laid down in subcutaneous tissue (hypodermis) Approximate crown-to-rump length at end of interval: 360 mm (14 inches); weight: 3.2 kg (7 lb)

28

(a) Before conception
(Uterus the size of a fist and resides in the pelvis.)

(b) 4 months
(Fundus of the uterus is between the pubic symphysis and the umbilicus.)

(c) 7 months
(Fundus is well above the umbilicus.)

(d) 9 months
(Fundus reaches the xiphoid process.)

Figure 28.16 **Relative size of the uterus before conception and during pregnancy.**

amount of growth occurs in the first 8 weeks of life, when the embryo grows from one cell to a fetus of 1 inch.

CHECK YOUR UNDERSTANDING

14. When does the fetal period begin?

For answers, see Appendix G.

Effects of Pregnancy on the Mother

▶ Describe functional changes in maternal reproductive organs and in the cardiovascular, respiratory, and urinary systems during pregnancy.

▶ Indicate the effects of pregnancy on maternal metabolism and posture.

Pregnancy can be a difficult time for the mother. Not only are there anatomical changes, but striking changes in her metabolism and physiology occur to support the pregnancy and prepare her body for delivery and lactation.

Anatomical Changes

As pregnancy progresses, the female reproductive organs become increasingly vascular and engorged with blood, and the vagina develops a purplish hue (*Chadwick's sign*). The enhanced vascularity increases vaginal sensitivity and sexual intensity, and some women achieve orgasm for the first time when they are pregnant. The breasts, too, engorge with blood and, prodded by

rising levels of estrogen and progesterone, they enlarge and their areolae darken. Some women develop increased pigmentation of facial skin of the nose and cheeks, a condition called *chloasma* (klo-az′mah; "to be green") or the "mask of pregnancy."

The degree of uterine enlargement during pregnancy is remarkable. Starting as a fist-sized organ, the uterus fills most of the pelvic cavity by 16 weeks (**Figure 28.16a, b**). Though the fetus is only about 140 mm long (crown-to-rump) at this time, the placenta is fully formed, uterine muscle is hypertrophied, and amniotic fluid volume is increasing.

As pregnancy continues, the uterus pushes higher into the abdominal cavity, exerting pressure on both abdominal and pelvic organs (Figure 28.16c). As birth nears, the uterus reaches the level of the xiphoid process and occupies most of the abdominal cavity (Figure 28.16d). The crowded abdominal organs press superiorly against the diaphragm, which intrudes on the thoracic cavity. As a result, the ribs flare, causing the thorax to widen.

The increasing bulkiness of the anterior abdomen changes the woman's center of gravity, and many women develop *lordosis* (accentuated lumbar curvature) and backaches during the last few months of pregnancy. Placental production of the hormone **relaxin** causes pelvic ligaments and the pubic symphysis to relax, widen, and become more flexible. This increased flexibility eases birth passage, but it may result in a waddling gait in the meantime. Considerable weight gain occurs during a normal pregnancy. Because some women are over- or underweight before pregnancy begins, it is almost impossible to state the ideal or desirable weight gain. However, summing up the weight increases resulting from fetal and placental growth, increased size of the maternal reproductive organs and breasts, and greater blood volume during pregnancy, a weight gain of approximately 13 kg (about 28 lb) usually occurs.

28

Good nutrition is necessary all through pregnancy if the developing fetus is to have all the building materials (especially proteins, calcium, and iron) needed to form its tissues. Additionally, multivitamins containing folic acid reduce the risk of having a baby with neurological problems, including such birth defects as spina bifida and anencephaly. However, a pregnant woman needs only 300 additional calories daily to sustain proper fetal growth. The emphasis should be on eating high-quality food, not just more food.

Not surprisingly, effects of the fetal environment may not show up until decades later. Below-normal birth weight, for instance, places females at risk for type 2 diabetes and increases the general risk of cardiovascular disease later in life for both men and women.

Metabolic Changes

As the placenta enlarges, it secretes increasing amounts of **human placental lactogen (hPL)**, also called **human chorionic somatomammotropin (hCS)**. hPL works cooperatively with estrogens and progesterone to stimulate maturation of the breasts for lactation, promotes growth of the fetus, and exerts a glucose-sparing effect in the mother. Consequently, maternal cells metabolize more fatty acids and less glucose than usual, sparing glucose for use by the fetus. Gestational diabetes mellitus occurs in about 10% of pregnancies, but over half of those women go on to develop type 2 diabetes later in life.

The placenta also releases **human chorionic thyrotropin (hCT)**, a glycoprotein hormone similar to thyroid-stimulating hormone of the anterior pituitary. hCT increases the rate of maternal metabolism throughout the pregnancy, causing hypermetabolism. Plasma levels of parathyroid hormone and activated vitamin D rise, so that pregnant women tend to be in positive calcium balance throughout pregnancy. This state ensures that the developing fetus will have adequate calcium to mineralize its bones.

Physiological Changes

Physiological changes take place in many systems during pregnancy. A few of these changes are described next.

Gastrointestinal System

Until their system adjusts to the elevated levels of progesterone and estrogens, many women suffer nausea, commonly called *morning sickness*, during the first few months of pregnancy. (Nausea is also a side effect of many birth control pills.) *Heartburn*, due to reflux of stomach acid into the esophagus, is common because the esophagus is displaced and the stomach is crowded by the growing uterus. *Constipation* occurs because motility of the digestive tract declines during pregnancy.

Urinary System

The kidneys produce more urine during pregnancy because of the mother's increased metabolic rate and the additional burden of disposing of fetal metabolic wastes. As the growing uterus compresses the bladder, urination becomes more frequent, more urgent, and sometimes uncontrollable (*stress incontinence*).

Respiratory System

The nasal mucosa responds to estrogens by becoming edematous and congested. Thus, nasal stuffiness and occasional nosebleeds may occur. Tidal volume increases markedly during pregnancy, while respiratory rate is relatively unchanged and residual volume declines. The increase in tidal volume is due to the mother's greater need for oxygen during pregnancy and the fact that progesterone enhances the sensitivity of the medullary respiratory center to CO_2. Many women exhibit *dyspnea* (disp-ne′ah), or difficult breathing, during the later stages of pregnancy.

Cardiovascular System

The most dramatic physiological changes occur in the cardiovascular system. Total body water rises, and blood volume increases 25–40% by the 32nd week to accommodate the additional needs of the fetus. The rise in blood volume also safeguards against blood loss during birth. Blood pressure and pulse typically rise and increase cardiac output by 20–40% at various stages of pregnancy. This helps propel the greater circulatory volume around the body. The uterus presses on the pelvic blood vessels, which may impair venous return from the lower limbs, resulting in *varicose veins* and leg edema.

HOMEOSTATIC IMBALANCE

A dangerous complication of pregnancy called **preeclampsia** results in an insufficient placental blood supply, which can starve a fetus of oxygen. The pregnant woman becomes edematous and hypertensive, and proteinuria occurs. This condition, which affects one in 10 pregnancies, is believed to be due to immunological abnormalities in some cases, because its occurrence seems to be positively correlated with the number of fetal cells that enter the maternal circulation. ■

CHECK YOUR UNDERSTANDING

15. What causes the difficult breathing that some women experience during pregnancy? What causes the waddling gait seen in some?

16. What is the cause of morning sickness?

17. What is the role of the hormone hCT?

For answers, see Appendix G.

Parturition (Birth)

▶ Explain how labor is initiated, and describe the three stages of labor.

Parturition (par″tu-rish′un; "bringing forth young") is the culmination of pregnancy—giving birth to the baby. It usually occurs within 15 days of the calculated due date (280 days from the last menstrual period). The series of events that expel the infant from the uterus are collectively called **labor**.

Initiation of Labor

Several events and hormones interlock to trigger labor. During the last few weeks of pregnancy, estrogens reach their highest levels in the mother's blood. Studies indicate that the fetus determines its own birth date. Rising levels of fetal adrenocortical hormones (especially cortisol) late in pregnancy are a major stimulus for the placenta to release such large amounts of estrogens. In addition, increased production of *surfactant protein A* (*SP-A*) by the fetal lungs in the weeks before delivery appears to trigger an inflammatory response in the cervix that stimulates its softening in preparation for labor.

The rise in estrogens has two important consequences. It stimulates the myometrial cells of the uterus to form abundant oxytocin receptors (Figure 28.17). It also antagonizes progesterone's quieting influence on uterine muscle. As a result, the myometrium becomes increasingly irritable, and weak, irregular uterine contractions begin to occur. These contractions, called *Braxton Hicks contractions*, have caused many women to go to the hospital, only to be told that they were in **false labor** and sent home.

As birth nears, two more chemical signals cooperate to convert these false labor pains into the real thing. Certain fetal cells begin to produce **oxytocin** (ok″sĭ-to′sin), which causes the placenta to release **prostaglandins** (pros″tah-glan′dinz) (Figure 28.17). Both hormones are powerful uterine muscle stimulants, and since the myometrium is now highly sensitive to oxytocin, contractions become more frequent and more vigorous. While elevated levels of oxytocin and prostaglandins sustain labor once it begins, many studies indicate that it is the prostaglandins (acting as paracrines) that actually trigger the rhythmic expulsive contractions of true labor. At this point, the increasing emotional and physical stresses (pain and uterine distension respectively) activate the mother's hypothalamus, which signals for oxytocin release by the posterior pituitary.

Once the hypothalamus is involved, a *positive feedback mechanism* is propelled into action—greater distension causes the release of more oxytocin, which causes greater contractile force, and so on (Figure 28.17). These expulsive contractions are aided by the fact that *fetal fibronectin*, a natural "stickum" (adhesive protein) that binds the fetal and maternal tissues of the placenta together throughout pregnancy, changes to a lubricant just before true labor begins.

As mentioned earlier, prostaglandins are essential for initiating labor in humans, and interfering with their production will hinder onset of labor. For example, antiprostaglandin drugs such as ibuprofen can inhibit the early stages of labor and such drugs are used occasionally to prevent preterm births.

Stages of Labor

Labor includes the dilation, expulsion, and placental stages illustrated in Figure 28.18.

Stage 1: Dilation Stage

The **dilation stage** is the time from labor's onset until the cervix is fully dilated by the baby's head (about 10 cm in diameter)

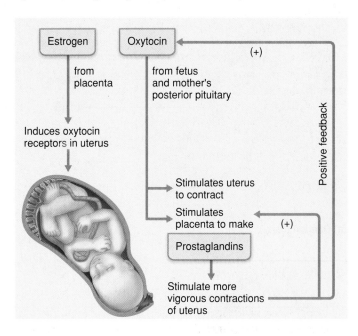

Figure 28.17 Hormonal induction of labor.

(Figure 28.18a). As labor starts, weak but regular contractions begin in the upper part of the uterus and move toward the vagina. At first, only the superior uterine muscle is active, the contractions are 15–30 minutes apart, and they last for 10–30 seconds. As labor progresses, the contractions become more vigorous and rapid, and the lower part of the uterus gets involved. As the infant's head is forced against the cervix with each contraction, the cervix softens and thins (*effaces*), and dilates. Eventually the amnion ruptures, releasing the amniotic fluid, an event commonly called "breaking the water."

The dilation stage is the longest part of labor, lasting 6–12 hours or more. Several events happen during this phase. *Engagement* occurs when the infant's head enters the true pelvis. As descent continues through the birth canal, the baby's head rotates so that its greatest dimension is in the anteroposterior line, which allows it to navigate the narrow dimensions of the pelvic outlet (Figure 28.18b).

Stage 2: Expulsion Stage

The **expulsion stage** lasts from full dilation to delivery of the infant, or actual childbirth (Figure 28.18c). By the time the cervix is fully dilated, strong contractions occur every 2–3 minutes and last about 1 minute. In this stage, a mother undergoing labor without local anesthesia has an increasing urge to push or bear down with the abdominal muscles. Although this phase may last 2 hours, it is typically 50 minutes in a first birth and around 20 minutes in subsequent births.

Crowning occurs when the largest dimension of the baby's head distends the vulva. At this point, an *episiotomy* (e-piz″e-ot′o-me) may be done to reduce tissue tearing. An episiotomy is an incision made to widen the vaginal orifice. The baby's neck extends as the head exits from the perineum, and once the head has been delivered, the rest of the baby's body is delivered much more easily. After birth, the umbilical cord is clamped and cut.

(a) Dilation (early)

(b) Dilation (late)

(c) Expulsion

28

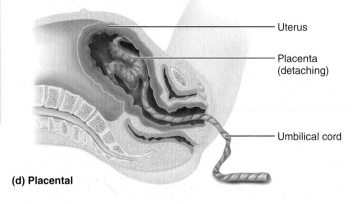

(d) Placental

Figure 28.18 Parturition. (a) Dilation stage (early). The baby's head is engaged in the true pelvis. The widest head dimension is along the left-right axis. **(b)** Late dilation. The baby's head rotates so that its greatest dimension is in the anteroposterior axis as it moves through the pelvic outlet. Dilation of the cervix is nearly complete. **(c)** Expulsion stage. The baby's head extends as it reaches the perineum and is delivered. **(d)** Placental stage. After the baby is delivered, the placenta is detached by the continuing uterine contractions and removed.

When the infant is in the usual *vertex*, or head-first, *presentation*, the skull (its largest diameter) acts as a wedge to dilate the cervix. The head-first presentation also allows the baby to be suctioned free of mucus and to breathe even before it has completely exited from the birth canal (Figure 28.18c). In *breech* (buttock-first) and other nonvertex presentations, these advantages are lost and delivery is much more difficult, often requiring the use of forceps, or a C-section (see below).

HOMEOSTATIC IMBALANCE

If a woman has a deformed or malelike pelvis, labor may be prolonged and difficult. This condition is called *dystocia* (dis-to′se-ah; *dys* = difficult; *toc* = birth). Besides extreme maternal fatigue, another possible consequence of dystocia is fetal brain damage, resulting in cerebral palsy or epilepsy. To prevent these outcomes, a *cesarean* (*C-*) *section* (se-sa′re-an) is performed in many such cases. A C-section is delivery of the infant through an incision made through the abdominal and uterine walls. ■

Stage 3: Placental Stage

The **placental stage**, or the delivery of the placenta and its attached fetal membranes, which are collectively called the **afterbirth**, is usually accomplished within 30 minutes after birth of the infant (Figure 28.18d). The strong uterine contractions that continue after birth compress uterine blood vessels, limit bleeding, and shear the placenta off the uterine wall (cause placental detachment). It is very important that all placental fragments be removed to prevent continued uterine bleeding after birth (*postpartum bleeding*).

CHECK YOUR UNDERSTANDING

18. What is a breech presentation?
19. What chemical is most responsible for triggering true labor?
20. Why does a baby turn as it travels through the birth canal?

For answers, see Appendix G.

Adjustments of the Infant to Extrauterine Life

▶ Outline the events leading to the first breath of a newborn.

▶ Describe changes that occur in the fetal circulation after birth.

The **neonatal period** is the four-week period immediately after birth. Here we will be concerned with the events of just the first few hours after birth in a normal infant. As you might suspect, birth represents quite a shock to the infant. Exposed to physical trauma during the birth process, it is suddenly cast out of its watery, warm environment and its placental life supports are severed. Now it must do for itself all that the mother had been doing for it—respire, obtain nutrients, excrete, and maintain its body temperature.

At 1 and 5 minutes after birth, the infant's physical status is assessed based on five signs: heart rate, respiration, color, muscle tone, and reflexes (tested by response to catheter in nostril). Each observation is given a score of 0 to 2, and the total is called the **Apgar score**. An Apgar score of 8 to 10 indicates a healthy baby. Lower scores reveal problems in one or more of the physiological functions assessed.

Taking the First Breath and Transition

The crucial first requirement is to breathe. Vasoconstriction of the umbilical arteries, initiated when they are stretched during birth, leads to loss of placental support. Once carbon dioxide is no longer removed by the placenta, it accumulates in the baby's blood, causing central acidosis. This excites respiratory control centers in the baby's brain and triggers the first inspiration. The first breath requires a tremendous effort—the airways are tiny, and the lungs are collapsed. However, once the lungs have been inflated in full-term babies, surfactant in alveolar fluid reduces surface tension in the alveoli, and breathing is easier. The rate of respiration is rapid (about 45 respirations/min) during the first two weeks and then gradually declines.

Keeping the lungs inflated is much more difficult for premature infants (those weighing less than 2500 g, or about 5.5 lb, at birth) because surfactant production occurs during the last months of prenatal life. Consequently, preemies are usually put on respiratory assistance (a ventilator) until their lungs are mature enough to function on their own.

For 6–8 hours after birth, infants pass through an unstable **transitional period** marked by alternating periods of increased activity and sleep, and during which they adjust to extrauterine life. During the activity periods, vital signs are irregular and the baby gags frequently as it regurgitates mucus and debris. After this, the infant stabilizes, with waking periods (dictated by hunger) occurring every 3–4 hours.

Occlusion of Special Fetal Blood Vessels and Vascular Shunts

After birth the special umbilical blood vessels and fetal shunts are no longer necessary (see Figure 28.14b). The umbilical arteries and vein constrict and become fibrosed. The proximal parts of the umbilical arteries persist as the *superior vesical arteries* that supply the urinary bladder, and their distal parts become the **medial umbilical ligaments**. The remnant of the umbilical vein becomes the **round ligament of the liver**, or **ligamentum teres**, that attaches the umbilicus to the liver. The ductus venosus collapses as blood stops flowing through the umbilical vein and is eventually converted to the **ligamentum venosum** on the liver's undersurface.

As the pulmonary circulation becomes functional, pressure in the left side of the heart increases and that in the right side of the heart decreases, causing the pulmonary shunts to close. The flap of the foramen ovale is pushed to the shut position, and its edges fuse to the septal wall. Ultimately, only a slight depression, the **fossa ovalis**, marks its position. The ductus arteriosus constricts and is converted to the cordlike **ligamentum arteriosum**, connecting the aorta and pulmonary trunk.

Except for the foramen ovale, all of the special circulatory adaptations of the fetus are functionally occluded within 30 minutes after birth. Closure of the foramen ovale is usually complete within the year. As we described in Chapter 18, failure of the ductus arteriosus or foramen ovale to close leads to congenital heart defects.

CHECK YOUR UNDERSTANDING

21. What two modifications of the fetal circulation allow most blood to bypass parts of the heart?
22. What happens to the special fetal circulatory modifications after birth?

For answers, see Appendix G.

Lactation

▶ Explain how the breasts are prepared for lactation.

Lactation is production of milk by the hormone-prepared mammary glands. Rising levels of (placental) estrogens, progesterone, and human placental lactogen toward the end of pregnancy stimulate the hypothalamus to release prolactin-releasing factors (PRFs). The anterior pituitary gland responds by secreting **prolactin**. (This mechanism is described below.) After a delay of two to three days following birth, true milk production begins.

During the initial delay (and during late gestation), the mammary glands secrete a yellowish fluid called **colostrum** (ko-los′trum). It has less lactose than milk and almost no fat, but it contains more protein, vitamin A, and minerals than true milk. Like milk, colostrum is rich in IgA antibodies. Since these antibodies are resistant to digestion in the stomach, they may help to protect the infant's digestive tract against bacterial infection. Additionally, these IgA antibodies are absorbed by endocytosis and subsequently enter the bloodstream to provide even broader immunity.

After birth, prolactin release gradually wanes, and continual milk production depends on mechanical stimulation of the nipples, normally provided by the suckling infant. Mechanoreceptors in the nipple send afferent nerve impulses to the hypothalamus, stimulating secretion of PRF. This results in a burstlike release of prolactin, which stimulates milk production for the next feeding.

The same afferent impulses also prompt hypothalamic release of oxytocin from the posterior pituitary via a *positive feedback mechanism*. Oxytocin causes the **let-down reflex**, the actual ejection of milk from the alveoli of the mammary glands

28

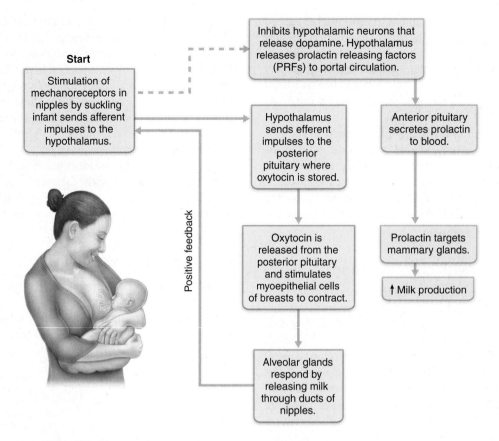

Figure 28.19 Milk production and the positive feedback mechanism of the milk let-down reflex.

(Figure 28.19). Let-down occurs when oxytocin binds to myoepithelial cells surrounding the glands, after which milk is ejected from *both* breasts, not just the suckled one. During nursing oxytocin also stimulates the recently emptied uterus to contract, helping it to return to (nearly) its prepregnant size.

Breast milk has advantages for the infant:

1. *Its fats and iron are better absorbed and its amino acids are metabolized more efficiently* than those of cow's milk.

2. *It has a host of beneficial chemicals,* including IgA, complement, lysozyme, interferon, and lactoperoxidase, that protect infants from life-threatening infections. Mother's milk also contains interleukins and prostaglandins that prevent overzealous inflammatory responses, and a glycoprotein that deters the ulcer-causing bacterium (*H. pylori*) from attaching to the stomach mucosa.

3. *Its natural laxative effect helps to cleanse the bowels of* **meconium** (mĕ-ko′ne-um), a tarry green-black paste containing sloughed-off epithelial cells, bile, and other substances. Since meconium, and later feces, provides the route for eliminating bilirubin from the body, clearing meconium as quickly as possible helps to prevent *physiological jaundice* (see the Related Clinical Terms section). It also encourages bacteria (the source of vitamin K and some B vitamins) to colonize the large intestine.

When nursing is discontinued, the stimulus for prolactin release and milk production ends, and the mammary glands stop producing milk. Women who nurse their infants for six months or more lose a significant amount of calcium from their bones, but those on sound diets usually replace lost bone calcium after weaning the infant.

While prolactin levels are high, the normal hypothalamic-pituitary controls of the ovarian cycle are damped, probably because stimulation of the hypothalamus by suckling causes it to release beta endorphin, a peptide hormone that inhibits hypothalamic release of GnRH and, for this reason, the release of gonadotropins by the pituitary. Because of this inhibition of ovarian function, nursing has been called natural birth control. Nonetheless, there is a good deal of "slippage" in these controls, and most women begin to ovulate even while continuing to nurse their infants.

CHECK YOUR UNDERSTANDING

23. What hormone causes the let-down reflex?

For answers, see Appendix G.

Assisted Reproductive Technology and Reproductive Cloning

▶ Describe some techniques of ART including IVF, ZIFT, and GIFT.

So far we have been describing how babies are made. But if a couple lacks that capability for some reason, what recourse do

28

A CLOSER LOOK
Contraception: To Be or Not To Be

In a society such as ours, where many women opt for professional careers or work for economic reasons, **contraception** (*contra* = against, *cept* = taking), commonly called birth control, is often seen as a necessity. An effective antisperm vaccine exists, but so far the only approved male contraceptive methods are vasectomy and condom use. Consequently, the burden for birth control still falls on women's shoulders, and most birth control products are female directed.

The key to birth control is dependability. As the red arrows in the accompanying flowchart show, the birth control techniques currently available have many sites of action for blocking reproduction. Let's examine a few of them more closely.

Coitus interruptus, or withdrawal of the penis just before ejaculation, is unreliable because control of ejaculation is never ensured. Additionally, sperm may be present in the preejaculatory fluid secreted by the bulbourethral glands.

Rhythm or *temporary abstinence methods* involve avoiding intercourse during periods of ovulation or fertility. This may be accomplished by (1) recording daily basal body temperatures (body temperature drops slightly immediately prior to ovulation and then rises slightly after ovulation) or (2) more simply by buying the over-the-counter *Ovulite Microscope*, which is the size of a lipstick. On awakening, a drop of saliva is placed on the microscope slide and examined for a particular pattern of crystals that indicate the optimal days for fertilization. These techniques require accurate record keeping for several cycles before they can be used with confidence, but have a high success rate for those willing to take the time necessary.

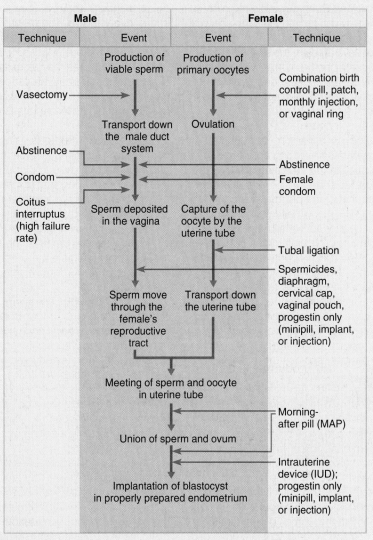

Mechanisms of contraception. Techniques or products that interfere with events from production of gametes to implantation are indicated by red arrows at the site of interference and act to prevent the next step from occurring.

With a failure rate of 10–20%, it is obvious that some people are willing and some are not.

Barrier methods, such as diaphragms, cervical caps, male and female condoms, spermicidal foams, gels, and sponges, are

they have? Hormone therapy may increase sperm or egg production in cases where that is the problem, and surgery can open blocked uterine tubes. Beyond that are *assisted reproductive technology* (*ART*) procedures that entail surgically removing oocytes from a woman's ovaries following hormone stimulation, fertilizing the oocytes, and then returning them to the woman's body. These procedures, now performed worldwide in major medical centers, have produced thousands of infants, but they are expensive, emotionally draining, and painful for

the oocyte donor. Unused oocytes, sperm, and embryos can be frozen for later attempts at accomplishing pregnancy.

In the most common ART process, *in vitro fertilization* (*IVF*), harvested oocytes are incubated with sperm in culture dishes (*in vitro*) for several days to allow fertilization to occur. In cases where the quality or number of sperm is low, the oocytes are injected with sperm. Embryos reaching the two-cell or blastocyst stage are then carefully transferred into the woman's uterus in the hope that implantation will occur.

quite effective, especially when used in combination—for example, condoms and spermicides. But many avoid them because they can reduce the spontaneity of sexual encounters.

For several years, the second most used contraceptive method was the *intrauterine device* (*IUD*), and it is still one of the most commonly used methods in the world, largely because of its economy. Developed in 1909, this plastic or metal device is inserted into the uterus and prevents the young embryo from implanting in the endometrial lining. Although IUDs' failure rate was nearly as low as that of the pill, they were taken off the U.S. market because of occasional contraceptive failure, uterine perforation, or pelvic inflammatory disease (PID). New IUD products that provide sustained local delivery of synthetic progesterone to the endometrium are particularly recommended for women who have given birth and are in monogamous relationships (i.e., who have a lower risk of developing PID).

The most-used contraceptive product in the United States is the *birth control pill*, or simply "the pill," first marketed in 1960. Supplied in 28-tablet packets, the first 20 or 21 tablets contain minute amounts of estrogens and progestins (progesterone-like hormones) taken daily; the last seven tablets are hormone free. The pill tricks the hypothalamic-pituitary axis and "lulls it to sleep," because the relatively constant blood levels of ovarian hormones make it appear that the woman is pregnant (both estrogen and progesterone are produced throughout pregnancy). Ovarian follicles do not develop, ovulation ceases, and menstrual flow is much reduced. However, since hormonal balance is one of

the most precisely controlled body functions, some women cannot tolerate these changes—they become nauseated and/or hypertensive. The pill has adverse cardiovascular effects in a small number of users and there is still debate about whether it increases the risk of uterine, ovarian, or (particularly) breast cancer. Presently, well over 50 million women use the pill, and its failure rate is less than 1%.

Other delivery methods using the combination hormone approach include two slow-release products approved in 2001—a flexible ring that is inserted into the vagina, and a transdermal (skin) patch. Failure rates and side effects of the vaginal ring and skin patch are comparable to those of the pill, although in clinical trials the patch was less effective in women weighing more than 198 pounds.

Combination birth control pills with substantially higher hormone concentrations used for *postcoital contraception* have a 75% effectiveness. Taken within three days of unprotected intercourse, these *morning-after pills* (*MAPs*), or *emergency contraceptive pills* (*ECPs*) as they are also called, "mess up" normal hormonal signals enough to prevent a fertilized egg from implanting or prevent fertilization altogether.

Other hormonal approaches to contraception use progestin-only products which thicken the cervical mucus enough to block sperm entry into the uterus, decrease the frequency of ovulation, and make the endometrium inhospitable to implantion. These include a tablet form (the *minipill*), match-size silicone rods implanted just under the skin that release progestin over a five-year period (Nor-

plant), and an injectable form that lasts for three months (Depo Provera). The failure rates of progestin treatments are even less than that of the "pill."

Abortion is the termination of a pregnancy that is in progress. Spontaneous abortion, also called miscarriage, is common and frequently occurs before a woman is aware that she has conceived. Additionally, over a million American women choose to undergo abortions performed by physicians. *Mifepristone* (RU-486), the so-called abortion pill developed in France, enables a woman to end a pregnancy during its first 7 weeks and has a 96–98% success rate with few side effects. RU-486 is an antihormone that, when taken along with a tiny amount of prostaglandin to stimulate uterine contractions, induces miscarriage by blocking progesterone's quieting effect on the uterus.

Sterilization techniques permanently prevent gamete release. *Tubal ligation* or vasectomy (cutting or cauterizing the uterine tubes or ductus deferentia, respectively) are nearly foolproof and are the choice of approximately 33% of couples of childbearing age in the United States. Both procedures can be done in the physician's office. However, these techniques are usually permanent, making them unpopular with individuals who still plan to have children but want to select the time.

This summary doesn't even begin to touch on the experimental birth control drugs now awaiting clinical trials, and other methods are sure to be developed in the near future. In the final analysis, however, the only 100% effective means of birth control is the age-old one—total abstinence.

In *zygote intrafallopian transfer* (*ZIFT*), oocytes fertilized in vitro are immediately transferred to the woman's uterine (fallopian) tubes. The goal is to have development to the blastocyst stage occur followed by normal implantation in the uterus.

In *gamete intrafallopian transfer* (*GIFT*), no in vitro procedures are used. Instead, sperm and harvested oocytes are transferred together into the woman's uterine tubes in the hope that fertilization will take place there.

Although there is a great deal of hubbub in the scientific community about using cloning as another possible avenue to produce offspring, humans have proved notoriously difficult to create and sustain past very early (blastocyst) development. Cloning entails insertion of a somatic cell nucleus into an oocyte from which the nucleus is removed and then an incubation period to dedifferentiate the inserted nucleus. This technique has proved more successful in creating stem cells for therapeutic use in treating selected diseases than for reproductive cloning to produce whole and healthy human offspring. Furthermore, human reproductive cloning is currently fraught with legal, moral, ethical, and political roadblocks.

■ ■ ■

In this chapter, we have focused on changes that occur during human development in utero. But having a baby is not always what the interacting partners have in mind, and we humans have devised a variety of techniques for preventing this outcome (see *A Closer Look* on p. 1095).

We must admit that the description of embryonic development here has fallen short because we have barely touched upon the phenomenon of differentiation. How does an unspecialized cell that can become *anything* in the body develop into a specific *something* (a heart cell, for example)? And what paces the developmental sequence, so that if a particular process fails to occur at a precise time, it never occurs at all? Scientists are beginning to believe that there are master switches in the genes. In Chapter 29, the final chapter of this book, we describe a small part of the "how" as we examine the interaction of genes and other components that determine who we finally become.

RELATED CLINICAL TERMS

Abortion (*abort* = born prematurely) Premature removal of the embryo or fetus from the uterus; may be spontaneous or induced.

Ectopic pregnancy (ek-top′ik; *ecto* = outside) A pregnancy in which the embryo implants in any site other than the uterus; most often the site is a uterine tube (tubal pregnancy). Since the uterine tube (as well as most other ectopic sites) is unable to establish a placenta or accommodate growth, the uterine tube ruptures unless the condition is diagnosed early, or the pregnancy spontaneously aborts.

Hydatid (hydatidiform) mole (hi′dah-tid; *hydat* = watery) Developmental abnormality of the placenta; the conceptus degenerates and the chorionic villi convert into a mass of vesicles that resemble tapioca. Signs include vaginal bleeding, which contains some of the grapelike vesicles.

Physiological jaundice (jawn′dis) Jaundice sometimes occurring in normal newborns within three to four days after birth. Fetal

erythrocytes are short-lived, and they break down rapidly after birth; the infant's liver may be unable to process the bilirubin (breakdown product of hemoglobin pigment) fast enough to prevent its accumulation in blood and subsequent deposit in body tissues.

Placenta abruptio (ah-brup′she-o; *abrupt* = broken away from) Premature separation of the placenta from the uterine wall; if this occurs before labor, it can result in fetal death due to anoxia.

Placenta previa (pre′ve-ah) Placental formation adjacent to or across the internal os of the uterus. Represents a problem because as the uterus and cervix stretch, tearing of the placenta may occur. Additionally, the placenta precedes the infant during labor.

Ultrasonography (ul″trah-son-og′rah-fe) Noninvasive technique that uses sound waves to visualize the position and size of the fetus and placenta (see *A Closer Look*, Chapter 1).

CHAPTER SUMMARY

1. The gestation period of approximately 280 days extends from the woman's last menstrual period to birth. The conceptus undergoes embryonic development for 8 weeks after fertilization, and fetal development from week 9 to birth.

From Egg to Zygote   (pp. 1072–1075)
Accomplishing Fertilization   (pp. 1072–1075)

1. An oocyte is fertilizable for up to 24 hours; most sperm are viable within the female reproductive tract for one to two days.
2. Sperm must survive the hostile environment of the vagina and become capacitated (capable of reaching and fertilizing the oocyte).
3. Hundreds of sperm must release their acrosomal enzymes to break down the egg's corona radiata and zona pellucida.
4. When one sperm binds to receptors on the egg, it triggers the slow block to polyspermy (release of cortical granules).
5. Following sperm penetration, the secondary oocyte completes meiosis II. Then the ovum and sperm pronuclei fuse (fertilization), forming a zygote.

Events of Embryonic Development: Zygote to Blastocyst Implantation   (pp. 1075–1078)
Cleavage and Blastocyst Formation   (pp. 1075–1076)

1. Cleavage, a rapid series of mitotic divisions without intervening growth, begins with the zygote and ends with a blastocyst. The blastocyst consists of the trophoblast and an inner cell mass. Cleavage produces a large number of cells with a favorable surface-to-volume ratio.

Implantation   (pp. 1076–1078)

2. The trophoblast adheres to, digests, and implants in the endometrium. Implantation is completed when the blastocyst is entirely surrounded by endometrial tissue, about 12 days after ovulation.
3. hCG released by the blastocyst maintains hormone production by the corpus luteum, preventing menses. hCG levels decline after four months.

Placentation   (p. 1078)

4. The placenta acts as the respiratory, nutritive, and excretory organ of the fetus and produces the hormones of pregnancy. It is formed

from embryonic (chorionic villi) and maternal (endometrial decidua) tissues. The chorion develops when the trophoblast becomes associated with extraembryonic mesoderm. Typically, the placenta is functional as an endocrine organ by the third month.

Events of Embryonic Development: Gastrula to Fetus   (pp. 1079–1087)

Formation and Roles of the Extraembryonic Membranes   (p. 1080)

1. The fluid-filled amnion forms from cells of the superior surface (epiblast) of the embryonic disc. It protects the embryo from physical trauma and adhesion formation, provides a constant temperature, and allows fetal movements.
2. The yolk sac forms from the hypoblast of the embryonic disc; it is the source of early blood cells.
3. The allantois, a caudal outpocketing adjacent to the yolk sac, forms the structural basis of the umbilical cord.
4. The chorion is the outermost membrane and takes part in placentation.

Gastrulation: Germ Layer Formation   (pp. 1081–1083)

5. Gastrulation involves cellular migrations that ultimately transform the inner cell mass into a three-layered embryo (gastrula) containing ectoderm, mesoderm, and endoderm. Cells that move through the midline primitive streak become endoderm if they form the most inferior layer of the embryonic disc and mesoderm if they ultimately occupy the middle layer. Cells remaining on the superior surface become ectoderm.

Organogenesis: Differentiation of the Germ Layers (pp. 1083–1087)

6. Ectoderm forms the nervous system and the epidermis of the skin and its derivatives. The first event of organogenesis is neurulation, which produces the brain and spinal cord. By the eighth week, all major brain regions are formed.
7. Endoderm forms the mucosa of the digestive and respiratory systems, and the epithelial cells of all associated glands (thyroid, parathyroids, thymus, liver, pancreas). It becomes a continuous tube when the embryonic body undercuts and fuses ventrally.
8. Mesoderm forms all other organ systems and tissues. It segregates early into (1) a dorsal superior notochord, (2) paired somites that form the vertebrae, skeletal trunk muscles, and part of the dermis, and (3) paired masses of intermediate and lateral plate mesoderm. The intermediate mesoderm forms the kidneys and gonads. The somatic layer of the lateral plate mesoderm forms the dermis of skin, parietal serosa, and bones and muscles of the limbs; the splanchnic layer forms the cardiovascular system and the visceral serosae.
9. The fetal cardiovascular system is formed in the embryonic period. The umbilical vein delivers nutrient- and oxygen-rich blood to the embryo; the paired umbilical arteries return oxygen-poor, waste-laden blood to the placenta. The ductus venosus allows most of the blood to bypass the liver; the foramen ovale and ductus arteriosus are pulmonary shunts.

Events of Fetal Development   (pp. 1087–1089)

1. All organ systems are laid down during the embryonic period; growth and tissue/organ specialization are the major events of the fetal period.
2. During the fetal period, fetal length increases from about 22 mm to 360 mm, and weight increases from less than an ounce to 7 pounds or more.

Effects of Pregnancy on the Mother   (pp. 1089–1090)

Anatomical Changes   (pp. 1089–1090)

1. Maternal reproductive organs and breasts become increasingly vascularized during pregnancy, and the breasts enlarge.
2. The uterus eventually occupies nearly the entire abdominopelvic cavity. Abdominal organs are pushed superiorly and encroach on the thoracic cavity, causing the ribs to flare.
3. The increased abdominal mass changes the woman's center of gravity; lordosis and backache are common. A waddling gait occurs as pelvic ligaments and joints are loosened by placental relaxin.
4. A typical weight gain during pregnancy in a woman of normal weight is 28 pounds.

Metabolic Changes   (p. 1090)

5. Human placental lactogen has anabolic effects and promotes glucose sparing in the mother. Human chorionic thyrotropin results in maternal hypermetabolism.

Physiological Changes   (p. 1090)

6. Many women suffer morning sickness, heartburn, and constipation during pregnancy.
7. The kidneys produce more urine, and pressure on the bladder may cause frequency, urgency, and stress incontinence.
8. Tidal volume increases, but residual volume decreases. The respiratory rate remains relatively unchanged. Dyspnea is common.
9. Total body water and blood volume increase dramatically. Heart rate and blood pressure rise, resulting in enhancement of cardiac output in the mother.

Parturition (Birth)   (pp. 1090–1092)

1. Parturition encompasses a series of events called labor.

Initiation of Labor   (p. 1091)

2. When estrogen levels are sufficiently high, they induce oxytocin receptors on the myometrial cells and inhibit progesterone's quieting effect on uterine muscle. Weak, irregular contractions begin.
3. Fetal cells produce oxytocin, which stimulates prostaglandin production by the placenta. Both hormones stimulate contraction of uterine muscle. Increasing distension of the uterus activates the hypothalamus, causing oxytocin release from the mother's posterior pituitary; this sets up a positive feedback loop resulting in true labor.

Stages of Labor   (pp. 1091–1092)

4. The dilation stage is from the onset of rhythmic, strong contractions until the cervix is fully dilated. The head of the fetus rotates as it descends through the pelvic outlet.
5. The expulsion stage extends from full cervical dilation until birth of the infant.
6. The placental stage is the delivery of the afterbirth (the placenta and attached fetal membranes).

Adjustments of the Infant to Extrauterine Life (pp. 1092–1093)

1. The infant's Apgar score is recorded immediately after birth.

Taking the First Breath and Transition   (p. 1093)

2. After the umbilical cord is clamped, carbon dioxide accumulates in the infant's blood, causing respiratory centers in the brain to trigger the first inspiration.
3. Once the lungs are inflated, breathing is eased by the presence of surfactant, which decreases the surface tension of the alveolar fluid.

4. During transition, the first 8 hours after birth, the infant is physiologically unstable and adjusting. After stabilizing, the infant wakes approximately every 3–4 hours in response to hunger.

Occlusion of Special Fetal Blood Vessels and Vascular Shunts (p. 1093)

5. Inflation of the lungs causes pressure changes in the circulation; as a result, the umbilical arteries and vein, ductus venosus, and ductus arteriosus collapse, and the foramen ovale closes. The occluded blood vessels are converted to fibrous cords; the site of the foramen ovale becomes the fossa ovalis.

Lactation (pp. 1093–1094)

1. The breasts are prepared for lactation during pregnancy by high blood levels of estrogen, progesterone, and human placental lactogen.
2. Colostrum, a premilk fluid, is a fat-poor fluid that contains more protein, vitamin A, and minerals than true milk. It is produced toward the end of pregnancy and for the first two to three days after birth.

3. True milk is produced around day 3 in response to suckling, which stimulates the hypothalamus to prompt anterior pituitary release of prolactin and posterior pituitary release of oxytocin. Prolactin stimulates milk production. Oxytocin triggers milk letdown. Continued breast-feeding is required for continued milk production.
4. At first, ovulation and menses are absent or irregular during nursing, but in most women the ovarian cycle is eventually re-established while still nursing.

Assisted Reproductive Technology and Reproductive Cloning (pp. 1094–1097)

1. Assisted reproductive technology (ART) procedures assist infertile couples to bear children. Among the most-used techniques are IVF, ZIFT, and GIFT. IVF and ZIFT attempt to fertilize harvested oocytes in vitro and then return the embryo or zygote to the woman's body. GIFT utilizes in vivo methods—sperm and oocytes are transferred together to the woman's uterine tubes.
2. Reproductive cloning in humans has proved difficult to achieve and the practice has met several roadblocks.

REVIEW QUESTIONS

Multiple Choice/Matching

(Some questions have more than one correct answer. Select the best answer or answers from the choices given.)

1. Indicate whether each of the following statements is describing (a) cleavage or (b) gastrulation.
   _____ (1) period during which a morula forms
   _____ (2) period when vast amounts of cell migration occur
   _____ (3) period when the three embryonic germ layers appear
   _____ (4) period during which the blastocyst is formed
2. Most systems are operational in the fetus by four to six months. Which system is the exception to this generalization, affecting premature infants? (a) the circulatory system, (b) the respiratory system, (c) the urinary system, (d) the digestive system.
3. The zygote contains chromosomes from (a) the mother only, (b) the father only, (c) both the mother and father, but half from each, (d) each parent and synthesizes others.
4. The outer layer of the blastocyst, which later attaches to the uterus, is the (a) decidua, (b) trophoblast, (c) amnion, (d) inner cell mass.
5. The fetal membrane that forms the basis of the umbilical cord is the (a) allantois, (b) amnion, (c) chorion, (d) yolk sac.
6. In the fetus, the ductus arteriosus carries blood from (a) the pulmonary artery to the pulmonary vein, (b) the liver to the inferior vena cava, (c) the right ventricle to the left ventricle, (d) the pulmonary trunk to the aorta.
7. Which of the following changes occur in the baby's cardiovascular system after birth? (a) Blood clots in the umbilical vein, (b) the pulmonary vessels dilate as the lungs expand, (c) the ductus venosus becomes obliterated, as does the ductus arteriosus, (d) all of these.
8. Following delivery of the infant, the delivery of the afterbirth includes the (a) placenta only, (b) placenta and decidua, (c) placenta and attached (torn) fetal membranes, (d) chorionic villi.
9. The umbilical vein carries (a) waste products to the placenta, (b) oxygen and food to the fetus, (c) oxygen and food to the placenta, (d) oxygen and waste products to the fetus.

10. The germ layer from which the skeletal muscles, heart, and skeleton are derived is the (a) ectoderm, (b) endoderm, (c) mesoderm.
11. Which of the following cannot pass through placental barriers? (a) blood cells, (b) glucose, (c) amino acids, (d) gases, (e) antibodies.
12. The most important hormone in initiating and maintaining lactation after birth is (a) estrogen, (b) FSH, (c) prolactin, (d) oxytocin.
13. The initial stage of labor, during which the neck of the uterus is stretched, is the (a) dilation stage, (b) expulsion stage, (c) placental stage.
14. Match each adult structure in column B with the embryonic structure it derives from in column A.

Column A	Column B
____ (1) notochord	(a) kidney
____ (2) ectoderm (not neural tube)	(b) peritoneal cavity
____ (3) intermediate mesoderm	(c) pancreas, liver
____ (4) splanchnic mesoderm	(d) parietal serosa, dermis
____ (5) sclerotome	(e) nucleus pulposus
____ (6) coelom	(f) visceral serosa
____ (7) neural tube	(g) hair and epidermis
____ (8) somatic mesoderm	(h) brain
____ (9) endoderm	(i) ribs

Short Answer Essay Questions

15. Why does testing for hCG work as a pregnancy test during early pregnancy but not late pregnancy?
16. Fertilization involves much more than a mere restoration of the diploid chromosome number. (a) What does the process of fertilization entail on the part of both the egg and sperm? (b) What are the effects of fertilization?
17. Cleavage is an embryonic event that mainly involves mitotic divisions. How does cleavage differ from mitosis occurring during life after birth, and what are its important functions?
18. The life span of the ovarian corpus luteum is extended for nearly three months after implantation, but otherwise it deteriorates. (a) Explain why this is so. (b) Explain why it is important that the corpus luteum remain functional following implantation.

19. The placenta is a marvelous, but temporary, organ. Starting with a description of its formation, show how it is an intimate part of both fetal and maternal anatomy and physiology during the gestation period.

20. Why is it that only one sperm out of the hundreds (or thousands) available enters the oocyte?

21. What is the function of gastrulation?

22. Cite two problems with a breech presentation.

23. What factors are believed to bring about uterine contractions at the termination of pregnancy?

24. Explain how the flat embryonic disc takes on the cylindrical shape of a tadpole.

Critical Thinking and Clinical Application Questions

1. Jennie, a freshman in your dormitory, tells you she just discovered that she is three months pregnant. She recently bragged that since she came to college she has been drinking alcohol heavily and experimenting with every kind of recreational drug she could find. From the following, select the advice you would give her, and explain why it is the best choice. (a) She must stop taking drugs, but they could not have affected her fetus during these first few months of her pregnancy. (b) Harmful substances usually cannot pass from mother to embryo, so she can keep using drugs. (c) There could be defects in the fetus, so she should stop using drugs and visit a doctor as soon as possible. (d) If she has not taken any drugs in the last week, she is okay.

2. During Mrs. Jones's labor, the obstetrician decided that it was necessary to perform an episiotomy. What is an episiotomy, and why is it done?

3. A woman in substantial pain called her doctor and explained (between sobs) that she was about to have her baby "right here." The doctor calmed her and asked how she had come to that conclusion. She said that her water had broken and that her husband could see the baby's head. (a) Was she right? If so, what stage of labor was she in? (b) Do you think that she had time to make it to the hospital 60 miles away? Why or why not?

4. Mary is a heavy smoker and has ignored a friend's advice to stop smoking during her pregnancy. On the basis of what you know about the effect of smoking on physiology, describe how Mary's smoking might affect her fetus.

5. While Mortimer was cramming for his anatomy test, he read that some parts of the mesoderm become segmented. He suddenly realized that he could not remember what segmentation is. Define segmentation, and give two examples of segmented structures in the embryo.

6. Assume a sperm has penetrated a polar body and their nuclei fuse. Why would it be unlikely for the resulting cell to develop into a healthy embryo?

29

Heredity

The wondrous growth and development of a new individual is guided by the gene-bearing chromosomes it receives from its parents in egg and sperm. As we described in Chapter 3, individual *genes*, or DNA segments, contain the "recipes" or genetic blueprints for proteins. Many of these proteins are enzymes that dictate the synthesis of virtually all the body's molecules. Consequently, genes are ultimately expressed in your hair color, sex, blood type, and so on.

Genes, however, do not act as free agents. As you will see, a gene's ability to prompt the development of a specific trait is enhanced or inhibited by interactions with other genes, as well as by environmental factors.

The science of genetics, which studies the mechanism of heredity (*genes* = give birth to), is relatively young, but our understanding of how human genes act and interact has advanced considerably since

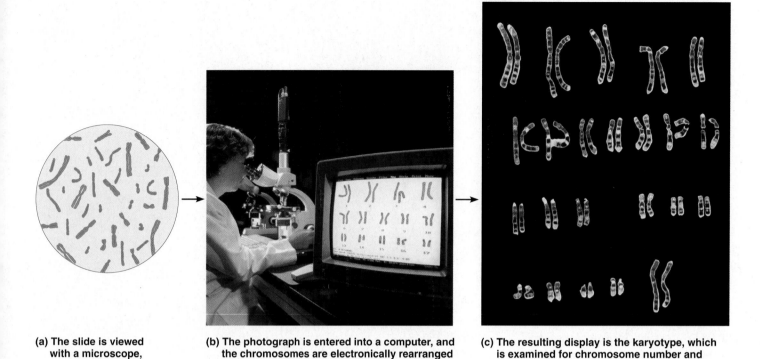

(a) The slide is viewed with a microscope, and the chromosomes are photographed.

(b) The photograph is entered into a computer, and the chromosomes are electronically rearranged into homologous pairs according to size and structure.

(c) The resulting display is the karyotype, which is examined for chromosome number and structure.

Figure 29.1 Preparing a karyotype. After lymphocytes are stimulated to divide and grow in culture for several days, they are treated with a drug that arrests mitosis in metaphase, a stage when the chromosomes are easily identified. The cells are harvested, treated with a solution that makes their chromosomes spread out, transferred to a microscope for photography, and then subjected to computer analysis and arrangement of the chromosomes into homologous pairs. The patterns of stained bands in the karyotype help to identify specific chromosomes and parts of chromosomes.

Gregor Mendel first proposed the basic principles of heredity in the mid-1800s. Mendel studied characteristics that vary in an either-or fashion, which is easier to understand than the more-or-less fashion in which many human traits vary.

However, the urge to understand human inheritance is powerful. Recent advances provided by the *Human Genome Project*, which scanned and determined the human DNA sequence, are enabling geneticists to manipulate and engineer human genes to examine their expression. This research has tremendous promise for more sophisticated genetic screening, and for drug development to treat or cure disease. Although we touch upon some of these newer topics, we will concentrate on the principles of heredity discovered by Mendel more than a century ago.

The Vocabulary of Genetics

▶ Define allele.

▶ Differentiate between genotype and phenotype.

The nuclei of all human cells except gametes contain the diploid number of chromosomes (46), consisting of 23 pairs of homologous chromosomes. Recall that *homologous chromosomes* are pairs of chromosomes—one from the father (sperm) and one

from the mother (egg)—that look similar and carry genes for the same traits, but do not necessarily bring about the same expressions of those traits. Two of the 46 chromosomes are **sex chromosomes** (X and Y), which determine genetic sex (male = XY; female = XX). The other 44 are the 22 pairs of **autosomes** that guide the expression of most other traits.

The complete human **karyotype** (kar′e-o-tīp), or diploid chromosomal complement displayed in homologous pairs, is illustrated in **Figure 29.1c**. The diploid **genome** (je′nōm), or genetic (DNA) makeup, represents two sets of genetic instructions—one from the egg and the other from the sperm.

Gene Pairs (Alleles)

Because chromosomes are paired, it follows that the genes in them are paired as well. Consequently, each of us receives *two* genes, one from each parent (for the most part), that interact to dictate each trait. Matched genes, which are at the same *locus* (location) on homologous chromosomes, are called **alleles** (ah-lēlz′) of each other. Alleles may code for the same or for alternative forms of a given trait. For example, of the alleles that dictate whether or not you have loose thumb ligaments, one allele might code for tight ligaments and the other for loose ligaments (the double-jointed thumb condition). When the two

Figure 29.2 Gamete variability resulting from independent assortment. During metaphase of meiosis I, the tetrads of homologous chromosomes align independently of other tetrads. The large circles depict the possible alignments in a mother cell having a diploid number of 6 (paternal homologues purple; maternal, green). The small circles show the gametes arising from each alignment. Some gametes contain all maternal or all paternal chromosomes; others have maternal and paternal chromosomes in various combinations.

alleles controlling a trait are the same, a person is said to be **homozygous** (homo-zi′gus) for that trait. When the two alleles are different, the individual is **heterozygous** (het″er-o-zi′gus) for the trait.

Sometimes, one allele masks or suppresses the expression of its partner. Such an allele is said to be **dominant**, whereas the allele that is masked is said to be **recessive**. By convention, a dominant allele is represented by a capital letter (for example, *J*), and a recessive allele by the lowercase form of the same letter (*j*). Dominant alleles are expressed, or make themselves "known," when they are present in either single or double dose. For recessive alleles to be expressed, they must be present in double dose, that is, the homozygous condition. Returning to our thumb example, a person whose genetic makeup includes either the gene pair *JJ* (the homozygous dominant condition) or the gene pair *Jj* (the heterozygous condition) will have double-jointed thumbs. The combination *jj* (the homozygous recessive condition) is needed to produce tight thumb ligaments.

Genotype and Phenotype

A person's genetic makeup is referred to as his or her **genotype** (jen′o-tīp). The way that genotype is expressed in the body is called one's **phenotype** (fe′no-tīp). For example, the double-jointed condition is the phenotype produced by a genotype of *JJ* or *Jj*.

CHECK YOUR UNDERSTANDING

1. When a geneticist orders a karyotype, why are cells in metaphase studied instead of those in interphase?
2. What term is given to chromosomes *other than* our sex chromosomes?
3. Is an allele represented by a capital letter presumed to be dominant or recessive?
4. Harold is homozygous for the dominant alleles *HH*, *CC*, and *LL*, and heterozygous for *Bb* and *Kk*. He is blond and blue-eyed and has a very hairy chest. Which of these descriptions refer to his phenotype?

For answers, see Appendix G.

Sexual Sources of Genetic Variation

▶ Describe events that lead to genetic variability of gametes.

Before we examine how genes interact, let us consider why (with the possible exception of identical siblings) each of us is one of a kind, with a unique genotype and phenotype. This variability reflects three events that occur before we are even a twinkle in our parents' eyes: independent assortment of chromosomes, crossover of homologues, and random fertilization of eggs by sperm.

Chromosome Segregation and Independent Assortment

As we described in Chapter 27, each pair of homologous chromosomes synapses during meiosis I, forming a tetrad. This happens during both spermatogenesis and oogenesis. Because chance determines how the tetrads align (line up) on the meiosis I metaphase spindle, maternal and paternal chromosomes are randomly distributed to daughter nuclei.

As illustrated in **Figure 29.2**, this simple event leads to an amazing amount of variation in gametes. The cell in our example has a diploid number of 6, and so three tetrads form. As you can see, the possible combinations of alignments of the three

29

Hair color genes — Eye color genes

Homologous chromosomes synapse during prophase of meiosis I. Each chromosome consists of two sister chromatids.

Chiasma

One chromatid segment exchanges positions with a homologous chromatid segment—in other words, crossing over occurs, forming a chiasma.

The chromatids forming the chiasma break, and the broken-off ends join their corresponding homologues.

Gamete 1
Gamete 2
Gamete 3
Gamete 4

At the conclusion of meiosis, each haploid gamete has one of the four chromosomes shown. Two of the chromosomes are recombinant (they carry new combinations of genes).

H Allele for brown hair   **E** Allele for brown eyes
h Allele for blond hair   **e** Allele for blue eyes

☐ Paternal chromosome ⎤
                       ⎬ Homologous pair
☐ Maternal chromosome ⎦

Figure 29.3 Crossover and genetic recombination. These meiosis I events increase genetic variability in the gametes formed. For simplicity, only two chromatids are shown taking part in crossover. Multiple crossovers result in more complex patterns.

tetrads result in eight gamete possibilities. Because the way each tetrad aligns is random, and because many cells are undergoing meiosis simultaneously, each alignment and each type of gamete occurs with the same frequency as all others.

Two important points about metaphase of meiosis I: (1) The two alleles determining each trait are **segregated**, which means that they are distributed to different gametes. (2) Alleles on different pairs of homologous chromosomes are distributed independently of each other. The net result is that each gamete has a single allele for each trait, and that allele represents only one of the four possible parental alleles.

The number of different gamete types resulting from this **independent assortment** of homologues during meiosis I can be calculated for any genome from the formula 2^n, where n is the number of homologous pairs. In our example, $2^n = 2^3$ ($2 \times 2 \times 2$), for a total of 8 different gamete types.

Note that the number of gamete types increases dramatically as the chromosome number increases. A cell with six pairs of homologues would produce 2^6, or 64, kinds of gametes. In a man's testes, the number of gamete types that can be produced on the basis of independent assortment alone is 2^{23}, or about 8.5 million—an incredible variety. The number of different gamete types produced simultaneously in a woman's ovaries is significantly less because her ovaries complete at most 500 reduction divisions in her lifetime. Still, each ovulated oocyte will most likely be novel genetically because of independent assortment.

Crossover of Homologues and Gene Recombination

Additional gamete variation results from the crossing over and exchange of chromosomal parts during meiosis I. Genes are arranged linearly along a chromosome's length, and genes on the same chromosome are said to be **linked** because they are transmitted as a unit to daughter cells during mitosis. However, as we described in Chapter 27, chromosomes can break and precisely exchange gene segments with their homologous counterparts during meiosis. This exchange gives rise to **recombinant chromosomes** that have mixed contributions from each parent.

In the hypothetical example shown in **Figure 29.3**, the genes for hair and eye color are linked. The paternal chromosome contains alleles coding for blond hair and blue eyes, and the maternal alleles code for brown hair and brown eyes. In the **crossover**, or **chiasma**, shown, the break occurs between these linked genes, resulting in one gamete with alleles for blond hair and brown eyes and another with alleles for brown hair and blue eyes. As a result of the crossover, two of the four chromatids present in the tetrad end up with a mixed set of alleles—some maternal and some paternal. This means that when the chromatids segregate, each gamete will receive a unique combination of parental genes.

Because humans have 23 tetrads, with crossovers going on in most of them during meiosis I, the variability resulting from this factor alone is tremendous.

Random Fertilization

At any point in time, gametogenesis is turning out gametes with all variations possible from independent assortment and random crossovers. Fertilization compounds this variety because a single human egg will be fertilized by a single sperm on a totally haphazard, or random, basis. If we consider variation resulting only from independent assortment and random fertilization, any offspring represents one out of the close to 72 trillion (8.5 million × 8.5 million) zygotes possible. The additional variation introduced by crossovers increases this number exponentially. Perhaps now you can understand why brothers and sisters are so different, and marvel at how they can also be so alike in many ways.

CHECK YOUR UNDERSTANDING

5. We said that genetic variability is introduced by independent assortment. Just what is assorting independently?
6. How does crossover increase genetic variability?

For answers, see Appendix G.

Types of Inheritance

A few human phenotypes can be traced to a single gene pair (as we will describe shortly), but most such traits are very limited in nature, or reflect variation in a single enzyme. Most human traits are determined by multiple alleles or by the interaction of several gene pairs.

Dominant-Recessive Inheritance

▶ Compare and contrast dominant-recessive inheritance with incomplete dominance and codominance.

Dominant-recessive inheritance reflects the interaction of dominant and recessive alleles. A simple diagram, called the **Punnett square**, is used to figure out, for a single trait, the possible gene combinations that would result from the mating of parents of known genotypes **(Figure 29.4)**. In the example shown, both parents can roll their tongue into a U because both are heterozygous for the dominant allele (*T*) that confers this ability. In other words, each parent has the genotype *Tt*. The alleles of one parent are written along one side of the Punnett square, and the alleles for the other parent are shown along an adjacent side. The alleles are then combined down and across to determine the possible gene combinations (genotypes) and their expected frequency in the offspring of these two parents.

As the completed Punnett square shows, the probability of these parents producing a homozygous dominant child (*TT*) is 25% (1 out of 4); of producing a heterozygous child (*Tt*), 50% (2 out of 4); and of producing a homozygous recessive child, 25% (1 out of 4). The *TT* and *Tt* offspring will be tongue rollers. Only the *tt* offspring will not be able to roll their tongues.

The Punnett square predicts only the *probability* of a particular genotype (and phenotype). The larger the number of offspring, the greater the likelihood that the ratios will conform to

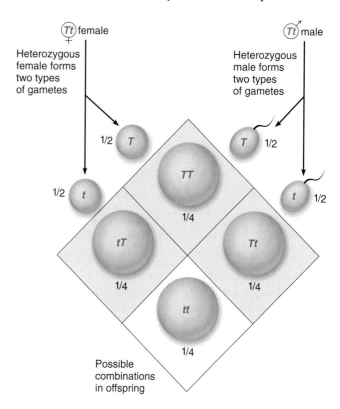

Figure 29.4 Genotype and phenotype probabilities resulting from a mating of two heterozygous parents. The Punnett square shows all possible combinations of a set of alleles in the zygote. In this example, the *T* allele is dominant and determines tongue-rolling ability; the *t* allele is recessive.

the predicted values—just as the chances of getting heads half the time and tails half the time increase with the number of tosses of a coin. If we toss only twice, we may well get heads both times. Likewise, if the couple in our example had only two children, it would not be surprising if both children had the genotype *Tt*.

What are the chances of having two children of the same genotype? To determine the probability of two events happening in succession, we must multiply the probabilities of the separate events happening. The probability of getting heads in one coin toss is 1/2, so the probability of getting two heads in a row is 1/2 × 1/2 = 1/4. Now consider the chances of our couple's having two children who are both non–tongue rollers (*tt*). The probability that one child will be *tt* is 1/4, so the probability that both children will be *tt* is 1/4 × 1/4 = 1/16, only slightly better than 6%.

Remember that the production of each child, like each coin toss in a series, is an *independent event* that does not influence the production of any other child by the same couple. If you get heads on the first toss, the chance of getting heads the second time is still 1/2. Likewise, if our couple's first child is a *tt*, they still have a 1/4 chance of getting a *tt* the next time.

Dominant Traits

Human traits dictated by dominant alleles include widow's peaks, dimples, and freckles.

TABLE 29.1	Traits Determined by Simple Dominant-Recessive Inheritance

PHENOTYPE DUE TO EXPRESSION OF:

DOMINANT GENES (*ZZ* OR *Zz*)	RECESSIVE GENES (*zz*)
Tongue roller	Inability to roll tongue into a U shape
Astigmatism	Normal vision
Freckles	Absence of freckles
Dimples in cheeks	Absence of dimples
PTC* taster	PTC nontaster
Widow's peak	Straight hairline
Double-jointed thumb	Tight thumb ligaments
Syndactyly (webbed digits)	Normal digits
Achondroplasia (heterozygous: dwarfism; homozygous: lethal)	Normal endochondral ossification
Huntington's disease	Absence of Huntington's disease
Normal skin pigmentation	Albinism
Absence of Tay-Sachs disease	Tay-Sachs disease
Absence of cystic fibrosis	Cystic fibrosis

*PTC is phenylthiocarbamide, a harmless bitter chemical.

Disorders caused by dominant genes are uncommon because *lethal dominant genes* are almost always expressed and result in the death of the embryo, fetus, or child. The deadly genes are not usually passed along to successive generations. However, in some dominant disorders the person is less impaired or at least survives long enough to reproduce. One example is *Huntington's disease*, a fatal nervous system disease involving degeneration of the basal nuclei. It involves a *delayed-action gene* that is expressed when the affected individual is about 40. Offspring of a parent with Huntington's disease have a 50% chance of inheriting the lethal gene. (The parent is heterozygous, because the dominant homozygous condition is lethal to the fetus.) Many informed offspring of such parents are opting not to become parents themselves.

These and other dominant gene–determined traits are listed in Table 29.1.

Recessive Traits

Some examples of recessive inheritance are the more desirable genetic condition. For example, normal vision is dictated by recessive alleles, whereas astigmatism is prescribed by dominant alleles. However, many if not most genetic disorders are inherited as simple recessive traits. These include conditions as different as *albinism* (lack of skin pigmentation); *cystic fibrosis*, a condition of excessive mucus production that impairs lung and pancreatic functioning; and *Tay-Sachs disease*, a disorder of brain lipid metabolism, caused by an enzyme deficit that shows itself a few months after birth.

Recessive genetic disorders are more frequent than those caused by dominant alleles because those who carry a *single* recessive allele for a recessive genetic disorder do not themselves express the disease. However, they can pass the gene on to offspring and so are called *carriers* of the disorder. Conversely, as we explained above, few individuals with dominant genetic disorders get a chance to pass on the detrimental gene.

Incomplete Dominance

In dominant-recessive inheritance, one allele variant completely masks the other. Some traits, however, exhibit **incomplete dominance**. In such instances, the heterozygote has a phenotype intermediate between those of homozygous dominant and homozygous recessive individuals. Incomplete dominance is uncommon in humans.

Perhaps the best human example is inheritance of the *sickling gene (s)*, which causes a substitution of one amino acid in the beta chain of hemoglobin. Hemoglobin molecules containing the abnormal beta chains crystallize when blood oxygen levels are low, causing the erythrocytes to assume a sickle shape (see Figure 17.8b, p. 642). Individuals with a double dose of the sickling allele (*ss*) have **sickle-cell anemia**, and any condition that lowers their blood oxygen level, such as respiratory difficulty or excessive exercise, can precipitate a *sickle-cell crisis*. The deformed erythrocytes jam up and fragment in small capillaries, causing intense pain.

Individuals heterozygous for the sickling gene (*Ss*) have **sickle-cell trait**. They make both normal and sickling hemoglobin, and as a rule, these individuals are healthy. However, they can suffer a crisis if there is prolonged reduction in blood oxygen levels, as might happen when traveling in high-altitude areas, and they can transmit the sickling gene to their offspring.

Multiple-Allele Inheritance

Although we inherit only two alleles for each gene, some genes exhibit more than two allele forms, leading to a phenomenon called **multiple-allele inheritance**. For example, three alleles determine the ABO blood types in humans: I^A, I^B and i. Each of us receives two of these. The I^A and I^B alleles are *codominant*, and both are expressed when present, resulting in the AB blood type. The i allele is recessive to the other two. Genotypes determining the four possible ABO blood groups are shown in **Table 29.2**.

TABLE 29.2	ABO Blood Groups			
BLOOD GROUP (PHENOTYPE)		FREQUENCY (% OF U.S. POPULATION)		
	GENOTYPE	WHITE	BLACK	ASIAN
O	*ii*	45	49	40
A	$I^A I^A$ or $I^A i$	40	27	28
B	$I^B I^B$ or $I^B i$	11	20	27
AB	$I^A I^B$	4	4	5

7. Why are there so few genetic disorders caused by dominant genes?

8. How does incomplete dominance differ from codominance?

For answers, see Appendix G.

Sex-Linked Inheritance

▶ Describe the mechanism of sex-linked inheritance.

Inherited traits determined by genes on the sex chromosomes are said to be **sex-linked**. The X and Y sex chromosomes are not homologous in the true sense. The Y, which contains the gene (or genes) that determines maleness, is much smaller than the X chromosome (Figure 29.5). The X bears over 2500 genes, and a disproportionately large number of them code for proteins important to brain function. Because the Y carries only 78 genes as of the last count, it lacks many of the genes present on the X. For example, genes coding for certain clotting factors, cone pigments, and even testosterone receptors are present on X but not on Y. A gene found only on the X chromosome is said to be **X-linked**.

Only relatively short regions at either end of the Y chromosome (corresponding to about 5% of the Y's DNA) code for nonsexual characteristics corresponding to those on the X. Those regions are the only areas that can participate in crossovers with the X.

When a male inherits an X-linked recessive allele—for example, for hemophilia or for red-green color blindness—its expression is never masked or damped, because there is no corresponding allele on his Y chromosome. Consequently, the recessive gene is always expressed, even when present only in single dose. In contrast, females must have two X-linked recessive alleles to express such a disorder, and as a result, very few females exhibit any X-linked conditions.

X-linked traits are typically passed from mother to son, never from father to son, because males receive no X chromosome from their father. Of course, the mother can also pass the recessive allele to her daughter, but unless the daughter receives another such allele from her father, she will not express the trait.

Polygene Inheritance

▶ Explain how polygene inheritance differs from that resulting from the action of a single pair of alleles.

So far, we have considered only traits inherited by mechanisms of classical Mendelian genetics, which are fairly easy to understand, and such traits typically have two, or perhaps three, alternate forms. However, many phenotypes depend on several gene pairs at different locations acting in tandem. Such **polygene inheritance** results in *continuous*, or *quantitative*, phenotypic variation between two extremes and explains many human characteristics. Examples of polygene traits in humans include skin color, height, metabolic rate, and intelligence.

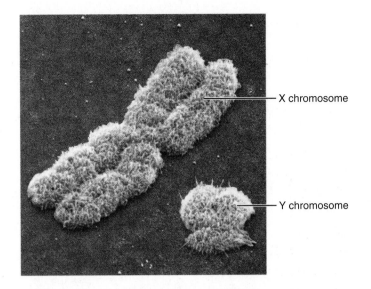

Figure 29.5 **Photograph of human sex chromosomes.**

Skin color, for instance, is controlled by three separately inherited genes, each existing in two allelic forms: *A*, *a*; *B*, *b*; *C*, *c*. The *A*, *B*, and *C* alleles confer dark skin pigment, and their effects are additive. The *a*, *b*, and *c* alleles confer pale skin tone. An individual with an *AABBCC* genotype would be about as dark-skinned as a human can get, while an *aabbcc* person would be very fair. However, when individuals heterozygous for at least one of these gene pairs mate, a broad range of pigmentation is possible in their offspring. Such polygene inheritance results in a distribution of genotypes and phenotypes that, when plotted, yields a bell-shaped curve (Figure 29.6).

CHECK YOUR UNDERSTANDING

9. Why does a male *always* express an X-linked recessive allele?

10. How can you explain why parents of average height can produce very tall or very short offspring?

For answers, see Appendix G.

Environmental Factors in Gene Expression

▶ Provide examples illustrating how gene expression may be modified by environmental factors.

In many situations environmental factors override or at least influence gene expression. Our genotype (discounting mutations) is as unchanging as the Rock of Gibraltar, but our phenotype is more like clay. If this were not the case, we would never get a tan, women bodybuilders would never be able to develop bulging muscles, and there would be no hope for treating genetic disorders.

Sometimes, such maternal factors as drugs or pathogens alter normal gene expression during embryonic development.

29

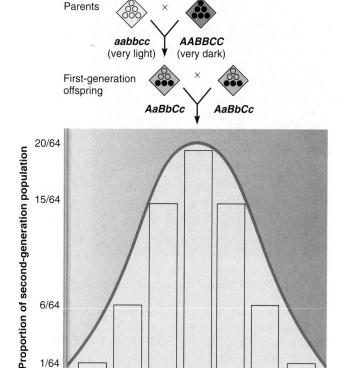

Figure 29.6 Simplified model for polygene inheritance of skin color based on three gene pairs. Alleles for dark skin are incompletely dominant over those for light skin. Each dominant gene (*A*, *B*, *C*) contributes 1 "unit" of darkness (indicated by a dark dot) to the phenotypes. Here the parents are homozygotes at opposite ends of the phenotype range.

Each child inherits 3 "units" of darkness (is a heterozygote) and has intermediate pigmentation. When they grow up and mate with those with the same alleles, their offspring (second generation) may have a wide variation in pigmentation, as shown by the plotted distribution of skin colors.

Take, for example, the case of the "thalidomide babies" (discussed on p. 1085). As a result of their mothers taking that sedative, the embryos developed phenotypes (flipperlike appendages) not directed by their genes. Such environmentally produced phenotypes that mimic conditions that may be caused by genetic mutations (permanent transmissible changes in the DNA) are called **phenocopies.**

Equally significant are environmental factors that may influence genetic expression after birth, such as the effect of poor infant nutrition on brain growth, general body development, and height. In this way, a person with "tall genes" can be stunted by insufficient nutrition. Furthermore, part of a gene's environment consists of the influence of other genes. For example, hormonal deficits during childhood can lead to abnormal skeletal growth and proportions, as in cretinism, a type of dwarfism resulting from hypothyroidism.

11. Which of the following factors may alter gene expression? Other genes, measles in a pregnant woman, lack of key nutrients in the diet.

For answers, see Appendix G.

Nontraditional Inheritance

Mendel's writings underlie mainstream thinking about heredity, but some genetic outcomes do not fit his rules. Among these nontraditional types of inheritance are influences due to RNA-only genes, to chemical groups attached to DNA or histone proteins, and to *extranuclear inheritance* conferred by mitochondrial DNA.

Beyond DNA: Regulation of Gene Expression

▶ Describe how RNA-only genes and epigenetic marks affect gene expression.

Our genome is a biochemical system of awesome complexity, with three basic levels of controls. The protein-coding genes that we have been describing to this point only make up the first level and account for less than 2% of the DNA of a human cell. This is the part of the genome traditionally considered to be a "blueprint" for protein structure.

Since the 1960s, scientists have been finding second and third layers of information important in directing development elsewhere—in the noncoding DNA and even totally outside the DNA sequences. So what are these other regulatory systems?

Small RNAs

The second layer appears to be the product of the abundant "RNA-only genes" (see p. 105), formerly believed to be "junk," that are found in the non-protein-coding DNA. They form a parallel regulatory system that generates single stranded microRNAs (miRNAs) and short interfering RNAs (siRNAs). These small RNA molecules can act directly on DNA, other RNAs, or proteins. They also can tame or inactivate aggressive (jumping) genes, called *transposons*, that tend to replicate themselves and then insert the copies into distant DNA sites, disabling or hyperactivating those genes.

Small RNAs control timing of programmed cell death during development and can also prevent translation of another gene. Mutations in these RNA-only areas have already been linked to several conditions including prostate and lung cancers and schizophrenia.

As a result of the Human Genome Project, nucleotide sequences of these RNA-specifying DNA areas are now worked out and biochemical companies are investing heavily in gene therapy research. They are especially hot on synthesizing RNA-interfering drugs to silence or shut down particular genes to treat age-related macular degeneration, Parkinson's disease, cancer, and a host of other disorders.

Epigenetic Marks

Epigenetic marks form the third layer of gene controls. This continually changing information is stored in the proteins and chemical groups that bind to the DNA and in the manner in which chromatin is packaged in the cell. Within cells, chemical tags such as methyl and acetyl groups bound to DNA segments and to histones determine whether the DNA is available for transcription (acetylation) or silenced (methylation). Epigenetic marks also account for the inactivation (by methylation) of one of the female's X chromosomes in the early embryo.

Epigenetic marks or lack of them may predispose a cell for transformation from normal to cancerous, and even slight deviations in the epigenetic marks on specific chromosomes can result in devastating human illness.

Epigenetic marks also underlie the phenomenon called genomic imprinting. For most genes, the maternal and paternal genes turn on or off at the same time. This balance is upset during gametogenesis when certain genes in both sperm and eggs are modified by the addition of a methyl ($-CH_3$) group, a process called **genomic imprinting**. Genomic imprinting is essential for normal development and somehow tags the genes as paternal or maternal and confers important functional differences in the resulting embryo. The developing embryo "reads" these tags, and then either expresses the mother's gene while the father's version remains idle or vice versa. The methylation process is reversible. In each generation, the old imprints are "erased" when new gametes are produced and all the chromosomes are newly imprinted according to the sex of the parents.

Mutations of imprinted genes may lead to pathology. For example, victims of Prader-Willi syndrome are mildly to moderately retarded, short, and grossly obese. Children with Angelman syndrome are severely retarded, unable to speak coherently, laugh uncontrollably, and exhibit jerky, lurching movements as if tied to a puppeteer's strings. The symptoms of these two disorders are very different, but the genetic cause is the same—deletion of a particular region of chromosome 15. If the defective chromosome comes from the father, the result is Prader-Willi syndrome; the mother's defective chromosome confers Angelman syndrome. Thus, it seems that the same allele can have different effects depending on which parent it comes from.

In short, protein-coding genes are not the only instructions to which cells refer. RNA matters, and so do the tiny chemical tags that attach to the chromatin.

Extranuclear (Mitochondrial) Inheritance

▶ Describe the basis of extranuclear (mitochondria-based) genetic disorders.

Although we have focused on the chromosomal basis of inheritance, remember that not all genes are in the cell's nucleus. Some 37 genes (referred to as mtDNA) are in mitochondria. Mitochondrial genes are transmitted to the offspring almost exclusively by the mother because the ovum donates essentially all the cytoplasm in the fertilized egg.

A growing list of disorders, all rare, is now being linked to errors (mutations) in mitochondrial genes. Most involve problems with oxidative phosphorylation within the mitochondria, but a few lead to unusual degenerative muscle disorders or neurological problems. Some researchers suggest that Alzheimer's and Parkinson's disease may be among them.

CHECK YOUR UNDERSTANDING

12. What process labels genes as paternal or maternal?

13. What is the source of the genes that confer extranuclear inheritance?

For answers, see Appendix G.

Genetic Screening, Counseling, and Therapy

▶ List and explain several techniques used to determine or predict genetic diseases.

▶ Describe briefly some approaches of gene therapy.

Genetic screening and *genetic counseling* provide information and options for prospective parents not even dreamed of 100 years ago. Newborn infants are routinely screened for a number of anatomical disorders (congenital hip dysplasia, imperforate anus, and others), and testing for phenylketonuria (PKU) and other metabolic diseases is mandated by law in many states. These tests alert the new parents that treatment is necessary to ensure the well-being of their infant. Anatomical defects are usually treated surgically, and PKU is managed by strict dietary measures that exclude most phenylalanine-containing foods.

Adult children of parents with Huntington's disease are obvious candidates for these services, but many other genetic conditions also place babies at risk. For example, a woman pregnant at age 35 may wish to know if her baby has trisomy-21 or Down syndrome (see Related Clinical Terms, p. 1112), a chromosome abnormality with a high incidence in children of older mothers.

Depending on the condition being investigated, screening can occur before conception, by carrier recognition, or during fetal testing.

Carrier Recognition

There are two major avenues for identifying carriers of detrimental genes: pedigrees and blood tests. A **pedigree** traces a genetic trait through several generations and helps predict the future. For prospective parents, a genetic counselor collects phenotype information on as many family members as possible and uses it to construct the pedigree.

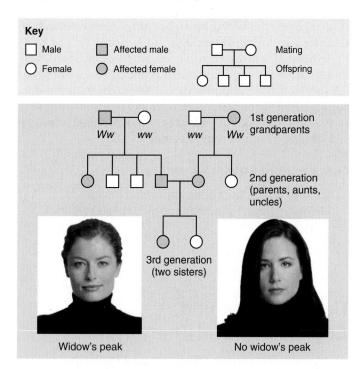

Key

☐ Male ▨ Affected male ☐—○ Mating
○ Female ◉ Affected female Offspring

1st generation grandparents

2nd generation (parents, aunts, uncles)

3rd generation (two sisters)

Widow's peak   No widow's peak

Figure 29.7 Pedigree tracing the trait called widow's peak through three generations. Notice in the third generation that the second-born daughter lacks a widow's peak, although both of her parents had the trait.

Figure 29.7 uses a normal trait, a widow's peak (pointed contour of the hair on the forehead) to illustrate how a pedigree is constructed and read. Widow's peak results from the presence of a dominant allele (*W*). Individuals with the widow's peak phenotype (blue symbols) have at least one dominant gene (*WW* or *Ww*), while those lacking a widow's peak must be homozygous recessive (*ww*).

By working backward from the bottom row and applying the rules of dominant-recessive inheritance, a counselor can deduce the genotypes of the parents (middle row). That one of their two offspring lacks a widow's peak (*ww*) tells the counselor that each parent must have at least one recessive gene (*Ww*), even though both parents exhibit a widow's peak. You should be able to take it from here and figure out the genotypes of the other individuals in their parents' generation. (Try it!)

Simple blood tests are used to screen for the sickling gene in heterozygotes, and sophisticated *blood chemistry tests* and *DNA probes* can detect the presence of other unexpressed recessive genes. At present, carriers of the Tay-Sachs and cystic fibrosis genes can be identified with such tests.

Fetal Testing

Fetal testing is used when there is a known risk of a genetic disorder. The most common type of fetal testing is **amniocentesis** (am″ne-o-sen-te′sis), in which a wide-bore needle is inserted into the amniotic sac through the mother's abdominal wall, and about 10 ml of fluid is withdrawn **(Figure 29.8a)**. Because there is a chance of injuring the fetus before ample amniotic fluid is

present, this procedure is not normally done before the 14th week of pregnancy. Using ultrasound to visualize the position of the fetus and the amniotic sac has dramatically reduced the risk of this procedure.

The fluid is checked for enzymes and other chemicals that serve as markers for specific diseases, but most tests are done on the sloughed-off fetal cells in the fluid. These cells are isolated and cultured in laboratory dishes over a period of several weeks. Then the cells are examined for DNA markers of genetic disease and karyotyped to check for chromosomal abnormalities (see Figure 29.1).

A type of cell that floats freely in the amniotic fluid has proven to be very interesting to stem cell investigators. Armed with many of the same traits as embryonic stem (ES) cells, including pluripotence (an ability to grow into brain, vascular, muscle, and bone tissues), it may prove useful to serve as a "repair kit" for birth defects. Only time will tell.

Chorionic villus sampling (CVS) suctions off bits of the chorionic villi from the placenta for examination (Figure 29.8b). A small tube is inserted through the vagina and cervical canal and guided by ultrasound to an area where a piece of placental tissue can be removed. CVS allows testing at 8 weeks (but waiting until after the 10th week is usually recommended). Karyotyping can be done almost immediately on the rapidly dividing chorionic cells, much earlier than in amniocentesis.

Both of these procedures are invasive, and they carry with them an inherent risk to both fetus and mother. (For example, increased fetal risk of finger and toe defects is linked to CVS.) These tests are routinely ordered for pregnant women over 35 (because of the enhanced risk of Down syndrome), but they are performed on younger women when the probability of finding a severe fetal disorder is greater than the probability of doing harm during the procedure. If a serious genetic or congenital defect is detected in the developing fetus, the parents must decide whether or not to continue the pregnancy.

Human Gene Therapy

As indicated earlier, the Human Genome Project has opened an exciting world to scientists investigating gene expression. Advances in diagnosing human genetic diseases have been followed quickly by new applications of "gene therapy" to alleviate or even cure the disorders, particularly in cases traced to a single defective gene or protein. Indeed, genetic engineering has the potential to replace a defective gene with a normal version.

One approach (used successfully in treatment of severe combined immunodeficiency disorders) is to "infect" the defective cells with a virus into which a functional gene has been inserted. Another is to inject the "corrected" DNA directly into the patient's cells. Such therapies have had mixed results in treating cystic fibrosis and muscular dystrophy. However, genetic engineering processes are prohibitively expensive and raise some thorny ethical, religious, and societal questions: Who will pay? Who determines who will be treated with the new therapies? Are we playing God?

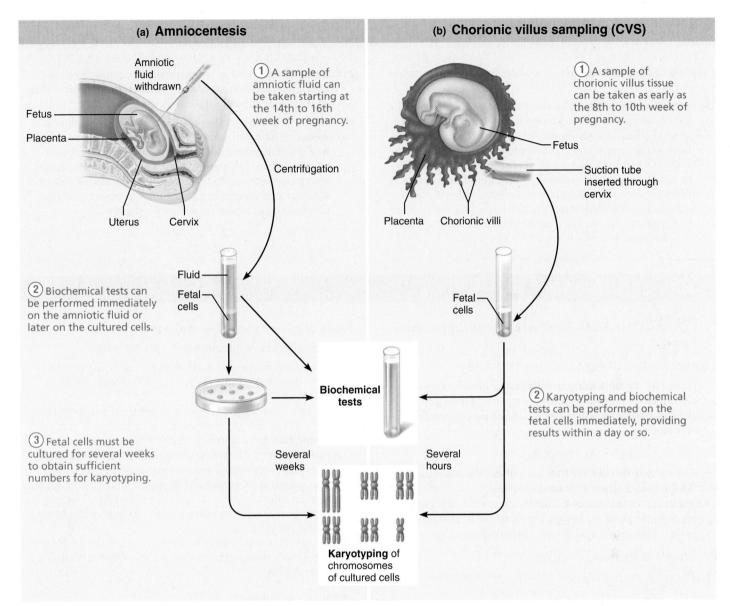

Figure 29.8 **Fetal testing—amniocentesis and chorionic villus sampling.**

CHECK YOUR UNDERSTANDING

14. Which fetal testing procedure depends on analyzing amniotic fluid?

15. What noninvasive imaging procedure is used to determine some aspects of fetal development? (You many want to check *A Closer Look* in Chapter 1 for this.)

For answers, see Appendix G.

In this chapter, we have explored some of the basic principles of genetics, the manner in which genes are expressed, and the means by which gene expression can be modified. Considering the precision required to make perfect copies of genes and chromosomes, and the incredible mechanical events of meiotic division, it is amazing that genetic defects are as rare as they are. Perhaps, after reading this chapter, you have a greater sense of wonder that you turned out as well as you did.

29

RELATED CLINICAL TERMS

Deletion Chromosomal aberration in which part of a chromosome is lost.

Down syndrome Formerly called mongolism, this condition usually reflects the presence of an extra autosome (trisomy of chromosome 21). The child has slightly slanted eyes, flattened facial features, a large tongue, and a tendency toward short stature and stubby fingers. Some, but not all, affected people are mentally retarded. Down syndrome individuals have mitochondrial defects, which have been associated with neurodegeneration in other disorders. A distinctive feature of Down syndrome is early onset of Alzheimer's disease. The most important risk factor appears to be advanced maternal (or paternal) age.

Mutation (*mutare* = change) A permanent structural change in a gene. The mutation may or may not affect function, depending on the precise site and nature of the alteration.

Nondisjunction Abnormal segregation of chromosomes during meiosis, resulting in gametes receiving two or no copies of a particular parental chromosome. It is more common in female meiosis than in male meiosis. If the abnormal gamete participates in fertilization, the resulting zygote will have an abnormal chromosomal complement (monosomy or trisomy) for that particular chromosome (as in Down syndrome).

CHAPTER SUMMARY

1. Genetics is the study of heredity and mechanisms of gene transmission.

The Vocabulary of Genetics (pp. 1102–1103)

1. A complete diploid set of chromosomes is called the karyotype of an organism; the complete genetic complement is the genome. A person's genome consists of two sets of instructions, one from each parent.

Gene Pairs (Alleles) (pp. 1102–1103)

2. Genes coding for the same trait and found at the same locus on homologous chromosomes are called alleles.

3. Alleles may be the same or different in expression. When the allele pair is identical, the person is homozygous for that trait; when the alleles differ, the person is heterozygous.

Genotype and Phenotype (p. 1103)

4. The actual genetic makeup of cells is the genotype; phenotype is the manner in which those genes are expressed.

Sexual Sources of Genetic Variation (pp. 1103–1105)

Chromosome Segregation and Independent Assortment (pp. 1103–1104)

1. During meiosis I of gametogenesis, tetrads align randomly on the metaphase plate, and chromatids are randomly distributed to the daughter cells. This is called independent assortment of the homologues. Each gamete receives only one allele of each gene pair.

2. Each different metaphase I alignment produces a different assortment of parental chromosomes in the gametes, and all combinations of maternal and paternal chromosomes are equally possible.

Crossover of Homologues and Gene Recombination (p. 1104)

3. During meiosis I, all four chromatids of each tetrad may cross over at one or more points and exchange corresponding gene segments. The recombinant chromosomes contain new gene combinations, adding to the variability arising from independent assortment.

Random Fertilization (p. 1105)

4. The third source of genetic variation is random fertilization of eggs by sperm.

Types of Inheritance (pp. 1105–1107)

Dominant-Recessive Inheritance (pp. 1105–1106)

1. Dominant genes are expressed when present in single or double dose; recessive genes must be present in double dose to be expressed.

2. For traits following the dominant-recessive pattern, the laws of probability predict the outcome of a large number of matings.

3. Genetic disorders more often reflect the homozygous recessive condition than the homozygous dominant or heterozygous condition because dominant genes are expressed and, if they are lethal genes, the pregnancy usually results in miscarriage. Genetic disorders caused by dominant alleles include achondroplasia and Huntington's disease; recessive disorders include cystic fibrosis and Tay-Sachs disease.

4. Carriers are heterozygotes who carry a deleterious recessive gene (but do not express the trait) and have the potential of passing it on to offspring.

Incomplete Dominance (p. 1106)

5. In incomplete dominance, the heterozygote exhibits a phenotype intermediate between those of the homozygous dominant and recessive individuals. Inheritance of sickle-cell trait is an example of incomplete dominance.

Multiple-Allele Inheritance (pp. 1106–1107)

6. Multiple-allele inheritance involves genes that exist in more than two allelic forms in a population. Only two of the alleles are inherited, but on a random basis. Inheritance of ABO blood types is an example of multiple-allele inheritance in which the I^A and I^B alleles are codominant.

Sex-Linked Inheritance (p. 1107)

7. Traits determined by genes on the X and Y chromosomes are said to be sex-linked. The small Y chromosome lacks most genes present on the X chromosome. Recessive genes located only on the X chromosome are expressed in single dose in males. Examples of such X-linked conditions, passed from mother to son, include hemophilia and red-green color blindness.

Polygene Inheritance (p. 1107)

8. Polygene inheritance occurs when several gene pairs interact to produce phenotypes that vary quantitatively over a broad range. Height, intelligence, and skin pigmentation are examples.

Environmental Factors in Gene Expression (pp. 1107–1108)

1. Environmental factors may influence the expression of genotype.
2. Maternal factors that cross the placenta may alter expression of fetal genes. Environmentally provoked phenotypes that mimic genetically determined ones are called phenocopies. Nutritional deficits or hormonal imbalances may alter anticipated growth and development during childhood.

Nontraditional Inheritance (pp. 1108–1109)

Beyond DNA: Regulation of Gene Expression (pp. 1108–1109)

1. Control of gene expression occurs at three levels: protein-coding genes, RNA-only genes, and epigenetic marks. The latter two account for many cases of inherited disease that fail to follow traditional genetics.
2. The products of the RNA-only genes (siRNA and miRNA) may silence genes or prevent their expression and appear to play a role in directing apoptosis during development.
3. Epigenetic marks involve attachment of small chemical groups (methyl or acetyl) to DNA or histone proteins. In general, methylation prevents access to the DNA whereas acetylation provides access to the DNA. Genomic imprinting, which involves methylation of certain genes during gametogenesis, confers different effects and phenotypes on maternal and paternal genes. It is reversible, and occurs anew each generation.

Extranuclear (Mitochondrial) Inheritance (p. 1109)

4. Cytoplasmic (mitochondrial) genes pass to offspring via the ovum and help to determine certain characteristics. Deletions or mutations in mitochondrial genes are responsible for some problems with oxidative phosphorylation and some rare genetic diseases.

Genetic Screening, Counseling, and Therapy (pp. 1109–1111)

Carrier Recognition (pp. 1109–1110)

1. The likelihood of an individual carrying a deleterious recessive gene may be assessed by constructing a pedigree. Some of these genes can be deduced by various blood tests and DNA probes.

Fetal Testing (p. 1110)

2. Amniocentesis is fetal testing based on aspirated samples of amniotic fluid. Fetal cells in the fluid are cultured for several weeks, then examined for chromosomal defects (karyotyped) or for DNA markers of genetic disease. Amniocentesis cannot be performed until the 14th week of pregnancy.
3. Chorionic villus sampling is fetal testing based on a sample of the chorion. This tissue is rapidly mitotic, so karyotyping can be done almost immediately. Samples may be obtained by the 8th week.

Human Gene Therapy (pp. 1110–1111)

4. The Human Genome Project has allowed research on diagnosis of genetic disease and on its treatment to surge forward. Thus far, gene therapy has been particularly useful for correcting single-gene disorders. The most common approach involves transferring a corrected gene via a virus to the affected cells to restore normal function.

REVIEW QUESTIONS

Multiple Choice/Matching

(Some questions have more than one correct answer. Select the best answer or answers from the choices given.)

1. Match one of the following terms (a–i) with each of the descriptions below:
   Key: (a) alleles (f) homozygote
   (b) autosomes (g) phenotype
   (c) dominant allele (h) recessive allele
   (d) genotype (i) sex chromosomes
   (e) heterozygote
   _____ (1) genetic makeup
   _____ (2) how genetic makeup is expressed
   _____ (3) chromosomes that dictate most body characteristics
   _____ (4) alternate forms of the same gene
   _____ (5) an individual bearing two alleles that are the same for a particular trait
   _____ (6) an allele that is expressed whether in single or double dose
   _____ (7) an individual bearing two alleles that differ for a particular trait
   _____ (8) an allele that must be present in double dose to be expressed

2. Match the following types of inheritance (a–f) with the descriptions below:
   Key: (a) dominant-recessive (d) polygene
   (b) incomplete dominance (e) sex-linked
   (c) multiple-allele (f) extranuclear
   _____ (1) only sons show the trait
   _____ (2) homozygotes and heterozygotes have the same phenotype
   _____ (3) heterozygotes exhibit a phenotype intermediate between those of the homozygotes
   _____ (4) phenotypes of offspring may be more varied than those of the parents
   _____ (5) inheritance of ABO blood types
   _____ (6) inheritance of stature
   _____ (7) reflects activity of mitochondrial DNA

Short Answer Essay Questions

3. Describe the important mechanisms that lead to genetic variations in gametes.
4. The ability to taste PTC (phenylthiocarbamide) depends on the presence of a dominant gene *T*; nontasters are homozygous for the recessive gene *t*. This is a situation of classical dominant-recessive inheritance. (a) Consider a mating between heterozygous

parents producing three offspring. What proportion of the offspring will be tasters? What is the chance that all three offspring will be tasters? Nontasters? What is the chance that two will be tasters and one will be a nontaster? (b) Consider a mating between *Tt* and *tt* parents. What is the anticipated percentage of tasters? Nontasters? What proportion can be expected to be homozygous recessive? Heterozygous? Homozygous dominant?

5. Most albino children are born to normally pigmented parents. Albinos are homozygous for the recessive gene (*aa*). What can you conclude about the genotypes of the nonalbino parents?

6. A woman with blood type A has two children. One has type O blood and the other has type B blood. What is the genotype of the mother? What are the genotype and phenotype of the father? What is the genotype of each child?

7. In skin color inheritance, what will be the relative range of pigmentation in offspring arising from the following parental matches? (a) *AABBCC* × *aabbcc*, (b) *AABBCC* × *AaBbCc*, (c) *Aabbcc* × *aabbcc*.

8. Compare and contrast amniocentesis and chorionic villus sampling as to the time at which they can be performed and the techniques used to obtain information on the fetus's genetic status.

Critical Thinking and Clinical Application Questions

1. A color-blind man marries a woman with normal vision. The woman's father was also color-blind. (a) What is the chance that their first child will be a color-blind son? A color-blind daughter? (b) If they have four children, what is the chance that two will be color-blind sons? (Be careful on this one.)

2. Brian is a college student. His genetics assignment is to do a family pedigree for dimples in the cheeks. Absence of dimples is recessive; presence of dimples reflects a dominant allele. Brian has dimples, as do his three brothers. His mother and maternal grandmother are dimple free, but his father and all other grandparents have dimples. Construct a pedigree spanning three generations for Brian's family. Show the phenotype and genotype for each person.

3. Mr. and Mrs. Lehman have sought genetic counseling. Mrs. Lehman is concerned because she is unexpectedly pregnant and her husband's brother died of Tay-Sachs disease. She can recall no incidence of Tay-Sachs disease in her own family. Do you think biochemical testing should be recommended to detect the deleterious gene in Mrs. Lehman? Explain your answer.

4. The Browns are both carriers of the recessive allele that causes the metabolic disorder called phenylketonuria. What is the probability of each of the following occurring? (a) All three children will have the disorder. (b) None of their three children will have the disorder. (c) One or more of their children will have the disorder. (d) At least one of their children will be phenotypically normal.

APPENDIX A The Metric System

MEASUREMENT	UNIT AND ABBREVIATION	METRIC EQUIVALENT	METRIC TO ENGLISH CONVERSION FACTOR	ENGLISH TO METRIC CONVERSION FACTOR
Length	1 kilometer (km)	= 1000 (10^3) meters	1 km = 0.62 mile	1 mile = 1.61 km
	1 meter (m)	= 100 (10^2) centimeters = 1000 millimeters	1 m = 1.09 yards 1 m = 3.28 feet 1 m = 39.37 inches	1 yard = 0.914 m 1 foot = 0.305 m
	1 centimeter (cm)	= 0.01 (10^{-2}) meter	1 cm = 0.394 inch	1 foot = 30.5 cm 1 inch = 2.54 cm
	1 millimeter (mm)	= 0.001 (10^{-3}) meter	1 mm = 0.039 inch	
	1 micrometer (μm) [formerly micron (μ)]	= 0.000001 (10^{-6}) meter		
	1 nanometer (nm)	= 0.000000001 (10^{-9}) meter		
	1 angstrom (Å)	= 0.0000000001 (10^{-10}) meter		
Area	1 square meter (m²)	= 10,000 square centimeters	1 m² = 1.1960 square yards 1 m² = 10.764 square feet	1 square yard = 0.8361 m² 1 square foot = 0.0929 m²
	1 square centimeter (cm²)	= 100 square millimeters	1 cm² = 0.155 square inch	1 square inch = 6.4516 cm²
Mass	1 metric ton (t)	= 1000 kilograms	1 t = 1.103 ton	1 ton = 0.907 t
	1 kilogram (kg)	= 1000 grams	1 kg = 2.205 pounds	1 pound = 0.4536 kg
	1 gram (g)	= 1000 milligrams	1 g = 0.0353 ounce 1 g = 15.432 grains	1 ounce = 28.35 g
	1 milligram (mg)	= 0.001 gram	1 mg = approx. 0.015 grain	
	1 microgram (μg)	= 0.000001 gram		
Volume (solids)	1 cubic meter (m³)	= 1,000,000 cubic centimeters	1 m³ = 1.3080 cubic yards 1 m³ = 35.315 cubic feet	1 cubic yard = 0.7646 m³ 1 cubic foot = 0.0283 m³
	1 cubic centimeter (cm³ or cc)	= 0.000001 cubic meter = 1 milliliter	1 cm³ = 0.0610 cubic inch	1 cubic inch = 16.387 cm³
	1 cubic millimeter (mm³)	= 0.000000001 cubic meter		
Volume (liquids and gases)	1 kiloliter (kl or kL)	= 1000 liters	1 kL = 264.17 gallons	1 gallon = 3.785 L
	1 liter (l or L)	= 1000 milliliters	1 L = 0.264 gallon 1 L = 1.057 quarts	1 quart = 0.946 L
	1 milliliter (ml or mL)	= 0.001 liter = 1 cubic centimeter	1 ml = 0.034 fluid ounce 1 ml = approx. $\frac{1}{5}$ teaspoon 1 ml = approx. 15–16 drops (gtt)	1 quart = 946 ml 1 pint = 473 ml 1 fluid ounce = 29.57 ml 1 teaspoon = approx. 5 ml
	1 microliter (μl or μL)	= 0.000001 liter		
Time	1 second (s)	= $\frac{1}{60}$ minute		
	1 millisecond (ms)	= 0.001 second		
Temperature	Degrees Celsius (°C)		$°F = \frac{9}{5}(°C) + 32$	$°C = \frac{5}{9}(°F - 32)$

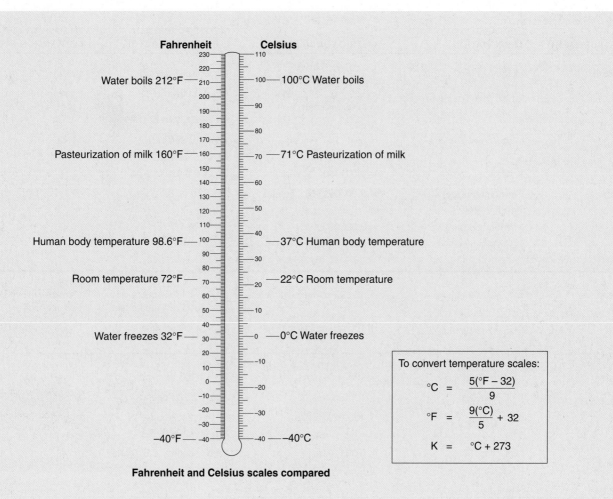

Fahrenheit and Celsius scales compared

APPENDIX B Functional Groups in Organic Molecules

Functional group	General formula	Name of compounds	Example	Where else found
Hydroxyl —OH (or HO—)	—O—H	Alcohols	Ethanol	Sugars; water-soluble vitamins
Carbonyl \CO	—C(=O)H	Aldehydes	Propanal	Some sugars; formaldehyde (a preservative)
	—C(=O)—	Ketones	Acetone	Some sugars; "ketone bodies" in urine (from fat breakdown)
Carboxyl —COOH	—C(=O)OH	Carboxylic acids	Acetic acid	Amino acids; proteins; some vitamins; fatty acids
Amino —NH₂ (or H₂N—)	—N(H)(H)	Amines	Methylamine	Amino acids; proteins; urea in urine (from protein breakdown)

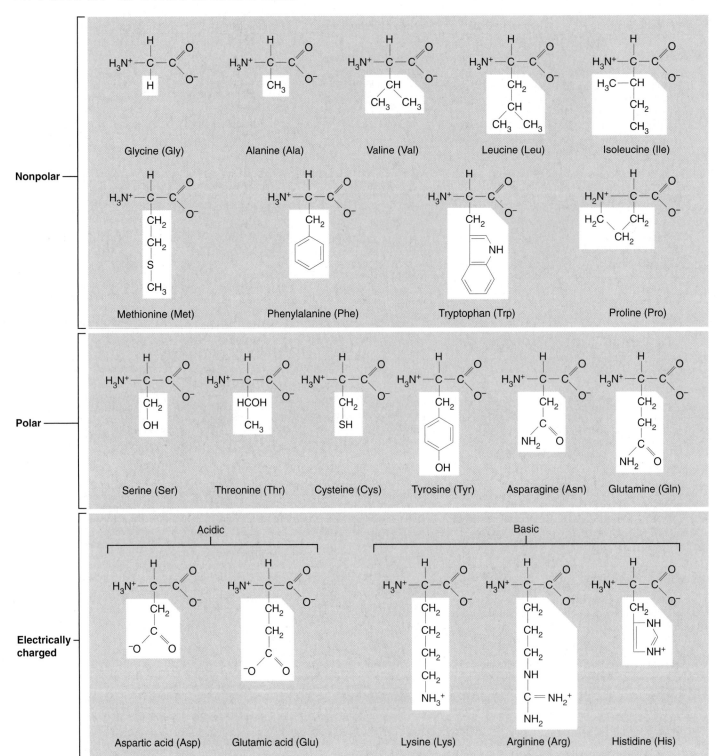

Nonpolar

Glycine (Gly)

Alanine (Ala)

Valine (Val)

Leucine (Leu)

Isoleucine (Ile)

Methionine (Met)

Phenylalanine (Phe)

Tryptophan (Trp)

Proline (Pro)

Polar

Serine (Ser)

Threonine (Thr)

Cysteine (Cys)

Tyrosine (Tyr)

Asparagine (Asn)

Glutamine (Gln)

Electrically charged

Acidic

Aspartic acid (Asp)

Glutamic acid (Glu)

Basic

Lysine (Lys)

Arginine (Arg)

Histidine (His)

① Glucose enters the cell and is phosphorylated by the enzyme hexokinase, which catalyzes the transfer of a phosphate group, indicated as ⓟ, from ATP to the number six carbon of the sugar, producing glucose-6-phosphate. The electrical charge of the phosphate group traps the sugar in the cell because the plasma membrane is impermeable to ions. Phosphorylation of glucose also makes the molecule more chemically reactive. Although glycolysis is supposed to *produce* ATP, ATP is actually consumed in step 1—an energy investment that will be repaid with dividends later in glycolysis.

② Glucose-6-phosphate is rearranged and converted to its isomer, fructose-6-phosphate. Isomers, remember, have the same number and types of atoms but in different structural arrangements.

③ In this step, still another molecule of ATP is used to add a second phosphate group to the sugar, producing fructose-1,6-bisphosphate. So far, the ATP ledger shows a debit of –2. With phosphate groups on its opposite ends, the sugar is now ready to be split in half.

④ This is the reaction from which glycolysis gets its name. An enzyme cleaves the sugar molecule into two different 3-carbon sugars: glyceraldehyde 3-phosphate and dihydroxyacetone phosphate. These two sugars are isomers of one another.

⑤ An isomerase enzyme interconverts the 3-carbon sugars, and if left alone in a test tube, the reaction reaches equilibrium. This does not happen in the cell, however, because the next enzyme in glycolysis uses only glyceraldehyde phosphate as its substrate and not dihydroxyacetone phosphate. This pulls the equilibrium between the two 3-carbon sugars in the direction of glyceraldehyde phosphate, which is removed as fast as it forms. Thus, the net result of steps 4 and 5 is cleavage of a 6-carbon sugar into two molecules of glyceraldehyde phosphate; each will progress through the remaining steps of glycolysis.

⑥ An enzyme now catalyzes two sequential reactions while it holds glyceraldehyde phosphate in its active site. First, the sugar is oxidized by the transfer of H from the number one carbon of the sugar to NAD, forming NADH + H$^+$. Here we see in metabolic context the oxidation-reduction reaction described in Chapter 24. This reaction releases substantial amounts of energy, and the enzyme capitalizes on this by coupling the reaction to the creation of a high-energy phosphate bond at the number one carbon of the oxidized substrate. The source of the phosphate is inorganic phosphate (P$_i$) always present in the cytosol. The enzyme releases NADH + H$^+$ and 1,3-bisphosphoglyceric acid as products. Notice in the figure that the new phosphate bond is symbolized with a squiggle (~), which indicates that the bond is at least as energetic as the high-energy phosphate bonds of ATP.

THE TEN STEPS OF GLYCOLYSIS Each of the ten steps of glycolysis is catalyzed by a specific enzyme found dissolved in the cytoplasm. All steps are reversible. An abbreviated version of the three major phases of glycolysis appears in the lower right-hand corner of the next page.

(1,3-Bisphosphoglyceric acid)

ADP — Phosphoglycerokinase

(7)

ATP

3-Phosphoglyceric acid (2 molecules)

OH
|
C=O
|
CHOH
|
CH_2—O— P

Phosphoglyceromutase

(8)

2-Phosphoglyceric acid (2 molecules)

OH
|
C=O
|
H—C—O— P
|
CH_2OH

Enolase

(9)

H_2O

2-Phosphoenolpyruvic acid (PEP) (2 molecules)

OH
|
C=O
|
C—O~ P
||
CH_2

ADP — Pyruvate kinase

(10)

ATP

Pyruvic acid (2 molecules)

OH
|
C=O
|
C=O
|
CH_3

Oxygen present / Oxygen deficit

Lactate dehydrogenase

$NADH+H^+$

NAD^+

To Krebs cycle (aerobic pathway)

Lactic acid (2 molecules)

OH
|
C=O
|
H—C—OH
|
CH_3

(7) Finally, glycolysis produces ATP. The phosphate group, with its high-energy bond, is transferred from 1,3-bisphosphoglyceric acid to ADP. For each glucose molecule that began glycolysis, step 7 produces two molecules of ATP, because every product after the sugar-splitting step (step 4) is doubled. Of course, two ATPs were invested to get sugar ready for splitting. The ATP ledger now stands at zero. By the end of step 7, glucose has been converted to two molecules of 3-phosphoglyceric acid. This compound is not a sugar. The sugar was oxidized to an organic acid back in step 6, and now the energy made available by that oxidation has been used to make ATP.

(8) Next, an enzyme relocates the remaining phosphate group of 3-phosphoglyceric acid to form 2-phosphoglyceric acid. This prepares the substrate for the next reaction.

(9) An enzyme forms a double bond in the substrate by removing a water molecule from 2-phosphoglyceric acid to form phosphoenolpyruvic acid, or PEP. This results in the electrons of the substrate being rearranged in such a way that the remaining phosphate bond becomes very unstable; it has been upgraded to high-energy status.

(10) The last reaction of glycolysis produces another molecule of ATP by transferring the phosphate group from PEP to ADP. Because this step occurs twice for each glucose molecule, the ATP ledger now shows a net gain of two ATPs. Steps 7 and 10 each produce two ATPs for a total credit of four, but a debt of two ATPs was incurred from steps 1 and 3. Glycolysis has repaid the ATP investment with 100% interest. In the meantime, glucose has been broken down and oxidized to two molecules of pyruvic acid, the compound produced from PEP in step 10.

Summary

Phase 1   Sugar activates by phosphorylation

Glucose (6C)

2 ATP

2 ADP

Fructose-1,6-bisphosphate (6C)

Phase 2   Sugar cleavage

Glyceraldehyde phosphate (3C) | Dihydroxyacetone phosphate (3C)

Phase 3 Sugar oxidation and formation of ATP

2 P_i

2 NAD^+

4 ADP

2 $NADH+H^+$

4 ATP

2 Pyruvic acid (3C)

Oxygen present | 2 $NADH+H^+$ | Oxygen deficit

2 NAD^+

Aerobic pathway | 2 Lactic acid

(1) Two-carbon acetyl CoA is combined with oxaloacetic acid, a 4-carbon compound. The unstable bond between the acetyl group and CoA is broken as oxaloacetic acid binds and CoA is freed to prime another 2-carbon fragment derived from pyruvic acid. The product is the 6-carbon citric acid, for which the cycle is named.

(2) A molecule of water is removed, and another is added back. The net result is the conversion of citric acid to its isomer, isocitric acid.

(3) The substrate loses a CO_2 molecule, and the remaining 5-carbon compound is oxidized, forming an α-ketoglutaric acid and reducing NAD^+.

(4) This step is catalyzed by a multienzyme complex very similar to the one that converts pyruvic acid to acetyl CoA. CO_2 is lost; the remaining 4-carbon compound is oxidized by the transfer of electrons to NAD^+ to form $NADH+H^+$ and is then attached to CoA by an unstable bond. The product is succinyl CoA.

(5) Substrate-level phosphorylation occurs in this step. CoA is displaced by a phosphate group, which is then transferred to GDP to form guanosine triphosphate (GTP). GTP is similar to ATP, which is formed when GTP donates a phosphate group to ADP. The products of this step are succinic acid and ATP.

(6) In another oxidative step, two hydrogens are removed from succinic acid (forming fumaric acid) and transferred to FAD to form $FADH_2$. The function of this coenzyme is similar to that of $NADH+H^+$, but $FADH_2$ stores less energy. The enzyme that catalyzes this oxidation-reduction reaction is the only enzyme of the cycle that is embedded in the mitochondrial membrane. All other enzymes of the citric acid cycle are dissolved in the mitochondrial matrix.

(7) Bonds in the substrate are rearranged in this step by the addition of a water molecule. The product is malic acid.

(8) The last oxidative step reduces another NAD^+ and regenerates oxaloacetic acid, which accepts a 2-carbon fragment from acetyl CoA for another turn of the cycle.

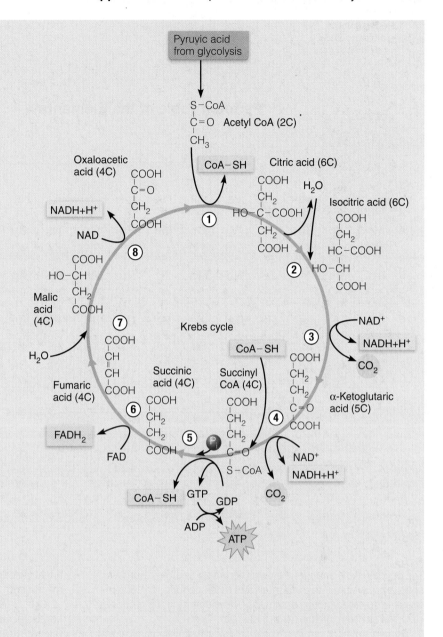

Krebs Cycle (Citric Acid Cycle) All but one of the steps (step 6) occur in the mitochondrial matrix. The preparation of pyruvic acid (by oxidation, decarboxylation, and reaction with coenzyme A) to enter the cycle as acetyl CoA is shown above the cycle. Acetyl CoA is picked up by oxaloacetic acid to form citric acid; and as it passes through the cycle, it is oxidized four more times [forming three molecules of reduced NAD ($NADH + H^+$) and one of reduced FAD ($FADH_2$)] and decarboxylated twice (releasing 2 CO_2). Energy is captured in the bonds of GTP, which then acts in a coupled reaction with ADP to generate one molecule of ATP by substrate-level phosphorylation.

Periodic Table of the Elements

Representative (main group) elements

Representative (main group) elements

Transition metals

	IA												IIIA	IVA	VA	VIA	VIIA	VIIIA
	1 **H** 1.0079	IIA																2 **He** 4.003
2	3 **Li** 6.941	4 **Be** 9.012											5 **B** 10.811	6 **C** 12.011	7 **N** 14.007	8 **O** 15.999	9 **F** 18.998	10 **Ne** 20.180
3	11 **Na** 22.990	12 **Mg** 24.305	IIIB	IVB	VB	VIB	VIIB	VIIIB			IB	IIB	13 **Al** 26.982	14 **Si** 28.086	15 **P** 30.974	16 **S** 32.065	17 **Cl** 35.453	18 **Ar** 39.948
4	19 **K** 39.098	20 **Ca** 40.078	21 **Sc** 44.956	22 **Ti** 47.867	23 **V** 50.942	24 **Cr** 51.996	25 **Mn** 54.938	26 **Fe** 55.845	27 **Co** 58.933	28 **Ni** 58.69	29 **Cu** 63.546	30 **Zn** 65.38	31 **Ga** 69.723	32 **Ge** 72.64	33 **As** 74.922	34 **Se** 78.96	35 **Br** 79.904	36 **Kr** 83.8
5	37 **Rb** 85.468	38 **Sr** 87.62	39 **Y** 88.906	40 **Zr** 91.224	41 **Nb** 92.906	42 **Mo** 95.96	43 **Tc** 98	44 **Ru** 101.07	45 **Rh** 102.906	46 **Pd** 106.42	47 **Ag** 107.868	48 **Cd** 112.411	49 **In** 114.82	50 **Sn** 118.71	51 **Sb** 121.76	52 **Te** 127.60	53 **I** 126.905	54 **Xe** 131.29
6	55 **Cs** 132.905	56 **Ba** 137.327	57 **La** 138.906	72 **Hf** 178.49	73 **Ta** 180.948	74 **W** 183.84	75 **Re** 186.207	76 **Os** 190.23	77 **Ir** 192.22	78 **Pt** 195.08	79 **Au** 196.967	80 **Hg** 200.59	81 **Tl** 204.383	82 **Pb** 207.2	83 **Bi** 208.980	84 **Po** 209	85 **At** 210	86 **Rn** 222
7	87 **Fr** 223	88 **Ra** 226	89 **Ac** 227	104 **Rf** 267	105 **Db** 268	106 **Sg** 271	107 **Bh** 272	108 **Hs** 270	109 **Mt** 276	110 **Ds** 281	111 **Rg** 280	112 **Uub** 285	113 **Uut** 284	114 **Uuq** 289	115 **Uup** 288	116 **Uuh** 293		118 **Uuo** 294

Rare earth elements

	58	59	60	61	62	63	64	65	66	67	68	69	70	71
Lanthanides	**Ce** 140.116	**Pr** 140.908	**Nd** 144.24	**Pm** 145	**Sm** 150.36	**Eu** 151.964	**Gd** 157.25	**Tb** 158.925	**Dy** 162.5	**Ho** 164.93	**Er** 167.26	**Tm** 168.934	**Yb** 173.054	**Lu** 174.967

	90	91	92	93	94	95	96	97	98	99	100	101	102	103
Actinides	**Th** 232.038	**Pa** 231.036	**U** 238.029	**Np** 237.048	**Pu** 244	**Am** 243	**Cm** 247	**Bk** 247	**Cf** 251	**Es** 252	**Fm** 257	**Md** 258	**No** 259	**Lr** 262

The periodic table arranges elements according to atomic number and atomic weight into horizontal rows called periods and 18 vertical columns called groups or families. The elements in the groups are classified as being in either A or B classes.

Elements of each group of the A series have similar chemical and physical properties. This reflects the fact that members of a particular group have the same number of valence shell electrons, which is indicated by the roman numeral of the group. For example, group IA elements have one valence shell electron, group IIA elements have two, and group VA elements have five. In contrast, as you progress across a period from left to right, the properties of the elements change in discrete steps, varying gradually from the very metallic properties of groups IA and IIA elements to the nonmetallic properties seen in group VIIA (chlorine and others), and finally to the inert elements (noble gases) in group VIIIA. This change reflects the con- tinual increase in the number of valence shell electrons seen in elements (from left to right) within a period.

Class B elements are referred to as transition elements. All transition elements are metals, and in most cases they have one or two valence shell electrons. (In these elements, some electrons occupy more distant electron shells before the deeper shells are filled.)

In this periodic table, the colors are used to convey information about the phase (solid, liquid, or gas) in which a pure element exists under standard conditions (25 degrees centigrade and 1 atmosphere of pressure). If the element's symbol is solid black, then the element exists as a solid. If its symbol is red, then it exists as a gas. If its symbol is dark blue, then it is a liquid. If the element's symbol is green, the element does not exist in nature and must be created by some type of nuclear reaction.

*Atomic weights of the elements per IUPAC Commission on Isotopic Abundances and Atomic Weights, 2007.

The reference values listed for the selected blood and urine studies are common ranges for adults, but specific "normals" are established by the laboratory performing the analysis. The values may be affected by a wide range of circumstances, including testing methods and equipment used, client age, body mass, sex, diet, activity level, medications, and extent of disease processes.

Reference values are identified in both standard or conventional units and in the system of international (SI) units. SI units (given in parentheses) are measurements of amount per volume and are used in most countries and scientific journals. SI units are often given as moles or millimoles per liter. Most clinical laboratories and textbooks in the United States use conventional or standard units, which measure mass per volume. These values are given as grams, milligrams, or milliequivalents per deciliter or liter. It is anticipated that the United States will eventually use SI units exclusively.

For enzymes, 1 international unit (IU) represents an arbitrary but defined amount of activity, whereas 1 katal (kat) is the amount of enzyme required to consume 1 mol of substrate per second.

Sample types in column 1 are serum (S), plasma (P), arterial whole blood (A), and whole blood (WB).

TEST (SAMPLE)	REFERENCE VALUES: CONVENTIONAL (SI)	PHYSIOLOGICAL INDICATION AND CLINICAL IMPLICATIONS
Blood Chemistry Studies		
Ammonia (P)	15–120 μg/dl (9–70 μmol/L)	Liver and renal function. Increased values in liver disease, renal failure, newborn hemolytic disease, heart failure, cor pulmonale. Decreased values in hypertension.
Amylase (S)	56–190 IU/L (0.4–2.1 μkat/L)	Pancreatic function. Increased values in pancreatitis, mumps, obstruction of pancreatic duct, ketoacidosis. Decreased values in kidney disease, pancreatic damage or cancer, toxemia of pregnancy.
Aspartate aminotransferase (AST, or SGOT) (S)	≤40 U/ml (≤0.7 μkat/L)	Cellular damage. Increased after myocardial infarction, acute liver disease, drug toxicity, muscle trauma. Decreased in pyridoxine (vitamin B_6) deficiency.
Bilirubin (S)	Total: 0.1–1.0 mg/dl (1.7–17.1 μmol/L) Direct: <0.4 mg/dl (<6.8 μmol/L) Indirect: 0.1–1.0 mg/dl (1.7–17.1 μmol/L) Newborn: <13.0 mg/dl (<222 μmol/L)	Liver function and red cell breakdown. Increased levels of direct in liver disease and biliary obstruction. Increased levels of indirect in hemolysis of red blood cells.
Blood urea nitrogen (S)	7–26 mg/dl (2.5–9.3 mmol/L)	Kidney function. Increased values in renal disease, dehydration, urinary obstruction, congestive heart failure, myocardial infarction, burns. Decreased values in liver failure, overhydration, impaired protein absorption, pregnancy.
Cholesterol	<200 mg/dl (<5.2 mmol/L)	Metabolism—fat utilization. Increased values in diabetes mellitus, pregnancy, use of oral contraceptives or anabolic steroids.
High-density lipoprotein (HDL) cholesterol (S)	20–30% of total >40 mg/dl (>1.0 mmol/L)	Increased levels in liver disease, aerobic exercise. Decreased levels in atherosclerotic heart disease, malnutrition.
Low-density lipoprotein (LDL) cholesterol (S)	60–70% of total <130 mg/dl (<3.4 mmol/L)	Increased values in hyperlipidemia, atherosclerotic heart disease. Decreased values in fat malabsorption and malnutrition.
Very low density lipoprotein cholesterol (VLDL) (S)	10–15% of total	Same as LDL.
Creatine kinase (CK) (S)	Female: ≤190 U/L (≤3.2 μkat/L) Male: ≤235 U/L (≤3.9 μkat/L)	Cellular damage. Increased values in myocardial infarction, muscular dystrophy, hypothyroidism, pulmonary infarction, cerebrovascular accident (CVA), shock, tissue damage, and trauma.
Creatinine (S)	0.5–1.2 mg/dl (44–106 μmol/L)	Renal function. Increased values in renal disease and acromegaly. Decreased in muscular dystrophy.

TEST (SAMPLE)	REFERENCE VALUES: CONVENTIONAL (SI)	PHYSIOLOGICAL INDICATION AND CLINICAL IMPLICATIONS
Blood Chemistry Studies (continued)		
Gases (A)		
Bicarbonate	22–26 mEq/L (22–26 mmol/L)	Acid-base balance. Increased values in metabolic alkalosis and respiratory acidosis. Decreased values in metabolic acidosis and respiratory alkalosis.
Carbon dioxide content	Arterial: 19–24 mEq/L (19–24 mmol/L) Venous: 22–30 mEq/L (22–30 mmol/L)	
Carbon dioxide partial pressure (P_{CO_2})	Arterial: 35–45 mm Hg Venous: 45 mm Hg	
Oxygen (O_2) saturation	95–98% (same)	Values increased slightly in hyperventilation. Decreased values (hypoxia) in pulmonary disease, hypoventilation, high altitude.
Oxygen partial pressure (P_{O_2})	80–105 mm Hg	
pH	7.35–7.45 (same)	Increased values in metabolic and respiratory alkalosis. Decreased values in metabolic and respiratory acidosis.
Glucose (S)	70–120 mg/dl (3.9–6.7 mmol/L)	Metabolic function. Increased values in diabetes mellitus, Cushing's syndrome, liver disease, acute stress, and acromegaly. Decreased levels in Addison's disease, insulinomas.
Immunoglobulins (S)		
IgG	560–1800 mg/dl (5.6–18 g/L)	Immune response. Increased levels in chronic infections, rheumatic fever, liver disease, rheumatoid arthritis. Decreased levels in amyloidosis, leukemia, and preeclampsia.
IgE	<43.2 µg/dl (<432 µg/L)	Allergic responses. Increased values in allergic responses. Decreased values in agammaglobulinemia.
IgA	85–563 mg/dl (0.85–5.6 g/L)	Immune integrity. Increased values in liver disease, rheumatic fever, chronic infection, inflammatory bowel disease. Decreased values in immunodeficiency disorders and immunosuppression.
IgM	55–375 mg/dl (0.5–3.8 g/L)	Immune integrity. Increased in autoimmune disease (e.g., rheumatoid arthritis), acute infections. Decreased in amyloidosis and leukemia.
IgD	0.5–14 mg/dl (5–140 mg/L)	Immune integrity. Increased values in myelomas.
Ketone bodies (S or P)	Negative Toxic level >20 mg/dl (0.2 g/L)	Fatty acid catabolism. Increased values (ketosis, ketoacidosis) in starvation, low-carbohydrate diet, uncontrolled diabetes mellitus, aspirin overdose.
Lactate dehydrogenase (LDH) (S)	105–333 U/L (1.7–5.6 µkat/L)	Tissue damage of organs or striated muscle. Increased in myocardial infarction, pulmonary infarction, liver disease, cerebrovascular accident, infectious mononucleosis, muscular dystrophy, fractures.
Lactic acid (lactate) (P)	9–16 mg/dl (1.0–1.8 mmol/L)	Anaerobic tissue metabolism. Increased values in congestive heart failure, shock, hemorrhage, strenuous exercise.
Osmolality (S)	280–300 mOsm/kg H_2O (280–300 mmol/kg H_2O)	Fluid and electrolyte balance. Increased levels in hypernatremia, dehydration, kidney disease, alcohol ingestion. Decreased levels in hyponatremia, overhydration, and syndrome of inappropriate ADH secretion (SIADH).
Phosphate (S) (phosphorus)	2.5–4.5 mg/dl (0.8–1.5 mmol/L)	Parathyroid function; bone disease. Increased levels in hypoparathyroidism, renal failure, bone metastasis, hypocalcemia. Decreased values in hyperparathyroidism, hypercalcemia, alcoholism, vitamin D deficiency, ketoacidosis, osteomalacia.
Potassium (S)	3.5–5.5 mEq/L (3.5–5.5 mmol/L)	Fluid and electrolyte balance. Increased levels in renal disease, Addison's disease, ketoacidosis, burns, and crush injuries. Decreased levels in vomiting, diarrhea, Cushing's syndrome, alkalosis, diuretics.

TEST (SAMPLE)	REFERENCE VALUES: CONVENTIONAL (SI)	PHYSIOLOGICAL INDICATION AND CLINICAL IMPLICATIONS
Blood Chemistry Studies (continued)		
Protein (S) Total	6.0–8.5 g/dl (60–85 g/L)	Osmotic pressure; immune system integrity. Increased values in multiple myeloma, dehydration, myxedema. Decreased values in protein malnutrition, burns, diarrhea, renal failure, liver failure.
Albumin	3.2–5.0 g/dl (32–50 g/L)	Osmotic pressure. Increased levels in dehydration. Decreased levels in liver disease, malnutrition, Crohn's disease, nephrotic syndrome, systemic lupus erythematosus.
Sodium (S)	135–145 mEq/L (135–145 mmol/L)	Fluid and electrolyte balance. Increased values in dehydration, diabetes insipidus, Cushing's syndrome. Decreased values in vomiting, diarrhea, burns, Addison's disease, myxedema, congestive heart failure, overhydration, syndrome of inappropriate ADH secretion (SIADH).
Triglycerides	10–150 mg/dl (0.1–1.5 g/L)	Increased values in diabetes mellitus, liver disease, nephrotic syndrome, pregnancy.
Uric acid (S)	Female: 2.0–7.3 mg/dl (119–434 μmol/L) Male: 2.1–8.5 mg/dl (125–506 μmol/L)	Renal function. Increased in lead poisoning, impaired renal function, gout, alcoholism, hematologic cancers. Decreased in Wilson's disease.
Hematology Studies		
Hemoglobin (S)	Female: 12–16 g/dl (120–160 g/L) Male: 13–18 g/dl (130–180 g/L)	Oxygenation status. Increased values in dehydration, polycythemia, congestive heart failure, chronic obstructive pulmonary disease, high altitudes. Decreased levels in anemia, hemorrhage, bone marrow cancer, renal disease, systemic lupus erythematosus, nutritional deficiency.
Hematocrit (WB)	Female: 37–47% (same) Male: 42–52% (same)	Oxygenation status. Increased levels in polycythemia, dehydration, congestive heart failure, shock, surgery. Decreased levels in anemia, hemorrhage, bone marrow disease, malnutrition, cirrhosis, rheumatoid arthritis.
Partial thromboplastin time (activated) (PTT or aPTT)	20–36 s (same)	Clotting mechanisms. Increased values in clotting factor deficiencies, cirrhosis, vitamin K deficiency, disseminated intravascular coagulation (DIC). Decreased values in early DIC, extensive cancer.
Platelet count (WB)	150,000–400,000/μl (150–400 × 10⁹/L)	Clotting mechanisms. Increased values in polycythemia, cancers, rheumatoid arthritis, trauma. Decreased values in liver disease, hemolytic uremic syndrome, disseminated intravascular coagulation (DIC), idiopathic thrombocytopenic purpura (ITP), systemic lupus erythematosus (SLE).
Prothrombin time (PT) (WB)	11–12.5 s (same) 1.5–2 × control (evaluating anticoagulant treatment)	Clotting mechanisms. Increased values in liver disease, vitamin K deficiency, salicylate intoxication. Decreased values in disseminated intravascular coagulation (DIC).
Red blood cell count (RBC) (WB)	Female: 4.2–5.4 million/μl (4.2–5.4 × 10¹²/L) Male: 4.7–6.1 million/μl (4.7–6.1 × 10¹²/L)	Oxygenation status. Increased values in high altitudes, polycythemia, hemoconcentration, cor pulmonale. Decreased values in hemorrhage, hemolysis, anemias, chronic illness, nutritional deficiencies, leukemia, overhydration.
Reticulocyte count (WB)	0.5–2.0% (same)	Bone marrow function. Increased values in hemolytic anemia, sickle-cell anemia, leukemia, pregnancy. Decreased values in pernicious anemia, folic acid deficiency, cirrhosis, chronic infection, bone marrow depression or failure.
White blood cell count (WBC) (WB) Total (males)	4800–10,800/μl (4.8–10.8 × 10⁹/L)	Immune system integrity. Increased values in infection, trauma, stress, tissue necrosis, inflammation. Decreased values in bone marrow depression or failure, drug toxicity, overwhelming infection, malnutrition.

TEST (SAMPLE)	REFERENCE VALUES: CONVENTIONAL (SI)	PHYSIOLOGICAL INDICATION AND CLINICAL IMPLICATIONS
Hematology Studies (continued)		
White blood cell count, differential (WB)		
Neutrophils	50–70% (same)	Immune system integrity. Increased values in acute bacterial infections, stress, Cushing's syndrome, inflammatory disorders, ketoacidosis, gout. Decreased levels in aplastic anemia, bone marrow suppression, and overwhelming bacterial infections.
Lymphocytes	25–40% (same)	Immune system integrity. Increased values in viral infections (e.g., mumps, rubella, infectious mononucleosis, hepatitis), lymphocytic leukemia, certain bacterial infections. Decreased levels in leukemia, immunodeficiency, lupus erythematosus, bone marrow depressive drugs.
Eosinophils	1–4% (same)	Immune system integrity. Increased levels in allergic reactions, parasitic infections, leukemia. Decreased levels in excess adrenosteroid production.
Monocytes	3–8% (same)	Immune system integrity. Increased levels in certain infections (e.g., tuberculosis, malaria), inflammatory disorders.
Basophils	0.5–1.0% (same)	Immune system integrity. Increased levels in myeloproliferative disorders, leukemia. Decreased levels in allergic reactions, hyperthyroidism, stress.
Urine Tests		
Amylase (24 h)	<6000 Somogyi units/24 h 0–500 U/24 h (0–8.3 μkat/24h)	Pancreatic function. Increased values in pancreatic disease or obstruction, inflammation of the salivary glands, and cholecystitis.
Bilirubin (random)	Negative (same)	Liver function. Increased values in liver disease, extrahepatic obstruction (gallstones, tumor, inflammation).
Blood (hemoglobin) (random)	Negative (same)	Urinary system function. Increased values in cystitis, renal disease, hemolytic anemia, transfusion reaction, prostatitis, burns.
Osmolality (random or fasting)	Random: 50–1200 mOsm/kg H_2O (50–1200 mmol/kg H_2O) Fluid restriction: ≥850 mOsm/kg H_2O (≥850 mmol/kg H_2O)	Fluid and electrolyte balance, renal function, and endocrine function. Increased levels in hypernatremia, syndrome of inappropriate ADH secretion (SIADH), congestive heart failure, metabolic acidosis. Decreased levels in diabetes insipidus, water intoxication, pyelonephritis, renal tubular necrosis, aldosteronism.
Phosphate (24 h)	0.9–1.3g/24 hr (same)	Parathyroid function. Increased levels in hyperparathyroidism, osteomalacia, certain renal diseases, vitamin D deficiency. Decreased levels in hypoparathyroidism.
Potassium (24 h)	25–120 mEq/24 h (25–120 mmol/24 h)	Fluid and electrolyte balance. Increased values in renal tubular necrosis, metabolic acidosis, dehydration, aldosteronism, Cushing's syndrome. Decreased values in Addison's disease, malabsorption, acute renal failure.
Protein (random)	<8 mg/dl (<80 mg/L)	Renal function. Increased levels in nephrotic syndrome, renal trauma, hyperthyroidism, diabetic nephropathy, lupus erythematosus.
Sodium (24 h)	40–220 mEq/24 h (40–220 mmol/24 h)	Fluid and electrolyte balance. Increased values in dehydration, ketoacidosis, syndrome of inappropriate ADH secretion (SIADH), adrenocortical insufficiency. Decreased levels in congestive heart failure, renal failure, diarrhea, aldosteronism.
Uric acid (24 h)	250–750 mg/24 h (1.5–4.5 mmol/24 h)	Renal function and metabolism. Increased in gout, leukemia, liver disease, ulcerative colitis. Decreased in renal disease, alcoholism, lead toxicity, folic acid deficiency.

TEST (SAMPLE)	REFERENCE VALUES: CONVENTIONAL (SI)	PHYSIOLOGICAL INDICATION AND CLINICAL IMPLICATIONS
Urine Tests (continued)		
Urinalysis (random)		
Color	Straw, yellow, amber	Fluid balance and renal function. Darker in dehydration. Lighter in overhydration, diabetes insipidus. Color varies with disease states, diet, and medications.
Odor	Aromatic	Metabolic function, infection. Abnormal odors in infection, ketonuria, rectal fistula, hepatic failure, phenylketonuria.
Specific gravity	1.001–1.035	An indirect measurement of urine concentration (osmolality). Same physiological indications and clinical implications as osmolality.
pH	4.5–8.0	A crude indicator of acid-base balance. Decreased by acidic diet (proteins). Increased by a vegetarian diet, prolonged vomiting, and bacterial infection of the urinary tract.
Urobilinogen (24 h)	0.2–1.0 mg/dl (2–10 mg/L)	Liver function. Increased in hemolytic anemias, hepatitis, cirrhosis, biliary disease. Decreased in common bile duct obstruction.
Volume (24 h)	800–2000 ml/24 h (0.8–2.0 L/24 h)	Fluid and electrolyte balance, renal function. Increased values in diabetes insipidus, diabetes mellitus, renal disease. Decreased values in dehydration, syndrome of inappropriate ADH secretion (SIADH), renal disease.

APPENDIX G Answers to Check Your Understanding, Clinical Connections, Multiple Choice, and Matching Questions

Chapter 1

Check Your Understanding 1. The operation or function of a structure is dictated (promoted or prevented) by its anatomy. For example, oxygen and carbon dioxide are exchanged across the very thin membranes of the lungs but not across the skin. **2.** Muscle shortening is a topic of physiology. The body location of the lungs is an anatomy topic. **3.** Cytologists study the cellular level of organization. **4.** The order in the structural hierarchy is cell, tissue, organ, and organism. **5.** Bones and cartilages are part of the skeletal system. The nasal cavity, lungs, and trachea are organs of the respiratory system. **6.** Living organisms are able to maintain their boundaries, move, respond to environmental changes, digest nutrients, carry out metabolism, dispose of wastes, reproduce, and grow. While inanimate objects may exhibit some of these properties, they do not exhibit all of them. **7.** Metabolism is the term that encompasses all the chemical reactions that occur in body cells. **8.** In flight, the cabin must be pressurized because the atmosphere is thinner at high altitudes and the amount of oxygen entering the blood under such conditions may be insufficient to maintain life. **9.** Negative feedback mechanisms allow us to adjust to conditions outside the normal temperature range by causing heat to be lost from the body (in hot conditions) and retained or generated by the body (in cold conditions). **10.** Thirst is part of a negative feedback control system because it prods us to drink, which ends the thirst stimulus and returns body fluid volume to the normal range. **11.** This is a positive feedback mechanism because it enhances the change (formation of a platelet plug) set into motion by the stimulus (damage to the blood vessel). The response ends when the platelet plug has plugged the hole in the blood vessel. **12.** The position in which a person is standing erect with feet slightly separated and palms facing anteriorly. Knowing the anatomical position is important because directional terms refer to the body as if it is in this position. **13.** Axillary region is the armpit. Acromial area is the tip of the shoulder. **14.** A frontal (coronal) section would separate the brain into anterior and posterior parts. **15.** He may have appendicitis if the pain is in the lower right quadrant of his abdomen. **16.** Of these organs, only the spinal cord is in the dorsal body cavity. **17.** As mobile organs (heart, lungs, digestive organs) work, friction is greatly reduced by the presence of serous fluid. Serous fluid allows the surrounding serous membranes to glide easily over one another.

Review Questions 1. c; **2.** a; **3.** e; **4.** a, d; **5.** (a) wrist (b) hip bone (c) nose (d) toes (e) scalp; **6.** neither c nor d would be visible in the median section; **7.** (a) dorsal (b) ventral (c) dorsal (d) ventral; **8.** b; **9.** b; **10.** c

Chapter 2

Check Your Understanding 1. Foods contain chemical energy. **2.** Electrical energy is the energy used by nerve cells to transmit messages in the body. **3.** Potential energy (PE) is available when we are still. PE is converted to kinetic (working) energy when we exercise. **4.** Besides hydrogen and nitrogen, carbon and oxygen help to make up the bulk of living matter. **5.** This element has 82 protons in its nucleus and 82 electrons in its orbitals (electron cloud). **6.** Atomic mass indicates the sum of the protons and neutrons in a given atom's nucleus. Atomic weight indicates the average mass of all the isotopes of a given element. **7.** A molecule is 2 or more atoms held together by chemical bonds. **8.** A compound is formed when two or more different kinds of atoms chemically bond together, as in NaCl. Oxygen gas is 2 oxygen atoms (the same kind of atom) bonded together. **9.** Blood is a mixture because its components are not changed by their combination and they can be separated by physical means. **10.** Hydrogen bonds (linking H of one water molecule to O of another) form between water molecules. **11.** Argon's valence shell is full:)2e)8e)8e. Hence it is nonreactive. **12.** Electrons would spend more time in the vicinity of the more electronegative atom in XY, whereas electrons in XX would orbit both X atoms to an equal extent. **13.** Fats are digested in the small intestine by decomposition reactions. **14.** Biochemical reactions in the body tend to be irreversible because (a) one or more of the products is removed from the reaction site or (b) the product is needed more than the reactants, so the cell would not provide energy to reverse the reaction. **15.** Decomposition reactions in which foods are broken down for energy are oxidation-reduction (O-R) reactions. **16.** Water is an excellent solvent because of its polarity. As a dipole, it can orient itself to the end of other molecules, causing them to dissociate or go into solution. **17.** Electrolytes are substances like salts that will conduct an electrical current in aqueous solution. **18.** H^+ is responsible for acidity. **19.** It is better to add a weak base, which will act to buffer the strong acid. **20.** Monomers of carbohydrates are called monosaccharides or simple sugars. Glucose is blood sugar. **21.** The animal form of stored carbohydrate is glycogen. **22.** Triglycerides, the major source of stored energy in the body, are composed of three fatty acid chains and a glycerol molecule and are found in fat tissue. Phospholipids consist of two fatty acid chains and a charged P-containing group. They are found in all cell membranes where they form the basis of those membranes. **23.** Hydrolysis reactions break down polymers or macromolecules to their monomers by adding water to each bond joining monomers. **24.** An "amino acid" has an amine group (NH_2) and a COOH group that has acidic properties. **25.** The primary structure of proteins is the stringlike chain of amino acids. **26.** The secondary structures of proteins are the alpha helix and the beta-pleated sheet. **27.** Molecular chaperones prevent inaccurate or inappropriate folding in the 3-D structure of a protein. **28.** Enzymes hold the substrate(s) in a desirable position to interact. **29.** DNA contains deoxyribose sugar and the bases A, T, G, C. RNA contains ribose sugar and the bases A, U, G, C. **30.** DNA dictates protein structure by its base sequence and reproduces itself before a cell divides to ensure that the genetic information in the daughter cells is identical. **31.** ATP stores energy in smaller packets that are more readily released and transferred (during ATP hydrolysis) than the energy stored in glucose. Hence the use of ATP as an energy source keeps energy waste to a minimum. **32.** When ATP releases energy, it loses a phosphate group and becomes ADP (also energy rich).

Review Questions 1. d; **2.** d; **3.** b; **4.** a; **5.** b; **6.** a; **7.** a; **8.** b; **9.** d; **10.** a; **11.** b; **12.** a, c; **13.** (1)a, (2)c; **14.** c; **15.** d; **16.** e; **17.** d; **18.** d; **19.** a; **20.** b; **21.** b; **22.** c

Chapter 3

Check Your Understanding 1. The three basic parts of a cell are the plasma membrane (the outer boundary of the cell), the nucleus (control center of the cell), and the cytoplasm (the fluid material between the nucleus and plasma membrane), which contains the organelles. **2.** It is the cell concept that includes structures and functions common to all cells. **3.** All cellular membranes consist of a double layer of phospholipids in which proteins are embedded. **4.** Hydrophobic regions (tails of phospholipid molecules) orient toward each other while the hydrophilic regions (phospholipid heads) orient to the aqueous fluid inside and outside the cell. **5.** The sugar residues of the glycocalyx provide recognizable biological markers for cells to recognize each other. **6.** The heart has desmosomes (anchoring junctions) that secure cardiac cells together as the heart works and gap junctions (communicating junctions) that allow ions to flow from cardiac cell to cardiac cell. **7.** Diffusion is driven by kinetic energy of the molecules. **8.** The relative concentration of the substance in different areas determines the direction of diffusion. Diffusion occurs from regions of high concentration to regions of low concentration. **9.** In channel-mediated diffusion, the diffusing substance moves through a membrane channel. In carrier-mediated diffusion, the diffusing substance attaches to a membrane (protein) carrier which moves it across the membrane. **10.** Phosphorylation of the Na^+-K^+ pump causes the pump protein to change shape so that it "pumps" Na^+ across the membrane. K^+ binding to the pump protein triggers the release of phosphate and the pump protein returns to its original shape. **11.** The plasma membrane expands as a result of exocytosis. **12.** Phagocytic cells engulf debris and a smoker's lungs would be laden with carbon particles and other debris from smoke inhalation. **13.** Cholesterol is taken in by receptor-mediated endocytosis. **14.** Diffusion of ions, mainly the diffusion of K^+ from the cell through leakage channels, establishes the resting membrane potential. **15.** In a polarized membrane, the inside is negative relative to its outside. **16.** Signaling chemicals that bind to membrane receptors are called ligands. G protein–linked receptors direct intracellular events by promoting formation of second messengers. **17.** Mitochondria are the major sites of ATP synthesis. **18.** Ribosomes are the sites of protein synthesis. The rough ER provides a site for ribosome attachment and its cisternae package in vesicles the proteins made on the ribosomes for transport to the Golgi apparatus. The Golgi apparatus modifies and packages the proteins it receives for various destinations within or outside the cell. **19.** The lysosomal enzymes digest foreign substances engulfed by the cell, nonuseful or deteriorating organelles, or even the cell itself to prevent the buildup of cellular debris. The enzymes in peroxisomes detoxify harmful chemicals and neutralize free radicals. **20.** Both microfilaments and microtubules are involved in organelle movements within the cell and/or movements of the cell as a whole. **21.** Intermediate filaments are the most important cytoskeletal elements in maintaining cell shape. **22.** The major function of microvilli is to increase the cell's surface area for absorption or filtration of substances. **23.** If a cell loses its nucleus, it is doomed to die because it will be unable to make proteins, which include the enzymes needed for all metabolic reactions. **24.** Nucleoli are the site of synthesis of ribosomal subunits. **25.** Histone proteins provide the means to pack DNA in a compact, orderly way and play a role in gene regulation. **26.** The base sequence of the corresponding strand will be GCTTAC. **27.** DNA is synthesized during the S phase. **28.** Nuclear envelope breaks up, spindle forms, nucleoli disappear, and the chromosomes coil and condense. **29.** Codons are three base sequences in mRNA, each of which specifies an amino acid. Anticodons are three-base sequences in tRNA that are complementary to the codons specifying the amino acid they transport to the ribosome during protein synthesis. **30.** A site = entry site for tRNA at the ribosome. P site = site where peptide bonds form between delivered amino acids. E site = the tRNA exit site from the ribosome. **31.** DNA provides the coded instructions (is the template) for protein synthesis via the mRNA synthesized on it. **32.** Ubiquitin attaches to misfolded, damaged, or unneeded proteins, tagging them for destruction by proteasomes. **33.** Blood plasma is extracellular fluid that transports nutrients, gases, hormones, and other substances throughout the body. Interstitial fluid is an important transport and dissolving medium. **34.** Apoptosis is a process of programmed cell death which rids the body of cells that are stressed, damaged, old, or no longer needed. **35.** The wear-and-tear theory of aging attributes aging to little chemical insults and free radicals which have cumulative detrimental effects.

Review Questions 1. d; **2.** a, c; **3.** b; **4.** b; **5.** e; **6.** c; **7.** d; **8.** a; **9.** d; **10.** a; **11.** b; **12.** d; **13.** c; **14.** b; **15.** d; **16.** a; **17.** b; **18.** d; **19.** c

Chapter 4

Check Your Understanding 1. Fixing tissue preserves it and prevents it from deteriorating. **2.** Organic dyes are used to stain tissues viewed by a light microscope. Heavy metal salts are used to stain tissues viewed by electron microscopes. **3.** Epithelial tissue lines body cavities and covers the body's external surface; thus polarity with one free (apical) surface is a requirement. **4.** Epithelial tissue can regenerate and its cells are joined by lateral contacts. **5.** Simple epithelia are "built" to provide for efficient absorption and filtration across their thin epithelial barriers. **6.** Pseudostratified epithelia appear to be stratified because their cells' nuclei lie at different distances from the basement membrane. However, all cells rest on the basement membrane. **7.** Transitional epithelium is found in the urinary bladder and other hollow urinary organs. The ability of this epithelium to thin allows the urinary organs to handle (store or transport) a larger urine volume when necessary. **8.** All unicellular exocrine glands secrete the protein mucin (which becomes mucus on mixing with water). **9.** These exocrine glands are classified by duct and secretory unit types. **10.** Holocrine glands have the highest rate of cell division. The secretory cells fragment and are lost in the secretion; thus the secretory cells must be continuously replaced. **11.** Connective tissue functions to bind, support, protect, and insulate body organs. In addition, blood acts to transport substances throughout the body. **12.** Reticular, collagen, and elastic fibers are found in the various connective tissues. **13.** Areolar connective tissue, because of its loose weblike nature, is capable of serving as a fluid reservoir. **14.** Dense regular connective tissue is damaged when you lacerate a tendon. **15.** Hyaline cartilage forms the growth plates. **16.** With extended processes, a neuron can conduct electrical signals a greater distance within the body. **17.** Cardiac muscle cells have striations and are branching cells. **18.** Skeletal muscle tissue is voluntary and is the muscle tissue injured when you "pull a muscle" while exercising. **19.** A mucous membrane consists of both connective tissue and epithelium. It lines body cavities open to the exterior. **20.** The serous membranes called pleurae line the thorax walls and cover the lungs. **21.** The three main steps of tissue repair are inflammation, organization, and regeneration and fibrosis (which is a permanent repair). **22.** More severe injuries damage and destroy more tissue, requiring greater replacement with scar tissue. **23.** The three embryonic germ layers are the ectoderm, mesoderm, and endoderm. **24.** Ectoderm gives rise to the nervous system. **25.** Epithelium and some connective tissues (areolar, dense irregular, and blood-forming tissue) remain highly mitotic all through life.

Review Questions 1. a, c, d, b; **2.** c, e; **3.** b, f, a, d, g, d; **4.** b; **5.** c; **6.** b

Chapter 5

Check Your Understanding 1. Since the sole of the foot has thick skin, the layers from most superficial to deepest would be the stratum corneum, stratum lucidum, stratum granulosum, stratum spinosum, and stratum basale. **2.** The stratum basale undergoes almost continuous mitosis to replace cells lost by abrasion. **3.** The skin is subjected to a lot of abrasion and physical trauma. The desmosomes, which are connecting junctions, help to hold the cells together during such stress. **4.** The stratum basale, which abuts the dermis where the blood supply is, has the best nourished cells. **5.** The papillary layer of the dermis gives rise to fingerprint patterns. **6.** Fatty tissue in the hypodermis gives it insulating and shock-absorbing properties. **7.** Because there is no bleeding, the cut has penetrated into the avascular epidermis only. **8.** The third pigment contributing to skin color is hemoglobin, the pigment found in red blood cells found in blood vessels of the dermis. **9.** Cyanosis is a bluish cast of the skin that indicates that hemoglobin in the red blood cells in the dermal capillaries is poorly oxygenated. **10.** Jaundice or a yellow cast to the skin due to the deposit of yellow bile pigments in body tissues may indicate a liver disorder. **11.** Sebaceous (oil) glands and apocrine glands are associated with the hair follicles. **12.** His sympathetic nervous system activated his eccrine sweat glands and caused heat-induced sweating in order to cool the body. **13.** Heat-induced sweating occurs all over the body when we are overheated. A cold sweat is emotionally induced sweating that begins on the palms, soles, and armpits and then spreads to other body areas. Both types of sweating are produced by the eccrine sweat glands, but activity of apocrine sweat glands is also likely during a cold sweat. **14.** The palms of the hands and soles of the feet are thick skin areas. It would be dangerous to have oily soles, and oily palms would decrease the ability of the hands to hang onto things. **15.** The regions of a hair from outside in are the cuticle, cortex, and medulla. **16.** There are no nerves in a hair, so cutting hair is painless. **17.** The arrector pili muscles pull the hair (normally slanted) to the upright position (when cold or scared). **18.** The hair papilla contains a knot of capillaries that supplies nutrients to cells of the hair bulb. **19.** The lunule of the nail is white because the thick nail matrix that underlies it blocks the rosy color of the dermal blood supply from showing through. **20.** Nails are hard because the keratin they contain is the hard keratin variety. **21.** The low pH of skin secretions (acid mantle) inhibits division of bacteria, and many bacteria are killed by bactericidal substances in sebum or by natural antibiotics called defensins. Damaged skin secretes cathelicidins that are effective against a certain strain of strep bacteria. **22.** The epidermal dendritic cells play a role in body immunity. **23.** Sunlight causes the skin to produce a precursor of vitamin D from cholesterol. **24.** The skin carries out chemical conversions that supplement some of the protective conversions carried out by the liver, convert some chemicals into carcinogens, activate some steroid hormones, and synthesize the vitamin D precursor. **25.** Basal cell carcinoma develops from the youngest epidermal cells. **26.** The ABCD rule helps one to recognize signs of melanoma. **27.** First- and second-degree burns can heal uneventfully by regeneration of epidermal cells as long as infection does not occur. Third-degree burns destroy the entire epidermis and regeneration is not possible. Infection and loss of body fluid and proteins are problematic. **28.** Burns to the face are serious because damage to the lungs can occur in such burns. **29.** Vernix caseosa is a product of the sebaceous glands. **30.** Loss of subcutaneous fat, common in the elderly, leads to cold intolerance seen in this group of people. **31.** UV radiation degrades collagen and leads to loss of skin elasticity and water-holding capacity.

Clinical Connections 1. The skin separates and protects the internal environment of the body from potentially dangerous elements in the external environment. Mrs. DeStephano's chart indicates epidermal abrasions, which represent the loss of this barrier. Epidermal loss will also cost Mrs. DeStephano the acid mantle of her skin, protection against UV radiation, and epidermal dendritic (Langerhans) cells, which protect against invasion by microorganisms. **2.** Macrophages found in the dermis can act as a backup system against bacterial and viral invasion when the epidermis is damaged. **3.** Suturing brings the edges of wounds close together and promotes faster healing because smaller amounts of granulation tissue need to be formed. This is termed *healing by first intention*. **4.** Cyanosis signals a decrease in the amount of oxygen carried by hemoglobin in the blood. Respiratory system and/or cardiovascular system impairments can lead to cyanosis.

Review Questions 1. a; **2.** c; **3.** d; **4.** d; **5.** b; **6.** b; **7.** c; **8.** c; **9.** b; **10.** a; **11.** d; **12.** b

Chapter 6

Check Your Understanding 1. Hyaline cartilage is the most plentiful in the adult body. **2.** The epiglottis and external ear cartilages are flexible elastic cartilage. **3.** Interstitial growth is growth from within. **4.** The components of the axial skeleton are the skull, the vertebral column, and the thoracic cage. **5.** The major function of the axial skeleton is to establish the long axis of the body and to protect structures that it encloses. The general function of the appendicular skeleton is to allow us mobility for propulsion and manipulation of our environment. **6.** The ribs and skull bones are flat bones. **7.** Skeletal muscles use bones as levers to cause movement of the body and its parts. **8.** Bone matrix stores minerals and growth factors. **9.** Bone marrow cavities serve as sites for blood cell formation and fat storage. **10.** Crests, tubercles, and spines are bony projections.

11. Compact bone looks fairly solid and homogeneous whereas spongy bones have an open network of bone spicules. **12.** Endosteum lines the internal canals and covers the trabeculae. **13.** Bone's inorganic component (bone salts) makes it hard. **14.** The osteoclast fits this description. **15.** Bones begin as fibrous membranes or hyaline cartilages. **16.** The cartilage model grows, then breaks down and is replaced by bone. **17.** The primary ossification center in a long bone is in the center of the shaft. The secondary ossification centers are in the epiphyses (bone ends). **18.** The chondrocytes are enlarging and their lacunae are breaking down and leaving holes in the cartilage matrix. **19.** If bone-destroying cells (osteoclasts) are more active than bone-forming cells (osteoblasts), bone mass will decrease. **20.** The hormonal stimulus maintains homeostatic blood calcium levels. **21.** In an open fracture, the bone ends are exposed to the external environment. In a closed fracture, the bone ends do not penetrate the external boundary of the skin. **22.** Bone growth increases bone mass, as during childhood or when exceptional stress is placed on the bones. Bone remodeling follows bone growth to maintain the proper proportions of the bone considering stresses placed upon it. **23.** Paget's disease is characterized by excessive deposit of weak, poorly mineralized bone. **24.** Sufficient vitamin D, calcium, and weight-bearing exercise all help to maintain healthy bone density. **25.** Adult rickets is called osteomalacia. **26.** At birth, most bones are well formed and ossified. Two areas of hyaline cartilage remain—in the epiphyseal plates and covering the bone ends (articular cartilage). **27.** The skull bones do not appear to lose mass with aging.

Clinical Connections 1. Mrs. DeStephano's broken leg has a transverse fracture of the open variety because the broken ends of the bone are protruding through the skin. **2.** The laceration of the skin caused by the broken end of the bone creates a breach in the protective barrier created by the skin, providing an entry point for bacteria and other microorganisms. In addition, the protruding ends of the bone have now been exposed to the nonsterile external environment. This could result in the development of osteomyelitis, a bacterial infection, which can be treated with antibiotics. **3.** Reduction of a fracture is the clinical term for "setting the bone." Mrs. DeStephano's physician chose internal reduction, in which surgery is performed and the broken ends of the bone are secured together by pins or wires. A cast was applied to keep the aligned ends of the bone immobile until healing of the fracture has occurred. **4.** Healing of Mrs. DeStephano's fracture will begin as bony callus formation fills the break in the bone with bony tissue. This process begins 3–4 weeks after the break occurs and is completed within 2–3 months. **5.** Nutrient arteries supply blood to the bone tissue. In order for Mrs. DeStephano's break to heal normally, the bony tissue must be supplied with oxygen (to generate ATP for energy) and nutrients in order to rebuild the bone. Damage to a nutrient artery will decrease the delivery of these building materials and could slow the process of healing. **6.** For a fracture that is slow to heal, new techniques that promote healing include electrical stimulation, which promotes the deposition of new bone tissue; ultrasound treatments, known to speed healing; and possibly the addition of bone substitutes to the fractured area. **7.** At age 45, Mrs. DeStephano will most likely not regenerate her knee cartilage. (Cartilage growth typically ends during adolescence.) Cartilage damage that occurs during adulthood is slow to heal, due to the avascular nature of cartilage, and is usually irreparable. Surgical removal of cartilage fragments to allow improved movement of the joint is the usual treatment for this type of damage.

Review Questions 1. e; **2.** b; **3.** c; **4.** d; **5.** e; **6.** b; **7.** c; **8.** b; **9.** d, e; **10.** c; **11.** b; **12.** c; **13.** a; **14.** b

Chapter 7

Check Your Understanding 1. The three main parts of the axial skeleton are the skull, vertebral column, and thoracic cage. **2.** The axial skeleton is more important in protecting internal organs. **3.** The frontal, parietal, temporal, sphenoid, and ethmoid bones are all cranial bones. **4.** The ethmoid bone forms the crista galli. **5.** The temporal bones house the external ear canals. **6.** The parietal bones abut each other at the sagittal suture. The occipital bone abuts the parietal bones at the lambdoid suture. **7.** The zygomatic bone are the cheekbones. **8.** Eating or talking, because the only freely movable joints of the skull are the temporomandibular joints of the jaw. **9.** The maxillae are the keystone bones of the facial skeleton. **10.** The sphenoid, ethmoid, frontal, and maxillary bones contain paranasal sinuses. **11.** The cribriform plates of the ethmoid bone form the roof of the nasal cavity. **12.** The maxillae form the bulk of the orbit floor. The eye is housed in the orbit. **13.** The five major regions of the vertebral column are the cervical, thoracic, lumbar, sacral, and coccygeal regions. **14.** The cervical and lumbar regions are concave posteriorly. **15.** The fibrocartilage discs contribute to the flexibility of the vertebral column. **16.** There are 7 cervical and 12 thoracic vertebrae. **17.** The dens is the axis on which the atlas rotates. If it's broken, movements of the atlas would be less controllable. **18.** A lumbar vertebra is heavier and its massive body is kidney shaped. Its spinous processes are short and project directly back. A thoracic vertebral body is generally heart shaped, its spinous process is long, sharp, and points downward, and its transverse processes have facets for articulating with the ribs. **19.** A true rib connects to the sternum by its own costal cartilage. A false rib connects to the sternum via costal cartilages of other ribs or not at all. **20.** The sternal angle is a ridge across the front of the sternum where the manubrium joins the sternal body. It acts as a hinge allowing the sternum to swing anteriorly when we inhale. Because it is aligned with the second rib, it is a handy cue for finding that rib and then counting the ribs during a physical exam. **21.** The thoracic vertebrae also contribute to the thoracic cage. **22.** Each pectoral girdle is formed by a scapula and a clavicle. **23.** The pectoral girdle attaches to the sternal manubrium of the axial skeleton via the medial end of its clavicle. **24.** A consequence of its flexibility is that it is easily dislocated. **25.** Together the ulna and humerus form the elbow joint. **26.** The ulna and the radius each have a styloid process distally. **27.** Carpals are found in the proximal region of the palm. They are short bones. **28.** The third bone of the os coxae is the ischium. **29.** The pelvic girdle (along with the sacrum) receives the weight of the upper body (trunk, head, and upper limbs) and transmits that weight to the lower limbs. **30.** The female pelvis is wider and has a shorter sacrum and a more movable coccyx. **31.** The tibia is the second largest bone in the body. **32.** The medial malleolus is located on the distalmost medial aspect of the tibia. **33.** The lateral condyles are not sites of muscle attachment, they are articular surfaces. **34.** Because of their springiness, the foot arches save energy during locomotion. **35.** The two largest tarsals are the talus, and the calcaneus which forms the heel. **36.** The enlargement of the facial skeleton between ages 6 and 13 is due to the enlargement of the nose and paranasal sinuses and the development of the permanent teeth. **37.** The lumbar curvature develops when the baby begins to walk.

Review Questions 1. (1)b, g; (2)h; (3)d; (4)d, f; (5)e; (6)c; (7)a, b, d, h; (8)i; **2.** (1)g, (2)f, (3)b, (4)a, (5)b, (6)c, (7)d, (8)e; **3.** (1)b, (2)c, (3)e, (4)a, (5)h, (6)e, (7)f

Chapter 8

Check Your Understanding 1. Joint and articulation are synonyms. **2.** The synarthroses are the least mobile of the joint types. **3.** Symphyses and synchondroses are cartilaginous joints. **4.** In general, the more stable a joint, the less mobile it is. **5.** The fibrous capsule and the synovial membrane make up the wall of the articular capsule. **6.** Bursae and tendon sheaths help to reduce friction during joint movement. **7.** The muscle tendons that cross the joint are typically the most important factor in stabilizing synovial joints. **8.** Weeping lubrication helps keep the joint

cartilages nourished and "lubricates" the joint surfaces. **9.** John's hip joint was flexed and his knees extended and his thumb was in opposition (to his index finger). **10.** The hinge and pivot joints are uniaxial joints. **11.** The knee and temporomandibular joints have menisci. The elbow and knee act mainly as a uniaxial hinge. The shoulder depends largely on muscle tendons for stability. **12.** Arthritis means inflammation of the joint. **13.** RA typically produces pain, swelling, and joint deformations that tend to be bilateral and crippling. OA patients tend to have pain, particularly on arising, which is relieved by gentle exercise, and enlarged bone ends (due to spurs) in affected joints. Affected joints may exhibit crepitus. **14.** Lyme disease is caused by spirochete bacteria and transmitted by a tick bite. **15.** Regular exercise strengthens joints and keeps them well nourished.

Review Questions 1. (1)c, (2)a, (3)a, (4)b, (5)c, (6)b, (7)b, (8)a, (9)c; **2.** b; **3.** d; **4.** d; **5.** b; **6.** d; **7.** d

Chapter 9

Check Your Understanding 1. Striated means "with stripes." **2.** He should have responded "smooth muscle," which fits the description. **3.** "Epimysium" literally translates to "outside the muscle" and this connective tissue sheath is the outermost muscle sheath which encloses the entire muscle. **4.** The thin myofilaments have binding sites for calcium on the troponin molecules forming part of those filaments. **5.** In a resting muscle fiber, the SR would have the highest concentration of calcium ions. The mitochondrion provides the ATP needed for muscle activity. **6.** The components of the neuromuscular junction are the axon terminal, the synaptic cleft and the junctional folds of the sarcolemma. **7.** The final trigger for contraction is a certain concentration of calcium ions in the cytosol. The initial trigger is depolarization of the sarcolemma. **8.** There are always some myosin cross bridges bound to the actin myofilament during the contraction phase. Thus, backward sliding of the actin filaments is prevented. **9.** Without ATP, rigor would occur because the myosin heads could not detach. **10.** A motor unit is an axon of a motor neuron and all the muscle fibers it innervates. **11.** During the latent period, events of excitation-contraction coupling are occurring. **12.** Immediately after Jay grabs the bar, his biceps muscles are contracting isometrically. As his body moves upward toward the bar, they are contracting isotonically and concentrically. As he lowers his body, the biceps are contracting isotonically and eccentrically. **13.** Eric was breathing heavily because it takes some time for his heart rate and overall metabolism to return to the resting state after exercise. Moreover, he had likely incurred an oxygen deficit. Although jogging is primarily an aerobic exercise, there is always some anaerobic respiration that occurs as well—the amount depends on exercise intensity. As fatigue occurs, potassium ions accumulate in the T tubules, and lactic acid and phosphate ions accumulate in the muscle cells. **14.** Factors that influence muscle contractile force include muscle fiber size, the number of muscle fibers stimulated, the frequency of stimulation, and the degree of muscle stretch. Factors that influence velocity of contraction include muscle fiber type, load, and the number of motor units contracting. **15.** Fast glycolytic fibers would provide for short periods of intense strength needed to lift and move furniture. **16.** To increase muscle size and strength, anaerobic exercise is best. Muscle endurance is enhanced by aerobic exercise. **17.** Both skeletal and smooth muscle fibers are elongated cells, but unlike smooth muscle cells, which are spindle shaped, uninucleate, and nonstriated, skeletal muscle cells are very large cigar-shaped, multinucleate, striated cells. **18.** Calcium binds to troponin on the actin filaments in skeletal muscle cells. In smooth muscle cells, it binds to a cytoplasmic protein called calmodulin. **19.** Hollow organs that have smooth muscle cells helping to form their walls often must temporarily store the organ's contents (urine, food residues, etc.), an ability ensured by the stress-relaxation response. **20.** During development of skeletal muscle fibers, the myoblast cells join together, forming multinucleate myotubes. **21.** The connective tissue in muscles increases with age, causing the muscles to get stringier. **22.** Regular exercise and strength training help to defer the loss in strength and muscle wasting that tends to occur with age, and improve neuromuscular function.

Clinical Connections 1. The first reaction to tissue injury is the initiation of the inflammatory response. The inflammatory chemicals increase the permeability of the capillaries in the injured area, allowing white blood cells, fluid, and other substances to reach the injured area. The next step in healing involves the formation of granulation tissue, in which the vascular supply for the injured area is regenerated and collagen fibers to knit the torn edges of the tissue together are formed. Skeletal muscle does not regenerate well, so the damaged areas of Mrs. DeStephano's muscle tissue will probably be repaired primarily by the formation of fibrous tissue, creating scar tissue. **2.** Healing is aided by good circulation of blood within the injured area. Vascular damage compromises healing because the supply of oxygen and nutrients to the tissue is reduced. **3.** Under normal circumstances, skeletal muscles receive electrical signals from the nervous system continuously. These signals help to maintain muscle tone and readiness. Severing of the sciatic nerve removes this continuous nervous input to the muscles and will lead to muscle atrophy. Immobility of muscles will lead to a replacement of contractile muscle tissue with noncontractile fibrous connective tissue. Distal to the point of transection, the muscle will begin to decrease in size within 3–7 days of becoming immobile. This process can be delayed by electrically stimulating the tissues. Passive range-of-motion exercises also help prevent loss of muscle tone and joint range, and improve circulation in the injured areas. **4.** Mrs. DeStephano's physician wants to supply her damaged tissues with the necessary building materials to encourage healing. A high-protein diet will provide plenty of amino acids to rebuild or replace damaged proteins, carbohydrates will provide the fuel molecules needed to generate the required ATP, and vitamin C is important for the regeneration of connective tissue.

Review Questions 1. c; **2.** b; **3.** (1)b, (2)a, (3)b, (4)a, (5)b, (6)a; **4.** c; **5.** a; **6.** a; **7.** d; **8.** a; **9.** (1)a, (2)a, c, (3)b, (4)c, (5)b, (6)b; **10.** a; **11.** c; **12.** c; **13.** c; **14.** b

Chapter 10

Check Your Understanding 1. The term "prime mover" refers to the muscle that bears the most responsibility for causing a particular movement. **2.** The iliacus overlies the iliac bone; the adductor brevis is a small (size) muscle that adducts (movement caused) the thigh; and the quadriceps (4 heads) femoris muscle follows the course of the femur. **3.** Of the muscles illustrated in Figure 10.1, the one with the parallel arrangement (sartorius) could shorten to the greatest degree. The stocky bipennate (rectus femoris) and multipennate (deltoid) muscles would be most powerful because they pack in the most fibers. **4.** Third-class levers are the fastest levers. **5.** A lever that operates at a mechanical advantage allows the muscle to exert less force than the load being moved. **6.** John was using the frontal belly of his epicranius to raise his eyebrows and the orbicularis oculi muscles to wink at Sarah. **7.** To make a sad clown's face you would contract your platysma, depressor anguli oris, and depressor labii inferioris muscles. **8.** The deltoid has a broad origin. When only its anterior fibers contract, it flexes and medially rotates the humerus. When only its posterior fibers contract, it extends and laterally rotates the humerus. **9.** The opponens pollicis does not have an insertion on the bones of the thumb.

Review Questions 1. c; **2.** c; **3.** (1)e, (2)c, (3)g, (4)f, (5)d; **4.** a; **5.** c; **6.** d; **7.** c; **8.** c; **9.** b; **10.** d; **11.** b; **12.** a; **13.** c; **14.** d; **15.** a, b; **16.** a

Chapter 11

Check Your Understanding 1. Integration involves processing and interpreting sensory information, and making a decision about motor output.

Integration occurs primarily in the CNS. **2.** (a) This "full stomach" feeling would be relayed by the sensory (afferent) division of the PNS (via its visceral afferent fibers). (b) The somatic nervous system, which is part of the motor (efferent) division of the PNS, controls movement of skeletal muscle. (c) The autonomic nervous system, which is part of the motor (efferent) division of the PNS, controls the heart rate. **3.** Astrocytes control the extracellular environment around neuron cell bodies in the CNS, whereas satellite cells perform this function in the PNS. **4.** Oligodendrocytes and Schwann cells form myelin sheaths in the CNS and PNS, respectively. **5.** A nerve fiber is a long *axon*, an extension of the cell. In connective tissue, fibers are extracellular *proteins* that provide support. In muscle tissue, a muscle fiber is a muscle *cell*. **6.** A nucleus within the brain is a cluster of cell bodies, whereas the nucleus within each neuron is a large organelle that acts as the control center of the cell. **7.** In the CNS, a myelin sheath is formed by oligodendrocytes that wrap their plasma membranes around the axon. The myelin sheath protects and electrically insulates fibers and increases the speed of transmission of nerve impulses. **8.** Burning a finger will first activate unipolar (pseudounipolar) neurons that are sensory (afferent) neurons. The impulse to move your finger away from the heat will be carried by multipolar neurons that are motor (efferent) neurons. **9.** The concentration gradient and the electrical gradient—together called the electrochemical gradient—determine the direction in which ions flow through an open membrane channel. **10.** There is more leakage of K^+ than of any other cations. **11.** Action potentials are larger than graded potentials and travel further. Graded potentials generally initiate action potentials. **12.** An action potential is regenerated anew at each membrane patch. **13.** Conduction of action potentials is faster in myelinated axons because myelin allows the axon membrane between nodes to change its voltage rapidly, and allows current to flow only at the widely spaced nodes. **14.** If a second stimulus occurs before the end of the absolute refractory period, no AP can occur because sodium channels are still inactivated. **15.** At an electrical synapse, neurons are joined by gap junctions. **16.** Voltage-gated ion (Ca^{2+}) channels are found in the presynaptic axon terminal and open when an action potential reaches the axon terminal. Chemically gated ion channels are found in the postsynaptic membrane and open when neurotransmitter binds to the receptor protein. **17.** IPSPs result from the flow of either K^+ or Cl^- through chemically gated channels. EPSPs result from the flow of both Na^+ and K^+ through chemically gated channels. **18.** Temporal summation is summation in *time* of graded potentials occurring in quick succession at the postsynaptic membrane. It can result from EPSPs arising from just one synapse. Spatial summation is summation in *space*—a postsynaptic neuron is stimulated by a large number of terminals at the same time. **19.** ACh interacts with more than one specific receptor type, and this explains how it can excite at some synapses and inhibit at others. **20.** cAMP is called a second messenger because it relays the message between the *first messenger* (the original chemical messenger) outside of the cell and effector molecules that will ultimately bring about the desired response within the cell. **21.** Reverberating circuits and parallel after-discharge circuits both result in prolonged output. **22.** The pattern of neural processing is serial processing. The response is a reflex arc. **23.** The pattern of neural processing is parallel processing. **24.** The growing tip of an axon is called a growth cone. Neurotropins are chemicals that signal the growth cone.

Review Questions 1. b; **2.** (1)d, (2)b, (3)f, (4)c, (5)a; **3.** b; **4.** c; **5.** a; **6.** c; **7.** b; **8.** d; **9.** c; **10.** c; **11.** a; **12.** (1)d, (2)b, (3)a, (4)c

Chapter 12

Check Your Understanding 1. The third ventricle is surrounded by the diencephalon. **2.** The cerebral hemispheres and the cerebellum have an outside layer of gray matter in addition to central gray matter and its surrounding white matter. **3.** Convolutions increase surface area of the cortex, which allows more neurons to occupy the limited space within the skull. **4.** The central sulcus separates primary motor areas from somatosensory areas. **5.** Motor functions on the left side of the body are controlled by the right hemisphere of the brain because motor tracts from the right hemisphere cross over (in the medulla oblongata) to the left side of the spinal cord to go to the left side of the body. **6.** Commissural fibers (which form commissures) allow the cerebral hemispheres to "talk to each other." **7.** The caudate nucleus, putamen, and globus pallidus together form the basal nuclei. **8.** Virtually all inputs ascending to the cerebral cortex synapse in the thalamus en route. **9.** The hypothalamus oversees the autonomic nervous system. **10.** The pyramids of the medulla are the corticospinal (pyramidal) tracts, the large voluntary motor tracts descending from the motor cortex. The result of decussation (crossing over) is that each side of the motor cortex controls the opposite side of the body. **11.** The cerebral peduncles and the colliculi are associated with the midbrain. **12.** There are many possible answers to this question—here are a few: Structurally, the cerebellum and cerebrum are similar in that they both have a thin outer cortex of gray matter, internal white matter, and deep gray matter nuclei. Also, both have body maps (homunculi) and large fiber tracts connecting them to the brain stem. Both receive sensory input and influence motor output. A major difference is that the cerebellum is almost entirely concerned with motor output, whereas the cerebrum has much broader responsibilities. Also, while a cerebral hemisphere controls the opposite side of the body, a cerebellar hemisphere controls the same side of the body. **13.** The hypothalamus is part of the limbic system and also an autonomic (visceral) control center. **14.** Taylor is increasing the amount of sensory stimuli she receives, which will be relayed to the reticular activating system, which, in turn, will increase activation of the cerebral cortex. **15.** Delta waves are typically seen in deep sleep in normal adults. **16.** Drowsiness (or lethargy) and stupor are stages of consciousness between alertness and coma. **17.** Most skeletal muscles are actively inhibited during REM sleep. **18.** Transfer of memory from STM to LTM is enhanced by (1) rehearsal, (2) association (tying "new" information to "old" information), and (3) a heightened emotional state (for example, alert, motivated, surprised, or aroused). **19.** The basal nuclei and premotor cortex are involved in procedural (skills) memory, but not in declarative memory. **20.** CSF, formed by the choroid plexuses as a filtrate of blood plasma, is a watery "broth" similar in composition to plasma. It protects the brain and spinal cord from blows and other trauma, helps nourish the brain, and carries chemical signals from one part of the brain to another. **21.** A TIA is a temporary loss of blood supply to brain tissue, and it differs from a stroke in that the resultant impairment is fully reversible. **22.** Mrs. Lee might have Parkinson's disease. **23.** Alar plate neuroblasts become interneurons, whereas basal plate neuroblasts become motor (efferent) neurons. **24.** The nerves serving the limbs arise in the cervical and lumbar enlargements of the spinal cord. **25.** In the spinothalamic pathway, the cell bodies of first-order sensory neurons are outside the spinal cord in a ganglion, cell bodies of second-order sensory neurons are in the dorsal horn of the spinal cord, and cell bodies of third-order sensory neurons are in the thalamus. (See also Figure 12.34b.) **26.** Roy had lower limb paralysis. This could be caused by a spinal cord injury in the thoracic region (between T_1 and L_1). If the spinal cord is transected, the result is paraplegia. If the cord is only bruised, he may regain function in the limbs. An MRI scan (or CT scan) of the spinal cord would be helpful. **27.** Premature babies have trouble regulating body temperature because the hypothalamus is immature. **28.** Reversible causes of dementia include prescription drug effects, low blood pressure, poor nutrition, hormone imbalances, depression, and dehydration.

Review Questions 1. a; **2.** d; **3.** c; **4.** a; **5.** (1)d, (2)f, (3)e, (4)g, (5)b, (6)f, (7)i, (8)a; **6.** b; **7.** c; **8.** a; **9.** (1)a, (2)b, (3)a, (4)a, (5)b, (6)a, (7)b, (8)b, (9)a; **10.** d; **11.** (1)d, (2)e, (3)c and d, (4)a; **12.** (c)

Chapter 13

Check Your Understanding 1. In addition to nerves, the PNS also consists of sensory receptors, motor endings, and ganglia. **2.** Nociceptors respond to painful stimuli. They are exteroceptors that are simple and unencapsulated (free nerve endings). **3.** The three levels of sensory integration are receptor level, circuit level, and perceptual level. **4.** Phasic receptors adapt, whereas tonic receptors exhibit little or no adaptation. Pain receptors are tonic so that we are reminded to protect the injured body part. **5.** Hot and cold are conveyed by different sensory receptors that are parts of separate "labeled lines." Cool and cold are two different intensities of the same stimulus, detected by frequency coding—the frequency of APs would be higher for a cold than a cool stimulus. Action potentials arising in the fingers and foot arrive at different locations in the somatosensory cortex via their own "labeled lines" and in this way the cortex can determine their origin. **6.** Ganglia are collections of neuron cell bodies in the PNS. **7.** Nerves also contain connective tissue, blood vessels, lymphatic vessels, and the myelin surrounding the axons. **8.** Schwann cells, macrophages, and the neurons themselves were all important in healing the nerve. **9.** The oculomotor (III), trochlear (IV), and abducens (VI) nerves control eye movements. Sticking out your tongue involves the hypoglossal nerve (XII). The vagus nerve (X) influences heart rate and digestive activity. The accessory nerve (XI) innervates the trapezius muscle, which is involved in shoulder shrugging. **10.** Roots lie medial to spinal nerves, whereas rami lie lateral to spinal nerves. Dorsal roots are purely sensory, whereas dorsal rami carry both motor and sensory fibers. **11.** The spinal nerve roots were C_3–C_5, the spinal nerve was the phrenic nerve, the plexus was the cervical plexus. The phrenic nerve is the sole motor nerve supply to the diaphragm, the primary muscle for respiration. **12.** Varicosities are the series of knoblike swellings that are the axon endings of autonomic motor neurons. You would find them on axon endings serving smooth muscle or glands. **13.** The cerebellum and basal nuclei, which form the precommand level of motor control, plan and coordinate complex motor activities. **14.** The five components of a reflex arc are receptor, sensory neuron, integration center, motor neuron, and effector. **15.** The stretch reflex is important for maintaining muscle tone and adjusting it reflexively by causing muscle contraction in response to increased muscle length (stretch). It maintains posture. The flexor or withdrawal reflex is initiated by a painful stimulus and causes automatic withdrawal of the painful body part from the stimulus. It is protective. **16.** This response is called Babinski's sign and it indicates damage to the corticospinal tract or primary motor cortex. **17.** The vertebral column, spinal nerves, and dermatomes are all examples of segmentation in the adult.

Review Questions 1. b; **2.** c; **3.** d; **4.** c; **5.** e; **6.** c; **7.** (1)d, (2)c, (3)f, (4)b, (5)e, (6)a; **8.** (1)f, (2)i, (3)b, (4)g, h, (5)e, (6)i, (7)c, (8)k, (9)l, (10)c, d, f, k; **9.** (1)b 6; (2)d 8; (3)c 2; (4)c 5; (5)a 4; (6)a 3, 9; (7)a 7; (8)a 7; (9)d 1; (10)a 3, 4, 7, 9; **10.** (1)a, 1 and 5; (2)a, 3 and 5; (3)a, 4; (4)a, 2; (5)c, 2; (6)b, 2; **11.** c

Chapter 14

Check Your Understanding 1. The effectors of the autonomic nervous system are cardiac muscle, smooth muscle, and glands. **2.** The somatic motor system relays instructions to muscles more quickly because it involves only one motor neuron, whereas the ANS uses a two-neuron chain. Moreover, axons of somatic motor neurons are typically heavily myelinated, whereas preganglionic autonomic axons are lightly myelinated and postganglionic axons are unmyelinated. **3.** While you relax in the sun on the beach, the parasympathetic branch of the ANS would probably predominate. When you perceive danger (as in a shark), the sympathetic branch of the ANS predominates. **4.** "Short preganglionic fibers," "origin from thoracolumbar region of spinal cord," "collateral ganglia," and "innervates adrenal medulla" are all characteristic of the sympathetic nervous system. Terminal ganglia are found in the parasympathetic nervous system. **5.** The major differences are (1) the ANS has visceral afferents rather than somatic afferents, (2) the ANS has a two-neuron efferent chain, whereas the somatic nervous system (SNS) has one, and (3) the effectors of the ANS are smooth muscles, cardiac muscles, and glands, whereas the effectors of the SNS are skeletal muscles. **6.** The parasympathetic nervous system increases digestive activity and decreases heart rate. The sympathetic nervous system increases blood pressure, dilates bronchioles, stimulates the adrenal medulla to release its hormones, and causes ejaculation. **7.** You would find nicotinic receptors on skeletal muscle and the hormone-producing cells of the adrenal medulla, but not on smooth muscle or glands. Virtually all types of receptors (including nicotinic receptors) are also found in the CNS (see Table 11.3 on p. 416). **8.** The main integration center of the ANS is the hypothalamus, although the most direct influence is through the brain stem reticular formation and the reflex centers in the pons and medulla oblongata. **9.** Jackson's doctor may have prescribed a beta-blocker because Jackson has hypertension. (Chronic stress is a factor in causing hypertension.) The beta-blocker will decrease blood pressure by blocking beta-adrenergic receptors in the heart and blood vessels, thereby decreasing heart rate and dilating blood vessels. **10.** The neural crest gives rise to both autonomic ganglia and the adrenal medulla.

Clinical Connections 1. The location of Jimmy's lacerations and bruises and his inability to rise led the paramedics to suspect a head, neck, or back injury. They immobilized his head and torso to prevent any further damage to the brain and spinal cord. **2.** The worsening neurological signs indicate a probable intracranial hemorrhage. The blood escaping from the ruptured blood vessel(s) will begin to compress Jimmy's brain and increase his intracranial pressure. Jimmy's surgery will involve repair of the damaged vessel(s) and removal of the mass of clotted blood pressing on his brain. **3.** Loss of motor and sensory function below the level of the nipples indicates a lesion at T_4. See Figure 13.12. **4.** Jimmy is suffering from spinal shock, which occurs as a result of injury to the spinal cord. Spinal shock is a temporary condition in which all reflex and motor activities caudal to the level of spinal cord injury are lost, so Jimmy's muscles are paralyzed. His blood pressure is low due to the loss of sympathetic tone in his vasculature. **5.** Jimmy's exaggerated reflexes are caused by damaged upper motor neuron axons in the spinal cord. These upper motor neurons normally inhibit spinal reflexes. He is incontinent because there are no longer pathways to support voluntary control of bowel and bladder emptying. **6.** This condition is called *autonomic dysreflexia* (or *autonomic hyperreflexia*). This is a condition in which a normal stimulus triggers a massive activation of autonomic neurons. **7.** Extremely high arterial blood pressure can cause a rupture of the cerebral blood vessels (as well as other blood vessels in the body) and put Jimmy's life at risk.

Review Questions 1. d; **2.** (1)S, (2)P, (3)P, (4)S, (5)S, (6)P, (7)P, (8)S, (9)P, (10)S, (11)P, (12)S; **3.** b; **4.** c; **5.** a

Chapter 15

Check Your Understanding 1. Tears (lacrimal fluid) are a dilute saline secretion that contains mucus, antibodies, and lysozyme. They are secreted by the lacrimal glands. **2.** The blind spot of the eye is the optic disc. It is the part of the retina where the optic nerve exits the eye and it is "blind" because it is a region of the retina that lacks photoreceptors. **3.** An increase in intraocular pressure is called glaucoma and is due to an accumulation of aqueous humor, usually because of impaired drainage of the fluid. **4.** Light passes through the cornea, aqueous humor, lens, vitreous humor, ganglion cells and bipolar cells before it reaches the photoreceptors. **5.** The ciliary muscles and sphincter pupillae relax for distant vision. (If you said the medial rectus muscles also relax, this is true, but remem-

ber that the rectus muscles are *extrinsic* eye muscles, not intrinsic.) **6.** The near point moves farther away as you age because the lens becomes less flexible (presbyopia), so that it is unable to assume the more rounded shape required for near vision. **7.** The following are characteristics of cones: "vision in bright light," "color vision," and "higher acuity." The following are characteristics of rods: "only one type of visual pigment," "most abundant in the periphery of the retina," "many feed into one ganglion cell," and "higher sensitivity." **8.** Breakdown of the retinal-opsin combination is called bleaching of the pigment. It occurs with exposure to light. **9.** A tumor in the right visual cortex would affect the left visual field. A tumor compressing the right optic nerve would affect both the left and right visual fields from the right eye only. **10.** The five taste modalities are sweet, sour, bitter, salty, and umami. The fungiform, circumvallate, and foliate papillae contain taste buds. **11.** The cilia and hairs of these receptor cells greatly increase the surface area for sensory receptors. **12.** The tympanic membrane separates the external from the middle ear. The oval and round windows separate the middle from the inner ear. **13.** The basilar membrane allows us to differentiate sounds of different pitch. **14.** You would not be able to locate the origin of a sound if the brain stem did not receive input from both ears. **15.** The "fullness" in Mohammed's ears is likely due to an accumulation of fluid in the middle ear as a result of his upper respiratory infection ("cold") spreading into his ear. He has a form of conduction deafness. **16.** The following apply to a macula: "contains otoliths," "responds to linear acceleration or deceleration," and "inside a saccule." The following apply to a crista ampullaris: "inside a semicircular canal," "has a cupula," "responds to rotational acceleration and deceleration." **17.** With age, the lens discolors and loses its clarity and the dilator pupillae muscles become less efficient, decreasing the amount of light that reaches the retinas at night.

Review Questions 1. c; **2.** d; **3.** a; **4.** b; **5.** c; **6.** c; **7.** b; **8.** a; **9.** b; **10.** b; **11.** b; **12.** d; **13.** d; **14.** a; **15.** d; **16.** c; **17.** d; **18.** b; **19.** b; **20.** c; **21.** d; **22.** b; **23.** b; **24.** e; **25.** b; **26.** c; **27.** c; **28.** c; **29.** c

Chapter 16

Check Your Understanding 1. The endocrine system is more closely associated with growth and development, and its responses tend to be long-lasting, whereas nervous system responses tend to be rapid and discrete. **2.** The thyroid and parathyroid glands are found in the neck. **3.** Hormones are released into the blood and transported throughout the body, whereas paracrines act locally, generally within the same tissue. **4.** The two major chemical classes of hormones are amino acid–based hormones and steroids. Steroids are all lipid soluble. Thyroid hormones are the only amino acid–based hormones that are lipid soluble. **5.** Water-soluble hormones act on receptors in the plasma membrane coupled most often via regulatory molecules called G proteins to intracellular second messengers. Lipid-soluble hormones act on intracellular receptors, directly activating genes and stimulating synthesis of specific proteins. **6.** Hormone release can be triggered by humoral, neural, or hormonal stimuli. **7.** The hypothalamus communicates with the anterior pituitary via *hormones* released into a special portal system of blood vessels. In contrast, it communicates with the posterior pituitary via *action potentials traveling down axons* that connect the hypothalamus to the posterior pituitary. **8.** LH and FSH are tropic hormones that act on the gonads, TSH is a tropic hormone that acts on the thyroid, and ACTH is a tropic hormone that acts on the adrenal cortex. (If you said growth hormone, that's also a good answer, as GH causing the liver to release IGFs might also be considered a tropic effect.) **9.** Drinking alcoholic beverages inhibits ADH secretion from the posterior pituitary and causes copious urine output and dehydration. The dehydration causes the hangover effects. **10.** Thyroid hormone increases basal metabolic rate (and heat production) in the body. Parathyroid hormone increases blood Ca^{2+} levels in a variety of ways.

Calcitonin at high (pharmacological) levels has a Ca^{2+}-lowering, bone-sparing effect. (At normal blood levels its effects in humans are negligible.) **11.** Thyroid follicle cells release thyroid hormone, chief cells in the parathyroid gland release parathyroid hormone, and parafollicular (C) cells in the thyroid gland release calcitonin. **12.** Glucocorticoids are stress hormones that, among many effects, increase blood glucose. Mineralocorticoids increase blood Na^+ (and blood pressure) and decrease blood K^+. Gonadocorticoids are male and female sex hormones that are thought to have a variety of effects (for example, onset of puberty, sex drive in women, pubic and axillary hair development in women). **13.** Melatonin is used by some individuals as a sleep aid, particularly to counter jet lag. **14.** When we say Sharon is diabetic, this means that she has insufficient insulin action in her body. The most likely explanation for Sharon's behavior is that she has taken too much insulin and is experiencing hypoglycemia. Ingesting some sugar will likely help her. **15.** Diabetes mellitus is due to a lack of insulin production or action, whereas diabetes insipidus is due to a lack of ADH. Both conditions are characterized by production of copious amounts of urine. You would find glucose in the urine of a patient with diabetes mellitus, but not in the urine of a patient with diabetes insipidus. **16.** The gonadal hormones are steroid hormones. A major endocrine gland that also secretes steroid hormones is the adrenal cortex. **17.** The heart produces atrial natriuretic peptide (ANP). ANP decreases blood volume and blood pressure by increasing the kidneys' production of salty urine. **18.** Vitamin D_3, produced in inactive form by the skin, increases intestinal absorption of calcium. **19.** The decline in growth hormone with age contributes to muscle atrophy. The decline in estrogen contributes to osteoporosis in women.

Clinical Connections 1. Rationale for orders: As Mr. Gutteman is unconscious, the level of damage to his brain is unclear. Monitoring his responses and vital signs every hour will provide information for his care providers about the extent of his injuries. Turning him every 4 hours and providing careful skin care will prevent decubitus ulcers (bedsores) as well as stimulating his proprioceptive pathways. **2.** Mr. Gutteman's condition is termed *diabetes insipidus*, a condition in which insufficient quantities of antidiuretic hormone (ADH) are produced or released. Diabetes insipidus patients excrete large volumes of urine but do not have glucose or ketones present in the urine. The head trauma could have damaged Mr. Gutteman's hypothalamus, which produces the hormone, or injured his posterior pituitary gland, which releases ADH into the bloodstream. **3.** Diabetes insipidus is not life threatening for most individuals with normal thirst mechanisms, as they will be thirsty and drink to replenish the lost fluid. However, Mr. Gutteman is comatose, so his fluid output must be monitored closely so that the volume lost can be replaced by IV line. His subsequent recovery may be complicated if he has suffered damage to his hypothalamus, which houses the thirst center neurons.

Review Questions 1. b; **2.** a; **3.** c; **4.** d; **5.** (1)c, (2)a and b, (3)f, (4)d, (5)e, (6)g, (7)a, (8)h, (9)b and e, (10)a; **6.** d; **7.** c; **8.** b; **9.** d; **10.** b; **11.** d; **12.** b; **13.** c; **14.** d

Chapter 17

Check Your Understanding 1. The hematocrit is the percentage of blood that is occupied by erythrocytes. It is normally about 45%. **2.** Blood can prevent blood loss by forming clots when a blood vessel is damaged. Blood can prevent infection because it contains antimicrobial proteins and white blood cells. **3.** Plasma proteins are not used as fuel for body cells because their presence in blood is required to perform many key functions. **4.** Each hemoglobin molecule can transport four O_2. The heme portion of the hemoglobin binds the O_2. **5.** The kidneys' synthesis of erythropoietin is compromised in advanced kidney disease, so RBC production decreases, causing anemia. **6.** Monocytes become macrophages in tissues. Neutrophils are also voracious phagocytes. **7.** "Thrombopoietin" is derived from the same word as "thrombocyte." It is the hormone that promotes platelet formation. **8.** Amos's red bone marrow is spewing out many abnormal white blood cells, which are crowding out the production of normal bone marrow elements. The lack of normal white blood cells allows the infections, the lack of platelets fails to stop bleeding, and the lack of erythrocytes is anemia. **9.** The three steps of hemostasis are vascular spasm, platelet plug formation, and coagulation. **10.** Fibrinogen is water soluble, whereas fibrin is not. Prothrombin is an inactive precursor, whereas thrombin acts as an enzyme. Most factors are inactive in blood before activation and become enzymes upon activation. (There are exceptions, such as fibrinogen and calcium.) **11.** Thrombocytopenia (platelet deficiency) results in failure to plug the countless small tears in blood vessels, and so manifests as small purple spots. Hemophilia A results from the absence of clotting factor VIII. **12.** Nigel has anti-A antibodies in his blood and type B agglutinogens on his RBCs. He can donate blood to an AB recipient, but he should not receive blood from an AB donor because his anti-A antibodies will cause a transfusion reaction. **13.** If Emily has a bacterial meningitis, a differential WBC count would likely reveal an increase in neutrophils because neutrophils are a major body defense against bacteria. **14.** Hemoglobin F has a higher affinity (binding strength) for oxygen than adult hemoglobin does.

Review Questions 1. c; **2.** c; **3.** d; **4.** b; **5.** d; **6.** a; **7.** a; **8.** b; **9.** c; **10.** d

Chapter 18

Check Your Understanding 1. The mediastinum is the medial cavity of the thorax within which the heart, great vessels, and trachea are found. **2.** The layers of the heart wall are the endocardium, the myocardium, and the epicardium. The epicardium is also called the visceral layer of the serous pericardium. This is surrounded by the parietal layer of the serous pericardium and the fibrous pericardium. **3.** The serous fluid decreases friction caused by movement of the layers against one another. **4.** The right side of the heart acts as the pulmonary pump, whereas the left acts as the systemic pump. **5.** (a) True. The left ventricle wall is thicker than the right. (b) True. The left ventricle pumps blood at much higher pressure than the right ventricle because the left ventricle supplies the whole body, whereas the right ventricle supplies only the lungs. (c) False. Each ventricle pumps the *same amount* of blood with each beat. If this were not true, blood would back up in either the systemic or pulmonary circulation (because the two ventricles are in series). **6.** The branches of the right coronary artery are the right marginal artery and the posterior interventricular artery. **7.** The papillary muscles and chordae tendineae keep the AV valve flaps from everting into the atria as the ventricles contract. **8.** (a) The refractory period is almost as long as the contraction in cardiac muscle. (b) The source of Ca^{2+} for the contraction is *only* SR in skeletal muscle. (c) The AP exhibits a plateau phase in cardiac muscle. (d) Both skeletal muscle and cardiac muscle have troponin. (e) Only skeletal muscle has triads. **9.** Cardiac muscle cannot go into tetany because the absolute refractory period is almost as long as the contraction. **10.** The Purkinje fibers excite ventricular muscle fibers. The depolarization wave travels upward from the apex toward the atria **11.** (a) The QRS wave occurs during ventricular depolarization. (b) The T wave of the ECG occurs during ventricular repolarization. (c) The P-Q interval of the ECG occurs during atrial depolarization and the conduction of the action potential through the rest of the intrinsic conduction system. **12.** The second heart sound is associated with the closing of the semilunar valves. **13.** The murmur of mitral insufficiency occurs during ventricular systole (because this is when the valve should be closed, and the murmur is due to blood leaking through the incompletely closed valve into the atrium). **14.** The periods when all four valves are closed are the isovolumetric contraction phase and the isovolumetric relaxation phase. **15.** Exercise activates the sympathetic nervous system. Sympathetic nervous system activity increases heart rate. It also directly increases ventricular contractility, thereby increasing Josh's stroke volume. **16.** If the heart is beating very rapidly, the amount of time for ventricular filling between contractions is decreased. This decreases the end diastolic volume, decreases the stroke volume, and therefore decreases the cardiac output. **17.** The foramen ovale and the ductus arteriosus both allow blood to bypass the fetal lungs. **18.** Elderly athletes may be hampered by sclerosis and thickening of heart valve flaps, a decline in cardiac reserve, fibrosis of cardiac muscle, and atherosclerosis.

Review Questions 1. a; **2.** c; **3.** b; **4.** c; **5.** b; **6.** b; **7.** c; **8.** d; **9.** b

Chapter 19

Check Your Understanding 1. The sympathetic nervous system innervates blood vessels. The sympathetic nerves innervate the tunica media. The effector cells in the tunica media are smooth muscle cells. **2.** When vascular smooth muscle contracts, the diameter of the blood vessel becomes smaller. This is called vasoconstriction. **3.** *Elastic arteries* play a major role in dampening the pulsatile pressure of heart contractions. Dilation or constriction of *arterioles* determines blood flow to individual capillary beds. *Muscular arteries* have the thickest tunica media relative to their lumen size. **4.** If you were doing calf raises, your capillary bed would be in the condition depicted in part (a). The true capillaries would be flushed with blood to ensure that the working calf muscles could receive the needed nutrients and dispose of their metabolic wastes. **5.** Valves prevent blood from flowing backwards in veins. They are formed from folds of the tunica intima. **6.** In the systemic circuit, veins contain more blood than arteries (see Figure 19.5). **7.** The three factors that determine resistance are blood viscosity, vessel length, and vessel diameter. Vessel diameter is physiologically most important. **8.** The rate of flow will decrease 81-fold from its original flow ($3 \times 3 \times 3 \times 3 = 81$). **9.** When you first stand up, mean arterial pressure (MAP) temporarily decreases and this is sensed by aortic and carotid baroreceptors. Medullary cardiac and vasomotor center reflexes increase sympathetic and decrease parasympathetic outflow to the heart. Heart rate and contractility increase, increasing cardiac output, and therefore MAP. Further, sympathetic constriction of arterioles increases peripheral resistance, also increasing MAP. (In addition, increased constriction of veins increases venous return, which increases end diastolic volume, increasing stroke volume, and therefore cardiac output and MAP.) See also Figure 19.9 (bottom). **10.** The kidneys help maintain MAP by influencing blood volume. In renal artery obstruction, the blood pressure in the kidney is lower than in the rest of the body (because it is downstream of the obstruction). Low renal blood pressure triggers both direct and indirect renal mechanisms to increase blood pressure by increasing blood volume. This can cause hypertension (called "secondary hypertension" because it is secondary to a defined cause—in this case the renal artery obstruction). **11.** In a bicycle race, autoregulation by intrinsic metabolic controls causes arteriolar smooth muscle in your legs to relax, dilating the vessels and supplying more O_2 and nutrients to the exercising muscles. **12.** Extrinsic mechanisms, primarily the sympathetic nervous system, prevent blood pressure from plummeting by constricting arterioles elsewhere (such as gut, kidneys). In addition, cardiac output increases, which also helps maintain MAP. **13.** (a) An increase in interstitial fluid osmotic pressure (OP_{if}) would tend to pull more fluid out of capillaries (causing localized swelling, or edema). (b) An increase of OP_{if} to 10 mm Hg would decrease the net osmotic pressure on both the arteriole and venule ends of the capillary to 16 mm Hg (26 mm Hg − 10 mm Hg). The NFP at the venous end would become 1 mm Hg (17 mm Hg − 16 mm Hg). (c) Fluid would flow *out of* the venous end of the capillary rather than in. **14.** Bob is in vascular shock due to anaphylaxis, a systemic allergic reaction to his medication. His blood pressure is low because of widespread vasodilation triggered by the massive release of histamine. Bob's rapid heart rate is a result of the baroreceptor reflex triggered by his low blood pressure. This activates the sympathetic nervous system, increasing heart rate, in an attempt to restore blood pressure. **15.** The external carotid arteries supply most of the tissues of the head except for the brain and orbits. **16.** The cerebral arterial circle (circle of Willis) is the arterial anastomosis at the base of the brain. **17.** The four unpaired arteries that emerge from the abdominal aorta are the celiac trunk, the superior and inferior mesenteric arteries, and the median sacral artery. **18.** You would palpate the popliteal artery behind the knee, the posterior tibial artery behind the medial malleolus of the tibia, and the dorsalis pedis artery on the foot. (See also Figure 19.12.) **19.** The vertebral arteries help supply the brain, but the vertebral veins do *not* drain much blood from the brain. **20.** The internal jugular veins drain the dural venous sinuses. Each internal jugular vein joins a subclavian vein to form a brachiocephalic vein. **21.** A portal system is a system where two capillary beds occur in series. In other words, in a portal system, a capillary bed is drained by a vein that leads into a second capillary bed. The function of the hepatic portal system is to transport venous blood from the digestive organs to the liver for processing before it enters the rest of the systemic circulation. This plays an important role in defense against absorbed toxins or microorganisms and also allows direct delivery of absorbed nutrients to the liver for processing. **22.** The leg veins that often become varicosed are the great and small saphenous veins. **23.** Three differences between arteries and veins are (1) arteries run deep while veins are both deep and superficial, (2) venous pathways are more interconnected than arterial pathways, and (3) the brain and digestive systems have unique venous drainage systems, whereas their arterial supply patterns are not substantially different from those of other organs. **24.** The foramen ovale and the ductus arteriosus both bypass the fetal lungs. The ductus venosus bypasses the fetal liver. **25.** Varicose veins, atherosclerosis, and hypertension are associated with aging.

Clinical Connections 1. The tissues in Mr. Hutchinson's right leg were deprived of oxygen and nutrients for at least one-half hour. When tissues are deprived of oxygen, tissue metabolism decreases and eventually ceases, so these tissues may have died due to anoxia. **2.** Mr. Hutchinson's vital signs (low BP; rapid, thready pulse) indicate that he is facing a life-threatening problem that must be stabilized before other, less vital problems can be addressed. As for surgery, he may be scheduled for open reduction of his crushed bone, depending upon the condition of the tissues in his crushed right leg. If tissue death has occurred in his leg, he may undergo amputation of that limb. **3.** Mr. Hutchinson's rapid, thready pulse and falling blood pressure are indications of hypovolemic shock, a type of shock resulting from decreased blood volume. Because his blood volume is low, his heart rate is elevated to increase cardiac output in an effort to maintain the blood supply to his vital organs. Mr. Hutchinson's blood volume must be increased as quickly as possible with blood transfusions or intravenous saline. This will stabilize his condition and allow his physicians to continue with his surgery.

Review Questions 1. d; **2.** b; **3.** d; **4.** c; **5.** e; **6.** d; **7.** c; **8.** b; **9.** b; **10.** a; **11.** b; **12.** c; **13.** b; **14.** d; **15.** (1)b, e, g; (2)c; (3)i; (4) f, h; (5) d

Chapter 20

Check Your Understanding 1. Lymph is the fluid inside lymphatic vessels. It enters lymphatic vessels from interstitial fluid. Interstitial fluid, in turn, is a filtrate of blood plasma. **2.** The right lymphatic duct receives lymph from the right upper limb and the right side of the head and thorax. The thoracic duct drains lymph from the rest of the body. **3.** Lymph movement is driven by the contraction of adjacent skeletal muscles, pressure changes in the thorax during breathing, and the pulsations of nearby arteries. (Valves in lymphatic vessels prevent backflow of lymph.) **4.** Lymphoid follicles are solid, spherical bodies consisting of tightly packed reticular elements and cells, often with a lighter-staining central region. They are regions where B cells predominate. **5.** Having fewer efferents causes lymph to accumulate in lymph nodes, allowing more time for its cleansing. **6.** MALT (mucosa-associated lymphatic tissue) is lymphoid tissue found in the mucosa of the digestive, respiratory, and genitourinary tracts. **7.** The spleen cleanses the blood, stores breakdown products of RBCs, stores platelets, and is thought to be a site of erythrocyte production in the fetus. **8.** The thymus develops first.

Clinical Connections 1. The red streaks radiating from Mr. Hutchinson's finger indicate that his lymphatic vessels are inflamed. This inflammation may be caused by a bacterial infection. If Mr. Hutchinson's arm had exhibited edema without any accompanying red streaks, the problem would likely have been impaired lymph transport from his arm back to his trunk, due to injury or blockage of his lymphatic vessels. **2.** Mr. Hutchinson's arm was placed in a sling to immobilize it, slowing the drainage of lymph from the infected area in an attempt to limit the spread of the infection. **3.** Mr. Hutchinson's low lymphocyte count indicates that his body's ability to fight infection by bacteria or viruses is impaired. The antibiotics and additional staff protection will protect Mr. Hutchinson until his lymphocyte count increases again. Gloving and gowning also protect the staff caring for Mr. Hutchinson from any body infection he might have. **4.** Mr. Hutchinson's recovery may be problematic, as he probably already has an ongoing bacterial infection and his ability to raise a defense to this infection is impaired.

Review Questions 1. c; **2.** c; **3.** a, d; **4.** c; **5.** a; **6.** b; **7.** a; **8.** b; **9.** d

Chapter 21

Check Your Understanding 1. The innate defense system is always ready to respond immediately, whereas it takes considerable time to mount the adaptive defense system. The innate defenses consist of surface barriers and internal defenses, whereas the adaptive defenses consist of humoral and cellular immunity, which rely on B and T lymphocytes. **2.** Surface barriers (the skin and mucous membranes) constitute the first line of defense. **3.** Opsonization is the process of making pathogens more susceptible to phagocytosis by decorating their surface with molecules that phagocytes can bind. Antibodies and complement proteins are examples of molecules that act as opsonins. **4.** Our own cells are killed by NK cells when they have been infected by viruses or when they have become cancerous. **5.** Redness, heat, swelling, and pain are the cardinal signs of inflammation. Redness and local heat are both caused by vasodilation of arterioles, which increases the flow of blood (warmed by the body core) to the affected area. The swelling (edema) is due to the release of histamine and other chemical mediators of inflammation, which increase capillary permeability. This increased permeability allows proteins to leak into the interstitial fluid (IF), increasing the IF osmotic pressure and drawing more fluid out of blood vessels and into the tissues, thereby causing swelling. The pain is due to two things: (1) the actions of certain chemical mediators (kinins and prostaglandins) on nerve endings, and (2) the swelling, which can compress free nerve endings. **6.** Three key characteristics of adaptive immunity are that it is specific, it is systemic, and it has memory. **7.** A complete antigen has both immunogenicity and reactivity, whereas a hapten has reactivity but not immunogenicity. **8.** Self-antigens, particularly MHC proteins, mark a cell as self. **9.** Development of immunocompetence of a B or T cell is signaled by the appearance on its surface of specific and unique receptors for an antigen. In the case of a B cell, this receptor is a membrane-bound antibody. (In T cells, it is simply called the T cell receptor.) **10.** The T cell that would survive is (c), one that recognizes MHC but not self-antigen. **11.** Dendritic cells, macrophages, and B cells can all act as APCs. Dendritic cells are most important for T cell activation. **12.** In clonal selection, the antigen does the selecting. What is being selected is a particular clone of B or T cells that

has antigen receptors corresponding to that antigen. **13.** The secondary response to an antigen is faster than the primary response because the immune system has already been "primed" and has memory cells that are specific for that particular antigen. **14.** Vaccinations protect by providing the initial encounter to an antigen—the primary response to that antigen. As a result, when the pathogen for that illness is encountered again, the pathogen elicits the much faster, more powerful secondary response, which is generally effective enough to prevent clinical illness. **15.** IgG antibody is most abundant in blood. IgM is secreted first in a primary immune response. IgA is most abundant in secretions. **16.** Antibodies can bring about destruction of pathogen via "PLAN"—**p**hagocytosis, **l**ysis (via complement), **a**gglutination, or **n**eutralization. **17.** Class II MHC proteins display exogenous antigens. Class II MHC proteins are recognized by CD4 T cells (which usually become helper T cells). APCs display class II MHC proteins. **18.** When antigens are bound in the absence of co-stimulators this causes the lymphocyte to develop *anergy*—a state of permanent unresponsiveness to that antigen. **19.** Helper T cells are central to both humoral and cell-mediated immunity because they are required for activation of both cytotoxic T cells and most B cells. **20.** The cytotoxic T cell releases perforins and granzymes onto the identified target cell. Perforins form a pore in the target cell membrane, and granzymes enter through this pore, triggering apoptosis (cell suicide). **21.** MHC proteins and blood type antigens (ABO, etc.) are carefully matched before an organ transplant. **22.** HIV is particularly hard for the immune system to defeat because (1) it destroys helper T cells, which are key players in adaptive immunity and (2) it has a high mutation rate and so it rapidly becomes resistant to drugs. **23.** Binding of an allergen onto specific IgE antibodies attached to mast cells triggers the mast cells to release histamine.

Review Questions 1. c; **2.** a; **3.** d; **4.** d, e; **5.** a; **6.** d; **7.** b; **8.** c; **9.** d; **10.** d; **11.** d; **12.** (1)b, g; (2)d, i; (3)a, e; (4)a, e, f, h; (5)e, h; (6)c, f, g

Chapter 22

Check Your Understanding 1. The structures that air passes by are the nasal cavity (nares, nasal vestibule, nasal conchae), nasopharynx (with pharyngeal tonsil), oropharynx (with palatine tonsil), laryngopharynx, and larynx (with epiglottis, vestibular fold, and vocal fold). **2.** The epiglottis seals the larynx when we swallow. **3.** The incomplete, C-shaped cartilage rings of the trachea allow it to expand and contract and yet keep it from collapsing. **4.** The many tiny alveoli together have a large surface area. This and the thinness of their respiratory membranes make them ideal for gas exchange. **5.** The peanut was most likely in the right main bronchus because it is wider and more vertical than the left. **6.** The two circulations of the lungs are the pulmonary circulation, which delivers deoxygenated blood to the lungs for oxygenation and returns oxygenated blood to the heart, and the bronchial circulation, which provides systemic (oxygenated) blood to lung tissue. **7.** The driving force for pulmonary ventilation is a pressure gradient created by changes in the thoracic volume. **8.** The intrapulmonary pressure decreases during inspiration because of the increase in thoracic cavity volume brought about by the muscles of inspiration. **9.** The partial vacuum (negative pressure) inside the pleural cavity is caused by the opposing forces acting on the visceral and parietal pleurae. The visceral pleurae are pulled inward by the lungs' natural tendency to recoil and the surface tension of the alveolar fluid. The parietal pleurae are pulled outward by the elasticity of the chest wall. If air enters the pleural cavity, the lung on that side will collapse. This condition is called pneumothorax. **10.** Airway resistance is low because (1) the diameters of most airways are relatively large, (2) for smaller airways there are many in parallel, making their combined diameter large, and (3) air has a low viscosity. **11.** A lack of surfactant increases surface tension in the alveoli and causes them to collapse between breaths. (In other words, it markedly decreases lung compliance.) **12.** Slow, deep breaths ventilate the alveoli more effectively because a smaller fraction of the tidal volume of each breath is spent moving air into and out of the dead space. **13.** In a sealed container, the air and water would be at equilibrium. Therefore, the partial pressures of CO_2 and O_2 (P_{CO_2} and P_{O_2}) will be the same in the water as in the air: 100 mm Hg each. More CO_2 than O_2 molecules will be dissolved in the water (even though they are at the same partial pressure) because CO_2 is much more soluble than O_2 in water. **14.** The difference in P_{O_2} between inspired air and alveolar air can be explained by (1) the gas exchange occurring in the lungs (O_2 continuously diffuses out of the alveoli into the blood), (2) the humidification of inspired air (which adds water molecules that dilute the O_2 molecules), and (3) the mixing of newly inspired air with gases already present in the alveoli. **15.** The arterioles leading into the O_2-enriched alveoli would be dilated. This response allows matching of blood flow to availability of oxygen. **16.** Both CO_2 and H^+ increase O_2 unloading by binding to Hb. This is called the Bohr effect. **17.** About 70% of CO_2 is transported as bicarbonate ion (HCO_3^-) in plasma. Just over 20% is transported bound to hemoglobin in the RBCs, and 7–10% is dissolved in plasma. **18.** As blood CO_2 increases, blood pH decreases. This is because CO_2 combines with water to form carbonic acid. (However, the change in pH in blood for a given increase in CO_2 is minimized by other buffer systems.) **19.** The ventral respiratory group of the medulla (VRG) is thought to be the rhythm-generating area. **20.** CO_2 in blood normally provides the most powerful stimulus to breathe. Central chemoreceptors are most important in this response (see Figure 22.25). **21.** The injured soccer player's P_{CO_2} is low. (Recall that normal P_{CO_2} = 40 mm Hg.) The low P_{CO_2} reveals that this is hyperventilation and not hyperpnea (which is not accompanied by changes in blood CO_2 levels). **22.** Long-term adjustments to altitude include an increase in erythropoiesis, resulting in a higher hematocrit; an increase in BPG, which decreases Hb affinity for oxygen; and an increase in minute respiratory volume. **23.** The obstruction in asthma is *reversible*, and acute exacerbations are typically followed by symptom-free periods. In contrast, the obstruction in chronic bronchitis is generally not reversible. **24.** The underlying defect in cystic fibrosis is an abnormality in a protein (CFTR protein) that acts as a membrane channel for chloride ions. **25.** Vital capacity declines with age because the thoracic wall becomes more rigid and the lungs lose their elasticity.

Clinical Connections 1. Spinal cord injury from a fracture at the level of the C_2 vertebra would interrupt the normal transmission of signals from the brain stem down the phrenic nerve to the diaphragm, and Barbara would be unable to breathe due to paralysis of the diaphragm. **2.** Barbara's head, neck, and torso should have been immobilized to prevent further damage to the spinal cord. In addition, she required assistance to breathe, so her airway was probably intubated to permit ventilation of her lungs. **3.** Cyanosis is a decrease in the degree of oxygen saturation of hemoglobin. As Barbara's respiratory efforts cease, her alveolar P_{O_2} will fall, so there is less oxygen to load onto hemoglobin. In her peripheral tissues, what little oxygen hemoglobin carries will be consumed leaving these tissues with a bluish tinge. **4.** Injury to the spinal cord at the level of the C_2 vertebra will cause quadriplegia (paralysis of all four limbs). **5.** Atelectasis is the collapse of a lung. Because it is the right thorax that is compressed, only her right lung is affected. Because the lungs are in separate pleural cavities, only her right lung collapsed. **6.** Barbara's fractured ribs probably punctured her lung tissue and allowed air within the lung to enter the pleural cavity. **7.** The atelectasis will be reversed by inserting a chest tube and removing the air from the pleural cavity. This will allow her lung to heal and reinflate.

Review Questions 1. b; **2.** a and c; **3.** c; **4.** c; **5.** b; **6.** d; **7.** d; **8.** b; **9.** c, d; **10.** c; **11.** b; **12.** b; **13.** b; **14.** c; **15.** b; **16.** b

Chapter 23

Check Your Understanding 1. The esophagus is found in the thorax. Three alimentary canal organs found in the abdominal cavity include the stomach, small intestine, and large intestine. **2.** The usual site of ingestion in a healthy person is the mouth. **3.** The process of absorption moves nutrients into the body. **4.** Reflexes associated with the GI tract promote muscle contraction and secretion of digestive juices or hormones. **5.** The term "gut brain" refers to the enteric nervous system or web of neurons closely associated with the digestive organs. **6.** The visceral peritoneum is the outermost layer of the digestive organ; the parietal peritoneum is the serous membrane covering the wall of the abdominal cavity. **7.** The pancreas is retroperitoneal. **8.** The hepatic portal circulation is the venous portion of the splanchnic circulation. **9.** From deep to superficial the layers of the alimentary canal are the mucosa, submucosa, muscularis externa, and serosa. **10.** He should temporarily refrain from eating because the parasympathetic nervous system oversees digestive activities. **11.** The vestibule is the region between the cheek and the teeth. The oral cavity proper is the area enclosed by the teeth. **12.** The palate forms the roof of the mouth. The hard palate supported by bone is anterior to the soft palate (no bony support). **13.** The tongue is important for speech, particularly for uttering consonants, and taste. **14.** The serous portion of saliva is rich in salivary amylase, an enzyme that chemically breaks down starch. Additionally, the serous portion of saliva helps to hydrate the foodstuffs and helps provide protection against microorganisms. **15.** Antimicrobial substances found in saliva include lysozyme, defensins, a cyanide compound, and IgA antibodies. **16.** Tina's "show and tell" tooth is a primary tooth, also called a deciduous tooth. **17.** Enamel is harder than bone. Pulp consists of nervous tissue and blood vessels. **18.** The molars are grinding teeth. **19.** The pharynx is part of the digestive and respiratory systems. **20.** The esophageal mucularis externa undergoes a transformation along its length from skeletal muscle superiorly to smooth muscle near the stomach. **21.** The esophagus is merely a chute for food passage and is subjected to a good deal of abrasion, which a stratified squamous epithelium can withstand. The stomach mucosa is a secretory mucosa served well by a simple columnar epithelium. **22.** The tongue mixes the chewed food with saliva and compacts the food into a bolus. **23.** During swallowing the larynx rises and the epiglottis covers its lumen so that foodstuffs are diverted into the esophagus posteriorly. **24.** The stomach has three layers of smooth muscle—longitudinal, circular, and oblique. Addition of the oblique layer allows the stomach to pummel food in addition to its peristaltic movements. **25.** The chief cells produce pepsinogen, which is the inactive pepsin enzyme, and the parietal cells secrete HCl needed to activate pepsinogen. **26.** The mucosal barrier consists of the thick alkaline mucus secreted by the mucous cells, the fact that the epithelial cells of the mucosa are joined by tight junctions, and the quick replacement of dead or dying cells by stem cells. **27.** The three phases of gastric secretion are the cephalic, gastric, and intestinal phases. **28.** The presence of food in the duodenum inhibits gastric activity by triggering the enterogastric reflex and the secretion of certain enterogastrones (hormones). **29.** Venous blood leaving the stomach during a meal becomes more alkaline due to the alkaline tide occurring during HCl secretion. **30.** All of these modifications increase the surface area of the small intestine. The circular folds force the chyme to spiral through the lumen. **31.** Brush border enzymes are enzymes associated with the microvilli of the small intestine mucosal cells. **32.** A lacteal is a blind-ended lymphatic capillary that picks up lymph (fluid and proteins leaked from the bloodstream), which is then returned to the blood. **33.** IgA, HCl, defensins, and lysozyme protect the intestinal cells from bacterial damage. **34.** A portal triad is a region at the corner of a hepatic lobule that contains a branch of the hepatic portal vein, a branch of the hepatic artery, and a bile duct. **35.** The enterohepatic circulation is an important recycling mechanism for retaining bile salts needed for fat absorption. **36.** Kupffer cells are macrophages that rid the blood of bacteria and dead cells. **37.** Zymogen granules contain digestive enzymes. **38.** The pancreas is the only important source of lipases, so fats will probably not be digested or absorbed during her illness. **39.** Pancreatic acini produce the exocrine products of the pancreas (digestive enzymes and bicarbonate-rich juice). The islets produce pancreatic hormones, most importantly insulin and glucagon. **40.** Fluid in the pancreatic duct is bicarbonate-rich, enzyme-rich pancreatic juice. Fluid in the cystic and bile ducts is bile. **41.** CCK is secreted in response to the entry of chyme rich in protein and fat into the duodenum. It causes the pancreatic acini to secrete digestive enzymes and stimulates the gallbladder to contract. **42.** Distension of stomach walls enhances stomach secretory activity. Distension of the walls of the small intestine reduces stomach secretory activity (to give the small intestine time to carry out its digestive and absorptive activities). **43.** Segmentation is more important for moving food along the small intestine. **44.** MMC is the migrating motility complex, a pattern of peristalsis seen in the small intestine that moves the last remnants of a meal plus bacteria and other debris into the large intestine. MMC is important to prevent the overgrowth of bacteria in the small intestine. **45.** Mass movements are unique to the large intestine. They are long, slow, powerful contractions that move over large areas of the colon three or four times a day, forcing the contents toward the rectum. **46.** Activation of stretch receptors in the rectal wall initiates the defecation reflex. **47.** Enteric bacteria synthesize B vitamins and most of the vitamin K the liver needs to synthesize clotting proteins. **48.** All food digestion depends on hydrolysis reactions. **49.** Amylase is to starch as lipase is to fats. **50.** Bile salts emulsify fats so that they can be acted on efficiently by lipase enzymes, and form micelles that aid fat absorption. **51.** The digestive system mucosa develops from the endoderm. **52.** The thick viscous mucus produced in cystic fibrosis patients clogs pancreatic ducts and prevents the delivery of pancreatic fluid to the duodenum, thus inhibiting fat digestion and absorption. **53.** Colon and stomach cancers are dangerous because they have few early signs and symptoms.

Clinical Connections 1. Mr. Gutteman's statement about the effects of milk on his digestive tract suggests that he may be deficient in lactase, a brush border enzyme that breaks down lactose (milk sugar). **2.** His responses to the questions reduced the possibility that he has gastric ulcers. Mr. Gutteman's diarrhea may be due to gluten enteropathy. To verify this diagnosis, Mr. Gutteman should be screened for specific IgA antibodies in his blood. If these tests are positive, a biopsy of the intestinal mucosa would be performed to verify or negate the diagnosis. A positive diagnosis of gluten enteropathy would lead to dietary restriction of all grains but rice and corn. In the meantime, grains should not be restricted.

Review Questions 1. c; **2.** d; **3.** d; **4.** b; **5.** b; **6.** a; **7.** d; **8.** d; **9.** b; **10.** c; **11.** c; **12.** a; **13.** d; **14.** d; **15.** b; **16.** c; **17.** a

Chapter 24

Check Your Understanding 1. The six major nutrients are carbohydrates, proteins, fats, water, minerals, and vitamins. **2.** Cellulose provides fiber, which helps in elimination. **3.** Triglycerides are used for ATP synthesis, body insulation and protective padding, and to help the body absorb fat-soluble vitamins. Cholesterol is the basis of our steroid hormones and bile salts, and stabilizes cellular membranes. **4.** Beans (legumes) and grains (rice) are good sources of protein, but neither is a complete one. Together they should provide all the essential amino acids. Like beans, the bread supplies carbohydrates. **5.** Vitamins serve as the basis for coenzymes, which work with enzymes to accomplish metabolic reactions. **6.** Vitamin B_{12} needs intrinsic factor to be absorbed by the intestine. **7.** Iodine is essential for thyroxine synthesis. Calcium in the form of bone salts is needed to make bones hard. Iron is needed to make functional hemoglobin.

8. A redox reaction is a combination of an oxidation and a reduction reaction. As one substance is oxidized, another is reduced. **9.** Some of the energy released during catabolism is captured in the bonds of ATP, which provides the energy needed to carry out the constructive activities of anabolism. **10.** The energy released during the oxidation of food fuels is used to pump protons across the inner mitochondrial membrane. **11.** In substrate-level phosphorylation, high-energy phosphate groups are transferred directly from phosphorylated intermediates to ADP to form ATP. In oxidative phosphorylation, electron transport proteins forming part of the mitochondrial cristae use energy released during oxidation of glucose to create a steep gradient for protons across the crista membrane. Then as protons flow back through the membrane, gradient energy is captured to attach phosphate to ADP. **12.** If oxygen and pyruvic acid are not available, glycolysis will stop because the supply of NAD^+ is limited and glycolysis can continue only if the reduced coenzymes ($NADH + H^+$) formed during glycolysis are relieved of their extra hydrogen. **13.** Oxidation (via removal of H) is common in the Krebs cycle; it is indicated by the reduction of a coenzyme (either NAD^+ or FAD). Decarboxylations are also common, and are indicated by the removal of CO_2 from the cycle. **14.** Glycogenolysis is the reaction in which glycogen is broken down to its glucose units. **15.** Carbo loading forces the skeletal muscles to store more glycogen than they ordinarily would. **16.** Glycerol, a breakdown product of fat metabolism, directly enters the glycolysis pathway. **17.** Acetyl CoA is the central molecule of fat metabolism. **18.** The products of beta oxidation are acetyl CoA (acetic acid + coenzyme A), $NADH^+ + H^+$, and $FADH_2$. **19.** The liver uses keto acids drained off the Krebs cycle and amino groups (from other nonessential amino acids) as substrates to make the nonessential amino acids that the body needs. **20.** The ammonia removed from amino acids is combined with carbon dioxide to form urea, which is then eliminated by the kidneys. **21.** The three organs or tissues that regulate the directions of interconversions in the nutrient pools are the liver, skeletal muscles, and adipose tissues. **22.** Anabolic reactions and energy storage typify the absorptive state. Catabolic reactions (to increase blood sugar levels) such as lipolysis and glycogenolysis, and glucose sparing occur in the postabsorptive state. **23.** The main antagonist of glucagon is insulin. **24.** A rise in amino acid levels in blood increases both insulin and glucagon release. **25.** High HDLs would be preferable because the cholesterol these particles transport is destined for the liver and elimination from the body. **26.** A total cholesterol level of 200 mg/dl of blood or lower is recommended. **27.** Trans fats are oils that have been hydrogenated (with H atoms). They are unhealthy because they cause LDLs to increase and HDLs to decrease, exactly the opposite of what is desirable. **28.** Among short-term stimuli influencing feeding behavior are neural signals from the digestive tract, nutrient signals related to energy stores, and GI tract hormones (CCK, insulin, glucagon, and ghrelin). **29.** Leptin is the most important long-term regulator of feeding behavior. **30.** Of the factors listed, breathing and kidney function contribute to BMR. **31.** Samantha has a larger relative body surface area and well-toned muscles, both of which promote a higher BMR. **32.** The bodys core is the organs within the skull, and the thoracic and abdominal cavities. **33.** Cindy's body temperature is rising as heat-promoting mechanisms (shivering, chills) are activated. Something (an infection?) has caused the hypothalamic thermostat to be set to a higher level (fever) temporarily. **34.** In conduction, heat is transferred directly from one object to another (a hot surface to your palm). In convection, air warmed by body heat is continually removed (warm air rises) and replaced by cooler air (cool air falls), which in turn will absorb heat radiating from the body. **35.** Metabolic rate falls in old age because muscle mass declines and physical activity tends to be reduced. **36.** Elderly nutrition can be influenced and impaired by alcoholism, certain antibiotics that interfere with food absorption, other drugs that may cause electrolyte imbalances, and use of mineral oil.

Review Questions 1. a; **2.** c; **3.** b; **4.** d; **5.** b; **6.** c; **7.** a; **8.** d; **9.** d; **10.** a; **11.** b; **12.** d; **13.** c; **14.** d; **15.** a

Chapter 25

Check Your Understanding 1. The lower part of his rib cage and the perirenal fat capsule protect his kidneys from blows. **2.** The layers of supportive tissue around each kidney are the fibrous capsule, the perirenal fat capsule, and the renal fascia. The parietal peritoneum overlies the anterior renal fascia. **3.** The renal pelvis, which has extensions called calyces, is continuous with the ureter. **4.** Filtrate is formed in the glomerular capsule and then passes through the proximal convoluted tubule (PCT), the descending and ascending limbs of the loop of Henle, and the distal convoluted tubule (DCT). **5.** The structural differences are (1) juxtamedullary nephrons have long loops of Henle (with long thin segments) and renal corpuscles that are near the cortex-medulla junction, whereas cortical nephrons have short loops of Henle and renal corpuscles that lie more superficially in the cortex; (2) efferent arterioles of juxtamedullary nephrons supply vasa recta, while efferent arterioles of cortical nephrons supply peritubular capillaries. **6.** The glomerular capillaries are fenestrated capillaries. (See Figure 19.3 on p. 699 to refresh your memory of capillary types.) Their function is to filter large amounts of plasma into the glomerular capsule. **7.** Intrinsic controls serve to maintain a nearly constant GFR in spite of changes in systemic blood pressure. Extrinsic controls serve to maintain systemic blood pressure. **8.** Net filtration pressure is 5 mm Hg [50 mm Hg − (25 mm Hg + 20 mm Hg)]. **9.** The two main ways in which angiotensin II increases blood pressure and blood volume are by causing vasoconstriction and by causing aldosterone release. (In addition, angiotensin II causes ADH release, activates the thirst mechanism, increases tubular reabsorption, and contracts mesangial cells, which decreases the GFR.) **10.** The majority of reabsorption occurs in the proximal convoluted tubule. **11.** In primary active transport, the energy for the process is provided directly by the cleavage of ATP. In secondary active transport, the energy for the process is provided by the Na^+ concentration gradient. As Na^+ moves down its own concentration gradient established by the active pumping of Na^+ occurring elsewhere in the cell, it drives the movement of another substance (e.g., glucose) against its concentration gradient. **12.** The reabsorption of Na^+ by primary active transport, in turn, drives reabsorption of amino acids and glucose by secondary active transport. It also drives passive reabsorption of chloride, and reabsorption of water by osmosis. The reabsorption of water leaves behind other solutes, which become more concentrated and can therefore be reabsorbed by diffusion. **13.** H^+, K^+, NH_4^+, creatinine, urea, and uric acid are all substances that are secreted into the kidney tubules. **14.** The descending limb of the loop of Henle is permeable to water and impermeable to NaCl. The ascending limb is impermeable to water and permeable to NaCl. **15.** ADH is released from the posterior pituitary in response to hyperosmotic extracellular fluid (as sensed by hypothalamic osmoreceptors). ADH causes insertion of aquaporins into the luminal membrane of the principal cells of the collecting ducts. **16.** The normal renal clearance value for amino acids is zero. You would expect this because amino acids are valuable as nutrients and as the building blocks for protein synthesis, so it would not be good to lose them in the urine. **17.** The three major nitrogenous wastes excreted in urine are urea, creatinine, and uric acid. **18.** A kidney stone blocking the ureter would interfere with urine flow to the bladder. The pain would occur in waves that coincide with the peristaltic contractions of the smooth muscle of the ureter. **19.** The trigone is a smooth triangular region at the base of the bladder. Its borders are defined by the openings for the ureters and the urethra. **20.** The prostatic urethra, membranous urethra, and spongy urethra are the three regions of the male urethra. **21.** The detrusor muscle contracts in response to increased firing of parasympathetic nerves. Contraction of the detrusor muscle opens the internal urethral sphincter.

22. The three sets of embryonic kidneys in the order that they develop are the pronephros, mesonephros, and metanephros. **23.** Both loss of bladder tone with age and an increase in size of the prostate can contribute to urinary retention in elderly men.

Review Questions 1. d; **2.** b; **3.** c; **4.** d; **5.** c; **6.** b; **7.** a; **8.** c; **9.** a; **10.** b

Chapter 26

Check Your Understanding 1. You have more intracellular than extracellular fluid and more interstitial fluid than plasma. **2.** Na^+ is the major cation in the ECF and K^+ is the major cation in the ICF. The intracellular counterparts to extracellular Cl^- are HPO_4^{2-} and protein anions. **3.** If you eat salty pretzels, your extracellular fluid volume will expand even if you don't ingest fluids. This is because water will flow by osmosis from the intracellular fluid to the extracellular fluid. **4.** An increases in osmolality of the plasma is most important for triggering thirst. This change is sensed by osmoreceptors in the hypothalamus. **5.** ADH cannot add water—it can only conserve what is already there. In order to reduce an increase in osmolality of body fluids, the thirst mechanism is required. **6.** (a) A loss of plasma proteins causes edema. (b) Copious sweating causes dehydration. (c) Using ecstasy (together with drinking lots of fluids) could cause hypotonic hydration because it promotes ADH secretion, which interferes with the body's ability to get rid of extra water. **7.** Insufficient aldosterone would cause Jacob's plasma Na^+ to be decreased and his plasma K^+ to be elevated. The decrease in plasma Na^+ would cause a decrease in blood pressure, because plasma Na^+ is directly related to blood volume, which is a major determinant of blood pressure. **8.** The kidneys' handling of K^+ can be summed up as "The kidneys reabsorb most of the filtered K^+ in the proximal parts of the kidney's tubules and then secrete just the right amount in the distal parts (cortical collecting duct)." **9.** The major regulator of calcium in the blood is parathyroid hormone. Hypercalcemia decreases excitability of neurons and muscle cells and may cause life-threatening cardiac arrhythmias. Hypocalcemia increases excitability and causes muscle tetany. **10.** Acidemia is an arterial pH below 7.35 and alkalemia is a pH above 7.45. **11.** A weak base would be better at minimizing the shift in pH caused by adding a strong acid to a solution because its ability to loosely tie up H^+ allows it to act as a buffer. **12.** The three major chemical buffer systems of the body are the bicarbonate buffer system, the phosphate buffer system, and the protein buffer system. The most important intracellular buffer is the protein buffer system. **13.** Joanne's ventilation would be increased. The acidosis caused by the accumulated ketone bodies will stimulate the peripheral chemoreceptors, and this will cause more CO_2 to be "blown off" in an attempt to restore pH to normal. **14.** Reabsorption of HCO_3^- is always linked with secretion of H^+. **15.** The most important urine buffer of H^+ is the phosphate buffer system. **16.** The tubule and collecting duct cells generate new HCO_3^- either by excreting ammonium ion (NH_4^+) or by excreting buffered H^+ ions. **17.** Key features of an uncompensated metabolic alkalosis are an increase in blood pH and an increase in blood HCO_3^-. Key features of an uncompensated respiratory acidosis are a decrease in blood pH and an increase in blood P_{CO_2}. **18.** The kidneys compensate for respiratory acidosis by excreting more H^+ and generating new HCO_3^- to buffer the acidosis. **19.** Infants' immature kidneys are not as proficient at concentrating urine. In addition, they have a high metabolic rate, so they produce more metabolic water and also have larger amounts of metabolic wastes and acids that need to be excreted with water.

Clinical Connections 1. Mr. Heyden's vital signs suggest that he is in hypovolemic shock, which is probably due to an internal hemorrhage. **2.** The spleen is a highly vascular organ due to its role as a blood-filtering organ. The macrophages in Mr. Heyden's liver and bone marrow will help compensate for the loss of his spleen. **3.** Elevation of renin, aldosterone, and antidiuretic hormone indicate that Mr. Heyden's body is trying to compensate for his falling blood pressure and blood loss. *Renin*: released when renal blood flow is diminished and blood pressure falls. The angiotensin-aldosterone response is initiated by renin. The formation of angiotensin II leads to vasoconstriction, which will increase blood pressure, and to the release of aldosterone. *Aldosterone*: increases Na$^+$ reabsorption by the kidney. The movement of this reabsorbed Na$^+$ into the bloodstream will promote the movement of water from the interstitial fluid, resulting in an increase in blood volume. *Antidiuretic hormone* (*ADH*): released when the hypothalamic osmoreceptors sense an increase in osmolality. ADH has two consequences: It is a potent vasoconstrictor and will increase blood pressure, and it promotes water retention by the kidney, increasing blood volume. **4.** Mr. Heyden's urine production may be decreased for several reasons. The severe drop in his blood pressure would reduce renal blood flow, thus reducing glomerular blood pressure and decreasing his glomerular filtration rate. The elevation in his ADH levels can reduce urine output due to increased water reabsorption by the kidney. He may also have damage to the kidney due to his crush injury in the left lumbar region. The presence of casts and a brownish-red color in his urine are probably damaged cells and blood. If he has suffered kidney damage due to being crushed, he may have nephron damage that would include disruption of the filtration membrane, allowing red blood cells to pass into the filtrate and therefore the urine. He may also have damaged renal tubules and peritubular capillaries, allowing entry of blood and damaged renal tubule epithelial cells into the filtrate.

Review Questions 1. a; **2.** c; **3.** b; **4.** a and b; **5.** h, i, j; **6.** c, g; **7.** a, e; **8.** b; **9.** a, b; **10.** j; **11.** b, d; **12.** a; **13.** c

Chapter 27

Check Your Understanding 1. The testes produce the male gametes (sperm) and testosterone. **2.** The sperm factories are the seminiferous tubules. **3.** When the ambient temperature is cold, the muscles contract, bringing the testes close to the warm body wall. When body temperature is high, the muscles relax, allowing the testes to hang away from the body wall. The pampiniform venous plexus absorbs heat from the arterial blood before it enters the testes. **4.** The erectile tissue of the penis allows the penis to become stiff so that it may more efficiently enter the female vagina to deliver sperm. **5.** The organs of the male duct system in order from the epididymis to the body exterior are the ductus deferens, ejaculatory duct, prostatic urethra, membranous urethra, and spongy urethra. **6.** These stereocilia pass nutrients to the sperm and absorb excess testicular fluid. **7.** The ductus deferens runs from the scrotum into the abdominal cavity. **8.** Adolph probably has a hypertrophied prostate, a condition which can be felt through the anterior wall of the rectum. **9.** The seminal vesicles produce the bulk of seminal fluid. **10.** Semen is sperm plus the secretions of the male accessory glands. **11.** Erection is the stiffening of the penis that occurs when blood in the cavernous tissue is prevented from leaving the penis. It is caused by the parasympathetic division of the autonomic nervous system. **12.** Resolution is a period of muscular and psychological relaxation that follows orgasm. It results as the sympathetic nervous system constricts the internal pudendal arteries, reducing blood flow to the penis, and activates small muscles that force blood out of the penis. **13.** Meiosis reduces the chromosomal count from $2n$ to n and introduces variability. **14.** The sperm head is the compacted DNA-containing nucleus. The acrosome that caps the head is a lysosome-like sac of enzymes. The midpiece contains the energy-producing mitochondria. The tail fashioned by a centriole is the propulsive structure. **15.** Sustentacular cells provide nutrients and essential development signals to the developing sperm and form the blood-testis barrier that prevents sperm antigens from escaping into the blood. Interstitial cells secrete testosterone. **16.** The HPG axis is the hormonal interrelationship between the hypothalamus, anterior pituitary, and gonads that regulates the production of gametes

and sex hormones (e.g., sperm production and testosterone in the male). **17.** Follicle-stimulating hormone indirectly stimulates spermatogenesis by prompting the sustentacular cells to secrete androgen-binding protein. Androgen-binding protein keeps the concentration of testosterone high in the vicinity of the spermatogenic cells, which directly stimulates spermatogenesis. **18.** Secondary sex characteristics of males include appearance of pubic, axillary, and facial hair, deepening of the voice, increased oiliness of the skin, and increased size (length and mass) of the bones and skeletal muscles. **19.** The female's internal genitalia include the ovaries and duct system (uterine tubes, uterus, and vagina). **20.** The ovaries produce the female gametes and secrete female sex hormones (estrogens and progesterone). **21.** A primary follicle has one layer of cuboidal follicle cells surrounding the oocyte; a secondary follicle has more than one layer of follicle cells, and small fluid-filled spaces form between the follicle cells. A vesicular follicle has several layers of follicle cells surrounding a fluid-filled cavity (antrum) that pushes the oocyte to one side. **22.** Women are more at risk for PID than men because the duct system of women is incomplete—there is no physical connection between the ovary and the uterine tubes, which are open to the pelvic cavity. In men, the duct system is continuous from the testes to the body exterior. **23.** The waving action of the fimbriae helps to direct the ovulated oocytes into the uterine tube. **24.** The usual site of fertilization is the uterine tube. The uterus serves as the incubator for fetal development. **25.** The greater vestibular glands are the female homologue of the male bulbourethral glands. **26.** Both the penis and clitoris are hooded by a skin fold and are largely erectile tissue. However, the clitoris lacks a corpus spongiosum containing a urethra, so the urinary and reproductive systems are completely separate in females. **27.** Developmentally, the mammary glands are modified sweat glands. **28.** Breast cancer usually arises from the epithelial cells of the small ducts. **29.** The products of meiosis in females are 3 polar bodies (tiny haploid cells with essentially no cytoplasm) and 1 haploid ovum (functional gamete). Meiosis in males yields 4 functional gametes, the haploid sperm. **30.** Identical twins develop from separation of a very young embryo (the result of fertilization by a single sperm) into two parts. Fraternal twins develop when different oocytes are fertilized by different sperm. **31.** In the luteal phase, the ovulated follicle develops into a corpus luteum, which then secretes progesterone (and some estrogen). **32.** Leptin is important in advising the brain of the girl's readiness (relative to energy stores) for puberty. **33.** FSH prompts follicle growth and LH prompts ovulation. **34.** Estrogen exerts positive feedback on the anterior pituitary that leads to a burstlike release of LH. **35.** Estrogen is responsible for the secondary sex characteristics of females. **36.** Estrogen promotes epiphyseal closure in both males and females. **37.** The human papillomavirus (HPV) is most associated with cervical cancer. **38.** Chlamydia is the most common bacterial sexually transmitted infection in the U.S. **39.** No. If the sex chromosomes are XY, a male baby will develop. **40.** The sexually indifferent stage of development is the early period when the presumptive reproductive structures can produce either male or female organs. **41.** The gubernaculum guides the descent of the testis into the scrotum. **42.** Early signs of puberty's onset in boys are enlargement of the testes and scrotum. **43.** Menopause has happened when ovulation and menstruation have not occurred for a year.

Clinical Connections 1. *Carcinoma* is the term for cancer originating from epithelial tissue. The primary source of Mr. Heyden's cancer is likely to be the prostate. **2.** Elevation of serum acid phosphatase levels is diagnostic for carcinoma of the prostate. (In addition, Mr. Heyden's age places him in a group that is at relatively higher risk for this type of cancer.) **3.** Digital examination of Mr. Heyden's prostate should detect the presence of carcinoma in this tissue. In addition, serum levels of prostate-specific antigen (PSA) should be checked, as an increase in this antigen is often indicative of prostate cancer. **4.** Mr. Heyden's carcinoma has advanced to the point of metastasis. He will probably undergo a treatment that reduces the levels of androgens in his body, as androgens promote growth of the prostate-derived tissue. These treatments could include castration or administration of drugs that block the production and/or effects of androgens.

Review Questions 1. a and b; **2.** d; **3.** a; **4.** d; **5.** b; **6.** d; **7.** d; **8.** c; **9.** a, c, e, f; **10.** (1)c, f; (2)e, h; (3)g; (4)a; (5)b, g, and e; (6)f; **11.** a; **12.** c; **13.** d; **14.** b; **15.** a; **16.** b; **17.** c

Chapter 28

Check Your Understanding 1. Sperm must be capacitated before they can penetrate an oocyte. **2.** The cortical reaction involves the release of enzymes from cortical granules to the oocyte exterior, which accomplishes the slow block to polyspermy. **3.** The blastocyst is only slightly larger than the zygote because, although cell division has been going on (cleavage divisions), there is essentially no time for growth between divisions, so the resulting cells get smaller and smaller. **4.** The trophoblast cells adhere to and secrete digestive enzymes onto the uterine endometrium, accomplishing implantation, and they contribute to the formation of the placenta. **5.** The syncytiotrophoblast actually accomplishes implantation. **6.** The blastocyst secretes the hormone human chorionic gonadotropin, which is detectable in the urine. **7.** The chorion develops from the trophoblast and a layer of extraembryonic mesoderm. **8.** The decidua basalis cooperates with the chorionic villi to form the placenta. **9.** The placenta is usually fully functional by the end of the third month of pregnancy. **10.** The amnion helps to maintain a constant temperature for the developing fetus and protects it from physical trauma. **11.** The allantois provides the basis of the umbilical cord, which provides a pathway for the embryonic blood vessels to reach the placenta. **12.** Before organogenesis can occur in earnest, the embryonic body must fold and undercut to form a tubular embryo. **13.** The mesoderm gives rise to essentially all body tissues except neural and epidermal tissue and mucosae. **14.** The fetal period begins at the end of 8 weeks. **15.** Difficult breathing during late pregnancy is due to the fact that the uterus is pressing against and crowding the diaphragm (and hence the lungs). The waddling gait is due to the relaxing effect of relaxin on the pelvic ligaments and the pubic symphysis. **16.** While the exact cause of morning sickness is unknown, it is thought to be due to the rising levels of female sex hormones in the mother's blood, which sometimes takes awhile to get used to. **17.** The hormone hCT increases the pregnant woman's metabolic rate. **18.** Breech presentation is a buttock-first presentation of the baby during labor. **19.** Prostaglandins are most responsible for triggering true labor. **20.** The descent of the baby's head (the largest part of its body) follows the widest dimensions of the bony pelvis.

21. The foramen ovale and ductus arteriosus allow most of the blood to bypass the heart. **22.** For the most part, the special fetal circulatory modifications are occluded at birth or shortly thereafter. **23.** Oxytocin causes the let-down reflex.

Review Questions 1. (1)a, (2)b, (3)b, (4)a; **2.** b; **3.** c; **4.** b; **5.** a; **6.** d; **7.** d; **8.** c; **9.** b; **10.** c; **11.** a; **12.** c; **13.** a; **14.** (1)e, (2)g, (3)a, (4)f, (5)i, (6)b, (7)h, (8)d, (9)c

Chapter 29

Check Your Understanding 1. Chromosomes are not visible during interphase. The DNA-containing material is in the form of dispersed strands of chromatin. As mitosis begins, the chromatin coils and condenses, becoming visible. Chromosomes continue to condense throughout prophase and are most visible during metaphase. **2.** Chromosomes other than sex chromosomes are called autosomes. **3.** An allele represented by a capital letter is presumed to be a dominant allele. **4.** Descriptions of his phenotype are blond, blue-eyed, and hairy chest. **5.** The alleles pertaining to the same trait are segregated independently of each other to different gametes. **6.** It causes separations of linked genes on the same chromosome, producing gametes with variable genomes. **7.** Dominant genes are expressed. Thus if the dominant gene is detrimental (lethal), the carrier will probably not live very long or will die during development. **8.** In incomplete dominance, the heterozygote has a phenotype intermediate between that of the dominant and recessive alleles [for example, for the sickling gene, the dominant homozygote (*SS*) has no evidence of sickling; the heterozygote (*Ss*) has sickle-cell trait; and the homozygote for the recessive gene (*ss*) has sickle-cell anemia]. In codominance, both dominant alleles are expressed (as in ABO blood types). **9.** A male always expresses an X-linked recessive allele because, unlike a female, he does not have a second X containing homologous alleles to blunt or counteract the effect. The Y chromosome lacks most of the genes carried on the X chromosome. **10.** Height is an example of a trait conferred by polygene inheritance in which several genes on different chromosomes contribute to the trait. Such traits show a distribution of phenotypes that yields a bell-shaped curve. **11.** Other genes, measles in a pregnant woman, and lack of key dietary nutrients all may alter gene expression. **12.** Genomic imprinting labels genes as maternal or paternal. **13.** Maternal mitochondrial DNA confers extranuclear inheritance. **14.** Amniocentesis analyzes chemicals and cells in amniotic fluid. **15.** Ultrasound imaging is used to determine some aspects of fetal development (fetal age for example) and is noninvasive.

Review Questions 1. (1)d, (2)g, (3)b, (4)a, (5)f, (6)c, (7)e, (8)h; **2.** (1)e, (2)a, (3)b, (4)d, (5)c, (6)d, (7)f

Glossary

Pronunciation Key

′ = Primary accent

″ = Secondary accent

Pronounce:

		as in					as in	
a, fa, āt		fate		o, no, ōt			note
ă, hă, at		hat		ŏ, frŏ, og			frog
ah		father		oo			soon
ar		tar		or			for
e, stre, ēt		street		ow			plow
ĕ, hĕ, en		hen		oy			boy
er		her		sh			she
ew		new		u, mu, ūt			mute
g		go		ŭ, sŭ, un			sun
i, bi, īt		bite		z			zebra
ĭ, hĭ, im		him		zh			measure
ng		ring					

Abduct (ab-dukt′) To move away from the midline of the body.

Absolute refractory period Period following stimulation during which no additional action potential can be evoked.

Absorption Process by which the products of digestion pass through the alimentary tube mucosa into the blood or lymph.

Accessory digestive organs Organs that contribute to the digestive process but are not part of the alimentary canal; include the tongue, teeth, salivary glands, pancreas, liver.

Accommodation The process of increasing the refractive power of the lens of the eye; focusing.

Acetabulum (as″ĕ-tab′u-lum) Cuplike cavity on lateral surface of the hip bone that receives the femur.

Acetylcholine (ACh) (as″ĕ-til-ko′lēn) Chemical transmitter substance released by some nerve endings.

Acetylcholinesterase (AChE) (as″ĕ-til-ko″lin-es′ter-ās) Enzyme present at the neuromuscular junction and synapses that degrades acetylcholine and terminates its action.

Achilles tendon *See* Calcaneal tendon.

Acid A substance that releases hydrogen ions when in solution (compare with Base); a proton donor.

Acid-base balance Situation in which the pH of the blood is maintained between 7.35 and 7.45.

Acidosis (as″ĭ-do′sis) State of abnormally high hydrogen ion concentration in the extracellular fluid.

Actin (ak′tin) A contractile protein of muscle.

Action potential A large transient depolarization event, including polarity reversal, that is conducted along the membrane of a muscle cell or a nerve fiber.

Activation energy The amount of energy required to push a reactant to the level necessary for action.

Active immunity Immunity produced by an encounter with an antigen; provides immunological memory.

Active site Region on the surface of a functional (globular) protein where it binds and interacts chemically with other molecules of complementary shape and charge.

Active (transport) processes (1) Membrane transport processes for which ATP is required, e.g., solute pumping and endocytosis. (2) "Active transport" also refers specifically to solute pumping.

Adaptation (1) Any change in structure or response to suit a new environment; (2) decline in the transmission of a sensory nerve when a receptor is stimulated continuously and without change in stimulus strength.

Adduct (a-dukt′) To move toward the midline of the body.

Adenine (A) (ad′ĕ-nēn) One of the two major purines found in both RNA and DNA; also found in various free nucleotides of importance to the body, such as ATP.

Adenohypophysis (ad″ĕ-no-hi-pof′ĭ-sis) Anterior pituitary; the glandular part of the pituitary gland.

Adenoids (ad′en-noids) Pharyngeal tonsil.

Adenosine triphosphate (ATP) (ah-den′o-sēn tri″fos′fāt) Organic molecule that stores and releases chemical energy for use in body cells.

Adipocyte (ad′ĭ-po-sīt) An adipose, or fat, cell.

Adipose tissue (ad′ĭ-pōs) Areolar connective tissue modified to store nutrients; a connective tissue consisting chiefly of fat cells.

Adrenal glands (uh-drē′nul) Hormone-producing glands located superior to the kidneys; each consists of medulla and cortex areas.

Adrenergic fibers (ad″ren-er′jik) Nerve fibers that release norepinephrine.

Adrenocorticotropic hormone (ACTH) (ah-dre′no-kor″tĭ-ko-trō′pik) Anterior pituitary hormone that influences the activity of the adrenal cortex.

Adventitia (ad″ven-tish′e-ah) Outermost layer or covering of some organs.

Aerobic (a′er-ōb″ik) Oxygen-requiring.

Aerobic endurance The length of time a muscle can continue to contract using aerobic pathways.

Aerobic respiration Respiration in which oxygen is consumed and glucose is broken down entirely; water, carbon dioxide, and large amounts of ATP are the final products.

Afferent (af′er-ent) Carrying to or toward a center.

Afferent (sensory) nerve Nerve that contains processes of sensory neurons and carries nerve impulses to the central nervous system.

Agglutination (ah-gloo″tĭ-na′shun) Clumping of (foreign) cells; induced by cross-linking of antigen-antibody complexes.

Agonist (ag′o-nist) Muscle that bears the major responsibility for effecting a particular movement; a prime mover.

AIDS Acquired immune deficiency syndrome; caused by human immunodeficiency virus (HIV); symptoms include severe weight loss, night sweats, swollen lymph nodes, opportunistic infections.

Albumin (al-bu′min) The most abundant plasma protein.

Aldosterone (al-dos′ter-ōn) Hormone produced by the adrenal cortex that regulates Na$^+$ reabsorption and K$^+$ secretion by the kidneys.

Alimentary canal (al″ĭ-men′tar-e) The continuous hollow tube extending from the mouth to the anus; its walls are constructed by the oral cavity, pharynx, esophagus, stomach, and small and large intestines.

Alkalosis (al″kah-lo′sis) State of abnormally low hydrogen ion concentration in the extracellular fluid.

Allantois (ah″lan′to-is) Embryonic membrane; its blood vessels develop into blood vessels of the umbilical cord.

Alleles Genes coding for the same trait and found at the same locus on homologous chromosomes.

Allergy A type of hypersensitivity (overzealous immune response to an otherwise harmless antigen) that involves IgE antibodies and histamine release.

Alopecia (al″o-pe′she-ah) Baldness.

Alpha (α)-helix The most common type of secondary structure of the amino acid chain in proteins; resembles the coils of a telephone cord.

Alveolar (acinar) gland (al-ve′o-lar) A gland whose secretory cells form small, flasklike sacs.

Alveolar ventilation rate (AVR) An index of respiratory efficiency; measures volume of fresh air that flows in and out of alveoli.

Alveolus (al-ve′o-lus) (1) One of the microscopic air sacs of the lungs; (2) tiny milk-producing glandular sac in the breast; (3) tooth socket.

Alzheimer's disease (AD) (altz′hi-merz) Degenerative brain disease resulting in progressive loss of memory and motor control, and increasing dementia.

Amino acid (ah-me′no) Organic compound containing nitrogen, carbon, hydrogen, and oxygen; building block of protein.

Ammonia (NH$_3$) Common waste product of protein breakdown in the body; a colorless volatile gas, very soluble in water and capable of forming a weak base; a proton acceptor.

Amniocentesis A common form of fetal testing in which a small sample of fluid is removed from the amniotic cavity.

Amnion (am′ne-on) Fetal membrane that forms a fluid-filled sac around the embryo.

Amoeboid motion (ah-me′boyd) The flowing movement of the cytoplasm of a phagocyte.

Amphiarthrosis (am″fe-ar-thro′sis) A slightly movable joint.

Ampulla (am-pul′lah) A localized dilation of a canal or duct.

Amylase Digestive system enzyme that breaks down starchy foods.

Anabolism (ah-nab′o-lizm) Energy-requiring building phase of metabolism in which simpler substances are combined to form more complex substances.

Anaerobic (an-a′er-ōb-ik) Not requiring oxygen.

Anaerobic glycolysis (gli-kol′ĭ-sis) Energy-yielding conversion of glucose to lactic acid in various tissues, notably muscle, when sufficient oxygen is not available.

Anaerobic threshold The point at which muscle metabolism converts to anaerobic glycolysis.

Anaphase Third stage of mitosis, meiosis I, and meiosis II in which daughter chromosomes move toward each pole of a cell.

Anastomosis (ah-nas″to-mo′sis) A union or joining of nerves, blood vessels, or lymphatics.

Anatomy Study of the structure of living organisms.

Androgen (an′dro-jen) A hormone such as testosterone that controls male secondary sex characteristics.

Anemia (ah-ne′me-ah) Reduced oxygen-carrying ability of blood resulting from too few erythrocytes or abnormal hemoglobin.

Aneurysm (an′u-rizm) Blood-filled sac in an artery wall caused by dilation or weakening of the wall.

Angina pectoris (an′jĭ-nah pek′tor-is) Severe suffocating chest pain caused by brief lack of oxygen supply to heart muscle.

Angiotensin II (an″je-o-ten′sin) A potent vasoconstrictor activated by renin; also triggers release of aldosterone.

Anion (an′i-on) An ion carrying one or more negative charges and therefore attracted to a positive pole.

Anoxia (ah-nŏk′se-ah) Deficiency of oxygen.

Antagonist (an-tag′o-nist) (1) Muscle that reverses, or opposes, the action of another muscle. (2) Hormone that opposes the action of another hormone.

Anterior pituitary *See* Adenohypophysis.

Antibody A protein molecule that is released by a plasma cell (a daughter cell of an activated B lymphocyte) and that binds specifically to an antigen; an immunoglobulin.

Anticodon (an″ti-ko′don) The three-base sequence complementary to the messenger RNA (mRNA) codon.

Antidiuretic hormone (ADH, also called **vasopressin)** (an″ti-di″yer-eh′tik) Hormone produced by the hypothalamus and released by the posterior pituitary; stimulates the kidneys to reabsorb more water, reducing urine volume.

Antigen (Ag) (an′tĭ-jen) A substance or part of a substance (living or nonliving) that is recognized as foreign by the immune system, activates the immune system, and reacts with immune cells or their products.

Antigen-presenting cell (APC) A specialized cell (dendritic cell, macrophage, or B cell) that captures, processes, and presents antigens on its surface to T lymphocytes.

Anucleate cell (a-nu′kle-āt) A cell without a nucleus.

Anus (a′nus) Distal end of digestive tract; outlet of rectum.

Aorta (a-or′tah) Major systemic artery; arises from the left ventricle of the heart.

Aortic body Receptor in the aortic arch sensitive to changing oxygen, carbon dioxide, and pH levels of the blood.

Apgar score Evaluation of an infant's physical status at 1 and 5 minutes after birth by assessing five criteria: heart rate, respiration, color, muscle tone, and reflexes.

Apnea Breathing cessation.

Apocrine sweat gland (ap′o-krin) The less numerous type of sweat gland; produces a secretion containing water, salts, proteins, and fatty acids.

Apoenzyme (ap′ō-en-zīm) The protein portion of an enzyme.

Aponeurosis (ap″o-nu-ro′sis) Fibrous or membranous sheet connecting a muscle and the part it moves.

Apoptosis A process of controlled cellular suicide; eliminates cells that are unneeded, stressed, or aged.

Appendicitis (ă-pen′dĭ-sī′tis) Inflammation of the appendix (wormlike sac attached to the cecum of the large intestine).

Appendicular Relating to the limbs; one of the two major divisions of the body.

Appositional growth Growth accomplished by the addition of new layers onto those previously formed.

Aquaporins (ă″kwă-por′ins) Transmembrane proteins that form water channels.

Aqueous humor (a′kwe-us) Watery fluid in the anterior segment of the eye.

Arachnoid (ah-rak′noid) Weblike; specifically, the weblike arachnoid mater, the middle layer of the three meninges.

Areola (ah-re′o-lah) Circular, pigmented area surrounding the nipple; any small space in a tissue.

Areolar connective tissue A type of loose connective tissue.

Arrector pili (ah-rek′tor pi′li) Tiny, smooth muscles attached to hair follicles; contraction causes the hair to stand upright.

Arrhythmia (a-rith′me-ah) Irregular heart rhythm, often caused by defects in the intrinsic conduction system.

Arteries Blood vessels that conduct blood away from the heart and into the circulation.

Arteriole (ar-tēr′e-ōl) A minute artery.

Arteriosclerosis (ar-tēr′e-o-skler-o′sis) Any of a number of proliferative and degenerative changes in the arteries leading to their decreased elasticity.

Arthritis Inflammation of the joints.

Arthroscopic surgery (ar-thro-skop′ik) Procedure enabling a surgeon to repair the interior of a joint through a small incision.

Articular capsule Double-layered capsule composed of an outer fibrous capsule lined by synovial membrane; encloses the joint cavity of a synovial joint.

Articular cartilage Hyaline cartilage covering bone ends at movable joints.

Articulation (joint) The junction of two or more bones.

Association areas Functional areas of the cerebral cortex that act mainly to integrate diverse information for purposeful action.

Astigmatism (ah-stig′mah-tizm) A condition in which unequal curvatures in different parts of the cornea or lens of the eye lead to blurred vision.

Astrocyte (as′tro-sīt) A type of CNS supporting cell; assists in exchanges between blood capillaries and neurons.

Atelectasis (at″ĕ-lik′tah-sis) Lung collapse.

Atherosclerosis (a″ther-o″skler-o′sis) Changes in the walls of large arteries consisting of lipid deposits on the artery walls; one form of arteriosclerosis.

Atmospheric pressure Force that air exerts on the surface of the body (760 mm Hg at sea level).

Atom Smallest particle of an elemental substance that exhibits the properties of that element; composed of protons, neutrons, and electrons.

Atomic number The number of protons in an atom.

Atomic symbol The one- or two-letter symbol used to indicate an element; usually the first letter(s) of the element's name.

Atomic weight The average of the mass numbers of all the isotopes of an element.

ATP (adenosine triphosphate) (ah-den′o-sēn tri″fos′fāt) Organic molecule that stores and releases chemical energy for use in body cells.

Atria (a′tre-ah) The two superior receiving chambers of the heart.

Atrial natriuretic peptide (ANP) (a′tre-al na″tre-u-ret′ik) A hormone released by certain cells of the heart atria that reduces blood pressure and blood volume by inhibiting nearly all events that promote vasoconstriction and Na^+ and water retention.

Atrioventricular (AV) bundle (a″tre-o-ven-trĭ′kyoo-ler) Bundle of specialized fibers that conduct impulses from the AV node to the right and left ventricles; also called bundle of His.

Atrioventricular (AV) node Specialized mass of conducting cells located at the atrioventricular junction in the heart.

Atrioventricular (AV) valve Valve that prevents backflow into the atrium when the connected ventricle is contracting.

Atrophy (at′ro-fe) Reduction in size or wasting away of an organ or cell resulting from disease or lack of use.

Auditory ossicles (ah′sih-kulz) The three tiny bones serving as transmitters of vibrations and located within the middle ear: the malleus, incus, and stapes.

Auditory tube *See* Pharyngotympanic tube.

Autoimmunity Production of antibodies or effector T cells that attack a person's own tissue.

Autolysis (aw″tol′ĭ-sis) Process of autodigestion (self-digestion) of cells, especially dead or degenerate cells.

Autonomic ganglion Collection of sympathetic or parasympathetic ganglionic neuronal cell bodies.

Autonomic nervous system (ANS) Efferent division of the peripheral nervous system that innervates cardiac and smooth muscles and glands; also called the involuntary or visceral motor system.

Autonomic (visceral) reflexes Reflexes that activate smooth or cardiac muscle and/or glands.

Autoregulation The automatic local adjustment of blood flow to a particular body area in response to its current requirements.

Autosomes Chromosomes number 1 to 22; do not include the sex chromosomes.

Avogadro's number (av″o-gad′rōz) The number of molecules in one mole of any substance, 6.02×10^{23}.

Axial Relating to the head, neck, and trunk; one of the two major divisions of the body.

Axolemma (ak″so-lem′ah) The plasma membrane of an axon.

Axon Neuron process that carries impulses away from the nerve cell body; efferent process; the conducting portion of a nerve cell.

Axon terminals (synaptic knobs, boutons) The bulbous distal endings of the terminal branches of an axon.

B cells Also called B lymphocytes; oversee humoral immunity; their descendants differentiate into antibody-producing plasma cells.

Baroreceptor (bayr″o-re-sep′tor) A sensory nerve ending in the wall of the carotid sinus or aortic arch sensitive to vessel stretching.

Basal body (ba′sal) An organelle structurally identical to a centriole and forming the base of a cilium or flagellum.

Basal ganglia *See* Basal nuclei.

Basal lamina (lam′ĭ-nah) Noncellular, adhesive supporting sheet consisting largely of glycoproteins secreted by epithelial cells.

Basal metabolic rate (BMR) Rate at which energy is expended (heat produced) by the body per unit time under controlled (basal) conditions: 12 hours after a meal, at rest.

Basal nuclei (basal ganglia) Specific gray matter areas located deep within the white matter of the cerebral hemispheres.

Basal surface The surface near the base or interior of a structure; nearest the lower side or bottom of a structure.

Base A substance capable of binding with hydrogen ions; a proton acceptor.

Basement membrane Extracellular material consisting of a basal lamina secreted by epithelial cells and a reticular lamina secreted by underlying connective tissue cells.

Basophil (ba′zo-fil) White blood cell whose granules stain purplish-black and nucleus purple with basic dye.

Benign (be-nīn′) Not malignant.

Bile Greenish-yellow or brownish fluid produced in and secreted by the liver, stored in the gallbladder, and released into the small intestine.

Bilirubin (bil″ĭ-roo′bin) Yellow pigment of bile.

Bipolar neuron Neuron with axon and dendrite that extend from opposite sides of the cell body.

Blastocyst (blas′to-sist) Stage of early embryonic development; the product of cleavage.

Blood pressure (BP) Force exerted by blood against a unit area of the blood vessel walls; differences in blood pressure between different areas of the circulation provide the driving force for blood circulation.

Blood-brain barrier Mechanism that inhibits passage of materials from the blood into brain tissues; reflects relative impermeability of brain capillaries.

Bolus (bo′lus) A rounded mass of food prepared by the mouth for swallowing; any soft round mass.

Bone marrow Fat- or blood-forming tissue found within bone cavities; called yellow and red bone marrow, respectively.

Bone (osseous tissue) (os′e-us) A connective tissue that forms the bony skeleton.

Bone remodeling Process involving bone formation and destruction in response to hormonal and mechanical factors.

Bone resorption The removal of osseous tissue; part of the continuous bone remodeling process.

Bowman's capsule (bo-manz) *See* Glomerular capsule.

Boyle's law States that when the temperature is constant, the pressure of a gas varies inversely with its volume.

Bradycardia (brad″e-kar′de-ah) A heart rate below 60 beats per minute.

Brain death State of irreversible coma, even though life-support measures may have restored other body organs.

Brain stem Collectively the midbrain, pons, and medulla of the brain.

Brain ventricle Fluid-filled cavity of the brain.

Branchial groove (brang′ke-al) An indentation of the surface ectoderm in the embryo; the external acoustic meatus develops from it.

Bronchioles Smaller (<1 mm in diameter) branching air passageways inside the lungs.

Bronchus (brong′kus) One of the two large branches of the trachea that leads to the lungs.

Buffer Chemical substance or system that minimizes changes in pH by releasing or binding hydrogen ions.

Burn Tissue damage inflicted by intense heat, electricity, radiation, or certain chemicals, all of which denature cell proteins and cause cell death in the affected areas.

Bursa (ber′sa) A fibrous sac lined with synovial membrane and containing synovial fluid; occurs between bones and muscle tendons (or other structures), where it acts to decrease friction during movement.

Bursitis Inflammation of a bursa.

Calcaneal tendon (kal-ka′ne-al) Tendon that attaches the calf muscles to the heelbone (calcaneus); also called the Achilles tendon.

Calcitonin (kal″sih-to′nin) Hormone released by the thyroid. Lowers blood calcium levels only when present at high (therapeutic). levels.

Calculus (kal′ku-lus) A stone formed within various body parts.

Callus (kal′lus) (1) Localized thickening of skin epidermis resulting from physical trauma; (2) repair tissue (fibrous or bony) formed at a fracture site.

Calorie (cal) Amount of energy needed to raise the temperature of 1 gram of water 1° Celsius. Energy exchanges associated with biochemical reactions are usually reported in kilocalories (1 kcal = 1000 cal), also called large calories (Cal).

Calyx (ka′liks) A cuplike extension of the pelvis of the kidney.

Canaliculus (kan″ah-lik′u-lus) Extremely small tubular passage or channel.

Cancer A malignant, invasive cellular neoplasm that has the capability of spreading throughout the body or body parts.

Capillaries (kap′il-layr″ēs) The smallest of the blood vessels and the sites of exchange between the blood and tissue cells.

Carbohydrate (kar″bo-hi′drāt) Organic compound composed of carbon, hydrogen, and oxygen; includes starches, sugars, cellulose.

Carbonic acid–bicarbonate buffer system Chemical system that helps maintain pH homeostasis of the blood.

Carbonic anhydrase (kar-bon′ik an-hi′drās) Enzyme that facilitates the combination of carbon dioxide with water to form carbonic acid.

Carcinogen (kar″sĭ′no-jin) Cancer-causing agent.

Cardiac cycle Sequence of events encompassing one complete contraction and relaxation of the atria and ventricles of the heart.

Cardiac muscle Specialized muscle of the heart.

Cardiac output (CO) Amount of blood pumped out of a ventricle in one minute.

Cardiac reserve The difference between resting and maximal cardiac output.

Cardiogenic shock Pump failure; the heart is so inefficient that it cannot sustain adequate circulation.

Cardiovascular system Organ system that distributes the blood to deliver nutrients and remove wastes.

Carotene (kar′o-tēn) Yellow to orange pigment that accumulates in the stratum corneum epidermal layer and in fatty tissue of the hypodermis.

Carotid body (kar-rot′id) A receptor in the common carotid artery sensitive to changing oxygen, carbon dioxide, and pH levels of the blood.

Carotid sinus (si′nus) A dilation of a common carotid artery; involved in regulation of systemic blood pressure.

Carrier A transmembrane protein that changes shape to envelop and transport a polar substance across the cell membrane.

Cartilage (kar′tĭ-lij) White, semiopaque connective tissue.

Cartilage bone (endochondral bone) Bone formed by using hyaline cartilage structures as models for ossification.

Cartilaginous joints (kar″tĭ-laj′ĭ-nus) Bones united by cartilage; no joint cavity is present.

Catabolism (kat-tab′o-lizm) Process in which living cells break down substances into simpler substances.

Catalyst (kat′ah-list) Substance that increases the rate of a chemical reaction without itself becoming chemically changed or part of the product.

Cataract Clouding of the eye's lens; often congenital or age-related.

Catecholamines (kat″ĕ-kol′ah-mēnz) Epinephrine, norepinephrine, and dopamine; a class of amines that act as chemical transmitters.

Cation (kat′i-on) An ion with a positive charge.

Caudal (kaw′dul) Literally, toward the tail; in humans, the inferior portion of the anatomy.

Cecum (se′kum) The blind-end pouch at the beginning of the large intestine.

Cell Structural unit of all living things.

Cell differentiation The development of specific and distinctive features in cells, from a single cell (the fertilized egg) to all the specialized cells of adulthood.

Cell life cycle Series of changes a cell goes through from the time it is formed until it reproduces itself.

Cell-mediated immunity Immunity conferred by activated T cells, which directly kill infected or cancerous body cells or cells of foreign grafts and release chemicals that regulate the immune response.

Cell membrane *See* Plasma membrane.

Cellular respiration Metabolic processes in which ATP is produced.

Cellulose (sel′u-lōs) A fibrous carbohydrate that is the main structural component of plant tissues.

Central (Haversian) canal (hah-ver′zhan) The canal in the center of each osteon that contains minute blood vessels and nerve fibers that serve the needs of the osteocytes.

Central nervous system (CNS) Brain and spinal cord.

Centriole (sen′tre-ol) Minute body found near the nucleus of the cell; active in cell division.

Centrosome (cell center) A region near the nucleus which contains paired organelles called centrioles.

Cerebellum (ser″ĕ-bel′um) Brain region most involved in producing smooth, coordinated skeletal muscle activity.

Cerebral aqueduct (ser′ĕ-bral, sĕ-re′bral) The slender cavity of the midbrain that connects the third and fourth ventricles.

Cerebral arterial circle (circle of Willis) An arterial anastomosis at the base of the brain.

Cerebral cortex The outer gray matter region of the cerebral hemispheres.

Cerebral dominance Designates the hemisphere that is dominant for language.

Cerebral palsy Neuromuscular disability in which voluntary muscles are poorly controlled or paralyzed as a result of brain damage.

Cerebral white matter Consists largely of myelinated fibers bundled into large tracts; provides for communication between cerebral areas and lower CNS centers.

Cerebrospinal fluid (CSF) (ser″ĕ-bro-spi′nal) Plasmalike fluid that fills the cavities of the CNS and surrounds the CNS externally; protects the brain and spinal cord.

Cerebrovascular accident (CVA) (ser″ĕ-bro-vas′ku-lar) Condition in which brain tissue is deprived of a blood supply, as in blockage of a cerebral blood vessel; a stroke.

Cerebrum (ser′ĕ-brum) The cerebral hemispheres and the structures of the diencephalon.

Cervical vertebrae The seven vertebrae of the vertebral column located in the neck.

Cervix Lower outlet of the uterus extending into the vagina.

Channel A transmembrane protein that forms an aqueous pore, allowing substances to move from one side of the membrane to the other.

Chemical bond An energy relationship holding atoms together; involves the interaction of electrons.

Chemical digestion A series of catabolic steps in which complex food molecules are broken down to their building blocks by enzymes.

Chemical energy Energy stored in the bonds of chemical substances.

Chemical equilibrium A state of apparent repose created by two reactions proceeding in opposite directions at equal speed.

Chemical reaction Process in which molecules are formed, changed, or broken down.

Chemoreceptor (ke″mo-re-sep′ter) Receptor sensitive to various chemicals in solution.

Chemotaxis (ke″mo-tak′sis) Movement of a cell, organism, or part of an organism toward or away from a chemical substance.

Cholecystokinin (CCK) (ko″le-sis″to-ki′nin) An intestinal hormone that stimulates gallbladder contraction and pancreatic juice release.

Cholesterol (ko-les′ter-ol″) Steroid found in animal fats as well as in most body tissues; made by the liver.

Cholinergic fibers (ko″lin-er′jik) Nerve endings that, upon stimulation, release acetylcholine.

Chondroblast (kon′dro-blast) Actively mitotic cell of cartilage.

Chondrocyte (kon′dro-sīt) Mature cell of cartilage.

Chorion (kor′e-on) Outermost fetal membrane; helps form the placenta.

Chorionic villi sampling (ko″re-on′ik vil′i) Fetal testing procedure in which bits of the chorionic villi from the placenta are snipped off and the cells karyotyped. This procedure can be done as early as 8 weeks into the pregnancy.

Choroid (ko′roid) The vascular middle layer of the eye.

Choroid plexus (ko′roid plex′sus) A capillary knot that protrudes into a brain ventricle; involved in forming cerebrospinal fluid.

Chromatin (kro′mah-tin) Structures in the nucleus that carry the hereditary factors (genes).

Chromosomes (kro′mo-somz) Barlike bodies of tightly coiled chromatin; visible during cell division.

Chronic obstructive pulmonary disease (COPD) Collective term for progressive, obstructive respiratory disorders; includes emphysema, chronic bronchitis.

Chyme (kīm) Semifluid, creamy mass consisting of partially digested food and gastric juice.

Cilia (sil′e-ah) Tiny, hairlike projections on cell surfaces that move in a wavelike manner.

Circumduction (ser″kum-duk′shun) Movement of a body part so that it outlines a cone in space.

Cirrhosis (sĭ-ro′sis) Chronic disease of the liver, characterized by an overgrowth of connective tissue or fibrosis.

Cisterna chyli (sis-ter′nah ki′li) An enlarged sac at the base of the thoracic duct; the origin of the thoracic duct.

Cisternae (sis-ter′ne) Any cavity or enclosed space serving as a reservoir.

Cleavage An early embryonic phase consisting of rapid mitotic cell divisions without intervening growth periods; product is a blastocyst.

Clonal selection (klo′nul) Process during which a B cell or T cell becomes activated by binding contact with an antigen.

Clone Descendants of a single cell.

Coagulation Process in which blood is transformed from a liquid to a gel; blood clotting.

Cochlea (kok′le-ah) Snail-shaped chamber of the bony labyrinth that houses the receptor for hearing [the spiral organ (of Corti)].

Codon (ko′don) The three-base sequence on a messenger RNA molecule that provides the genetic information used in protein synthesis; code for a given amino acid.

Coenzyme (ko-en′zīm) Nonprotein substance associated with and activating an enzyme, typically a vitamin.

Cofactor Metal ion or organic molecule that is required for enzyme activity.

Collagen fiber The most abundant of the three fibers found in the matrix of connective tissue.

Colloid (kol′oid) (1) A mixture in which the solute particles (usually proteins) do not settle out readily. (2) Substance in the thyroid gland containing thyroglobulin protein.

Colloid osmotic pressure (kol′oid ahz-mah′tik) Pressure created in a fluid by large nondiffusible molecules, such as plasma proteins that are prevented from moving through a (capillary) membrane. Such substances tend to draw water to them.

Colon Regions of the large intestine; includes ascending, transverse, descending, and sigmoid portions.

Combination (synthesis) reaction Chemical reaction in which larger, more complex atoms or molecules are formed from simpler ones.

Complement A group of bloodborne proteins, which, when activated, enhance the inflammatory and immune responses and may lead to cell lysis.

Complementarity of structure and function The relationship between a structure and its function; i.e., structure determines function.

Complementary base Refers to how a given nitrogenous base of DNA or RNA bonds to another nitrogenous base. For example, adenine (A) is the complementary base of thymine (T). The result is base pairing.

Complete blood count (CBC) Clinical test that includes counts of all formed elements, a hematocrit, and measurements of erythrocyte size and hemoglobin content.

Compound Substance composed of two or more different elements, the atoms of which are chemically united.

Concentration gradient The difference in the concentration of a particular substance between two different areas.

Conducting zone Includes all respiratory passageways that provide conduits for air to reach the sites of gas exchange (the respiratory zone).

Conductivity Ability to transmit an electrical impulse.

Cones One of the two types of photoreceptor cells in the retina of the eye; provide for color vision.

Congenital (kun-jeh′nih-tul) Existing at birth.

Congestive heart failure (CHF) Condition in which the pumping efficiency of the heart is depressed so that circulation is inadequate to meet tissue needs.

Conjunctiva (kon″junk-ti′vah) Thin, protective mucous membrane lining the eyelids and covering the anterior surface of the eye itself.

Connective tissue A primary tissue; form and function vary extensively. Functions include support, storage, and protection.

Consciousness The ability to perceive, communicate, remember, understand, appreciate, and initiate voluntary movements.

Contraception The prevention of conception; birth control.

Contractility Muscle cell's ability to move by shortening.

Contraction To shorten or develop tension, an ability highly developed in muscle cells.

Contralateral Relating to the opposite side.

Cornea (kor′ne-ah) Transparent anterior portion of the eyeball; part of the fibrous layer.

Corona radiata (kor-o′nah ra-de-ah′tah) (1) Arrangement of elongated follicle cells around a mature ovum; (2) crownlike arrangement of nerve fibers radiating from the internal capsule of the brain to every part of the cerebral cortex.

Coronary circulation The functional blood supply of the heart; shortest circulation in the body.

Cortex (kor′teks) Outer surface layer of an organ.

Corticosteroids (kor″tĭ-ko-stĕ′roidz) Steroid hormones released by the adrenal cortex.

Cortisol (hydrocortisone) (kor′tih-sol) Glucocorticoid produced by the adrenal cortex.

Covalent bond (ko-va′lent) Chemical bond created by electron sharing between atoms.

Cranial nerves The 12 nerve pairs that arise from the brain.

Craniosacral division Another name for the parasympathetic division of the autonomic nervous system.

Cranium (cranial bones) (kra′ne-um) Bony protective encasement of the brain and organs of hearing and equilibrium; also called the skull.

Creatine kinase (kre′ah-tin) Enzyme that catalyzes the transfer of phosphate from creatine phosphate to ADP, forming creatine and ATP; important in muscle contraction.

Creatine phosphate (CP) (fos-fāt) Compound that serves as an alternative energy source for muscle tissue.

Creatinine (kre-at′ĭ-nin) A nitrogenous waste molecule which is not reabsorbed by the kidney; this characteristic makes it useful for measurement of the GFR and glomerular function.

Crista ampullaris Sensory receptor organ within the ampulla of each semicircular canal of the inner ear; dynamic equilibrium receptor.

Cross section A cut running horizontally from right to left, dividing the body or an organ into superior and inferior parts.

Cutaneous (ku-ta′ne-us) Pertaining to the skin.

Cutaneous sensory receptors Receptors located throughout the skin that respond to stimuli arising outside the body; part of the nervous system.

Cyclic AMP Intracellular second messenger that mediates the effects of the first (extracellular) messenger (hormone or neurotransmitter); formed from ATP by a plasma membrane enzyme (adenylate cyclase).

Cystic fibrosis (CF) Genetic disorder in which secretion of overly viscous mucus clogs the respiratory passages, predisposes to fatal respiratory infections.

Cytochromes (si′to-krōmz) Brightly colored iron-containing proteins that form part of the inner mitochondrial membrane and function as electron carriers in oxidative phosphorylation.

Cytokines Small proteins that act as chemical messengers between various parts of the immune system.

Cytokinesis (si″to-kĭ-ne′sis) The division of cytoplasm that occurs after the cell nucleus has divided.

Cytoplasm (si′to-plazm) The cellular material surrounding the nucleus and enclosed by the plasma membrane.

Cytosine (C) (si″to-sēn) Nitrogen-containing base that is part of a nucleotide structure.

Cytoskeleton Literally, cell skeleton. An elaborate series of rods running through the cystol, supporting cellular structures and providing the machinery to generate various cell movements.

Cytosol Viscous, semitransparent fluid substance of cytoplasm in which other elements are suspended.

Cytotoxic T cell (T$_C$ cell) Effector T cell that directly kills foreign cells, cancer cells, or virus-infected body cells by inducing apoptosis (cell suicide).

Deamination (de′am″ih-na′shun) Removal of an amine group from an organic compound.

Decomposition reaction Chemical reaction in which a molecule is broken down into smaller molecules or its constituent atoms.

Defecation (def″ih-ka′shun) Elimination of the contents of the bowels (feces).

Deglutition (deg″loo-tish′un) Swallowing.

Dehydration (de″hi-dra′shun) Condition of excessive water loss.

Dehydration synthesis Process by which a large molecule is synthesized by removing water and covalently bonding smaller molecules together.

Dendrite (den′drīt) Branching neuron process that serves as a receptive, or input, region; transmits an electrical signal toward the cell body.

Dendritic cells Protective cells that phagocytize antigens, migrate to lymph nodes, and present the antigen to T cells, causing them to activate and mount an immune response; called epidermal dendritic cells or Langerhans cells in the skin.

Depolarization (de-po″ler-ah-za′shun) Loss of a state of polarity; loss or reduction of negative membrane potential.

Dermatome (der′mah-tōm) Portion of somite mesoderm that forms the dermis of the skin; also the area of skin innervated by the cutaneous branches of a single spinal nerve.

Dermis Layer of skin deep to the epidermis; composed mostly of dense irregular connective tissue.

Desmosome (dez′muh-sōm) Cell junction composed of thickened plasma membranes joined by filaments.

Diabetes insipidus (di″ah-be′tēz in-sih′pih-dus) Disease characterized by passage of a large quantity of dilute urine plus intense thirst and dehydration caused by inadequate release of antidiuretic hormone (ADH).

Diabetes mellitus (DM) (meh-li′tus) Disease caused by deficient insulin release or by insulin resistance, leading to inability of the body cells to use carbohydrates.

Dialysis (di-al′ah-sis) Diffusion of solute(s) through a semipermeable membrane.

Diapedesis (di″ah-pĕ-de′sis) Passage of white blood cells through intact vessel walls into tissue.

Diaphragm (di′ah-fram) (1) Any partition or wall separating one area from another; (2) a muscle that separates the thoracic cavity from the lower abdominopelvic cavity.

Diaphysis (di-af′ĭ-sis) Elongated shaft of a long bone.

Diarthrosis (di″ar-thro′sis) Freely movable joint.

Diastole (di-as′to-le) Period of the cardiac cycle when either the ventricles or the atria are relaxing.

Diastolic pressure (di-as-tah′lik) Arterial blood pressure reached during or as a result of diastole; lowest level of any given cardiac cycle.

Diencephalon (interbrain) (di″en-seh′fuh-lon) That part of the forebrain between the cerebral hemispheres and the midbrain including the thalamus, the epithalamus, and the hypothalamus.

Differential white blood cell count Diagnostic test to determine relative proportion of individual leukocyte types.

Diffusion (dĭ-fu′zhun) The spreading of particles in a gas or solution with a movement toward uniform distribution of particles; driven by kinetic energy.

Digestion Chemical or mechanical process of breaking down foodstuffs to substances that can be absorbed.

Digestive system System that processes food into absorbable units and eliminates indigestible wastes.

Dipeptide A combination of two amino acids united by means of a peptide bond.

Diploë (dip′lo-e) The internal layer of spongy bone in flat bones.

Diploid chromosomal number The chromosomal number characteristic of an organism, symbolized as $2n$; twice the chromosomal number (n) of the gamete; in humans, $2n = 46$.

Diplopia (dĭ-plo′pe-ah) Double vision.

Dipole (polar molecule) Nonsymmetrical molecules that contain electrically unbalanced atoms.

Disaccharide (di-sak′ah-rīd″, di-sak′ah-rid) Literally, double sugar; e.g., sucrose, lactose.

Dislocation (luxation) Occurs when bones are forced out of their normal alignment at a joint.

Displacement (exchange) reaction Chemical reaction in which bonds are both made and broken; atoms become combined with different atoms.

Distal (dis′tul) Away from the attached end of a limb or the origin of a structure.

Diuretics (di″u-ret′iks) Chemicals that enhance urinary output.

Diverticulum (di″ver-tik′u-lum) A pouch or sac in the walls of a hollow organ or structure.

DNA (deoxyribonucleic acid) (de-ok″sĭ-ri″bo-nu-kla′ik) A nucleic acid found in all living cells; it carries the organism's hereditary information.

DNA replication Process that occurs before cell division; ensures that all daughter cells have identical genes.

Dominant traits Occurs when one allele masks or suppresses the expression of its partner.

Dominant-recessive inheritance Reflects the interaction of dominant and recessive alleles.

Dorsal (dor′sul) Pertaining to the back; posterior.

Dorsal root ganglion Peripheral collection of cell bodies of first-order afferent neurons whose central axons enter the spinal cord.

Double helix The secondary structure assumed by two strands of DNA, held together throughout their length by hydrogen bonds between bases on opposite strands.

Duct (dukt) A canal or passageway; a tubular structure that provides an exit for the secretions of a gland, or for conducting any fluid.

Ductus (vas) deferens Extends from the epididymis to the urethra; propels sperm into the urethra by peristalsis during ejaculation.

Duodenum (du″o-de′num) First part of the small intestine.

Dura mater (du′rah ma′ter) Outermost and toughest of the three membranes (meninges) covering the brain and spinal cord.

Dynamic equilibrium Sense that reports on angular (rotatory) acceleration or deceleration of the head in space.

Dyskinesia (dis-kĭ-ne′ze-ah) Disorders of muscle tone, posture, or involuntary movements.

Dyspnea (disp-ne′ah) Difficult or labored breathing; air hunger.

Eccrine glands (ek′rin) Sweat glands abundant on the palms, soles of feet, and the forehead.

Ectoderm (ek′to-derm) Embryonic germ layer; forms the epidermis of the skin and its derivatives, and nervous tissues.

Edema (ĕ-de′mah) Abnormal increase in the amount of interstitial fluid; causes swelling.

Effector (ef-ek′ter) Organ, gland, or muscle capable of being activated by nerve endings.

Efferent (ef′er-ent) Carrying away or away from, especially a nerve fiber that carries impulses away from the central nervous system.

Elastic cartilage Cartilage with abundant elastic fibers; more flexible than hyaline cartilage.

Elastic fiber Fiber formed from the protein elastin, which gives a rubbery and resilient quality to the matrix of connective tissue.

Electrical energy Energy formed by the movement of charged particles across cell membranes.

Electrocardiogram (ECG or EKG) (e-lek″tro-car′de-o-gram″) Graphic record of the electrical activity of the heart.

Electrochemical gradient The combined difference in concentration and charge; influences the distribution and direction of diffusion of ions.

Electroencephalogram (EEG) (e-lek″tro-en-sef′ah-lo-gram″) Graphic record of the electrical activity of nerve cells in the brain.

Electrolyte (e-lek′tro-līt) Chemical substances, such as salts, acids, and bases, that ionize and dissociate in water and are capable of conducting an electrical current.

Electrolyte balance Refers to the balance between input and output of salts (sodium, potassium, calcium, magnesium) in the body.

Electromagnetic radiation Emitted photons (wave packets) of energy, e.g., light, X ray, infrared.

Electron Negatively charged subatomic particle; orbits the atom's nucleus.

Electron shells (energy levels) Regions of space that consecutively surround the nucleus of an atom.

Element One of a limited number of unique varieties of matter that composes substances of all kinds; e.g., carbon, hydrogen, oxygen.

Embolism (em′bo-lizm) Obstruction of a blood vessel by an embolus (blood clot, fatty mass, bubble of air, or other debris) floating in the blood.

Embryo (em′bre-o) Developmental stage extending from fertilization to the end of the eighth week.

Emesis Reflexive emptying of the stomach through the esophagus and pharynx; also known as vomiting.

Encephalitis (en″seh-fuh-lī′tis) Inflammation of the brain.

Endergonic reaction Chemical reaction that absorbs energy, e.g., an anabolic reaction.

Endocardium (en″do-kar′de-um) Endothelial membrane that lines the interior of the heart.

Endochondral ossification (en″do-kon′dral) Embryonic formation of bone by the replacement of calcified cartilage; most skeletal bones are formed by this process.

Endocrine glands (en′do-krin) Ductless glands that empty their hormonal products directly into the blood.

Endocrine system Body system that includes internal organs that secrete hormones.

Endocytosis (en″do-si-to′sis) Means by which fairly large extracellular molecules or particles enter cells, e.g., phagocytosis, pinocytosis, receptor-mediated endocytosis.

Endoderm (en′do-derm) Embryonic germ layer; forms the lining of the digestive tube and its associated structures.

Endogenous (en-doj′ĕ-nŭs) Originating or produced within the organism or one of its parts.

Endometrium (en″do-me′tre-um) Mucous membrane lining of the uterus.

Endomysium (en″do-mis′e-um) Thin connective tissue surrounding each muscle cell.

Endoplasmic reticulum (ER) (en″do-plaz′mik rĕ-tik′u-lum) Membranous network of tubular or saclike channels in the cytoplasm of a cell.

Endosteum (en-dos′te-um) Connective tissue membrane covering internal bone surfaces.

Endothelium (en″do-the′le-um) Single layer of simple squamous cells that line the walls of the heart, blood vessels, and lymphatic vessels.

Energy The capacity to do work; may be stored (potential energy) or in action (kinetic energy).

Energy intake Energy liberated during food oxidation.

Energy output Sum of energy lost as heat, as work, and as fat or glycogen storage.

Enzyme (en′zīm) A protein that acts as a biological catalyst to speed up a chemical reaction.

Eosinophil (e″o-sin′o-fil) Granular white blood cell whose granules readily take up an acid stain called eosin.

Ependymal cell (ĕ-pen′dĭ-mul) A type of CNS supporting cell; lines the central cavities of the brain and spinal cord.

Epidermis (ep″ĭ-der′mis) Superficial layer of the skin; composed of keratinized stratified squamous epithelium.

Epididymis (ep″ĭ-dĭ′dĭ-mis) That portion of the male duct system in which sperm mature. Empties into the ductus (or vas) deferens.

Epidural space Area between the bony vertebrae and the dura mater of the spinal cord.

Epiglottis (eh″puh-glah′tis) Elastic cartilage at the back of the throat; covers the opening of the larynx during swallowing.

Epileptic seizures Abnormal electrical discharges of groups of brain neurons, during which no other messages can get through.

Epimysium (ep″ĭ-mis′e-um) Sheath of fibrous connective tissue surrounding a muscle.

Epinephrine (ep″ĭ-nef′rin) Chief hormone produced by the adrenal medulla. Also called adrenaline.

Epiphyseal plate (e″pĭ-fis′e-ul) Plate of hyaline cartilage at the junction of the diaphysis and epiphysis that provides for growth in length of a long bone.

Epiphysis (e-pif′ĭ-sis) The end of a long bone, attached to the shaft.

Epithalamus Most dorsal portion of the diencephalon; forms the roof of the third ventricle with the pineal gland extending from its posterior border.

Epithelium (epithelial tissue) (ep″ĭ-the′le-ul) Pertaining to a primary tissue that covers the body surface, lines its internal cavities, and forms glands.

Erythrocytes (e-rith′ro-sīts) Red blood cells.

Erythropoiesis (ĕ-rith″ro-poi-e′sis) Process of erythrocyte formation.

Erythropoietin (EPO) (ĕ-rith″ro-poi′ĕ-tin) Hormone that stimulates production of red blood cells.

Esophagus (ĕ-sof′ah-gus) Muscular tube extending from the laryngopharynx through the diaphragm to join the stomach; collapses when not involved in food propulsion.

Estrogens (es′tro-jenz) Hormones that stimulate female secondary sex characteristics; female sex hormones.

Eupnea (ūp-ne′ah) Normal respiratory rate and rhythm.

Exchange (displacement) reaction Chemical reaction in which bonds are both made and broken; atoms become combined with different atoms.

Excitability (irritability) Ability to respond to stimuli.

Excitation-contraction (E-C) coupling Sequence of events by which transmission of an action potential along the sarcolemma leads to the sliding of myofilaments.

Excitatory postsynaptic potential (EPSP) Depolarizing graded potential in a postsynaptic neuron.

Excretion (ek-skre′shun) Elimination of waste products from the body.

Exergonic reaction Chemical reaction that releases energy, e.g., a catabolic or oxidative reaction.

Exocrine glands (ek′so-krin) Glands that have ducts through which their secretions are carried to a particular site.

Exocytosis (ek″so-si-to′sis) Mechanism by which substances are moved from the cell interior to the extracellular space as a secretory vesicle fuses with the plasma membrane.

Exons Amino acid–specifying informational sequences (separated by introns) in the genes of higher organisms.

Extension Movement that increases the angle of a joint, e.g., straightening a flexed knee.

Exteroceptor (ek″ster-o-sep′tor) Sensory end organ that responds to stimuli from the external world.

Extracellular fluid (ECF) Internal fluid located outside cells; includes interstitial fluid, blood plasma, and cerebrospinal fluid.

Extracellular matrix Nonliving material in connective tissue consisting of ground substance and fibers that separates the living cells.

Extrasystole (ek″strah-sis′to-le) Premature heart contraction.

Extrinsic (ek-strin′sik) Of external origin.

Extrinsic eye muscles The six skeletal muscles which attach to and move each eye.

Facilitated diffusion Passive transport process used by certain molecules, e.g., glucose and other simple sugars too large to pass through plasma membrane pores. Involves movement through channels or movement facilitated by a membrane carrier.

Fallopian tube (fah-lo′pē-un) *See* Uterine tube.

Fascia (fash′e-ah) Layers of fibrous tissue covering and separating muscle.

Fascicle (fas′ĭ-kl) Bundle of nerve or muscle fibers bound together by connective tissue.

Fatty acids Linear chains of carbon and hydrogen atoms (hydrocarbon chains) with an organic acid group at one end. A constituent of fat.

Feces (fe′sēz) Material discharged from the bowel; composed of food residue, secretions, bacteria.

Fenestrated (fen′es-tra-tid) Pierced with one or more small openings.

Fertilization Fusion of the sperm and egg nuclei.

Fetus Developmental stage extending from the ninth week of development to birth.

Fiber A slender threadlike structure or filament. *See also* Nerve fiber, Muscle fiber.

Fibrillation Condition of rapid and irregular or out-of-phase heart contractions.

Fibrin (fi′brin) Fibrous insoluble protein formed during blood clotting.

Fibrinogen (fi-brin′o-jin) A soluble blood protein that is converted to insoluble fibrin during blood clotting.

Fibrinolysis Process that removes unneeded blood clots when healing has occurred.

Fibroblast (fi′bro-blast) Young, actively mitotic cell that forms the fibers of connective tissue.

Fibrocartilage The most compressible type of cartilage; resistant to stretch. Forms vertebral discs and knee joint cartilages.

Fibrocyte (fi′bro-sīt) Mature fibroblast; maintains the matrix of fibrous types of connective tissue.

Fibrosis Proliferation of fibrous connective tissue called scar tissue.

Fibrous joints Bones joined by fibrous tissue; no joint cavity is present.

Filtrate A plasma-derived fluid that is processed by the renal tubules to form urine.

Filtration Passage of a solvent and dissolved substances through a membrane or filter.

First-degree burn A burn in which only the epidermis is damaged.

Fissure (fih′sher) (1) A groove or cleft; (2) the deepest depressions or inward folds on the brain.

Fixator (fix′a-ter) Muscle that immobilizes one or more bones, allowing other muscles to act from a stable base.

Flagellum (flah-jel′lum) Long, whiplike cellular extension containing microtubules; propels sperm and some single-celled eukaryotes.

Flexion (flek′shun) Movement that decreases the angle of the joint, e.g., bending the knee from a straight to an angled position.

Flexor (withdrawal) reflex Reflex initiated by a painful stimulus (actual or perceived); causes automatic withdrawal of the threatened body part from the stimulus.

Fluid mosaic model A depiction of the structure of the membranes of a cell as phospholipid bilayers in which proteins are dispersed.

Follicle (fah′lih-kul) (1) Ovarian structure consisting of a developing egg surrounded by one or more layers of follicle cells; (2) colloid-containing structure of the thyroid gland; (3) B cell–rich region in lymphoid tissue.

Follicle-stimulating hormone (FSH) Hormone produced by the anterior pituitary that stimulates ovarian follicle production in females and sperm production in males.

Fontanelles (fon″tah-nelz′) Fibrous membranes at the angles of cranial bones that accommodate brain growth in the fetus and infant.

Foramen (fo-ra′men) Hole or opening in a bone or between body cavities.

Forebrain (prosencephalon) Anterior portion of the brain consisting of the telencephalon and the diencephalon.

Formed elements Cellular portion of blood.

Fossa (fos′ah) A depression, often an articular surface.

Fovea (fo′ve-ah) A pit.

Fracture A break in a bone.

Free radicals Highly reactive chemicals with unpaired electrons that can scramble the structure of proteins, lipids, and nucleic acids.

Frontal (coronal) plane Longitudinal (vertical) plane that divides the body or an organ into anterior and posterior parts.

Fulcrum The fixed point on which a lever moves when a force is applied.

Fundus (fun′dus) Base of an organ; part farthest from the opening of the organ. For example, the posterior wall of the eye.

G protein Protein that relays signals between extracellular first messengers (hormones or neurotransmitters) and intracellular second messengers (such as cyclic AMP) via an effector enzyme.

Gallbladder Sac beneath the right lobe of the liver used for bile storage.

Gallstones (biliary calculi) Crystallized cholesterol that obstructs the flow of bile from the gallbladder.

Gamete (gam′ēt) Sex or germ cell.

Gametogenesis (gam″eh-to-jen′eh-sis) Formation of gametes.

Ganglion (gang′gle-on) Collection of nerve cell bodies outside the CNS.

Ganglionic neuron (gan″gle-ah′nik) Autonomic motor neuron that has its cell body in a peripheral ganglion and projects its (postganglionic) axon to an effector.

Gap junction A passageway between two adjacent cells; formed by transmembrane proteins called connexons.

Gastrin Hormone secreted in the stomach; regulates gastric juice secretion by stimulating HCl production.

Gastroenteritis Inflammation of the gastrointestinal tract.

Gastrulation (gas″troo-la′shun) Developmental process that produces the three primary germ layers (ectoderm, mesoderm, and endoderm).

Gene One of the biological units of heredity located in chromatin; transmits hereditary information.

Genetic code Refers to the rules by which the base sequence of a DNA gene is translated into protein structures (amino acid sequences).

Genitalia (jen″i-ta′le-ă) The internal and external reproductive organs.

Genome The complete set of chromosomes derived from one parent (the haploid genome); or the two sets of chromosomes, i.e., one set from the egg, the other from the sperm (the diploid genome).

Genotype (jen′o-tīp) One's genetic makeup or genes.

Germ layers Three cellular layers (ectoderm, mesoderm, and endoderm) that represent the initial specialization of cells in the embryonic body and from which all body tissues arise.

Gestation period (jes-ta′shun) The period of pregnancy; about 280 days for humans.

Gland Organ specialized to secrete or excrete substances for further use in the body or for elimination.

Glaucoma (glaw-ko′mah) Condition in which intraocular pressure increases to levels that cause compression of the retina and optic nerve; results in blindness unless detected early.

Glial cells (gle′al) *See* Neuroglia.

Glomerular capsule (glo-mer′yoo-ler) Double-walled cup at end of a renal tubule; encloses a glomerulus. Also called Bowman's capsule.

Glomerular filtration rate (GFR) Rate of filtrate formation by the kidneys.

Glomerulus (glo-mer′u-lus) (1) Cluster of capillaries forming part of the nephron; forms filtrate; (2) odor-specific processing unit in olfactory bulb.

Glottis (glah′tis) Opening between the vocal cords in the larynx.

Glucagon (gloo′kah-gon) Hormone formed by alpha cells of pancreatic islets; raises the glucose level of blood.

Glucocorticoids (gloo″ko-kor′tĭ-koidz) Adrenal cortex hormones that increase blood glucose levels and aid the body in resisting long-term stressors.

Gluconeogenesis (gloo″ko-ne″o-jen′ĕ-sis) Formation of glucose from noncarbohydrate molecules.

Glucose (gloo′kōs) Principal blood sugar; a hexose.

Glycerol (glis′er-ol) A modified simple sugar (a sugar alcohol); a building block of fats.

Glycocalyx (cell coat) (gli″ko-kal′iks) A layer of externally facing glycoproteins on a cell's plasma membrane that determines blood type; involved in the cellular interactions of fertilization, embryonic development, and immunity, and acts as an adhesive between cells.

Glycogen (gli′ko-jin) Main carbohydrate stored in animal cells; a polysaccharide.

Glycogenesis (gli″ko-jen′ĕ-sis) Formation of glycogen from glucose.

Glycogenolysis (gli″ko-jĕ-nol′ĭ-sis) Breakdown of glycogen to glucose.

Glycolipid (gli″ko-lip′id) A lipid with one or more covalently attached sugars.

Glycolysis (gli-kol′ĭ-sis) Breakdown of glucose to pyruvic acid—an anaerobic process.

Goblet cells Individual cells (unicellular glands) that produce mucus.

Golgi apparatus (gol′je) Membranous system close to the cell nucleus that packages protein secretions for export, packages enzymes into lysosomes for cellular use, and modifies proteins destined to become part of cellular membranes.

Golgi tendon organs Proprioceptors located in tendons; monitor muscle tension to prevent tearing and help smooth onset and termination of muscle contraction.

Gonad (go′nad) Primary reproductive organ; i.e., the testis of the male or the ovary of the female.

Gonadocorticoids (gon″ah-do-kor′tĭ-koidz) Sex hormones, primarily androgens, secreted by the adrenal cortex.

Gonadotropins (gon″ah-do-trōp′inz) Gonad-stimulating hormones produced by the anterior pituitary.

Graafian follicle (graf′e-an) *See* Vesicular follicle.

Graded muscle responses Variations in the degree of muscle contraction by changing either the frequency or strength of the stimulus.

Graded potential A local change in membrane potential that varies directly with the strength of the stimulus, declines with distance.

Graves' disease Disorder resulting from hyperactive thyroid gland.

Gray matter Gray area of the central nervous system; contains neuronal cell bodies and their dendrites.

Growth hormone (GH) Hormone that stimulates growth in general; produced in the anterior pituitary; also called somatotropin (STH).

Guanine (G) (gwan′ēn) One of two major purines occurring in all nucleic acids.

Gustation (gus-ta′shun) Taste.

Gyrus (ji′rus) An outward fold of the surface of the cerebral cortex.

Hair follicle Structure with outer and inner root sheaths extending from the epidermal surface into the dermis and from which new hair develops.

Hapten (hap′ten) An incomplete antigen; has reactivity but not immunogenicity.

Haversian system (hah-ver′zhen) *See* Osteon.

Heart attack (coronary) *See* Myocardial infarction.

Heart block Impaired transmission of impulses from atrium to ventricle resulting in abnormally slow heart rhythms.

Heart murmur Abnormal heart sound (usually resulting from valve problems).

Heimlich maneuver Procedure in which the air in a person's own lungs is used to expel an obstructing piece of food.

Helper T cell Type of T lymphocyte that orchestrates cellular immunity by direct contact with other immune cells and by releasing chemicals called cytokines; also helps to mediate the humoral response by interacting with B cells.

Hematocrit (he-mat′o-krit) The percentage of total blood volume occupied by erythrocytes.

Hematoma (he″mah-to′mah) Mass of clotted blood that forms at an injured site.

Hematopoiesis (hem″ah-to-poi-e′sis) Blood cell formation; hemopoiesis.

Heme (hēm) Iron-containing pigment that is essential to oxygen transport by hemoglobin.

Hemocytoblast (he″mo-si′to-blast) Bone marrow cell that gives rise to all the formed elements of blood; hematopoietic stem cell.

Hemoglobin (he′muh-glo-bin) Oxygen-transporting protein of erythrocytes.

Hemolysis (he-mah′lĕ-sis) Rupture of erythrocytes.

Hemophilia (he″mo-fil′e-ah) A term loosely applied to several different hereditary bleeding disorders that exhibit similar signs and symptoms.

Hemopoiesis (he″mo-poi-e′sis) *See* Hematopoiesis.

Hemorrhage (hem′or-ij) Loss of blood from the vessels by flow through ruptured walls; bleeding.

Hemostasis (he″mo-sta′sis) Stoppage of bleeding.

Heparin Natural anticoagulant secreted into blood plasma.

Hepatic portal system (hĕ-pat′ik) Circulation in which the hepatic portal vein carries dissolved nutrients to the liver tissues for processing.

Hepatitis (hep″ah-ti′tis) Inflammation of the liver.

Hernia (her′ne-ah) Abnormal protrusion of an organ or a body part through the containing wall of its cavity.

Heterozygous (het″er-o-zi′gus) Having different allelic genes at a given locus or (by extension) many loci.

Hilton's law Any nerve serving a muscle that produces movement at a joint also innervates the joint and the skin over the joint.

Hilum (hi′lum) The indented region of an organ from which blood and/or lymphatic vessels and nerves enter and exit.

Hippocampus Limbic system structure that plays a role in converting new information into long-term memories.

Histamine (his′tuh-mēn) A chemical messenger (neurotransmitter or paracrine); causes vasodilation and increased capillary permeability; in stomach causes acid secretion.

Histology (his-tol′o-je) Branch of anatomy dealing with the microscopic structure of tissues.

HIV (human immunodeficiency virus) Virus that destroys helper T cells, thus depressing adaptive immunity; symptomatic AIDS gradually appears when lymph nodes can no longer contain the virus.

Holocrine glands (hol′o-krin) Glands that accumulate their secretions within their cells; secretions are discharged only upon rupture and death of the cell.

Homeostasis (ho″me-o-sta′sis) A state of body equilibrium or stable internal environment of the body.

Homologous (ho-mol′ŏ-gus) Parts or organs corresponding in structure but not necessarily in function.

Homozygous (ho-mo-zi′gus) Having identical genes at one or more loci.

Hormones Steroidal or amino acid–based molecules released to the blood that act as chemical messengers to regulate specific body functions.

Humoral immunity (hu′mer-ul) Immunity conferred by antibodies present in blood plasma and other body fluids.

Huntington's disease Hereditary disorder leading to degeneration of the basal nuclei and the cerebral cortex.

Hyaline cartilage (hi′ah-līn) The most abundant cartilage type in the body; provides firm support with some pliability.

Hydrochloric acid (HCl) (hi″dro-klor′ik) Acid that aids protein digestion in the stomach; produced by parietal cells.

Hydrogen bond Weak bond in which a hydrogen atom forms a bridge between two electron-hungry atoms. An important intramolecular bond.

Hydrogen ion (H^+) A hydrogen atom minus its electron and therefore carrying a positive charge (i.e., a proton).

Hydrolysis (hi″drah′lă-sis) Process in which water is used to split a substance into smaller particles.

Hydrophilic (hi″dro-fil′ik) Refers to molecules, or portions of molecules, that interact with water and charged particles.

Hydrophobic (hi″dro-fo′bik) Refers to molecules, or portions of molecules, that interact only with nonpolar molecules.

Hydrostatic pressure (hi″dro-stă′tic) Pressure of fluid in a system.

Hydroxyl ion (OH^-) (hi-drok′sil) An ion liberated when a hydroxide (a common inorganic base) is dissolved in water.

Hyperalgesia Pain amplification.

Hypercapnia (hi″per-kap′ne-ah) High carbon dioxide levels in the blood.

Hyperemia An increase in blood flow into a tissue or organ; congested with blood.

Hyperglycemic (hi″per-gli-se′mik) Term used to describe hormones such as glucagon that elevate blood glucose level.

Hyperopia (hi″per-o′pe-ah) A condition in which visual images are routinely focused behind rather than on the retina; commonly known as farsightedness.

Hyperplasia (hi″per-pla′ze-ah) Accelerated growth, e.g., in anemia, the bone marrow produces red blood cells at a faster rate.

Hyperpnea (hi″perp-ne′ah) An increase in ventilation in response to metabolic need (e.g., during exercise).

Hyperpolarization An increase in membrane potential in which the membrane becomes more negative than resting membrane potential.

Hypersensitivity Overzealous immune response to an otherwise harmless antigen.

Hypertension (hi″per-ten′shun) High blood pressure.

Hypertonic (hi″per-ton′ik) Excessive, above normal, tone or tension.

Hypertonic solution A solution that has a higher concentration of nonpenetrating solutes than the reference cell; having greater osmotic pressure than the reference solution (blood plasma or interstitial fluid).

Hypertrophy (hi-per′trah-fe) Increase in size of a tissue or organ independent of the body's general growth.

Hyperventilation An increase in the depth and rate of breathing that is in excess of the body's need for removal of carbon dioxide.

Hypocapnia Low carbon dioxide levels in the blood.

Hypodermis (superficial fascia) Subcutaneous tissue just deep to the skin; consists of adipose plus some areolar connective tissue.

Hypoglycemic (hi″po-gli-se′mik) Term used to describe hormones such as insulin that decrease blood glucose level.

Hyponatremia Abnormally low concentrations of sodium ions in extracellular fluid.

Hypoproteinemia (hi″po-pro″te-ĭ-ne′me-ah) A condition of unusually low levels of plasma proteins causing a reduction in colloid osmotic pressure; results in tissue edema.

Hypotension Low blood pressure.

Hypothalamic-hypophyseal tract (hi″po-thah-lam′ik–hi″po-fiz′-e-al) Nerve bundles that run through the infundibulum and connect the neurohypophysis and the hypothalamus.

Hypothalamus (hi″po-thal′ah-mus) Region of the diencephalon forming the floor of the third ventricle of the brain.

Hypotonic (hi″po-ton′ik) Below normal tone or tension.

Hypotonic solution A solution that is more dilute (containing fewer nonpenetrating solutes) than the reference cell. Cells placed in hypotonic solutions plump up rapidly as water rushes into them.

Hypoventilation A decrease in the depth and rate of breathing; characterized by an increase in blood carbon dioxide.

Hypovolemic shock (hi″po-vo-le′mik) Most common form of shock; results from extreme blood loss.

Hypoxia (hi-pok′se-ah) Condition in which inadequate oxygen is available to tissues.

Ileocecal valve (il″e-o-se′kal) Site where the small intestine joins the large intestine.

Ileum (il′e-um) Terminal part of the small intestine; between the jejunum and the cecum of the large intestine.

Immune system A functional system whose components attack foreign substances or prevent their entry into the body.

Immunity (im″ūn′ĭ-te) Ability of the body to resist many agents (both living and nonliving) that can cause disease; resistance to disease.

Immunocompetence Ability of the body's immune cells to recognize (by binding) specific antigens; reflects the presence of plasma membrane–bound receptors.

Immunodeficiency Any congenital or acquired condition causing a deficiency in the production or function of immune cells or certain molecules (complement, antibodies, etc.) required for normal immunity.

In vitro (in ve′tro) In a test tube, glass, or artificial environment.

In vivo (in ve′vo) In the living body.

Incompetent valve Valve which does not close properly.

Incontinence Inability to control micturition or defecation voluntarily.

Infarct (in′farkt) Region of dead, deteriorating tissue resulting from a lack of blood supply.

Infectious mononucleosis Highly contagious viral disease; marked by excessive agranulocytes.

Inferior (caudal) Pertaining to a position toward the lower or tail end of the long axis of the body.

Inferior vena cava Vein that returns blood from body areas below the diaphragm.

Inflammation (in″flah-ma′shun) An innate (nonspecific) defensive response of the body to tissue injury; includes dilation of blood vessels and an increase in vessel permeability; indicated by redness, heat, swelling, and pain.

Infundibulum (in″fun-dib′u-lum) (1) A stalk of tissue that connects the pituitary gland to the hypothalamus; (2) the distal end of the uterine (fallopian) tube.

Inguinal (ing′wĭ-nal) Pertaining to the groin region.

Inhibitory postsynaptic potential (IPSP) A graded potential in a postsynaptic neuron that inhibits action potential generation; usually hyperpolarizing.

Inner cell mass Accumulation of cells in the blastocyst from which the embryo develops.

Innervation (in″er-va′shun) Supply of nerves to a body part.

Inorganic compound Chemical substances that do not contain carbon, including water, salts, and many acids and bases.

Insertion Movable attachment of a muscle.

Insula Lobe of the cerebral cortex that is buried in the lateral sulcus beneath portions of the parietal, frontal, and temporal lobes.

Insulin A hormone that enhances the carrier-mediated diffusion of glucose into tissue cells, thus lowering blood glucose levels.

Insulin resistance State in which a greater than normal amount of insulin is required to maintain normal glucose blood levels.

Integration The process by which the nervous system processes and interprets sensory input and makes decisions about what should be done at each moment.

Integumentary system (in-teg″u-men′tar-e) Skin and its derivatives; provides the external protective covering of the body.

Intercalated discs (in-ter′kah-la″ted) Specialized connections between myocardial cells containing gap junctions and desmosomes.

Interferons (IFNs) (in-ter-fēr′ons) Proteins released from virus-infected (and other) cells that protect uninfected cells from viral takeover. Also inhibit some cancers.

Internal capsule Band of projection fibers that runs between the basal nuclei and the thalamus.

Internal respiration Exchange of gases between blood and tissue fluid and between tissue fluid and cells.

Interneuron (association neuron) Nerve cell located between motor and sensory neurons that shuttles signals through CNS pathways where integration occurs.

Interoceptor (in″ter-o-sep′tor) Sensory receptor nerve ending in the viscera, which is sensitive to changes and stimuli within the body's internal environment; also called visceroceptor.

Interphase One of two major periods in the cell life cycle; includes the period from cell formation to cell division.

Interstitial cells Cells located in the loose connective tissue surrounding the seminiferous tubules; they produce androgens (most importantly testosterone), which are secreted into the surrounding interstitial fluid.

Interstitial fluid (IF) (in″ter-stish′al) Fluid between the cells.

Interstitial lamellae Incomplete lamellae that lie between intact osteons, filling the gaps between forming osteons, or representing the remnants of an osteon that has been cut through by bone remodeling.

Intervertebral discs (in″ter-ver′teh-brul) Discs of fibrocartilage between vertebrae.

Intracapsular ligament Ligament located within and separate from the articular capsule of a synovial joint.

Intracellular fluid (ICF) (in″trah-sel′u-ler) Fluid within a cell.

Intrinsic factor Substance produced by the stomach that is required for vitamin B_{12} absorption.

Intron Noncoding segment or portion of DNA that ranges from 60 to 100,000 nucleotides long.

Involuntary muscle Muscle that cannot ordinarily be controlled voluntarily (e.g., smooth and cardiac muscle).

Involuntary nervous system The autonomic nervous system.

Ion (ī′on) Atom with a positive or negative electric charge.

Ionic bond (ī-ah′nik) Chemical bond formed by electron transfer between atoms.

Ipsilateral (ip″sih-lă′ter-ul) Situated on the same side.

Ischemia (is-ke′me-ah) Local decrease in blood supply.

Isograft Tissue graft donated by an identical twin.

Isomer (i′so-mer) One of two or more substances that has the same molecular formula but with its atoms arranged differently.

Isometric contraction (i″so-mě′trik) Contraction in which the muscle does not shorten (the load is too heavy) but its internal tension increases.

Isotonic contraction (i″so-tah′nik) Contraction in which muscle tension remains constant at a given joint angle and load, and the muscle shortens.

Isotonic solution A solution with a concentration of nonpenetrating solutes equal to that found in the reference cell.

Isotopes (i′so-tōps) Different atomic forms of the same element, vary only in the number of neutrons they contain; the heavier species tend to be radioactive.

Jejunum (jĕ-joo′num) The part of the small intestine between the duodenum and the ileum.

Joint (articulation) The junction of two or more bones.

Joint kinesthetic receptor (kin″es-thet′ik) Receptor that provides information on joint position and motion.

Juxtaglomerular apparatus (JGA) (juks″tah-glo-mer′u-lar) Cells of the distal part of the ascending limb of the loop of Henle and afferent arteriole located close to the glomerulus; involved in blood pressure regulation (via release of the hormone renin) and autoregulation of GFR.

Karyotype (kar′e-o-tīp) The diploid chromosomal complement, typically shown as homologous chromosome pairs arranged from longest to shortest (X and Y are arranged by size rather than paired).

Keratin (ker′ah-tin) Fibrous protein found in the epidermis, hair, and nails that makes those structures hard and water resistant; precursor is keratohyaline.

Ketones (ketone bodies) (ke′tōnz) Fatty acid metabolites; strong organic acids.

Ketosis (kē-tō′sis) Excess levels of ketone bodies in blood. Called ketoacidosis if blood pH is low.

Killer T cell *See* Cytotoxic T cell.

Kilocalories (kcal) *See* Calorie.

Kinetic energy (ki-net′ik) The energy of motion or movement, e.g., the constant movement of atoms, or the push given to a swinging door that sets it into motion.

Krebs cycle Aerobic metabolic pathway occurring within mitochondria, in which food metabolites are oxidized and CO_2 is liberated, and coenzymes are reduced. Also called the citric acid cycle.

Labia (la′be-ah) Lips; singular: labium.

Labor Collective term for the series of events that expel the infant from the uterus.

Labyrinth (lab′ĭ-rinth″) Bony cavities and membranes of the inner ear.

Lacrimal (lak′ri-mal) Pertaining to tears.

Lactation (lak-ta′shun) Production and secretion of milk.

Lacteal (lak′te-al) Special lymphatic capillaries of the small intestine that take up lipids.

Lactic acid (lak′tik) Product of anaerobic metabolism, especially in muscle.

Lacuna (lah-ku′nah) A small space, cavity, or depression; lacunae in bone or cartilage are occupied by cells.

Lamella (lah-mel′ah) A layer, such as of bone matrix in an osteon of compact bone.

Lamina (lam′ĭ-nah) (1) A thin layer or flat plate; (2) the portion of a vertebra between the transverse process and the spinous process.

Large intestine Portion of the digestive tract extending from the ileocecal valve to the anus; includes the cecum, appendix, colon, rectum, and anal canal.

Larynx (lar′ingks) Cartilaginous organ located between the trachea and the pharynx; voice box.

Latent period Period of time between stimulation and the onset of muscle contraction.

Lateral Away from the midline of the body.

Leptin Hormone released by fat cells that signals satiety.

Leukemia Refers to a group of cancerous conditions of white blood cells.

Leukocytes (loo′ko-sīts) White blood cells; formed elements involved in body protection that take part in inflammatory and immune responses.

Leukocytosis An increase in the number of leukocytes (white blood cells); usually the result of a microbiological attack on the body.

Leukopenia (loo″ko-pe′ne-ah) Abnormally low white blood cell count.

Leukopoiesis The production of white blood cells.

Lever system Consists of a lever (bone), effort (muscle action), resistance (weight of object to be moved), and fulcrum (joint).

Ligament (lig′ah-ment) Band of regular fibrous tissue that connects bones.

Ligands Signaling chemicals that bind specifically to membrane receptors.

Limbic system (lim′bik) Functional brain system involved in emotional response and memory formation.

Lipid (lih′pid) Organic compound formed of carbon, hydrogen, and oxygen; examples are fats and cholesterol.

Lipolysis (lĭ-pol′ĭ-sis) The breakdown of stored fats into glycerol and fatty acids.

Liver Lobed accessory organ that overlies the stomach; produces bile to help digest fat, and serves other metabolic and regulatory functions.

Lumbar (lum′bar) Portion of the back between the thorax and the pelvis.

Lumbar vertebrae The five vertebrae of the lumbar region of the vertebral column, commonly called the small of the back.

Lumen (loo′min) Cavity inside a tube, blood vessel, or hollow organ.

Luteinizing hormone (LH) (lu′te-in-īz″ing) Anterior pituitary hormone that aids maturation of cells in the ovary and triggers ovulation in females. In males, causes the interstitial cells of the testis to produce testosterone.

Lymph (limf) Protein-containing fluid transported by lymphatic vessels.

Lymph node Small lymphoid organ that filters lymph; contains macrophages and lymphocytes.

Lymphatic system (lim-fat′ik) System consisting of lymphatic vessels, lymph nodes, and lymph; drains excess tissue fluid from the extracellular space. The nodes provide sites for immune surveillance.

Lymphatics General term used to designate the lymphatic vessels that collect and transport lymph.

Lymphocyte Agranular white blood cell that arises from bone marrow and becomes functionally mature in the lymphoid organs of the body.

Lysosomes (li′so-sōmz) Organelles that originate from the Golgi apparatus and contain strong digestive enzymes.

Lysozyme (li′so-zīm) Enzyme in sweat, saliva, and tears that is capable of destroying certain kinds of bacteria.

Macromolecules Large, complex molecules containing from 100 to over 10,000 subunits.

Macrophage (mak′ro-fāj″) Protective cell type common in connective tissue, lymphoid tissue, and many body organs; phagocytizes tissue cells, bacteria, and other foreign debris; presents antigens to T cells in the immune response.

Macula (mak′u-lah) (1) Static equilibrium receptor within the vestibule of the inner ear; (2) a colored area or spot.

Malignant (muh-lig′nent) Life threatening; pertains to neoplasms that spread and lead to death, such as cancer.

Malignant melanoma (mel″ah-no′mah) Cancer of the melanocytes; can begin wherever there is pigment.

Mammary glands (mam′mer-e) Milk-producing glands of the breast.

Mandible (man′dĭ-bl) Lower jawbone; U shaped, largest bone of the face.

Mass number Sum of the number of protons and neutrons in the nucleus of an atom.

Mast cells Immune cells that function to detect foreign substances in the tissue spaces and initiate local inflammatory responses against them; typically found clustered deep to an epithelium or along blood vessels.

Mastication (mas″tĭ-ka′shun) Chewing.

Meatus (me-a′tus) External opening of a canal.

Mechanical advantage (power lever) Condition that occurs when the load is close to the fulcrum and the effort is applied far from the fulcrum; allows a small effort exerted over a relatively large distance to move a large load over a small distance.

Mechanical disadvantage (speed lever) Condition that occurs when the load is far from the fulcrum and the effort is applied near the fulcrum; the effort applied must be greater than the load to be moved.

Mechanical energy The energy directly involved in moving matter; e.g., in bicycle riding, the legs provide the mechanical energy that moves the pedals.

Mechanoreceptor (meh″kĕ-no-re-sep′tor) Receptor sensitive to mechanical pressure such as touch, sound, or exerted by muscle contraction.

Medial (me′de-ahl) Toward the midline of the body.

Median (midsagittal) plane Specific sagittal plane that lies exactly in the midline.

Mediastinum (me″de-ah-sti′num) The medial cavity of the thorax containing the heart, great vessels, and trachea.

Medulla (mĕ-dul′ah) Central portion of certain organs.

Medulla oblongata (mĕ-dul′ah ob″long-gah′tah) Inferiormost part of the brain stem.

Medullary cavity Central cavity of a long bone. Contains yellow or red (bone) marrow.

Meiosis (mi-o′sis) Nuclear division process that reduces the chromosomal number by half and results in the formation of four haploid (*n*) cells; occurs only in certain reproductive organs.

Melanin (mel′ah-nin) Dark pigment formed by cells called melanocytes; imparts color to skin and hair.

Melatonin (mel′ah-to′nin) A hormone secreted by the pineal gland; secretion peaks at night and helps set sleep-wake cycles; also a powerful antioxidant.

Membrane potential Voltage across the plasma membrane.

Membrane receptors A large, diverse group of integral proteins and glycoproteins that serve as binding sites for signaling molecules.

Memory cells Members of T cell and B cell clones that provide for immunological memory.

Menarche (mĕ-nar′ke) Establishment of menstrual function; the first menstrual period.

Meninges (mĕ-nin′jēz) Protective coverings of the central nervous system; from the most external to the most internal, the dura mater, arachnoid mater, and pia mater.

Meningitis (mĕ-nin-ji′tis) Inflammation of the meninges.

Menopause Period of life when, prompted by hormonal changes, ovulation and menstruation cease.

Menstruation (men″stroo-a′shun) The periodic, cyclic discharge of blood, secretions, tissue, and mucus from the mature female uterus in the absence of pregnancy.

Merocrine glands (mer′o-krin) Glands that produce secretions intermittently; secretions do not accumulate in the gland.

Mesencephalon (mes″en-sef′ah-lon) One of the three primary vesicles of the developing brain; becomes the midbrain.

Mesenchyme (meh′zin-kīm) Common embryonic tissue from which all connective tissues arise.

Mesenteries (mes″en-ter′ēz) Double-layered extensions of the peritoneum that support most organs in the abdominal cavity.

Mesoderm (mez′o-derm) Primary germ layer that forms the skeleton and muscles of the body.

Mesothelium (mez″o-the′le-um) The epithelium found in serous membranes lining the ventral body cavity and covering its organs.

Messenger RNA (mRNA) Long nucleotide strands that reflect the exact nucleotide sequences of the genetically active DNA and carry the message of the latter.

Metabolic (fixed) acid Acid generated by cellular metabolism that must be eliminated by the kidneys.

Metabolic rate (mĕt″ah-bol′ik) Energy expended by the body per unit time.

Metabolic water (water of oxidation) Water produced from cellular metabolism (about 10% of our body's water).

Metabolism (mĕ-tab′o-lizm) Sum total of the chemical reactions occurring in the body cells.

Metaphase Second stage of mitosis.

Metastasis (mĕ-tas′tah-sis) The spread of cancer from one body part or organ into another not directly connected to it.

Metencephalon (afterbrain) A secondary brain vesicle; anterior portion of the rhombencephalon of the developing brain; becomes the pons and the cerebellum.

MHC (major histocompatibility complex) proteins Molecules on the outer plasma membrane of all cells; help the immune system distinguish self from nonself. T cells recognize antigens only when combined with these proteins.

Microfilaments (mi″kro-fil′ah-ments) Thin strands of the contractile protein actin.

Microglia (mi-kro′gle-ah) A type of CNS supporting cell; can transform into phagocytes in areas of neural damage or inflammation.

Microtubules (mi″kro-tu′būlz) One of three types of rods in the cytoskeleton of a cell; hollow tubes made of spherical protein that determine the cell shape as well as the distribution of cellular organelles.

Microvilli (mi″kro-vil′i) Tiny projections on the free surfaces of some epithelial cells; increase surface area for absorption.

Micturition (mik″tu-rish′un) Urination, or voiding; emptying the bladder.

Midbrain (mesencephalon) Region of the brain stem between the diencephalon and the pons.

Midsagittal (median) plane Specific sagittal plane that lies exactly in the midline.

Milliequivalents per liter (mEq/L) The units used to measure electrolyte concentrations of body fluids; a measure of the number of electrical charges in 1 liter of solution.

Mineralocorticoid (min″er-al″ō-kor′tih-koyd) Steroid hormone of the adrenal cortex that regulates Na^+ and K^+ metabolism and fluid balance.

Minerals Inorganic chemical compounds found in nature; salts.

Mitochondria (mi″to-kon′dre-ah) Cytoplasmic organelles responsible for ATP generation for cellular activities.

Mitosis Process during which the chromosomes are redistributed to two daughter nuclei; nuclear division. Consists of prophase, metaphase, anaphase, and telophase.

Mitotic (M) phase One of two major periods in the cell life cycle; involves the division of the nucleus (mitosis) and the division of the cytoplasm (cytokinesis).

Mitral (bicuspid) valve (mi′tral) The left atrioventricular valve.

Mixed nerves Nerves containing the processes of motor and sensory neurons; their impulses travel to and from the central nervous system.

Molar (mo′lar) (1) A solution concentration determined by mass of solute—1 liter of solution contains an amount of solute equal to its molecular weight in grams. (2) Broad back teeth that grind and crush.

Molarity (mo-lar′ĭ-te) A way to express the concentration of a solution; moles per liter of solution.

Mole (mōl) A mole of any element or compound is equal to its atomic weight or its molecular weight (sum of atomic weights) measured in grams.

Molecule Particle consisting of two or more atoms joined together by chemical bonds.

Monoclonal antibodies (mon″o-klo′nal) Pure preparations of identical antibodies that exhibit specificity for a single antigen.

Monocyte (mon′o-sīt) Large single-nucleus white blood cell; agranular leukocyte.

Monosaccharide (mon″o-sak′ah-rīd) Literally, one sugar; building block of carbohydrates; e.g., glucose.

Morula (mor′u-lah) The mulberry-like solid mass of blastomeres resulting from cleavage in the early conceptus.

Motor areas Functional areas in the cerebral cortex that control voluntary motor functions.

Motor (efferent) nerves Nerves that carry impulses leaving the brain and spinal cord, and destined for effectors.

Motor unit A motor neuron and all the muscle cells it stimulates.

Mucous membranes (mucosae) Membranes that form the linings of body cavities open to the exterior (digestive, respiratory, urinary, and reproductive tracts).

Mucus (myoo′kus) A sticky, thick fluid secreted by mucous glands and mucous membranes; keeps the free surface of membranes moist.

Multinucleate cell (mul″tĭ-nu′kle-āt) Cell with more than one nucleus, e.g., skeletal muscle cells, osteoclasts.

Multiple sclerosis (MS) Demyelinating disorder of the CNS; causes hardened patches (sclerosis) in the brain and spinal cord.

Multipolar neurons Neurons with three or more processes; most common neuron type in the CNS.

Muscarinic receptors (mus″kah-rin′ik) Acetylcholine-binding receptors of the autonomic nervous system's target organs; named for activation by the mushroom poison muscarine.

Muscle fiber A muscle cell.

Muscle spindle (neuromuscular spindle) Encapsulated receptor found in skeletal muscle that is sensitive to stretch.

Muscle tension The force exerted by a contracting muscle on some object.

Muscle tone Low levels of contractile activity in relaxed muscle; keeps the muscle healthy and ready to act.

Muscle twitch The response of a muscle to a single brief threshold stimulus.

Muscular dystrophy A group of inherited muscle-destroying diseases.

Muscular system The organ system consisting of the skeletal muscles of the body and their connective tissue attachments.

Myelencephalon (spinal brain) A secondary brain vesicle; lower part of the developing hindbrain, especially the medulla oblongata.

Myelin sheath (mi′ĕ-lin) Fatty insulating sheath that surrounds all but the smallest nerve fibers.

Myoblasts Embryonic mesoderm cells from which all muscle fibers develop.

Myocardial infarction (MI) (mi″o-kar′de-al in-fark′shun) Condition characterized by dead tissue areas in the myocardium; caused by interruption of blood supply to the area. Commonly called heart attack.

Myocardium (mi″o-kar′de-um) Layer of the heart wall composed of cardiac muscle.

Myofibril (mi″o-fi′bril) Rodlike bundle of contractile filaments (myofilaments) found in muscle fibers (cells).

Myofilament (mi″o-fil′ah-ment) Filament that constitutes myofibrils. Of two types: actin and myosin.

Myoglobin (mi″o-glo′bin) Oxygen-binding pigment in muscle.

Myogram A graphic recording of mechanical contractile activity produced by an apparatus that measures muscle contraction.

Myometrium (mi″o-me′tre-um) Thick uterine musculature.

Myopia (mi-o′pe-ah) A condition in which visual images are focused in front of rather than on the retina; nearsightedness.

Myosin (mi′o-sin) One of the principal contractile proteins found in muscle.

Myxedema (mik″sĕ-de′mah) Condition resulting from underactive thyroid gland.

Nares (na′rez) Nostrils.

Natural killer (NK) cell Defensive cell (a type of lymphocyte) that can kill cancer cells and virus-infected body cells before the adaptive immune system is activated.

Necrosis (nĕ-kro′sis) Death or disintegration of a cell or tissues caused by disease or injury.

Negative feedback mechanisms The most common homeostatic control mechanism. The net effect is that the output of the system shuts off the original stimulus or reduces its intensity.

Neonatal period The four-week period immediately after birth.

Neoplasm (ne′o-plazm) An abnormal mass of proliferating cells. Benign neoplasms remain localized; malignant neoplasms are cancers, which can spread to other organs.

Nephron (nef′ron) Structural and functional unit of the kidney; consists of the glomerulus and renal tubule.

Nerve A bundle of axons in the peripheral nervous system.

Nerve fiber Axon of a neuron.

Nerve growth factor (NGF) Protein that promotes survival and development of neurons; secreted by their target cells and many other cell types.

Nerve impulse A self-propagating wave of depolarization; also called an action potential.

Nerve plexuses Interlacing nerve networks that occur in the cervical, brachial, lumbar, and sacral regions and primarily serve the limbs.

Nervous system Fast-acting control system that triggers muscle contraction or gland secretion.

Neural tube Fetal structure which gives rise to the brain, spinal cord, and associated neural structures; formed from ectoderm by day 23 of embryonic development.

Neuroglia (nu-rog′le-ah) Nonexcitable cells of neural tissue that support, protect, and insulate the neurons; glial cells.

Neurohypophysis (nu″ro-hi-pof′ĭ-sis) Posterior pituitary plus infundibulum; portion of the pituitary gland derived from the brain.

Neuromuscular junction Region where a motor neuron comes into close contact with a skeletal muscle cell.

Neuron (nerve cell) (nu′ron) Cell of the nervous system specialized to generate and transmit electrical signals (action potentials and graded potentials).

Neuron cell body The biosynthetic center of a neuron; also called the perikaryon, or soma.

Neuronal pools Functional groups of neurons that process and integrate information.

Neuropeptides (nu″ro-pep′tīds) A class of neurotransmitters including beta endorphins and enkephalins (which act as euphorics and reduce perception of pain) and gut-brain peptides.

Neurotransmitter Chemical messenger released by neurons that may, upon binding to receptors of neurons or effector cells, stimulate or inhibit those neurons or effector cells.

Neutral fats Consist of fatty acid chains and glycerol; also called triglycerides or triacylglycerols. Commonly known as oils when liquid.

Neutralization reaction Displacement reaction in which mixing an acid and a base forms water and a salt.

Neutron (nu′tron) Uncharged subatomic particle; found in the atomic nucleus.

Neutrophil (nu′tro-fil) Most abundant type of white blood cell.

Nicotinic receptors (nik″o-tin′ik) Acetylcholine-binding receptors of all autonomic ganglionic neurons and skeletal muscle neuromuscular junctions; named for activation by nicotine.

Nitric oxide (NO) A gaseous chemical messenger; diverse functions include participation in memory formation in the brain, and causing vasodilation throughout the body.

Nociceptor (no″se-sep′tor) Receptor sensitive to potentially damaging stimuli that result in pain.

Nondisjunction Failure of sister chromatids to separate during mitosis or failure of homologous pairs to separate during meiosis; results in abnormal numbers of chromosomes in the resulting daughter cells.

Nonpolar molecules Electrically balanced molecules.

Norepinephrine (NE) (nor″ep-ĭ-nef′rin) A catecholamine neurotransmitter and adrenal medullary hormone, associated with sympathetic nervous system activation.

Nuclear envelope The double membrane barrier of a cell nucleus.

Nucleic acid (nu-kle′ik) Class of organic molecules that includes DNA and RNA.

Nucleoli (nu-kle′o-li) Dense spherical bodies in the cell nucleus involved with ribosomal RNA (rRNA) synthesis and ribosomal subunit assembly.

Nucleosome (nu′kle-o-sōm) Fundamental unit of chromatin; consists of a strand of DNA wound around a cluster of eight histone proteins.

Nucleotide (nu′kle-o-tīd) Building block of nucleic acids; consists of a sugar, a nitrogen-containing base, and a phosphate group.

Nucleus (nu′kle-is) (1) Control center of a cell; contains genetic material; (2) clusters of nerve cell bodies in the CNS.

Nutrients Chemical substances taken in via the diet that are used for energy and cell building.

Oblique section A cut made diagonally between the horizontal and vertical plane of the body or an organ.

Occlusion (ah-kloo′zhun) Closure or obstruction.

Octet rule (rule of eights) (ok-tet′) The tendency of atoms to interact in such a way that they have eight electrons in their valence shell.

Olfaction (ol-fak′shun) Smell.

Oligodendrocyte (ol″ĭ-go-den′dro-sīt) A type of CNS supporting cell that composes myelin sheaths.

Oocyte (o′o-sīt) Immature female gamete.

Oogenesis (o″o-jen′ĕ-sis) Process of ovum (female gamete) formation.

Ophthalmic (of-thal′mik) Pertaining to the eye.

Optic (op′tik) Pertaining to the eye or vision.

Optic chiasma (op′tik ki-az′muh) The partial crossover of fibers of the optic nerves.

Organ A part of the body formed of two or more tissues and adapted to carry out a specific function; e.g., the stomach.

Organ system A group of organs that work together to perform a vital body function; e.g., the nervous system.

Organelles (or″gah-nelz′) Small cellular structures (ribosomes, mitochondria, and others) that perform specific metabolic functions for the cell as a whole.

Organic compound Any compound composed of atoms (some of which are carbon) held together by covalent (shared electron) bonds.

Organic Pertaining to carbon-containing molecules, such as proteins, fats, and carbohydrates.

Organism The living animal (or plant), which represents the sum total of all its organ systems working together to maintain life.

Origin Attachment of a muscle that remains relatively fixed during muscular contraction.

Osmolality The number of solute particles dissolved in 1 kilogram (1000 g) of water; reflects the solution's ability to cause osmosis.

Osmolarity (oz″mo-lar′ĭ-te) The number of solute particles present in 1 liter of a solution.

Osmoreceptor (oz″mo-re-sep′tor) Structure sensitive to osmotic pressure or concentration of a solution.

Osmosis (oz-mo′sis) Diffusion of a solvent through a membrane from a dilute solution into a more concentrated one.

Osmotic pressure A measure of the tendency of water to move into a more concentrated solution.

Ossicles *See* Auditory ossicles.

Ossification (os″ĭ-fi-ka′shun) *See* Osteogenesis.

Osteoblasts (os′te-o-blasts) Bone-forming cells.

Osteoclasts (os′te-o-klasts) Large cells that resorb or break down bone matrix.

Osteocyte (os′te-o-sīt) Mature bone cell.

Osteogenesis (os″te-o-jen′e-sis) The process of bone formation; also called ossification.

Osteoid (os′te-oid) Unmineralized bone matrix.

Osteomalacia (os″te-o-mah-la′she-ah) Disorder in which bones are inadequately mineralized; soft bones.

Osteon (os′te-on) System of interconnecting canals in the microscopic structure of adult compact bone; unit of bone; also called Haversian system.

Osteoporosis (os″te-o-po-ro′sis) Decreased density and strength of bone resulting from a gradual decrease in rate of bone formation.

Ovarian cycle (o-vayr′e-an) Monthly cycle of follicle development, ovulation, and corpus luteum formation in an ovary.

Ovary (o′var-e) Female reproductive organ in which ova (eggs) are produced; female gonad.

Ovulation (ov″u-la′shun) Ejection of an immature egg (oocyte) from the ovary.

Ovum (o′vum) Female gamete; egg.

Oxidases Enzymes that catalyze the transfer of oxygen in oxidation-reduction reactions.

Oxidation (oks′ĭ-da″shun) Process of substances combining with oxygen or the removal of hydrogen.

Oxidation-reduction (redox) reaction A reaction that couples the oxidation (loss of electrons) of one substance with the reduction (gain of electrons) of another substance.

Oxidative phosphorylation (ok″sĭ-da″tiv fos″for-ĭ-la′shun) Process of ATP synthesis during which an inorganic phosphate group is attached to ADP; occurs via the electron transport chain within the mitochondria.

Oxygen deficit The volume of oxygen required after exercise to replenish stores of O_2, ATP, creatine phosphate, and glycogen and oxidize the lactic acid formed during exercise.

Oxyhemoglobin (ok″sĭ-he″mo-glo′bin) Oxygen-bound form of hemoglobin.

Oxytocin (ok″sĭ-to′sin) Hormone synthesized in the hypothalamus and secreted by the posterior pituitary; stimulates contraction of the uterus during childbirth and the ejection of milk during nursing.

Paget's disease (paj′ets) Disorder characterized by excessive bone breakdown and abnormal bone formation.

Palate (pal′at) Roof of the mouth.

Pancreas (pan′kre-us) Gland located behind the stomach, between the spleen and the duodenum; produces both endocrine and exocrine secretions.

Pancreatic juice (pan″kre-at′ik) Bicarbonate-rich secretion of the pancreas containing enzymes for digestion of all food categories.

Papilla (pah-pil′ah) Small, nipple-like projection; e.g., dermal papillae are projections of dermal tissue into the epidermis.

Paracrine (par′ah-krin) A chemical messenger that acts locally within the same tissue and is rapidly destroyed. Examples are prostaglandins and nitric oxide.

Parasagittal planes All sagittal planes offset from the midline.

Parasympathetic division The division of the autonomic nervous system that oversees digestion, elimination, and glandular function; the resting and digesting subdivision.

Parasympathetic tone Normal (background) level of parasympathetic output; sustains normal gastrointestinal and urinary tract activity, lowers heart rate.

Parathyroid glands (par″ah-thi′roid) Small endocrine glands located on the posterior aspect of the thyroid gland.

Parathyroid hormone (PTH) Hormone released by the parathyroid glands that regulates blood calcium level.

Parietal (pah-ri′ĕ-tal) Pertaining to the walls of a cavity.

Parietal serosa The part of the double-layered membrane that lines the walls of the ventral body cavity.

Parkinson's disease Neurodegenerative disorder of the basal nuclei due to insufficient secretion of the neurotransmitter dopamine; symptoms include tremor and rigid movement.

Partial pressure The pressure exerted by a single component of a mixture of gases.

Parturition (par″tu-rish′un) Culmination of pregnancy; giving birth.

Passive immunity Short-lived immunity resulting from the introduction of "borrowed antibodies" obtained from an immune animal or human donor; immunological memory is not established.

Passive (transport) processes Membrane transport processes that do not require cellular energy (ATP), e.g., diffusion, which is driven by kinetic energy.

Pathogen (path′o-jen) Disease-causing organism.

Pectoral (pek′tor-al) Pertaining to the chest.

Pectoral (shoulder) girdle Bones that attach the upper limbs to the axial skeleton; includes the clavicle and scapula.

Pedigree Traces a particular genetic trait through several generations and helps predict the genotype of future offspring.

Pelvic girdle (hip girdle) Consists of the paired coxal bones that attach the lower limbs to the axial skeleton.

Pelvis (pel′vis) (1) Basin-shaped bony structure composed of the pelvic girdle, sacrum, and coccyx; (2) funnel-shaped tube within the kidney continuous with the ureter.

Penis (pe′nis) Male organ of copulation and urination.

Pepsin Enzyme capable of digesting proteins in an acid pH.

Peptide bond (pep′tīd) Bond joining the amine group of one amino acid to the acid carboxyl group of a second amino acid with the loss of a water molecule.

Perforating canals Canals that run at right angles to the long axis of the bone, connecting the vascular and nerve supplies of the periosteum to those of the central canals and medullary cavity; also called Volkmann's canals.

Pericardium (per″ĭ-kar′de-um) Double-layered sac enclosing the heart and forming its superficial layer; has fibrous and serous layers.

Perichondrium (per″ĭ-kon′dre-um) Fibrous, connective-tissue membrane covering the external surface of cartilaginous structures.

Perimysium (per″ĭ-mis′e-um) Connective tissue enveloping bundles of muscle fibers.

Perineum (per″ĭ-ne′um) That region of the body spanning the region between the ischial tuberosities and extending from the pubic arch to the coccyx.

Periosteum (per″e-os′te-um) Double-layered connective tissue that covers and nourishes the bone.

Peripheral congestion Condition caused by failure of the right side of the heart; results in edema in the extremities.

Peripheral nervous system (PNS) Portion of the nervous system consisting of nerves and ganglia that lie outside of the brain and spinal cord.

Peripheral resistance A measure of the amount of friction encountered by blood as it flows through the blood vessels.

Peristalsis (per″i-stal′sis) Progressive, wavelike contractions that move foodstuffs through the alimentary tube organs (or that move other substances through other hollow body organs).

Peritoneum (per″ĭ-to-ne′um) Serous membrane lining the interior of the abdominal cavity and covering the surfaces of abdominal organs.

Peritonitis (per″ĭ-to-ni′tis) Inflammation of the peritoneum.

Permeability That property of membranes that permits passage of molecules and ions.

Peroxisomes (pĕ-roks′ĭ-sōmz) Membranous sacs in cytoplasm containing powerful oxidase enzymes that use molecular oxygen to detoxify harmful or toxic substances, such as free radicals.

Peyer's patches (pi′erz) Lymphoid organs located in the small intestine; also called aggregated lymphoid nodules.

pH unit (pe-āch) The measure of the relative acidity or alkalinity of a solution.

Phagocytosis (fag″o-si-to′sis) Engulfing of foreign solids by (phagocytic) cells.

Phagosome (fag′o-sōm) Vesicle formed as a result of phagocytosis.

Pharmacological dose A drug dose that is dramatically higher than normal levels of that substance (e.g., hormone) in the body.

Pharyngotympanic tube Tube that connects the middle ear and the pharynx. Also called auditory tube, eustachian tube.

Pharynx (fayr′inks) Muscular tube extending from the region posterior to the nasal cavities to the esophagus.

Phenotype (feʹno-tīp) Observable expression of the genotype.

Phospholipid (fosʺfo-lipʹid) Modified lipid, contains phosphorus.

Phosphorylation A chemical reaction in which a phosphate molecule is added to a molecule; for example, phosphorylation of ADP yields ATP.

Photoreceptor (foʺto-re-sepʹtor) Specialized receptor cells that respond to light energy; rods and cones.

Physiological acidosis (asʺĭ-doʹsis) Arterial pH lower than 7.35 resulting from any cause.

Physiological dose A drug dose that replicates normal levels of that substance (e.g., hormone) in the body.

Physiology (fizʺe-olʹo-je) Study of the function of living organisms.

Pineal gland (body) (pinʹe-al) A hormone-secreting part of the diencephalon of the brain thought to be involved in setting the biological clock and influencing reproductive function.

Pinocytosis (peʺno-si-toʹsis) Engulfing of extracellular fluid by cells.

Pituitary gland (pĭ-tuʹih-tayrʺe) Neuroendocrine gland located beneath the brain that serves a variety of functions including regulation of gonads, thyroid, adrenal cortex, lactation, and water balance.

Placenta (plah-senʹtah) Temporary organ formed from both fetal and maternal tissues that provides nutrients and oxygen to the developing fetus, carries away fetal metabolic wastes, and produces the hormones of pregnancy.

Plasma (plazʹmah) The nonliving fluid component of blood within which formed elements and various solutes are suspended and circulated.

Plasma cells Members of a B cell clone; specialized to produce and release antibodies.

Plasma membrane Membrane, composed of phospholipids, cholesterol, and proteins, that encloses cell contents; outer limiting cell membrane.

Platelet (plātʹlet) Cell fragment found in blood; involved in clotting.

Pleurae (plooʹre) Two layers of serous membrane that line the thoracic cavity and cover the external surface of the lung.

Pleural cavity (plooʹral) A potential space between the two layers of pleura; contains a thin film of serous fluid.

Plexus (plekʹsus) A network of converging and diverging nerve fibers, blood vessels, or lymphatics.

Polar molecules Nonsymmetrical molecules that contain electrically unbalanced atoms.

Polarized State of a plasma membrane of an unstimulated neuron or muscle cell in which the inside of the cell is relatively negative in comparison to the outside; the resting state.

Polycythemia (polʺe-si-theʹme-ah) An abnormally high number of erythrocytes.

Polymer A substance of high molecular weight with long, chainlike molecules consisting of many similar (repeated) units.

Polypeptide (polʺe-pepʹtīd) A chain of amino acids.

Polyps Benign mucosal tumors.

Polysaccharide (polʺe-sakʹah-rīd) Literally, many sugars, a polymer of linked monosaccharides; e.g., starch, glycogen.

Pons (1) Any bridgelike structure or part; (2) the part of the brain stem connecting the medulla with the midbrain, providing linkage between upper and lower levels of the central nervous system.

Pore The surface opening of the duct of a sweat gland.

Positive feedback mechanisms Feedback that tends to cause the level of a variable to change in the same direction as an initial change.

Posterior pituitary *See* Neurohypophysis.

Postganglionic axon (fiber) (postʺgang-gle-ahʹnik) Axon of a ganglionic neuron, an autonomic motor neuron that has its cell body in a peripheral ganglion; the axon projects to an effector.

Potential energy Stored or inactive energy.

Preganglionic neuron Autonomic motor neuron that has its cell body in the central nervous system and projects its axon to a peripheral ganglion.

Presbyopia (presʺbe-oʹpe-ah) A condition that results in the loss of near focusing ability; typical onset is around age 40.

Pressure gradient Difference in pressure (hydrostatic or osmotic) that drives movement of fluid.

Primary active transport A type of active transport in which the energy needed to drive the transport process is provided directly by hydrolysis of ATP.

Prime mover Muscle that bears the major responsibility for effecting a particular movement; an agonist.

Process (1) Prominence or projection; (2) series of actions for a specific purpose.

Progesterone (pro-jesʹter-ōn) Hormone partly responsible for preparing the uterus for the fertilized ovum.

Prolactin (PRL) (pro-lakʹtin) Adenohypophyseal hormone that stimulates the breasts to produce milk.

Pronation (pro-naʹshun) Inward rotation of the forearm causing the radius to cross diagonally over the ulna—palms face posteriorly.

Prophase The first stage of mitosis, consisting of coiling of the chromosomes accompanied by migration of the two daughter centrioles toward the poles of the cell, and nuclear membrane breakdown.

Proprioceptor (proʺpre-o-sepʹtor) Receptor located in a joint, muscle, or tendon; concerned with locomotion, posture, and muscle tone.

Prostaglandin (PG) (prosʺtah-glanʹdin) A lipid-based chemical messenger synthesized by most tissue cells that acts locally as a paracrine.

Prostate Accessory reproductive gland; produces one-third of semen volume, including fluids that activate sperm.

Protein (proʹtēn) Complex substance containing carbon, oxygen, hydrogen, and nitrogen; composes 10–30% of cell mass.

Prothrombin time Diagnostic test to determine status of hemostasis system.

Proton (proʹton) Subatomic particle that bears a positive charge; located in the atomic nucleus.

Proton acceptor A substance that takes up hydrogen ions in detectable amounts. Commonly referred to as a base.

Proton donor A substance that releases hydrogen ions in detectable amounts; an acid.

Proximal (prokʹsi-mul) Toward the attached end of a limb or the origin of a structure.

Pseudounipolar neuron (sooʺdo-uʺnĭ-poʹlar) Another term for unipolar neuron.

Puberty Period of life when reproductive maturity is achieved.

Pulmonary (pulʹmuh-nayr-e) Pertaining to the lungs.

Pulmonary arteries Vessels that deliver blood to the lungs to be oxygenated.

Pulmonary circuit System of blood vessels that serves gas exchange in the lungs; i.e., pulmonary arteries, capillaries, and veins.

Pulmonary edema (ĕ-deʹmuh) Leakage of fluid into the air sacs and tissue of the lungs.

Pulmonary veins Vessels that deliver freshly oxygenated blood from the respiratory zones of the lungs to the heart.

Pulmonary ventilation Breathing; consists of inspiration and expiration.

Pulse Rhythmic expansion and recoil of arteries resulting from heart contraction; can be felt from outside the body.

Pupil Opening in the center of the iris through which light enters the eye.

Purkinje fibers (pur-kin′je) Modified ventricular muscle fibers of the conduction system of the heart.

Pus Fluid product of inflammation composed of white blood cells, the debris of dead cells, and a thin fluid.

Pyloric sphincter (pi-lor′ik sfink′ter) Valve of the distal end of the stomach that controls food entry into the duodenum.

Pyramidal (corticospinal) tracts Major motor pathways concerned with voluntary movement; descend from pyramidal cells in the frontal lobes of each cerebral hemisphere.

Pyruvic acid An intermediate compound in the metabolism of carbohydrates.

Radioactivity The process of spontaneous decay seen in some of the heavier isotopes, during which particles or energy is emitted from the atomic nucleus; results in the atom becoming more stable.

Radioisotope (ra″de-o-i′so-tōp) Isotope that exhibits radioactive behavior.

Ramus (ra′mus) Branch of a nerve, artery, vein, or bone.

Rapid eye movement (REM) sleep Stage of sleep in which rapid eye movements, an alert EEG pattern, and dreaming occur.

Reactant A substance taking part in a chemical reaction.

Receptor (re-sep′tor) (1) A cell or nerve ending of a sensory neuron specialized to respond to particular types of stimuli; (2) protein that binds specifically with other molecules, e.g., neurotransmitters, hormones, paracrines, antigens.

Receptor-mediated endocytosis One of three types of endocytosis in which engulfed particles attach to receptors before endocytosis occurs.

Receptor potential A graded potential that occurs at a sensory receptor membrane.

Recessive traits A trait due to a particular allele that does not manifest itself in the presence of other alleles that generate traits dominant to it; must be present in double dose to be expressed.

Reduction Chemical reaction in which electrons and energy are gained by a molecule (often accompanied by gain of hydrogen ions) or oxygen is lost.

Referred pain Pain felt at a site other than the area of origin.

Reflex Automatic reaction to stimuli.

Refraction The bending of a light ray when it meets a different surface at an oblique rather than right angle.

Regeneration Replacement of destroyed tissue with the same kind of tissue.

Regulatory T cells (T_{Reg} cells) Population of T cells (usually expressing CD4) that suppress the immune response.

Relative refractory period Follows the absolute refractory period; interval when a threshold for action potential stimulation is markedly elevated.

Renal (re′nal) Pertaining to the kidney.

Renal autoregulation Process the kidney uses to maintain a nearly constant glomerular filtration rate despite fluctuations in systemic blood pressure.

Renal clearance The volume of plasma from which a particular substance is completely removed in a given time, usually 1 minute; provides information about renal function.

Renin (re′nin) Hormone released by the kidneys that is involved with raising blood pressure.

Rennin Stomach-secreted enzyme that acts on milk protein; not produced in adults.

Repolarization Movement of the membrane potential to the initial resting (polarized) state.

Reproductive system Organ system that functions to produce offspring.

Resistance exercise High-intensity exercise in which the muscles are pitted against high resistance or immovable forces and, as a result, muscle cells increase in size.

Respiration The processes involved in supplying the body with oxygen and disposing of carbon dioxide.

Respiratory system Organ system that carries out gas exchange; includes the nose, pharynx, larynx, trachea, bronchi, lungs.

Resting membrane potential The voltage that exists across the plasma membrane during the resting state of an excitable cell; ranges from -90 to -20 millivolts depending on cell type.

Reticular activating system (RAS) (re-tik′u-lar) Diffuse brain stem neural network that receives a wide variety of sensory input and maintains wakefulness of the cerebral cortex.

Reticular connective tissue Connective tissue with a fine network of reticular fibers that form the internal supporting framework of lymphoid organs.

Reticular formation Functional system that spans the brain stem; involved in regulating sensory input to the cerebral cortex, cortical arousal, and control of motor behavior.

Reticular lamina A layer of extracellular material containing a fine network of collagen protein fibers; together with the basal lamina it is a major component of the basement membrane.

Reticulocyte (rě-tik′u-lo-sīt) Immature erythrocyte.

Retina (ret′ĭ-nah) Neural layer of the eyeball; contains photoreceptors (rods, cones).

Rhombencephalon (hindbrain) (romb″en-sef′ah-lon) Caudal portion of the developing brain; constricts to form the metencephalon and myelencephalon; includes the pons, cerebellum, and medulla oblongata.

Ribosomal RNA (rRNA) A constituent of ribosome; exists within the ribosomes of cytoplasm and assists in protein synthesis.

Ribosomes (ri′bo-sōmz) Cytoplasmic organelles at which proteins are synthesized.

RNA (ribonucleic acid) (ri′bo-nu-kle′ik) Nucleic acid that contains ribose and the bases A, G, C, and U. Carries out DNA's instructions for protein synthesis.

Rods One of the two types of photosensitive cells in the retina.

Rotation The turning of a bone around its own long axis.

Rugae (ru′ge) Elevations or ridges, as in stomach mucosa.

Rule of nines Method of computing the extent of burns by dividing the body into a number of areas, each accounting for 9% (or a multiple thereof) of the total body area.

S (synthetic) phase The part of the interphase period of the cell life cycle in which DNA replicates itself, ensuring that the two future cells will receive identical copies of genetic material.

Sagittal plane (saj′ĭ-tal) A longitudinal (vertical) plane that divides the body or any of its parts into right and left portions.

Saliva Secretion of the salivary glands; cleanses and moistens the mouth and begins chemical digestion of starchy foods.

Saltatory conduction Transmission of an action potential along a myelinated fiber in which the nerve impulse appears to leap from node to node.

Sarcolemma The plasma membrane surface of a muscle fiber.

Sarcomere (sar′ko-mēr) The smallest contractile unit of muscle; extends from one Z disc to the next.

Sarcoplasm The nonfibrillar cytoplasm of a muscle fiber.

Sarcoplasmic reticulum (SR) (sar″ko-plaz′mik rĕ-tik′u-lum) Specialized endoplasmic reticulum of muscle cells.

Schwann cell A type of supporting cell in the PNS; forms myelin sheaths and is vital to peripheral nerve fiber regeneration.

Sclera (skle′rah) White opaque portion of the fibrous layer of the eyeball.

Scrotum (skro′tum) External sac enclosing the testes.

Sebaceous glands (oil glands) (se-ba′shus) Epidermal glands that produce an oily secretion called sebum.

Sebum (se′bum) Oily secretion of sebaceous glands.

Second-degree burn A burn in which the epidermis and the upper region of the dermis are damaged.

Second messenger Intracellular molecule generated by the binding of a chemical (hormone or neurotransmitter) to a plasma membrane receptor; mediates intracellular responses to the chemical messenger.

Secondary sex characteristics Anatomic features, not directly involved in the reproductive process, that develop under the influence of sex hormones, e.g., male or female pattern of muscle development, bone growth, body hair distribution.

Secretion (se-kre′shun) (1) The passage of material formed by a cell to its exterior; (2) cell product that is transported to the exterior of a cell.

Secretory vesicles (granules) Vesicles that migrate to the plasma membrane of a cell and discharge their contents from the cell by exocytosis.

Section A cut through the body (or an organ) that is made along a particular plane; a thin slice of tissue prepared for microscopic study.

Segregation During meiosis, the distribution of the members of the allele pair to different gametes.

Selectively permeable membrane A membrane that allows certain substances to pass while restricting the movement of others; also called differentially permeable membrane.

Semen (se′men) Fluid mixture containing sperm and secretions of the male accessory reproductive glands.

Semilunar valves (sĕ″me-loo′ner) Valves that prevent blood return to the ventricles after contraction; aortic and pulmonary valves.

Seminiferous tubules (sem″ĭ-nif′er-us) Highly convoluted tubes within the testes; form sperm.

Sense organs Localized collections of many types of cells working together to accomplish a specific receptive process.

Sensory (afferent) nerves Nerves that contain processes of sensory neurons and carry impulses to the central nervous system.

Sensory areas Functional areas of the cerebral cortex that provide for conscious awareness of sensation.

Sensory receptor Dendritic end organs, or parts of other cell types, specialized to respond to a stimulus.

Serosa (serous membrane) (se-ro′sah) The moist membrane found in closed ventral body cavities.

Serous fluid (sēr′us) Clear, watery fluid secreted by cells of a serous membrane.

Serum (sēr′um) Amber-colored fluid that exudes from clotted blood as the clot shrinks; plasma without clotting factors.

Sesamoid bones (ses′ah-moid) Short bones embedded in tendons, variable in size and number, many of which influence the action of muscles; largest is the patella (kneecap).

Severe combined immunodeficiency syndromes (SCIDs) Congenital conditions resulting in little or no protection against disease-causing organisms of any type.

Sex chromosomes The chromosomes, X and Y, that determine genetic sex (XX = female; XY = male); the 23rd pair of chromosomes.

Sex-linked inheritance Inherited traits determined by genes on the sex chromosomes, e.g., X-linked genes are passed from mother to son, Y-linked genes are passed from father to son.

Sexually transmitted infection (STI) Infectious disease spread through sexual contact.

Signal sequence A short peptide segment present in a protein being synthesized that causes the associated ribosome to attach to the membrane of rough ER.

Simple diffusion The unassisted transport across a plasma membrane of a lipid-soluble or very small particle.

Sinoatrial (SA) node (si″no-a′tre-al) Specialized myocardial cells in the wall of the right atrium; pacemaker of the heart.

Sinus (si′nus) (1) Mucous-membrane-lined, air-filled cavity in certain cranial bones; (2) dilated channel for the passage of blood or lymph.

Skeletal muscle Muscle composed of cylindrical multinucleate cells with obvious striations; the muscle(s) attached to the body's skeleton; voluntary muscle.

Skeletal system System of protection and support composed primarily of bone and cartilage.

Skull Bony protective encasement of the brain and the organs of hearing and equilibrium; includes the facial bones. Also called the cranium.

Small intestine Convoluted tube extending from the pyloric sphincter to the ileocecal valve where it joins the large intestine; the site where digestion is completed and virtually all absorption occurs.

Smooth muscle Spindle-shaped cells with one centrally located nucleus and no externally visible striations (bands). Found mainly in the walls of hollow organs.

Sodium-potassium (Na$^+$-K$^+$) pump A primary active transport system that simultaneously drives Na$^+$ out of the cell against a steep gradient and pumps K$^+$ back in.

Sol-gel transformation Reversible change of a colloid from a fluid (sol) to a more solid (gel) state.

Solute (sol′yoot) The substance that is dissolved in a solution.

Solute pump Enzyme-like protein carrier that mediates active transport of solutes such as amino acids and ions uphill against their concentration gradients.

Somatic nervous system (so-ma′tik) Division of the peripheral nervous system that provides the motor innervation of skeletal muscles; also called the voluntary nervous system.

Somatic reflexes Reflexes that activate skeletal muscle.

Somatosensory system That part of the sensory system dealing with reception in the body wall and limbs; receives inputs from exteroceptors, proprioceptors, and interoceptors.

Somite (so′mīt) A mesodermal segment of the body of an embryo that contributes to the formation of skeletal muscles, vertebrae, and dermis of skin.

Spatial discrimination The ability of neurons to identify the site or pattern of stimulation.

Special senses The senses of taste, smell, vision, hearing, and equilibrium.

Specific gravity Term used to compare the weight of a substance to the weight of an equal volume of distilled water.

Sperm (spermatozoon) Male gamete.

Spermatogenesis (sper″mah-to-jen′ĕ-sis) The process of sperm (male gamete) formation; involves meiosis.

Sphincter (sfink′ter) A circular muscle surrounding an opening; acts as a valve.

Spinal cord The bundle of nervous tissue that runs from the brain to the first to third lumbar vertebrae and provides a conduction pathway to and from the brain.

Spinal nerves The 31 nerve pairs that arise from the spinal cord.

Splanchnic circulation (splangk′nik) The blood vessels serving the digestive system.

Spleen Largest lymphoid organ; provides for lymphocyte proliferation, immune surveillance and response, and blood-cleansing functions.

Spongy bone Internal layer of skeletal bone. Also called cancellous bone.

Sprain Ligaments reinforcing a joint are stretched or torn.

Static equilibrium Sense of head position in space with respect to gravity.

Stenosis (stĕ-no′sis) Abnormal constriction or narrowing.

Steroids (stĕ′roidz) Group of chemical substances including certain hormones and cholesterol; they are fat soluble and contain little oxygen.

Stimulus (stim′u-lus) An excitant or irritant; a change in the environment that evokes a response.

Stomach Temporary reservoir in the gastrointestinal tract where chemical breakdown of proteins begins and food is converted into chyme.

Stressor Any stimulus that directly or indirectly causes the hypothalamus to initiate stress-reducing responses, such as the fight-or-flight response.

Stroke *See* Cerebrovascular accident.

Stroke volume (SV) Amount of blood pumped out of a ventricle during one contraction.

Stroma (stro′mah) The basic internal structural framework of an organ.

Structural (fibrous) proteins Consist of extended, strandlike polypeptide chains forming a strong, ropelike structure that is linear, insoluble in water, and very stable; e.g., collagen.

Subcutaneous (sub″kyu-ta′ne-us) Beneath the skin.

Substrate A reactant on which an enzyme acts to cause a chemical action to proceed.

Sudoriferous gland (su″do-rif′er-us) Epidermal gland that produces sweat.

Sulcus (sul′kus) A furrow on the brain, less deep than a fissure.

Summation Accumulation of effects, especially those of muscular, sensory, or mental stimuli.

Superficial Located close to or on the body surface.

Superior Toward the head or upper body regions.

Superior vena cava Vein that returns blood from body regions superior to the diaphragm.

Supination (soo″pĭ-na′shun) The outward rotation of the forearm causing palms to face anteriorly.

Surfactant (ser-fak′tant) Secretion produced by certain cells of the alveoli that reduces the surface tension of water molecules, thus preventing the collapse of the alveoli after each expiration.

Suspension Heterogeneous mixtures with large, often visible solutes that tend to settle out.

Suture (soo′cher) An immovable fibrous joint; with one exception, all bones of the skull are united by sutures.

Sweat gland *See* Sudoriferous gland.

Sympathetic division The division of the autonomic nervous system that prepares the body for activity or to cope with some stressor (danger, excitement, etc.); the fight, fright, and flight subdivision.

Sympathetic (vasomotor) tone State of partial vasoconstriction of the blood vessels maintained by sympathetic fibers.

Symphysis (sim′fih-sis) A joint in which the bones are connected by fibrocartilage.

Synapse (sin′aps) Functional junction or point of close contact between two neurons or between a neuron and an effector cell.

Synapsis (sĭ-nap′sis) Pairing of homologous chromosomes during the first meiotic division.

Synaptic cleft (si-nap′tik) Fluid-filled space at a synapse.

Synaptic delay Time required for an impulse to cross a synapse between two neurons.

Synaptic vesicles Small membranous sacs containing neurotransmitter.

Synarthrosis (sin″ar-thro′sis) Immovable joint.

Synchondrosis (sin″kon-dro′sis) A joint in which the bones are united by hyaline cartilage.

Syndesmosis (sin″des-mo′sis) A joint in which the bones are united by a ligament or a sheet of fibrous tissue.

Synergist (sin′er-jist) (1) Muscle that aids the action of a prime mover by effecting the same movement or by stabilizing joints across which the prime mover acts, preventing undesirable movements. (2) Hormone that amplifies the effect of another hormone at a target cell.

Synostosis (sin″os-to′sis) A completely ossified joint; a fused joint.

Synovial fluid Fluid secreted by the synovial membrane; lubricates joint surfaces and nourishes articular cartilages.

Synovial joint Freely movable joint exhibiting a joint cavity; also called a diarthrosis.

Synthesis (combination) reaction A chemical reaction in which larger, more complex atoms or molecules are formed from simpler ones.

Systemic (sis-tem′ik) Pertaining to the whole body.

Systemic circuit System of blood vessels that serves gas exchange in the body tissues.

Systole (sis′to-le) Period when either the ventricles or the atria are contracting.

Systolic pressure (sis-tah′lik) Pressure exerted by blood on the blood vessel walls during ventricular contractions.

T cells Lymphocytes that mediate cellular immunity; include helper, cytotoxic, regulatory, and memory cells. Also called T lymphocytes.

T tubule (transverse tubule) Extension of the muscle cell plasma membrane (sarcolemma) that protrudes deeply into the muscle cell.

Tachycardia (tak″e-kar′de-ah) A heart rate over 100 beats per minute.

Taste buds Sensory receptor organs that house gustatory cells, which respond to dissolved food chemicals.

Telencephalon (endbrain) (tel″en-seh′fuh-lon) Anterior subdivision of the primary forebrain that develops into olfactory lobes, cerebral cortex, and basal nuclei.

Telophase The final phase of mitosis; begins when migration of chromosomes to the poles of the cell has been completed and ends with the formation of two daughter nuclei.

Tendon (ten′dun) Cord of dense fibrous tissue attaching muscle to bone.

Tendonitis Inflammation of tendon sheaths, typically caused by overuse.

Terminal branches Branching ends of an axon that allow it to form many axon terminals; telodendria.

Testis (tes′tis) Male primary reproductive organ that produces sperm; male gonad.

Testosterone (tes-tos′tĕ-rōn) Male sex hormone produced by the testes; during puberty promotes virilization, and is necessary for normal sperm production.

Tetanus (tet′ah-nus) (1) A smooth, sustained muscle contraction resulting from high-frequency stimulation; (2) an infectious disease caused by an anaerobic bacterium.

Thalamus (thal′ah-mus) A mass of gray matter in the diencephalon of the brain.

Thermogenesis (ther″mo-jen′ĕ-sis) Heat production.

Thermoreceptor (ther″mo-re-sep′ter) Receptor sensitive to temperature changes.

Third-degree burn A burn that involves the entire thickness of the skin; also called a full-thickness burn. Usually requires skin grafting.

Thoracic cage (bony thorax) Bones that form the framework of the thorax; includes sternum, ribs, and thoracic vertebrae.

Thoracic duct Large duct that receives lymph drained from the entire lower body, the left upper extremity, and the left side of the head and thorax.

Thorax (tho′raks) That portion of the body trunk above the diaphragm and below the neck.

Threshold stimulus Weakest stimulus capable of producing a response in an irritable tissue.

Thrombin (throm′bin) Enzyme that induces clotting by converting fibrinogen to fibrin.

Thrombocyte (throm′bo-sīt) Platelet; cell fragment that participates in blood coagulation.

Thrombocytopenia (throm″bo-si″to-pe′ne-ah) A reduction in the number of platelets circulating in the blood.

Thrombus (throm′bus) A clot that develops and persists in an unbroken blood vessel.

Thymine (T) (thi′mēn) Single-ring base (a pyrimidine) in DNA.

Thymus (thi′mus) Lymphoid organ and endocrine gland active in immune response; site of maturation of T lymphocytes.

Thyroid gland (thi′roid) One of the largest of the body's endocrine glands; straddles the anterior trachea.

Thyroid hormone (TH) The major hormone secreted by thyroid follicles; stimulates enzymes concerned with glucose oxidation.

Thyroid-stimulating hormone (TSH) Adenohypophyseal hormone that regulates secretion of thyroid hormones.

Thyroxine (T₄) (thi-rok′sin) Iodine-containing hormone secreted by the thyroid gland; accelerates cellular metabolic rate in most body tissues.

Tight junction Area where plasma membranes of adjacent cells are fused.

Tissue A group of similar cells and their intercellular substance specialized to perform a specific function; primary tissue types of the body are epithelial, connective, muscle, and nervous tissue.

Tissue perfusion Blood flow through body tissues or organs.

Tonicity (to-nis′ĭ-te) A measure of the ability of a solution to cause a change in cell shape or tone by promoting osmotic flows of water.

Tonsils A ring of lymphoid tissue around the entrance to the pharynx. *See also* Adenoids.

Trabecula (trah-bek′u-lah) (1) Any of the fibrous bands extending from the capsule into the interior of an organ; (2) strut or thin plate of bone in spongy bone.

Trachea (tra′ke-ah) Windpipe; cartilage-reinforced tube extending from larynx to bronchi.

Tract A collection of axons in the central nervous system having the same origin, termination, and function.

Transcription One of the two major steps in the transfer of genetic code information from a DNA base sequence to the complementary base sequence of an mRNA molecule.

Transduction (trans-duk′shun) The conversion of the energy of a stimulus into an electrical event.

Transepithelial transport (trans-ep″ĭ-the′le-al) Movement of substances through, rather than between, adjacent epithelial cells connected by tight junctions, such as absorption of nutrients in the small intestine.

Transfer RNA (tRNA) Short-chain RNA molecules that transfer amino acids to the ribosome.

Transfusion reaction Agglutination and destruction of red blood cells following transfusion of incompatible blood.

Translation One of the two major steps in the transfer of genetic code information, in which the information carried by mRNA is decoded and used to assemble polypeptides.

Transverse (horizontal) plane A plane running from right to left, dividing the body or an organ into superior and inferior parts.

Tricuspid valve (tri-kus′pid) The right atrioventricular valve.

Triglycerides (tri-glis′er-īdz) Fats and oils composed of fatty acids and glycerol; are the body's most concentrated source of energy fuel; also known as neutral fats.

Triiodothyronine (T₃) (tri″i-o″do-thi′ro-nēn) Thyroid hormone; secretion and function similar to those of thyroxine (T₄).

Trophoblast (tro′fo-blast) Outer sphere of cells of the blastocyst.

Tropic hormone (trōp′ik) A hormone that regulates the secretory action of another endocrine organ.

Trypsin Proteolytic enzyme secreted by the pancreas.

Tubular reabsorption The movement of filtrate components from the renal tubules into the blood.

Tubular secretion The movement of substances (such as drugs, urea, excess ions) from blood into filtrate.

Tumor An abnormal growth of cells; a swelling; may be cancerous.

Tunica (too′nĭ-kah) A covering or tissue coat; membrane layer.

Tympanic membrane (tim-pan′ik) Eardrum.

Ulcer (ul′ser) Lesion or erosion of the mucous membrane, such as gastric ulcer of stomach.

Umbilical cord (um-bĭ′lĭ-kul) Structure bearing arteries and veins connecting the placenta and the fetus.

Umbilicus (um-bĭ′lĭ-kus) Navel; marks site where umbilical cord was attached in fetal stage.

Unipolar neuron Neuron in which embryological fusion of the two processes leaves only one process extending from the cell body.

Unmyelinated fibers (un-mi′ĕ-lĭ-nāt″ed) Axons lacking a myelin sheath and therefore conducting impulses quite slowly.

Uracil (U) (u′rah-sil) A smaller, single-ring base (a pyrimidine) found in RNA.

Urea (u-re′ah) Main nitrogen-containing waste excreted in urine.

Ureter (u-re′ter) Tube that carries urine from kidney to bladder.

Urethra (u-re′thrah) Canal through which urine passes from the bladder to outside the body.

Uric acid The nitrogenous waste product of nucleic acid metabolism; component of urine.

Urinary bladder A smooth, collapsible, muscular sac that stores urine temporarily.

Urinary system System primarily responsible for water, electrolyte, and acid-base balance and removal of nitrogenous wastes.

Uterine tube (u′ter-in) Tube through which the ovum is transported to the uterus. Also called fallopian tube.

Uterus (u′ter-us) Hollow, thick-walled organ that receives, retains, and nourishes fertilized egg; site where embryo/fetus develops.

Uvula (u′vu-lah) Tissue tag hanging from soft palate.

Vaccine Preparation that provides artificially acquired active immunity.

Vagina Thin-walled tube extending from the cervix to the body exterior; often called the birth canal.

Valence shell (va′lens) Outermost electron shell (energy level) of an atom that contains electrons.

Varicosities Knoblike swellings of certain autonomic axons containing mitochondria and synaptic vesicles.

Vas (vaz′) A duct; vessel.

Vasa recta (va′sah rek′tah) Capillary branches that supply loops of Henle in the medulla region of the kidney.

Vascular Pertaining to blood vessels or richly supplied with blood vessels.

Vascular spasm Immediate response to blood vessel injury; results in constriction.

Vasoconstriction (vas″o-kon-strik′shun) Narrowing of blood vessels.

Vasodilation (vas″o-di-la′shun) Relaxation of the smooth muscles of the blood vessels, producing dilation.

Vasomotion (vas″o-mo′shun) Intermittent contraction or relaxation of the precapillary sphincters, resulting in a staggered blood flow when tissue needs are not extreme.

Vasomotor center (vas″o-mo′ter) Brain area concerned with regulation of blood vessel resistance.

Vasomotor fibers Sympathetic nerve fibers that cause the contraction of smooth muscle in the walls of blood vessels, thereby regulating blood vessel diameter.

Veins (vānz″) Blood vessels that return blood toward the heart from the circulation.

Ventral Pertaining to the front; anterior.

Ventricles (1) Paired, inferiorly located heart chambers that function as the major blood pumps; (2) cavities in the brain.

Venule (ven′ūl) A small vein.

Vertebral column (spine) (ver′tĕ-brul) Formed of a number of individual bones called vertebrae and two composite bones (sacrum and coccyx).

Vesicle (vĕ′sĭ-kul) A small liquid-filled sac or bladder.

Vesicular (bulk) transport The movement of large particles and macromolecules across a plasma membrane.

Vesicular follicle Mature ovarian follicle.

Vestibule An enlarged area at the beginning of a canal, i.e., inner ear, nose, larynx.

Villus (vil′us) Fingerlike projections of the small intestinal mucosa that tremendously increase its surface area for absorption.

Visceral (vis′er-al) Pertaining to an internal organ of the body or the inner part of a structure.

Visceral muscle Type of smooth muscle; its cells contract as a unit and rhythmically, are electrically coupled by gap junctions, and often exhibit spontaneous action potentials.

Visceral organs (viscera) A group of internal organs housed in the ventral body cavity.

Visceral serosa (se-ro′sah) The part of the double-layered membrane that lines the outer surfaces of organs within the ventral body cavity.

Viscosity (vis′kos′ĭ-te) State of being sticky or thick.

Visual field The field of view seen when the head is still.

Vital capacity (VC) The volume of air that can be expelled from the lungs by forcible expiration after the deepest inspiration; total exchangeable air.

Vital signs Includes pulse, blood pressure, respiratory rate, and body temperature measurements.

Vitamins Organic compounds required by the body in minute amounts.

Vocal folds Mucosal folds that function in voice production (speech); also called the true vocal cords.

Volatile acid An acid that can be eliminated by the lungs; carbonic acid is converted to CO_2, which diffuses into the alveoli.

Volkmann's canals *See* Perforating canals.

Voluntary muscle Muscle under strict nervous control; skeletal muscle.

Voluntary nervous system The somatic nervous system.

Vulva (vul′vuh) Female external genitalia.

Wallerian degeneration (wal-er′ē-an) A process of disintegration of an axon that occurs when it is crushed or severed and cannot receive nutrients from the cell body.

White matter White substance of the central nervous system; myelinated nerve fibers.

Xenograft Tissue graft taken from another animal species.

Yolk sac (yōk) One of the extraembryonic membranes; involved in early blood cell formation.

Zygote (zi′gōt) Fertilized egg.

Photo and Illustration Credits

Photo Credits

Chapter 1
Chapter Opener: Jorge Silva/Corbis.
1.1: GoGo Images/Jupiter Images.
1.3: Pearson Science.
1.8.1: Jenny Thomas/Addison Wesley Longman.
1.8.2: Howard Sochurek.
1.8.3: James Cavallini/Photo Researchers.
1.8.4: CNRI/Science Photo Library/Photo Researchers.
1.12a: Custom Medical Stock Photo, Inc.
A Closer Look: a: Clinique Ste Catherine/CNRI/
Science Photo Library/Photo Researchers.
b: Willam Klunk, Chet Mathis, University of
Pittsburgh, PET Amyloid Imaging Group.
c: Custom Medical Stock Photography.

Chapter 2
Chapter Opener: Chuck Haney Outdoor Photography/
Danita Delimont.
2.4.1: Stockbyte/Getty Images.
2.4.2: Marc O. Finley, Stock Food Creative/Getty Images.
2.4.3: Cristina Pedrazzini/Photo Researchers.
2.10b: Bernard Photo Productions/Animals
Animals/Earth Sciences.
2.22c: Computer Graphics Laboratory, University of
California, San Francisco.

Chapter 3
Chapter Opener: Paul Burns/Getty Images.
3.9a–c: David M. Philips/Photo Researchers.
3.14b: Birgit H. Satir, Dept. of Anatomy and Structural Biology, Albert Einstein College of Medicine.
3.17c: Professors P. Motta & T. Naguro/SPL/Photo
Researchers.
3.18b: R. Bolender and Donald Fawcett/Visuals
Unlimited.
3.19b: P. Motta & T. Naguro/SPL/Photo Researchers.
3.21: K. G. Murti/Visuals Unlimited.
3.23a: Mary Osborn, Max Planck Institute.
3.23b: Frank Solomon and J. Dinsmore, Massachusetts Institute of Technology.
3.23c: Mark S. Ladinsky and J. Richard McIntosh,
University of Colorado.
3.25b: David M. Philips/Visuals Unlimited.
3.26.1: OMIKRON/Science Source/Photo Researchers.
3.26.2 and 3: W. L. Dentler/Biological Photo Service.
3.28: Don W. Fawcett/Photo Researchers.
3.29b.1: From L. Orci and A. Perrelet, *Freeze-Etch Histology.* (Heidelberg: Springer-Verlag, 1975) © 1975
Springer-Verlag.
3.29b.2: From A. C. Faberge, *Cell Tiss. Res.* 151
(1974):403. © 1974 Springer-Verlag.
3.29b.3: U. Aebi et al. *Nature* 323 (1996):560–564,
Figure 1a. Used by permission.

3.30.1: Dr. Victoria E. Foe.
3.30.2: GF Bahr, Armed Forces Institute of Pathology.
3.33.1–6: Conly Rieder.
3.38b: Barbara Hamkalo.

Chapter 4
Chapter Opener: Mark Karrass/Corbis.
4.3a: G. W. Willis/Visuals Unlimited.
4.3b, f: Allen Bell, University of New England;
Pearson Science.
4.3c: Cabisco/Visuals Unlimited.
4.3d: Ed Reschke.
4.3e: Nina Zanetti, Pearson Science.
4.4a: SPL/Photo Researchers.
4.8a, e, g, k: Ed Reschke.
4.8b, f, h: Nina Zanetti, Pearson Science.
4.8c, i, j: Allen Bell, University of New England;
Pearson Science.
4.8d: Ed Reschke/Peter Arnold.
4.9: Biophoto Associates/Photo Researchers.
4.10a: Eric Graves/Photo Researchers.
4.10b: Ed Reschke.
4.10c: SPL/Photo Researchers.

Chapter 5
Chapter Opener: Creasource/Corbis.
5.2a: Ed Reschke/Peter Arnold.
5.3a: Ed Reschke/Peter Arnold.
5.3b, c: Kessel and Kardon/Visuals Unlimited.
5.4a: Kessel and Kardon/Visuals Unlimited.
5.5a: Cabisco/Visuals Unlimited.
5.5b: John D. Cunningham/Visuals Unlimited.
5.6b: Carolina Biological Supply/Phototake.
5.6d: Manfred Kage/Peter Arnold.
5.8a: Bart's Medical Library/Phototake.
5.8b: P. Marazzi/SPL/Photo Researchers.
5.8c: Zeva Oelbaum/Peter Arnold.
5.10a: Scott Camazine/Photo Researchers.
5.10b: Dr. M.A. Ansary/Photo Researchers.

Chapter 6
Chapter Opener: Luciana Ellington/age fotostock.
6.5.1: seelevel.com.
6.5.2: Steve Gschmeissner/Photo Researchers.
6.7c.1: Kessel and Kardon/Visuals Unlimited.
6.7c.2: Ed Reschke/Peter Arnold.
6.10: Ed Reschke.
6.14a: Martin Rose/Bongarts/Getty Images.
6.16a, b: P. Motta, Department of Anatomy, University
"La Sapienza," Rome/Science Photo Library/Photo
Researchers.
6.17: Carolina Biological Supply.
Table 6.2.1: Lester Bergman/Corbis.
Table 6.2.2: ISM/Phototake.
Table 6.2.3: SIU/Peter Arnold.

Table 6.2.4: SIU/Visuals Unlimited.
Table 6.2.5: William T. C. Yuh.
Table 6.2.6: Charles Stewart MD.

Chapter 7
Chapter Opener: George Shelley/Masterfile.
7.5c: Ralph T. Hutchings.
7.6b: Ralph T. Hutchings.
7.7b: Ralph T. Hutchings.
7.8: Ralph T. Hutchings.
7.9a, b: Ralph T. Hutchings.
7.10: Ralph T. Hutchings.
7.11c: Ralph T. Hutchings/Pearson Science.
7.13a: Ralph T. Hutchings.
7.17d: Neil Borden/Photo Researchers.
7.22b: Dissection by Shawn Miller, photography by
Mark Nielsen and Alexa Doig.
7.23c: Pearson Science.
7.30c, d: Ralph T. Hutchings.
7.32c, d: Ralph T. Hutchings.
7.32.e: Biophoto Associates/Science Source/Photo
Researchers.
7.34b: Elaine N. Marieb.
7.36: Center For Cranialfacial Anomalies, University
of California, San Francisco.
7.37: Reik/age fotostock.
Table 7.4.2–5: From *A Stereoscopic Atlas of Human
Anatomy* by David L. Bassett.

Chapter 8
Chapter Opener: ANP/AFP/Getty Images.
8.5a–f: John Wilson White, Pearson Science.
8.6a–f: John Wilson White, Pearson Science.
8.8f: L. Bassett/Visuals Unlimited.
8.10b: Mark Neilsen, University of Utah; Pearson Science.
8.10e: VideoSurgery/Photo Researchers.
8.12b: From *A Stereoscopic Atlas of Human Anatomy*
by David L. Bassett.
8.14: Elaine Marieb.
8.15: CNRI/Science Photo Library/Photo Researchers.
A Closer Look: 1: Lawrence Livermore National
Laboratory/Photo Researchers. 2: Elaine Marieb.

Chapter 9
Chapter Opener: Robert Michael/Corbis.
9.1b: John D. Cunningham/Visuals Unlimited.
9.2a: Marian Rice.
9.4: John Heuser.
9.6.1, 3: James Dennis/Phototake.
9.13b: Eric Graves/Photo Researchers.
9.24: National Library of Medicine.
A Closer Look: Moritz Steiger/Riser/Getty Images.
Table 9.3.4: Eric Graves/Photo Researchers.
Table 9.3.5: Marian Rice.
Table 9.3.6: SPL/Photo Researchers.

Chapter 10
Chapter Opener: Goodshoot/Jupiter Images.
10.8b: Creative Digital Visions, Pearson Science.
10.9c: Dissection by Shawn Miller, photography by Mark Nielsen and Alexa Doig.
10.10c: From *A Stereoscopic Atlas of Human Anatomy* by David L. Bassett.
10.13b: Ralph T. Hutchings.
10.13d, e: Dissection by Shawn Miller, photography by Mark Nielsen and Alexa Doig.
10.14d: Dissection by Shawn Miller, photography by Mark Nielsen and Alexa Doig.
10.20b: Ralph T. Hutchings.

Chapter 11
Chapter Opener: Hulton Archive Photos/Getty Images.
11.4a: Manfred Kage/Peter Arnold.
11.5d: Don W. Fawcett/Photo Researchers.
11.17b: Oliver Meckes/Ottawa/Photo Researchers.
11.24: Tibor Harkany, Science Magagzine.
A Closer Look: Brookhaven National Laboratory/PictureQuest.

Chapter 12
Chapter Opener: Getty Images.
12.6c: Robert A. Chase.
12.6d: A. Glauberman/Photo Researchers.
12.7: Volker Steger/Peter Arnold.
12.10b: Ralph T. Hutchings.
12.11b: Pat Lynch/Photo Researchers.
12.14: Ralph T. Hutchings/Visuals Unlimited.
12.17a: Ralph T. Hutchings.
12.17c: L. Bassett/Visuals Unlimited.
12.20a: Hank Morgan/Photo Researchers.
12.25b: From *A Stereoscopic Atlas of Human Anatomy* by David L. Bassett.
12.27: Carroll H. Weiss.
12.29b–d: L. Bassett/Visuals Unlimited.
12.36: Biophoto Associates/Science Source/Photo Researchers.

Chapter 13
Chapter Opener: AP Photo/Andy Wong.
13.3a: Kessel and Kardon/Visuals Unlimited.
13.9b: Ralph T. Hutchings.
13.11c: Ralph T. Hutchings.
Table 13.2.8: William Thompson, Pearson Science.

Chapter 14
Chapter Opener: Dorling Kindersley.

Chapter 15
Chapter Opener: LWA/Dann Tardif/Jupiter Images.
15.1a: Richard Tauber, Pearson Science.
15.4b: From *A Stereoscopic Atlas of Human Anatomy* by David L Bassett.
15.6c: Ed Reschke/Peter Arnold.
15.7: A. L. Blum/Visuals Unlimited.
15.9: NMSB/Custom Medical Stock Photography.
15.11: Charles D. Wintrer/Photo Researchers.
15.19b: Stephen Spector/Benjamin Cummings.
15.23d: Carolina Biological Supply Company/Phototake, NYC.
15.28d: P. Motta/Department of Anatomy/University "La Sapienza," Rome/Science Photo Library/Photo Researchers.
15.32: *Science* Vol.279 March 1998, p. 1870.
15.36b: I. M. Hunter-Duvar, Department of Oto-laryngology, The Hospital for Sick Children, Toronto.

Chapter 16
Chapter Opener: Creasource/Corbis.
16.8b: Ed Reschke.
16.10a: John Paul Kay/Peter Arnold.
16.10b: Photo Researchers.

16.11b: From *Color Atlas of Histology* by Leslie P. Garner and James L. Hiatt, © Williams and Wilkins, 1990.
16.13b: Ed Reschke.
16.15a, b: Charles B. Wilson, Neurological Surgery, University of California Medical Center, San Francisco.
16.17: Carolina Biological Supply/Phototake NYC.
A Closer Look: Saturn Stills/Science Photo Library/Photo Researchers.

Chapter 17
Chapter Opener: Mark Scoggins/Jupiter Images.
17.2: Ed Reshke/Peter Arnold.
17.8a, b: Stan Flegler/Visuals Unlimited.
17.10a–e: Nina Zanetti, Pearson Science.
17.15: Meckes/Ottawa/Photo Researchers.
17.16.1–4: Jack Scanlon, Holyoke Community College.

Chapter 18
Chapter Opener: Brian Bahr/Getty Images.
18.4a: A. & F. Michler/Peter Arnold.
18.4c: L. Bassett/Visuals Unlimited.
18.4f: *Color Atlas of Anatomy: A Photographic Study of the Human Body*. Germany: © Schattauer Publishing.
18.8b: From *A Stereoscopic Atlas of Human Anatomy* by David L. Bassett.
18.8c: Lennart Nilsson, *The Body Victorious*, New York: Dell, © Boehringer Ingelheim International GmbH.
18.8d: L. Bassett/Visuals Unlimited.
18.11a: Manfred Kage/Peter Arnold.
18.19: Phil Jude/Science Photo Library/Photo Researchers.
18.22: Chris Cole/Getty Images.

Chapter 19
Chapter Opener: Jim Cummins/Getty Images.
19.1a: Gladden Willis/Visuals Unlimited.
19.13: Asia Images Group/Getty Images.
19.22c: Science Photo Library/Photo Researchers.
A Closer Look: 1: Sheila Terry/Science Photo Library/Photo Researchers. 2: ISM/Phototake.

Chapter 20
Chapter Opener: Stockbyte/Getty Images.
20.3: Francis Leroy, Biocosmos/Science Photo Library/Photo Researchers.
20.4b: Biophoto Associates/Photo Researchers.
20.6c: Mark Neilsen/Benjamin Cummings.
20.6d: LUMEN Histology, Loyola University Medical Education Network, http://www.lumen.luc.edu/lumen/MedEd/Histo/frames/histo_frames.html.
20.7: Astrid and Hanss-Freider Michler/Science Photo Library/Photo Researchers.
20.8: John Cunningham/Visuals Unlimited.
20.9: Biophoto Associates/Science Source/Photo Researchers.

Chapter 21
Chapter Opener: Jim Cummins/Getty Images.
21.2a: Dr. David M. Phillips/Visuals Unlimited/Getty Images.
21.10: David Scharf/Photo Researchers, Inc.
21.14b: Eduardo A. Padlan, National Institutes of Health.
21.20b: Andrejs Liepins/Science Photo Library/Photo Researchers.

Chapter 22
Chapter Opener: AP World Wide Photos.
22.2a: Jenny Thomas/Benjamin Cummings.
22.3a: From *A Stereoscopic Atlas of Human Anatomy* by David L. Bassett.
22.4c, d: From *A Stereoscopic Atlas of Human Anatomy* by David L. Bassett.
22.6b: Nina Zanetti, Pearson Science.

22.6c: Science Photo Library/Photo Researchers.
22.8b: Carolina Biological Supply/Phototake.
22.9b: Kessel and Kardon/Visuals Unlimited.
22.10a: Richard Tauber/Benjamin Cummings.
22.10b: From *A Stereoscopic Atlas of Human Anatomy* by David L. Bassett.

Chapter 23
Chapter Opener: Al Bello/Allsport/Getty Images.
23.9b: Science Photo Library/Photo Researchers.
23.10.b: Elaine N. Marieb.
23.12a: Biophoto Associates/Photo Researchers.
23.12b: From *Color Atlas of Histology* by Leslie P. Garner and James L. Hiatt, © Williams and Wilkins, 1990.
23.14.b: From *A Stereoscopic Atlas of Human Anatomy* by David L. Bassett.
23.16.a: Javer Domingo/Phototake NYC.
23.16.b: Oliver Meckes/Ottawa/Photo Researchers.
23.22d: Steve Gschmeissner/Photo Researchers, Inc.
23.23a: P. Motta/Department of Anatomy/University "La Sapienza," Rome/Science Photo Library/Photo Researchers.
23.23b: Secchi-Lecaque-Roussel-UCLAF/CNRI/Science Photo Library/Photo Researchers.
23.24a, b: From *A Stereoscopic Atlas of Human Anatomy* by David L. Bassett.
23.25b: From *A Stereoscopic Atlas of Human Anatomy* by David L. Bassett.
23.26b: Victor Eroschenko, University of Idaho; Benjamin Cummings.
23.30a: From *A Stereoscopic Atlas of Human Anatomy* by David L. Bassett.

Chapter 24
Chapter Opener: Stewart Cohen/Getty Images.
24.10: Andreas Engel and Daniel J. Müller.
24.CL: Bartomeu Amengual/age footstock.
24.26: Jeff Greenberg/Omni-Photo.

Chapter 25
Chapter Opener: Zefa RF/age fotostock.
25.2b: Richard Tauber, Benjamin Cummings.
25.3a: Ralph T. Hutchings.
25.6a: Biophoto Associates/Photo Researchers.
25.6b: Dennis Kunkel/PhotoTake.
25.7b: Kessel and Kardon/Visuals Unlimited.
25.9b: P. Motta and M. Castellucci/Science Photo Library/Photo Researchers.
25.19: National Institute of Health.
25.20: Biophoto Associates/Photo Researchers.

Chapter 26
Chapter Opener: Jim Cummins/Getty Images.
26.5: Spencer Grant/Stock Boston.

Chapter 27
Chapter Opener: Lisette Le Bon/SuperStock.
27.3b: From *A Stereoscopic Atlas of Human Anatomy* by David L. Bassett.
27.3c: Ed Reschke.
27.8a: Kessel and Kardon/Visuals Unlimited.
27.8b: Juergen Berger/Photo Researchers, Inc.
27.9b: Manfred Kage/Peter Arnold.
27.11b: Biophoto Associates/Photo Researchers, Inc.
27.12b: From *A Stereoscopic Atlas of Human Anatomy* by David L. Bassett.
27.13a: Carolina Biological Supply Company/Phototake.
27.16a: Mark Thomas/Photo Researchers, Inc.
27.16b, c: Leonard Lessin/Peter Arnold.
27.18.1–3: Science Pictures Ltd./Photo Researchers, Inc.
27.18.4: ISM/Phototake.
27.18.5: Ed Reschke/Peter Arnold.
27.18.6: C. Edelman/La Vilette/Photo Researchers.
27.18.7: Lester V. Bergman/Corbis.

Chapter 28
Chapter Opener: John Lund/Drew Kelly/Blend Images/Jupiter Images.
28.2b: Lennart Nilsson, *A Child Is Born*, New York: Dell, © Boehringer Ingelheim International GmbH.
28.3b: CC Studio/Science Photo Library/Photo Researchers, Inc.
28.5b: R. O'Rahilly and R. Muller, *Human Embryology and Teratology*. This material is reproduced with permission of Wiley-Liss, Inc., a subsidiary of John Wiley & Sons, Inc.
28.5d: Allen C. Enders, University of California, Davis/Carnegie Collection.
28.15a: From *A Stereoscopic Atlas of Human Anatomy* by David L. Bassett.
28.15b, c: From Lennart Nilsson/Albert Bonniers Forlag.

Chapter 29
Chapter Opener: Ariel Skelley/Corbis.
29.1b: Lester Lefkowitz/Corbis.
29.1c: L.Williatt, East Anglian Regional Genetics/SPL/Photo Researchers.
29.5: Andrew Syred/Photo Researchers.
29.7.1, 2: PhotoDisc/Getty Images.

Illustration Credits
All illustrations by Imagineering STA Media Services unless otherwise noted.

Chapter 1
1.3: Vincent Perez/Wendy Hiller Gee.
1.7: Imagineering STA Media Services/Precision Graphics
1.10a: Adapted from Seeley, Stephens, and Tate, *Anatomy & Physiology*, 4e, F1.15a, New York: WCB/McGraw-Hill, © McGraw-Hill, 1998.

Chapter 3
3.2: Imagineering STA Media Services/Precision Graphics
3.3: Imagineering STA Media Services/Precision Graphics
3.19: Tomo Narashima.
3.20: Imagineering STA Media Services/Precision Graphics
3.24: Adapted from Campbell, *Biology*, 4e, F7.21, © Benjamin Cummings, 1996.
3.27: Imagineering STA Media Services/Precision Graphics
3.29: Tomo Narashima.

Chapter 4
4.6: From Mathews, Van Holde, and Ahern, *Biochemistry*, 3e, F9.24, © Benjamin Cummings, 2000.

Chapter 5
5.1, 5.2, 5.5: Electronic Publishing Services, Inc.
Making Connections: Vincent Perez/Wendy Hiller Gee.

Chapter 6
6.9: Imagineering STA Media Services/Precision Graphics
Making Connections: Vincent Perez/Wendy Hiller Gee.

Chapter 7
7.3, 7.5, 7.6, 7.7, 7.8: Nadine Sokol.

Chapter 9
9.1: Imagineering STA Media Services/Precision Graphics
9.2: Imagineering STA Media Services/Precision Graphics
9.8, 9.9, 9.11, 9.12, 9.13, 9.26, 9.27, 9.28: Electronic Publishing Services, Inc.
Making Connections: Vincent Perez/Imagineering STA Media Services.

Chapter 11
11.2, 11.17, 11.23: Electronic Publishing Services, Inc.
11.3: Imagineering STA Media Services/Precision Graphics
11.5: Imagineering STA Media Services/Precision Graphics

Chapter 12
12.1–12.6, 12.8–12.11, 12.13, 12.15–12.19, 12.23–12.26: Electronic Publishing Services, Inc.
12.12: Electronic Publishing Services, Inc./Precision Graphics
12.31: Imagineering STA Media Services/Electronic Publishing Services, Inc.
12.32–12.35: Electronic Publishing Services, Inc.

Chapter 13
13.1, 13.3–13.5, 13.13, 13.14, 13.17, 13.18, 13.19: Electronic Publishing Services, Inc.
13.T02.06: Imagineering STA Media Services/Precision Graphics
13.15: Imagineering STA Media Services/Precision Graphics

Chapter 14
14.1–14.4, 14.6, 14.7, 14.9: Electronic Publishing Services, Inc.
Making Connections: Vincent Perez/Wendy Hiller Gee.

Chapter 15
15.1–15.6, 15.8, 15.15, 15.16, 15.18, 15.20, 15.21, 15.23–15.24, 15.26, 15.27, 15.28, 15.31, 15.33–15.36 : Electronic Publishing Services, Inc.
15.25: Electronic Publishing Services, Inc./Precision Graphics

Chapter 16
16.1: Electronic Publishing Services, Inc.
Making Connections: Vincent Perez/Wendy Hiller Gee.
16.8: Imagineering STA Media Services/Precision Graphics

Chapter 18
18.1: Electronic Publishing Services, Inc./Precision Graphics
18.4, 18.8, 18.11, 18.14: Electronic Publishing Services, Inc.
18.9: Imagineering STA Media Services/Precision Graphics

Chapter 19
19.1, 19.4, 19.21–19.30: Electronic Publishing Services, Inc.
Making Connections: Vincent Perez/Wendy Hiller Gee.

Chapter 20
Making Connections: Vincent Perez/Wendy Hiller Gee.

Chapter 21
21.16: Adapted from Johnson, *Human Biology*, 2e, F9.13, © Benjamin Cummings, 2003.

Chapter 22
22.1: Electronic Publishing Services, Inc./Precision Graphics
22.3, 22.4, 22.7–22.10, 22.26: Electronic Publishing Services, Inc.
Making Connections: Vincent Perez/Wendy Hiller Gee.

Chapter 23
23.1, 23.6–23.9, 23.14, 23.15, 23.21, 23.22, 23.29–23.31: Electronic Publishing Services, Inc.
Making Connections: Vincent Perez/Wendy Hiller Gee.
23.25: Electronic Publishing Services, Inc./Precision Graphics
23.28: Imagineering STA Media Services/Precision Graphics

Chapter 24
24.1b: Willett, W.C., Eat, Drink, and Be Healthy. Nutrition Source, Simon & Schuster, Harvard School of Public Health, Food Pyramids, 2001. www.hsph.harvard.edu/nutritionsource/pyramids.html.

Chapter 25
25.1, 25.5, 25.7–25.9, 25.21: Electronic Publishing Services, Inc.
25.12: Imagineering STA Media Services/Precision Graphics

Chapter 26
Making Connections: Vincent Perez/Wendy Hiller Gee.
26.09: Imagineering STA Media Services/Precision Graphics

Chapter 27
27.1–27.4, 27.10–27.12: Electronic Publishing Services, Inc.
Making Connections: Vincent Perez/Wendy Hiller Gee.

Chapter 28
28.4, 28.13: Electronic Publishing Services, Inc.

Index

NOTE: Page numbers in **boldface** indicate a definition. A *t* following a page number indicates tabular material, an *f* indicates an illustration, and a *b* indicates boxed material.

Word Roots, Prefixes, Suffixes, and Combining Forms

Prefixes and Combining Forms

a-, an- *absence or lack*; acardia, lack of a heart, anaerobic, in the absence of oxygen

ab- *departing from, away from*; abnormal, departing from normal

acou- *hearing*; acoustics, the science of sound

ac-, acro- *extreme or extremity, peak*; acrodermatitis, inflammation of the skin of the extremities

ad- *to or toward*; adorbital, toward the orbit

aden-, adeno- *gland*; adeniform, resembling a gland in shape

adren- *toward the kidney*; adrenal gland, adjacent to the kidney

aero- *air*; aerobic respiration, oxygen-requiring metabolism

af- *toward*; afferent neurons, which carry impulses to the central nervous system

agon- *contest*; agonistic and antagonistic muscles, which oppose each other

alb- *white*; corpus albicans of the ovary, a white scar tissue

aliment- *nourish*; alimentary canal, or digestive tract

allel- *of one another*; alleles, alternative expressions of a gene

amphi- *on both sides, of both kinds*; amphibian, an organism capable of living in water and on land

ana- *apart, up, again*; anaphase of mitosis, when the chromosomes separate

anastomos- *come together*; arteriovenous anastomosis, a connection between an artery and a vein

aneurysm *a widening*; aortic aneurysm, a weak spot that causes enlargement of the blood vessel

angi- *vessel*; angiitis, inflammation of a lymph vessel or blood vessel

angin- *choked*; angina pectoris, a choked feeling in the chest due to dysfunction of the heart

ant-, anti- *opposed to, preventing or inhibiting*; anticoagulant, a substance that prevents blood coagulation

ante- *preceding, before*; antecubital, in front of the elbow

aort- *great artery*; aorta

ap-, api- *tip, extremity*; apex of the heart

append- *hang to*; appendicular skeleton

aqua-, aque- *water*; aqueous solutions

arbor *tree*; arbor vitae of the cerebellum, the treelike pattern of white matter

areola- *open space*; areolar connective tissue, a loose connective tissue

arrect- *upright*; arrector pili muscles of the skin, which make the hairs stand erect

arthr-, arthro- *joint*; arthropathy, any joint disease

artic- *joint*; articular surfaces of bones, the points of connection

atri- *vestibule*; atria, upper chambers of the heart

auscult- *listen*; auscultatory method for measuring blood pressure

aut-, auto- *self*; autogenous, self-generated

ax-, axi-, axo- *axis, axle*; axial skeleton, axis of vertebral column

azyg- *unpaired*; azygous vein, an unpaired vessel

baro- *pressure*; baroreceptors for monitoring blood pressure

basal *base*; basal lamina of epithelial basement membrane

bi- *two*; bicuspid, having two cusps

bili- *bile*; bilirubin, a bile pigment

bio- *life*; biology, the study of life and living organisms

blast- *bud or germ*; blastocyte, undifferentiated embryonic cell

brachi- *arm*; brachial plexus of peripheral nervous system supplies the arm

brady- *slow*; bradycardia, abnormally slow heart rate

brev- *short*; peroneus brevis, a short leg muscle

broncho- *bronchus*; bronchospasm, spasmodic contraction of bronchial muscle

bucco- *cheek*; buccolabial, pertaining to the cheek and lip

calor- *heat*; calories, a measure of energy

capill- *hair*; blood and lymph capillaries

caput- *head*; decapitate, remove the head

carcin- *cancer*; carcinogen, a cancer-causing agent

cardi-, cardio- *heart*; cardiotoxic, harmful to the heart

carneo- *flesh*; trabeculae carneae, ridges of muscle in the ventricles of the heart

carot- *(1) carrot, (2) stupor*; (1) carotene, an orange pigment, (2) carotid arteries in the neck, blockage causes fainting

cata- *down*; catabolism, chemical breakdown

caud- *tail*; caudal (directional term)

cec- *blind*; cecum of large intestine, a blind-ended pouch

cele- *abdominal*; celiac artery, in the abdomen

cephal- *head*; cephalometer, an instrument for measuring the head

cerebro- *brain, especially the cerebrum*; cerebrospinal, pertaining to the brain and spinal cord

cervic-, cervix *neck*; cervix of the uterus

chiasm- *crossing*; optic chiasma, where optic nerves cross

chole- *bile*; cholesterol, cholecystokinin, a bile-secreting hormone

chondr- *cartilage*; chondrogenic, giving rise to cartilage

chrom- *colored*; chromosome, so named because they stain darkly

cili- *small hair*; ciliated epithelium

circum- *around*; circumnuclear, surrounding the nucleus

clavic- *key*; clavicle, a "skeleton key"

co-, con- *together*; concentric, common center, together in the center

coccy- *cuckoo*; coccyx, which is beak-shaped

cochlea *snail shell*; the cochlea of the inner ear, which is coiled like a snail shell

coel- *hollow*; coelom, the ventral body cavity

commis- *united*; gray commissure of the spinal cord connects the two columns of gray matter

concha *shell*; nasal conchae, coiled shelves of bone in the nasal cavity

contra- *against*; contraceptive, agent preventing conception

corn-, cornu- *horn*; stratum corneum, outer layer of the skin composed of (horny) cells

corona *crown*; coronal suture of the skull

corp- *body*; corpse, corpus luteum, hormone-secreting body in the ovary

cort- *bark*; cortex, the outer layer of the brain, kidney, adrenal glands, and lymph nodes

cost- *rib*; intercostal, between the ribs

crani- *skull*; craniotomy, a skull operation

crypt- *hidden*; cryptomenorrhea, a condition in which menstrual symptoms are experienced but no external loss of blood occurs

cusp- *pointed*; bicuspid, tricuspid valves of the heart

cutic- *skin*; cuticle of the nail

cyan- *blue*; cyanosis, blue color of the skin due to lack of oxygen

cyst- *sac, bladder*; cystitis, inflammation of the urinary bladder

cyt- *cell*; cytology, the study of cells

de- *undoing, reversal, loss, removal*; deactivation, becoming inactive

decid- *falling off*; deciduous (milk) teeth

delta *triangular*; deltoid muscle, roughly triangular in shape

den-, dent- *tooth*; dentin of the tooth

dendr- *tree, branch*; dendrites, telodendria, both branches of a neuron

derm- *skin*; dermis, deep layer of the skin

desm- *bond*; desmosome, which binds adjacent epithelial cells

di- *twice, double*; dimorphism, having two forms

dia- *through, between*; diaphragm, the wall through or between two areas

dialys- *separate, break apart*; kidney dialysis, in which waste products are removed from the blood

diastol- *stand apart*; cardiac diastole, between successive contractions of the heart

diure- *urinate*; diuretic, a drug that increases urine output

dors- *the back*; dorsal, dorsum, dorsiflexion

duc-, duct *lead, draw*; ductus deferens which carries sperm from the epididymis into the urethra during ejaculation

dura *hard*; dura mater, tough outer meninx

dys- *difficult, faulty, painful*; dyspepsia, disturbed digestion

ec-, ex-, ecto- *out, outside, away from*; excrete, to remove materials from the body

ectop- *displaced*; ectopic pregnancy, ectopic focus for initiation of heart contraction

edem- *swelling*; edema, accumulation of water in body tissues

ef- *away*; efferent nerve fibers, which carry impulses away from the central nervous system

ejac- *to shoot forth*; ejaculation of semen

embol- *wedge*; embolus, an obstructive object traveling in the bloodstream

en-, em- *in, inside*; encysted, enclosed in a cyst or capsule

enceph- *brain*; encephalitis, inflammation of the brain

endo- *within, inner*; endocytosis, taking particles into a cell

entero- *intestine*; enterologist, one who specializes in the study of intestinal disorders

epi- *over, above*; epidermis, outer layer of skin

erythr- *red*; erythema, redness of the skin, erythrocyte, red blood cell

eso- *within*; esophagus

eu- *well*; euesthesia, a normal state of the senses

excret- *separate*; excretory system

exo- *outside, outer layer*; exophthalmos, an abnormal protrusion of the eye from the orbit

extra- *outside, beyond*; extracellular, outside the body cells of an organism

extrins- *from the outside*; extrinsic regulation of the heart

fasci-, fascia- *bundle, band*; superficial and deep fascia

fenestr- *window*; fenestrated capillaries

ferr- *iron*; transferrin, ferritin, both iron-storage proteins

flagell- *whip*; flagellum, the tail of a sperm cell

flat- *blow, blown*; flatulence

folli- *bag, bellows*; hair follicle

fontan- *fountain*; fontanelles of the fetal skull

foram- *opening*; foramen magnum of the skull

foss- *ditch*; fossa ovalis of the heart, mandibular fossa of the skull

gam-, gamet- *married, spouse*; gametes, the sex cells

gangli- *swelling, or knot*; dorsal root ganglia of the spinal nerves

gastr- *stomach*; gastrin, a hormone that influences gastric acid secretion

gene *beginning, origin*; genetics

germin- *grow*; germinal epithelium of the gonads

gero-, geront- *old man*; gerontology, the study of aging

gest- *carried*; gestation, the period from conception to birth

glauc- *gray*; glaucoma, which causes gradual blindness

glom- *ball*; glomeruli, clusters of capillaries in the kidneys

glosso- *tongue*; glossopathy, any disease of the tongue

gluco-, glyco- gluconeogenesis, the production of glucose from noncarbohydrate molecules

glute- *buttock*; gluteus maximus, largest muscle of the buttock

gnost- *knowing*; the gnostic sense, a sense of awareness of self

gompho- *nail*; gomphosis, the term applied to the joint between tooth and jaw

gon-, gono- *seed, offspring*; gonads, the sex organs

gust- *taste*; gustatory sense, the sense of taste

hapt- *fasten, grasp*; hapten, a partial antigen

hema-, hemato-, hemo- *blood*; hematocyst, a cyst containing blood

hemi- *half*; hemiglossal, pertaining to one-half of the tongue

hepat- *liver*; hepatitis, inflammation of the liver

hetero- *different or other*; heterosexuality, sexual desire for a person of the opposite sex

hiat- *gap*; the hiatus of the diaphragm, the opening through which the esophagus passes

hippo- *horse*; hippocampus of the brain, shaped like a seahorse

hirsut- *hairy*; hirsutism, excessive body hair

hist- *tissue*; histology, the study of tissues

holo- *whole*; holocrine glands, whose secretions are whole cells

hom-, homo- *same*; homeoplasia, formation of tissue similar to normal tissue; homocentric, having the same center

hormon- *to excite*; hormones

humor- *a fluid*; humoral immunity, which involves antibodies circulating in the blood

hyal- *clear*; hyaline cartilage, which has no visible fibers

hydr-, hydro- *water*; dehydration, loss of body water

hyper- *excess*; hypertension, excessive tension

hypno- *sleep*; hypnosis, a sleeplike state

hypo- *below, deficient*; hypodermic, beneath the skin, hypokalemia, deficiency of potassium

hyster-, hystero- *uterus or womb*; hysterectomy, removal of the uterus, hysterodynia, pain in the womb

ile- *intestine*; ileum, the last portion of the small intestine

im- *not*; impermeable, not permitting passage, not permeable

inter- *between*; intercellular, between the cells

intercal- *insert*; intercalated discs, the end membranes between adjacent cardiac muscle cells

intra- *within, inside*; intracellular, inside the cell

iso- *equal, same*; isothermal, equal, or same, temperature

jugul- *throat*; jugular veins, prominent vessels in the neck

juxta- *near, close to*; juxtaglomerular apparatus, a cell cluster next to a glomerulus in the kidneys

karyo- *kernel, nucleus*; karyotype, the assemblage of the nuclear chromosomes

kera- *horn*; keratin, the water-repellent protein of the skin

kilo- *thousand*; kilocalories, equal to 1000 calories

kin-, kines- *move*; kinetic energy, the energy of motion

labi-, labri- *lip*; labial frenulum, the membrane which joins the lip to the gum

lact- *milk*; lactose, milk sugar

lacun- *space, cavity, lake*; lacunae, the spaces occupied by cells of cartilage and bone tissue

lamell- *small plate*; concentric lamellae, rings of bone matrix in compact bone

lamina *layer, sheet*; basal lamina, part of the epithelial basement membrane

lat- *wide*; latissimus dorsi, a broad muscle of the back

laten- *hidden*; latent period of a muscle twitch

later- *side*; lateral (directional term)

leuko- *white*; leukocyte, white blood cell

leva- *raise, elevate*; levator labii superioris, muscle that elevates upper lip

lingua- *tongue*; lingual tonsil, adjacent to the tongue

lip-, lipo- *fat, lipid*; lipophage, a cell that has taken up fat in its cytoplasm

lith- *stone*; cholelithiasis, gallstones

luci- *clear*; stratum lucidum, clear layer of the epidermis

lumen *light*; lumen, center of a hollow structure

lut- *yellow*; corpus luteum, a yellow, hormone-secreting structure in the ovary

lymph *water*; lymphatic circulation, return of clear fluid to the bloodstream

macro- *large*; macromolecule, large molecule

macula *spot*; macula lutea, yellow spot on the retina

magn- *large*; foramen magnum, largest opening of the skull

mal- *bad, abnormal*; malfunction, abnormal functioning of an organ

mamm- *breast*; mammary gland, breast

mast- *breast*; mastectomy, removal of a mammary gland

mater *mother*; dura mater, pia mater, membranes that envelop the brain

meat- *passage*; external acoustic meatus, the ear canal

medi- *middle*; medial (directional term)

medull- *marrow*; medulla, the middle portion of the kidney, adrenal gland, and lymph node

mega- *large*; megakaryocyte, large precursor cell of platelets

meio- *less*; meiosis, nuclear division that halves the chromosome number

melan- *black*; melanocytes, which secrete the black pigment melanin

men-, menstru- *month*; menses, the cyclic menstrual flow

meningo- *membrane*; meningitis, inflammation of the membranes of the brain

mer-, mero-, *a part*; merocrine glands, the secretions of which do not include the cell

meso- *middle*; mesoderm, middle germ layer

meta- *beyond, between, transition*; metatarsus, the part of the foot between the tarsus and the phalanges

metro- *uterus*; endometrium, the lining of the uterus

micro- *small*; microscope, an instrument used to make small objects appear larger

mictur- *urinate*; micturition, the act of voiding the bladder

mito- *thread, filament*; mitochondria, small, filament-like structures located in cells

mnem- *memory*; amnesia

mono- *single*; monospasm, spasm of a single limb

morpho- *form*; morphology, the study of form and structure or organisms

multi- *many*; multinuclear, having several nuclei

mur- *wall*; intramural ganglion, a nerve junction within an organ

muta- *change*; mutation, change in the base sequence of DNA

myelo- *spinal cord, marrow*; myeloblasts, cells of the bone marrow

myo- *muscle*; myocardium, heart muscle

nano- *dwarf*; nanometer, one-billionth of a meter

narco- *numbness*; narcotic, a drug producing stupor or numbed sensations

natri- *sodium*; atrial natriuretic peptide, a sodium-regulating hormone

necro- *death*; necrosis, tissue death

neo- *new*; neoplasm, an abnormal growth

nephro- *kidney*; nephritis, inflammation of the kidney

neuro- *nerve*; neurophysiology, the physiology of the nervous system

noci- *harmful*; nociceptors, receptors for pain

nom- *name*; innominate artery, innominate bone

noto- *back*; notochord, the embryonic structure that precedes the vertebral column

nucle- *pit, kernel, little nut*; nucleus

nutri- *feed, nourish*; nutrition

ob- *before, against*; obstruction, impeding or blocking up

oculo- *eye*; monocular, pertaining to one eye

odonto- *teeth*; orthodontist, one who specializes in proper positioning of the teeth in relation to each other

olfact- *smell*; olfactory nerves

oligo- *few*; oligodendrocytes, neuroglial cells with few branches

onco- *a mass*; oncology, study of cancer

oo- *egg*; oocyte, precursor of female gamete

ophthalmo- *eye*; ophthalmology, the study of the eyes and related disease

orb- *circular*; orbicularis oculi, muscle that encircles the eye

orchi- *testis*; cryptorchidism, failure of the testes to descend into the scrotum

org- *living*; organism

ortho- *straight, direct*; orthopedic, correction of deformities of the musculoskeletal system

osm- *smell*; anosmia, loss of sense of smell

osmo- *pushing*; osmosis

osteo- *bone*; osteodermia, bony formations in the skin

oto- *ear*; otoscope, a device for examining the ear

ov-, ovi- *egg*; ovum, oviduct

oxy- *oxygen*; oxygenation, the saturation of a substance with oxygen

pan- *all, universal*; panacea, a cure-all

papill- *nipple*; dermal papillae, projections of the dermis into the epidermal area

para- *beside, near*; paranuclear, beside the nucleus

pect-, pectus *breast*; pectoralis major, a large chest muscle

pelv- *a basin*; pelvic girdle, which cradles the pelvic organs

peni- *a tail*; penis; penile urethra

penna- *feather*; unipennate, bipennate muscles, whose fascicles have a feathered appearance

pent- *five*; pentose, a 5-carbon sugar

pep-, peps-, pept- *digest*; pepsin, a digestive enzyme of the stomach; peptic ulcer

per-, permea- *through*; permeate, permeable

peri- *around*; perianal, situated around the anus

phago- *eat*; phagocyte, a cell that engulfs and digests particles or cells

pheno- *show, appear*; phenotype, the physical appearance of an individual

phleb- *vein*; phlebitis, inflammation of the veins

pia *tender*; pia mater, delicate inner membrane around the brain and spinal cord

pili *hair*; arrector pili muscles of the skin, which make the hairs stand erect

pin-, pino- *drink*; pinocytosis, the engulfing of small particles by a cell

platy- *flat, broad*; platysma, broad, flat muscle of the neck

pleur- *side, rib*; pleural serosa, the membrane that lines the thoracic cavity and covers the lungs

plex-, plexus *net, network*; brachial plexus, the network of nerves that supplies the arm

pneumo- *air, wind*; pneumothorax, air in the thoracic cavity

pod- *foot*; podiatry, the treatment of foot disorders

poly- *multiple*; polymorphism, multiple forms

post- *after, behind*; posterior, places behind (a specific) part

pre-, pro- *before, ahead of*; prenatal, before birth

procto- *rectum, anus*; proctoscope, an instrument for examining the rectum

pron- *bent forward*; prone, pronate

propri- *one's own*; proprioception, awareness of body parts and movement

pseudo- *false*; pseudotumor, a false tumor

psycho- *mind, psyche*; psychogram, a chart of personality traits

ptos- *fall*; renal ptosis, a condition in which the kidneys drift below their normal position

pub- *of the pubis*; puberty

pulmo- *lung*; pulmonary artery, which brings blood to the lungs

pyo- *pus*; pyocyst, a cyst that contains pus

pyro- *fire*; pyrogen, a substance that induces fever

quad-, quadr- *four-sided*; quadratus lumborum, a muscle with a square shape

re- *back, again*; reinfect

rect- *straight*; rectus abdominis, rectum

ren- *kidney*; renal, renin, an enzyme secreted by the kidney

retin, retic- *net, network*; endoplasmic reticulum, a network of membranous sacs within a cell

retro- *backward, behind*; retrogression, to move backward in development

rheum- *watery flow, change, or flux*; rheumatoid arthritis, rheumatic fever

rhin-, rhino- *nose*; rhinitis, inflammation of the nose

ruga- *fold, wrinkle*; rugae, the folds of the stomach, gallbladder, and urinary bladder

sagitt- *arrow*; sagittal (directional term)

salta- *leap*; saltatory conduction, the rapid conduction of impulses along myelinated neurons

sanguin- *blood*; consanguineous, indicative of a genetic relationship between individuals

sarco- *flesh*; sarcomere, unit of contraction in skeletal muscle

saphen- *visible, clear*; great saphenous vein, superficial vein of the thigh and leg

sclero- *hard*; sclerodermatitis, inflammatory thickening and hardening of the skin

seb- *grease*; sebum, the oil of the skin

semen *seed, sperm*; semen, the discharge of the male reproductive system

semi- *half*; semicircular, having the form of half a circle

sens- *feeling*; sensation, sensory

septi- *rotten*; sepsis, infection, antiseptic

septum *fence*; nasal septum

sero- *serum*; serological tests, which assess blood conditions

serrat- *saw*; serratus anterior, a muscle of the chest wall that has a jagged edge

sin-, sino- *a hollow*; sinuses of the skull

soma- *body*; somatic nervous system

somn- *sleep*; insomnia, inability to sleep

sphin- *squeeze*; sphincter

splanchn- *organ*; splanchnic nerve, autonomic supply to abdominal viscera

spondyl- *vertebra*; ankylosing spondylitis, rheumatoid arthritis affecting the spine

squam- *scale, flat*; squamous epithelium, squamous suture of the skull

steno- *narrow*; stenocoriasis, narrowing of the pupil

strat- *layer*; strata of the epidermis, stratified epithelium

stria- *furrow, streak*; striations of skeletal and cardiac muscle tissue

stroma *spread out*; stroma, the connective tissue framework of some organs

sub- *beneath, under*; sublingual, beneath the tongue

sucr- *sweet*; sucrose, table sugar

sudor- *sweat*; sudoriferous glands, the sweat glands

super- *above, upon*; superior, quality or state of being above others or a part

supra- *above, upon*; supracondylar, above a condyle

sym-, syn- *together, with*; synapse, the region of communication between two neurons

synerg- *work together*; synergism

systol- *contraction*; systole, contraction of the heart

tachy- *rapid*; tachycardia, abnormally rapid heartbeat

tact- *touch*; tactile sense

telo- *the end*; telophase, the end of mitosis

templ-, tempo- *time*; temporal summation of nerve impulses

tens- *stretched*; muscle tension

terti- *third*; fibularis tertius, one of three fibularis muscles

tetan- *rigid, tense*; tetanus of muscles

therm- *heat*; thermometer, an instrument used to measure heat

thromb- *clot*; thrombocyte, thrombus

thyro- *a shield*; thyroid gland

tissu- *woven*; tissue

tono- *tension*; tonicity, hypertonic

tox- *poison*; toxicology, study of poisons

trab- *beam, timber*; trabeculae, spicules of bone in spongy bone tissue

trans- *across, through*; transpleural, through the pleura

trapez- *table*; trapezius, the four-sided muscle of the upper back

tri- *three*; trifurcation, division into three branches

trop- *turn, change*; tropic hormones, whose targets are endocrine glands

troph- *nourish*; trophoblast, from which develops the fetal portion of the placenta

tuber- *swelling*; tuberosity, a bump on a bone

tunic- *covering*; tunica albuginea, the covering of the testis

tympan- *drum*; tympanic membrane, the eardrum

ultra- *beyond*; ultraviolet radiation, beyond the band of visible light

vacc- *cow*; vaccine

vagin- *a sheath*; vagina

vagus *wanderer*; the vagus nerve, which starts at the brain and travels into the abdominopelvic cavity

valen- *strength*; valence shells of atoms

venter, ventr- *abdomen, belly*; ventral (directional term), ventricle

vent- *the wind*; pulmonary ventilation

vert- *turn*; vertebral column

vestibul- *a porch*; vestibule, the anterior entryway to the mouth and nose

vibr- *shake, quiver*; vibrissae, hairs of the nasal vestibule

villus *shaggy hair*; microvilli, which have the appearance of hair in light microscopy

viscero- *organ, viscera*; visceroinhibitory, inhibiting the movements of the viscera

viscos- *sticky*; viscosity, resistance to flow

vita- *life*; vitamin

vitre- *glass*; vitreous humor, the clear jelly of the eye

viv- *live*; in vivo

vulv- *a covering*; vulva, the female external genitalia

zyg- *a yoke, twin*; zygote

Suffixes

-able *able to, capable of*; viable, ability to live or exist

-ac *referring to*; cardiac, referring to the heart

-algia *pain in a certain part*; neuralgia, pain along the course of a nerve

-apsi *juncture*; synapse, where two neurons communicate

-ary *associated with, relating to*; coronary, associated with the heart

-asthen *weakness*; myasthenia gravis, a disease involving paralysis

-bryo *swollen*; embryo

-cide *destroy or kill*; germicide, an agent that kills germs

-cipit *head*; occipital

-clast *break*; osteoclast, a cell that dissolves bone matrix

-crine *separate*; endocrine organs, which secrete hormones into the blood

-dips *thirst, dry*; polydipsia, excessive thirst associated with diabetes

-ectomy *cutting out, surgical removal*; appendectomy, cutting out of the appendix

-ell, -elle *small*; organelle

-emia *condition of the blood*; anemia, deficiency of red blood cells

-esthesi *sensation*; anesthesia, lack of sensation